Great Chemists

Great Chemists

Edited by Eduard Farber

Interscience Publishers · New York · London

1961

Acknowledgments

This book could not have been produced without the cooperation of the authors of the individual biographies, nor without the gracious help of many publishers and authors who kindly consented to reproduction or translation of biographies published previously, and the Editor hereby extends to them, as well as to the authors of the original biographies, his gratitude. Further detailed credit is given at the end of each biography; here we can mention briefly: Verlag Chemie; Springer Verlag; Taylor & Francis, Ltd.; Gazzetta Chimica Italiana; The Washington Academy of Sciences; American Pharmaceutical Association; *American Dyestuff Reporter;* American Chemical Society (*Journal of Chemical Education; JACS*); The Smithsonian Institution; University of Pennsylvania Press; The Royal Society (London); Society of the Chemical Industry; *Nature;* National Academy of Sciences (U.S.); Sociéte Chimique de France; The Chemical Society (London); American Institute of Mining, Metallurgical and Petroleum Engineers; University Press, Cambridge; Princeton University Press; New York Academy of Science; Nobel Foundation; Yale University Press; American Institute for the History of Pharmacy; American Association for the Advancement of Science (*Science* and *Scientific Monthly*); University of Chicago Press; Salmon (Paris); University of Wisconsin Press; USSR Academy of Science; Oxford Bibliographical Society; *Naturwissenschaften;* The Cavendish Society; *American Journal of Science,* the Royal Swedish Academy of Science, and Akademie-Verlag.

In addition, grateful acknowledgment is hereby made to those who supplied many of the illustrations used in this book: Mrs. Dorothea H. Williams, Custodian of the Smith Collection, Philadelphia, for her invaluable help; The University Museum, Philadelphia, for the illustrations on pg. 2; Instituto Nazionale Medico Farmacologico, Rome, pp. 42 and 44; The Smithsonian Institution, pp. 48, 202, 536, 832, 854, 960, 1014, 1086, 1120, 1146, 1204, and 1264; The Library of Congress, pp. 66, 150, 178, and 284; Bettmann Archive, pg. 82; Duveen Historical Library, pp. 228, 240, 254, and 264; Academic Press, pp. 326, 750, 1326, 1334, and 1344; *J. Chem. Ed.,* pp. 704, 1376, 1422, and 1470; Mrs. James B. Conant, pg. 806 (Richards); University of Wisconsin, pg. 806 (Babcock); Mrs. Harvey W. Wiley, pg. 806 (Wiley); Alexander Silverman, University of Pittsburgh, pg.

908; La Wall and Harrison, Philadelphia, pg. 926; Deutsches Museum München, pg. 982; Professor Terje Enkvist, Helsinki, pg. 1112; *Endeavor,* pp. 1158 and 1454; *Cornell Chemist,* pg. 1182; Arthur D. Little, Inc., pg. 1192; The Dow Chemical Company, pg. 1220; Verlag Chemie, pp. 1300, 1366, and 1442; Dr. Robert Tiffeneau, Paris, pg. 1390; Professor Janick Bjerrum, Copenhagen, pg. 1490; Österreichische Nationalbibliothek, Bild-Archiv and Porträt-Sammlung, Wien, pg. 1552; Massachusetts Institute of Technology, pg. 8.

Preface

THE present collection of more than a hundred biographies is united by its subject, the development of chemistry in the last three thousand years, and it is diversified by a roster of authors from the last two centuries.

The selection of great chemists to be included in this publication was not too difficult for the more distant past. There were few chemists then, and their work has frequently been explored in books on the history of chemistry. The difficulties increased with the approach to our time. This may be illustrated by a few statistical figures. When the first edition of "American Men of Science" appeared in 1906, it contained about 4000 biographies; the eighth edition in 1949 listed about 50,000 for all sciences, and the ninth had over 43,000 in 1955 for the physical sciences alone. "Chemical Who's Who" contained short biographies of about 6500 American chemists in its third edition of 1951, and this number was more than a third greater in the fourth edition of 1956.

No living chemist is included in the present collection of biographies. Although there are no rules for determining greatness, nevertheless certain guides are available. The consensus of the historians in their publications, the acclaim of contemporaries expressed in citations and awards, suggestions offered by colleagues, and some personal preferences of the editor affected the selection of a few representative great chemists. Other selections could have been made and many more chemists included, particularly from the very recent past.

These biographies are arranged in the sequence of the birth dates. To form groups according to chemical subjects would have been artificial and, in many instances, impossible because usually one man worked in many, later divided fields.

Some among these chemists have left us their autobiographies, many of them rich sources for the historian of science and still more interesting for the student of human nature. Yet the biographer has to go beyond them. He must, as Schleiermacher once said, understand the author better than he did himself. Many of the biographers in the present volume are great chemists themselves, and some of their biographies are included here.

The lengths of these biographies are in no way related to the relative importance of the chemists. For example, much space is given to J. B. van Helmont not because of his exceptional greatness, but because his biography, by J. R. Partington, reveals so much about the state of chemistry after Paracelsus and before Robert Boyle.

In the presentation of the lives of these men, as individuals who created our science in their particular way, uniformity was not sought; in fact it was avoided. The reader may try to find similarities among the different stories, or construct harmonic relationships from the different events in one individual's life. He may attempt to derive a certain constant, called character, from the decisions reported for various occasions. When he looks more closely, he may also discover contradictions and something of that complementarity which the new physics found to solve fundamental problems. On the other hand, he may feel that such relationships and analogies do not exist and exclaim with Shakespeare:

Fate, show thy force; ourselves we do not owe;
What is decreed must be, and be this so!
(*Twelfth Night*, ACT 1, SCENE 5.)

Still more problematic, and yet intriguing, are comparisons between chemists and other creative personalities in arts and sciences. Thus, without claiming total equality, certain traits could be found to link Michelangelo with Paracelsus, Rembrandt with Boerhaave, Voltaire with Proust, Gauss with Liebig, Mozart with Victor Meyer, or Goethe with Emil Fischer, and George Bernard Shaw with Henry Edward Armstrong. There would be no end to such combinations—and certainly much disagreement.

Nevertheless, comparisons can aid memory and prevent premature generalizations. It has been claimed that the first-born are the brightest, and Gay-Lussac or Davy could be cited to support such an assumption; however, van Helmont, Boyle, Faraday, Mendeleev, Bunsen, Cannizzaro, and Moureu were the youngest in rather large families. An older brother greatly influenced the lives of Duhamel du Monceau, Buchner, and Moureu. Some of the great chemists started chemical experiments at an early age, like Ostwald, Werner, Baeyer, and Zsigmondy; others found their way to chemistry after pursuing interests in entirely different fields, like Mitscherlich, Kekulé, and Windaus. Great teachers, like the older Rouelle, Strohmeyer, and Emil Fischer, diverted students of arts, languages, and medicine to chemistry. Black, Dalton, Cavendish were bachelors—typically English? No, see Scheele, Bunsen, and Gomberg.

Comparisons between such single features will be less fruitful than attention to the skills and tools, the aims and incentives, the thoughts and emotions in the lives of these great chemists. They did not have the secure foreknowledge of great achievements, they had difficulties and problems similar to ours. To observe how others behaved in their predicaments may help us in emergencies, even to foresee both their coming and the results of our reactions. The contact with great men through their biographies may add to our own experiences by mental and emotional participation. This participation can involve situations of personal life or discoveries outside of our immediate activities. Certain parts of this book may be directly stimulating for actual chemical work, when some well-known facts appear in a new connection, and when some almost forgotten old achievements are brought to light. Other parts may have less immediate influences on the reader. Long after he has closed the book, a situation or a saying reported in it may come to his mind when he is confronted with a special personal dilemma or chemical difficulty.

Some of these answers to our potential problems may be derived from just a brief remark in one of the biographies. For example: not everybody who fails as an apprentice for a business career will become a great chemist, but there is hope to be found in Emil Fischer's experience.

The evolution of chemistry is a drama written and enacted by the great chemists. At least some of the most important scenes of this drama are here presented.

EDUARD FARBER

Washington, D. C.
August 1961

Contributors

ADAMS, Roger, 1889–; Ph.D. Harvard (1912); professor of organic chemistry, University of Illinois, 1919; author of several texts, editor, *Organic Reactions*. Chapter 114, Carothers.

AMBERG, Lyle O., 1914–; grad. chem. (1939); industrial chemist. Chapter 33, Chevreul (with D. Weeks).

ANSCHÜTZ, Richard, 1852–1937; Dr. phil. Heidelberg (1874); professor at Bonn University, 1898–1922. Chapter 50, Kekulé.

ARAGO, François, 1786–1853; director of the Paris observatory, 1830; minister of war in the Provisional Government, 1848. Chapter 28, Gay-Lussac.

BACHER, Alfred A., 1905–; Dr. phil. Vienna and D. Sc. Oxford; professor Vienna, 1935, Dublin, 1937; consulting practice, 1946; with Department of the Navy, 1956. Chapter 111, Spaeth.

BACHMANN, Werner Emmanuel, 1901–1951; Dr. phil. (1926); professor of organic chemistry at Ann Arbor, 1929. Chapter 85, Gomberg (with C. S. Schoeppfle).

BELL, Ronald Percy, 1907–; lecturer in physical chemistry, Balliol College, Oxford, 1932; president, Faraday Society. Chapter 106, Brønsted.

BENFEY, Otto Theodor, 1925–; Ph.D. London (1947); professor Haverford, 1948, Earlham College, 1956. Chapter 51, Couper.

BONHOEFFER, Karl Friedrich, 1899–1957; Haber's assistant at the Kaiser Wilhelm Institut; director, Max Planck Institut für Physikalische Chemie, Göttingen, 1949. Chapter 91, Haber.

BRINER, Émile, 1879–; Dr. phil. Geneva (1902); professor of theoretical and technical chemistry, Geneva, 1922. Chapter 78, Guye.

BROUGHAM, Lord Henry, 1778–1863; Scottish jurist and political leader, a founder of London University, 1828. Chapter 16, Black.

BUGGE, Friedrich Detlef Günther, 1885–1944; Dr. phil. (1908); director, div. of patents and literature, Holzverkohlungs-Industrie, A. G., Konstanz, 1918; editor, *Buch der Grossen Chemiker,* vol. 1, 1929; vol. 2, 1930. Chapter 22, Klaproth.

CHADWICK, Sir James, 1891–; professor at the University of Liverpool, 1935; Master of Gonville and Caius College, Cambridge, 1948. Chapter 95, Rutherford (with A. S. Eve).

CHALLENGER, Frederick, 1887–; Dr. phil. in Wallach's institute, (1912); professor of organic chemistry, University of Leeds, 1930. Chapter 81, Kipping.

COHEN, Ernst, 1869–1944; Dr. phil. under van't Hoff (1893); professor at Amsterdam University. Chapter 66, van't Hoff.

COURTOT, Charles, 1888–1955; Dr. phil. at Nancy (1915); professor of organic and dyestuff chemistry, Nancy, 1926. Chapter 94, Grignard.

CRELL, Lorenz Florenz Friedrich, 1744–1816; professor of chemistry in Braunschweig, 1771; editor of several chemical journals and archives, Göttingen, 1810. Chapter 19, Scheele.

CURTIUS, Theodor, 1857–1928; professor at Kiel, 1889, Heidelberg, 1898. Chapter 42, Bunsen.

CUVIER, Georges, 1769–1832; studied at Karlsschule, Stuttgart; professor at École Normale, Paris, 1795, at Collège de France, 1800; State Councilor, 1814, Pair de France, 1831; author of *Le Règne Animal,* 1817. Chapter 17, Cavendish.

DUFRAISSE, Charles Robert, 1885–; Dr. ès-sciences physiques, Paris (1921); professor of organic chemistry, Paris. Chapter 80, Moureu.

DUVEEN, Denis I., 1910–; First Class Diploma in chemistry, Battersea Polytechnic, London (1936); at Ministry of Supply, 1940–1944; president, Duveen Soap Corporation, New York, 1949. Chapter 20, Lavoisier.

EDELSTEIN, Sidney M., 1912–; B.S. at M.I.T. (1932); president, Dexter Chemical Corp., 1944. Chapter 55, Perkin.

EINSTEIN, Albert, 1879–1955; Dr. phil. Zürich (1905); professor at university of Prag, 1910, Zürich, 1912; director, Kaiser Wilhelm Institut für Physik, Berlin-Dahlem, 1914; at Institute for Advanced Study, Princeton, 1933–1945. Chapter 84, Nernst.

ÉTIENNE, René, 1875–1950; director of the Société Solvay, Paris, 1919; director of research, Brussels, 1928–1938. Chapter 56, Solvay.

EVE, Arthur Stuart, 1862–1948; D.Sc. McGill University (1910); professor of physics, Cambridge, 1913. Chapter 95, Rutherford (with J. Chadwick).

FABRE, Jean-Marie René, 1889–; Dr. ès-sciences Paris (1922); professor of toxicology, 1931; Doyen de la Faculté de Pharmacie de Paris, 1946. Chapter 75, Ciamician.

FARBER, Eduard, 1892–; Dr. phil. Leipzig (1916); assistant at Kaiser Wilhelm Institut, Berlin-Dahlem, 1916 and 1919; industrial chemical research since 1920. Chapters 2, 4, 21, 64—Interludes; 24, Berthollet; 25, Proust; 48, Berthelot; 71, Ostwald; 96, Willstätter; 103, Wieland.

FELIX, Kurt, 1888–1960; Dr. phil. under A. Kossel (1912); professor and director of the institute of vegetable physiology, Frankfurt-Main, 1934. Chapter 72, Kossel.

FINDLAY, Alexander, 1874–; at Stanford University, 1925, Aberdeen University. Chapter 88, Bancroft.

FLOURENS, Pierre Jean-Marie, 1794–1867; lectures on physiology, 1821; professor of comparative anatomy, 1832; Pair de France, 1846. Chapter 27, Thenard.

FONTENELLE, Bernard Le Bovier, 1657–1757; permanent secretary of the Académie des Sciences 1699–1744. Chapter 10, Lemery.

FOURNEAU, Ernest, 1872–1949; diploma in pharmacy (1898); at Institut Pasteur, 1911. Chapter 98, Tiffeneau.

GUGGENHEIM, Edward Armand, 1901–; studied under R. H. Fowler, J. N. Brønsted, and N. Bjerrum; teaching posts at Danish Royal Agri. College 1928–1929; Stanford U. 1932–1933; Reading U. 1933–1935; London U. 1936–1939; Scientific Staff of Admiralty 1939–1944; Montreal Lab. of Atomic Energy 1944–1946; Reading U. since 1946. Chapter 107, Bjerrum.

HABER, Fritz, 1868–1934; see biography by K. F. Bonhoeffer (91). Chapter 40, Liebig.

HALL, Marie Boas, 1919–; Ph.D. Cornell University; professor of history, University of California, Los Angeles. Chapter 9, Boyle.

HARTLEY, Sir Harold, 1878–; lecturer in physical chemistry Oxford 1901–1931; research fellow 1931–1941; chairman Fuel Research Board 1922–1947; president World Power Conference, 1950–1956. Chapter 62, Armstrong.

HAYNES, Williams, 1886–; editor of chemical-industrial journals; author of a history of American chemical industry. Chapters 64, Frash; 82, Baekeland; 83, Little; 86, Dow; 100, Teeple; 113, Midgley.

HELFERICH, Burckhardt, 1887–; assistant to Emil Fischer, 1911; professor of chemistry Frankfurt-Main, 1922; Greifswald, 1925; Leipzig, 1930; Bonn, 1945. Chapter 68, Emil Fischer.

HENRY, William, 1774–1836; medical doctor and owner of chemical manufacturing plants; author of *The Elements of Experimental Chemistry,* London, 1799, 11th ed., 1829. Chapter 18, Priestley.

HOFMANN, August Wilhelm von, 1818–1892; see biography by B. Lepsius (45). Chapter 38, Wöhler.

HOLDERMANN, Karl Friedrich, 1882–; Dr. ing. Karlsruhe; chemist with the Badische Anilin- und Soda Fabrik 1906–1947; from 1929 a director and chairman of the patent division. Chapter 99, Carl Bosch.

HOPWOOD, Arthur, of Carlisle, England. Chapter 26, Dalton.

HÜCKEL, Walter, 1895–; Dr. phil. (1920); professor of organic chemistry Freiburg, 1927; Greifswald, 1930; Breslau, 1935; Tübingen, 1948. Chapter 77, Aschan.

IHDE, Aaron J. 1909–; Ph.D. Wisconsin (1941); professor at the University of Wisconsin, 1948. Chapters 30, Berzelius; 35, Faraday; 58, Babcock, Wiley, Remsen, Richards, and Smith.

KAMERLINGH ONNES, Heike, 1853–1926; Dr. phil. Groningen (1879); professor of experimental physics, Leiden, 1882–1923. Chapter 54, van der Waals.

KERKER, Milton, 1920–; Ph.D. Columbia (1949); professor at Clarkson College of Technology, 1949. Chapter 11, Boerhaave.

KINGDON, Kenneth H., 1894–; Ph.D. in physics (1920); research associate, General Electric Co. 1920; technical manager, Knolls Atomic Power Laboratory, 1946–1953. Chapter 108, Langmuir.

KOCH, Herbert, 1904–; Dr. phil. Kaiser Wilhelm Institut für Kohle-Chemie, Mülheim-Ruhr (1928); department head, 1935; scientific member, 1947. Chapter 102, Franz Fischer.

KOCH, Richard, 1882–1949; Dr. med. Leipzig (1908); professor for the history of medicine at Frankfurt University till 1933. Chapters 46, Pasteur; 73, Ehrlich.

KRAUS, Charles A., 1875–; Ph.D. (1908); professor of chemistry at Brown University, 1924–1951. Chapter 57, Gibbs.

LEICESTER, Henry M., 1906–; Ph.D. Stanford University (1930); professor of biochemistry at the College of Physicians and Surgeons, San Francisco, 1938. Chapters 15, Lomonosov; 49, Butlerov; 52, Mendeleev.

LEMAY, Pierre, 1893–; Dr. chem. Institut Pasteur, Paris (1921). Chapter 44, Deville (with R. E. Oesper).

LETSIUS, Bernhard, 1854–1934; Dr. phil. Göttingen (1880); director, Chem. Fabrik Griesheim-Elektron, 1891–1910. Chapter 45, Hofmann.

LEVEY, Martin, 1913–; Ph.D. in history of science (1952); professor of mathematics at Temple University, 1956. Chapters 1, Babylonian Chemists; 3, Arabic Chemists.

LIEB, Hans, 1887–; Ph.D. Graz (1912); succeeded Pregl as professor for medical and physiological chemistry, Graz, 1931. Chapter 93, Pregl.

LIPPMANN, Edmund O. von, 1857–1940; Dr. phil. Heidelberg (1878); from 1877 on in the sugar industry; first in his father's plant; director of the sugar refining plant Halle, 1889–1926; professor of history, University of Halle, 1926–1933. Chapter 14, Marggraf.

MAROTTA, Domenico, 1886–; laureate in chemistry, University of Palermo; at Lab. Chimica della Sanità under Paternò, 1913; initiated Società Italiana Chimica, 1919; director Inst. Superiore di Sanità 1935. Chapter 47, Cannizzaro.

MARQUAND, Carl Bertram, 1895–; Ph.D. in physiological chemistry (1936); Edgewood Arsenal, 1940; exec. director, Chemical Corps Advisory Council, 1950. Chapter 90, Ipatieff (with Helen E. Marquand).

MEYER, Richard Emil, 1846–1926; Dr. phil. Göttingen (1868); Privat Dozent Munich, 1886; professor of chemistry, Technische Hochschule Braunschweig, 1889–1919; lecturer in the history of chemistry Leipzig, 1922. Chapter 60, Victor Meyer.

MILES, Wyndham, 1916–; Ph.D. in the history of science, Harvard (1955); historian at Army Chemical Center, 1953. Chapters 23, Rush; 31, Silliman; 32, Hare.

MULTHAUF, Robert P., 1919–; Ph.D. Berkeley (1953); head curator, Dept. of Science & Technology, U. S. National Museum, Smithsonian Institution, 1954. Chapters 5, Paracelsus; 6, Libavius; 10, Notes to Lemery.

MOUREU, Charles, 1863–1929; see biography by Dufraisse (80). Chapter 69, Ramsay.

NAUCKHOFF, Sigurd Adolf, 1879–1954; civil engineer (chemistry), Royal Institut of Technology, Stockholm, 1900; active in nitroglycerin and dynamite industry, 1900–1942; president, Royal Swedish Academy of Science, 1952–1953. Chapter 61, Klason.

NOELTING, Emilio, 1851–1922; Dr. phil. Zürich (1875); director of Chemie-Schule Mülhausen (Elsass), 1880–1922. Chapter 70, Witt.

ODLING, William, 1829–1921; demonstrator of chemistry at Guy's Hospital, 1850; professor of chemistry, University of Oxford, 1886. Chapter 41, Graham.

OESPER, Ralph E., 1886–; Ph.D. Cincinnati (1914); professor of analytical chemistry, University of Cincinnati, 1918. Chapter 44, Deville (with P. Lemay).

PALMAER, Knut Wilhelm, 1868–1942; Dr. phil. Uppsala (1895); professor of chemistry, Stockholm, 1907; director of the corrosion laboratory, Nobel Institut, Academy of Science, Stockholm. Chapter 76, Arrhenius.

PARTINGTON, James Riddick, 1886–; D.Sc. Manchester (1919); professor of chemistry, University of London, 1919. Chapter 7, Van Helmont.

PFEIFFER, Paul, 1875–1951; Dr. phil. (1897); professor at Rostock, 1916; Karlsruhe, 1919; Bonn, 1922. Chapter 87, Werner.

PHILLIPS, Max, 1894–1957; Ph.D. George Washington University (1923); U. S. Dept. of Agriculture, Bureau of Chemistry, 1919. Chapter 37, Payen.

PIETSCH, Ernst Hermann Erich, 1906–; Dr. phil. Berlin (1926); collaborator, 1925; chief editor of Gmelin's Handbuch der Anorganischen Chemie, 1936. Chapter 34, Gmelin (with E. Beyer).

ROSBAUD, Paul, 1896–; Dr. ing. Berlin (1926); crystallographic work at Kaiser Wilhelm Institut, Berlin; European Editor, Interscience Publishers. Chapter 112, Goldschmidt.

ROSE, Gustav, 1798–1873; Dr. phil. Berlin (1820); professor of mineralogy, Berlin, 1826; director of mineralogical museum, University of Berlin, 1856. Chapter 36, Mitscherlich.

RUSSELL, Alexander Smith, 1888–; studied with Soddy, 1909; Nernst, 1910; Rutherford, 1911–1913; professor at University of Oxford, 1920–1955. Chapter 105, Soddy.

RUZICKA, Leopold, 1887–; Dr. ing. Karlsruhe (1910); professor of organic chemistry, Utrecht, 1926; Eidgenössische Technische Hochschule, Zürich, 1929. Chapter 59, Wallach.

SCHOEPPFLE, Chester Seitz, 1892–1957; D.Sc. under Gomberg (1918); professor of organic chemistry, University of Michigan, Ann Arbor, 1936. Chapter 85, Gomberg (with W. E. Bachmann).

SECRÉTAN, Claude, 1897–; Dr. phil. Lausanne; professor of chemistry, Gymnases Cantonaux, Lausanne. Chapter 13, Rouelle.

SIEGFRIED, Robert, 1921–; Ph.D. in history of science at University of Wisconsin (1952); Professor of chemistry, University of Illinois, 1958. Chapter 29, Davy.

SILVERMANN, Alexander, 1881–; Ph.D. Pittsburgh (1902); chemist in glass works; Pittsburgh University, 1905; professor 1912–1951. Chapter 63, Le Chatelier.

STOCK, Alfred, 1876–1946; see biography by E. Wiborg (101). Chapter 67, Moissan.

THOMSON, Sir George Paget, 1892–; professor of natural philosophy, University of Aberdeen, 1922; of physics at Imperial College of Science, 1930–1952; chairman of first British Committee of Atomic Energy 1940–1941; master of Corpus Christi, Cambridge, 1953. Chapter 104, Aston.

THORPE, Thomas Edward, 1845–1925; Ph. D. Heidelberg (1868); professor of chemistry, College of Science and Technology, London 1885–1912. Chapter 43, Kopp.

TIZARD, Sir Henry Thomas, 1885–1959; studied chemistry at Oxford and Berlin; was largely responsible for developing Radar; president of Magdalen College, Oxford. Chapter 97, Sidgwick.

URBAIN, Georges, 1872–1938; graduated from the École de Physique et de Chimie, Paris (1894); professor of mineral chemistry there, 1908; director of the Institut de Chimie de Paris and co-director of the Institut de Biologie Physico-chimique, 1928. Chapter 39, Dumas and Wurtz.

VICQ-d'AZYR, Félix, 1748–1794; physician and anatomist, one of the founders of the Société Royale de Médicine; succeeded Buffon at the Académie de France, 1788. Chapter 12, Duhamel du Monceau.

WALDEN, Paul, 1863–1957; Dr. phil. Leipzig (1891); professor at Riga, 1892; Odessa, 1894; rector of the University of Riga, 1902–1906; Petersburg, 1908; Rostock, 1919; guest professor at Cornell, 1927–1928; Tübingen, 1946. Chapter 8, Glauber.

WEEKS, Mary Elvira, 1892–; Ph.D. Kansas (1927); professor and associate scientific librarian Kresge-Hooker Library; scientific librarian at Wayne University, 1944–1954. Chapter 33, Chevreul (with L. O. Amberg).

WEISSBERGER, Arnold, 1898–; professor emeritus; Ph.D. Leipzig (1924); Privat Dozent there, 1928–1933; at Oxford, 1933–1936; with Eastman Kodak Co. since 1936. Chapter 74, Hantzsch.

WIBERG, Egon, 1901–; Dr. phil. Karlsruhe (1927); professor of chemistry, Karlsruhe, 1940; University of München, 1951. Chapter 101, Stock.

WIELAND, Heinrich, 1877–1957; see biography by E. Farber (103). Chapter 109, Hans Fischer.

WILLSTÄTTER, Richard, 1872–1942; see biography by E. Farber (96). Chapter 53, Baeyer.

WOLFROM, Melvin Lawrence, 1900–; Ph.D. in organic chemistry (1927); National Research Fellow at Bureau of Standards; Rockefeller Institute and Ohio State, 1927–1928; at Ohio State, 1929; professor, 1940; head of organic chemistry division, 1948. Chapters 79, Nef; 92, Levene; 110, Hudson.

WOOD, Francis Carter, 1869–1951; M.S. Columbia (1894); assistant in clinical pathology, 1896–1898; professor, 1906; director of Cancer Institut, 1912. Chapter 89, Marie Curie.

Contents

xxi

Great Chemists

·· 1 ··

Babylonian Chemists

The oldest still known at present, dating back to about 3600 B. C. It was found at Tape Gowra in Mesopotamia and is 48 cm. high, 53 cm. in largest diameter. The channel contains about 2 liters, the inner pot about 37 liters. It was probably used to make perfumes.

THE EARLIEST mentioned chemists in history are found on cuneiform tablets of ancient Mesopotamia. Their names are *Tapputi-Belatekallim,* the Perfumeress, and [- - -] *ninu,* the Perfumeress.[1] Unfortunately, the latter's name is not known in full owing to lacunae in the tablet. The second part of the former name signifies that Tapputi was a mistress of the household. It seems evident that she was in charge of the manufacture of perfume products and had worked out the various steps of preparation by her own methods.

Both tablets are written in Akkadian, a Semitic language which predominated in the second millennium B.C. in Mesopotamia. There are, in all, seven tablets dealing with the technological aspects of perfumery. Six of these, including the two tablets which contain the names, resemble each other in style and method. One of these states that the date was the twentieth day of the month of Muhur-ilani in the year of the Limmu Qatnu-qardu. This places the tablets in the reign of Tukulti-Ninurti I (1256–1209 B.C.).[2]

The early history of chemistry is thus indebted to these women of over 3000 years ago as well as to their feminine successors in the early centuries of the Christian Era. Among the latter were Mary the Jewess, Paphnutia the Virgin, Cleopatra the Alchemist, and Theosebeia, the sister of Zosimos.[3]

With women as chief chemists, it is of interest to examine the texts—first to study the type of apparatus they used and second, the actual processes which were in operation.

In the period when the perfume texts were written, the Babylonians were producers of excellent bronze pots as well as fine clay containers of a variety of sizes and shapes capable of withstanding a high degree of heat.[4] In the above texts, the perfumeresses used an assortment of containers, such as a bowl or plate, a metal pot (called a *diqaru*) having a lid and used for heating over long periods of time, other types of pots, a cup serving as a measure (.4 liter), a flask for the perfume product, a sieve, and a stirrer.

3

The *diqaru* pot is the most interesting of all. It has been shown that this was a type of distillatory or sublimatory apparatus similar to some found at Tepe Gawra, in northern Mesopotamia dating back to ca. 3500 B.C. One is now in the Government Museum in Baghdad; the other is in the University Museum in Philadelphia.[5]

In one tablet, after the well-soaked aromatic botanical has been macerated and warmed with oil, the instructions read:

"You do not remove the organic material. Do not take away the charcoal. The fire rises; the oil throws up foam. You will repeatedly wipe up the inner section of the *diqaru* vessel with a handcloth. You stir and cover up. . . ."[6]

This passage is the earliest description of the process of Babylonian distillation. Here, the chemists used a sublimatory with a wide brim or lip having a slight depression in its center to retain the distillate after it had run down the inclined cover. The method is similar to that described by al-Razi in *"Al-Madkhal al-Talimi"* who used a vessel with a wide brim on which the sublimate settled after having risen due to the heat.[7] It was common in Arabic times (800–1200 A.D.) to soak up the distillate and then express it into a container by means of a cloth just as the Babylonians did.

The apparatus used in the perfumery operations by the women chemists might easily have been culinary utensils. The only exception is the *diqaru* pot which may be conceived simply as an evolutionary product of an ordinary kitchen pot used in food-heating processes.

As to the method, this also represents a combination of various types of operations often carried out by women in cooking. A typical set of operations reads in part:[8]

"At its seventh time that you mix ingredients, you will heat *tabilu* [an aromatic botanical] in fresh, good water of the well. You will pour into a vessel, ½ qa [.4 liter] of myrrh, ½ qa calamus, crushed and filtered [onto the heated liquid]. It soaks overnight. At dawn, filter the liquid and this aromatic through a straining cloth. Clarify it from this vessel into another. Discard the residue. You measure ½ qa of this liquid. Process, as earlier, purified cypress, myrrh, calamus and ½ qa . . . . You mix it together. Kindle a fire under the *diqaru* vessel; you heat . . . . If

4

it bothers the lip of the *diqaru* vessel . . . . You will cause your finger to poise over the *diqaru* vessel . . . ; if it is as warm as water for bathing [and the fire] rises, then your liquid is heated for the purpose of mixing. You pour oil into it and agitate with a stirrer. When they interpenetrate, just as though dissolving in one another, you will rake up the fire under the *diqaru* vessel; you will cover the *diqaru* vessel. For 2–3 days it remains . . . . You will kindle a fire. If the components continue to dissolve in one another, do not agitate strongly. Cover the *diqaru* vessel; cool. Remove the oil. Wash the *diqaru* vessel . . . , you will wipe. This is the purification of the seventh time."

The chemists used a combinatory process of maceration and extraction, first with water, then with oil as vehicles for the essential oils of perfume. The Babylonians worked with small batches at a time as seen from the text. Raw material (comminuted or expressed botanical material) was added in small amounts at a time to the larger, already worked batch. This resembled the medieval process of cohobation. At times, extraction was carried out with heat and oil or with oil alone or water alone. Extraction was often performed in as many as twenty repetitive operations.

In the case of water of perfume, the Babylonians may be quoted to advantage:[9]

"The following is the preparation in perfumery for 10 qa of commercial quality oil which is produced in the case of balsam. You clarify it with a fine sieve then pour it into a small flask. Let it rest a full month. Then, you return it to its *diqaru* vessel. You manufacture it with forty washings (aqueous extractions) of balsam. One calls it 'washing water for the king'."

Because of the slight solubility of most essential oils in aqueous solution, it is not surprising that the process was repeated forty times to obtain a greater yield. Even though apparatus and methods were somewhat improved later,[10] the idea of many repetitive operations persisted throughout the entire period of alchemical work.[11]

In addition to aqueous solutions, the Babylonian literature mentions perfumes in other forms, such as oil solutions and salves, both pure and compounded with other aromatics:[12]

"If you prepare *asanitu* (unknown plant) oil as perfume, for

5

10 qa of oil, 1 talent *asanitu;* 1 mina myrrh, 1 mina calamus, 1 mina . . . , 1 qa honey . . . ."

Babylonian women chemists were thoroughly empirical in their approach to perfumery operations. It would seem, from the evidence in the Babylonian tablets, that women were responsible for the early types of apparatus and for the repetitive processes later found in Greek and Muslim chemistry. The practical and objective methods utilized were such as to be expected from women who were not only experts in food preparation but already had made progress in some of the more specialized processes of distillation, extraction, and sublimation.[13]

NOTES AND REFERENCES

1 E. Ebeling, "Parfümrezepte and Kultische Texte aus Assur" (Roma: Pontifical Institute, 1950), pp. 32, 46.
2 *Ibid.,* p. 15.
3 M. Levey, *J. Chem. Ed. 31,* 374 (1954).
4 O. Streu, *Zeit. der Deut. Morgenl. Ges. 98,* p. 359 (1944).
5 M. Levey, *Centaurus* 4, pp. 23–33 (1955).
6 E. Ebeling, *op. cit.,* p. 20.
7 Stapleton, Azo and Husain, *Memoirs Asiatic Soc. Bengal,* VIII (1922–29).
8 E. Ebeling, *op. cit.,* pp. 33–4.
9 *Ibid.,* pp. 40–41.
10 Cf. Karl Garbers, ed., transl., Al-Kindi's, "Kitab Kimiya Al-Itr Wattasidat," *Abhandlungen für die Kunde des Morgenländes* XXX (Leipzig: 1948).
11 F. Sherwood Taylor, "The Alchemists" (New York: 1949), p. 85
12 E. Ebeling, *op. cit.,* p. 47.
13 M. Levey, *Osiris* XII, p. 389; cf. "Chemistry and Chemical Technology in Ancient Mesopotamia," Elsevier, Amsterdam (1959).

MARTIN LEVEY

Philosophers and Practitioners

from About 800 BC to AD 800

PLATO AND ARISTOTLE

CHEMISTRY as a science has its roots in the experiences of artisans and the thoughts of philosophers. Very little is known about the metal workers and stone masons, the jewelers and dyers, the brewers and druggists of ancient times—not much more than the names and dates of some of its philosophers. They were not scientists, yet they exerted great influence on the development of science. A few of these men who became important in the growth of chemistry will be mentioned here.

It seems appropriate to start with Hesiod, who lived after Homer, perhaps toward the end of the eighth century. First, because many of the ancient philosophers were also poets; second, because of Hesiod's remarkable story of the five ages of the world from his poem "Work and Days." Four of these five ages are characterized by metals: "The age of gold which was the age of peace and perfection; the age of silver, less pure and less noble; the age of bronze; the fourth age which seems to refer to the Minoan revival the glorious remembrance of which had inspired Homer; finally the age of iron, the present age of sorrow, hatred, and strife." (Quoted from George Sarton's "History of Science," Cambridge, 1952, p. 148.) Obviously, these metals are to designate a moral and aesthetic character, not a prevalent technology. Yet the knowledge of gold, silver, bronze, and iron must have been common enough to invite using them as symbols.

Thales of Miletos, on the western coast of Asia Minor (about 624 to about 545 B.C.), proclaimed water as the original substance from which everything was derived. This poetical and mystical concept had Babylonian predecessors and strange consequences as late as our seventeenth century.

Anaximandros of Miletos (610–545 B.C.) was primarily an astronomer. His concept of a primary substance was the *apeiron,* itself undetermined and undefinable, but potentially everything.

His younger compatriot, Anaximenes, saw air as the primary substance, whereas Heracleitos of Ephesos, in the beginning of the fifth century, ascribed that role to fire.

9

Empedocles of Agrigentum (Sicily), born about 492, agreed with all three and added earth to the number of elements. They are subjected to two moving forces: love and hatred. Philosophical reasoning convinced him that the propagation of light must occur with a finite velocity.

Democritos of Abdera, a widely traveled man, was believed to have been born about 460. His name is connected with the concept of the theory of atoms. He propagated and elaborated it, but its origins may go back to earlier times and other places. At least we know more about him than about Leucippos, who is said to have written about atoms some thirty years before Democritos. His atoms are absolutely simple, indivisible parts, all alike except in shape, order, and position.

Plato was born in Athens in 428. After twelve years of travel in Greece, Egypt, Italy, and Sicily he returned to Athens. On land which originally belonged to Academos, a hero of ancient times, Plato established a school which was called the Academia. He died in Athens, in 347 B.C. His philosophy influenced the development of science in many ways, specifically through his acceptance of the four elements and of the analogy between the universe, the macrocosmos, and the small world of our body, the microcosmos.

Aristotle (384–322) was born in Stageira (Thrace), the son of a physician. For twenty years (367–347) he was connected with the Academia as Plato's student. He lived in Macedonia as the educator of Alexander, who became the great king in 336. Aristotle then returned to Athens and founded the School of the Peripatetics at the Lykeion (Lyceum) which he directed for twelve years. Through his teaching and writing he dominated the development of science, particularly during the Middle Ages, as the unquestioned authority. He gave new depth to the concept of the basic four elements. For Empedocles, they had been absolute and unchangeable; through Aristotle they became the basis for explaining all substantial changes, involving combinations of the four primary qualities: hot, cold, dry, wet. To the four elements he added a fifth, ether, which he conceived as the first in rank. It was later called *quinta essentia*.

Matter, or *hyle*, is one of the four Aristotelian principles besides form (or *morphe*), cause, and purpose. Form is the realization, the entelechy or actuality, of matter which is poteniality, the passive principle which becomes reality through form. These thoughts have been as important for the course of chemistry as the concept of the elements.

Theophrastos of Eresos (about 372–288) was appointed by Aristotle as his successor at the Lyceum and remained head of the school for thirty-five years. His greatest fame is that of father of botany, but he also was a geologist and mineralogist who classified rocks according to the action of fire upon them. Precious stones interested him particularly. His description of the process of making white lead (lead acetate) shows his familiarity with the "chemical industry" of his time.

Epikuros (341–271) continued and modified the concept of atoms which have no qualities except size, shape, and gravity. His ideas were made popular by the Roman poet, T. Lucretius Carus (96?–55 B.C.).

The writings from the following centuries give us the dim outlines of a few persons and the names of many legendary authorities on thoughts and recipes.

Zosimos, who lived in the third or fourth century of our era, was an encyclopedic writer who claimed Egyptian gods and priests, Moses, and the Greek philosophers as his authorities. He described the "weighing" and "combining" of substances, the conversion (*metabolé*) of base metals into gold through the influence of spirits (*pneumata*), the way to "the great mystical substance" called *xerion* which, in small quantities, causes great masses of metal to be converted into gold, acting like yeast of which very little is needed to ferment a large batch of dough. Among his more recent authorities is Mary the Jewess, who invented heating in a water bath as an effective method for gentle operations.

In addition to books about "the mystical art of the philosophers," "the divine and sacred art," collections of sober recipes on ores, metals, drugs, and dyes have survived. They contain some amazing techniques and observations which proved valuable and remained in practice for many centuries.

We may be strongly inclined to attribute greater chemical value to these carefully developed experiences than to the exalted speculations. The historical facts show, however, that both were needed in the development of chemistry as a science. We should not project our concepts of science as goal and yardstick into those times when the greatest need was to reconcile ancient mysteries and rites with new experiences and thoughts.

NOTES AND REFERENCES

M. Berthelot, "Collections des Anciens Alchimistes Grecs," G. Steinheil, Paris, 1888.

Marshall Clagett, "Greek Science in Antiquity," Abelard-Schumann, New York, 1955.

M. Cohen and I. E. Drabkin, "A Source Book in Greek Science," McGraw-Hill, New York, 1948.

A. J. Hopkins, "Alchemy, Child of Greek Philosophy," Columbia University Press, New York, 1934.

Edmund O. von Lippmann, "Entstehung und Ausbreitung der Alchemie," Julius Springer, Berlin, 1919.

George Sarton, "A History of Science—Ancient Science through the Golden Age of Greece," Harvard University Press, Cambridge, 1952.

George Sarton, "Introduction to the History of Science," vols. I–III, Carnegie Institution of Washington, Williams & Wilkins, Baltimore, 1927–1947.

EDUARD FARBER

·· 3 ··

Arabic Chemists[1]

AVICENNA

W ITH the expulsion of the scholarly Nestorian Christians from Constantinople in 431 A.D., what was left of Greek learning moved to Edessa, in northern Syria. From there, in 489, it went to Nisibis, Mesopotamia and finally, shortly after 500, to Jundishapur, north of Basra in Persia. The Nestorians[2] were for many centuries a major link between East and West. Their culture, in fact, eventually diffused as far as Pekin. The hard-working Nestorians translated into Syriac Greek works on medicine, religion, astronomy, mathematics, and alchemy. Later on, translations were made into Arabic from the many Near-Eastern languages including Persian, Greek, Syriac, and others.

Because of their geographical location, the Nestorians were able to draw upon their Greek heritage and also utilized the knowledge made available to them from the peoples of Mesopotamia. Greek and Mesopotamian learning and technology thus made its way to the Muslims.[3] The latter learned from the Egyptians as well as from the artisans and craftsmen of the many countries conquered by them after the death of Mohammed. Thus, there was a fusion of the Greek, Egypto-Babylonian, and Muslim cultures to produce a new, highly viable product.

In the chemistry and the alchemy of the Muslims, there are often allusions to the operational methods well-known to the ancient Mesopotamians, who were the earliest chemists in history. For example, it has already been pointed out that the apparatus used by the ninth century chemist, al-Kindi, is similar to that in the twelfth century B.C. cuneiform tablets on perfumery.[4] Similarly, many of the actual operations strikingly resemble those of ancient Mesopotamia in many details. A huge debt is owed the Muslims for carrying on chemical tradition after Greek culture deteriorated markedly. It is also to the credit of the Muslims that, as conquerors, they chose to nurture and adopt the chemical knowledge of the Persians, Egyptians, Syrians, Greeks, and other peoples who had been overwhelmed by their armies. Significant also, as shown by the works of Jabir, al-Razi, and others, is that

15

their experiments were planned, material was well organized, and elaborate and careful notations of results were made.

Transmutation of the elements in the works of the outstanding Muslim chemists is not the central core of their thinking. In almost all cases of any consequence, it occupies a position of secondary importance. Alchemy, compared with chemistry, was no more important in the Golden Age of the Arabs (750–1150) than was numerology in relation to mathematics. The development of chemistry proceeded apace in this period despite the attempts of some to fasten the elements of mysticism upon the growing science.

For the development of chemistry, it was necessary in the Arabic period that the science be expanded quantitatively, just as it had been done in its first great historic period of growth in ancient Mesopotamia from 3000 to 500 B.C. Although the Mesopotamians, and later the Muslims, had their own theories on chemical matters, they were inadequate since qualitative understanding was still dependent on further experimental results and observations. The following biographies, with their bird's-eye views of the respective accomplishments, will serve to underline the unique position of the Muslims in the history of chemistry.

JABIR IBN HAYYAN

Abu Abdallah Jabir ibn Hayyan b. Abdallah al-Kufi, also known as al-Sufi or Jabir, was born probably between 720 and 723 and flourished ca. 760 A.D. In al-Nadim's "Fihrist,"[5] the bibliography of the Muslim world which was completed in 987 A.D., Jabir occupies an important place. Al-Nadim ascribed hundreds of works to Jabir, who is listed in the alchemical section. Later manuscripts, in abundance, bear Jabir's Latinized name, Geber, up to the thirteenth century. According to Taylor,[6] the works ascribed to Geber, although very orderly, as are those of Jabir, and having other similar characteristics, are nevertheless sufficiently different to prove separate authorship. Therefore he believed that the Geberian corpus should be considered as distinct from the Jabirian works. It was Paul Kraus,[7, 13] who came to the conclusion, now accepted by most historians of chemistry, that the famous name was used over and over by other writers in the expansion of Jabir's writings or in original works of members of the Ismaelite sect. This group, by the way, is still in existence today under the Aga Khan and believes that its system embraces all religions since they all have elements of truth in them.

Stapleton[8] believes that Jabir was a real person and practicing alchemist. The works under the signature of Jabir are supposed to have been re-edited to a large extent in the ninth century.[9]

It seems that doubt as to the existence of Jabir was already prevalent in the last part of the tenth century, as shown in the "Fihrist":[10] "Many scholars and elders of the Booksellers' Corporation say that this man, I mean Jabir, did not exist at all, whilst some of them say that, if he really did exist, he composed nothing but the Book of Mercy, *Kitab al-Rahma,* and that those books (supposed to have been composed by him) were written by other people and then ascribed to him. But I say that for an eminent man to sit down, and weary himself out with the composition of a book comprising 2000 folios, fatiguing his talents and thoughts in composing it and [tiring] his hand and body in writing it down, and then to assign it to another person, either real or imaginary this, I say, is a kind of foolishness . . . [No,] the man [Jabir] really existed: his circumstances are too clear and well known and his writings too important and numerous."

In the "Fihrist," the earliest source for Jabir, al-Nadim writes:[11]

> People differ about him, for the Shiites [a Muslim sect] say that he is one of their great men and one of the spiritual guides [religious officials who instructed novices], and they assert that he was a companion of Jafar al-Sadiq—Peace be upon him—and that he was a Kufan. Some philosophers, however, maintain that he was one of themselves, and that he composed books on logic and philosophy, whereas the seekers after the Philosopher's Stone assert, that the leading position [in this art] in his days was held by him, but that he lived in concealment. They maintain that he kept roaming about the countries without settling in a place because he feared the government would attempt his life [as a subversive]. It is also said, however, that he belonged to the circle of the Barmacides, was devoted to them and showed respect [as a student] to Jafar b. Yahya; for those who maintain this, say that he means by this, Jafar al-Sadiq—Peace be upon him!

From this paragraph, it is evident that by 987 A.D. there was already considerable difference of opinion regarding Jabir. The Shiites, philosophers, and alchemists all claimed him as one of them.

Quoting al-Nadim further:[11] "A reliable man who practiced the Art told me that he [the narrator] used to live in the street of the Syrian Gate, in a lane known as 'Gold Lane'. Now this man told me that Jabir for the most part lived at Kufa and, owing to the city's good air, prepared there the elixir. When, at Kufa, the cellar was discovered in which a golden mortar weighing 200 pounds was found, the place—said this man—where they had found it [the mortar] was the actual house of Jabir b. Hayyan, but they found nothing else in the cellar except the mortar and a place for carrying out [the process of] solution and fixation. This happened in the days of Muizz al Daula [reigned 967–977]. The chamberlain Abu Sabuktagin told me that he himself went to receive this [treasure]."

Jafar's father, Yahya ibn Khalid, is also mentioned in the "Fihrist" under alchemists and may, therefore, have been Jabir's teacher rather than the other Jafar mentioned. Kufa, on the western arm of the Euphrates, just south of the ruins of Babylon, in Iraq, was then a rapidly growing and thriving city. At one time it was one of the principal cities of the Umayyad Caliphate and had 200,000 inhabitants.

Jabir finally established himself as an alchemist at the court of Harun al-Rashid and as a friend of the Iman Jafar al-Sadiq (700–765).[12] At that time Jabir was identified with the Barmacides, a group including the ministers of the Caliph. These later became a menace to the ruler and were finally expelled. Jabir then returned to Kufa. One account has it that he served under Caliph al-Mamun (reigned 813–833), another that he died in 815 in Tus, the capital of Khorasan.[13]

As to the works of Jabir, al-Nadim writes:[14] "A big catalogue by him exists, which comprises everything he has written on alchemy and the other subjects, and there exists also a small catalogue by him, which comprises only what he has written on the art; and we shall mention a number of his books which either we have seen, or which reliable people have seen and mentioned to us."

Then follow 112 book titles on alchemy,[15] listing works on red tincture, hair, blood, plants, eggs, ferments, salts, stones, urine, perfume, milk, arsenics, amalgams, light, mines or minerals, and a number of other subjects.[16]

Following this most important group are in succession the "Seventy Books," the "Ten Books," including works on balance and others covering the entire field of alchemy as well as its history, the philosophy of the Greeks and of the Muslim sects, astrology, anatomy, astronomy, and physics.

After the list of 306 titles ascribed to Jabir, al-Nadim quotes him as saying:[17] "Then I composed books on asceticism and sermons and I composed books on pneumatic-magic, and I composed many books on matters that act by their specific properties. Then I composed 500 books to refute the philosophers; then I composed a book on the art known as the "Book of the Kingdom," another book, known as the "Book of the Luxuriant Gardeners."

The chemical knowledge of Jabir resembles that of al-Razi in many important respects, both being believers in the process of transmutation as well as having a similar objectivity, logic, and order in their works. The idea of transmutation, however, was not the fundamental spring of Jabir's concepts.

It may be of interest to examine parts of one of Jabir's works, "The First Book of the Element of the Foundation," *Ustuqus al-Uss,* the first work listed by al-Nadim. One may note here the clear-cut classification of the substances used in his chemistry.

"The advocates of [the use of] stone say that the knowledge [of alchemy] lies only in stone, and that certainly no knowledge or result lies in animal or vegetable. They say that the alchemists, in giving the description of The Stone hinted at mineral bodies and not at anything else, and these are the sulphurs, the arsenic sulphides, mercury and the bodies. The alchemists have made distinctions between them, and say that spirits are those that volatilize over fire. These are of two varieties, and their total is six—viz., the sulphurs, the arsenic sulphides and oil. The other three volatilize over fire, and neither are themselves consumed nor do they consume anything; and these are sal ammoniac, mercury and camphor."[8]

Stapleton is of the opinion that when Jabir first began his work,

19

he did not realize the reactivity of ammonium chloride. Later, he excluded camphor and the oils from the list of "spirits" given in his sixty-first treatise of the "Seventy." These facts tend to show that Jabir was, according to his own claim, a careful experimenter and recorder of his own work.

Jabir goes on to elaborate on definitions of terms which he uses: "The meaning of the word 'spirit' as used by the alchemists is 'active tincture' because it imparts to 'bodies' a large amount of 'spirit'." It is said in this connection: "Verily in our substances the amounts of *Jism* [inert matter] are small but the amounts of 'spirit' are very large. Thus a small quantity [stone or elixir] of it tinctures a great quantity of the amounts of inorganic substance."

"Between 'soul' and 'spirit' there is this difference, viz., that in the 'spirit' there is no oily property, while the 'soul' in its very nature is oily. Every oil catches hold of, and enters into, and unites with, the 'bodies,' so that the property of admixture is found in 'souls' only, viz., the oils. According, therefore, to this [classification] there are three 'souls': sulphur, oil, and arsenic sulphide: and three 'spirits'—mercury, sal ammoniac and camphor. There is an element of doubt regarding mercury because, with 'spirits,' it is a 'spirit' and, with 'souls,' a 'soul.' Hence it has much resemblance to the planet Mercury because when the latter is in conjunction with an auspicious star it becomes auspicious and when in conjunction with an inauspicious star it becomes inauspicious, and so on. Owing to this, the distinction between 'soul' and 'spirit' is in regard to admixture, and inability to mix. That which has the capacity of admixture is in reality 'soul': but it is also 'spirit' on account of volatilization: and that which has no power to mix is 'spirit' only, owing to its volatilization, and to there being no 'soul' [i.e., oil] in it."

In this early work, Jabir considered glass to be a useless substance but later in his "Book of the Seventy" ranked it as a metal. Probably he was able to effect different colorations in glass and this color ["spirit"] acted on "bodies" [the glass].

Jabir believed that the prime natures were heat, cold, dryness, and moistness. These were separable from chemical materials and could be recombined with other materials to produce new properties more desirable. Neo-Pythagorean numerology was enlisted to determine the proper amounts of the prime natures to be utilized in new preparations. Astrological considerations were also of great importance.

Metals were formed of sulfur and mercury with the prime natures admixed in various proportions. Impurities accounted for the existence of different metals. An equilibrium of prime natures was depended upon to achieve a "balance" which accounted for various property changes in substances.

Although previous alchemists used mineral substances almost exclusively in preparation of their elixirs, Jabir introduced materials of botanical and zoological origin into his work, thus going back to the ideas of the Sumerians.[18]

Repetition of chemical processes was of great importance. Jabir, for example, repeated his distillations and extractions many times, just as the Babylonians did in the second millennium B.C. in their perfumery operations.[4]

Jabir deserves credit in that he did not spend all his time on efforts to transmute metals but contributed much to the development of chemistry by experiment and observation. In his works, nitric acid is prepared. Technological processes like dyeing, metallurgy, glass-making, and many other chemical operations are discussed and improved upon in Jabir's works to provide a solid base for future chemical workers.

AL-KINDI

Abu Yusuf Yaqub b. Ishaq al-Kindi (ca. 800–870), called the "philosopher of Arabia," was born of southern Arabian stock probably at the beginning of the ninth century A.D. at Kufa, now in Iraq. In this early Abbaside period, there was a blossoming of Islamic science and learning as well as considerable translation and the writing of commentaries on considerable important Greek works.[19]

Al-Kindi's father was then Governor at Kufa.[20] As a young man, al-Kindi studied at Basra and Baghdad, where many of the great Muslim scientists and philosophers had gathered under the aegis of the Caliph Mamun. Later, al-Kindi became the tutor of the succeeding Caliph's son. It was at this court, under the Caliph's protection that al-Kindi was introduced to the ancient masters, such as Hippocrates, Plato, Aristotle, Euclid, Hypsicles, Ptolemy, and many others. It is of interest that al-Kindi spent much time interpreting their favorite Greek philosophers to the Muslims in a number of philosophical works.[21] Since al-Kindi was a devout Mutazilite, for a while he was persecuted and his library was confiscated. However, he was still living in 870 when he predicted that the Abbaside empire would last 450 years in spite of the fact that it was threatened by the configurations of the stars and by the Karmathians, a rival Mohammedan sect.

All his mature life al-Kindi worked on making available to the Muslims the ancient science and philosophy of the Greeks. This he did mainly by writing commentaries and works of his own in explanation. In the "Fihrist," written by al-Nadim,[22, 28] we find a list of al-Kindi's works. Here we learn that al-Kindi wrote 25 philosophical opera, including works on Aristotle and Porphyry, 9 works on logic, 11 treatises on arithmetic, 8 works on the sphere, 8 writings on music, 24 on astronomy, 27 on geometry, 21 on the celestial orbit, 24 on medicine, 9 on astrology, 17 on polemics, 17 on the soul, 12 on politics, 14 on the atmosphere and meteorology, 10 on determination of distances, 5 on preconception, and finally 36 works on technology and chemistry.

The latter collection is of great interest in the history of science and particularly chemistry since the works include such titles as "Treatise on Distillation of Aromatics," "Treatise on the Construction of a Burning Glass," "Treatise on the Origin of Thunder, Lightning, Snow, Cold, Thunderbolt and Rain," "Treatise on Various Kinds of Philosopher's Stones," "Treatise on Dyes," "On the Futility of the Claim of Those Who Pretend the Making of Gold and Silver and Their Deceits," "Treatise on Sundry Types of Precious Stones and Similar Things," "Treatise on Various Types of Swords and Iron," "Aromatics and their Different Types," "Preparation of Spices," "Treatise on the Fraudulent Arts of the Alchemist," and other similar writings on physics and biology.

Al-Kindi[23] was an eclectic philosopher in the neo-Platonic sense. In mathematics, he was a neo-Pythagorean; he considered it basic to all the sciences and applied it practically in medicine and in physics. Geometric proportion was adapted to the preparation of remedies in the proper use of heat, cold, dryness, and humidity.

Although al-Kindi was celebrated as an astrologer,[24] he was a natural philosopher above all. Al-Kindi was much occupied with the history of the development of the neo-Platonist-Aristotelianism in Islam as shown in his work now called "Liber de Intellectu."

In regard to alchemy, much practiced in his day, al-Kindi displayed skepticism.[25] He believed that silver and gold could not be prepared by man in a transmutation process but had to be obtained naturally. Al-Razi defended alchemy against the attacks of al-Kindi, who claimed that man cannot do what nature alone can, and that the practices of the alchemists are fraudulent and deceitful. In this, al-Kindi was probably the first Muslim to dispute the alchemists. Later, he was followed in these beliefs by Avicenna. Emphasizing the opposition of al-Kindi to alchemy is the manner in which al-Nadim, in the "Fihrist," listed Dubais, a disciple of al-Kindi:[22]

"He is Muhammad ibn Yazid, known as Dubais, one of those who dealt with the Art and the External Practices. By him are the following books: 1. The book of the collector, and 2. The book of the making of dyes, and of black and colored ink."

What is interesting is that the title of the latter work indicates no attempt at transmutation but rather "external practices" in the making of dyes and inks.

It is regrettable that most of al-Kindi's works have not yet been found or brought to light in critical editions or translations. Karl Garbers, however, in 1948 published the original Arabic and German translation of one of al-Kindi's most significant works, *Kitab fi-kimiya al-itr wat-tasidat,* "Book on the Chemistry of Perfume and Distillations." This treatise contains 107 recipes for the preparation of aromatic oils, salves, and water of perfume. Also included is the preparation of adulterants for costly drugs; ersatz mixtures were an important part of the perfumery trade of the time. It is of some interest that a man of al-Kindi's stature had no compunction about advising his readers on the preparation of substitutes which could be sold on the market as more costly products without the buyer being aware of the deception. The adulterated drug was labeled as "best quality" and sold at a high price. In one recipe, al-Kindi takes pride in the fact that he sold drugs, which escaped detection even by apothecaries as having been falsified.[23]

The use of aromatics was a cultural carry-over from Sumerian, Babylonian, and Egyptian methods of treating the sick.[18] In ancient times, going back to 3000 B.C., scores of aromatics were well known. It is therefore not surprising that al-Kindi shows an acquaintance with a great variety of perfumes of zoological and botanical origin, such as saffron, aloe wood, musk, Nemecylon tinctorum, oil from apricot kernels, jasmine, roses, stock gillyflower, camphor, sweet gum, sandalwood, and many others.

In the recipes of al-Kindi, a division into three categories may be made: (a) falsification of drugs and perfumes, (b) preparation of aromatic oils and salves, and (c) distillation of aromatic water of perfume.

In the falsification of musk, for example, the usual process is to comminute dry botanical substances and mix with dye, fatty oil, some genuine musk, and knead to a doughlike consistence.

FIG. 1. Sublimation apparatus in al-kindi (after Karl Garbers). A = beaker in which impure camphor is placed; B = beaker receiver; C = lid luted on beaker A; D = hearth base.

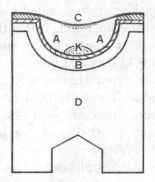

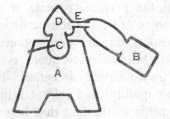

FIG. 2. Still of al-Kindi (after Karl Garbers, "Kitāb Kīmiyā . . . von al-Kindī," p. 19). A = hearth base; B = receiver; C = cucurbit; D = alembic; E = air condenser.

24

Then it is dried, made into small pieces, some genuine musk added, and placed in a musk bottle or in a small glass flask. The musk bottle is stopped with gum arabic and dried somewhat in an oven. The doughlike material is processed through a porous cloth many times. The drug is sold as a liquid or as a dough. In one recipe, musk is mixed with the running blood of a slaughtered young goat.[25]

By far the most interesting sections of this work on perfumery are those relating to the types of apparatus used in distillation and sublimation. It is of importance when one realizes that the representations are almost exactly like those of the Alexandrian chemists who preceded the Arabs and very much, in turn, like the apparatus used by the Babylonians in the second millennium B.C.[26] The original drawings are labeled in the Arabic manuscript. Figures 1 and 2 have been redrawn from those given by Garbers but the labels are given in English (or transliterated Arabic if no English equivalent is known).[27]

These representations are not very different from those of earlier Greek works but their importance lies in the fact that al-Kindi intended his apparatus to be used on a commercial scale. The size, however, of the apparatus is not given and so its feasibility is therefore uncertain.

AL-RAZI

Al-Razi, called Rhazes in medieval Europe, was born at Raiy[29] in 866. This was a town just south of the Caspian Sea, near modern Teheran. Few details of his life are known. It is related by a biographer[30] that al-Razi as a youth "played on the lute and cultivated vocal music, but, on reaching the age of manhood, he renounced these occupations, saying that music, proceeding from between mustaches and a beard had no charms to recommend it."

Ibn Khallikan, in his biography, says of al-Razi that he was past 40 when he turned to medicine and probably to his other scientific pursuits in more serious fashion. This took place, it is believed, in Baghdad, then the capital of the Abbasides, who had been supporting science and learning for many years. This patronage was carried out by such Muslim rulers as al-Mansur (754–75), Harun al-Rashid, and al-Mamun without regard to the re-

25

ligion or origin of the scholars.[31] As a result, when al-Razi came to Baghdad, he found institutes for the study of Greek science, and translations done mainly by the Christian Hunain ibn Ishaq (809–77) and his school, of writings of Plato, Aristotle, Plotinus, Hippocrates, Galen, Oribasius, and many more philosophers, mathematicians, and learned men. There were also great libraries and hospitals as well as famous teachers who had inherited the mantle of scientific tradition.

Al-Razi studied medicine under the well-known doctor, Abul Hasan Ali bin Sahl bin Rabban, a Jewish apostate to Islam. Showing great skill, al-Razi soon became head of a hospital, first in Raiy, his home town, then in Baghdad. Due to the shifting political situation, al-Razi found himself going from court to court enjoying the patronage of enlightened princes.[32] Al-Razi achieved fame as the greatest physician the Muslim world ever produced.

Al-Biruni[33] relates that al-Razi had many publications to his credit: 33 works on natural science; 11 on mathematics, astrology, and astronomy; 45 on philosophy, logic, and theology; and over 100 medical treatises. In alchemy, al-Razi wrote a "Compendium of Twelve Treatises" and a dozen other books. Two of the latter are dedicated to the defense of alchemy and are refutations of works of doubters such as al-Kindi.

The titles[34] of the twelve books on alchemy are: (1) "Introduction to the Doctrine"; (2) "Introduction to the Theory of the Art"; (3) "Book of the Sure Exposition of the Art"; (4) "Book of the Stone"; (5) "Book of Practice"; (6) "Book of the Elixir"; (7) "Book of the Nobility of the Art"; (8) "Book of Progression"; (9) "Book of the Practical Method"; (10) "Book of Solution of Enigmas (Opinions of Ancient Philosophers on the Art)"; (11) "Book of Tests"; (12) "Book of Secrets of the Wise and Their Enumeration."

Other titles relating to alchemy are: (13) "Book of the Secret"; (14) "Book of the Secret of Secrets"; (15) "Book of Perfection"; (16) "Book of Refutation of al-Kindi"; (17) "Book of Stones"; (18) "Communication to the Experimenters"; (19) "Book of the Yellow Stone"; (20) "Book on the Letters to the Kings." Other works are ascribed to al-Razi by al-Biruni and Ibn Abi Usaibia. The latter claims that al-Razi wrote "Book on—That the Art of

Alchemy Is an Art, in Which Actuality Is Closer Than Impossibility." Perhaps this title reflects an alchemist's views on his own subject.

Al-Razi claimed to have prepared the Philosophers' Stone but was not able to prove it.[35] However, the significance of al-Razi's work lies rather in the fact that he was a careful observer. Stapleton believes that al-Razi was the first in history to systematize chemical facts, reactions, and apparatus in a language almost completely free of mysticism and ambiguity.[36]

Al-Biruni said of al-Razi: "Regarding his life, I only know with certainty that he was occupied with alchemy. Finally his sight failed thus leading him to the study of medicine, in which he became famous. The most powerful kings brought him to their courts as a physician. He was a sincere scholar with many students. He would put a lamp in the niche of a wall and stand nearby supporting the book against the wall so that, when sleep came, it would fall from his hand and awaken him. This was the primary cause of the loss of his sight; the second was his fondness for beans. He finally lost the sight of both eyes. From Tabaristan, a pupil came to treat him and was of the opinion that a cataract operation was necessary. Whereupon, al-Razi replied that the end of his life was close and that pain would be unpleasant then. Soon after, al-Razi died at Raiy on the fifth of Shaban, 313 A. H. [Oct. 26, 925 A.D.], aged 62 lunar years and 5 days [approx. 60 solar years]."[37]

Although this anecdote shows in general the character of al-Razi, its accuracy is uncertain. Ibn Abi Usaibia relates that when al-Razi was urged to submit to cupping, he is alleged to have replied, "No I have seen the world so long that I am tired of it."[38]

Condemned as heretical by almost all Muslim opinion, al-Razi's philosophical writings[39] are very revealing of the man himself. He believed that religions, in addition to being hostile to philosophical and scientific research, were the sole cause of the wars that ravage humanity. Furthermore, al-Razi believed not only that the alleged holy scriptures are books of no value but that of much greater service to humanity were the works of such ancients as Plato, Aristotle, Hippocrates, and Euclid. Al-Razi had confidence in the progress of scientific and philosophical knowledge.[40]

27

A direct quote by al-Nadim, author of the "Fihrist" reads: "Al-Razi asserts that no one can succeed in the science of philosophy, nor can a scholar be called a philosopher unless he [first] succeeds in the science of the alchemical art, so that he becomes by this independent of everybody, whilst everybody else stands in need of him by reason of his knowledge and resources."[41]

Only four of al-Razi's chemical works have been found and examined: (a) "Elementary Introduction," *Kitab al-mudhal al-talimi*;[42] (b) "Book of Solution of Enigmas," *Kitab al-shawahid*;[36] (c) "Book of the Secret," *Kitab al-asrar*; and (d) "Book of the Secret of Secrets," *Kitab sirr al-asrar*.[43]

Al-Razi, in a very orderly manner, classified chemical substances into: (1) earthy; (2) botanical; (3) zoological; and (4) derivative. The first was divided into (a) "spirits," such as mercury, sal ammoniac, arsenic sulfide, and sulfur; (b) fusible "bodies" or metals, gold, silver, copper, iron, tin, lead, and possibly zinc; (c) "stones," such as pyrites, light and dark earthy minerals, iron oxide (?), azurite, hematite, arsenic oxide, lead sulfide, mica, asbestos, gypsum, and glass.

Then there are the "vitriols" which include black vitriol, alum, and four uncertain substances. There are six boraces—bread borax, (sodium sesquicarbonate), goldsmith's borax, gum of the willow and acacia, and others. The final grouping of "salts" includes sweet, bitter (a magnesium salt ?), a type of rock salt, microcosmic salt, slaked lime, potassium carbonate, and others more or less ucertain.

Vegetable substances were rarely used with the exception of the ashes of a plant called *ushnan*. The ashes are rich in sodium carbonate.

Zoological substances include hair, skulls, brains, bile, blood, milk, urine, eggs, mother-of-pearl, and horn. Dry distillation of hair yielded the important substance, ammonium chloride. Derivative substances include PbO, Pb_3O_4, tin oxide, copper acetate, CuO, iron rust, black oxide of iron, cinnabar, calcium silicate, lye, and others.

Al-Razi classifies apparatus used in chemistry into (a) instruments for melting metals and (b) those for general manipulation. The first group contains the hearth, bellows, crucible, descensory,

28

mold, etc.; the instruments include the cucurbit, alembic, receiving flask, aludel, beakers, oven, mortar and pestle, and other usual small apparatus.

Of greater interest are the processes described by al-Razi.[44] These methods were conditioned by his theory that substances were potentially "active matter" in combination with certain amounts of "spirit" and "soul." Since the essential material of all matter is the same, to effect any transmutation was to change the relative proportions of "spirit" and "soul" and the "active matter." Impurities were therefore to be removed in order to change proportions. Purification was first followed by reduction of these substances to a fluidity such that they would penetrate into other substances in the proper proportion. Lastly, solvents or "cerated" substances like water were removed to return to the solid state.

Purification was brought about by distillation, sublimation, filtration, roasting, digestion, amalgamation, calcination, lavation, and decantation. Then, an easily fusible condition was induced by "ceration," followed by solution. Various solutions of the proper proportion were then admixed by the process of "combination." Lastly, a solidification was effected by "coagulation." The product was then supposed to be the elixir which had the special property of being capable, in small quantities when mixed with base metal, of converting it into silver. If silver was employed instead of base metal, gold was produced.

Details of all these processes are given in the al-Razi manuscripts in a very logical and convincing fashion. He makes no resort to supernatural material or occultism in any way. Al-Razi was an organizer and true experimenter much ahead of his time. Al-Razi, himself, mentions Jabir in "Book of the Secret" as his mentor.

This may, however, have been an addendum by a later writer. There is, nevertheless, a striking similarity between the works of al-Razi and Jabir, for example, in their discussions of "sharp liquids," as pointed out by Ruska,[34] Garbers,[45] and Stapleton, Azo, and Husain.[46] Their descriptions of apparatus and methods are very much the same except that al-Razi's are much briefer. Both authors, although believing in transmutation, did not conceive of it as occupying the main cornerstone of their scientific corpus.

Al-Razi did, nevertheless, defend the idea of transmutation vigorously.

AVICENNA

Abu Ali al-Husain Ibn Abdallah Ibn Sina (980–1037) or Avicenna (Lat.) as he was known in the West (from the Hebrew *Aven Sina*), is still considered as the "prince of all learning" in the Muslim world today. His biography, taken largely from the notes of a pupil by Ibn Abi Usaibia (thirteenth century),[47] is known to us in fair detail.

Avicenna was born in Afshana, a village then in Persia. When Avicenna was a young boy, the father, who was a minor official in the Muslim government, moved his family to Bukhara. Here the future doctor, scientist, and philosopher began his studies, first in the Koran, then in Arabic poetry, jurisprudence, and philosophy under tutors. The boy soon outgrew his teachers and began the study of science and medicine before the age of 16.

Avicenna worked day and night to make himself master of the sciences. Before he was 18, he had read all available Greek mathematics, medicine, and other scientific works.

Shortly after, the Sultan of Bukhara, Nuh ibn Mansur became ill. It was Avicenna who was able to cure him and, as a reward, he became attached to the court. In this position, he was allowed to examine the private library of the Samanides and to read the books on medicine. This was a fascinating experience for Avicenna, for he described the library in his biography:

"In one section, there were books on language and poetry, in another law, etc.; each section was for books on one science. I looked through the catalogue of the ancient Greeks and asked for those I required. I saw books whose names are still unknown to many . . . . I read these books taking note of their contents. I came to realize the place each man occupied in his particular science."[48] The Samanide royal library with all its books was later put to the torch by the Turks when they overthrew the rule of this forward looking dynasty.

At the age of about 21, Avicenna began to write, mainly in Arabic and infrequently in Persian in a style not very easy to read;[49] the earliest works were on prosody, the law, and ethics. His writing was interrupted from time to time by the political unrest of the day. In this period, Avicenna was forced to journey from one court to another—Jurjan, Raiy, Hamadhan, Isfahan and others. However, he did find time to produce his greatest works on medicine in this period. It is important that Avicenna became the model universal encyclopedist who fixed the system of learning for future centuries.[50] Of over 100 works, his principal contributions to science are in the "Book of the Remedy," *Kitab al Shifa,* an encyclopedic commentary on the works of Aristotle, and in the "Canon of Medicine," *Qanun fi-l-tibb,* based mainly on Galen and other Greek and Arabic physicians.

For a time, because of political conditions, Avicenna was imprisoned but continued his writing. He was later released. The last years of Avicenna's life were spent under the protection of Ala al-Daula in Isfahan. Here, Avicenna completed his greatest work, the *Shifa,* mentioned above.

According to Jusjani, Avicenna became ill during one of his patron's campaigns against Hamadhan in 1037.[51] Attacked by colic, and not relaxing the indulgence of his sexual appetites, Avicenna exhausted his strength and, at the age of fifty-eight, died. His grave is known there today.

It is unfortunate that Avicenna lived in a period of such great political fluidity and strife. No doubt, it affected his work much of which was produced while he was engaged in military campaigns.

Crombie has put his finger on the greatest contribution to science made by Avicenna.[52] Prior to Galen, scientists followed the old Greek tradition of giving the definitions and then following them up with the body of logical development. The investigator was then obliged merely to define the various types of "natures" to be found. With Galen, this procedure was changed. Instead of hunting for these natures and defining more and more of them, Avicenna, although his work largely reproduces Aristotle's ideas,[53] planned inductive and experimental approaches to determine the conditions producing observable results.[54]

In the "Canon," Avicenna followed the method of Galen. Here, Avicenna related the effects of drugs to the proportions of their

31

qualities as they were then known. To this end, Avicenna set up the rules that made for the proper experimental investigation of the causes of the effects of drugs.

Aside from Avicenna's medical writings, one of his most influential works was from the "Book of the Remedy," particularly the chapters on natural science. The Latin translation was made by Alfred of Sareshal about 1200. The early parts of the book contain writings on minerals, fossils, geology, and metals and their reactions.

Conditions for the formation of mountains and stone are discussed by Avicenna.[55] "Stone is formed in two ways only (a) through the hardening of clay, and (b) by the congelation [of waters] . . . . In my childhood I saw, on the bank of the Oxus, deposits of the clay which people used for washing their heads; subsequently I observed that it had become converted into a soft stone, and that was in the space of approximately 23 years.

"Mountains have been formed by one of the causes of the formation of stone, most probably from agglutinative clay which slowly dried and petrified during ages of which we have no record. It seems likely that this habitable world was in former days uninhabitable and, indeed, submerged beneath the ocean . . . petrifaction occurred after the earth had been exposed . . .

"It is for this reason [i.e., that the earth was once covered by the sea] that in many stones, when they are broken, are found parts of aquatic animals, such as shells, etc."[56]

In this passage, Avicenna advanced a modern theory of fossils. Much of it was later introduced to the West by Albertus Magnus in his "De mineralibus."

In the section on the formation of minerals, Avicenna divided mineral bodies into four groups: stones, fusible substances, sulfurs, and salts. "Some of the mineral bodies are weak in substance and feeble in composition and union while others are strong in substance. Of the latter, some are malleable and some are not malleable. Of those which are feeble in substance, some have the nature of salt and are easily dissolved by moisture, such as alum, vitriol, sal ammoniac and *qalqand* while others are oily in nature and are not easily dissolved by moisture alone, such as sulphur and arsenic (sulphides).[57]

"The material of malleable bodies [all of which are fusible] is an aqueous substance united so firmly with an earthy substance that the two cannot be separated from one another. This aqueous substance has been congealed by cold after heat has acted upon it . . . .

"As regards the stony kinds of naturally occurring mineral substances, the material of which they are made is also aqueous, but they have not been congealed by cold alone [but also] . . . by dryness which has converted the aquosity into terrestreity.[58]

"Alum and sal ammoniac are considered to belong to a family of salts. The latter may be sublimed. In the case of sulphurs, their aquosity has suffered a vigorous leavening with earthiness and aeriness under the leavening action of heat, so far as to become oily in nature and subsequently to be solidified by cold.

"The vitriols are composed of a salty principle, a sulphurous principle and stone, and contain the virtue of some of the fusible bodies [metals].[59]

"Mercury . . . is the essential constituent element of all the fusible bodies, for all of them are converted into mercury on fusion. Most of them, however, fuse only at a very high temperature, so that their mercury appears red."[60]

Avicenna, at the end of this section, makes some very sharp statements on the alchemists of his day:[61] "There is very little doubt that, by alchemy, the adepts can contrive solidifications in which the qualities of the solidifications of mercury by the sulphurs are perceptible to the senses, though the alchemical qualities are not identical in principle or in perfection with the natural ones, but merely bear a resemblance and relationship to them. Hence the belief arises that their natural formation takes place in this way or in some similar way, though alchemy falls short of nature in this respect and, in spite of great effort, cannot overtake her.

"As to the claims of the alchemists, it must be clearly understood that it is not in their power to bring about any true change of species. They can, however, produce excellent imitations, dyeing the red [metal] white so that it closely resembles silver, or dyeing it yellow so that it closely resembles gold. They can, too, dye the white [metal] with any color they desire, until it bears a close resemblance to gold or copper; and they can free the leads [i.e., lead and tin] from most of their defects and impurities. Yet in these [dyed metals] the essential nature remains unchanged; they are merely so dominated by induced qualities that errors may be made concerning them, just as it happens that men are deceived by salt, *qalqand,* sal ammoniac, etc.

"I do not deny that such a degree of accuracy may be reached as to deceive even the shrewdest, but the possibility of eliminating or imparting the specific difference has never been clear to me. On the contrary, I regard it as impossible, since there is no way of splitting up one combination into another. Those properties which are perceived by the senses are probably not the differences which separate the metals into species, but rather accidents or consequences, the specific differences being unknown. And if a thing is unknown, how is it possible for anyone to endeavor to produce it or to destroy it?

"As for the removal or imparting of the dyes, or such accidental properties as odors and densities, these are things which one ought not to persist in denying merely because of lack of knowledge concerning them, for there is no proof whatever of their impossibility.

"It is likely that the proportion of the elements which enter into the composition of the essential substance of each of the metals enumerated is different from that of any other. If this is so, one metal cannot be converted into another unless the compound is broken up and converted into the composition of that into which its transformation is desired. This, however, cannot be effected by fusion, which maintains the union and merely causes the introduction of some foreign substance or virtue."

A debt is thus owed to Avicenna for his clear vision of the experimental lack and ignorance in alchemy as it was then known.[62] Avicenna, thus, with his logic and understanding, clarified the purposes of medieval chemistry. The passages above were well known in the times following Avicenna, particularly through Albertus Magnus[63] and other writers. Unfortunately, the works of Avicenna were so complete and so well known that his encyclopedic method, in the long run of the following centuries, discouraged original investigations and so had the net effect of retarding progress.[64]

Chemistry, in the work of the great chemists from Jabir to the time of Avicenna, was concerned chiefly not so much with alchemy but with concrete technical matters such as the development of apparatus, the preparation of chemicals, and the study of their reactions. The development of chemistry in this period, although almost entirely empirical, was of great importance in that a new high level was attained in the accumulation of chemical data. The previous period of such great growth had taken place long before, 3000–500 B.C., in Mesopotamia. In many ways, Muslim chemistry grew in the same manner as it did in Mesopotamia with the difference that the Arabs were more careful in their larger number of experiments, made careful notations of their laboratory results, and developed their laboratory apparatus to a high point of perfection. This was the real beginning of scientific method in the science of chemistry. Not only did the Muslims organize their scientific knowledge as did the ancient Mesopotamians before them, but they used experiments to gain scientific data. Because of this accent on experiment in later times, there is much more practical discussion of the categories of matter in the Muslim literature than may be found in the Mesopotamian literature where appearances were of prime consideration.

Alongside experiment, logical speculation took its place in chemical science as an important adjunct. Although Muslim theorizing was grossly inadequate, it was, however, carried out by important chemists in an effort to explain results of laboratory work and not necessarily to add to the so-called "natures." This was a distinct Muslim advancement over their Greek, Egyptian, and Mesopotamian predecessors.

NOTES AND REFERENCES

1 The transliteration of Arabic names and terms has been very much simplified. The author hopes that no one will be inconvenienced by this procedure.
2 G. Sarton, "Introduction to the History of Science," Williams and Wilkins, Baltimore, 1927, I, 381–2.

35

3 The Muslims, so-called, were of many different nationalities but almost always wrote in Arabic, the lingua franca of the Arabic conquest from ca. 750 A.D. to ca. 1200 A.D.

4 M. Levey, *J. Chem. Ed.*, *31*, 373–375 (1954).

5 J. W. Fück, transl.; "The Arabic Literature on Alchemy According to Al-Nadim," *Ambix* IV, 95 ff, 124 ff (1951). Cf. B. Carra de Vaux, Encyclopedia of Islam, E. J. Brill, Leyden, 1908, I, 987–8.

6 F. Sherwood Taylor, "The Alchemists," Schuman, New York, 1949, pp. 78 ff.

7 E. O. von Lippmann, "Entstehung und Ausbreitung der Alchemie," Springer, Berlin, 1919, pp. 363–369; J. Ruska, Chapter on "Dschabir" in Gunther Bugge," ed., "Der Buch der Grossen Chemiker," Verlag Chemie, Berlin, 1929, I, 19. In the latter, Ruska has made the division into the Jabirian corpus and the pseudo-Geberian works.

8 H. E. Stapleton, R. F. Azo and M. Hidayat Husain, "Chemistry in Iraq and Persia in the Tenth Century A.D.," *Memoirs of the Asiatic Society of Bengal,* 8, 394–397 (1927).

9 M. Berthelot, "La Chimie au Moyen Age," III, Leroux, Paris, 1893, 23.

10 Fück, *op. cit.*, p. 96.

11 Fück, *op. cit.*, 95, 6.

12 E. J. Holmyard, "Alchemy," Penguin, Harmondsworth, 1951, p. 69: E. J. Holmyard, "An Essay on Jabir ibn Hayyan, Festgabe für E. O. von Lippmann, Springer, Berlin, 1927, pp. 28 ff.

13 Paul Kraus, "Dschabir ibn Hayyan und die Ismailja, "Dritter Jahresber. d. Forschungs—Instituts für Gesch. der Naturwiss. in Berlin, 23–42 (1930).

14 Fück, *op. cit.,* 97.

15 E. J. Holmyard, "The Arabic Works of Jabir ibn Hayyan," Geuthner, Paris, 1928, I, 1. For a list of Jabir's works, see Holmyard's *Proceedings of the Royal Society of Medicine* (1923), XVI, pp. 48 ff. See also Fück, *op. cit.*, pp. 127 ff.

16 J. Ruska, "Die 70 Bucher" in Studien z. Gesch. der Chemie, Festgabe für E. O. von Lippmann, Berlin, 1927, pp. 38–47.

17 Fück, *op. cit.*, p. 104, pp. 135–6.

18 M. Levey, *J. Chem. Ed.*, **32,** 11–13 (1955).

19 Tj. de Boer, "Encyclopedie de L'Islam," Vol. 2, pt. 2, pp. 1078–79 (1913).

20 G. Flügel, "Al-Kindi genannt der Philosoph der Araber," Brockhaus, Leipzig, 1857, pp. 1–5.

21 Albino Nagy, "Die Philosophischen Abhandlungen," Munster, 1897.

22 G. Flügel, *op. cit.*, pp. 20 ff. contains translation into German and the Arabic of the section on al-Kindi.

23 Karl Garbers, ed. and translator, "Kitab fi kimiya al-itr wat-tasidat, Buch über die chemie der parfums und die destillationen von Yaqub B. Ishaq Al-Kindi, Brockhaus, Leipzig, 1948.

24 O. Loth, "Al-Kindi als Astrolog," "Morgenl. Forschung; Festschrift . . .
H. L. Fleischer," Brockhaus, Leipzig, 1875.

25 Karl Garbers, *op. cit.,* p. 11.

26 M. Levey, *J. Chem. Ed.* 32, 180–184 (1955); *Centaurus* IV, 23–33
(1955)

27 Garbers, *op. cit.,* pp. 19, 20 and photocopy of folio 84a of manuscript
opposite p. 400.

28 J. W. Fück, transl., "The Arabic Literature on Alchemy According to
Au-Nadim," Ambix IV; p. 108 (1951). The famous *Kitab al-Fihrist*
"Book of the Catalogue," writen by al-Nadim in A. H. 377–8 deals in its
tenth and last discourse with Islamic and pre-Islamic alchemists. It is
primarily a bibliography of the works of these men. It is probable that
al-Nadim was a bookseller, as was his father, and that he had actually
seen most of the works included in his "Catalogue."

29 P. Kraus and S. Pines, in "Encyclopedia of Islam," Brill, Leiden, 1936;
III, 1137; Max Meyerhof, "The Legacy of Islam," Clarendon Press,
Oxford, 1931, pp. 323 ff.

30 B. MacGuckin de Slane, travel, "Ibn Khallikan's biographical dictionary,"
Oriental Translation, Paris, 1842–71, 892.541, Ib 56.2 For al-Razi's
autobiography, cf. *Kitab al-sirat al-falsafiyya"* in *Orientalia* 4, 309–334
(1935).

31 A. J. Arberry, "The Spiritual Physick of Rhazes," J. Murray, London,
1950, p. 2. Cf. also G. S. A. Ranking, "The Life and Works of Rhases
(Abu Bakr Muhammad bin Zakariya ar-Razi" XVII Int. Cong. of Medicine, Hist. of Med., London, 1914, 237–268.

32 August Mueller, ed. "Ibn Abi Usaibiah, *Uyum al-anba fi Tabaqat al-
atiba."* "Sources of Information for the classes of physicians by Ibn Abi
Usaibi," A. Mueller, Konigsberg, 1884.

33 J. Ruska, *Isis* V, pp. 320 ff. (1922).

34 J. Ruska, "Die Alchemie ar-Razi's" *Der Islam* 22, 283–286 (1935).

35 Ibn Khallikan, *op. cit.,* III, 314.

36 H. E. Stapleton, R. F. Azo and M. Hidayat Husain, "Chemistry in Iraq
and Persia in the Tenth Century A.D. *Memoirs Asiatic Society of Bengal,*
VIII/6, 320 (1927).

37 Ruska, *op. cit.,* p. 32.

38 Mueller, *op. cit.,* 315.

39 P. Kraus, "Raziana I, II," *Orientalia* 5, 35–56 (1936).

40 P. Kraus and S. Pines, *op. cit.,* p. 1136

41 J. W. Fück, "The Arabic Literature on Alchemy According to An-Nadim,"
Ambix IV, 88 (1951).

42 H. E. Stapleton and R. F. Azo, "An Alchemical Compilation of the Thirteenth Century A.D., *Memoirs Asiatic Society Bengal,* III, 57–94
(1910) also Stapleton, Azo and Husain, *op. cit.*

43 J. Ruska, *op. cit.,* pp. 293 ff.

44 Stapleton, Azo and Husain, *op. cit.*, pp. 327 ff.
45 J. Ruska and K. Garbers, "Vorschriften Zur Herstellung von scharfen Wassern bei Gabir und Razi," *Der Islam* 25, 1–34 (1939).
46 Stapleton, Azo and Husain, *op. cit.*, pp. 336–7.
47 August Müller, ed., "Ibn Abi Useibia," Konigsberg, 1884, II, pp. 2 ff. Cf. also C. Brockelmann, "Gesch der arab. Litteratur, E. J. Brill, Leiden, 1898–1902, I, 452 ff.
48 A. S. Arberry in Chap. I of "Avicenna Scientist and Philosopher," ed. by G. M. Wickens, Luzac, London, 1952, pp. 18, 19; F. Rahman, "Avicenna's Psychology," Oxford U. Press, Oxford, 1952, Chapters I, II; M. Achena et H. Masse, translator, "Avicenne, Le Livre de Science," Société d'Édition Les Belles Lettres, Paris, 1955.
49 Henry Corbin, "Avicenne, Le Recit de Hayy ibn Yaqzan," Commission des monuments nationaux de l'Iran, Teheran, 1953, p. vii.
50 T. J. de Boer, "Encyclopedia of Islam," Leyden, 1913, p. 419.
51 Arberry, *op. cit.*, p. 26.
52 A. C. Crombie, in Chap. V of "Avicenna: Scientist and Philosopher," ed. by G. M. Wickens, London, 1952, pp. 88 ff.
53 A. F. Mehren, "Vues Theosophiques D'Avicenne," Peeters, Louvain, 1886, p. 3.
54 Carra de Vaux, "Avicenne," Paris, 1900, p. 176. Also cf. A.–M. Goichon, "Livre des Directives et Remarques," Vrin, Paris, 1951, pp. 1–74 for philosophical development of Avicenna.
55 E. J. Holmyard and D. C. Mandeville, "Avicennae, De Congelatione et Conglutinatione Lapidum," Geuthner, Paris, 1927, pp. 18, 19.
56 *Ibid.*, p. 28.
57 *Ibid.*, pp. 33, 34.
58 *Ibid.*, pp. 34, 35.
59 *Ibid.*, p. 36.
60 *Ibid.*, p. 39.
61 *Ibid.*, pp. 40–42.
62 J. R. Partington, Ambix I, pp. 3 ff. (1937).
63 B. Haneberg, "Zur Erkenntnisslehre von Ibn Sina und Albertus Magnus," München Akademie der Wissenschaften, München, 1886, p. 21.
64 E. J. Holmyard, "Makers of Chemistry," Clarendon Press, Oxford, 1931, p. 84.

MARTIN LEVEY

Philosophical Alchemists and Practical Metallurgists

Thirteenth to Sixteenth Centuries

LULLUS

BACON

THE following sketches are brief accounts of a few outstanding men who lived in the period between the Arabic chemists of the previous chapter and Paracelsus of the succeeding one.

Albertus, Count of Bollstadt, later called Albertus the Great ("Magnus") lived from 1193 to 1280. He became a Dominican monk, perhaps at Cologne in 1223, taught theology at various schools, and was consecrated bishop at Regensburg in 1260. After only a few years there he resigned in order to return to his scientific studies. He died in the Dominican cloister at Cologne.

"He was great in Magia naturali, greater in philosophy, greatest in theology" (Joh. Trithemius). With thorough knowledge of alembics for distillation, aludels for sublimation, and lutes for connecting stills with coolers and receivers, he leaned toward alchemical thoughts and practices. Through him and his famous pupil, Thomas Aquinas (1225(?)–1274) Aristotle's philosophy was revived and propagated.

Roger Bacon (1214–1294) was called "Doctor Mirabilis" because of his great universal knowledge. In his "Liber claritatis" he expects alchemy to make noble metals and many other things by artifice better than they are made by nature. Not for metals as elements, but for alloys and "many other things" modern chemistry is fulfilling this expectation. The elixir, of which a sixth of a pound will "purge" a million pounds of base metal, is also supposed to restore sick bodies to health (Opus minus).

Raymundus Lullus (1235(?)–1315(?)), born on Mallorca, was profligate as a youth, but soon turned to evangelistic and missionary work as a member of the Franciscan Order. About 4000 books were ascribed to his name. Among his genuine writings were descriptions of *aqua fortis* (nitric acid) and *aqua ignis,* a mixture of *sal ammoniacum* and nitric acid. He redistilled wine over *sal vegetabile* (burnt tartar, potassium carbonate) and obtained an *aqua ardens,* concentrated alcohol. Many recipes for tinctures and quintessences came from his pen. In his testament he claimed to have converted 22 tons of silver, lead, and tin into gold.

41

The picture, from an Italian manuscript of the early 14th century, shows Pater Hermes philosophorum; his great turban is surmounted by an imaginary heraldic crown. In the upper right corner is an eight-pointed star with rays.

FROM GIOVANNI CARBONELLI: SULLE FONTI STORICHE DELLA CHIMICA E DELL' ALCHIMIA IN ITALIA. ISTITUTO NAZIONALE MEDICO FARMACOLOGICO, ROMA, 1925.

Arnaldus Bachuone, called de Villanova after his birthplace in the Languedoc, France (1235–1313?), acquired great fame as a physician but was persecuted for his unorthodox teachings. He was reputed to have taught the "great art" to Lullus.

These men and their times were concerned with theology and metaphysics; to them the science of nature was an inseparable part of the theological-philosophical systems they sought to erect. To prove by argument and logic was more important than to test by experiment. We may deplore this attitude from the standpoint of our concepts of science and we may criticize as wasteful the devotion to dialectics and scholasticism. However, it is a historical fact that centuries were spent in these pursuits. Instead of belatedly wishing it had been different, we would do better to try to understand this phase of history as the endeavor to clarify thoughts and define words. Could we have developed science without the development of these tools?

During these centuries, old metallurgical practices and mining experiences continued to be slowly developed. In the year 1500, Ulrich Rülein von Calw published his "Bergbüchlein" which was reprinted many times. Subsequently, Vannoccio Biringuccio, Georgius Agricola, and Lazarus Ercker composed magnificent books on mining and assaying. A parallel literature on the art of distillation began to appear from 1479 on.

Ulrich Rülein (1465/9–1523) studied and graduated in Leipzig. Perhaps he also taught mathematics there while studying medicine. In 1497 he was a physician in Freiberg and wrote a book on mining, ores, and assaying which appeared in 1500. He believed that all metals are composed of sulfur and mercury. The sun and the planets govern the various compositions of the ores from the two primary substances and create the seven metals: gold, silver, tin, copper, iron, lead, and mercury.

Vannoccio Biringuccio (1480–1538 or 1539) was born in Siena and became manager of iron and silver works. After many years of traveling, partly necessitated by political upheavals, he returned to Siena and directed the construction of the cathedral. In 1538 he managed the foundry of the Pope. In the last years of his life he collected his many-sided experiences in a book on "The Technique of Fire," *Pirotechnia*. Aristotle and Albertus Magnus were the authorities for his general explanations. He wrote about ores and metals, sulfur, gunpowder, wire-drawing, and fireworks.

Georgius Agricola (1494–1555) was born in Glauchau (Saxony). He studied in Leipzig, Bologna, Padua, and Venice. Theology, philosophy, and philology were his first interests, although he also studied medicine. One outlet of this many-sidedness was the collaboration on a new edition of Galen (130–201, physician of Roman emperors and prolific writer on medical subjects) in 1525. Two years later he became town physician in Joachimsthal. From 1533 on he lived in Chemnitz as a physician, chemist, and mineralogist. He published books on metals ("Bermannus, sive de re metallica," Basle, 1530), on "fossils," and on water. He knew the alchemistic literature and quoted Arnaldus the Villanova among others. In 1533 he published a book on weights and measures. His greatest work had the title "De re metallica" and appeared posthumously, like the book of his predecessor whom he

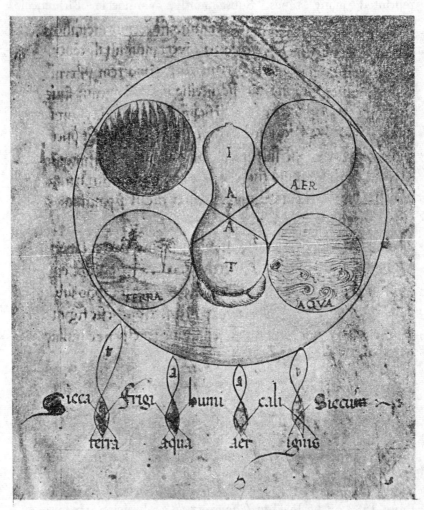

In the center is the philosophical vessel, upright on a straw ring, inscribed with the initials I A A T of the four elements Ignis, Aqua, Aer, Terra. The four disks, surrounding the vase and connected by cross-lines, represent the four elements: earth by a landscape with trees, water by a turbulent sea, air by a light-blue tint, fire by a red flame. All of this is symbolically enclosed in a circle. At the bottom are the four qualities sicca frigi(da), humi(da or dus), cali(da or dus), and the elements containing pairs of these qualities; their symbols t a a i, recur in the loops.

44

gratefully acknowledges. According to his biographer, Ernst Darmstaedter, he was more a systematizer than an originally creative chemist.

Lazarus Ercker (1530?–1594?) was born at Annaberg, a mining town in Saxony. He studied at Wittenberg and, perhaps, abroad. Shortly after he became assay master in Dresden in 1555, he published a small book on assaying, a "Probierbüchlein," in 1556. It was an elementary text, written for the Electoral Prince of Saxony and dedicated to him. The Prince was delighted, but personal and political intrigues made life difficult for Ercker. He emigrated to Goslar where he was mint master for several years from 1558 on. Ten years later he was in Bohemia, trying to improve operations and accounting methods in mines under complicated legal restrictions and fighting against narrow business interests. He collected reliable descriptions of mineral ores and mining practices in a large book which first appeared in Prague, 1574. It was reprinted many times and in many translations. An edition of 1672 added to the cumbersome original title the intriguing superscript "Aula Subterranea" which saw new editions until 1556. The German Glauber, the Dutch Boerhaave, and the Swede Torbern Bergman (1735–1784) praised Ercker's work.

In 1586 Emperor Rudolf II conferred on him nobility and a coat of arms. His device was: Test it before you praise it (*Erst probs dan lobs*). The cause of his death, at sixty-four or sixty-five, is not known.

NOTES AND REFERENCES

Georgius Agricola, "De re metallica," Basel, 1556. Translated by Herbert C. Hoover and Lou H. Hoover, London, 1912.

Paul Reinhard Beierlein, "Lazarus Ercker," Freiberger Forschungshefte, D 12. Akademie– Verlag, Berlin, 1955.

Vannoccio Biringuccio, "Pirotechnia," Venedig, 1540. Übersetzt und erläutert von Otto Johannsen, Vieweg, Braunschweig, 1925. Translated from the Italian by Cyril Stanley Smith and Martha Teach Gnudi, The American Institute of Mining and Metallurgical Engineers, New York, 1942.

Lazarus Ercker, "Treatise on Ores and Assaying," translated from the German edition of 1580 by Anneliese Grünhardt Sisco and Cyril Stanley Smith, The University of Chicago Press, Chicago, 1951.

Ernst Darmstaedter, "Georg Agricola," München, 1926.

Wilhelm Pieper, "Ulrich Rülein von Calw und sein Bergbüchlein," Freiberger Forschungshefte, D7. Akademie– Verlag, Berlin, 1955.

A. G. Sisco and C. St. Smith, "Bergwerk– und Probierbüchlein," A translation from the German, The American Institute of Mining and Metallurgical Engineers, New York, 1949.

Lynn Thorndike, "History of Magic and Experimental Science," 8 vols., Columbia University Press, New York, 1923–1958.

Arthur Edward Waite, "Lives of Alchemical Philosophers," based on materials collected in 1815 and supplemented by recent researches, to which is added a bibliography of "Alchemy and Hermetic Philosophy," George Redway, London, 1888.

EDUARD FARBER

·· 5 ··

Paracelsus

1493-1541

IN 1493 Christopher Columbus returned to Spain to announce the discovery of a sea passage to the Indies. Leonardo da Vinci, forty-one, and at the height of his powers, had just finished the colossal monument of Francesco Sforza, for which he had come to Milan a decade earlier; Nicholas Koppernigk (later Copernicus) was a twenty-year-old student at Cracow University, and had just interested himself in collecting books on mathematics and astronomy; Martin Luther was a ten-year-old schoolboy at Mansfeld in Germany. In that year Paracelsus was born near Einsiedeln, Switzerland, the son of a German country doctor and his Swiss wife, a subject of the local sovereign.[1]

When Theophrastus—for that was Paracelsus' given name—was 9 his mother died and he and his father moved to the important imperial city of Villach, in Carinthia (now in Austria near the Yugoslav border) where his father became town physician. There Theophrastus attended the school at the Benedictine Cloister, and made the aquaintance of science through the tutelage of his father. Through the proximity of the mine at Hutenberg he became familiar with the common metallurgical processes.

About 1507 Theophrastus began an irregular course of university study, which took him to various academic centers in Germany, France, Austria, and Italy. Details of his academic activity are uncertain, but he seems to have attended the medical course at Ferrara, where Niccolo Leoniceno and Giovanni Manardi were already breathing new life into the ancient dogmas of medicine. His formal education ended about 1515, with or without a degree, a hotly disputed question which seems less important than the likelihood that he did devote himself for some time to formal academic study in medicine. Leaving Ferrara he spent several years wandering through most of western Europe, from Ireland to Poland and from Sweden to Sicily. It is possible that his travels extended to more remote parts, including Russia and Egypt. His employment may have been that of a military surgeon; at any rate he emerged from this period a practiced, if not established, physician. During these years he also formed in general outline his views on science, philosophy, and religion and began to write them down. What may be his earliest work, on the origin, causes, symptoms, and cure of several diseases, is thought to have been written in 1520. The first theological tracts were written about 1524, and his most important chemical work, "Archidoxies," in the following year. Like most of the other writings that poured from his prolific pen, these remained unpublished until after his death, for Paracelsus was a controversial figure and had difficulty in finding a publisher.

His wanderings continued from 1524 to 1527, within the smaller compass of the Rhine-Danube region, during which he came before the public eye as a suspected partisan of the peasantry in their controversy with the nobility of Salzburg. This period terminated with his cure of the ailing Johannes Froben, a famous Basle publisher, which brought him to the attention of influential persons in that city and led to Paracelsus' acceptance of an invitation to go to that city as town physician.

This invitation testifies to the fame that already surrounded him, although a number of other considerations entered into the Basle invitation. At that time the Protestant majority in Basle was endeavoring to dislodge the Catholic minority from its principal stronghold, the university. The town physician, who was also on the medical faculty, had been discharged by the city council, but the effectiveness of that move appeared to depend upon his being replaced by a man acceptable to some degree to both factions. Paracelsus, who was sympathetic to the Reformation but had not repudiated Catholicism, seemed to be the man.

The calculations of the Basle city council seem to have been correct so far as Paracelsus' ambiguous religious position was concerned. But he lost no time in making clear the divergence of his position from that of the medical faculty so far as medicine was concerned. His outspoken criticism of the traditional medicine which dominated the university is symbolized by the incident of St. John's Day in the summer of 1527, when he flaunted his opinion of the authoritative texts of medicine by burning one of them publicly. He attempted to counter the consequent hostility of the medical faculty by uncompromising demands for full support from the council, which ultimately resulted in the alienation of that body. In February, 1528, he abruptly forsook the city, allegedly under the stimulus of impending arrest.

The remaining thirteen years of Paracelsus' life were a continuation of the wandering he had interrupted to take a position at Basle. Now a famous doctor, he stopped briefly with many influential persons, but always moved on in a relatively short time. Occasional brief periods were spent at the home of his father, who lived until 1534. During this time he continued to write, an amazing accomplishment in view of the circumstances of his life, and, even more amazing, to pursue the labors of the chemical laboratory wherever the requisite apparatus could be assembled. The fame that has made his name so prominent in the history of medicine and chemistry seems due principally to these voluminous writings, and to date from their publication during the half century after his death.

Paracelsus' collected works were first published in 1589, again in 1658, and, in editions of varying completeness, up to the most recent in 1949. None of these contains all of his works, as some still remain unpublished; most contain treatises of questionable authenticity. The earlier collections were inspired by an interest in his medical and chemical writings; some of the later by theosophical interest. Chemical matters are discussed in virtually all of his medical works, although in many cases only in the form of a recitation of a list of chemical remedies. Authorities are unanimous—as near as unanimity ever occurs among students of Paracelsus—in regarding "Archidoxies" as his fundamental chemical work. "De natura rerum," written toward the end of his career, supplements "Archidoxies" interestingly. The works called "Paramirum" and "Paragranum" express, in its clearest form, his conception of a chemical physiology and pathology. The specific application of his chemistry appears in some detail in his works on surgery and the tartaric diseases and in several small tracts on chemistry, notably that on the spirit of vitriol.

GENERAL CHEMISTRY

Paracelsus' fame in the history of chemistry is rooted principally in his association with a sixteenth century movement for the application of chemistry to medicine. In that century the preparation of "chemical" remedies succeeded gold-making alchemy as the main object of chemical activity, and remained the principal justification of the science until medical chemistry was itself succeeded by modern chemistry in the eighteenth century, both successions signifying a change in the objective of the majority of prominent chemists rather than an actual abandonment of the earlier science. Medical chemistry was formerly regarded as an important intermediate step between alchemy and modern chemistry, but it has been judged less favorably in recent years, as its practice has been revealed as less "modern" than that of contemporary chemical technology (especially metallurgy), and the theories associated with it scarcely more tenable than those of alchemy itself. The decline of Paracelsus' own reputation has been even sharper, for as his predecessors and contemporaries have become better known, and his own works studied more critically, he has been divested of the majority of discoveries once thought to have been his.

This judgment seems, however, to presuppose that the history of chemistry is nothing more than a linear succession of discoveries and theories accepted as proved by modern chemistry. Moreover it assumes that the aberrations of the past, once they are so regarded, have no positive significance. Medical chemistry is now regarded as an aberration, or rather as one aspect of an aberration known in the history of chemistry as iatrochemistry. The use of this mysterious sounding term to cover a tenuously related group of practical discoveries and theories, some of which were separated in time by three centuries, testifies to the superficiality of our knowledge of the chemistry of this period. By contrast, metallurgical chemistry has proved quite understandable in modern terms, in part because of its barrenness of theory, and has been cultivated widely by seekers after a more respectable ancestry for the science. Because of its peculiar interest, a considerable expenditure of effort has been made toward the elucidation of alchemy, which has inevitably made the contents of a leading works a matter of general knowledge among students of the history of chemistry. Paracelsus spoke neither the first nor the last word in medical chemistry, hence his biography is no history of the subject. But his biography as a chemist is embedded in the subject, which must therefore be somewhat clarified if his career is to be coherently described.

Galenic medicine as practiced in the sixteenth century was particularly vulnerable before the new critical spirit. Its once simple pharmacopoea had grown mightily through the classification of diseases and remedies according to their supposed degrees of the four qualities, hot, cold, wet, and dry; yet it was powerless against a number of "incurable" diseases, to which syphilis had been added by many at the beginning of the century. Under these circumstances folk, empirical, and other unofficial forms of medicine flourished, including one which advocated the use in internal medicine of the products of the alchemical laboratory. This was medical chemistry. Its fundamental idea was inherent from a very early period in alchemy, in the idea of the life-preserving qualities of the elixir. But as a matter of serious rather than incidental concern to the alchemist it dates, according to present knowledge, from the fourteenth century, when we find its main arguments outlined in a treatise, "On the Consideration of the Fifth Essence," written by a Franciscan friar, John of Rupescissa. According to this treatise, medicines, chiefly for the prolongation of life, can be obtained by the chemical treatment of various materials, but especially from mercury, antimony, and gold. The chemical treatment involved was usually distillation, combined with mineral acid dissolution. Both of these processes and the materials used were popular sources of metal ennobling elixirs among contemporary gold-making alchemists, and it would appear that the originality of the doctrine lay in the idea of preparing instead a series of medical quintessences or elixirs.[2] This treatise was evidently widely known, as many manuscripts survive, and its influence is clear from the close similarity of subsequent treatises on this subject, including the "Archidoxies" of Paracelsus.

Thus medical chemistry represented a change in the objective of chemistry rather than in its content. The medical chemist, like the alchemist, was an indefatigable theorist, and habitually referred the products of his experiments to an idealized substance —the quintessence—which bore a more than incidental resemblance to the alchemical elixir. In his works, as in those of the alchemist, the historian seeking first notices of various chemical substances has been obliged to interpret his way through a mass of—to us—irrelevant verbiage involving the author's description of the substances according to the then-prevailing ideology. The inevitable uncertainty in the result has led to a continuing dispute as to the accuracy of claims made for various chemists in this regard.

Since the thirteenth century the evolution of chemical practice had involved the exploitation of the mineral acids. The addition of sulfuric and nitric acids, and aqua regia to the armory of the chemist made possible the synthesis of a large number of salts through their interaction with the metals and other minerals. The predilection of the thirteenth century alchemist for random experimentation makes it probable that many of the products of acid-mineral interaction were known to him, but the difficulty of identifying reaction products which are habitually described in terms of the elixir has prevented our converting this probability to a certainty. A few were known to the metallurgist, but the clarity of his description also reveals the narrowness of his interest, for he was evidently not an experimenter. The alchemist of the late Middle Ages and his successor, the medical chemist of the fifteenth and early sixteenth centuries, evolved a theory of pure substance which equated it to the elixir (among medical chemists the quintessence), an idealized substance resembling Aristotle's fifth element in its physical and the modern catalyst in its chemical properties. This mode of thought, which was anything but conducive to the emergence of a modern system of classification, prevailed in Paracelsus' time, but productive experimentation with the acids appears again in the later sixteenth century when we find the first evidence of chemical processes conducted under controlled conditions, with the isolation of intermediate products.

Paracelsus may have made some discoveries in elucidating the chemistry of those favorite materials of the medical chemist, mercury and antimony. His own favorite remedy seems to have been red mercuric oxide, of which he says in "De natura rerum" (Bk. 5), "This is the principal arcanum, for all wounds and ulcers and the Gallic disease . . . moreover [it] brightens up despondent al-chemists . . . you ought therefore to rejoice over it and to thank God and me for it." But his discovery, if it was such, related to its medical use, not to its preparation, for it had long been known to alchemists, as had most if not all other mercury compounds mentioned by him. Paracelsus does not appear to have used anti-mony as extensively in medicine, but was the first to mention the important preparation, butter of antimony (antimony trichloride) according to the most probable interpretation of this passage in "Archidoxies."[3] The problem of his involvement with antimony is one of the principal Paracelsian mysteries. The elaborate descrip-tion of antimony chemistry in the famous "Triumphal Chariot" attributed to the pseudonymous Basil Valentine is probably the first systematic discussion of the chemistry of a single substance, even if the treatise was written after 1600, as is now thought. When this work was thought to belong to the fourteenth century, Para-celsus was thought to have plagarized it, for it contains many of his ideas and is decidedly Paracelsian in tone. Now that it is recognized to be post-Paracelsian his influence on its author is evident. Is its chemical practice also from Paracelsus? If so his prestige as an experimental chemist would have to be considerably enhanced. His acknowledged works do not answer the question.

Thus despite its elaborations "Archidoxies" remained subject to the limitations of medical chemical theory, and mentions few if any new chemical substances. The effect of this inhibition is illustrated by its account of the "separation of the elements." Speaking of this (having in mind the four elements of antiquity, fire, air, water, and earth) Paracelsus makes the earliest approach we know of to a systematic observation of the result of dissolution through cementation and acid action on each of the seven classical metals. But after calling attention to the resultant colored solu-tions, he proceeds to distill them, casting away the residues ac-cording to the convention of the medical chemist. This inhibition may also account for his failure to exploit other advanced observa-tions made in "Archidoxies" and elsewhere which portended such discoveries as that of ether and the existence of nonaerial gases.

Paracelsus' principal chemical treatise appears, therefore, not very significant for the introduction of new chemical substances, processes, or theories. It does have another significance, however, when considered in the light of the subsequent course of medical chemistry, for it exhibits an unprecedented awareness that a system of chemistry should go beyond alchemy and medical chemistry. No antimony maniac, he proclaimed the general applicability of chemistry to medicine, and urged the alchemist to apply himself to the production of medicines rather than gold. He also declared the whole world to be a druggist's shop, and in "Archidoxies" went beyond his predecessors in seeking quintessences (the term had already tended to become plural while remaining singular in theory) in a wide range of raw materials of animal, vegetable, and mineral origin. No less important, he professed to prepare other entities, arcana, magisteria, specifics, and elixirs—classificatory terms mentioned earlier by various chemists, but never brought to the juxtaposition which would have stimulated mutual comparisons.[4] Although they hardly deserve to be called members of a system of chemistry as they appear in "Archidoxies," they do have the characteristics of classificatory categories. From this beginning the next generation converted them into a crude system, chiefly by abandoning Paracelsus' hierarchical arrangement, and this system proved remarkably durable; in fact it was essentially the system against which the "chemical revolution" of the eighteenth century bore its arms.

Despite its formal adherence to the dogma of medical chemistry and the consequent limitation on its practice, "Archidoxies" therefore implies something new, a belief in the utility of—and hence the possibility of—a general science of chemistry. However tortured his mode of expression, it was clearly Paracelsus' intention to apply chemistry as he understood it to all species of matter whatever. The chemistry of "Archidoxies," practiced and described without strict adherence to medicochemical theory, yielded a great increase in the range of chemicals effectively known to the chemist. Some indication of this appears in Paracelsus' own late work, "De natura rerum," where, in an extended discussion of the "mortification" (meaning decomposition) of metals, he describes a number of decomposition reactions without reference to medicochemical theory or alchemy. His procedures were heroic and it remained for gentler hands to draw forth the full range of synthetic products from metals (which he calls products of their decomposition), but he had provided the incentive for that investigation, and had begun the framework for its fruitful pursuit.

BIOCHEMISTRY

Galen himself betrayed some uneasiness over the mechanistic character of his physiology and medicine, an uneasiness which continued to manifest itself in such sixteenth century Galenists as Fernel. The question was a peripheral one, however, and Galenic medicine remained wedded to its geometric basis in Greek cosmology, in the doctrines of the four elements, four qualities, and four humors. Paracelsus' claim to a place in the history of biochemistry is based on his critique of this doctrine.

He disposed of the four elements, not by denying them, but by regarding them as more remote than three "principles" which he called mercury, sulfur, and salt. The first two had long been regarded by alchemists as the elements of metals, and probably originated in the observation of the sulfurous effluent gas and liquid metal residue which typified the smelting process. Paracelsus saw them representative of the properties of volatility and inflammability, and added salt to represent the properties of fire resistance and coagulation (usually meaning precipitation).

Thus Paracelsus is credited with the addition of a solid element to the alchemical prima materia, despite the medicochemical theoretician's disdain for residues, which we have noted in "Archidoxies." But the three principles are not mentioned in "Archidoxies," and although they seem to be mentioned in some of his earliest works it is only in his later works (after about 1530) that they figure prominently, and even there equivocally.[5] A close scrutiny of his evidence for elementary salt reveals that it rests exclusively, or nearly so, on the analysis of animal and vegetable matter. In "De natura rerum," written in 1537, he speaks of salt, together with mercury and sulfur, as the products of the separation of the elements of animal and vegetable matter, although in "Archidoxies" he had separated them into fire, air, water, and earth. But speaking of minerals, in 1537 he still speaks of these four as their elements. He does frequently call the three principles the prima materia of minerals at this time, except in theoretical treatises such as "De mineralibus," where his discussions are highly speculative in character and do not relate to experiment or analysis. His fullest discussion of salt from this point of view appears in his treatises on the tartaric diseases, in which he reveals himself to have been much impressed with the saline character of concretions found in the body, their physical resemblance to the solid residue of the wine cask, and their supposed chemical resemblance to the corrosive inorganic salts. It is well known that the difficulty of extracting elementary salt from metals long plagued the adherents of the three principles. Paracelsus may never have tried it, for, paradoxical as it seems, this system of elements, derived from alchemy, had its foundation in his experience with the animal and vegetable kingdoms.

The significance of the three principles resided in their further substitution for the four humors, which, unlike the four elements, were specifically denied by Paracelsus, who attacked them as a Galenic fiction. In making this substitution he re-established communication between the sciences of the organic and inorganic realms which had been very tenuous if not severed through the dogmatization of the four element and four humor ideology. Paracelsus saw the body as a chemical laboratory, in which resided a sentient entity, the *archeus* (an internal chemist) which performed the chemical operations involved in the functioning of the organism. He saw a similar agent at work in the formation of minerals in the earth. This chemical physiology is given great empasis by Paracelsus and had undoubted consequences in advancing this science, in the inspiration of Van Helmont and others in the seventeenth century to the resumption of research in physiology along chemical lines. Its relationship to Paracelsus' own theory is anything but clear. Beyond occasional references to the use of sulfurous remedies for sulfurous diseases, etc. (like for like, against the Galenic therapy of cure by opposites), he has little to say of the three principles when speaking of his remedies. The *archeus* acted spontaneously to counteract disease, a theory which resembled Hippocrates' doctrine of the self-healing powers of the body. The purpose of drugs was to aid the *archeus* in this function. In many instances, however, Paracelsus seems to apply his doctrine of three principles to the body almost as though they

58

were humors, for no more than the Galenists did he succeed in maintaining consistency between his theory and his therapy. Like the relationship of his three principles to the mineral kingdom, the relationship of his chemical medicines to his chemical theory of physiology and therapy remains a speculative extrapolation of other doctrines actually founded in experience.[6]

This system as such was hardly an improvement upon that of the Galenists, for it proved in his hands and those of his disciples even more conducive to confusion. The selection of the names mercury and sulfur for the principles of volatility and inflammability also led to endless controversy over their relationship to common mercury and sulfur, and fixed upon the Paracelsians the stigma of gold-making alchemy. But the Paracelsian system did play an important role in the dislodgment of medical theory from the dead level it had occupied since the time of Galen, and marked the beginning of chemical investigation of the human body. The influence of Paracelsus is clear in the work of Van Helmont, who in the seventeeth century initiated the study of gastric digestion from a chemical point of view. In chemistry the Paracelsian system provided a bridge between the organic and inorganic realms which made a general science of chemistry possible, and provided a theoretical justification for medical chemistry which contributed much to its rise from obscurity to prominence in the late sixteenth century.

HIS CHARACTER AS A SCIENTIST

Perhaps the works of no other scientist present so bewildering an entanglement of personal and professional subject matter as those of Paracelsus. Had he not been the son of a doctor, living in the environment of a community of miners and chemists, we might surmise that his inclination toward mysticism and religion might have led him to a career among the multitude of apocalyptic theologians who flourished in sixteenth century Germany. As it was he attracted attention early in his career through his involvement in one of these politicoreligious outbreaks, and the latter part of his life seems to have been devoted more to theology than to science. Christian mysticism and cabbalistic lore invade his scientific writing at every point. Unless one remembers that Para-

59

celsus was a scientist who literally grew up in the Middle Ages and who wrestled with the most intractable of all sciences, it is easy to dismiss the whole of Paracelsus' work as nonsense, and indeed it is often done.

Paracelsus had a respectable medical knowledge for the time, and enjoyed a wide reputation as a healer during his lifetime; in fact this reputation seems to have saved him repeatedly from falling into the anonymity of an ordinary quack, a fate toward which he was continuously pushed by the enemies he made with his sharp tongue and sharper pen. A perusal of the affair of Basle and other imbroglios suggests that his uncompromising and combative nature contributed very much to his spectacular role as an anti-Galenist, and to his reaction toward the empirics and practitioners of folk medicine. The extent to which his medical practice actually deviated from that of contemporary Galenists is open to some question.

Paracelsus' reputation as a physician has been subject to much fluctuation. The specific character of most of his medicines is today regarded as imaginary, and it is questionable that many, if any, were actually introduced by him for the first time. But the harsh judgment commonly made of him today reflects a reaction against his personality and against the doctrinaire chemical medicine of the eighteenth century from which modern medicine had to free itself. In seeking specific remedies Paracelsus was striking an overdue blow against an even more rigidly crystallized doctrine, for which he deserves credit whatever the merits of his specifics. His medicine involved much more, however, that was pregnant for the future, in his constant concern with dosage (which led him to a more rational definition of poison and nutriment), his concern for the "incurable" diseases, and his awareness of those aspects of medical science now known as psychiatry and biochemistry.

Similar fluctuation has characterized his reputation as a chemist, which has been supposed to depend upon his alleged introduction of new inorganic chemicals. After being freed of the charge of plagiarism from such shadowy "predecessors" as the pseudo Basil Valentine, it is now clear that he had not one or two mysterious predecessors, but an entire line of medical chemists

60

stretching back at least a century and a half before his time. His contribution to medical chemistry was principally that of a publicist. To chemistry in general he made more important contributions than the introduction of a few new substances, in (1) beginning the generalization of the disconnected observations and theories of his predecessors into a form which, however strange it appears to us, did prove a suitable vehicle for the advancement of chemistry, and (2) breaking down the traditional distinction between the organic and inorganic kingdoms, thus attaching chemistry to the triumphal chariot of medicine and creating the incentive for that advancement.

These developments seem to have set in motion a chain of events that carried chemistry far along the road from alchemy to modern chemistry. The influence of the system of chemical classification which appears in its nascent form in "Archidoxies" is easily detected in most chemical textbooks of the next two centuries. The five-element system of the seventeenth century, distinguished by its claim to a solid foundation in analysis, was a corrected version of Paracelsus' three principles. These fruitful ideas, added to his bequest of a corpus of medicochemical writings which constituted an attractive and not entirely unproductive mine for his successors, left a legacy the importance of which cannot be dismissed. His successors, however reluctantly, acknowledged this. Themistius, the Aristotelian in Boyle's "Sceptical Chymist," saw "Paracelsus and some few other sooty empirics" of the previous century as the villains who, "troubled with the smoak of their own furnaces, began to rail at the peripatetic doctrine." It is not clear who the other sooty empirics could have been, except the followers of Paracelsus. In the seventeenth century chemists frequently took elaborate pains to disassociate themselves from him. Libavius remarked defensively that "chemistry was not invented by Paracelsus," and Hendrik de Roy, the translator of Beguin's "Tyrocinium Chymicum" (1610) expressed this sentiment in a rather extreme form. Declaring himself "a foster-child of the Paris school" (of medicine, the principal antagonists of medical chemistry) and "a sworn enemy of the sect of Paracelsists" he goes so far as to advocate their banishment from society! But looking into the works of these critics one finds a practical chemistry built

61

around a system of quintessences, magisteria, tinctures, etc., and a theory dominated by the doctrine of the three principles. Boyle recognized this and remarks on the difficulty of conceding to these "later spagyrists" the originality they claim. Not without reason does he set Paracelsus, as the representative of chemistry, against Aristotle as the representative of philosophy. To Paracelsus, more than any other, the science of chemistry owes its establishment. After him the phrase, "Chymia quid?" was introduced by authors as a matter of pedagogical convenience, not of necessity.

NOTES AND REFERENCES

1 On Paracelsus' biography see R. Julius Hartmann, "Theophrast von Hohenheim," Stuttgart und Berlin, 1904; Henry M. Pachter, "Paracelsus," New York, 1951. On his chronology see Walter Artelt, "Paracelsus und seine Zeit," in "Theophrastus Paracelsus," Hrsg. Fritz Jaeger, Salzberg, 1941, and Owsei Temkin, "The Elusiveness of Paracelsus," Bulletin of the History of Medicine, XXVI (1952), pp. 201–17.

2 The idea of a wholesale transfer of chemicals from alchemical to medical use will seem less bizarre if one recalls that chemicals which exhibit reactivity in the laboratory are likely also to exhibit it in the body, whereas a substance inert in the one case is more likely to be so in both. Reaction, in the form of vomitive, laxative, or sweating effects was the aim of many Galenic remedies at this time, and some prominent pharmacopoeias were organized according to these effects. They are also producible with proper doses of chemical medicines, and were so listed in the chemical pharmacopoeias of the late sixteenth and seventeenth centuries. Paracelsus' evident care in dosage and that of other prominent chemical physicians weaken if it does not disprove the charge of poisoner hurled against them, although violent remedies were certainly not unknown, especially among the empirici who came to represent the lunatic fringe of medical chemistry.

3 Concerning *mercurius vitae*, Book 5. Statistically Paracelsus' most common chemical remedies would appear to have been oil and spirit of vitriol, mixed with a great variety of less active ingredients. But his amanuensis' Oporinus, later on professor in Basle, described precipitati pulver reduced to pills with several vegetable ingredients as his remedy for "all illnesses." Paracelsus' adversary Erastus also mentions calcined mercury in this vein.

4 The term "quintessence" flourished among alchemists and medical chemists of the later middle ages; "elixir" was a more ancient term meaning approximately the same thing. "Magisteria" was popularized by the Latin Geber, having a meaning something like "masterpiece." "Specifics" were specific medicines, a few of which were listed in most Galenic pharmacopoeias. The name was also applied to remedies classified as laxative, vomi-

tive, etc. in pharmacopoeias organized in this manner. The term "arcanum" seems to have enjoyed no particular notoriety prior to Paracelsus. It is noteworthy, however, that books of secret remedies resembling Paracelsus' arcana were enjoying great popularity just at this time. In general writers on Paracelsus' chemistry attribute peculiar importance to his conception of "arcana," but this seems justifiable only if one emphasizes the frequency and ignores the looseness of his use of it.

5 In his earliest work (On . . . the several diseases, ca. 1520) he says "Each (Ein ietliche) element consists in three things, mercury, sulphur and salt; thus there are 4 mercuries, 4 sulphurs and 4 salts," a statement enigmatic enough to fix the problem. Most references to his writing on the three principles refer to "Opus Paramirum" (1531–32) and other late works.

6 Such elements of Paracelsus' philosophy as the archeus and the three principles sometimes appear in his nonchemical works. There is an inescapable danger in considering from the point of view of a single science, a terminology evidently aimed to propound a general world view. These terms, however, seem to have originated in his consideration of chemistry. The explanation of their permutations as they were integrated into his whole philosophy is probably the principal justification for the continued large scale prosecution of Paracelsian studies.

7 Walter Pagel, "Paracelsus, an introduction to philosophical medicine in the era of the renaissance," Basel & New York, S. Karger, 1958.

ROBERT P. MULTHAUF

·· 6 ··

Libavius and Beguin

Sixteenth Century to Early Seventeenth

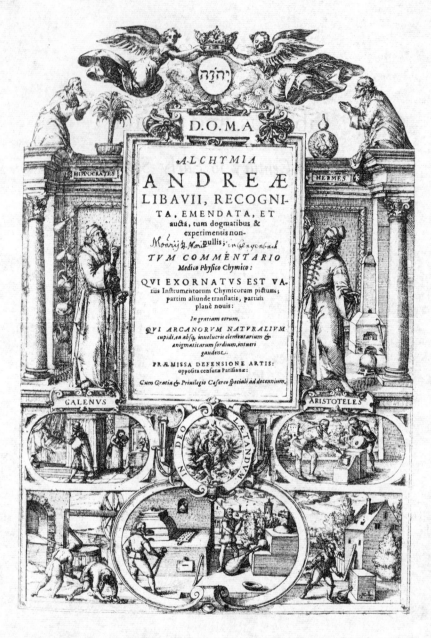

Title page of *Alchymia Andreae Libavii*, Frankfurt, 1606.

THE medieval alchemist increasingly abandoned the attempt to achieve transmutation through conventional metallurgical procedures. He sought the elixir, and regarded chemistry as a sequence of operations leading to the preparation of this single product. Under the domination of this ideology he not only ignored the problem of classification of chemical species, but tended to concern himself less with the nature of these operations than with their sequence. The writings of the Latin Geber represent a premature beginning of a more modern approach to the description of chemical operations, and those of Paracelsus the beginning of an attempt to classify the products of those operations. Embedded as they were in voluminous effusions of conventional thought, these beginnings only become apparent as their consequences are seen in later writings, notably in two chemists who took the next step in defining the science, Andreas Libavius and Jean Beguin.

Little biographical data have been unearthed on either Libavius or Beguin. Libavius was born in Halle, about 1540–50, and appeared on the public scene in 1588, as Professor of History and Poetry at Jena. He seems to have arrived at this respectable university position prior to acquiring an interest in chemistry. Four years later he moved to Rothenberg an der Tauber, where he introduced the teaching of science and began the publication of a series of critiques of both the Paracelsians and their adversaries, which he soon expanded into his own version of chemistry. In 1597 he published his major work, "Alchemia," a massive tome recognizably affiliated with Paracelsus' "Archidoxies," but fundamentally different in its approach. Libavius is regarded as the first academic professor of chemistry and was the more remarkable in being no literary scientist, but a real practitioner to whom some discoveries are credited. He continued to write at length on chemistry, and by his death in 1616 had produced a body of scientific writing more voluminous than that of Paracelsus himself.

Beguin was very nearly an exact contemporary of Libavius.

He was a native of Lorraine, where he apparently received a good education, but his later life was spent in Germany and Paris, where he offered instruction in chemistry. He tells of visits to the mining regions of central Europe in 1604 and in 1611, between which he first issued, at the request of his students, his textbook of chemistry, "Tyrocinium chymicum." This small volume, published in 1610, was his second publication, as he had edited two years earlier the popular alchemical work, "Novum lumen chymicum." The "Tyrocinium" appeared in Germany in 1611 in a pirated edition and the following year Beguin published an enlarged version which became the basis for subsequent editions. He died between 1616 and 1620.

Paracelsus had died in 1541, leaving behind a few publications which he had succeeded in getting out despite a generally hostile press, and a mass of manuscript material, some of which still remains unpublished.[1] The floodgates were about to open, however, on a deluge of Paracelsian literature which was to make his name commonplace among booksellers for centuries. In the generation after his death a number of his medicochemical works were edited by obscure disciples of questionable repute—such as Michael Toxites and Leonard Thurneysser—but persons of more solid reputation occasionally had the temerity to associate with medical chemistry, and perforce with Paracelsus. The rapidity with which medical chemistry became merged in Paracelsianism testifies to the rise of his fame, but also to the degree of the obscurity of this school prior to Paracelsus.

With the adoption of medical chemistry by some of the prominent physicians in the last quarter of the sixteenth century, the stage was set for a battle between medical "conservatives" and "radicals." The eventual loss of this battle by the conservatives was not unconnected with their essentially static and negative position, for the Paracelsians not only edited the works of the master, but enlarged upon them in their own medicochemical writings. It is evident that there was a ready market for the pharmacopoeia of chemical medicines, and the works of the Paracelsians assumed the format of the conventional pharmacopoeia more than had anything written by Paracelsus himself. Their chemical explorations also went considerably beyond anything recorded in Paracelsus' writings, and the number of inorganic substances synthesized by such men as Quercetanus[2] was considerably greater than can be claimed with any certainty for Paracelsus. But with remarkable consistency they swore allegiance to the theories of the master, and the relationship between theory and practice, never close, became increasingly tenuous.

The incompatibility between the theory and practice of Paracelsian chemistry was a consequence of its basis in the ideology of medical chemistry, which was in turn based on that of medieval European alchemy. This ideology regarded the manifest differences in forms of matter as evidences of a gradual qualitative variation of matter from an extremely pure and active substance—the alchemist's elixir and medical chemist's quintessence—to an equally impure and inert substance, which, being the dross which the chemist's operations aimed to dispose of, was scarcely deemed worthy of a name. This theory was closely bound up with the operation of distillation—an innovation of the later Middle Ages— and the behavior of substances under distillation was the principal criterion of their definition. In "Archidoxies," Paracelsus had organized a miscellany of chemical entities—quintessences, arcana, magisteria, specifics, and elixirs—into a crude system, useful as a starting point for chemical work, but fundamentally unsound in its preoccupation with distillation and the ideology of the quintessence, for it provided no place for the nondistillable residues which constituted the real basis of inorganic chemistry. By the end of the century these residues constituted the major part of the chemical pharmacopoeia, which could accommodate them thanks to its conventional organization into diaphoretics, sudorifics, etc., but they still had no home in any chemical system. The Paracelsians had exploited chemistry about as thoroughly as was possible within this peculiar theoretical framework. They had created a condition in which chemistry as an art and science could exist on its own merits—albeit with medicine as its "aim"—and had produced the data for its reconstruction. That reconstruction had to wait for the appearance of the chemist who was free of the Paracelsian theoretical predilections.

LIBAVIUS

In Libavius' time it appears that all chemists were commonly regarded as Paracelsians. His works are an extended protest against this point of view, and the harshness of his judgment of the Paracelsians was scarcely less than that of their arch-enemies among the Galenists. He begins his "Rerum chymicarum epistolica" (1595) with a criticism of the Paracelsians which he has not ameliorated in his "Syntagmatis" written almost twenty years later. In the earlier work he defends the "honor" of true chemistry against them, saying that "it is a far different matter from the deceits of the Paracelsians." He similarly begins the "Syntagmatis" with an attack on the Paracelsians, "who arrogate to themselves the key to the science." In both works he follows these remarks with a brief and somewhat unconvincing discussion of the contributions to chemistry of other *"physici, philosophi, et sapientes,"* impressive in its testimony to his familiarity with the literature, but unconvincing in its vagueness as to their contributions.

Libavius labors at length over the definition and scope of chemistry. He finds unsatisfactory the Paracelsian definition of their "spagyrics" as "the separation of the pure from the impure." Chemists, he says, either resolve mixtures into parts and purify the latter according to the prescriptions of the art; or they elaborate the whole to bring it to its maximum strength (*vires*); or they belabor the ignoble to transmute it into the noble, with rejection of the useless impurities. But in the last analysis "chemistry is to segregate the heterogeneous, resolve the composite, and to utilize the principles per se or to purify, correct, or exalt them to be recomposed for the most effective use of the components."

Libavius' specific criticisms are usually directed at aspects of medicochemical theory which considerably predate Paracelsus, such as the equation of chemistry with distillation, and the ideology of the quintessence. Chemistry, he declares in "Rerum chymicarum epistolica," rules itself and serves medicine only accidentally. The foundation of his reconstruction of the science was in his ingenious redefinition and rearrangement of the categories of "Archidoxies," and particularly in his adoption of the category of magisterium as a general one comprehending, for the most part, the nondistillable residues. The term, magisterium, was not invented by Paracelsus, as Libavius points out. Its most familiar prior use was by the Latin Geber, but Libavius curiously fails to mention him where he discusses this in "Syntagmatis," and it is clear that Paracelsus was his principal source on the subject. The magisterium was the vaguest of Paracelsus' categories. He called it "that which, apart from separation or any preparation of the elements, can be extracted out of things." In "Alchemia" Libavius adopts this conveniently amorphous concept as the most comprehensive subdivision of chemistry, but redefines it as "pure chemical species," and emphasizes its independence of distillation by coining the category "extracta" as a second subdivision of chemistry within which he places most of the other categories of "Archidoxies." He defines the extracta as "that which can be extracted from solid bodies, leaving behind the crassness of the elements." His third and last category is the composite species, by which he means mixture.

One is tempted to credit Libavius with the accomplishment of the miracle of a system compatible both with the chemistry of his own time and with modern chemistry. In his heroic attempt to comprehend within a single system what was in his time a formidable body of disorganized knowledge, he fails, however, to fulfill the promise of this definition. He further subdivides magisteria into those of quality and those of substance, the former relating to physical changes, such as the polishing of gems, but including such curiosities as the magisterium of weight, which he exemplifies by a chemical process designed to rectify the deficiency in underweight coins! In general it appears that his magisteria of quality are simply processes defined by easily recognizable physical properties of the product, whereas those of substance are defined by the chemical operation involved. The result is that some of the processes and many of the products appear under both headings and the classification is in general anything but rigorous. The significance of his magisterium is rather in that he used it in such a way as to signify something like that which we now call general chemistry; it retained scarcely any alchemical or medical connotations. As a classification of chemical phenomena, Libavius' "Alchemia" is not very satisfactory, but as a guide to the

71

future and as a compilation of the whole practice of chemistry it far surpasses any earlier work. It culminates an era during which the principal technological factor underlying chemistry had been the exploitation of the mineral acids. In "Alchemia" they appear in almost every chapter, usually as solvents, in which capacity Libavius appears to regard them as nonparticipating agents for bringing about the operation of dissolution. Through them he renders metals potable, powdered, fixed, and volatile. By processes beginning with acid dissolution he calcines, vitrifies, separates, and transmutes them, and through acids he converts them to their "crocuses" (usually any yellowish powder), and separates from them the elements, principles, quintessences, tinctures, oils, and flowers. In respect to clarity, however, the process descriptions are not generally superior to those of Paracelsus, where the latter did not resort to deliberate obscurity. Despite a tendency to repeat the same few acid dissolution processes for different purposes, Libavius mixes them with other common processes, such as vinegar extraction, amalgamation, and various cementations, in numerous combinations which must have yielded a great variety of inorganic materials, although the identity of the product is often a matter of considerable doubt.

Libavius has been credited at various times with a number of chemical "firsts," the preparation of tin tetrachloride, glass of antimony (oxidized antimony sulfide), bismuth hydroxide, ammonium sulfate, succinnic acid, carbonic acid, and hydrochloric acid; the use of gold for coloring glass red, the distinction of inflammable from noninflammable gases, the analysis of mineral waters, recognition of the identity of the acids (sulfuric) obtained by distillation of vitriol and from burning sulfur in the presence of niter. Since his "Alchemia" was the first work to treat comprehensively the reactions of sulfuric and nitric acids, and aqua regia, it seems probable that he did first describe some of these. But that he recognized many of them as unique substances is questionable. It seems clear that he prepared hydrochloric acid by distilling sodium chloride with clay, and sulfuric acid by burning sulfur, and in the latter case recognized the identity of this acid with that obtained from vitriol. These discoveries, which certainly justify his reputation as an experimental chemist, were evidently made in his later years as they are first described in the "Syntagmatis." Tin tetrachloride, which was long named Libavius' fuming spirit, was also described in that work. It was prepared by heating tin with corrosive sublimate, and not through the direct use of hydrochloric acid, which remained unexploited long after Libavius' time.

On the question of the elements, that ancient bugaboo of the chemist, Libavius' ideas show an interesting development. In "Rerum chymicarum epistolica" he solemnly derives both the four elements of antiquity and the three chemical principles from the cogitations of the ancient geometers, concluding "Now since the ancient philosophers have found ternaries and quaternaries useful, the said principles and elements are designated in nature." He acknowledges the chemist's mercury, sulfur, and salt as convenient to their "anatomy," but declares that the four elements are drawn from mixed bodies.

In "Alchemia" he appears to be relatively indifferent to the question of the elements and satisfies himself with a quotation from "Archidoxies," but in the "Syntagmatis" he is positively unsympathetic, and remarks that it is no wonder that the beginner in chemistry is disturbed by the variety of judgments on the anatomy of the science, where all others are condemned and only one's own phantasies are held to be genuine. "In Ulstad[4] mention is made of the distillation of wine, and one is taught to extract the quintessence and phlegm, leaving a black material. From this on another occasion phlegm and oil are elicited, leaving black earth. This is calcined and salt segregated, leaving an empty cinder, which is called 'terra damnata.' From the salt again tincture is sought, and it is necessary that another earth remain. Thus such cutting-up exhibits seven things, spirit, phlegm, oil, salt, terra damnata, tincture and fixed earth. How are these made congruent with the elements and principles? If we take phlegm and terra damnata for elements the others must be principles, that is the salt, oil, and spirit . . ." After more of this, he concludes, "If you want to know more on the cultivation of elements, see Paracelsus, in Book 3 of "Archidoxies."

BEGUIN

Beguin[5] himself does not seem to have been especially concerned at being grouped with the Paracelsians, in fact he placed a quotation from Paracelsus at the beginning of the early editions of "Tyrocinium," but the same cannot be said for some of his supporters. Jean de Roy, who edited the 1620 French version of "Tyrocinium," even outdid Libavius, describing himself as "the sworn enemy" of the "sect of Paracelsists," and "being a foster-child of the Paris school . . . would be very glad to give them the chase as profanators and unworthy of being admitted to the mysteries of chemistry." He even speaks of procuring their banishment from society! Beguin does appear to be less directly dependent upon Paracelsus than Libavius, and more upon Geber. We can reach this conclusion from the number of citations of each, but only very tentatively, for the vast literature of chemistry at that time was largely repetitive, and the choice of citations depended largely upon one's taste.

In dealing with the definition and aims of chemistry, and similar questions, Beguin is less philosophical and, one is tempted to say, more to the point, that Libavius. "Chemistry is an art which teaches the dissolution of natural mixed bodies and, upon their dissolution, their coagulation to make medicines more agreeable, salubrious and assured." Its object "is mixed and composed bodies, not in motion, for in that consideration it belongs to [physics] but insofar as it is soluble and coagulable." "If," he declares, "anyone calls chemistry alchemy, he, in the Arabian manner, declares the excellency thereof. If he calls it the spagyric art, he shows its principal offices, conjunction and separation; if the hermetic art, he demonstrates its author and antiquity; if the distillatory science, he shows its authority and function. But since all disciplines are either theoretical or practical, chemistry not acquiescing in the knowledge and contemplation of mixed bodies, as a natural science, but having regard to the work or business, viz to magisteria, tinctures, quintessences, and such like, unto it is worthily granted a place among practical arts and disciplines."

It is evident from this that the "magisteria, tinctures, quintessences, and such like" brought into prominence by "Archidoxies," continued to preoccupy the chemist of the first decades of the seventeenth century. Beguin was a more conventional chemist than Libavius in his preoccupation with medicine, but his approach differed from that of both Paracelsus and Libavius in that his description of chemistry was not organized around these entities, but around the chemical operations. In this he was reverting to the old alchemical system, but his spirit is as independent as that of Libavius, and it would surely be incorrect to see in his system any significant reversion to pre-Paracelsian chemistry. He does comment on the entities, and his comments are interesting. Speaking on the "effects" of solution and coagulation (his subdivisions of chemistry) he says, "there are effects, or, as by some they are called, chymical species, of solution and coagulation, which are either liquid, or soft, or hard. To the liquid may be referred the various kinds of aqua fortis, spirits, vinegar, oils, and liquid tinctures . . . to the soft balsams, various extracts, soft tinctures; to the hard, salts, flowers, magisteria, calxes, dry tinctures or crocus." Further on, however, he gives a definition of magisteria nearly identical with that of Libavius.

Here we see another approach which avoids the dilemma which distillation chemistry brought to chemical classification. In the chapter subdivisions of his book Beguin mixes operations and chemical species in somewhat the same way as Libavius, but he does show his deeper interest in classification—unlike Libavius—by exposing his ideas nakedly in the form of a table, a table in which chemistry is described entirely in terms of the operations. As to the ideal of distillation chemistry, the quintessence, he disposes of it in precisely the same way as had Libavius, by giving it a separate section in his book, scarcely related to anything that had gone before.

Beguin's peculiar independence is also shown in his handling of the elements. He emphasizes the importance of the principles of the science and their not conflicting with those of physics and medicine. The physicist and physician consider the same body diversely, the first according to physical principles, as natural, capable of movement and repose, the second as capable of receiving health, examined by the first principles which cause or destroy health, established by the four first qualities, cold, hot, dry, and wet, which constitute the temperament of bodies with the result of health or illness. The chemist considers the body again in his fashion, to know how far it can be resolved or coagulated, and that it has numerous virtues in its interior which can be manifested by art and rendered more useful; and finally that mercury, sulfur, and salt are the principles which render mixed bodies soluble and coagulable, and the reasons of its internal virtues, or the true chemical substances. The chemist must proceed in all his examinations, theories, and operations by these three principles, otherwise his observations and artifices would be without foundation, and outside his principles. His emphasis on "principles" (a word which he takes in more than one sense) continues as he notes that physicians have found the four qualities and four elements to be their first principles, whereas chemists have found the *tria prima* (mercury, sulfur, and salt) to be theirs. He then defines mercury as an acid liquor, permeable, penetrating, ethereal and very pure; sulfur is a sweet balm, oleaginous and viscous, which he compares to fire. Salt is a dry, salty body which impedes corruption and has admirable faculties for dissolving, coagulating, purifying, and evacuating. They are between bodies and spirits, and philosophers have given them various names, such as body, soul and spirit, material, form and idea . . . at which point he plunges briefly into the philosophical mists from which chemistry was at this time emerging.

Beguin is also credited with the first mention of certain hitherto unknown substances, most notably acetone, obtained by distillation of lead acetate, and called "burning spirit of Saturn (lead)." Less certain is his alleged priority in mentioning ammonium hydrogen sulfate, one of his "oils" of sulfur. He also describes the preparation of hydrochloric acid by the same process as Libavius; in fact it is not entirely clear that Beguin's is not the earlier account.[6]

SUMMARY

Libavius and Beguin represent two independent reinterpretations of chemistry which marked the beginning of its reorganization into "modern" chemistry. The former, taking a view independent of the contending schools of alchemy, metallurgy, medical chemistry, and "Galenic" pharmacology, saw with remarkable

76

perspicacity the common ground upon which a better structure could be built. The latter, showing an awareness of this new approach—which he may well have gained from reading Libavius—went on to draw up a practical textbook designed to appeal to the practical chemist of his time, as Libavius' ponderous works could not.

Libavius, while an excellent laboratory chemist, was primarily interested in theory—or philosophy as it was then called—and brought criticism to bear on the chemistry of his time just where it was needed, on the chemist's preoccupation with the supposed entities of distillation chemistry and on their exclusive concern with that process. His definition of the magisterium as a pure chemical species, while subsuming the distillation entities under the category of extracta, redirected the science of chemical classification toward a more attainable goal.

It is not easy, however, to evaluate the effect of Libavius' reform, for the chemists of succeeding generations are not conspicuously aware of it. Perhaps the virulence of his antagonism towards the Paracelsians mitigated against him, for their heyday was far from over. Perhaps also chemistry was not sufficiently well established as an art in the seventeenth century to be appreciated as a science, for Libavius' works, although containing much on chemical practice, are heavily overweighted with a philosophy which is discouragingly profuse, while neither dogmatic enough for the system-seeker nor lucid enough for the scientist. The very size of his books must have discouraged many a practical chemist, and it seems that none of them was translated from Latin, even into his native tongue.[7] Although like practically every other writer on chemistry, he was frequently cited, appreciation of Libavius seems really to have begun among modern students of the history of chemistry.

Perhaps Libavius' failure to create a greater impact was also due to the contemporary appearance of the simple textbook of chemistry which was to set the pattern for generations, that is, Beguin's "Tyrocinium." Beguin had the benefit of access to Libavius' early works and cites him (as Libavius in his later work cites Beguin), but Beguin was certainly no disciple of Libavius, but rather an independent product of the same trend toward sober rationalism in

77

chemistry. Beguin's occasional excursions into theory are no less philosophical than those of Libavius, but they are far less numerous and, as has been noted, he seems to have shrugged off his own philosophy by declaring chemistry not to be a science at all, but rather an art. His single work, about one third the length of "Alchemia," was translated into the major European languages, issued in 35 to 50 editions,[8] and set a pattern followed by the important series of textbooks issued in France later in the seventeenth century. It can scarcely be doubted that Beguin had an influence on chemistry considerably beyond that exercised by Libavius.

In their attitude toward the "elements" Libavius and Beguin show themselves free of dogmatism, but they do little to advance this aspect of chemical theory, and they do not actually appear to be much concerned with the question. In this they were not revolutionary, for even before them chemists were less concerned with the elements than a reading of Boyle's "Sceptical Chymist" would lead one to suppose. Paracelsus' struggles with the Galenists over his three principles relate more to physiology than to chemistry, and he seems in "Archidoxies" to regard the elements as simply another category in distillation chemistry.

The processes cultivated by Beguin and Libavius did not differ greatly from those of their predecessors, but in the fullness of their exploitation of earlier sources and the comprehensiveness of their exposition of chemistry they put on record the full complexity of the science in this time. Some of the materials they are thought to have first described are clear in that record, others are nebulous but possible products of the processes they mention. Libavius can more certainly be regarded as a discoverer, and his observation of the identity of two types of (sulfuric) acid justifies our ranking him among the foremost research chemists of his time. His principal claim to fame, however, like that of Beguin, is for his reformation of the curious and mystical science of chemistry into something which the modern chemist can recognize as his own.

NOTES AND REFERENCES

1 The work still unpublished is chiefly, if not exclusively, theological.
2 Quercetanus, the Latinized name of Joseph Duchesne (circa 1544–1609) was one of the most "controversial" of the Paracelsians. At the end of the

sixteenth century he was physician-in-ordinary to King Henry IV of France. Beguin served the same sovereign.

3 The most extensive biography of Libavius is that of Ludwig Darmstaedter in G. Bugge, ed., "Das Buch der Grossen Chemiker," Berlin, 1929, Vol. I. The present discussion is based upon "Rerum chymicarum epistolica . . ." (Francofurti: Joannes Saurius, 1595); "Alchymia . . ." (Title page missing. Handwritten notation lists this as the edition of Francofurti, 1597. Library of Yale University); "Syntagmatis selectorum undiquaque et perspicue traditorum alchymiae arcanorum," Francofurti, Nicholaus Hoffmannus, 1615.

4 Philip Ulstad, of Nurnberg, was a contemporary of Paracelsus who published in 1525—the same year *Archidoxies* is supposed to have been written (but not published)—a similar work called "Coelum philosophorum." Both works were derived from earlier books on distillation chemistry, but *Archidoxies* is considerably more original.

5 On Beguin see also, T. S. Patterson, "Jean Beguin and his *Tyrocinium chymicum,*" *Annals of Science* 2(1937)243–98. Patterson gives a summary of Beguin's book and an exhaustive discussion of the derivation of its various editions. The present discussion is based upon the editions of Rouen: Jean Behourt, 1647; Wittebergae: A. Hartmann, 1656; and London: T. Passenger, 1669. The Rouen edition is a French translation, edited by Hendrik de Roy. The Wittenberg edition contains three letters from Beguin to his German student Jeremia Barth.

6 According to Darmstaedter (see note 3) Book I of the *Syntagmatis,* which contained the description of hydrochloric acid, was published in 1611 by Hoffmann. The edition I have seen from this publisher carries the date 1615. Beguin described the acid as early as 1612, according to Patterson. I have no information on the 1610 edition of *Tyrocinium.*

7 A French translation entitled, "Secrets de médicine et de la philosophie chimique" is mentioned by L. Reutter de Rosemont, "Histoire de la Pharmacie," Paris, 1931, but I have found no other reference to this.

8 Patterson (see note 5) has given particular attention to the interrelationship of the various editions. He questions the existence of a German translation and takes the more conservative view in estimating the total number of editions.

ROBERT P. MULTHAUF

·· 7 ··

Joan Baptista Van Helmont

1577-1644

LIFE AND CHARACTER

JOAN BAPTISTA VAN HELMONT was born in Brussels in 1577[1] or 1580,[2] and died December 30, 1644, either in Brussels or Vilvorde (near Brussels). He was descended from a noble and ancient family: his mother was Marie de Stassert, and he belonged to the family of Mérode through his wife, Margaret Van Ranst. His father died in 1580, and Joan Baptista was the youngest child.

He studied arts at Louvain until 1594 but took no degree, since he considered academic honours a mere vanity. He then went to the Jesuits' School at Louvain, recently founded in spite of the prohibition of the King, the University and Pope Clement VIII, where he studied the Qabbalah under Martin Del Rio, who expounded his celebrated *Disquisitiones magicarum*.[3] Still dissatisfied, van Helmont turned to the mystics, and studied the works of Thomas à Kempis (1379–1471) and Johann Tauler (1290–1361), both of whom wrote "On the Imitation of Jesus Christ." He then took up medicine and read the works of Hippocrates, Galen, Avicenna and a great number of modern authors, from which he says he "noted all that seemed certain and incontrovertible but was dismayed on reading my notes to find that the pains I had bestowed and the years I had spent were altogether fruitless."[4] He says he gave away to students books worth 200 crowns but wished afterwards that he had burnt them.[5] He had visions, in one of which he saw his own soul in the form of a resplendent crystal,[6] and he regarded all science and wisdom as a gift of God.[7] He took the degree of M.D. at Louvain in 1609[8] after ten years of study and travel, in which he visited the Alps, Switzerland, Italy, Spain, France and England (1604–5).[9]

D'Elmotte says he was admitted to the Rosicrucian order in Bavaria, but gives no authority.[10] Among other lucrative offers he declined one from the Emperor Rudolph II at Vienna. In 1609 he married Margaret Van Ranst, and he says: "God has given me a pious and noble wife. I retired with her to Vilvorde and there for seven years I dedicated myself to pyrotechny [i.e., Chemistry] and to the relief of the poor."[11] Boerhaave[12] says he was told that Helmont was "wholly taken up in chemical operations night and day" and that "he was scarce known in his neighborhood; that he did not apply himself to practice; nor scarce ever stirr'd out of doors." He was a very influential and highly respected man, with a great reputation, although Boyle,[13] who constantly quotes Helmont as an authority, remarks that he was "an author more considerable for his experiments than many learned men are pleased to think him." Helmont's harsh although deserved criticism of the conventional medicine of his time made him many enemies and retarded the general acceptance of his views.

Van Helmont was proud of his claim to be called a chemist, and calls himself (e.g., in the introduction to his "De lithiasi") "Philosophus per ignem." He represents the transition from alchemy to chemistry. Van Helmont made a careful study of the chemical as well as the medical writings of Paracelsus (which he later found full of errors) and carried out a large number of chemical experiments in his house at Vilvorde. He loved his apparatus, and tells us of a beautiful receiver which he thought he had spoiled through neglect: a vessel "exceeding great, clear, Crystalline and precious . . . easily capable of containing three Gallons . . . I sequestred from the long snout of an Alembick," and "was grieved that a Glass so precious was stained about so sordid a matter." The stain put him in train of an important truth, and was easily removed by acid, so that "those things which I judged I had committed through my own carlessnesse I knew had come to pass by divine Goodnesse so disposing it."[14]

Autobiographical details and a notice by his son, Francis Mercurius, are given in Helmont's works,[15] and there are several studies of his life and works.[16]

With their wide scope, critical attitude, varied interests, and intimate blending of the practical and mystical, the writings of van Helmont as printed convey the impression of a complex personality and, in fact, all shades of opinion are represented in the various appreciations of their author. I shall permit myself to give an independent opinion on those parts of his writings which are of chemical interest. Some parts of van Helmont's works show the credulity we should expect in his time. He tells a story of a church tower at Leyden having been struck by lightning in 1554

and disappearing entirely into the ground, where it was afterwards found complete by digging;[17] he asserts that he and many
others were cured of diseases by taking oil into which a stone had
been dipped by an Irishman, Butler, imprisoned at Vilvorde;[18]
and he gives a very circumstantial account of the transmutation
of nearly 2000 times its weight of mercury into gold by means of
a quarter of a grain of the Philosopher's Stone given him by a
stranger.[19] This was a heavy red powder glittering like powdered
glass and smelling of saffron; it was enclosed in wax and projected
on the mercury heated to the melting-point of lead, when the
metal grew thick and, on raising the fire, melted into pure gold.
Helmont did not believe that the Philosopher's Stone was also the
elixir of life, as Paracelsus assumed. He gives directions for preparing a powerful elixir by dissolving cedar wood in the alkahest
and distilling off an oil, of which a drop given in wine cures serious illnesses in a few hours.[20] He says that by means of the alkahest of Paracelsus he had converted vegetables or oak charcoal
into water.[21] He calls the alkahest *ignis aqua*, and it was probably
nitric acid. In some of the examples which he gives of converting
bodies into water, he neutralizes acids with chalk and distils off
water. Schmieder[22] gives a derivation of the name alkahest from
al+καυστής, a Greek-Arabic word. J. le Pelletier[23] after a long dissertation on the nature of the alkahest, and extracts from Ripley,
Philalethes and Starkey, leaves the matter where he found it.
The idea probably came originally from the water of Styx, which
could be kept only in an ass's hoof, whereas the alkahest should
dissolve any vessel in which it is put and gradually bore its way to
the center of the earth, so that Kunckel[24] said the name should be
"Alles Lügen est."[25]

An unknown contemporary says Helmont was pious, learned,
and famous. He was called usually to patients who were abandoned by other physicians as incurable, and they were never long
in his hands, since on the second or third day they were either
dead or cured.[26]

Van Helmont believed in spontaneous generation: he asserts
that full-grown mice are produced in three weeks from wheat in a
glass stopped with dirty linen, and that scorpions are formed from
the herb basil crushed in a cavity between two bricks, but he also

gives some good observations in natural history which seemed to support the theory,[27] which was accepted as late as the last century.

He made extensive use of sympathetic remedies and the usual *Dreckapotheke* of his period, prescribing the most disgusting remedies even for his own illnesses.[28] His remedy from toads (Zenexton)[29] was used as an amulet against plague.[30] He taught that plants are produced from a primordial juice called Leffas, and metals and minerals are generated in the earth from a whitish-green paste (*Saponis liquidi*) called Bur.[31]

Cap[32] regarded Helmont as much superior to Paracelsus in learning, patience, and logic, and above all in the nobility and elevation of his character, and Moon[33] gives an expert appreciation of his medical views: "fanciful explanations in medicine, as in other things, are often stimulating and fertilizing and are perhaps better than none at all." In chemistry van Helmont was certainly very considerably superior to Paracelsus, both in theory and experiment. Thomson[34] says that Helmont, "notwithstanding his attachment to the fanatical opinions" of his time, overturned "a vast number of errors, both theoretical and practical." Although he "has been frequently placed on the same level with Paracelsus, and treated like him with contempt," his merits were very much greater: "his erudition was great, his understanding excellent, and his industry indefatigable."[34] The recent attempts to prove the great dependence of Helmont on Paracelsus have gone too far, and are often too vaguely expressed.[35] Delacre[36] more correctly emphasizes the great change in philosophic outlook between Paracelsus and Helmont. Helmont thought[37] young men should be taught in their three and seven years in the universities, not the pagan philosophy of Aristotle, but Mathematics, Geography, Political Economy, Natural History and Mineralogy, and especially practical chemistry—"to know and separate the first principles of bodies . . . their fixedness, volatility, separation, life, death, transformations, alteration, weakness, corruption, transplanting, solution, coagulation, resolution and new operations . . . not by naked discourse but by handicraft demonstration of the fire . . . by distilling, moistening, drying, calcining, resolving, as Nature works."

He wrote a treatise[38] on the therapeutic properties of animal magnetism which he published only after being urged to do so by Jesuits. This at once brought him in contact with the Inquisition, which considered his case for thirteen years. He was a good Catholic, and offered to have the book burned if condemned. In 1634 he was sent to a Franciscan prison in Brussels, but after the intervention of powerful friends—including, it is said, Marie de Medici, he was released after a few weeks and confined to his own house, which he was not allowed to leave without a dispensation of the Archbishop of Malines. The gentle and pious Brotherhood was thus balked of a second Roger Bacon, but the treatment of van Helmont was by no means mild: when the plague broke out, his family refused to leave without him, and as a result two of his sons died. He appears to have been left alone by his persecutors after 1638. Some of his papers were confiscated and were unknown until they were found and published by C. Broeckx.[39]

His *Supplementum de Spadanis fontibus* (on Spa water) in six chapters, published at Liège (Leodii) in 1624,[40] criticized a work of Henri de Heer (or Heers), a Liège physician, published at Liège in 1614 (*Spadacrene, Hoc est Fons Spadanus*, 8°, Leodii, 1614; *Les Fontaines de Spa*, 8°, Liège, 1616) and made him some medical enemies. In 1642 he published his important work on fevers,[41] which was reprinted in 1644 with three new tracts, one on the stone (*De Lithiasi*), one on the plague (*De Peste*) and one criticizing the theories of Galen (*De humoribus Galeni*), as *Opuscula medica inaudita*.[42]

WORKS

Shortly before his death van Helmont gave his papers, which he had thought of burning, to his son Francis Mercurius (1614–1699), who had studied and practiced medicine, but led an irregular life among gypsies,[43] charging him to publish them all, even the crude and incorrect. The result was the work, containing parts previously published separately, entitled *Ortus medicinæ*, or the "Origins of Medicine," dedicated to Jehova ("Verbo ineffabili"), the first edition of which appeared in 1648 and the last in 1707.[44]

Boerhaave,[45] who calls van Helmont "the greatest and most

experienced of all the chemists that have yet appeared," says the Venice and German editions contain "morsels not in the fashion of the author," but it is a mistake to say that the later editions are very different from the first, of 1648. The English translation[46] is by John Chandler, of Merton Hall, Oxford.

The French translation[47] by Jean le Conte is incomplete; the German translation[48] is by Knorr von Rosenroth with the assistance of F. M. van Helmont: Rixner and Siber[49] say that the translator compared the Latin and Flemish texts, and his version is literal but obscure. Three treatises (*Of the magnetic cure of wounds; The nativity of tartar in wine;* and *The Image of God in man*) were translated by Walter Charleton (1619–1707; physician to Charles I) and published in 1650 as "A Ternary of Paradoxes."[50]

An interesting work of van Helmont's is that written in Flemish: *Dageraed oft Nieuwe Opkomst der Geneeskonst, in verborgen grondt-regelen der Natuere* ("Dawn of the revival of medicine and the concealed fundamental rules of nature"), *Nooyt in't licht gesien, en van den Autheur selve in't Nederduyts beschreven.*[51] The 1660 edition is sometimes called, incorrectly, a Dutch translation of the *Ortus medicinæ.* Rixner and Siber say the manuscript was given by van Helmont to his daughter, from whom it was obtained by a friend who had it printed. An edition of Leyden, 4°, 1615, has been reported. The first mention I have found is in Rixner and Siber[52] with the title as *Dagereat ef the nieuwe Opkonst der Gennees-Konst in verborgen Grond-Regulen des Nature,* Leiden, 1615, 4°: they also mention (p. 27) an Antwerp edition of the Latin works which seems imaginary. Dezeimeris[53] quotes the title as above with a reference to Rixner and Siber. In the *Catalogue des livres* of Dezeimeris' library,[54] the only work of van Helmont mentioned is the French translation of the *Ortus* by le Conte. Boerhaave[55] quotes an "Aurora medicinæ Belgice edita," but gives no date, hence he probably means the 1659 edition; the 1615 edition is also mentioned by Rommelaere[56] and Broeckx:[57] none of these authors appears to have seen the book, which probably does not exist[58] since no one claims to have seen a copy.

The title page of the German translation of the *Ortus medicinæ* states that the text is completed from the Femish edition ("mit Beyfügung dessen was in der Ersten auf Niederländisch gedruckten Edition, genannt Die Morgen-Röthe, mehr, oder auch anders, als in der Lateinischen").[59] The *Dageraed* contains fundamental ideas which are expanded in the *Ortus medicinæ,* including the criticism of Galenical medicine, and the ideas of *gas* and *blas* but not the important treatise *Complexionum atque mistionum elementalium,* etc. The Flemish text is said by Rommelaere to be clearer than the Latin in the *Ortus medicinæ,* but it is less detailed. The editions of 1659 and 1660 contain, in the second part, treatises on the plague which were probable written late in the author's life.

A list of some of the treatises contained in the 1659 and 1660 editions is given below. I have also indicated in the later discussions what is to be found on the subject in the *Dageraed*: —

1. Van tijdt, duringe, oft weringe, p. 1; 2. Van reden, en verstandt, p. 16; 3. Van de ziele, en beeldt Godts, p. 30; 4. D'oorsaecken der naturelijcke dingen, p. 37; 5. Van den inwendigen werck-meester der saden [Archeus], p. 43; 6. Van verscheyde teeringen des lijfs, p. 48; 7. Wat tarter zy by Paracelso, p. 51; 8. Hoe alle zaet, by middel van eenigen heve, uytwerckt alle . . . . afgemaelt wesen, p. 53; 9. Van de Elementen, p. 61; 10. Der Elementen en Meteoren rechte kennisse, p. 83 (including "Gas-maeckinge", p. 92); 11. Dat de leere van Blas en Gas tot nut streckt, p. 106; 12. Oorsaecken om den Tarter te vinden, p. 119; 13. Den grooten oportet . . . , p. 126; 14. Naerder bediet des middel-levens, p. 130; 15. De geboorte des Wijn-steens, p. 140; 16. Dat'er geenen tarter en is in onse Spijsen . . . , p. 144; 17. Tarter en is niet in den dranck, p. 156; Van de drie eerste beginselen aller lichaemen, p. 164 (on the three principles); . . . De steenwordinge des bergh-wercks, p. 199; De winden der menschen, p. 206 (*De flatibus*); De steenwordinge in ons, p. 219; Oorsaecken van de duelech de Ouden van ons verscheyden, p. 238; Genesinge des duelechs, p. 253. The second part contains the treatises on plague (De Pest) in 19 parts, including Genesinge der pest, p. 376.

THE CHEMICAL WORK OF VAN HELMONT

An important feature of van Helmont's chemical work is its quantitative character: he made extensive use of the balance, expressed clearly the law of indestructibility of matter, and emphasized that metals when dissolved in acids are not destroyed but can be recovered again by suitable means. He also realized that when one metal precipitates another from a solution of a salt, there is no transmutation as Paracelsus thought.[60] Helmont says that Paracelsus taught that "although a metal is destroyed ten thousand times, it will always rise again more perfect by its destruction."[61] When silver is dissolved in *aqua fortis* (*chrysulca*), it is not destroyed but is concealed in the clear liquid as salt is contained in a solution in water and can be recovered (*permanet tamen in pristina sui essentia*).[62] When gold is distilled seven times with sal ammoniac, antimony, and mercury sublimate, it is converted into a red oil, but this is easily reduced again into its former weight and body (*in pristinum auri pondus et corpus*).[63] Dissolved copper is precipitated by iron, which takes its place (*putatus est ferrum in æs mutare, delusionem scilicet viri metallarii vix agnoscentes; eo quod ferri absumit locum, æris succedentes atomi explerent*), and copper similarly precipitates silver.[64] Nothing is made of nothing, therefore weight is made of another body of equal weight in which there is only an apparent transmutation of the matter (*ut materiæ sit transmutatio*).[65] When mercury is boiled with oil of vitriol it forms a white precipitate like snow (*præcipitatus albus nivis instar*) which on washing with water turns yellow, and on revivification gives the same weight of mercury.[66] He describes the preparation of blue vitriol by concentrating mine water; by lixiviating roasted pyrites exposed to air; by throwing sulfur on melted copper and putting the mass (cuprous sulfide) in rain water; and by boiling copper plates with oil of vitriol, when a black mass is obtained which is dissolved to a blue solution in water. Contrary to the statements of Isaac Hollandus, Georg Agricola and "other moderns" (i.e., Paracelsus), copper vitriol yields little or no acid on distillation, but when common (iron) vitriol is distilled by a strong fire in a coated glass retort it yields a very acid oil (*oleum acidissimum*) of vitriol[67]—a clear distinction between copper and iron vitriols, not made by Paracelsus.

VIEWS ON THE ELEMENTS

Van Helmont's criticism of prevailing views on the elements is contained especially in the treatise entitled *Complexionum atque mistionum elementalium figmentum* ("The fiction of elementary complexions and mixtures"), the summary of which, given at the head, is very suggestive:[68]

(1) Why earth does not seem to be a primary element. (2) Fire is neither an element nor a substance. (3) All visible things are formed of water only. (4) Why the place of the air, called the middle region, is cold. (5) What the three chemical principles may be. (6) Some bodies are not reducible into the three principles (*tria prima*). (7) The inconsistency of Paracelsus. (8) The errors of the chemists. (9) Demonstration of the reduction of the three principles into the water of a cloud. (10) The volatile salt of simple bodies is fixed by melting (*colliquationem*). (11) The three principles are not pre-existent but are formed in separation, and indeed a new body (*et quidem nova creatura*). (12) The oil of things is only water, the seed of the compound body being abstracted (*ablato concreti semine*). (13) The same is true of charcoal. (14) What gas sylvestre of things is (*quid gas sylvestre rerum*). (15) Why gas is generated in the grape (*uva*). (16) Gas of wines. (17) Why many grapes spoil. (18) Gas of must is not spirit of wine (*spiritum vini*). (19) Opinion of Paracelsus erroneous. (20) Twofold (*duplex*) sulphur in tin, which is why it is light. (21) Gunpowder proves gas. (22) Some things change themselves into gas. (23) Incompatibility of some things melted together. (24) Gas, materially, is not earth or air . . . . (27) An experiment with alkahest. (28) Gas is wholly from the element of water. (29) Proof by an experiment with charcoal. (30) By experiment (*per mechanicam*) every vegetable is wholly and materially made from water only. (31) So a stone is wholly water. (32) Fish and everything unctuous are wholly of water. (33) Every smoke (*fuligo*) is solely water. (34) All sulphurs are reduced into smoke and gas and these into water. (35) Why fire cannot produce air from water. (36) Ashes and glass are wholly water. (37) Gas of salts is only insipid water. (38) Gas of fruits is only water. (39) Commentaries of the schools on exhalations.

(40) Physics is obscure without chemistry. (*Physica in tenebris absque Pyrotechnia*). (41) The vital spirit is materially gas of water. (42) Sweat before death is not sweat but the dregs of a liquid (*liquamen liquoris*). (43) We are easily killed by endemic gas.

Van Helmont's views on the elements are important.[69] He rejects the theory of the four elements and three principles as taught by Paracelsus, and the "heathen" theory of a primary matter of Aristotle.[70] Neither of the two primary elements (air and water) is convertible into the other[71] and an element cannot be reduced to a simpler state.[72] Van Helmont proceeds to show that the other two so-called elements, viz., fire and earth, do not deserve the title, since fire is not a form of matter at all, and earth can be formed from water.

GAS

Van Helmont says that flame, which is only burning smoke (*non est nisi accensa fuligo*),[73] perishes at once in a closed vessel, and charcoal may be heated continuously in a closed vessel without wasting. Yet if 62 lb. of oak charcoal contain 1 lb. of ashes, the remaining 61 lb. are "wild spirit" (*spiritus silvester*) which cannot escape from the shut vessel. (These ideas contain the germ of Stahl's theory of combustion.) "I call this spirit, hitherto unknown, by the new name of gas, which can neither be retained in vessels nor reduced to a visible form, unless the seed is first extinguished" (*Hunc, spiritum, incognitum hactenus, novo nomine Gas voco, qui nec vasis cogi, nec in corpus visibile reduci, nisi extincto prius semine, potest*). The last part of this famous definition he explains by saying that the gas of flame is not yet water (the fundamental element) because, "although the fire has consumed the seminal forces of the burning body, yet some primitive fermentive differentiations of the body remain (*primae fermentales aliquot concreti notae*) which being at last consumed and extinguished, the gas returns to the element of water (*redit istud Gas in elementum aquæ*)."[74] Flame is ignited smoke and smoke is gas (1. *Imprimus indubium est, quin flamma sit fumus ascensus.* 2. *Quod fumus sit corpus Gas*).[75] Van Helmont[76] describes an experiment of burning a candle in air in a cupping glass over water, when the water rises and the flame goes out: the suction is caused by consumption of part of the air. "There is in the air something that is less than a body, which fills up the vacuities in the air and is wholly annihilated by fire." The contraction is due to the pressing together of the empty spaces in the air by the smoke from the burning candle, the air having been "created to be a receptacle of exhalations". The air in mines, saturated with exhalations from minerals, extinguishes a flame. All this shows, he says, that a vacuum, which Aristotle thought impossible, is "something quite ordinary" (*aliquid valde ordinarium*). The vacuities of the air, he supposed, are normally filled by *magnale,* which is not light but a special form (*forma quædam assistens aeri*); on heating the air, the matter is really condensed, but the *magnale* in the pores is extended.

The name *gas sylvester* (*sylvestris,* "of the wood") is given to the "wild spirit", "untameable gas", which breaks vessels and escapes into the air (*vasis incoercibile, foras in aëra prorumpit*). If nitric acid is poured on sal ammoniac in a glass vessel which is closed by cement or by melting the glass, a gas is produced which bursts the vessel: "the vessel is filled with plentiful exhalation (yet an invisible one) and however it may be feigned to be stronger than iron, yet it straightway dangerously leapeth asunder into broken pieces."[77] The Flemish text[78] says: "Gas veel subtijlder is dan eenigen damp", and it is interesting that in describing the experiment (*De winden der menschen,* p. 216 f.) he uses the word "wind", not gas: "In het [glass] maecken das Koninckswaeters komt'er uyt het wercken beyder geesten, te weten des salpeters, en van het zout armoniac, eenen onsienelijcken windt, die oock in de koude van selfs werckende, geboren wordt, en niet tot sienelijck waeter off stoffe en mach gebrocht, noch gehouden worden, hoe groot het vat zy." This explosive property explains the effects of gunpowder (*historiam enim Gas exprimit proxime pulvis tormentarius.*[79] The name gas is almost certainly derived by van Helmont from the Greek word *chaos* (*non longe a Chao veterum secretum*).[80] Juncker's derivation[81] from *Gäscht,* "froth", and a favourite derivation from *Geist* (spirit), are incorrect.[82] The

Flemish text[83] has: *Gas-maeckinge: uyt het water eenen gas (dat is eenen griexschen water-chaos).*

Paracelsus[84] uses the name *chaos* for the "element air", but there is no indication that he had any idea of the existence of separate gases, and the statement[85] that he used the name *spiritus sylvestris* for the gas evolved in fermentation, effervescence and combustion, I have been unable to confirm. The statement that Paracelsus describes the production of hydrogen from metals and acids is completely mistaken.[86] Paracelsus seems to have regarded air as formed from water and fire.[87]

Van Helmont also deals with gas in his treatise *De flatibus*[88] in which he speaks of *gas ventosum, gas pingue, gas siccum, gas fuliginosum sive endemicum, gas sylvester (sive incoërcibile, quod in corpus cogi non potest visibile), gas sulphureum, gas uvæ, gas vini, gas musti, gas flammeum,* etc., some of which are really the same. He was the first clearly to realize the production of gas in various chemical processes.[89] In Spa water, which had been said to contain all manner of dissolved substances, he observed only a little iron vitriol (it really contains ferrous bicarbonate) and *gas sylvester,* on the escape of which in bubbles it deposits an ochry sediment.[90] The common assertion that the name "gas" was not used after van Helmont until it was revived by Macquer[91] is incorrect, since the name appears repeatedly in earlier authors, such as Becher.[92] It seems to have been intentionally avoided by English authors after Boyle (who speaks of "air"). Van Helmont says more than once that he was the "inventor" of gas (*halitum illum Gas vocavi*) which Paracelsus was ignorant of (*ignoravit . . . . quidditatem Gas, meum scil. inventum*),[93] and there is no doubt that Paracelsus had no such ideas on gases as he. Van Helmont definitely distinguishes gases from condensible vapours and from air, and from one another.[94] He says that gas is composed of invisible atoms which can come together by intense cold and condense to minute liquid drops (*atomi Gas, ob nimiam exiguitatem invisibiles, . . . frigoris excessum, in minimas rursus guttulas concidant*).[95]

It is usually asserted[96] that van Helmont confused various kinds of gas together, so that it is necessary to point out: (1) that he sometimes uses the name *gas sylvester* as a general name for gas and sometimes for one particular gas (as one of a group), and

(2) that he realized clearly that there were gases with different properties. He speaks of gas in a number of treatises,[97] mentioning: (i) The poisonous gas, extinguishing a candle flame, which collects in mines and in the Grotto del Cane (pp. 70, 78, 90, 126, 863; *in crypta Canis*), i.e., carbon dioxide. (ii) The *gas carbonum* formed by burning charcoal and other combustibles (pp. 86, 88, 90, 111, 329 f., 490, 868), which is usually carbon dioxide but sometimes carbon monoxide, since van Helmont says he was himself once nearly poisoned at the age of 65 by the fumes of burning charcoal (pp. 242, 720) and gives the symptoms of carbon monoxide poisoning. (iii) The gas forming in cellars, especially from fermenting wine (carbon dioxide). Grapes can be dried to raisins if the skin remains whole, but if the skin is broken they ferment and evolve *gas sylvester,* which makes them appear to boil and is contained in wines which have been closed up in casks before the fermentation is ended and makes them effervescent (*vina furiosa reddit*). Since the fresh grape on distillation is reduced by art to elementary water, but gives rise to gas in presence of a ferment, it follows that gas itself is water (pp. 87, 89, 90, 126, 343, 490). (iv) Gas formed by effervescence of sulfuric acid and salt of tartar (p. 768), or distilled vinegar and calcium carbonate (carbon dioxide) (p. 343: *acetum stillatitium, dum lapides cancrorum solvit . . . eructatur spiritus sylvester*: crab's eyes was a form of calcium carbonate).[98] (v) A poisonous red gas formed when aqua fortis (*chrysulca*) acts on metals such as silver (pp. 343, 490: *chrysulca argentum, eructatur spiritus sylvester*). The *Dageraed* (1659, p. 216) also mentions this red gas: *maer soo het sterckwaeter koper oft silver eet, soo maeckt hen een selven rooden roock, die nu wint ist.* The *Explicatio aliquot verborum artis,* preceding the preface in the 1644 edition of *De lithiasi,* has: "Gas, qualis è fermentante vino; itemque ruber ille, qui chrysulca operante, eructatur," etc. This was nitric oxide, which Juncker[99] still called *gas sylvester.* (vi) The gas evolved from aqua fortis and sal ammoniac in the cold (p. 343: chlorine and nitrosyl chloride). (vii) The gas evolved in bubbles from Spa water, which then deposits an ochry sediment (p. 679: carbon dioxide). (viii) The gas evolved in eructations (*gas sylvester; gas ventosum*), i.e., carbon dioxide, sharply distinguished from inflammable intestinal gas

(pp. 94, 341, 349), i.e., (ix) *Gas pingue,* which is inflammable, is evolved in putrefaction, and is contained in intestinal gas which he (as did Albertus Magnus, see ref.[73]) knew was inflammable (p. 341: *ructus sive flatus originalis in stomacho . . . extinguant flammam candelæ. Stercoreus autem flatus, qui in ultimis formatur intestinis, atque per anum erumpit, transmissus per flammam candelæ, transvolando accenditur, ac flamman diversocolorem, Iridis instar exprimit*) (hydrogen, methane, with fetid impurities). (x) A gas, different from (ix), which inflates the tympanum (? in gas gangrene) (pp. 341, 416). (xi) A combustible gas (*gas pingue, siccum, fuliginosum, endemicum*) formed on dry distillation of organic matter (p. 336) (a mixture of hydrogen, methane, and carbon monoxide). (xii) A sulfurous gas (*gas sulfuris; sal acidum,* i.e., sulfur dioxide) which flies off from burning sulfur, which is a material wholly fatty and combustible (*totum sit pingue et* φλογιστὸν): this gas when formed in a vessel filled with air extinguishes a candle-flame: it can be condensed in a bell-jar into a juice (*per campanam in succum cogitur;* sulfuric acid) (pp. 550, 888: the word φλογιστὸν is given in both places; it also occurs in the Flemish *Dageraed,* p. 378: *Dit is't het welck wy levende swavel noemen, en* φλογιστὸν *uyt den swavel-plaets getrocken*). (xiii) A *gas sylvester* from fused saltpetre and charcoal (carbon dioxide) (p. 343). Van Helmont missed the oxygen from heated saltpetre, although he says (p. 87) that when saltpeter is strongly heated it gives off a little acid water and leaves salt of tartar (really potassium nitrite or oxide. (xiv) Gunpowder when inflamed evolves gas which bursts vessels, yet the charcoal, sulfur, and saltpeter when heated separately do not explode: the detonation of the mixture is due to a mutual antipathy by which they try to destroy one another (*ergo illa apposita se mutuo in gas convertunt, per destructionem*) (p. 87). (xv) An ethereal or vital gas (*gas æthereum ac vitale*), a kind of vital spirit of a gaseous nature (*spiritum vitæ nostræ materialem de natura gas esse*), which is the reason why other gases act so swiftly and powerfully on the body; this is a preservative balsam, formed in the blood in the heart and not inspired from the outer air. From the arterial blood no dregs or filth are expelled, smoky vapours being wanting where there is no adustion; but venous blood in wasting itself by the guidance of heat produces a gas, as water does a vapour, and this gas is subsequently of necessity expelled (pp. 89, 146, 149, 155 f.).

In respiration, the air mingles in the lungs with the venous blood, which would otherwise coagulate; it mingles with the sulfur of the blood, and exhales together with watery vapor in an unperceivable gas (*per gas insensibile transpiratum*, p. 151). Van Helmont criticizes Galen for teaching that the object of respiration is refrigeration,[100] and says its purpose is to maintain animal heat, by a ferment in the left ventricle of the heart changing the arterial blood into a vital spirit (*vita humana est lux formalis*). The friction together of saline and sulfurous particles in the blood, caused by the beating of the heart, produces heat and a "formal" light in the blood.[101]

THE ELEMENT WATER

In his treatise "On the causes and beginnings of natural things"[102] van Helmont criticizes the teachings of Aristotle, and in the contents he has the following propositions: "(13) Tria Paracelsi corporum initia non habere naturam causarum. (22) Chimicorum principia non habere vim principiandi." Van Helmont still occasionally makes use of the three principles of Paracelsus, as when he says that water contains salt, sulphur and mercury, but this is only "to meet the weakness of our understanding" (*ut intelligendi imbecillitati nostræ*).[103] He says the three principles ("borrowed from Basil Valentine") are not in bodies actually nor are they separated unchanged by fire:[104] mercury is a simple actually existing body, not a constituent of things.[105] Metals can combine only with themselves without losing their luster.[106] Van Helmont asserts that the true elements are air and water (*duo dixi primitiva elementa, aërem et aquam*), and points out that water, with heaven and earth, was formed on the first day in the account of Creation in Genesis.[107] He describes the famous "Tree Experiment" to prove that "all vegetables proceed out of the element of water only:"[108] "I took an Earthen Vessel, in which I put 200 pounds of Earth that had been dried in a Furnace, which I moystened with Rain-water, and I implanted therein the Trunk or Stem of a Willow Tree, weighing five pounds; and at length, five years being finished, the Tree sprung from thence, did weigh

169 pounds, and about three ounces: But I moystened the Earthen Vessel with Rain-water, or distilled water (always when there was need) and it was large, and implanted into the Earth, and least the dust that flew about should be co-mingled with the Earth, I covered the lip or mouth of the Vessel, with an Iron plate covered with Tin (*lamina ferrea, stanno obducta*), and easily passable with many holes. I computed not the weight of the leaves that fell off in the four Automnes. At length, I again dried the Earth of the Vessel, and there were found the same 200 pounds, wanting about two ounces. Therefore 164 pounds of Wood, Barks, and Roots, arose out of water onely." The conclusion is mainly correct, since the tree is largely water (about 50 per cent of fresh willow wood is free water), but it is an irony of fate that van Helmont did not know the part played by the carbon dioxide in the air, since, as has been shown, he was the first to realize the existence of this gas, to which he gave a special name. In the idea, but apparently not in the performance of this famous experiment, van Helmont had been anticipated by a century and a half in a work of Nicolaus of Cusa.

The Cardinal Nicolaus Kryfts of Cusa (1401–1464), born at Cusa (Kues) on the Moselle, was a mystic and a Lullist; although in some respects in advance of the science of his time, his importance has been exaggerated by German authors.[109] The only part of his works of interest to us is the one written in 1450 at Fabriano, with the title: *Idiotæ, dialogus IIII.*[110] In an interesting chapter *de staticis experimentis* he anticipates van Helmont's tree experiment but does not seem actually to have performed it:[111] *Si quis positis centum libris terræ in poto testaceo, colligeret successiue, ex herbis, aut seminibus, in terram iactis, prius ponderatis, centum libras, et iterum terram ponderaret: in pauco, ipsam in pondere reperiret diminutam. Ex quo haberet, collectas herbas pondus exaqua potius habere. Aquæ igitur in terra ingrossatæ, terrestreitatem attraxerunt, et operante Sole in herbam, sunt condensatæ. Si herbæ illæ incinerentur, nonne per coniecturam, ex ponderum omnium diuersitate, attingeres, quantum terræ plus centum libris experires, et illud aquam attulisse manifestum est. Conuertuntur enim elementa, unum in aliud per partes, uti ex-*

98

perimur uitro in niue posito, aerem in uitro in aquam condensari, quam in uitro fluidam reperimus.

There is a saying that no pure element is to be given, how is this prov'd by the ballance? *Id.* If a man should put an hundred weight of earth into a great earthen pot, and should then take some Herbs, and Seeds, & weigh them, and then plant and sow them in that pot, and then should let them grow there so long, untill hee had successively by little and little, gotten an hundred weight of them, hee would finde the earth but very little diminished, when he came to weigh it again, by which he might gather, that all the aforesaid herbs, had their weight from the water. . . . If those Herbs be then burn't to ashes, mayest not thou guesse by the diversity of weights of all; How much earth thou foundest more then the hundred weight, and then conclude that the water brought us all that?

Van Helmont's theory (*doctrinam illam de aqua omnium rerum principis*) was severely criticized by Morhof, who says the tree experiment is unconvincing (*nihil plane probat*).[112] Although Prescott accuses van Helmont of plagiarizing Cusa's experiment, Pagel does not think he did so intentionally.

As further proofs of his thesis, van Helmont says that spirit of wine carefully dephlegmated (dehydrated) with salt of tartar gives only water on combustion, and that fish are nourished and their fatty matter produced from the water in which they swim.[113] He establishes links between materials to prove that they are formed from water; for example, since wood was shown to be formed from water in the tree experiment, all the products obtained from wood, such as charcoal and ash, must also consist of water. If gold is to be formed from water, this will involve a compression to one-sixteenth the volume, which is quite possible to Nature, although water has no pores. Grain by fermentation is converted into beer, which still leaves a solid residue on evaporation. But beer can undergo a further fermentation, becoming sour and consuming its dregs, and finally it returns of its own accord into water.[114]

Van Helmont sharply criticizes the theory of the four elements.[115] Earth is not an element, but is formed from water. For if sand is fused with excess of alkali it forms a glass. If this glass is exposed to the air, it liquefies to water (*resolvi in aquam*), and if sufficient *aqua fortis* is added to saturate the alkali (*quantum saturando alcali sufficit*), the sand settles out again of the same weight as was used to make the glass.[116] Fire, which is clearly distinguished from light,[117] is not an element, cannot form a material constituent of bodies (*nec materialiter corporibus commiscetur*), and is "a positive death of things, a singular creature, second to no other", which can pierce glass.[118] Air cannot be condensed to water (*aërem et aquam esse corpora impermutabilia*), as is proved by the experiment with the air-gun (*in canna ferrea . . . . instar sclopeti*), in which compressed air remains elastic and can propel a ball through a board.[119]

An air thermoscope described and shown in a figure consists of two glass bulbs, separated by a U-shaped tube with a long and a short leg, and containing sulfuric acid colored with roses. The upper bulb is closed and contains air, the lower bulb communicates with the atmosphere by a small hole. The instrument was used to measure the temperature of the body.[120] Van Helmont gives a scale of temperatures with fifteen "fixed points," instead of the usual four of the alchemists: the greatest cold, melting ice (?, *aqua nondum glaciata*), well water, gentle lukewarm, human body temperature, feverish temperature, May sun, distillatory, boiling (water), subliming sulfur, melting pyrites, dark red heat, bright red heat, reverberatory with bellows. He points out that touch is an uncertain guide near body temperature.[121]

ON THE STONE

Of all Helmont's works, that on urinary calculi (*De Lithiasi*) is said by Boerhaave[122] to be "incomparable, and the best," and it also contains the greatest number of chemical experiments, which must have occupied him for a long period of time. He criticizes Paracelsus's theory of tartar, gives a fairly accurate description of the formation of tartar in wine casks, and says tartar is not contained in food and does not cause the disease of the stone.[123] In his *De Lithiasi*, in nine chapters, he says the stone, called *duelech* by Paracelsus, is not tartar, since it does not dissolve in boiling water. Although urine is clear when voided, even if it has been retained for several hours, it soon deposits a sandy sediment or crust if allowed to stand in a vessel. By mixing spirit of urine (ammonium carbonate solution) with spirit of wine he observed the formation of a white precipitate (*ambo simul in offam albam coagulata sunt*), afterwards called *offa Helmontii*.[124] He discusses a number of ways in which solid concretions and coagulations are formed in nature and concludes that they are all different from the formation of *duelech*. This is deposited from urine in the bladder by the concurrence of three things: the spirit of urine, spirit of wine (*aqua vitæ*), and a corrupting ferment from the kidneys.[125] This conclusion is faulty, since spirit of wine does not occur in the body, and the spirit of urine which he used, containing ammonium carbonate, does not occur in fresh urine. Van Helmont isolated from urine two fixed salts, one of them common salt, which he asserted was that taken with the food, and another of different crystalline form—probably microcosmic salt.[126]

For the volatile ammonium salt (ammonium carbonate) van Helmont uses the names *spiritus urinæ, sal volatile* (also for ammonium chloride in soot), *spiritus lotii,* etc.[127] A spirit can be distilled from blood which cannot be distinguished by smell or taste from spirit of urine, but cures epilepsy, which spirit of urine does not.[128]

By distilling a calculus (*duelech*) van Helmont obtained a fetid spirit of urine, yellow crystals, and an oil like that from dried urine; a black unsavory earth remained.[129]

FERMENTS

Van Helmont's theory of ferments is very original and interesting. He says the name of ferment was unknown before, except for the leaven used for making bread, whereas there is no change or transmutation brought about by the sleeping affinity of matter except by the work of the ferment (*nulla in rebus fiat vicissitudo, aut transmutatio, per somniatum appetitum hyles: sed duntaxat solius fermenti opera*). The two chief beginnings of bodies (*prima initia*) are water and ferment or seminal origin (*fermentum sive initium seminale*); the ferment is an indwelling formative energy, "hardly 1/8200 part of a body", which disposes (*disponit*) the material of water so that a seed is produced and life (*vita*), and the mass develops into a stone, metal, plant, or animal.[130] These

101

ideas, and that of the Archeus, are derived from Seton (or Sendi-vogius)[131] (*juxta Chymicorum Cosmopolitam*).

Helmont's theory of the Archeus[132] is a modification of Para-celsus's,[133] and is a peculiar vitalism.[134] He uses the "new name *Blas*" to designate the principle of movement of the stars (*Blas motivum stellarum est virtus pulsiva, ratione itineris, per loca et secundum aspectus*), which pours its influences on the earth.[135] The Archeus or efficient cause (the name Archeus is used by Basil Valentine[136]) causes matter to develop from within to certain forms: "the seed is a substance in which the Archeus is already contained, a spiritual gas containing in it a ferment, the image of the thing, and moreover a dispositive knowledge of things to be done. . . . One thing is not changed into another without a ferment and a seed." The ferment pre-exists in the seed, which is devel-oped by it, and this contains also a second ferment of the seed, the product of the first. The ferment exhales an odor, which at-tracts the generating spirit of the Archeus. This spirit (*aura vitalis*) creates bodies after its own Idea: it disappears only at the instant of death to produce a new creation of the body, which then enters for the second time into fermentation. Seed is not indispensable for generation: animals produced when the Archeus acts on a suit-able ferment are as perfect as those produced from eggs.

The Stoic theory of Seminal Reasons (*rationes seminales*) was perhaps borrowed by van Helmont from St. Augustine.[137] The latter taught that God deposited in matter a hidden treasure of active forces or seminal reasons or principles (*rationes seminales*), which, by successive germination in the matrix of matter as occasion presented (*acceptis opportunitatibus*), produced each a different species of corporeal being.[138]

Van Helmont taught that there are specific ferments and *archeæ* in the stomach, the liver, and other parts of the body, which bring about digestions and other physiological changes (*in aliis locis continuo aliis fermentis*).[139] His ideas on ferments, al-though naturally rather crude and undeveloped, were in the right direction and in many ways resemble the modern theory of en-zymes.[140] The acid of the gastric juice is necessary for digestion, but an excess of acid causes discomfort and illness, since it cannot be neutralized into salt by the alkali of the gall in the duodenum

102

(*aciditatem sui in salem commutat*).[141] The pylorus, opening and closing under the influence of the Archeus, regulates the transfer of chyme (*cremor*) from the stomach to the doudenum.[142] Van Helmont compared the interactions of various juices in the organs with chemical reactions between liquids outside the body. He showed by experiment that salt can pass with water through a bladder, and explains how the digested food (chyle) can pass through the walls of the intestines into the veins;[143] He did not know of the lacteals, discovered by Aselli of Cremona in 1622, but first published in 1627. He distinguished six fermentations of the food in passing through the body. The stomach and spleen, acting under the direction of the Archeus, constitute a *duumvirate* and cannot act separately.[144] They produce an acid liquor (which van Helmont said had been tasted in the saliva of birds) which carries out the first digestion. The mass passes through the pylorus into the duodenum, where it is neutralized by the gall (*fel*) of the gall bladder, a vital balsam different from the excrementitious biliary principle in the mass of the blood, and this is the second digestion. The third digestion takes place in the mesentery, to which the gall bladder sends the prepared fluid. The fourth digestion occurs in the heart, where the red blood becomes more yellow by the addition of vital spirit; the fifth digestion consists in the conversion of arterial blood into vital spirit, and occurs mainly in the brain; and the sixth digestion consists in the elaboration of the nutritive principle in each separate member from the blood, by a separate ferment. There are, thus, six digestions: the number seven is chosen by Nature for a state of repose.[145] The seat of the Archeus is in the stomach, as Helmont proved by an experiment.[146] He took aconite (*Napellus*) and felt himself thinking in the stomach, not in the head, an experiment he could not repeat. Diseases are caused by the Archeus in the stomach sending acid ferments or juices to various parts of the body.[147] Van Helmont's theory of the connection between fermentation and digestion was soon replaced by other less accurate views. The Iatromathematical school as represented by J. A. Borelli (1608–1679) regarded digestion as mere trituration, and estimated the force exerted by the walls of the stomach as 1350 pounds.[148] The chief antagonist of van Helmont's views was Archibald Pitcairn (1652–1713), who objected that if digestion were effected by a ferment, this should also dissolve the walls of the stomach.[149]

MISCELLANEOUS CHEMICAL OBSERVATIONS

In addition to the important chemical ideas and observations described above, a large number of others of considerable interest occur in the works of van Helmont. He was well acquainted with sulfuric acid both from the distillation of vitriol and by burning sulfur under a bell. He describes the preparation of nitric acid by distilling equal parts of saltpeter (*salispetræ*), vitriol, and alum, first dried and then mixed together,[150] and apparently knew that it converted sulfur into sulfuric acid (*salispetræ spiritus elevat sulfur humidum et embryonatum vitrioli*).[151] He mentions aqua regia, made from nitric acid and sal ammoniac, and the gas (chlorine and nitrosyl chloride) evolved from it.[152] He describes the distillation of spirit of sea salt (*spiritus salis marini*), i.e., hydrochloric acid, from salt and dried potter's clay.[153] Quicklime contains a twofold alkaline salt, one lixivial and the other acid, as may be perceived by the taste (*in calce viva est duplex sal alcalizatum. Unum quidem lixiviale, et alterum acidum*); by the action of water these salts become hot, as when acid spirit of vitriol is poured upon salt of tartar.[154] Fixed alkali is not present (as such) in plants but is produced by combustion (*alkali fixum in vegetabilibus non præexstitisse: fixari vero cremando*).[155] Alkali neutralizes all acidity (*quatenus alkali quodvis omnem aciditatem, quam attingit, perimit*).[156] Van Helmont uses the name *sal salsum* for a neutral salt.[157] When strong spirit of vitriol is poured on salt of tartar, heat is produced, and when sugar of lead is calcined the residue takes fire when exposed to the air—van Helmont thought because the alkali in it took up moisture from the air.[158]

The volatile red oil obtained by repeatedly distilling sulfur (with ammonia?) was probably ammonium sulfide,[159] usually credited to Boyle.

In the Flemish text van Helmont describes the solution of precipitated silver chloride (apparently containing a little copper) in the spirit (ammonia) distilled from urine: *ick stelde hem op kalck van silver gemaeckt door't scheydt-waeter, en met zeesout neder-*

geslaegen, en seer nauw afgesoet, door veel warme waeteren, en ten lesten gedrooght. Ick sagh den voorschreven pis-geest met kleynder lauwheyt hemels-blaeuw worden.[160]

Van Helmont rejected the old Galenical pharmacopeia and used many mineral remedies, following Paracelsus.[161] He gives a list of the *arcana* of Paracelsus, including antimony and mercury compounds (*corralatum Paracelsi, arcanum corrallinum, mercurius præcipitatus, mercurius diaphoreticus, corallatum dulci mercurii diaphoretici, præcipitatus diaphoreticus*), the latter probably including red oxide of mercury and Turpeth mineral (basic sulfate), which he used in venereal cases, gout, fevers, dropsy, and many other diseases. He says, however, that potable gold is useless, and he considered with Paracelsus that arsenic compounds, however prepared, were unsuitable for internal use.[162]

Arsenic gives a salt fixed in the fire [potassium arsenate] when fused with saltpeter (*sal-petræ et arsenicum, ambo volatilia, per colliquationem, fixantur*).[163] The three colors of the rainbow [red, yellow and blue] are those of the three sulfurs in burnt minerals (*trium sulfurum in mineralibus concrematis*).[164]

What van Helmont calls Aroph[165] has been identified with ferric ammonium chloride. He prescribed burnt sponge (containing iodine) for goiter.[166] He says that wine is strengthened by freezing out the water,[167] that the common people distil spirit (*aqua vitæ*) from beer, mead, fruits, grains, etc., as well as from wine, and that a sweet oil, different from the spirit, can be separated from wine.[168]

CONCLUSIONS

When we review the work of van Helmont, we cannot deny that he represents the transition from alchemy to chemistry, and is a worthy predecessor of Boyle, who studied him carefully and adopted many of his ideas. That he was "a great chemist, undoubtedly the greatest prior to Lavoisier"[169] is an overstatement which van Helmont himself would, if he could look back over the period between his experiments at Vilvorde and the work of the great Frenchman, the the first to correct.

I have to thank Dr. Douglas McKie for very generously placing at my disposal reprints of the three articles by Vandevelde and some notes on the *Dageraed*: I had then completed my study of the latter work but was able to compare my account with that of Dr. McKie.

NOTES AND REFERENCES

1 His own statement: *Ortus medicinæ*, Amsterdam, 1652, p. 14.
2 12 Jan. 1579 (Old Style), 1580 (New Style); birth register of St. Gudula, Brussels, quoted by A. J. J. Vandevelde, "Helmontiana, I–III," *Koninklijke Vlaamsche Academie voor Taal-en Letterkunde, Verslagen en Mededeelingen*, 1929, 453, 716.
3 Louvain, 1599.
4 Van Helmont, *Ortus medicinæ*, 1652, p. 14 f.: *Studia Authoris*.
5 *Ib.*, p. 837.
6 *Ib.*, p. 565: *Imago Dei*.
7 *Ib.*, p. 8, *Promissa Authoris*.
8 *Ib.*, p. 11.
9 *Astra necessitant*, § 48; *Ignotus hydrops*, § 11; *De lithiasi*, cap. 2: *Ortus*, 1652, pp. 103, 408, 667.
10 W. Rommelaere, "Etudes sur J. B. van Helmont," *Mémoires des concours et des savants étrangers publ. par l'Académie Royale de Médicine de Belgique*, Brussels, 1866, 6, 281–541; 301.
11 *Tumulus Pestis: Ortus*, 1652, p. 835.
12 *New Method of Chemistry*, transl. Shaw and Chambers, 4°, London, 1727, p. 31 f.
13 *Sceptical Chymist*, 1680, p. 112.
14 Van Helmont, *Oriatrike, or Physick Refined*, London, 1662, p. 847.
15 *Ortus medicinæ*, 1652, *Præfatio; Studia authoris*, p. 14 f.; *Tumulus pestis*, p. 834.
16 Boerhaave, *New Method of Chemistry*, trans. by Shaw and Chambers, 1727, p. 30 f.; N. F. J. Eloy, *Dictionnaire historique de la médicine ancienne et moderne*, 2 vols., Liège, 1755, ii, p. 20; *ib.*, 4 vols., 4°, Mons, 1778, ii, p. 478; Wiegleb, *Geschichte der Chemie*, 1792, p. 200—very unfavourable; Sprengel, *Histoire de la médicine*, Paris, 1815, v, p. 22 f.; Gmelin, *Geschichte der Chemie*, Göttingen, 1797, i, pp. 524–55, summary of chemical contributions; *P. d'Elmotte, *Essai philosophique et critique sur . . . van Helmont*, Brussels, 1817; J. E. Dezeimeris, *Dictionnaire historique de la médicine ancienne et moderne*, 4 vols., Paris, 1828–39, iii (1836), p. 99; J. J. Loos, *J. B. van Helmont*, 12°, Heidelberg, 1807; *H. Masson, *Essai sur la vie et les ouvrages de van Helmont*, Brussels, 1857; T. A. Rixner and T. Siber, *Leben und Lehrmeinungen berühmter Physiker am Ende des XVI und am Anfange des XVII Jahrhunderts, als Beyträge zur Geschichte der Physiologie*, 7 vols., Sulzbach, 1826, vii (Helmont); J. A. Mandon, "J. B. van Hel-

mont, sa Biographie, Histoire critique de ses œuvres, etc., *Mémoires des concours et des savants étrangers publ. par l'Académie Royale de Médicine de Belgique,* Brussels, 1866, 6, 553–739; P. A. Cap, "Notice biographique sur J. B. van Helmont," *Journal de Pharmacie,* Antwerp, 1852, 8, 265, 319; Melsens, "Note historique sur J. B. van Helmont à propos de la definition et de la théorie de la flamme," *Mém. couronnés et autres mémoires publ. par l'Acad. Roy.,* 8°, Brussels, 1875, 24, 1 f.— omits to mention Aristotle and Albertus Magnus; *Nouvelle Biographie Universelle* (NBU), xxiii, p. 853, and bibliography; British Museum MS. Sloane 617, ff. 142–151, life by F. M. van Helmont; some treatises by the latter, translated by Dr. D. Foote, are in Sloane 530 (Alchemical Enquiries) and Sloane 3984, ff. 151–2 (Chymical Processes); R. O. Moon, *Proc. Roy. Soc. Med.,* 1931, Sect. Hist. of Med., 25, 23; F. Strunz, *J. B. van Helmont,* Leipzig and Vienna, 1907; H. S. and M. L. Redgrove, *J. B. van Helmont,* 1922; Walden, "Von Iatrochemie zur organischen Chemie," *Z. angew. Chem.,* 1927, 40, 1; Delacre, "Le rôle de Van Helmont dans l'histoire des sciences," *Rev. gén. des Sciences,* 1924, 35, 703; Prescott, *Archiv für Geschichte der Mathematik, der Naturwissenschaften und der Technik,* Leipzig, 1929, 12, 70 f.; W. Pagel, "Helmont, Leibniz, Stahl," *Archiv für Geschichte der Medizin,* Leipzig, 1931, 24, 19–59; *ib., Jo. Bapt. van Helmont, Einführung in die philosophische Medizin des Barock,* Berlin, 1930; G. de Mengel, *J. Alchemical Soc.,* 1913, 1, 49; Sir M. Foster, *Lectures on the History of Physiology,* Cambridge, 1901, p. 128 f.; Bibliography of essays on the life and works of Helmont in **Gazette médicale de Paris,* 1868, 457; **J. M. Caillau, Mémoire sur Jean Baptiste van Helmont et ses écrits,* Bordeaux, 1819; **F. Giesecke, Die Mystik Joh. Bapt. van Helmont,* Dissert. Erlangen, 1908. Starred references I have been unable to see.

17 *Meteoron Anomalum, Ortus,* 1652, p. 74.

18 *Butler, Ortus,* 1652, p. 466; on Butler see Lenglet du Fresnoy, *Histoire de la philosophie hermetique,* Paris, 1742, i, p. 398.

19 *Demonstratur thesis,* § 58; *Vita æterna; Arbor vitæ; Ortus,* 1652, pp. 534, 590, 630.

20 *Arbor vitæ; Ortus,* 1652, p. 633.

21 *Complexionum atque mistionum,* § 29; *Ignota actio regiminis,* § 11; *Arbor vitæ; Ortus,* 1652, pp. 88, 265, 635.

22 *Geschichte der Alchemie,* Halle, 1832, p. 86.

23 *L'Alkaest ou le dissolvant universel de van Helmont. Revelé dans plusieurs Traitez qui en découvrent le Secret,* Rouen, 1704; *cf.* Kopp, *Geschichte der Chemie,* ii, p. 241.

24 *Laboratorium Chymicum,* Hamburg and Leipzig, 1716, p. 506.

25 O. Tachenius, **Epistola de famoso liquore Alkahest,* 4°, Venice 1655; *ib., Echo ad Vindicias Chirosophi. In que de liquore Alcæist, Paracelsi et Helmontij Veterum vestigia perquiruntur,* 4°, Venice, 1656; Boer-

haave, *New Method of Chemistry*, transl. by Shaw and Chambers, 4°, London, 1727, p. 362.

26 Rixner and Siber, *op. cit.*, vii, p. 243.

27 *Imago Fermenti*, § 9; *Demonstratur thesis*, § 97 f.; *Ortus*, 1652, pp. 92, 542 f.

28 E. g., *Pleura furens*, § 35; *Ortus*, 1652, p. 322; *sumsi cervi genitale carptum . . . mox bibi drachman cruoris hircini.*

29 *Tumulus pestis*, ib., p. 879; the name is due to Paracelsus.

30 *Cf.* C. H. La Wall, *Four Thousand Years of Pharmacy*, 1927.

31 *Elementa*, § 13; *Magnum oportet; Ortus*, 1652, pp. 43, 127; Cap, *op. cit.*, thought Bur was synonymous with "affinity."

32 *Op. cit.*, p. 325.

33 *Op. cit.*, p. 28.

34 *History of Chemistry*, i, p. 192.

35 E. g., Pagel, *J. B. van Helmont*, 1930, p. 41: views of Helmont can be found in Paracelsus "in höchst sublimierter Form und als Niederschlag intuitiver Ganzheitsschau"; *ib., A. Med.*, 1931, *34*, 19 f.: Helmont's complex "Faust-like" personality was influenced by the Qabbalah and Campanella.

36 *Rev. gén. des Sciences*, 1924, *34*, 704.

37 *Physica Aristotelis et Galeni ignara, Ortus*, 1652, p. 40.

38 **De magnetica vulnerum naturalis et legitima curatione*, Paris, 1621, Liège, 1624; reprinted in *Ortus medicinæ*, Amsterdam, 1648, p. 746, and later editions.

39 *Interrogatoires du docteur J. B. van Helmont sur le magnétisme animal*, Antwerp, 1856; ib., *Documents pour servir à l'histoire de la bibliographie médicale Belge*, 1858; ib., *Prodrome de l'histoire de la faculté de médicine de l'ancien Universite de Louvain depuis son origine jusqu'à son suppression*, 1865; Rommelaire, *op. cit.*

40 I have not seen the original issue: Hoefer says it was published at Cologne; Reprinted in *Ortus medicinæ*, 1648, p. 685 f.

41 *Febrium doctrina inaudita*, 12°, Antwerp, 1642; *French transl. by Bauda, 8°, Paris, 1653.

42 Cologne, 8°; reprinted as a supplement to *Ortus medicinæ*, 1648, and later editions; G. A. Mercklein, *Lindenius renovatus, sive J. A. van der Linden de scriptis medicis libri duo . . . continuati . . . et purgati*, 4°, Norimbergæ, 1686, p. 528; A. J. J. Vandevelde, "Helmontiana," *Koninklijke Vlaamsche Academie voor Taal-en Letterkunde*, Ledeberg-Gent, 1929, 857.

43 NBU, xxiii, p. 864; M. J. Nicolson, *Conway Letters*, 1930, pp. 84 f., 309 f.; Vandevelde, *op. cit.*

44 *Ortvs medicinæ, Id est, initia physicæ inavdita. Progressus medicinæ novus, in morborum ultionem, ad vitam longam. Avthore Joanne Baptista van Helmont, Toparchä in Merode, Royenborch, Oorschot, Pellines*, etc., 4°, Elzevir, Amsterdam, without index, 1648; 2 ed., fol., Venice,

1651, with index by Tachenius; 3 ed., 4°, Elzevir, Amsterdam, 1652, with index—this is usually considered the best edition, and all references are to it unless otherwise stated; later eds. are: fol., Lyons, 1655 and 1667; 4°, *Opera omnia additis de novo Tractatibus aliquot posthumis ejusdem Authoris . . . antehac non in lucem editis,* Francofurti, Sumptibus Johannis Justi Erythropili. Typis Johannis Phillippi Andreae, 1682; *ib.,* Francofurti, Apud Hier. Christ. Paulli, ex Bibliopolio Hafniense, 1707; these editions (all in my possession) appear to be the only ones ever published in Latin, those quoted by Ferguson, *Bibliotheca Chemica,* 1906, i, p. 381, being mostly imaginary.

45 *New Method of Chemistry,* transl. by Shaw, 1741, p. 45; *cf.* T. L. Davis, *J. Chem. Educ.,* 1928, 5, 678.

46 *Oriatrike or Physick Refined . . .,* 4°, London, 1662; reissued with new t.p. and prelim. matter as *Works, containing his most excellent Philosophy, Physick, Chirurgery, Anatomy . . .,* 1664, 2 vols.

47 *Oevvres . . . traittant des Principes de Medicine et Physique, pour la Guérison assurée des Maladies,* 4°, Lyon, 1670, and 1671.

48 *Aufgang der Artzney-Kunst,* Sultzbach, fol., 1683.

49 *Op. cit.*

50 London, 4°, 144 pp., dedicated to Viscount Brouncker.

51 T'Amsterdam by Jan Jacobsz. Schipper, 4°, 1659, 404 pp.—the edition seen and quoted; *Tot Rotterdam by Joannes Narranus, 4°, 1660, also quoted by Vandevelde, who says the two editions are identical except for spelling variants: the book is exceedingly rare.

52 1826, vii, p. 25.

53 *Dictionnaire hist. de la méd.,* 1836, iii, p. 101.

54 Paris, 1852.

55 *Elementa Chemiæ,* Leyden, 1732, ii, p. 527.

56 *Op. cit.,* pp. 307, 327; also by A. Le Roy, *Biographie Nationale de Belgique,* 1880–83, vii, p. 919: "il est assez curieux de noter que celle de Rotterdam (1660) présente le livre comme inédit"; also by Strunz, 1907, p. 5.

57 *Essai sur l'histoire de la médicine Belge avant le XIX siècle,* Antwerp, 1837, p. 85 f.

58 Delacre, *Revue gen. des sciences,* 1924, 35, 703; A. J. J. Vandevelde, "Helmontiana I–III," *Koninklijke Vlaamsche Academie voor Taal-en Letterkunde,* Ledeberg-Gent, 1929, 453, 715, 857, gives reasons why the book as it was published in 1659 could not have appeared in 1615, *e. g.,* dates after this occur in the text.

59 From an actual copy.

60 Delacre, *Revue gén. des sciences,* 1924, 35, 704.

61 *Tria prima chymicorum principia,* § 59; *Ortus,* 1652, p. 331—"in vexatione præfata": the reference is probably to the vague statement: destructio bonum perficit," in the preface to Paracelsus's *Cœlum philosophorum sive liber vexationum, Opera,* Geneva, 1658, ii, p. 120.

62 *Terra*, § 14; *Progymnasma meteori*, § 17; *Ignota actio regiminis*, § 11; *De febribus*, cap. viii; *Ortus*, 1652, pp. 45, 57, 265, 765.

63 *Progymnasma meteori*, § 6; *De lithiasi*, cap. iv, § 9, cap. viii, § 10; *Ortus*, 1652, pp. 55, 678, 706; *Dageraed*, 1659, p. 86.

64 *Supplementum de Spadanis fontibus, paradoxum tertium*, § 14, *paradoxum quintum*, § 11; *Opera*, 1652, pp. 550, 554; *cf.* Kircher, *Mundus subterraneus*, Amsterdam, 1668, i, p. 319, Paracelsus an impostor: *ib.*, 1665, ii, pp. 185, 223, report from Hungary.

65 *Progymnasma meteori*, § 18; *Ortus*, 1652, p. 57.

66 *De lithiasi*, cap. iv, § 13; *Ortus*, 1652, p. 679.

67 *Supplementum de Spadanis fontibus*, paradox iii, § 12 f.; *De lithiasi*, cap. viii, § 11 f.; *Ortus*, 1652, pp. 550 f., 706.

68 *Ortus*, 1652, p. 84 f.

69 *Cf.* Delacre, *Rev. gén. des sciences*, 1924, *35*, 704.

70 *Causæ et initia naturalium; Ortus*, 1652, p. 26.

71 *Complex. atque mist. element.*, § 1; *Ortus*, 1652, p. 85.

72 *Progymnasma meteori*, § 5; *Ortus*, 1652, p. 55.

73 Although Van Helmont is usually credited with this definition, *e. g.*, by Roscoe and Schorlemmer, *Treatise on Chemistry*, 1905, i, p. 811, it is due to Aristotle: *De cœlo*, iii, 4; *De gen. et corr.*, ii, 4; *Meteor.*, iv. 9, who also frequently uses the word φλογιστά. Kopp, *Beiträge*, iii, p. 84, incorrectly attributes the definition of flame to Albertus Magnus: see Partington, *Nature*, 1935, *135*, 916.

74 *Complex. atque mist. element.*, § 14; *Formarum ortus*, § 31; *De lithiasi*, cap. iii, § 13; *Ortus*, 1652, pp. 86, 111, 670.

75 *Vacuum naturæ*, § 7; *Ortus*, 1652, p. 68.

76 *Vacuum naturæ*, § 8; *Ortus*, 1652, p. 68.

77 *Complex, atque mist. element. figmentum*, § 37; *Ortus*, 1652, p. 89; *Oriatrike*, 1662, p. 96.

78 *Dageraed*, 1659, p. 90.

79 *Complexionum*, etc., § 21; *Ortus*, 1652, p. 87.

80 *Progymnasma meteori*, § 28; *Ortus*, 1652, p. 59.

81 *Conspectus chemiæ*, Halle, 1730, i, p. 365.

82 Lippmann, "Zur Geschichte des Namens Gas," *Abhandlungen und Vorträge*, Leipzig, 1913, ii, p. 360 f.; *cf.* Kirkby, *Chem. and Ind.*, 1923, *42*, 325.

83 *Dageraed*, 1659, p. 92.

84 Lippmann, *Abh.*, ii, p. 360 f.; Stillman, *Paracelsus*, 1920, p. 102 f.; Strunz, *J. B. van Helmont*, 1907, p. 30.

85 Bergman, *Essays*, Edinburgh, 1791, iii, p. 155; Gmelin, *Geschichte der Chemie*, i, p. 217; Escher, Ersch-Gruber, *Encyclopädie*, 1838, [iii] xi, p. 293.

86 Stillman, *Story of Early Chemistry*, 1924, p. 357 f.; Dobbin, *Isis*, 1933, *19*, 262; already in Kopp, *Beiträge*, iii, p. 241.

87 Dorn, *Congeries Paracelsicæ*, Frankfurt, 1581; Manget, *Bibliotheca Chemica Curiosa*, Geneva, 1702, ii, p. 426.

88 *Ortus*, 1652, p. 335 f.

89 Delacre, *Rev. gén. des. sciences*, 1924, 35, 707.

90 *Supplementum de Spadanis fontibus*, paradox. iv; *De lithiasi*, cap. iv, §§ 5, 7: *bullas atque silvestre Gas excitant, ac tandem se vasi affigunt; Ortus*, 1652, pp. 551, 677.

91 *Dictionnaire de Chymie*, 2 ed., Paris, 1778, ii, p. 240 f., art. Gas; Lavoisier uses the name "gaz."

92 Lippman, *op. cit.*

93 *Progymnasma meteori*, § 27; *Gas aquæ*, § 1; *Ortus*, 1652, pp. 58, 59: *Gas et Blas nova quidem suut nomina, à me introducta, eo quod illorum cognitio veteribus fuerit ignota.* Brucker, *Historia critica philosophiae*, Leipzig, 1743, IV, i, p. 721, says: *qualia sunt Gas et Blas ejus, quibus tamen inventionibus mire gaudet, licet nec perspicuitatem gignant, nec solidi quid dicant, nec distinctam notionem faciant.*

94 *Progymn. meteori*, § 29; *Ortus*, 1652, p. 59—*Sat mihi interim sciri, quod Gas, vapore, fuligine, et stillatis oleositatibus, longe sit subtilius, quamquam multoties aëre adhuc densius; De Lithiasi; Explicatio aliquot verborum artis*, preceding the preface in the 1648 ed.; *Gas est spiritus non coagulabilis.*

95 *Blas meteoron*, § 11; *Ortus*, 1652, p. 66.

96 Thomson, *History of Chemistry*, i, p. 185; Kopp, *Beiträge*, iii, p. 155; Delacre, *Revue gén. des sciences*, 1924, 35, 706; but *cf.* Hoefer, *Hist. de la Chimie*, 1869, ii, p. 140.

97 The page references in the text are to the *Ortus*, 1652, the treatises corresponding being: 60, *Gas aquæ*; 70, *Vacuum naturæ*, 78, *Terræ tremor;* 86–90, *Complexionum*, etc.; 91–94, *Imago fermenti;* 111, *Formarum ortus;* 126, *Magnum oportet;* 146–151, *Blas humanum;* 155, *Endemica;* 242, *Jus duumviratus;* 323, *Pleura furens;* 336–43, *De flatibus;* 349, *Catarrhi deliramenta;* 416, *Ignotus hydrops;* 490, *De inspiratio;* 550, *Supplement. de Spadanis font.;* 621, *In sole tabernaculum;* 677, *De lithiasi*, c. iv; 720, *De lithiasi*, c. ix; 768, *De febribus*, c. ix; 863–888, *Tumulus pestis.*

98 Lemery, *Traité universal des drogues simples*, 1698, p. 141: *oculus cancri, pierre d'écrevisse.*

99 *Conspectus Chemiæ*, Halle, 1730, i, p. 569.

100 Unjustly according to Adams, *Paulus Aegineta*, 1844, i, p. 214.

101 *Blas humanum; In sole tabernaculum; Ortus*, 1652, pp. 147, 621; *cf.* Willis.

102 *Causæ et initia naturalium; Ortus*, 1652, p. 26 f.

103 *Gas aquæ*, § 8; *Ortus*, 1652, p. 60.

104 *Imago fermenti*, § 7; *Tria prima; Ortus*, 1652, pp. 91, 323.

105 *De lithiasi*, cap. iii, § 17; *Ortus*, 1652, p. 671.

106 *Arbor vitae; Ortus,* 1652, p. 630.

107 *Elementa; Complexionum,* etc.; *Ortus,* 1652, pp. 43 f., 85 f.

108 *Complexionum, etc.,* § 30; *Ortus,* 1652, p. 88; the passage is quoted from the English translation, 1662, p. 109.

109 *D. Nicolai de Cvsa Cardinalis, vtriusque Iuris Doctoris, in omnique Philosophia incomparabilis viri, Opera,* 3 vols., with continuous pagination, pp. 1176, Basle, 1565, ex officina Henricipetrina—good index; Thorndike, *Science and thought in the 15th cent.,* New York, 1929, p. 133 f.; *ib., History of Magic,* 1934, iv, p. 387 f.—unfavorable; Stones, *Isis,* 1928, *10,* 446; *ib.,* 1934, *20,* 457; *ib.,* 1935, *21,* 562.

110 *Opera,* 1656, pp. 172–180; English transl., 12°, London, 1650, *The Idiot in four books. The first and second of Wisdom. The third of the Minde. The fourth of Statick experiments, or experiments of the Ballance;* and by Viets, **Annals of Medical History,* 1922, *4,* 115–35, q. by Thorndike, *Magic,* iv, p. 389; Pagel, *Archiv für Gesch. der Med.,* 1931, *24,* 42; Prescott, *Archiv für Gesch. der Math., der Naturwiss. und der Technik,* 1929, *12,* 70.

111 *Opera,* 1565, p. 176.

112 *Polyhistor,* 4 ed., Lübeck, 1747, ii, p. 210.

113 *Progymnasma meteori; Complexionum, etc.; Ortus,* 1652, pp. 57, 58, 86.

114 *Imago fermenti,* § 2; *Ortus,* 1652, p. 91; vinegar, in fact, loses its acidity by attack of organisms.

115 *Elementa; Ortus,* 1652, p. 42 f.; *elementorum doctrina, in medendo, impertinens tota.*

116 *Terra,* § 16; *De lithiasi,* cap. iii, § 28; *Ortus,* 1652, pp. 46, 672: the use of the term "saturation" is noteworthy.

117 *Formarum ortus,* § 22; *Ortus,* 1652, p. 108.

118 *Terra,* § 1; *Formarum ortus,* § 31; *Ortus,* 1652, pp. 44, 111.

119 *Aër,* §§ 3, 11; *Supplement. de Spadanis font.,* ii, § 10 f.; *Ortus,* 1652, pp. 50 f., 548.

120 *Aër,* § 12; *Humidum radicale; Ortus,* 1652, pp. 52, 574.

121 *Calor efficienter,* § 35; *Ortus,* 1652, p. 165.

122 Boerhaave, *op. cit.,* transl. Shaw, 1741, i, p. 45.

123 *Tartari historia; Tartari vini historia; Inventio tartari, in morbis temeraria; Alimenta tartari insontia; Tartarum non in potu; Ortus,* 1652, p. 186 f.

124 *De lithiasi,* iii; *Ortus,* 1652, p. 668; in the Flemish text, 1659, p. 243, the passage reads: *ick goot dit leste waeter, dat over den helm was gekomen, in een fleschjen met den besten brande-wijn, die op eenen oogenblick in een schoon wit vluchtigh sout worde verkeert, niet min, als den geest des wijns, oft der pisse.*

125 *De lithiasi,* cap. iii, v f.; *Ortus,* 1652, pp. 669, 683 f.: Rommelaere, *op. cit.,* p. 448, who says spirit of urine = uric acid.

126 *De lithiasi, cap.* iii, § 19—man as the microcosm is also mentioned;

112

Sextuplex digestio alimenti humani, § 58; *Ortus,* 1652, pp. 177, 671.

127 *Complexionum, etc.,* § 37; *De lithiasi,* cap. iii; *Ortus,* 1652, pp. 89, 669 f., 675, etc.

128 *Aura vitalis; Ortus,* 1652, p. 577; *cf.* Boyle.

129 *De lithiasi,* cap. v, § 9; *Ortus,* 1652, p. 684: a very interesting chemical experiment.

130 *Causæ et initia naturalium; Complexionum atque mistionum, etc.; Imago fermenti imprægnat massam semine; Tractatus de morbis; Ortus,* 1652, pp. 86 f., 90 f., 428 f.

131 *Novum lumen chemicum,* in Albineus, *Bibliotheca chemica contracta,* Geneva, 1652, 1 f.; Becher's ideas are also very similar.

132 Martin Heer, *Introductio in Archivum Archei vitale et fermentali viri magnifici Johannes Baptistæ van Helmont, Philosophi per ignem,* 4°, Laubæ, 1703; *Helmont disguised,* by J[as.] T[hompson], 16°, London, 1657.

133 Strunz, *Paracelsus,* 1903, p. 18.

134 *Cf.* Pagel, *op. cit.;* Sprengel, *Hist. de la médicine,* 1815, v, p. 22 f.; Rixner-Siber, *op. cit.,* vii, p. 125 f.; A. Lemoine, *Le vitalisme et animisme de Stahl,* Paris, 1864.

135 *Blas meteoron; Ortus,* 1652, p. 65 f.; *Blas humanum; ib.,* p. 143 f.; *Causæ; Archeus faber; Imago fermenti; Magnum oportet; Ortus,* 1652, pp. 30, 33, 91, 120 f.

136 Heer, *Introductio in Archivum Archei,* p. 56.

137 Prescott, *op. cit.*

138 De Wulf, *History of Medieval Philosophy,* 1909, p. 93.

139 *Imago fermenti,* § 23; *Sextuplex digestio alimenti humani; Aura vitalis; Ortus,* 1652, pp. 93, 167, 577.

140 Brucker, *Historia critica philosophiæ,* Leipzig, 1743, IV, i, p. 715; Sir M. Foster, *Lectures on the History of Physiology,* Cambridge, 1901, p. 135; W. M. Bayliss, *Principles of General Physiology,* 1915, p. 307; Partington, *Everyday Chemistry,* 1929, pp. 508, 551, 555.

141 *Sextuplex digestio etc.,* § 56; *Ortus,* 1652, p. 176.

142 *Pylorus rector; Ortus,* 1652, p. 180.

143 *Sextuplex digestio,* § 48; *Ortus,* 1652, p. 174—an early experiment on osmosis.

144 *Ignota actio regiminis; Ortus,* 1652, p. 273.

145 *Sextuplex digestio alimenti humani; Ortus,* 1652, p. 166 f. I have made use of the summaries of Sprengel, and of Thomson on the subject; see also Pagel, *J. B. van Helmont,* 1930, p. 115.

146 *Demens idea; Ortus,* 1652, p. 222.

147 *A sede animæ ad morbos; Ortus,* 1652, 234 f.; *De febribus,* cap. ix; *Ortus,* p. 767; details in Sprengel and Thomson.

148 Sprengel, *Hist. de la médicine,* 1815, v, p. 142.

149 Sprengel, *op. cit.,* p. 123. Pitcairn was the teacher of Boerhaave.

150 *Complexionum, etc.,* §§ 33, 37; *Ortus,* 1652, p. 89.

151 *Potestas medicaminum*, § 65; *Ortus*, 1652, p. 387.

152 *Complexionum*, § 37; *Ortus*, 1652, p. 89, etc.

153 *Butler; De lithiasi*, cap. vii, § 28; *Ortus*, 1652, pp. 475, 702.

154 *De febribus*, cap. ix; *Ortus*, 1652, p. 768.

155 *Tria prima*, etc.; *Ortus*, 1652, p. 329.

156 *Blas humanum*, § 53, *Ortus*, 1652, p. 153.

157 *Sextuplex digestio*, § 27; *Ortus*, 1652, p. 170.

158 *De febribus*, cap. ix; *Ortus*, 1652, p. 768.

159 *Quaedam imperfectoria; Ortus*, 1652, p. 458.

160 *Dageraed*, 1659, p. 242; the passage is not in the Latin edition.

161 *Pharmacopolium ac dispensatorium modernum; Ortus*, 1652, pp. 366 f., 556.

162 *Ortus*, 1652, pp. 134, 151, 248, 315, 375, 384, 416 f., 455, 498, etc.

163 *Complexionum*, etc., § 10; *Ortus*, 1652, p. 86.

164 *Meteoron anomalum; Ortus*, 1652, p. 72—flame colors.

165 *Supplement. de Spadanis font., paradox. numero criticum*, § 53; *Ortus*, 1652, p. 560.

166 *Tartarus non in potu*, § 15; *Ortus*, 1652, p. 205.

167 *Tartari vini historia*, § 3 f.; *Ortus*, 1652, p. 188; in Paracelsus.

168 *Aura vitalis: Arbor vitæ; Ortus*, 1652, pp. 576, 633.

169 J. Campbell Brown, *History of Chemistry*, 1913, p. 202.

GENERAL REFERENCES

Henry de Waele, "J. B. van Helmont" (Collection Nationale No. 78). Bruxelles, Office de Publicité, S. C., 1947.

From: *Annals of Science.*
"A Quarterly Review of the History of Science Since the Renaissance," *1*, 359–384 (1936).

J. R. PARTINGTON

·· 8 ··

Rudolph Glauber

1604-1670

THE sixteenth century was an epoch of renaissance for chemistry. An active collecting of chemical facts from the technical arts and practices began; the urge to acquire chemical knowledge that was firmly grounded on planned new experiments received heightened attention. The practitioners and technical operators turned from the search for the "Philosopher's Stone" and abandoned the blind belief in the authority of the ancient "hermetic philosophers." There began an independent, vigorous experimenting with the ordinary stones and minerals; metals, ores, earths, and glass, these raw materials for chemical operations, were moved into the center of chemical work.

The leading figures of the new era were Vannoccio Biringuccio (1494–?1538) and his eminent successor, Georg Agricola or Bauer (1494–1555). Paracelsus (1493–1541) erected a bridge between this chemistry of inanimate materials and the chemistry of the living organism. Chemistry benefited from the new chemical preparations; iatrochemistry (chemiatrics, spagyric medicine) took its place at the side of technical chemistry. Here, too, was waged the battle against tradition and authority, against speculation and in favor of practical experience.

It was a bold step when the great ceramic artist Bernard Palissy (1499–1589 or 1510–1590), who had no command of Latin or Greek, calmly and with no regard for the renowned ancient philosophers, published, in his "Oeuvres" (1557–1580) his own views and ideas of Nature, based on his personal observations and experiments. It was a new approach when he warned against the so-called knowledge emanating from "cabinets par une théorique imaginative" or "par imagination de ceux qui n'ont rien practique," and recommended instead the direct reading of the great book of Nature, namely "practice," i.e., experimenting and observation. Palissy, an autodidact, proceeded by this experimental inductive method. Through his own indefatigable studies he greatly enriched technical chemistry (especially ceramic chemis-

117

try) and also directed the attention of agriculturists to the importance of salts as fertilizers.

Another variety of scholar is represented by the polyhistor (universal scholar) Giovanni Battista della Porta (1538–1615). His knowledge, derived from the most varied sources, was acquired during extensive travels in Italy, France, and Spain. His chief work "Magiae naturalis libri IV" (1558) and "libri XX" (Naples 1689) appeared in five living languages. As a collective work of facts and fictions it exhibits so many facets that it is justly regarded as a storehouse of the knowledge of the sixteenth century. In Book VI, Porta gives the elements of the manufacture of glass, colored enamels, and artificial gems, in XIV and XV an extended treatment of poisons and antidotes, and in XX a description of the production (by distillation) of fresh water from sea water.

In similar manner, a third man of this period was active as a technical chemist, namely, the "mining master and bookkeeper in the Kingdom of Bohemia," Lazarus Ercker (died 1593). His "Aula subterranea" (first edition: Prague, 1574; last edition: Frankfurt, 1736) served for more than a century and a half as the basic work on metallurgy and assaying.[1]

Another representative of his time was the Florentine abbot Antonio Neri (died 1614). On his journeys through Italy and the Low Countries, he assembled information regarding the manufacture of enamels, colored glasses, gems, metallic mirrors, etc. His resulting "L'Arte Vetraria" (Florence, 1612) is the earliest textbook on the making of glass; in it he describes lead glass and red copper glass and suggests the use of gold oxide for coloring glass.

In 1679 Kunckel issued a translation of this text at Leipzig and Frankfurt as part of his "Ars Vitraria experimentalis oder vollkommene Glasmacher Kunst;" the last edition in this form appeared at Nurnberg in 1756. (see also Christopher Hemet, "The Art of Glass," London, 1662, which contains considerable additions by the translator. Here again, a text derived from actual practice served for the teaching of applied chemistry for about 150 years. R.E.O.)

In the meantime Libavius had published a first textbook of chemistry and works on applied parts of chemistry. Iatrochemistry was further developed by the physician, J. B. van Helmont ("Ortus medicinae," Amsterdam, 1648). Franz de le Boe Sylvius (1614–1672), also a physician, carried the van Helmont theories to the conclusion that everything occurring in the living organism, healthy or diseased, is based on chemical processes. Two chemical principles are decisive here, the acidic (an occult sharp acid) and the alkaline (volatile alkali), insofar as most ailments arise from the predominance of one or the other in the body fluids. Sylvius compared respiration with combustion; gastric digestion is fundamentally supported by the saliva, which contains a definite spiritual ingredient; the effervescence of the alkalis (alkali carbonates) on the addition of acids is not a fermentation phenomenon but the result of a combination (salt-formation). The writings of this physician, which in some instances have a quite modern flavor, appeared partly as disputations (from 1659 on) and partly collected in his "Opera medica," first at Paris in 1671 and then in Amsterdam, 1679.

In addition to a wealth of factual material, the seventeenth century is also characterized by the abundance of problems. A new kind of chemistry was approaching, a scientific chemistry which sought to clarify and explain the chemical changes in general and to discover the composition of the various substances. If the tested methods of experimentation and observation were pursued further, would not the solution of all these problems be within reach soon? However, this logical course of development was hampered by world events of far-reaching influence: the Thirty Years' War (1618–48) darkened Central Europe with calamitous clouds. During these war-torn years there came on the scene a man who knowingly and unknowingly elucidated the now matured problems, and who through his accomplishments deserves a place of honor in the history of chemistry.

The facts of Glauber's life were not uncovered until rather recently; they were gleaned for the most part from his own writings and reconstructed. This service was rendered especially by Walter Brieger (1917, 1918).

Johann Rudolph Glauber was born at Karlstadt (Franconia) in 1604; his father was a barber. Orphaned at an early age, he wandered about and so came to know "a considerable portion of Europe." At twenty-one, he had found his way to Vienna, supporting himself on the road by making mirrors. He came down with a serious attack of the "Hungarian sickness" (spotted typhus) and was advised by sympathetic persons—so he himself reports— "to take the waters of a spring which issues near a vineyard one hour from Neustadt." He dragged himself there, drank the water and was cured. "Astounded at this miraculous change, I enquired about the nature of this water and was told that it is saltpeter water." Actually, the water contained no nitrate but his analysis showed the presence of a salt "which Paracelsus called sal enixum and which I called sal mirabile."

This event can be regarded as the turning point in his life, as orienting his future and mental interests. He tells of being in Salzburg, where he visited the gravestone of Paracelsus, whom he had always revered. He also was in Paris and Basle for a time. He must have seen and learned much and have tested many things experimentally, because after a training period, which presumably extended from 1626 to 1644, he found himself in Giessen where he is reported to have been active as the director of the "Fürstliche Apothek." However, because of the "Hessian War" he left this post the next year, went to Bonn, and then to Amsterdam (1646). The unfavorable climate drove him to Utrecht and Armheim, but "because of the lack of needed requisites and materials" he was soon back in Amsterdam. He moved into a large house that had formerly been occupied by an alchemist and there fitted up a fine laboratory. During this period of his life, when he was still healthy and took great joy in experimenting, Glauber certainly did much laboratory work, tested new procedures, and devised and constructed new apparatus. A notable fruit of this first Amsterdam period (1646–50) was his fundamental and chief chemical work "Furni Novi Philosophici. . . ." issued at Amsterdam 1648–50 in five parts, a work which Ferguson regarded as "certainly one of the most remarkable books on chemistry of the seventeenth century."

In October, 1648, the Thirty Years' War came to a close. Glauber then thought it "time to see the beloved Fatherland again" and he planned to go up the Rhine as far as Frankfurt. But the captain of the river boat demanded a fare of 500 thalers "because due to foreign occupation or garrisons on the Rhine there is great

120

danger at various places." Consequently, in the spring of 1649 Glauber went to Wertheim via Bremen, Cassel, and Hanau. He set up a laboratory, occupied himself "with this and that," among other things the improvement of wine. But by 1651 he was in Kitzingen, where he bought a spacious stone house (the "little castle") and again fitted up a laboratory. The Elector of Mainz granted him a license for his process for "pressing the wine from the lees, for making vinegar, and for drawing the tartar in great amount from the sediment." In Kitzingen he also prepared his *Panacea antimonialis* (antimony pentasulfide) which, because of its healing power, brought so many ailing persons to him that each day "he had to devote an hour to give them an audience and medicine, and this not at all for money, but rich and poor without payment." Here also began his religious disputes. Farner, "steward of the Speyer cathedral," who against promises to pay obtained from Glauber several "secrets" but later, instead of paying, spread scurrilous reports and distributed libelous pamphlets about him. From the literary standpoint the Kitzingen period is noteworthy in that he composed there his principal iatrochemical text, the "Pharmacopoea spagyrica," whose first part was published in 1654 at Nürnberg and Amsterdam. Around the turn of the year he left Kitzingen, which had become uncomfortable for him because of the Farner affair and also because the wine coopers were on the outs with him.

He went to Frankfurt and then to Cologne, and finally back to Amsterdam (1655 or 56). He moved into a house in a prominent location and it was no "alchemical kitchen" that he installed there. A French visitor (1660) reports that Glauber had four laboratories (workrooms?) in the rear house of a large structure and 5 or 6 co-workers; in the adjacent garden he cultivated a test field whose sandy soil was enriched with mineral fertilizers. "His laboratories are magnificent . . . they are of prodigious size and have a very particular structure." However, these admirable working quarters housed a sick chemical master. As early as 1660 Glauber became paralyzed in one leg; by 1666 he was entirely bedfast. In 1668 he complained that "all of the flesh on my body has been consumed and has disappeared because of the many

121

successive serious illnesses I have endured over these many years and I believe that hardly 6, 8 or at the most 10 pounds of flesh [not including skin and bones] still remain." It is not improbable that his illness was due to mercury, arsenic, or antimony poisoning, because Glauber, like most of the chemists of his time, frequently made experiments involving these elements under conditions of inadequate ventilation. His experimental labors were suspended; the many and varied "Furni Novi Philosophici" stood cold and empty along the walls; he offered them for sale and gave up his laboratory. The exact date of his death is not known but he was buried in the Wester Kerk at Amsterdam on March 10, 1670.

Glauber set down his findings, methods, and ideas, and described his apparatus in about forty printed works which were written in German and given Latin titles. They extend over the period 1646 to 1669. The most important appeared as "Opera omnia" in seven volumes at Amsterdam in 1661, in four volumes (1651–1656), and under the title "Glauberus concentratus" at Leipzig and Breslau, 1715. As "Opera chymica" they appeared in two volumes in Frankfurt, 1658–59, in French translation by du Teil at Paris, 1659. (The English translation of the "Opera omnia" bears the title: "The Works of the highly experienced and famous John Rudolph Glauber. Containing great variety of choice secrets in medicine and alchymy, in the working of metallick mines and the separation of metals. Also, various cheap and easie ways of making saltpetre, and improving of barren land and fruits of the earth. Together with many other things very profitable for all lovers of art and industry. Translated into English, and published for publick good by the labour, care and charge of Christopher Packe, Philochymico-Medicus, London, 1689. 3 Parts and an Index." R.E.O.)

Among his single volumes, special note should be given to "Furni Novi Philosophici oder Beschreibung einer Neuerfundenen Distillir-Kunst" whose complete text appeared in German at Frankfurt in 1652, in Latin at Amsterdam, in French by du Teil, 1659, and at London, 1651 by John French. (See also the Packe translation, Part 1: "Philosophical Furnaces"; in five parts and an Appendix.)

Glauber exhibited an unusual mental productivity. The seven volumes of his "Opera omnia" contain in fact only his work during the years 1648–60. These approximately 30 treatises were composed by a man who was active almost without interruption despite his frequent changes of residence. The importance of his work and its influence on his contemporaries and successors are apparent from the many translations as well as new editions that were printed as late as 1715. His eminent contemporaries (Boyle, Lemery, Kunckel, Becher) could not fail to read his discoveries and carry them further.

The discussion of his accomplishments can well begin with the acids, their preparation and their use by Glauber. He did not yet employ this term for his products but, in keeping with the physical designations of his day (volatile, spirituous, oily, etc.), he referred to them as spirits, olea, and the like. A large portion of his principal work: "Furni" is devoted to the preparation of acids.

Oleum acidum vitrioli (sulfuric acid); *Spiritus volatilis vitrioli* (sulfurous acid): Glauber dry-distilled iron vitriol that had been purified by recrystallization. The spiritus passed over, followed by the phlegm. The former was concentrated and divided from the oleum by separate (i.e., fractional) distillation. Because of its "miraculous effects" on the human organism, this spiritus was highly recommended as a medicament. The oleum is "to be found in almost all apothecary shops," it "cools internally the parts of the body. Externally it purifies all unclean wounds." "In addition, various metals can be dissolved in it and made into their vitriols." ("Furni," II. p. 14.)

These same products can also be obtained by distilling alum. "However, the *oleum aluminis* has almost the same action as the oleo vitrioli: but the *spiritus volatilis* from both is alike in nature and properties." The same is true of the *spiritus* or *oleum acidum* obtained from distilled zinc vitriol. Similar products can also be obtained directly from sulfur by burning it in a crucible and collecting the fumes in a superimposed glass bell which has a high rim filled with water. ("Furni," II, p. 186.)

Glauber regards the products that may be obtained from iron vitriol, alum, and zinc vitriol as "of the same action." Iron vitriol yields oleum, and this oleum dissolves iron, zinc, and other metals to yield iron vitriol, zinc vitriol, etc.

The burning of sulfur in the air produces chiefly *spiritus volatilis vitrioli* i.e., sulfur dioxide. The latter, which Glauber obtained (1648) by two methods, was isolated as a new species of gas in 1775 by Priestley.

Spiritus nitri (red, fuming nitric acid): Slow distillation of a mixture of 2 parts of alum and 1 part of saltpeter yields a *spiritus acidus* along with a *spiritus volatilis* (therefore a pound of water should be placed in the receiver for each pound of the mixture); by a subsequent "gentle rectification" the two are separated: "namely when the volatile goes, the [content of] the receiver is very dark red; later, when the phlegm comes, the receiver again becomes entirely white, finally, when the heavy spiritus acidus goes, the receiver again becomes red, but not exactly as when the first volatile came over." This spiritus can likewise be obtained, but not as well, from *nitrum* mixed with twice as much bole, brick, dust, or clay ("Furni," II, p. 38). The volatile spiritus "remains red always" (consequently is red nitric acid), the heavy spirit is white. "This spiritus nitri also turns the hair, nails, feathers quite gold-colored." ("Opera chymica," 1658, p. 188.)

It is not difficult to recognize the "volatile spiritus," which is separated by subsequent "gentle rectification" as nitrogen dioxide and trioxide, which pass over along with some water. A closer study of these gaseous products did not come until about 150 years later. It is interesting to note the method of obtaining these products by a kind of "dry distillation" of saltpeter with bole, etc.

Glauber also discovered the method of preparing concentrated nitric acid by the direct action of saltpeter and sulfuric acid. He did not publish this procedure but revealed it to individuals for a fee. As late as around 1800, concentrated nitric acid was still referred to as *spiritus nitri fumans Glauberi* or *acidum nitri fumans Glauberi*.

Aqua regis: "If ignited table salt is dissolved in this spiritus nitri acido and rectified in a glass retort, set in sand, with a strong fire, it becomes so strong that it can dissolve gold and all other metals and minerals except Luna (silver) and sulfur . . . much better than aqua regis that has been prepared by adding sal ammoniac."

Spiritus arsenic nitros: If white arsenic and nitrum purum are mixed in equal weights, and distilled, there results "a blue spiritus, which is very strong, but no water must be present, otherwise it will turn white . . ." ("Furni," II, p. 72.)

Spiritus salis (spirit of salt, hydrochloric acid): To have prepared this valuable acid by simplified methods and in large batches for the first time and to have studied its chemical and medical actions was one of Glauber's permanent contributions. He begins by describing the faulty methods previously used. His own processes were: glowing charcoals are saturated with a solution of common salt, and then burned in a furnace, whereby the spiritus salis is evolved and caught in a glass receiver; or common salt is mixed with some vitriol or alum, the mixture is well ground and added a spoonful at a time to glowing coals ("Furni," I, p. 32). Glauber then points out that all methods yield one and the same spiritus, and that the *spiritus salis* obtained with the aid of vitriol or alum is a pure *spiritus salis* (hence not contaminated with *spiritus vitrioli* or *aluminis*). A detailed description is given of the properties of the spirit of salt, and various metal chlorides are prepared with its help: "because all metals and minerals, except Luna, and almost all lapides . . . are dissolved in it and made into medicaments of different excellence." ("Furni," I, p. 32.)

Illustrative of Glauber's chemical sagacity is the third and simplest method which he discovered (and long kept secret). If spirit of salt can be prepared from sodium chloride and vitriol and, on the other hand, *oleum vitrioli* (sulfuric acid) is formed when vitriol is heated alone, then the spirit of salt must likewise be obtained directly and more easily from common salt and sulfuric acid. It is worth examining, in this connection, the empirical quantity relations which he recommended, namely, 1 part of common salt to 1.25 parts of oil of vitriol. Theoretically, (with 100 per cent sulfuric acid), 117 parts of sodium chloride must be brought into reaction with 98 parts of sulfuric acid, but 140 parts of 70 per cent acid must be used, which is almost equal to the ratio prescribed by Glauber.

This direct reaction yielded two important products simultaneously: the spirit of salt (hydrochloric acid) and Glauber's salt (*sal mirabile Glauberi*). The improved process made hydrochloric acid available at various concentrations, in higher states of purity, and at a reasonable price. Glauber, therefore, had prepared gaseous hydrogen chloride around 1648. As late as 150 years ago, fuming hydrochloric acid was generally known as *spiritus salis fumans Glauberi* or *acidum salis fumans Glauberi*.

The chemical activity of acids with metals, metal calces (oxides), carbonates, etc. was well known to Glauber, and he employed this knowledge for the preparation of new salts. Some procedures were syntheses of new salts, some were the preparation of known salts in purer or crystalline form, for instance Glauber's salt ($Na_2SO_4.10\ H_2O$) from common salt and sulfuric acid): *sal ammoniacum secretum Glauberi* (ammonium sulfate by saturation of sulfuric acid with ammonia); green vitriol (from iron and sulfuric acid); blue vitriol (from copper or copper calx and sulfuric acid); white vitriol (zinc sulfate); saltpeter (from potash and nitric acid); sal ammoniac (from ammonia and hydrochloric acid); auric and ferric chloride, the chlorides of zinc, copper, tin, antimony (butter of antimony); nitrate of silver, copper, etc. It may be said, in brief, that Glauber (1) possessed a well-developed technique for preparing mineral acids; (2) that he could produce considerable amounts of these acids and deliver them to his customers at a reasonable price and from various starting materials; (3) that he was fully aware of the influence of the purity of the starting materials on the purity of the acids; (4) that he knew how to prepare pure acids in various concentrations; and (5) that with the aid of these acids he had prepared the corresponding neutral salts—nitrates, chlorides, sulfates—from all the then known metals (and metal oxides) and had brought these salts into technical and medicinal use. Glauber and his chemical laboratory can readily be viewed as a small-scale precursor of the chemical large-scale industry.

Spirit of wine, *spiritus vini* or *ardens,* as well as vinegar (acetic acid) were purified and concentrated by Glauber through fractional distillation and rectification. He removed the water or dephlegmated the alcohol (spirit of wine), as well as the "subtile oils" in general and the nonacidic *spiritus* by means of ignited potash. The following reaction is described and leads to a new material: "If a dephlegmated spirit is added to such a strong spiritus salis, and digests for a time, it causes a separation in the spiritus vini, kills its volatile, so that a pleasant clear oleum floats on its surface" ("Furni," I, p. 66). This could be ethyl chloride. Glauber gave also another method of preparation in which he used the concentrated (oily) acid solution of zinc chloride and very pure spirit of wine. Is this not similar to the technical method of Groves used today?

Wood vinegar and salts: In his "Furni," Glauber states: "How to prepare an acid spirit or acetum from all vegetable materials such as herbs, roots, seeds and the like." By distillation of wood, there is obtained "wood acid" which "does not differ much in taste from an ordinary vinegar," and after rectification this "acetum" can serve for the dissolution of metal calces, etc., since it "is as good for such a task as is acetum vini." On reaction with wood ashes, it yields a "beautifully bright and clear salt, which is not lixivial alkaline but pleasant in taste," i.e., crystalline potassium acetate. This is certainly the earliest description of the preparation of wood vinegar.

Acetone: Vinegar dissolves flowers of zinc and lead calx, hence forms zinc acetate and lead acetate. If zinc acetate, for example, is distilled (as a concentrated solution) along with pure sand (the same holds true of lead acetate)" . . . there passes over first a tasteless phlegm [water?], then a subtile [volatile] spirit, and finally a red and yellow oleum, which must be kept apart from the spirit." Since nothing had been known previously concerning the medical use of this spirit and oleum, Glauber states, "I too will not write anything about them, but will try to leave the matter in other hands." Of course it was a long time before these "others" made similar experiments with the distillation products of the acetates of metals and alkaline earth metals (Macaire and Marcet, 1823). What Glauber had separated as *spiritus* was a mixture of mesityl oxide, phorone, and other compounds.

Acrolein: Glauber also distilled the fatty oils (olive, rape, nut, hemp, linseed). He saturated balls of potter's clay with the oil, for instance, olive oil "which is the best for this," and dropped them into a glowing distilling furnace; the collected distillation product was then rectified over calcined alum or vitriol (to free it of the ill-smelling impurities), and if necessary, this is repeated "and each time what passed over first was collected alone, thus there was obtained a fine clear and bright oleum, which is incomparably subtile, but what comes over later is somewhat yellow and also not so penetrating as the first. . . . The first and clear is of very penetrating nature and character." This latter exceedingly subtile oleum with "a very penetrating nature" was doubtless acrolein. (Brandes, in 1838, prepared acrolein by dry-distilling coconut oil and studied it in further detail.)

Benzene: Coal was likewise distilled. In this case "there passes over not only a sharp spiritus, but also a burning and blood red oleum, which powerfully dries and heals all moist ulcers." His "Pharmacopoea Spagyrica" (Part III, 1654) contains the following additional statement: "I have found that mineral coals have in them a pleasant-smelling oil and valuable healing balsams . . . fill a retort with coals and distill from them a black oleum, separate this from the acid water that has come over with it, and rectify it per spiritum salis, there passes over first a clear and bright oil, and then a yellow one that is not so pleasant as the clear oil, and a thick black one remains behind . . . the yellow can again be rectified with fresh spiritu, so that it too becomes clear, white and pleasant, and if you now wish to make still another separation from these clear oils and again rectify with fresh spiritu, then you can collect separately first the very purest part, which is not at all inferior to the natural oleo petri with regard to heat, subtility, and fragrance, which can also be kept separately and used internally and externally in cold accidents." Looking back, shall we interpret the nature of these two coal tar fractions? They could only have been the "benzene hydrocarbons and phenols." Especially interesting is the treatment (distillation) with hydrochloric acid (*spiritus salis*) whereby—as in the modern treatment with sulfuric acid—all of the basic products, olefines, etc., are held back. As to the "pleasant aromatic oil" described by Glauber, is it not clearly recognizable as the first "aromatic" hydrocarbon, namely benzene, which was not discovered until 1825 by Faraday, while the less "subtile" (volatile), i.e., higher boiling portions of the mixtures, were the homologs, toluene, xylenes, etc.? Their discovery by Glauber thus dates back to 1648, and their technical production (by Mansfield) did not come until 1849 (a full two centuries later). The "fiery and blood red oleum" must have contained the phenols and middle oils; the medical healing effect on all "moist ulcers" which it "powerfully dries and cures," is perhaps worthy of particular attention as a precursor of the antiseptic treatment of wounds in the nineteenth centry.

Alkaloids: Plant materials were of course included in Glauber's study of the pharmaceutical and medical substances derived from the various natural kingdoms. He went further than his predecessors in that he desired to strengthen the curative action of these materials and accordingly subjected the medicaments to a special chemical pretreatment. To this end he subjected the crushed or divided plant parts to a warm extraction with *spiritus nitri rectific,* i.e., he formed nitrates, filtered the suspension with care, and treated the clear liquid with a solution of *liquor nitri fixi* (potash) and thus precipitated "the corrected Vegetabile or Animale in forma pulveris" ("Opera chymica," I, p. 50 f.). Alternatively, if dissolution can be readily accomplished, the reverse course is followed, in that the first step is an extraction with a potash solution, followed by treatment of the clear extract with nitric acid. The "active substance" is thrown down as a "fine powder." Among other plant materials, he treated nux vomica and powdered opium in this fashion; he also employed sulfuric in place of nitric acid for the extraction. Obviously, this procedure involves an extraction of the vegetable bases (strychnine, brucine, or morphine) as their soluble nitrates and sulfates, followed by a precipitation of the bases by means of potassium carbonate. There can be no doubt that his "fine powders" were actually considerably purified specimens of these alkaloids and that his process was chemically the most suitable. In fact, it was employed in the isolation of the alkaloids in 1805, and in Liebig's "Handbuch der organischen Chemie" (1843) the prescribed general method was to extract the plant parts with dilute hydrochloric or sulfuric acid, concentrate the extract, and precipitate the plant base by means of soluble alkalis.

Aromatic oils (Olea aromatum): Glauber followed his own way in the preparation of pure aromatic oils (*olea vegetabilium* or *olea aromatum, seminum, florum, herbarum,* etc.). The plant parts, broken down to a sufficient degree, were covered with salt water, allowed to steep for several days (salting out of the colloidal components?) and then distilled. After the watery distillate had settled, the supernatant oil layer was removed "by a heated separating glass" and rectified ("Furni," III, p. 27). Repeated fractional distillation over a calcined salt, such as potassium carbonate, was found necessary for removal of the water (dephlegmation). "In this way they leave their occult wateriness and pass over quite subtilely."

Another procedure was thought to give better yields. The proper plant parts were covered with *spiritus salis* (hydrochloric acid). On distilling "all of the oil passes over with but little phlegm, because the spiritus sali, by virtue of its sharpness, penetrated the lignum, frees the oil, so that it preferably passes over" ("Furni," I, p. 34). Even old and viscous (resinified) oils can be reconverted into clear ones by distillation with *spiritus sali*. ". . . If now you desire to have the oil that has passed over still more fragrant, rectify it again with fresh spiritus salis and repeat this until you are satisfied with the odor and color."

He made a special study of the preparation and use of tartar. He published an improved method for preparing tartar emetic. As early as 1654, he observed the occurrence of crystalline grape sugar (from honey, raisins, etc.).

His suggestion to use copper tartrate in place of verdigris is interesting, since the latter pigment ruins the paintings. The field of coloring also includes his proposal to blacken feathers, furs, and wood using a solution of silver nitrate. He pointed out that iron dissolved in acid can be used for the black mordanting of leather, wood, etc. ("Explic. miraculi mundi," 1656, p. 188 f.).

Glauber may justly be considered as the great pioneer of the coming organic chemistry. He put forth ideas which in many respects are in harmony with modern concepts. He demonstrated that spirit of sal ammoniac (*sal volatile urinae*) or *salis armoniaci* (ammonia) can be obtained by adding a solution of tartar, lime, zinc oxide, etc. to sal ammoniac (ammonium chloride) and distilling. He assumed that the salts contain two components of opposing natures; one of the components is acidic, the other is alkaline: salt $\rightleftharpoons$ acidum $+$ alkali. The salt can be synthesized from these components and decomposed into them. Thus, for instance, he prepared artificial saltpeter from nitric acid and potassium carbonate (calc. *sal tartari*) both in solution. He also had a correct idea of the neutral point: the addition of the potash solution was to be continued as long as the effervescence (carbon dioxide) was still audible. Instead of the present-day reliance on sight (color changes of indicators) he employed an "acoustic" indicator for the determination of the end point.

He was well aware that the various mineral acids have different "strengths" and made use of this fact; oil of vitriol displaces nitric or hydrochloric acid. Solubilities were differentiated, and the abilities of acids to dissolve metals are not always the same since, for instance, oil of vitriol "will not attack Mars [iron] or Venus [copper] readily unless ordinary water is added." "Zinc or iron are readily soluble in spiritus nitri" and "if it is strong enough, it dissolves the highest metal to the highest mineral [i.e., Ag, Hg, Cu, Fe, Sn, Pb] while the very lowest, namely sulfur, it leaves unaffected, but always one metal rather than the other, according to whether it is more closely related to it by nature and attracted to it." The concept of affinity is clearly evident here. ("Opera chymica," p. 50.)

Glauber was moving in the same world of ideas and expressions when he undertook to interpret the reaction between a solution of gold (in aqua regia) and *tinctura silicum* (soluble potassium silicate), prepared by fusion of *sal tartari* (potassium carbonate) with sand. The gold precipitates as a yellow powder and the solution becomes colorless; after being washed and dried, the gold weighs twice as much as before it was dissolved. ("Furni," II, p. 147.)

He gave an extensive treatment of the separation of metals by "the wet method" by means of acids, particularly "the separation of gold, silver and copper from each other without casting," namely by means of *spiritus salis nitrosus* (hydrochloric-nitric acid) ("Furni," IV, p. 22).

Addition of zinc to solutions of copper and iron salts (vitriols) leads to precipitation of copper and iron. On treatment with solutions of potash (*sal tartari*), solutions of the metal salts give precipitates, and likewise on the addition of ammonia water (*spiritus volatilis* from sal ammoniac).

Aqueous acid solutions serve for the dissolution of metals and metal oxides. The resulting salt solutions are boiled to dryness, the dry salts dissolved in pure water and fractionally crystallized. Glauber used this process for purifying salts, and it is noteworthy that he employed the formation of perfectly formed crystals as a criterion of purity. He described—perhaps as the first— the details of the crystal forms of carefully purified salts (sodium chloride, potassium nitrate, sodium sulfate, vitriols).

From the technical standpoint, Glauber exercised a permanent influence on the constantly expanding large-scale manufacture of acids. He not only improved the design of the "philosophical furnace" and distillation and condensing apparatus, but also the materials from which chemical apparatus and vessels were constructed. In addition to glass retorts for distilling concentrated mineral acids, he also employed glass funnels for extractions, filtrations, etc., as well as "heated parting glasses" for the separation of liquids. Bottles with ground stoppers were used for storing fuming acids, and extremely volatile materials were kept in flasks provided with a mercury seal. He tried to attain more effective extraction of plant parts by using a mechanical stirrer. He influenced the glass industry in still another direction. As early as 1549 he described the preparation of gold purple, and hence, prior to Boyle, Cassius (1685), and Kunckel, he independently discovered gold or ruby glass. His process was an application of the yellow precipitate described above, i.e., the mixture of gold hydroxide and colloidal silicic acid. If it is placed in a dry crucible, and the latter is put "between glowing coals, so that it begins to glow, but not for too long, the yellow will change into the most beautiful purple color." Red glass pastes (artificial rubies) can be prepared in this way. The same method of precipitation (*tinctura silicum* plus solutions of metals) yields pastes of artificial gems of

132

various colors, such as sea green with copper salts, hyacinth yellow with iron salts, amethyst with pyrolusite (manganese dioxide), and sapphire with zaffre (cobalt oxide). According to Kunckel, Cassius was led to his discovery through Glauber's publications.

Glauber observed that strong alkaline solutions make linen threads much finer and softer. Is this not akin to the discovery by Mercer (1844) of the process that bears his name? Glauber noted that glue is rendered permanently tacky by hydrochloric or sulfuric acid, an early discovery of the alteration by hydrogen ions of the state of dispersion and solvation of this typical colloid.

He recommended that malt wort be boiled down and the resulting extract, after dilution with water, be used as a nutrient beverage and as an antiscorbutic. Finally it should be pointed out that Glauber had a persistent interest in the origin and production of saltpeter. He also studied the preparation of fulminating gold and tried to render it insensitive to heat. He conceived, described, and succeeded in the large-scale manufacture of a special group of substances intended for the defense of the country against invasions by the unbelievers. Walter Brieger has devoted an extended discussion to Glauber's activities in the field of explosives (Z. f. Schiess- und Sprengwesen, Vol. 12 (1917), p. 305).

There is no justification for including Glauber among the "alchemists," if by the latter are meant those itinerant, boastful gold-makers, who could produce gold only if they had previously been given gold. Admittedly, he wrote about the fundamental alchemical problem, i.e., the philosophical notion of the transmutability of the metals or a development of this concept, and set down his speculations on this subject at great length. Glauber believed in the theoretical possibility of transmutation but specifically denied that he had ever accomplished such a change.

Because of his chemical versatility, Boyle has often been called the "father of chemistry." The accomplishments of Glauber preceded in time the successes of Boyle and Stahl and provided the foundations of the chemical thinking of the eighteenth century. Is he therefore not deserving of an honorific title, such as "the German Boyle?"

NOTES AND REFERENCES

1 Lazarus Ercker, "Treatise on Ores and Assaying," translated from the German edition of 1580 by A. S. Sisco and C. S. Smith, Chicago, 1951. (R.E.O.)

Erich Pietsch, "Johann Rudolph Glauber, Der Mensch Sein Werk und Seine Zeit," Verlag R. Oldenbourg, Munich, 1956.

From: Bugge, "Buch der grossen Chemiker," vol. 1, pp. 151–172 (abbreviated). Translation and additions by Ralph E. Oesper.

PAUL WALDEN

·· *9* ··

Robert Boyle

1626/7-1691

THE HON. ROBERT BOYLE.

URING the first thirty years of the Royal Society's existence
Robert Boyle (1626/7–1691)—chemist, natural philosopher, patron of learning, philanthropist, amateur of medicine and theology, essayist, linguist, gentleman—was regarded as the chief English scientist. His name was known throughout the learned world as a leading advocate of experimental philosophy, the perfector of the air pump (whose vacuum was named after him), and when fashionable or scholarly tourists came to London even the most distinguished and aristocratic regarded it as an honor to meet and converse with the "ornament of English science." In a period when the Renaissance tradition of polymathy still lingered, Boyle could compete with any; he was a master of, and indeed a contributor to the seventeenth century's scientific innovation, the mechanical philosophy which finally drove out the scholastic method of interpretation of the phenomena of the universe; he was honored by scientists, by theologians, by literary figures, and by royalty, equally and impartially. Although Newton, his younger contemporary, was soon to eclipse him in fame, Newton himself studied and honored Boyle, and the eighteenth century rightly associated Bacon, Galileo, Boyle, and Newton in their catalogues of saints of the experimental science of the new age. Boyle's influence on chemistry was the more important because he was both a natural philosopher and a chemist, and was one of the first to include chemistry in natural philosophy, in an age when chemistry was usually regarded as either a mystic science or a practical art useful to metallurgy or to medicine but ignored, as Boyle put it, "by those that aim at curing no disease but ignorance."

Like most men of the seventeenth century who devoted themselves to science Boyle was a self-taught amateur; unlike most he came from a distinguished family and was wealthy enough to support not only his own scientific experiments but also those of others. His father was that great Earl of Cork who, starting as a penniless adventurer in Ireland in the reign of Queen Elizabeth, accumulated such wealth, rank, and influence that he and his family were able both to shine at court under successive monarchs and to play a leading political role in the turbulent Anglo-Irish affairs of the mid-seventeenth century. His youngest son alone resisted the acquisition of title and inclined, like his brother Roger, Lord Broghill, and sister Katherine, Lady Ranelagh, toward a literary life.

Robert Boyle, as a future scientist, had the advantage of escaping the Aristotelian education of a university; his education was mainly undertaken by a French-speaking Protestant citizen of Geneva named Marcombes, who taught Robert and his next older brother only the rudiments of scholastic philosophy before turning to what they all preferred, modern languages and the mathematical sciences, which included fortification and surveying. The young Boyle was fortunate enough to be introduced to what he called "the new paradoxes of the great star-gazer Galileo" in Galileo's own city of Florence. This completed his rejection of Aristotelian tenets; he later remembered how much foreign travel had influenced him in this regard. At this point Boyle's formal education was interrupted. The Civil Wars broke out in Ireland, to be followed by Civil War in England. His father died in 1643, and the next year Boyle returned, penniless, to London, where he luckily found his sister Lady Ranelagh in residence; she not only provided a home, but also, being a staunch parliamentarian, prevented his joining the royalist army. She was a most distinguished and intelligent lady, a friend of the poet Milton and through him of Samuel Hartlib, originally from Poland, the learned and able leader of a group of public-spirited men who hoped to make the ideas of the Czech educator, J. A. Comenius, a reality under the Commonwealth. Boyle soon retired to the country, to look after his manor house of Stalbridge in Dorset; to enjoy country pursuits; to write moral and pious essays (some later published as "Occasional Reflections"); to interest himself in agriculture and the useful arts (which included medicine) "according to the precepts of our new philosophic college, that values no knowledge, but as it hath a tendency to use," (this "invisible college" was the Comenian scheme of Hartlib and his friends); to study the new natural philosophy, especially the plea for empiricism of Francis

Bacon; and to set up a furnace and undertake chemical experiments. These interests and activities were supported by a tremendous program of reading (his references to contemporary literature, especially to medicine and chemistry, are extraordinarily numerous) and by a wide correspondence with family, friends, scholars, scientists, and advocates of useful knowledge. This life was interrupted by visits to Ireland in 1652–3, where he looked after his estates, extended his anatomical knowledge with the help of William Petty, M.D. (friend of Hartlib and later famous as a political economist), and gained first-hand knowledge of mining techniques.

He became sufficiently well known as an amateur of science to make the acquaintance of some of the men who before this had begun meeting at Gresham College to discuss the new, experimental, anti-Aristotelian science; in 1653 one of them, John Wilkins, mathematician and divine, then Warden of Wadham College, urged Boyle to join the group now domiciled at Oxford. They included the mathematicians, John Wallis and Seth Ward, the physicians, Goddard and Willis, and soon the brilliant young scholars, Christopher Wren (not yet famous as an architect) and Robert Hooke (later first to hold the position of demonstrator to the Royal Society, and to be its leading physicist before the advent of Newton). Boyle had already written a number of essays on theology (one, written in 1648, was published as his first book, "Seraphick Love"; others, on the theological uses of natural philosophy, were incorporated into the "Usefulness of Natural Philosophy," published in 1663), and had attempted a number of chemical essays. Most were never published; only fragments remain in the Royal Society's collection of Boyle Papers. One, which circulated in manuscript, was a brief summary of the thesis later expanded into the literary, Galileo-like dialogue, the "Sceptical Chymist." What attracted attention to Boyle in scientific circles was his passionate interest in experimental natural philosophy, and his rejection of Aristotelianism. Settled in Oxford, Boyle proceeded to undertake a vast project of experimentation on six or seven topics all at once and to begin work on several diverse treatises. This was the method he pursued all his life, a method made possible only by the help of laboratory assistants, by amanuenses, and by a most discursive system of publication.

To understand what Boyle was doing in this period one needs to consider briefly the state of natural philosophy at this time, as well as the state of chemistry. To Boyle and his friends the great innovation in natural philosophy was the attack on the Aristotelian system symbolized by the mechanical philosophy. To accept the mechanical philosophy meant to accept the concept that the world was composed of matter and motion and of these only; that is, it meant complete rejection of the Aristotelian concept that matter must always be accompanied by "form" and returned to the earlier Democritean concept that matter was made up of small, hard particles whose physical properties, especially size and shape, determined the properties of matter. The mechanical philosophy appeared in many guises, from the combination of non-Aristotelian particles with Aristotelian forms, to pure Democritean atomism. The Oxford group were influenced primarily by those philosophers who emphasized the motion of the particles as the cause of physical properties, as Bacon had done in his inquiry into the cause of heat (in the "Novum Organum"), and as Galileo had suggested. Descartes in his "Principles of Philosophy" of 1644 was the first natural philosopher to incorporate a mechanical theory of matter into a total mechanical philosophy, that is to present a system of the world framed on the properties of matter and the laws of motion. Boyle found much to admire in Descartes' system, but he could not accept any universal system; besides, he disagreed with some of Descartes' laws of motion; unlike Descartes he firmly believed in the existence of a vacuum, from the evidence of Torricelli's experiment before he had made his own experiments with the air pump; and he was unable to find any trace of a Cartesian ether in a series of experiments expressly designed for the purpose. The account of the attempt to revive Epicurean atomism, made by Pierre Gassendi, was published after Boyle had already made up his mind, but it was, in any case, far too systematic an approach for the Baconian that Boyle so firmly was. He therefore devised his own "corpuscular philosophy," nonsystematic in that it dealt only with a limited branch of natural philosophy, the explanation of the properties of matter; and peculiar to him especially because firmly based upon experimental evidence.

The experimental evidence on which Boyle relied was in general chemical experiment. Chemistry he thought was the ideal experimental science, and he deprecated the fact that his Oxford friends tended to regard chemistry as useful only to medicine. Not that Boyle was unmindful of medical chemistry; he loved preparing drugs for dosing himself and his friends. But he felt that the ordinary chemist, the textbook writer, spent too much time on chemistry as a practical art to the detriment of chemistry as a theoretical science. It was perhaps from J. B. van Helmont that Boyle first came to think it possible to make chemistry a science, although Helmont's science was a mystic one with no connection with the new, nonmystic, mechanical philosophy. Boyle quickly came to feel that chemistry could benefit natural philosophy by providing experiments, while natural philosophy could benefit chemistry by providing a background of theory. To this end he felt it necessary to replace the chemist's theory of matter with a physicist's, and hence his attack on the three "chymical principles" and the four Aristotelian elements which he was writing when he went to Oxford, and which he later published as the "Sceptical Chymist." This attack was designed to show on logical and experimental grounds that, granted the contemporary definition of elements as substances found in *all* compounds and as substances into which *all* compounds were reduced, there was no such thing except for physical corpuscles. For not all substances could be analyzed into the same salt, sulfur, and mercury, or earth, air, fire, water, or phlegm, oil, spirit; further, these substances were doubtfully of an uncompounded nature; further still, they were by no means immutable. That being so, it was absurd to talk of the saline or watery or spirtuous part of a substance; one should logically either talk in terms of physical principles, the corpuscles, or else in terms of simple chemical entities. How these chemical entities changed their properties, physical and chemical, when they adhered to other substances became one of his great preoccupations, both because it gave insight into chemical composition and because it helped in the interpretation of the corpuscular philosophy. It was in the course of his investigation into color

141

changes in chemical solutions (discussed in the "History of Colours") that Boyle began developing chemical indicators for the systematic identification of substances.

Life in Oxford, where Boyle studied the theological languages of the East and was esteemed for his piety as well as for his pursuit of science, must have been singularly congenial until it was interrupted by political events. Cromwell died, to be succeeded by his son Richard, so manifestly inept that all men's minds turned to the desirability of a Royal restoration. The Oxford group broke up, some to Cambridge and some to London, and although Boyle had nothing to fear politically—he had never taken an active role in affairs, half his family were royalists, and although his brother Broghill had gone over to Cromwell he was active in negotiating for the return of Charles II—he had no taste for what he called "the disturbances of this troubled time" and retired into the country. There, to beguile a country visit, and probably to show what he and his friends had accomplished, he wrote up the series of experiments on which he had been working for the past two years and in 1660 published "New Experiments, Physico-Mechanical, Touching the Weight of the Air and Its Effects." This was the first scientific book he had published, and it made an instant stir. Aristotelians and Cartesians alike attacked his insistence that he had created a vacuum, although able Cartesians like the physicist Christian Huygens welcomed the ingenious experiments with delight. In two years' time Boyle published a second edition with answers to a number of his critics and included what we call Boyle's Law, but which he called an hypothesis. Having begun to publish Boyle continued, with a spate of books experimental, chemical, theological, and medical, based on the work begun at Oxford. This set the pattern for an extraordinarily prolific life, with one or more treatises appearing every year, a pattern only possible because, like a modern scientist, he had many of his experiments carried out by assistants, and because he dictated his books to amanuenses.

Boyle continued to live in Oxford for the next five or six years, after which he took up his residence in London with his sister Lady Ranelagh, in her house on Pall Mall. He was active in London affairs even earlier. He was present at Gresham College toward the end of 1660 when, after one of Wren's lectures, a number of the Oxford group and a number of royalist virtuosi decided to formalize and found a philosopical society. Boyle's presence was politically important, for he alone among the original scientists was in a social position to be favorably received at court. When the Royal Society was incorporated by the King in 1663, Boyle was one of the original members of council. He chose the demonstrator, Hooke, and the secretary, Henry Oldenburg. He was often on the council in succeeding years, and was several times president during the few years when presidents were elected monthly. He was again chosen president in 1680, but declined for reasons of conscience. He was widely honored in this period. In 1662 the King, presumably through the intervention of friends (for Boyle was not personally involved) secured him the grant of several forfeited estates in Ireland, which he used for the furtherance of Protestantism. At the same time the King appointed him one of the governors of the Corporation for Propagating the Gospel in New England, in which he was very active. In 1664 he was elected to the company of the Royal Mines. Oxford made him an M.D. He became a director of the East India Company. He was occasionally at court, and always the center of a fashionable as well as a scientific circle. He was always willing to help scientists, as shown by the number who dedicated their books to him. Even those like Henry Stubbe, the physician and polemicist, who vehemently attacked the Royal Society (1668–70) refrained from attacking its leading scientist, so highly valued for his public-spirited charity and promotion of religion as well as for his wit, learning, piety, and goodness. Newton, newly elected to the Royal Society, sought out and corresponded with the man who had so deeply influenced him, although by 1675 Boyle, never strong in health, was gradually withdrawing more and more from the world, to devote his strength and leisure to continuing his work.

Boyle never wrote a systematic treatise on chemical theory, although he produced numerous essays which he hoped showed what he had in mind for a chemical philosophy. One important later work is the "Icy Noctiluca," the first systematic treatise on phosphorus. Boyle learned of phosphorus from a German named

Kraft, a friend of the chemist Johann Kunckel, isolated it by a method of his own, and then systematically explored its properties in such great detail that nothing more was learned for 150 years. It is an admirable investigation, carried out with excellent experimental technique.

Most of Boyle's ideas and accomplishments belong to no one period of his life. As frequently happens with scientists, he discovered when young the subjects he wished to explore and his method of work was such that he was always able to work on several topics at once. Because he believed in the experimental essay, he published numerous works on many subjects, filled with a fascinating array of experiments, and published no systematic treatises. He wrote always in English, and in a semiliterary style, intending thereby to popularize science among the nonscientists. When one comes to appraise his chemical achievements, one must say in praise what some of his contemporaries said in criticism, that he treated chemistry like a branch of natural philosophy. This is particularly true in his explanation of physical and chemical properties by means of the matter and motion of the corpuscles of matter. All "occult" explanations and properties he detested, and under his influence they rapidly disappeared from chemistry. This was a great step forward, more particularly because with no appeal to occult properties possible, the only alternative was the explanation of *how* chemical substances behaved, rather than *why* they behaved as they did; in chemistry final causes were indeed, as Bacon had proclaimed them for natural philosophy, barren virgins.

It was partly from his dislike of occult qualities, partly from his convictions about particles as the only true ultimate agents, and partly from much experimental evidence that Boyle came to reject elements and principles and to conclude that none, in fact, existed. Yet on the same basis he was willing to accept classification of simple substances. Although like everyone else at the time he thought of metals as compound substances, he accepted them as a class. In the same way, while carefully differentiating between blue and green vitriol (copper and iron sulfate) he recognized the class formed by the combination of metals with oil of vitriol (sulfuric acid) and beyond that, the class of metallic salts of mineral acids. He rejected the fashionable alternative to the salt, sulfur, and mercury theory, the acid-alkali theory of chemistry, most stoutly defended by Otto Tachenius, German apothecary and M.D., and medical chemist, who insisted that all substances were either acid or alkali, and all reactions were acid-alkali neutralizations; but this did not prevent him from accepting acids and alkalies as classes of substances. He merely insisted that this classification be determined experimentally: he used indicators, especially dyes like blue vegetable solutions to determine acids, alkalies and neutral substances, and he further differentiated the two alkalies he knew, carbonates from vegetable sources and ammonia compounds from animal sources, by means of their reactions with corrosive sublimate. These tests showed clearly that some substances were neither acid nor alkali, but neutral.

Besides the indicator tests for acids, Boyle devised or adapted numerous other techniques for chemical identification. In many cases the reactions were known, but Boyle was the first to develop a systematic body of technique for identifying diverse substances, a technique which made use of both physical characteristics (like specific gravity and crystal form) and chemical characteristics. Thus in his "Natural History of Mineral Waters" he carefully described the tests to which the chemist or physician should subject samples of new mineral springs, and very good tests they are. It had long been known that copper compounds exhibited bright blue and green colors in strong acid and alkaline solutions (although in Boyle's time some chemists still maintained that silver would show this color too); Boyle was the first to suggest that this could be used as a test for copper in compounds. He also suggested that the green color revealed by another solvent—fire—might be useful in detecting copper, and attempted to establish a whole series of flame tests. He used the actinic blackening of *luna cornea* (silver chloride) as an identification test.

These identification tests were a far better means of determining chemical composition than any used earlier. Analysis was the usual means, but analysis too often meant analysis by fire, which was really destructive distillation, when inorganic compounds were supposed to produce the same range of substances that organic compounds did produce. Boyle had pointed out exhaustively

145

the difficulties inherent in analysis by fire, and he used it only sparingly; never, in fact, unless checked by synthesis. Synthesis was useful but not always convincing; we tend to forget that in Boyle's day technique was still so poor that, as he pointed out, chemists often threw away important parts of the reaction in the *caput mortuum,* or added substances unaware that they were reactive, or through ignorance and confusion mistook the composition of substances. Thus Boyle took some pains to show definitively that sulfur (the entity, not the element) entered into the composition of oil of vitriol, which was identical with oil of sulfur *per campanam,* sulfur burned under a bell jar. So, too, he carefully showed that potashes and salt of tartar and various other carbonates were the same substance, though of different origin.

These were the difficulties inherent in seventeenth century chemistry, and it was only by persistent experimental effort, as Boyle insisted, that chemists could emancipate themselves from old methods of thought. It was not only that chemists persisted, when discussing a reaction, in talking about the effect of the element of salt in causing precipitation, or the action of the sulfur of a metal, or the effect of the oily part of a substance deserting the residue. This indicated a habit of mind, again an addiction to final causes, which prevented chemists from trying to discuss the mechanism of a reaction, that is, what actually happened in a reaction. Boyle, emancipated from final causes, was intensely interested in what happened in a reaction. Although lack of a clear understanding of pneumatic chemistry prevented him from understanding the total composition of substances and hence of everything that took place in a reaction, he went far along the correct road.

Boyle's work in combustion was equally influential, although perhaps less fortunately so. Like other chemists of his day he thought of air as a physical substance, not a chemical one, and this in spite of the fact that he discovered hydrogen and recognized it as different from atmospheric air (he prepared it from strong mineral acids and iron filings) and detected, in his air pump, the "fixed air" present in vegetables. But because air no longer fit to support combustion and respiration was still elastic, and because he knew how heavily saturated with water particles air might be, Boyle assumed that the elastic part of air—what made it a gas—was permanent, although only a part of normal atmospheric air. This elastic air carried in solution a wide variety of solid particles, water, salts, and so on, and it was his hope (expressed in the posthumously published "General History of Air") that some one would take the trouble to make the tests necessary to determine just what particles air did carry in solution. He himself could find no evidence for "nitrous" particles and hence he rejected the theories of such men as Kenelm Digby, Hooke, and John Mayow, themselves based on earlier theories, that "nitro-aerial corpuscles" were responsible for combustion. Boyle, although convinced from air pump experiments that air was absolutely essential to life and fire, fought shy of trying to explain the reason for this, except to assume that it must be caused by particles contained in the air. For air did not, he was sure, take part in any chemical reactions, although some could not take place without air. When a substance was calcined it often gained weight, Boyle knew; indeed, metals and minerals like sulfur always did, strikingly so, and he made careful quantitative experiments to find out how much weight they gained. Since he excluded air, a priori, and since he was predisposed, for philosophic reasons, to believe that fire was corporeal (it seemed more mechanical and less occult, even though he knew well that heat was only from the motion of the particles, as was abundantly proved by the mechanical production of heat), he decided that the gain in weight on calcination must come from the fire. This was generally accepted, with adaptations, by eighteenth-century chemists, even when, paradoxically, they rejected Boyle's careful experimental evidence of constant gain in weight on calcination. But it should not be forgotten that Lavoisier read Boyle.

Boyle's greatest influence was personal. Through his enormous prestige as a leading anti-Aristotelian, Baconian, natural philosopher, the archetype of the English school, whatever he wrote attracted attention. Most of his books were rapidly translated from English to Latin. Many were summarized in French in the *Journal des Scavans,* and in Latin in the *Acta Eruditorum.* The registers of the physical section of the French Academy of Science show a constant awareness that Boyle's prolific output was essential reading for the scientist. And he always influenced the men working in his laboratory. Most of these assistants were what he called "laborants," mere technical men, "lab boys," more or less trained by him. But many were essentially research students. Hooke's first published work was on a subject connected with his work for Boyle—on capillarity. Denis Papin, the inventor of the digester, worked for Boyle. The German chemist Becher worked in Boyle's laboratory; though Becher's theory of matter was far removed from Boyle's, it still contained much of Boyle's corpuscular philosophy. Guillaume Homberg, who had also worked with Boyle, changed the chemical interests of the French Academy of Science from old-fashioned analytical chemistry to the newer theoretical chemistry. We can abundantly agree with Boerhaave, the influential Dutch chemist of the eighteenth century, who wrote that Boyle was one of the first to "treat of chemistry with a view to natural philosophy." Without this treatment, chemistry could not have advanced as it did.

NOTES AND REFERENCES

John F. Fulton, "Bibliography of the Hon. Robert Boyle," *Oxford Bibliographical Society, Proceedings and Papers,* 3, part I, 1932; part 3, 1933.

George Sarton, "Boyle and Bayle," *Chymia,* 3, 155–189, University of Pennsylvania Press, Philadelphia, 1950.

Marie Boas, "The establishment of the mechanical philosophy," *Osiris, 10,* pp. 412–541, 1952.

Marie Boas, "Robert Boyle and Seventeenth Century Chemistry," The University Press, Cambridge, 1958.

MARIE BOAS HALL

·· 10 ··

Nicolas Lemery

1645-1715

MEDECIN DE NICOLAS ANDRY DOCTEUR EN

L. Ferdinand pinxit   C. Vermeulen Sculpsit

NICOLAS LEMERY was born at Rouen on Nov. 17, 1645, to Julien Lemery, Procurator to the Parliament of Normandy, who was of the so-called reformed religion (Huguenot). He pursued his education in his birthplace and, following his natural inclination, determined to learn pharmacy from a Rouen apothecary who was a member of his family. He soon perceived that that which was called chemistry, of which he scarcely knew more than the name, could be a more extended science than his master and his associates realized. In 1666 he went to seek that chemistry in Paris.

He addressed himself to Glazer, then demonstrator of chemistry at the Jardin du Roi, and took lodging in Glazer's home to be near a good source of experiment and analysis. But he unfortunately found that Glazer was a true chemist, full of obscure ideas, covetous of these ideas, and unsociable. Lemery quit him after six months and resolved to travel through France, to see those skilled in the art, one after another, and to compose a science for himself from the diverse information that he would draw from this trip. Thus it was that, before the learned nations communicated with each other by books, one scarcely studied except through travel. Chemistry was still so imperfect and so little cultivated that it was necessary, to make any progress, to take up that ancient method of self-instruction.

He remained at Montpellier three years, a pensioner of Verchant, master apothecary, where he had the convenience of working and, what was more important, the advantage of giving lessons to a number of his host's young students. He did not fail to profit much from his own lessons and soon drew all the professors of the faculty of medicine and the curious of Montpellier, for he already had novelties to offer the most adept. Although he was not a doctor, he practiced medicine in that city, where it had been at all times so well practiced. His reputation became his title.

After having toured the whole of France he returned to Paris in 1672. Meetings still took place at the homes of various private persons. Those who had a taste for the true sciences assembled in small bands, like rebels who conspired against ignorance and the dominant prejudices. Such were the meetings of the abbé Bourdelot, physician to the prince of le grand Condé, and those of Justel. Lemery was present at them all, and scintillated in this company. He associated himself with Martin, apothecary to the prince, and profited from the laboratory that his friend had at the mansion of Condé. He there gave a course of chemistry which soon earned him the honor to be known and esteemed by the prince in whose laboratory he worked. He was often called to Chantilly where, surrounded by spirited and learned men, he lived as would an idle Caesar.

Lemery finally decided to have his own independent laboratory. He had the opportunity to make of himself a doctor of medicine or master apothecary. Chemistry determined him upon the latter, and he soon opened public courses in chemistry in the rue Galande where he lodged. His laboratory was less a room than a cave, and nearly a magic cavern illuminated only by the light of the furnaces. But the crowd of vistitors was so great that he scarcely had a place for his operations. The most famous names entered the list of his hearers, the Rohauts, Berniers, Auzouts, Regis, Tourneforts.[1] Even women, caught up by the fashion, had the audacity to show themselves in these learned assemblies. At the same time, du Verney gave courses in anatomy with the same brilliance, and all the nations of Europe provided them with students.[2] In one of these years forty Scotsmen came to Paris only to hear these two masters, and returned home as soon as their courses were completed. As Lemery took boarders, it was important that his house should be large enough to lodge all those who wanted to be there, and the rooms of the quarter were filled with half-boarders, who wished at least to eat with him. His reputation had also a considerable utility, as the preparations coming from his hands were in vogue. He made a prodigious sale of them in Paris and in the provinces; the sale of magistery of bismuth alone sufficed for all the expenses of his house. This magistery, however, was not a remedy. It is that which we call "Spanish white," and he alone in Paris then possessed that treasure.[3]

Chemistry had been until then a science in which, to borrow its own terms, a little truth was so dissolved in a great quantity of false that it had become invisible, and the two were nearly inseparable. To the few natural properties that one recognized in these two mixtures was added as much as one wished of more spectacular imaginary properties. The metals sympathized with the planets and with the principal parts of the human body. An alkahest which no one had ever seen dissolved everything. The greatest absurdities were revered by the grace of a mysterious obscurity with which they were enveloped or entrenched against reason. One took pride in speaking only in a barbaric language resembling the sacred languages of the ancient theology of Egypt, understood by the priests alone, and apparently devoid of sense. Chemical operations were described in books in an enigmatic manner and often deliberately charged with so many impossible or useless circumstances that it was clear that the authors wished only to assure to themselves the glory of understanding them and to throw others into a despair of succeeding. However, very often these same authors did not know so much about it, or had not done as much as they would have liked to have credit for. Lemery was the first who dissipated the natural or artificial shadows of chemistry; who reduced it to more clear and simple ideas; who abolished the useless barbarism of its language; who only promised from it what was within its power, and that which he knew it could accomplish. From this came its great success. There is not only a spirit of honesty; there is a sort of grandeur of spirit in thus stripping a false dignity from the science in which one works.

To render his course even more popular he published, in 1675, his "Cours de Chymie." The glory deriving from quick sale is not for learned works, but this was an exception. It sold like a work of gallantry or satire. Editions followed each other nearly from year to year, not counting a large number of pirate editions, honorable as well as injurious to the author. It was a new science which saw the light and which stirred the curiosity of everyone.

The book has been translated into Latin, German, English, and Spanish. We have seen in the "Éloge to Tschirnhaus" (Fontenelle's) that he, through his passion for the science, had Lemery's work translated into German at his own expense. The English translator, who had been a student of Lemery, regrets that he is no longer, and treats chemistry as a science indebted almost entirely to his master. The Spaniard, founder and president of the Royal Society of Medecine of Seville, said that in "the subject of chemistry the authority of the great Lemery is more unique than recommendable."

Although he had divulged secrets of chemistry in his book, he reserved some of them for himself. For example, an emetic, very gentle and more certain than the ordinary, and a mesenteric opiate with which he was said to have made surprising cures, and which none of those who worked under him had been able to discover. He was also content to render some operations easier without revealing the last degree of facility known to him. And he did not doubt that of so many riches which he liberally spread before the public it was permitted to him to reserve some small part for his own use.

In 1681 his life began to be troubled because of his religion. He received an order to rid himself of its burden within a certain time. The Elector of Brandenberg seized this occasion to propose, through Spanheim, his envoy in France, that Lemery come to Berlin where the Elector would create for him a commission as chemist. Love of country, the inconvenience of transporting his family to a distant place, hope—although very uncertain—of some distinction, all this held him back. And even after his time had expired he still gave some courses of chemistry to a large number of students who hastened forward to profit from them. But, at last, rigor succeeded the tolerance with which he had been favored, and he went to England in 1683. He had the honor to pay his respects to King Charles II and to present him with the fifth edition of his book. This prince, although sovereign of a learned nation, and accustomed to savants, marked Lemery with particular esteem and gave him expectations. But Lemery felt the effects would be long in following if they followed at all. The troubles which seemed to be on the increase in England menaced him with a life as agitated as in France. His family, who had remained in France, gave him concern, and he resolved to return there, although still without any clearly determined resolution.

He believed that he would be more undisturbed under the shelter of the rank of Doctor of Medicine. Toward the end of 1683 he took the cap at the University of Caen, which repaid him with great honors for the preference he had given it. When he had returned to Paris he soon found there an ample practice but not much of the tranquility of which he had need. The concerns of his religion worsened from day to day. Finally, the Edict of Nantes having been revoked in 1685, the practice of medicine was forbidden to the members of the so-called reformed religion. He remained without function and without resources, his house entirely denuded of furnishings through a melancholy precaution. His effects were dispersed almost at random and hidden wherever he could. His wealth, which was not substantial, was destroyed. His spirit was incessantly occupied both by chagrin for the present and fears for the future, which could scarcely be as terrible as he fancied them.

However, Lemery still gave two courses of chemistry, but under powerful protection, one for the two youngest brothers of the Marquis of Seignelay, Secretary of State, and the other for Lord Salisbury, who did not believe it possible to obtain the same instruction in England.

In the midst of these vexations and misfortunes, Lemery finally came to fear a greater evil, that of suffering for a bad cause, and to no purpose. He applied himself to the practices of the Catholic religion, and soon after, in the beginning of 1686, he was reunited to the Church with his whole family.

He resumed by full right the exercise of medicine, but for a course in chemistry and the sale of his remedies or preparations he needed letters from the King, for he was no longer an apothecary. He easily obtained them, but when it was a question of registering them at Parliament, La Reynie, lieutenant general of police, the faculty of medicine, and the master and warden apothecaries opposed it, apparently less by sincere design to vex him than to make such arrangements rare and difficult. Happily the apothecaries, the most interested of the opposition, soon desisted and ceded gracefully to the personal merit of Lemery and the fact of his conversion. Tranquil days returned and with them the students, the sick, the large sale of chemical preparations—all redoubled by the interruption.

The ancient physicians, beginning with Hippocrates, were physicians, apothecaries, and surgeons. But subsequently medicine had

155

been divided into three parts; not that one old physician was worth three modern ones, but because the three functions and the knowledge necessary to them were much augmented. Lemery, however, united all three, for he was also a surgeon, and in his youth had conducted surgical operations, in which he had succeeded very well, especially in bleeding. Because of his great knowledge of pharmacy and the actual practice of that art, he was the double of an ordinary physician. He proved it by two great works which appeared in 1697, one entitled "Pharmacopée universelle," and the other "Traité universel des drogues simples," for which he asked a copyright of fifteen years; the judge, believing it too short, granted him twenty.

The "Pharmacopée universelle" is a comprehensive collection of the compound remedies described in the books of pharmacy of all the European nations. It is so arranged that a particular country which, either by the differences of climate and temperament, or by ancient usages, used different remedies, could find, as in a grand pharmacopeia, the particular remedy which best suited it. One found there even those secrets which so many physicians were accused of ignoring and which were admired all the more because they were distributed by ignorant hands. But the collection is purged of all the false compounds reported by authors who had little knowledge of the diseases they treated.

Of all of the medicines that Lemery retained, of which the number is prodigious, he advises as to their virtues and gives the method of preparation, thus facilitating preparation or curtailing useless ingredients. For example, from the famous theriac of Andromachus, composed of sixty-four drugs, he omitted twelve, and that perhaps too few. But strongly entrenched things can only be attacked by degrees.

The "Traité universel des drogues simples" is the basis of the "Pharmacopée universelle." It is an alphabetical collection of all of the materials—mineral, animal, and vegetable—that enter into the accepted remedies. Since there were few that were not involved, a good part of the treatise is natural history. One finds there the description of drugs, their virtues, how to choose them, and their history. As regards foreign drugs, Lemery furnishes all available information. There were many drugs in common use at that time about which little was known. For example, he points out that the common opinion that true opium is a tear is false; also that coffee is not a bean.[4]

The immense heap of simple and compound remedies contained in the "Pharmacopée" or in the "Traité des drogues" would seem to hold out a promise of a sure cure for any malady. But as in life, where many promises are made and few are kept, in that horde of nostrums are few true remedies. Lemery, who knew them well, trusted but a few. He employed chemical remedies only with great circumspection, although he might have been predisposed in their favor. He gave most of the analyses merely to satisfy the curiosity of physicians, and believed that as far as medicine was concerned, chemistry, because it has to reduce mixtures to their principles, often reduces them to nothing. He believed that the day would come when it would take a contrary route, and that chemistry, from being a decomposing science, would become a composing one, that is to say, forming new remedies and better ones by the compounding of different mixtures. The most skillful in an art are not those who praise it the most but those who are superior to it.

When the Academy was revived in 1699, Lemery's reputation alone urged and obtained for him the place of associate chemist. Toward the end of the same year he became a pensioner through the death of Bourdelin. He then commenced a great work which he read in parts to the Academy until it was finally published in 1707. This is the "Traité de l'antimoine." There that most useful mineral is changed in all ways by dissolutions, sublimations, distillations, and calcinations; it takes all the forms that art can give it and is allied with everything capable of augmenting or modifying its virtues. It is considered both in regard to medicine and in regard to natural philosophy, but unfortunately curiosity in natural philosophy is much more extensive than medicinal usage. One could understand by that example that the study of a single mixture is nearly unlimited and that each could have its own chemist.

After the printing of this book Lemery began to feel many of the infirmities of old age. He had several attacks of apoplexy followed by paralysis of one side; this did not, however, prevent his going out. He always attended the Academy for which he had

157

conceived that affection which it rarely fails to inspire. He fulfilled its functions more than his health seemed to permit. But finally he had to renounce assemblies and remain at home. He gave up his place as pensioner, which was given to the elder of his two sons. He was stricken by a last attack of apoplexy which lasted six or seven days and died on June 19, 1715.

Nearly all of Europe learned chemistry from him and most of the great chemists, French and foreign, rendered him homage for their knowledge. He was an indefatigable worker, knowing only the sickroom of his patients, his study, laboratory, and the Academy, and he well understood that he who wastes no time has plenty of it. He was a good friend; he had always lived with Regis in a close relationship that suffered no alteration. The same probity and simplicity of manners united them. It is a commendation that belongs often enough to that particular and rare category of men whom scientific activity separates from ordinary men.

ADDITIONAL NOTES ON LEMERY

This glowing tribute by Fontenelle[5] might lead us to speculate that Lemery has been neglected by historians of chemistry, were we unmindful of the nature of such communications. But our neglect of Lemery, who was, after all, one of the best known chemists of his time, does have some significance. He was one of the chemists who, as historians of science are wont to say, "discovered no new facts." His primary service to science was that of a teacher and textbook writer. As Fontenelle has shown, the teacher of chemistry was not necessarily underrated in the seventeenth century. Another reason for our neglect of Lemery would appear to be the rapid eclipse of the peculiar atomism of Descartes, which he adopted as dogma. He did not merely teach practical chemistry; he also taught a theory which had a wonderful plausability when compared to alchemical and iatrochemical theories, but which was not much more solidly grounded and which seems now an isolated incident in the history of chemistry. In his own time it probably contributed to his popularity.

Lemery's role as an innovator in chemistry has been overrated by Fontenelle. Lemery was only one of a series of seventeenth century French chemists—and nearly the last of the series—who published usable manuals of instruction in practical chemistry. The first of this line was Beguin; Glazer, Lemery's instructor in Paris, was another. The obscurities which Lemery is credited with dropping, concerning sympathies between metals and planets, the alkahest, etc., had been fading from the literature of his French predecessors. Glazer's work was not so unlike Lemery's as Fontenelle suggests. But as Lemery was the last of this series, so also was he freest of the taint of these antique notions. He deserves to be remembered as an outstanding member of the group that did so much to clear the ground for the construction of the science we now know as chemistry.

As already noted, Fontenelle's Éloge gives an incorrect impression that Lemery had nothing to say on the subject of chemical theory. In fact, the "Cours," while treating theory in an incidental fashion, does offer an explanation of chemical activity. It defines chemistry as "that art which teaches the separation of different substances encountered in a mixture," a definition that seems less satisfactory than those of some of Lemery's predecessors. Its "sensible principles," which he does not regard as elementary, he found by analysis to be mercury or spirit, sulfur or oil, salt, phlegm, and earth. These modest and, for the time, sensible observations are not, however, the basis of his explanations of chemical activity. That role is played by his doctrine of figured particles which derived both from contemporary atomism and from Descartes. This doctrine seems to have been worked out in explaining the lively question of the interaction of acids and alkalis and the mild character of the resulting substances. In this case the acid particles were supposed to be characterized by sharp points, the alkaline by holes into which the former fitted, thus yielding a less abrasive product. In a highly speculative manner Lemery plays on this theme again and again in the explanations he provides for most of the preparations described in the "Cours." In this geometric atomism he differed markedly from chemists both before and after him.

Lemery also has more to say than had his predecessors concerning weight balances. Most of his preparations are recounted in terms of weights, usually in the manner of a cookbook, but frequently he gives an explanation of the gains and losses in weights.

159

These explanations involve, when such are needed, the loss of "volatile parts," the retention of fire particles, and the like. But they are often clearly given merely as a sop to the curious. Lemery would seem to be a transitional figure in his offhand and almost flippant concern with weight balances.

Lemery was not, as has been frequently claimed, connected with the Jardin du Roi, although most of his predecessors were, and his son was. This institution seems to have been the economic factor which made possible this continuity of chemical instruction in seventeenth-century France. In view of his eminence it is reasonable to suppose that his religion was the obstacle.

NOTES AND REFERENCES

1 Illustrious bearers of these names in Lemery's time were Jacques Rohault (for Rohaut?), a zealous Cartesian who is described in the *Biographie Universal* as "the first professor of physics who united observation and experience to reason." Lemery's close friend, Pierre Sylvain Regis, was a disciple of Rohault. Regis gave lectures on Cartesian philosophy at Lemery's house, but his school was closed by the archbishop who favored the "ancient philosophy." Rohault was accused of heresy for similar reasons in the 1670's. Adrian Auzout, also from Rouen, was an astronomer, remembered for the invention of the micrometer. Joseph P. de Tournefort was one of the most illustrious botanists of the time.

2 Joseph-Guichard Duverney, professor of anatomy at the Jardin Royal from 1679, is remembered for notable work on the anatomy of the ear.

3 Magistery of bismuth, a cosmetic, was prepared by dissolving bismuth in nitric acid and precipitating out basic bismuth nitrate with salt water. Although Fontenelle says that it was not a remedy, it was; oddly enough, it outlasted most of the other early chemical medicines as a remedy in chronic diarrhea and cholera. It is not clear why Lemery "alone in Paris" should have possessed it. It was known to Libavius, and was not only mentioned in Lemery's own "Cours de chymie," but its preparation was featured in his courses, according to his student and English translator, Keil.

4 "Opium is a tear which flows from the wounded heads or leaves of the black poppy being ripe," according to Wm. Salmon, "New London Dispensatory" (London, 1691) p. 167. However, the term "tear," as used in materia medica, often refers only to the shape. With regard to the coffee bean, Europeans seem to have known long before Lemery that it was the product of a tree. The term "bean" seems to have derived from the Arabic term *bon,* or *ban,* referring to coffee.

160

5 Fontenelle (1657–1757), one of the most prominent and long-lived literary figures of his time, was, like Lemery, a native of Rouen. He was a member of the Academy of Sciences from 1691 and its perpetual secretary for forty-two years. The Éloges, published between 1708 and 1722, were customarily read to the Academy at the first meeting following the death of the member.

From: Fontenelle, "Oeuvres," Paris, Salmon, 1825, Vol. I, pp. 296–306. Translated by Robert P. Multhauf. All notes are by the translator.

BERNARD LE BOUVIER DE FONTENELLE

·· 11 ··

Herman Boerhaave

1668-1738

HERMAN BOERHAAVE was the renowned chemist-physician of the early eighteenth century who, in the estimation of his contemporaries in the scientific world, stood second only to Isaac Newton. A native of Holland, he became a fellow of the Royal Society and also a foreign associate of the Academy of Sciences at Paris. The Philosophical Transactions of 1737 was dedicated to him. Admired and respected by both his colleagues and the public at large, he is probably the only scientist whose life has been the subject of a highly successful play. "Il Medico Olandise," a prose comedy avowedly based on Boerhaave's life, proved immensely popular when produced in Venice in 1756 and remained in the repertory of the Italian comic theater until 1832.

Despite this general acclaim, there are very few scientific discoveries associated with his name. Boerhaave's reputation was due primarily to his success as a teacher at the University of Leiden where he influenced a generation of students who flocked there from all over Europe. His influence extended many years beyond his death through his textbooks, especially the "Elementa Chemiae." This chemical treatise, which went through nearly thirty editions, became one of the touchstones of eighteenth century chemistry and played a central role in the development of chemical thought leading to the revolution in chemistry associated with the name of Lavoisier.

Herman Boerhaave was born in the village of Verhout, two miles from Leiden, on December 31, 1668. His father, James, a minister of scholarly attainments, was especially well versed in historical and classical studies. His mother, Hagar, was the daughter of an Amsterdam merchant. She died in 1673 and James remarried shortly thereafter. The new wife, Eve du Bois, daughter of a Leiden minister, endeared herself to her seven young stepchildren, Herman and his six sisters, who came to regard her as their own mother.

Boerhaave displayed extraordinary ability at an early age and his father planned him for the ministry. When twelve years old

165

he was afflicted with an extremely painful ulcer on the left thigh from which he suffered for five years. In order that he be closer to medical care, he was placed in a school at Leiden where his scholastic performance was brilliant.

James Boerhaave died in 1682 leaving the most meager funds for his wife and now, nine children. His patrimony sufficed to carry Herman through school; when he entered the University of Leiden in 1684, the burgomaster of Leiden, Daniel Van Alphen, generously became his patron.

By this time Boerhaave had developed a voracious appetite for learning and he ranged over the entire curriculum. Although aiming at the ministry, he took courses in medicine, in which he had developed an interest as a result of his illness, mathematics, natural philosophy, chemistry, botany, and languages. He took his first degree in 1687 in natural philosophy and in 1690 received a doctor of philosophy degree based on a thesis on the distinction between the nature of soul and body. After this he supplemented his income by giving lectures in mathematics and plunged into a serious study of medicine, botany, and chemistry. He was an omnivorous reader, working through the medical classics from Hippocrates to Sydenham and the works of Boyle and Newton.

His interest in medicine was so overwhelming that he decided to acquire a medical degree, but still as a preliminary to entering the ministry. As Samuel Johnson pointed out, he "proposed, when he had made himself master of the whole art of physick, and obtained the honor of a degree in that science to petition regularly for a licence to preach and to engage in the cure of souls."

He chose to travel to Harderwijk to complete his medical studies, a move that has been hard to explain in view of Leiden's preeminence. The current saying was that "Harderwijk is a trading town where sour herrings, whortleberries and medical diplomas are sold." Certainly this reputation should have been a deterrent to so brilliant and conscientious a student. It has been suggested that economy may have been a motive or perhaps the avoidance of the limelight of notoriety that might have been associated with a professed theologian showing such undue interest in the sciences.

In fact, upon his return to Leiden after acquiring a medical

166

degree in 1693, he found himself accused of impiety. It seems that Boerhaave was present in a public boat when a discussion arose of the doctrines of Spinoza. One rather intemperate participant resorted to violent invective, and Boerhaave demanded to know whether he had ever actually read Spinoza, letting all know that he himself was quite familiar with the work of that heterodox philosopher. The storm that arose made his decision to forget the ministry and to practice medicine an easy one. His natural inclination was with medicine; besides which, in Leiden at that moment, there was little choice for him.

Boerhaave did not find private medical practice lucrative but it did provide him with sufficient time in which to continue his studies. He ranged beyond his books and also began to carry out extensive experimentation in chemistry.

In 1701 he started teaching medicine at the University and shortly thereafter was asked by his students to lecture privately on chemistry. His success as a teacher was tremendous and the story of his career from this time is one of continual academic advancement to the point where Boerhaave and the medical faculty of Leiden were almost synonymous.

He declined the offer of a chair at Groningen in 1703 and in gratitude the governors at Leiden raised his salary and promised him the first vacant professorship. This turned out to be Hotten's chair in medicine and botany to which he succeeded in 1709. As Professor of Botany his duties included, in addition to lecturing, the care of the botanical garden.

In 1710 he married Marie, the twenty-four-year-old daughter of his friend, Dr. Abraham Drolenvaux, one of Leiden's leading citizens. Of their four children, only one, Joanne Maria, survived infancy.

Boerhaave became Professor of Physick and Physician to St. Augustin's Hospital in 1714. It was here that clinical instruction took place. In the same year he was elected Rector of the University, a position which he gave up one year later. Boerhaave had been lecturing in chemistry since his initial appointment and upon the death in 1718 of his colleague in chemistry, James Le Mort, succeeded to his chair. Thus, Boerhaave occupied simultaneously chairs in medicine, clinical medicine, botany and chemistry. He not only lectured actively in all these fields but wrote definitive treatises in each one.

He was a superb teacher. His personality and character were such as to inspire his students. He was a tall, robust man of rustic appearance, simple, and yet refined and courteous in manner. He was patient, of good humor, and possessed a gentle wit. He was known to the leading men of his age; all who met him came away with a feeling that bordered on veneration. His learning was amazing and he was able to converse in all of the special fields of knowledge with profound insight. But strongest of all is the impression of an original and forceful character, of a fully integrated personality, of the whole man.

About a hundred students would attend each of his lectures and it was necessary to arrive early to obtain a seat. He had an unaffected way of speaking, his language was simple, and he could be approached for personal consultation. He made the students feel he had a sincere desire to instruct them.

His lectures were elegant but it was their content as much as his powers of exposition that attracted students. In each of the special sciences with which he dealt, medicine, botany, and chemistry, Boerhaave provided a new synthesis. Building on the method of Boyle and Newton, he was able to organize the theory and practice of each of these sciences into a system that was logical and that incorporated the most advanced ideas of the day. The medical faculty of Leiden was already renowned and, as Boerhaave's reputation spread, medical students flocked there in increasing numbers.

The delegation of British and German students at Leiden was especially numerous for in neither country could adequate clinical training be found. Of the 178 students who took their medical degree at Leiden under Boerhaave as promoter, there were 76 from the United Netherlands, 48 from the Germanies, 43 from Britain and the British Colonies, and 1 each from Austria, Sweden, Hungary, Turkey, and Greece.

His lectures were eventually worked up into treatises which were to become the standard textbooks of the age. The "Institutiones medicae," a theoretical work, and its practical companion volume, "Book of Aphorisms," were published in 1708 and 1709. Among the most famous medical texts of all times, they were used for the greater part of a century and provided the basis for medical courses in scores of universities. In botany he published the "Index plantarum" (1710) and a supplementary volume, the "Index alter plantarum" (1720) which catalogued the holdings of his botanical garden. His students published an unauthorized edition of his botanical lectures in 1727 under the title of the "Historia plantarum."

Boerhaave's treatise in chemistry, "Elementa chemiae," became his most famous work and his influence on the course of eighteenth century chemistry was due almost entirely to this book. It is remarkable, then, to consider that Boerhaave was reluctant to publish it. His students, however, were less reticent and in 1724 they brought out what they felt to be the substance of his lectures under the title "Institutiones et experimenta chemiae." This was not an uncommon practice and their action may have been precipitated by the publication of Senac's "A New Course in Chemistry According to the Principles of Newton and Stahl." Stahl was Boerhaave's principal rival in both the fields of medicine and chemistry and his supporters may have felt that the publication of Boerhaave's chemical lectures would provide an antidote to the doctrines of Stahl.

Boerhaave was horrified at what was purported to be his own work and immediately disowned and denounced it. He pointed out that it contained errors on every page, but in spite of this disavowal, it became an instant success and was even translated into English. In his preface, the English translator, Peter Shaw, unabashedly acknowledged that " 'Tis no secret, [he] has abandoned this his latest offspring. . . . This mov'd us to take the unhappy fugitive under our care, and supply in some measure, the wanted office of the natural parent. What we have done for it let others say; the most transient view of its former, compared with its present state, will easily shew it. In short, we adjusted and composed its dislocated parts; pared off the redundant ones, dress'd it anew, nay, and adorn'd and enrich'd it, with a concern and affection rarely shewn to the productions of other people." Boerhaave therefore had no choice but to prepare an authorized edition which was published in 1732 as the two-volume "Elementa chemiae."

In 1722 Boerhaave was afflicted with a serious case of the gout that confined him to his bed for several months. The esteem in which he was held by both town and university is attested to by the celebration that marked his recovery. A public holiday was proclaimed and the city of Leiden especially illuminated in honor of the occasion of his return to classes. His colleague, Peter Burman, wrote a poem of considerable length in his honor. This general approbation remained undiminished until his death from heart disease in 1738, at the age of sixty-nine.

During his lifetime, Boerhaave's reputation was based primarily upon his prominence in medicine and his ability as a teacher. He was known as the Batavian Hippocrates, the prototype of the perfect physician, not only possessed of vast encyclopedic knowledge and imbued with the scientific approach, but also full of good sense, sympathy, and good faith.

As a medical theorist, Boerhaave attempted to apply the atomic and mechanical views of Boyle and Newton. He taught that the nerves were canals conducting vital spirit from the brain to the motor apparatus, that absorption and secretion involved a simple filtering action, and that hydraulics would provide the key to understanding blood circulation. Disease was due to a physical alteration of the organs which prevented the normal movement of the particles, and fever was a result of the friction of globules of blood against the walls of the blood vessels. These iatromechanical views were part of a tradition that went back to early Alexandrian medicine and Democritan atomism but Boerhaave did avoid the extreme mechanical doctrines of such Italians as Borelli and Bellini. He was sufficiently broad in his point of view to include what he felt were the good ideas of his adversaries, such as Stahl and Hoffmann. However, success as a medical practitioner was not dependent upon one's theoretical point of view since one was no more substantial than another and it was upon the more subjective factors that success depended. Boerhaave was neither an experimentalist nor a diagnostician. His significant contributions to medicine were pedagogical. It was the comprehensive synthesis of all the subject matter of medicine and the incorporation into the medical curriculum of a well-ordered and modern treatment of chemistry, physics, and botany that was his claim to fame. In addition, he brought new importance to the use of clinical instruction in medical education.

We now realize that Boerhaave's most important contribution was not to medicine but to the development of the science of chemistry. His influence here was greatest after his death and was advanced chiefly through his treatise, the "Elementa chemiae." In fact, Boerhaave would probably not even appear in the history of chemistry were it not for this textbook, for there are very few actual discoveries credited to him.

That the "Elementa chemiae" was widely used is attested to by the numerous editions which appeared throughout the eighteenth century including translations into English, French, German, Turkish, and Russian. There was a Latin edition as late as 1777 and the last of the German and Russian translations appeared in 1791 and 1781, respectively. Thomas Thomson, the eminent British chemist and historian of chemistry, in 1811 referred to this work "as the most learned and most luminous treatise on chemistry that the world has yet seen . . . and when we compare it with any other system of chemistry that preceded it, the superiority of Boerhaave's information will appear in a very conspicuous point of view." This popularity may have been due to some extent to the influence of his students who occupied chairs at leading universities all over Europe, but it must have been its intrinsic virtues that commended it to such chemists as Black, MacBride, Cavendish, and Lavoisier, a full generation removed from Boerhaave.

From the point of view of style alone, the "Elementa chemiae" had much to recommend itself. Boerhaave was past sixty when the book was published so that it was a mature effort. His classical training and years of experience as a writer and teacher ensured an orderly presentation and crystal-clear exposition. Such qualities were not at all characteristic of the chemical treatises of the period which were frequently a confused collection of recipes and experiments in haphazard order related in a jargon that was meaningful only to the adept.

171

In the first volume are found the history and theory of chemistry, the latter being almost a physical chemistry. There is a very substantial treatment of heat which is so complete in itself that it is frequently referred to as Boerhaave's "Treatise on Fire." Similarly there is a long section on "air" which contains, in addition to the chemical relations of "air," a rather complete treatment of Boyle's law. The second volume consists principally of the descriptive and preparative aspects of chemistry, but it also contains a "Treatise on Menstrums" which deals with solutions.

Although Boerhaave's main interest was in medicine, he did not treat chemistry merely as the handmaiden of medicine. He included subjects such as metallurgy and industrial arts which were not usually part of a medical school course. Chemistry had not yet emerged as a truly learned profession and was still associated with either the alchemist's den, the apothecary's workshop, or the metallurgist's mine. In his inaugural address on succeeding to the chair of chemistry in 1718, Boerhaave said "Chemistry . . . ! accounted crude, savage, toilsome, divorced from all intercourse among Savants, a stranger or object of suspicion among the Learned, belching forth fire, fumes, ashes and filth, with scarcely any kind of beauty to recommend it." It was one of his aims to elevate chemistry to a branch of natural philosophy so that it might become an honorable part of university learning.

His early training in natural philosophy made Boerhaave an enthusiastic supporter of Newton and Boyle. Although there is no trace of his having direct contact with Newton, he was well acquainted with many of Newton's closest associates. He realized that the general truths of physics must also be applied to chemistry and so he gave careful consideration to the influence of light, heat, density, and pressure to chemical phenomena. He used Boyle's air pump to investigate pressure effects and he carefully used Fahrenheit's thermometer in thermal investigations. He subjected his materials to scrutiny under the microscope and made use of the balance, the barometer, and the burning glass.

Yet more than the specific techniques and theories of Newton and Boyle, Boerhaave applied their method. To Newton's contemporaries this implied as much the empirical, inductive method exemplified by his work in optics as the vast deductive system of the "Principia." Boerhaave was scrupulous in avoiding speculations that were far removed from the possibility of direct experimental confirmation. In this respect he differed from Freind, another disciple of Newton, who freely speculated on the possibility of a gravitational attraction among the particles of matter as the fundamental physical basis of chemical phenomena.

Boerhaave's most celebrated chemical research was that dealing with the constitution of mercury and it illustrates his attitude toward hypothesis and theory. The problem was whether mercury is pure and elemental or compounded with either sulfur or with "fire as some celebrated modern chemists have said it was." Although this must refer to phlogiston and Stahl, Boerhaave consistently refused to use this word or to mention his rival's name in a controversial context.

For years he subjected mercury samples to the most drastic of laboratory operations and finally concluded: "The Nature of Mercury is constant, simple and cannot be separated into dissimilar Parts by Distillation; not into fix'd and volatile; not into pure and unpure; not into faeces and defecated; not into different elements. . . . To make Gold or Silver of Mercury does not proceed. Ignorant Men are given up to Imagination, easy to Promise, rich in Hope. The Mercury remained Mercury."

In this conclusion Boerhaave stood in direct opposition to Stahl whose phlogiston theory was predicated on the compound nature of metals. Boerhaave's views on the combustion of nonmetals were not too different from Stahl's although here again he refrained from the use of the term, phlogiston, since he considered *ignis* or fire to be a material substance rather than a principle. However, on the nature of metals he took a stand in direct opposition to Stahl and indeed to the point of view that had been part of chemistry from the very beginning. He insisted that at least those substances that he had exhaustively studied, such as mercury and lead, were simple substances. In this he was using Boyle's operational definition of an element. He offered no alternative doctrine of calcination to rival that of Stahl, preferring to be undogmatic. He avoided the restraints of a rigid philosophical system and tried to remain as close as possible to what could be ascertained empirically. In his words, "We must check the Forwardness of the Imagination by the Weight of Experiments."

In a sense, the work of Stahl and Boerhaave complemented each other. The one was philosophical and speculative, the other practical, empirical, and quantitative; the one presented a theory which contained the significant knowledge then available, the other a method for the accumulation of new knowledge; the one summed up, the other pointed the direction ahead. No wonder, then, in the years after his death, when the phlogiston theory was in the ascendancy, that Boerhaave's book still remained the standard work for teaching and for reference. Independent of a hypothetical basis and thus not subject to the vagaries of the success or failure of any system, it remained the standard textbook of chemistry. No matter how convinced one might be of the value of Stahl's theory, the best way to obtain a practical working knowledge of chemistry was to study Boerhaave. When, finally, Stahl's theory was overthrown, much of Boerhaave's work, which was rooted in observation, could still be incorporated into the new system so that his influence even spilled over into the post-Lavoisier period.

But the "Elementa chemiae" was more than a convenient reference work. Its treatment of "air" was sufficiently original to play, along with Stephen Hales' "Vegetable Staticks," a major part in the subsequent discovery of gases and their role in chemical phenomena. Like Hales, and possibly before him, Boerhaave was familiar with the fixation of "air" and even considered the possibility of its entering into chemical combination in addition to its well-understood behavior as a physical agent.

That there might be gases chemically distinct from air had been suggested by Van Helmont, who had identified *gas sylvestre,* a product of fermentation and combustion, as distinct from common air. Boerhaave was familiar with Van Helmont's idea and speculated upon it as an explanation for the variety of conditions leading to the evolution of air.

Boerhaave formulated the laws of solubility of air in liquids on a sound basis and in so doing provided the framework for later determinations of gaseous solubility by Cavendish and Priestley.

174

He established the reversibility of the solution process and the fact that each liquid is characterized by a specific solubility of the air.

The revolution in chemistry at the end of the eighteenth century was a result of the synthesis by Lavoisier of two currents, British pneumatic chemistry and the quantitative analytical techniques developed on the continent. The achievements in pneumatic chemistry were based upon an understanding of the chemical role of gases and the possibility of the existence of gaseous species chemically distinct from air. The quantitative interpretation of experiments in which gases were collected over water depended upon an appreciation of the nature of gaseous solubility. In all of these considerations the "Elementa chemiae" must, at the very least, have established a favorable frame of reference which pointed out the path ahead and may have even directly stimulated the discoveries of pneumatic chemists such as Black, Cavendish, and Priestley.

Boerhaave insisted on the necessity for a thorough knowledge of heat as a preliminary to the study of chemistry; for chemists his textbook became the prime source of study in this field. He describes his experiments and views on a variety of calorimetric and heat transfer problems. He not only provided the background for much of the work on heat done by Black, who constantly referred to Boerhaave, but when Lavoisier, who also acknowledged him, dispensed with phlogiston as an unnecessary hypothesis and proposed instead caloric, he assigned to this element the very physical properties of Boerhaave's *ignis*.

No matter how useful the phlogiston theory was in organizing mid-eighteenth century chemical thought into a logical theory, the chief influence directing the course of actual research in chemistry at this time was the emphasis on observation and quantitative experiment and the use of both physical tools and physical concepts. The originators of this method were Boyle and Newton and its fruition was in the work of Black, Cavendish, Priestley, and Lavoisier. Boerhaave's importance for the history of chemistry is that his work on heat and gases and his views on the methods of chemical research provided a link between these generations.

Boerhaave's influence, not only upon his contemporaries, but especially upon those who followed, cannot be overestimated. Endowed with the instinct of the research director, he formulated the research program and pointed out the direction that eighteenth century chemistry was to follow. If modern chemistry is the offspring of Lavoisier, then Boerhaave was its grandsire.

NOTES AND REFERENCES

William Burton, "An Account of the Life and Writings of Herman Boerhaave," 2nd ed., London, 1746. The first edition was published anonymously in London, 1743.

Samuel Johnson, "Life of Boerhaave," *Gentlemen's Magazine,* 1739. This has been reprinted in *J. Chem. Educ., 19,* 103 (1942).

Fontenelle, "Éloge de Boerhaave," *Oeuvres,* tome 7, Paris, 1792.

Bugge, "Das Buch Der Grossen Chemiker," Vol. I. *Janus, 23,* 193 (1918); and *Memoralia Herman Boerhaave,* Haarlem, 1939.

Some recent studies of Boerhaave's significance to the history of chemistry are found in *Janus, loc. cit.,* "Memoralia Herman Boerhaave," *loc. cit.,* Hélène Metzger, "Newton, Stahl, Boerhaave et la Doctrine Chimique," Paris, 1930, Tenny L. Davis, *Isis, 10,* 33 (1928); and Milton Kerker, *Isis, 46,* 36 (1955).

F. W. Gibbs, "The Life and Work of Herman Boerhaave," Ph.D. Thesis, University College, London, 1949.

The author is indebted to Dr. Gibbs for the point of view regarding the relation between the work of Boerhaave and Stahl during the mid-eighteenth century.

MILTON KERKER

·· *12* ··

Duhamel du Monceau

1700-1782

Henri-Louis Duhamel, seigneur du Monceau, Vrigni, et Secval, naval inspector of the Royal Academy of Sciences and the Navy, member of the Royal Society of London, of the academies of Saint Petersburg, Stockholm, Palermo, Padua, of the Institute of Bologna, the Royal Society of Edinburgh, of the Societies of Agriculture in Paris and Leyden, and free associate of the Royal Society of Medicine, was born in Paris in the year 1700.

His family originated from a Dutch nobleman, Loth Duhamel, whose son came to France in 1400.

The education he received at college was of little use to him. Finally, after several years of disgust and boredom, he heard his professor speak of physics, and for the first time he enjoyed lectures and showed that he could apply himself to his work.

He received sound instruction in different branches of physics from Dufay, Geoffroy, Lemeri, Jussien, Duverney, and Winslow. The lessons these great masters gave at the Jardin du Roi impressed him as so interesting that he did not leave their school and took lodgings near the garden to be able to work more.

In the midst of these agreeable occupations his parents demanded that he obtain a law degree. He consented, provided he could do it in Orléans where many ateliers and manufacturers interested him. Although he spent his time at Orléans studying the arts and their processes, he nevertheless was graduated in law, and he returned to Paris with a degree he never used. Duhamel worked on designing, studied mathematics, constructed a chemical laboratory and arranged everything on his land to serve the numerous studies he was planning.

These wise measures were the source of long and useful projects which brought Duhamel great distinction. In discussing Duhamel's achievements we also have to include a brother who was as eager to promote the sciences and arts, as exact and assiduous as Duhamel himself. His brother was completely self-effacing; he took part in all the work without asking for any part

179

in the fame. Such rare and honorable accord calls for a similar attitude on our part: we shall speak only of Duhamel and attribute to him that surprising series of trials and experiments, although we know that it was the work of two great men.

The Government needed information on the cultivation of saffron and approached Antoine de Jessieu. Instead of grabbing it for himself, as so many would have done, de Jessieu turned the inquiry over to Duhamel, whose work he praised and for whom he thus prepared the confidence of the Ministry and a subsequent place in the Academy.

For a long time the culture of saffron had suffered great losses in the Gatinois, which is located in the north central portion of France. Duhamel observed that to transport one of the sick bulbs or a part of the infested soil into a field was sufficient to communicate the disease. He had the good fortune, in 1728, to discover its origin, a parasitical plant with very long filaments which penetrated into the saffron bulbs and diverted their juices.

The researches of Duhamel and Tillet on the disease of the grains of the Augoumois, in western France, were carried out under similar auspices in 1760. They found that the great damage was the work of a very small insect belonging to the looper moths. This insect, hidden under a cocoon, penetrated into the grain where its hull was the thinnest and offered the least resistance.

From 1745 on Duhamel studied the means for conserving grains and flours without which it would be impossible to transport them to distant places. Drying is an indispensable preliminary measure. Duhamel went to great expense to have a great oven built in which the corn was exposed to mild heat and so lost part of the water which it contained. In this oven blowers were activated by the wings of a windmill, so that air circulated between the grains, and the whole apparatus was built into a tower.

Duhamel strongly protested against two abuses, both of which are contrary to domestic economy and the interest of the State, namely the devastation of the forests and the excessive burning of wood in our ovens. Our century is really prodigal in everything. . . .

There is no part of physics that he did not enrich with new

180

observations. In experiments on the strength of wood (1742) he obtained the astonishing result that a beam two-thirds sawed through and with a thin slice of another wood inserted to fill the saw kerf has a greater strength than the original whole beam.

In a study published in 1747 on lime he reported the effects of different acids on this substance. He observed that a precipitate formed upon mixing lime water with alkalies (soda or potash). He attributed this to an acid contained in the lime where it is combined with an earth that is set free by the alkalies. Joseph Black has proved that, on the contrary, the acid ("chalky" acid) is contained in the alkalies and, by separating from the alkalies and combining with the lime, forms chalk.

It is known that the kali plant (glasswort) grown in coastal areas contains only the basis of marine salt (i.e., sodium). Duhamel planted it in the Gatinois region and recovered from it as much vegetable alkali as mineral base; the change in location did not in the least reduce the vigor of the plant. We also know how that tamarisk, which furnishes Glauber salt when grown at the coast, gives only vitriolated tartar (potassium sulfate) when cultivated at a distance from the sea. It was, therefore, erroneous to consider the salts formed in the plants as inherent in their substance and as an immediate or invariable product of plant life.

Most of these studies were aided by Grosse, a very skillful chemist and member of the Royal Academy of Sciences. A contemporary of Boulduc, Grosse was, like him, distinguished by the exactness of knowledge, the spirit of research, and a great dexterity in the practice of his science.

An English surgeon, Belehier, had seen in the shop of a dyer in London the bones of a pig which were red in color, and he had found out that this color came from the madder mixed in with the animal's food. Belehier communicated this fact to the Royal Society whose president passed it on to Geoffroy. Duhamel undertook to repeat these experiments which became for him a source of discoveries and strange observations.

As a result of his many experiments he found that young animals, after eating madder-containing food, have cartilages which turn red only at the time when they change into bone substance;

that the color is deeper in the middle of the bones, and that 36 or 48 hours are often sufficient to show the progress of the coloration. In older animals he saw the color developing mainly on the surface of the bone, where it was deposited in layers which he considered as leaves successively detached from the periosteum. He concluded that the periosteum was the organ of ossification.

Duhamel eagerly used all occasions where his work could be useful for medicine. He was the first to plant rhubarb in France. He introduced the use of milkwort (*Polygala amara*) from Virginia and from France for the treatment of pleurisy, but he did not himself administer these drugs. His enlightened generosity did not by far resemble that of certain rich inhabitants of the country side who offer help or hospitals to the poor only under the express condition that they shall have the privilege of administering medicines to their charges, thus risking to destroy by their empiricism the advantages which could result from their benevolence.

Duhamel is the first to publish, in France, an elementary study on the art of conserving the health of sailors (1750). He demonstrated that the evils so often attributed to the atmosphere at sea have their origin in the ship itself. He provided ventilators for the ships and extended their use to the renewal of air in hospitals.

On his voyages he visited the fishermen whenever he could, went out to sea with them and studied in all its details this art which is ingenious because it is based on ruse, and very ancient because it provides nourishment. All of this art is disclosed in a great book which was the fruit of his last travels: Traité des pêches, et histoire des poissons qu'elles fournissent. . . . 3 volumes in-folio, le premier chez Saillant, Nyon, et veuve Dessaint; le troisième chez la veuve Dessaint, 1782. (Treatise on fishing, and history of the fish which they furnish . . . 3 volumes in-folio, the first at Saillant, Nyon, and widow Dessaint; the third at the widow Dessaint, 1782.)

Duhamel had only one great sorrow in his life; that was the death of de Denainvilliers, his brother. He did not long survive his brother. In one of the sessions of the Royal Academy of Sciences, July 22, 1782, he felt the first attacks of the illness to which he succumbed 22 days later.

Selection from: Éloge de M. Duhamel—Lu le 11 mars 1783 par M. Vicq—d'Azyr, Secrétaire perpetuel. From: Histoire de la Société Royale de Médecine, années 1780 et 1781. Paris 1785, pp. 101–135. Translated by Éduard Farber.

FELIX VICQ-D'AZYR

·· *13* ··

Guillaume-François Rouelle

1703-1770

GUILLAUME-FRANÇOIS ROUELLE was born in 1703, in a village near Caen, and died in Paris, in 1770. He was an apothecary and professor of chemistry, and an associate member of the Academy of Sciences. He published only five papers.

In the first (1744) he proposed a classification of the neutral salts based, at the same time, on the form of their crystals, on the proportion of water of crystallization they contain, and on the temperature at which their solutions are conveniently concentrated by evaporation.

The following year, Rouelle devoted his second paper to the crystallization of marine salt (sodium chloride).

The third (1747) describes the inflammation of the essential oils, particularly turpentine, by means of nitric acid. Since the time when the Dane, Borch (better known by his Latinized name Olaus Borrichius, 1626–1690), had found and described this difficult reaction, three chemists, the Germans, Dippel and Hofmann, and the French, Geoffroy, had succeeded in reproducing it only when they added concentrated sulfuric acid to their nitric acid. According to the historians, F. Hoefer and R. Jagnaux, Rouelle is supposed to have used the hygroscopic action of concentrated sulfuric acid for dewatering the nitric acid. (See F. Hoefer: Histoire de la Chimie, Paris, Hachette, 1843, p. 390 who quotes from the manuscript of Rouelle's lecture notes; R. Jagnaux: Histoire de la Chimie. Paris, Baudry, 1891, vol. I, p. 617.)

In the fourth paper, the question of the embalming methods used by the Egyptians is discussed. Besides sodium carbonate (*natron*) which forms efflorescences in the desert sand and which was still used in Egypt in the eighteenth century, they used materials like amber and bitumen which Rouelle analyzed.

Finally, in 1754, Rouelle presented his last paper to the Academy. In it he distinguished acid salts from neutral salts. His viewpoints aroused heated discussions. Rouelle's ideas were attacked particularly by Baumé, who later became one of the most

187

tenacious adversaries of Lavoisier. Baumé, said Jagnaux, was an opinionated adversary; he always took the wrong side.

Guillaume-François Rouelle is best known as a teacher. His course in chemistry, first given privately, then at the Jardin du Roi, where he had been elected professor-demonstrator in 1742 and taught till 1768, had the same great success as that of Lemery and, later, Fourcroy.

His students included those chemists who stood out by their independence from tradition, the great noblemen who were scientific amateurs, and a number of "enlightened spirits."

Among the titled amateurs was the Marquis of Courtanvaux, great-grandson of Louvois and author of works in physics, astronomy, and chemistry. He studied particularly the composition of "marine ether" (ethyl chloride) and the inflammability of acetic acid.

Among the scientists, there was Hilaire-Marin Rouelle, who was to succeed his older brother at the Jardin du Roi. His name is frequently mentioned even today, because, in 1773, he isolated urea. Jean Darcet had been tutor to the son of Montesquieu; later on he specialized in applied chemistry. His name remains connected with an alloy of bismuth, tin, and lead which melts at 93°C. He became Guillaume-François Rouelle's son-in-law posthumously.

Another of Rouelle's students was Pierre Bayen, who almost put his finger on the correct explanation of the oxidation of metals. (See: P. A. Cap: Pierre Bayen, Paris, Masson. 1865.)

G.-F. Venel, who later on worked in the laboratory of the Duc d'Orléans, then taught medicine at Montpellier, became known particularly through his analyses of mineral waters and research on the properties of brown coal for which uses were then not known. Furthermore, he collaborated on Diderot's "Encyclopédie" and, finally, he became a rival of his jealous teacher.

In the highest rank of these brilliant students are Lavoisier and J.-B.-M. Bucquet, who became Fourcroy's teacher but died young.

Of the philosophers, we shall name only Diderot, who was excited about Rouelle's teaching, and Jean-Jacques Rousseau, who soon felt he could write a treatise of chemistry. Together with de Francueil, whose secretary he was, Rousseau had heard Rouelle's course since 1743. Jean-Jacques Rousseau's "Institutions chymiques" has never been printed. The manuscript was given to the library of the city of Geneva by the heirs of Rousseau's friend, Paul Moulton; Théophile Dufour, a citizen of Geneva, has published a study of it (1905).

Talking about citizens of Geneva, let us also mention Horace-B. de Saussure. In 1768, when he was in Paris, he attended a course by Rouelle, his swan song, because in the same year poor health forced Rouelle to retire.

The personality of Guillaume-François Rouelle is immortalized in the "Correspondance litéraire" by Melchior Grimm. This is the source on which all who subsequently wrote about this chemist relied. Rouelle appears as a picturesque figure bordering on the grotesque. He is described as stuttering, his reddish hair showing under the wig, with a distraction comparable to that of Newton or Ampère, causing handicaps in social gatherings and explosions in his lecture experiments, and so jealous that he used strong words in public against those chemists he accused of having plagiarized him.

In his book on Melchior Grimm, Edmond Scherer (Paris, 1887) writes concerning the "Correspondance litéraire": "His necrologues sometimes present remarkable portraits. In that of Rouelle, there is a certain gaiety and, perhaps, a little caricature."

Rouelle had hoped to publish his course of chemistry. Although poor health in his last years prevented him from doing that, several more or less complete copies of the manuscript are known.

Rouelle still believed in the four elements of the ancient philosophers: phlogiston (the principle of flammability, combined fire), earth, water, and air. It seemed to him that these four elements are better able to explain the properties of matter and chemical phenomena than the three elements of Paracelsus and of the so-called Basilius Valentinus.

However, Rouelle interpreted the four elements very freely. "The principles do not themselves form the substances without intermediaries, as Aristotle claimed for his elements and Epicurus for his atoms; rather, several principles of different natures combine to form the mixed bodies" (p. 8 of the Lausanne manuscript.)

Of these "mixed bodies" there are only a few. Rouelle declared that he knew only a dozen, among which are our present elements. For example, the metals result from the union of an earth that provides their solid texture with the phlogiston that is responsible for the metallic character. Light and electricity are aspects or effects of the element fire.

Since we are talking about the teacher of Lavoisier, we might be especially interested in Rouelle's thoughts about the rôle of air in combustion and fermentation. Not in his introduction, but in describing the manipulations he occasionally drops some rare remarks about a subject which seems to us today of greatest importance. After distilling rosmarine by direct fire he obtained a residual char which he subjected to some experiments: "No matter how much fire one gives to the charcoal of rosmarine, it never burns in closed vessels; it needs the contact with air. Why is that? This is again a problem that has not been solved" (p. 121 of the Lausanne manuscript).

About water, Rouelle begins

"There is almost nothing more difficult to know than water. It is everywhere, it permeates all bodies, and can be separated from them only with difficulty."

Earth "It is a great question to know whether there is only one earth in nature, or whether there are several."

In his lectures Rouelle repeatedly described the importance of dissolving actions. The fixed alkalies, for example, are strong agents (*menstrua*) through which substances can be melted or fats can be saponified.

Petroleum oil and spirit of wine are energetic solvents. Distillation and rectification of alcohol were included in Rouelle's course.

Resins had an important place in his lectures, and he had many questions about them. About the latex of certain plants he remarked:

This milky juice is just resin of the plant diluted with much water. It is in about the same state as the resins which one dissolves in the spirit of wine and then separates from it by means of water.

190

This liquid is opaque because the resin never contracts a real union with the water. It is white because the resin is in a state of astonishing division. . . . If somebody doubted that this milky liquid contained the resin of the plant, he could convince himself of this fact very easily; all that needs to be done is to take a little of the milk and let it rest. The resin separates, and the water does not retain any of its acrid taste. One can separate the resin more easily by beating this liquid with a small stick; the resin is soft, clings to the stick and is easily removed (p. 215/16 of the Lausanne manuscript).

Rouelle was always conversant with the latest discoveries. In 1740 and 1741, Belchier and Duhamel had found that when the stock feed was mixed with the coloring substance of madder it passed into the periosteum and the bones. Rouelle adds the question: "This seems to be capable of producing changes which could perhaps remedy the sicknesses which occur in these parts" (p. 350).

Rouelle calls "perfect neutral salts . . . those in which the acid and its base are so combined that neither one nor the other retains its properties. Those salts do not effervesce with the acids or with the alkalies. They do not change the blue colors of flowers."

In his lectures, Rouelle took a much less exclusively medical point of view than Lemery in his book (Cours de Chimie, 1675, 10th ed., 1713, the last by Lemery's hand; in 1756, Théodore Baron published an edition with his notes). Although Rouelle was an apothecary, he liked to initiate his audience in the mysteries of industry and manufacturing almost as much as in pharmacy and medicine.

When Hilaire-Marin Rouelle took over the instruction in chemistry at the Jardin du Roi, he adopted with a few changes the plan followed by his older brother who had used the division into three realms proposed by Boerhaave. In his "Tableau de l'analyse chimique" (Paris, 1774), Rouelle, Jr. felt obliged to defend his brother:

A great critic of our time has said that my brother took the plan of Boerhaave and copied Boerhaave, but that the changes he made only spoiled it. It is true that my brother has adopted the great division into three realms of Boerhaave. As to the subdivisions, as to the analytical order and the method he pursued, nothing resembles Boerhaave, if this great critic will pardon me. Has my brother done better? It is up to enlightened men who are just and without interest or passion, to judge that.

In his necrologue, Grimm said of Rouelle:

... before him, in France one knew only the principles of Lemery who introduced the chemistry of Stahl and made here known that theory which nobody put in doubt, and which a number of great men in Germany developed to a high degree of perfection. Rouelle could not read all of them, but his instinct was ordinarily as strong as their science. Therefore, he has to be considered as the founder of chemistry in France; and nevertheless ... those who have, in our time, written estimated works on this science and who have all gone through his school, have never given their teacher the acknowledgment they owed him.

NOTES AND REFERENCES

Pierre Lemay, "Rouelle," *Rev. hist. pharmacie,* No. 123, 436/42, March 1949.

Rhoda Rappaport, "Rouelle," *Chymia,* 6, 68–101, University of Pennsylvania Press, Philadelphia, 1960.

Selections from Claude Secrétan: Un aspect de la chimie pre-lavoisienne; in Mémoires de la Société Vaudoise des Sciences Naturelles, No. 50, vol. 7, No. 4, 1943, pp. 219–444. Translation by Eduard Farber.

CLAUDE SECRÉTAN

·· *14* ··

Andreas Sigismund Marggraf

1709-1782

Born March 3, 1709, in Berlin, the son of an apothecary, Marggraf received his education from Professor Neumann, a distinguished pupil of the famous Stahl. Marggraf continued his studies in Strassburg, Halle, and Freiberg and returned to Berlin in 1735. In 1738 he became a member of the Royal Society of Sciences in Berlin, and in 1760 the director of its physicomathematical class.

Not an extrovert, and keeping away from the bitter strife and personal jealousies of Berlin's society of scholars, this modest and selfless man devoted his time exclusively to science and to his students, among whom Achard later on carried Marggraf's most important discovery to its first practical application. Gradually Marggraf's name became known throughout Europe. In spite of delicate health he remained constantly active until a stroke in 1774 initiated a long illness, ending in his death on August 7, 1782.

Trained in the school of Stahl, the father of phlogiston, Marggraf adhered faithfully to the phlogiston theory. His work comprises subjects from inorganic, organic, and analytical chemistry. A brief review of the most important of his findings follows.

At the beginning of the eighteenth century phosphorus, which in 1669 Brand and in 1676–1678 Kunckel had discovered in their search for the Philosophers' Stone, still was a very rare substance, surrounded by the allure of a magic secret and worth more than its weight in gold. Some vague indications by Neumann (1725) and Henckel (1734) led Marggraf to a simple method of preparation. It gave good yields and remained in favor until 1769, when Scheele discovered the phosphorus content of bones. Marggraf started from putrefied urine which he concentrated by evaporation. The salts separating from the concentrated urine were mixed with chloride of lead, sand, and coal. Within four hours at red heat, "the most beautiful white phosphorus" appeared. After redistillation it was "purely white and clear like ice." Melting under warm water and pouring into glass tubes gave the typical form of

195

small rods. Marggraf noticed particularly that this phosphorus burned with an increase in weight to form a white, very hygroscopic, featherlike mass (the anhydride of phosphoric acid). Dissolved in water, it is a new acid, phosphoric acid, also obtainable by reacting phosphorus with nitric acid. This is a strong, heat-stable acid which at high temperatures displaces even sulfuric acid. Heating with coal, however, regenerates phosphorus. With alkalies or ammonia, phosphoric acid forms white, easily crystallizing salts, and these are identical with those obtained from urine and used for preparing phosphorus.

Although the salts of phosphoric acid undergo many reactions in solution or upon melting at high temperatures, they are not formed in the human body. Instead, they are absorbed, ready-made, from vegetables used as food. Hoffmann, Pott, and Boerhaave demonstrated that phosphorus can be obtained from the ash of several plants; therefore, they contain phosphates.

Phosphorus also combines with almost all metals and, when heated with sulfur, forms a distillable compound (phosphorus sulfide) which ignites upon heating in the air and then forms sulfurous acid and phosphoric acid.

Marggraf found that substances resembling phosphoric acid anhydride can be obtained from other acids. Upon heating oil of vitriol he obtained "a dry concretum, of wool-like appearance, and smoking terribly, which ignites when water is added," our sulfur trioxide. Concentrated nitric acid gave, when heated, "a terribly smoking, turbulent and volatile" product, now designated as nitrous acid.

Although Stahl and Duhamel (1736) had shown differences between the mineral and the vegetable alkalies (soda and potash), the two were still often considered as identical, or the alkali of marine salt (sodium chloride) was held to be analogous to lime. Marggraf demonstrated the two as definitely different by the folfollowing experiment:

He prepared potassium chloride from tartar and hydrochloric acid. He converted it into nitrate by treatment with nitric acid in exactly the required amount and noticed that the needlelike, crystallized salt colored a flame a blue-violet color.

196

Pure marine salt, however, gave cubic crystals of soda-saltpeter and colored the flame yellow. The two different nitrates could also be obtained by reacting potassium chloride or sodium chloride with silver nitrate. The sulfates of the two are also different; one is only sparingly soluble (potassium sulfate), the other much more so and identical with Glauber's salt (sodium sulfate).

Ignition with coal gave the alkali of wood ashes from potassium nitrate, and an analogous yet different alkali from sodium nitrate. The latter dissolves with effervescence in acids, forming marine salt with muriatic acid, Glauber's salt with sulfuric acid, and combining with tartar to form Seignette's salt.

Marggraf concluded that the two different alkalies are not, as assumed at that time, produced in the process of ashing, but that they are each present in the ashed plant material to begin with. And even the plant does not form these salts, but it "attracts them out of the soil, out of water and air."

A new kind of earth, magnesia, was discovered by Marggraf when he investigated a serpentine mineral from Saxony. When it is decomposed by sulfuric acid, silica remains and the solution contains "neither lime nor alumina earths, as has been believed up to now, but a genuine and true terra alcalina sui generis." Magnesia occurs in nature quite commonly. The mother liquors from the crystallization of marine salt contain magnesium chloride.

Another new earth, wrongly identified with the earth from chalk by Pott, Stahl, and Neumann, was alumina. It can be precipitated from solutions of alum by the addition of alkalies as a new, particular earth, related to the alkalies but not identical with them. It is a principal constituent of lapis lazuli. The common opinion that this mineral owed its wonderful blue color to the presence of gold, copper, or iron were wrong, since it contains only silica, an alkali, and sulfur.

Marggraf spent much time in the investigation of the so-called luminous stones. He proved that selenite (lapis specularis) is chemically the same as gypsum. He analyzed mineral waters and devoted many studies to gold, silver, and mercury. By distilling galmey (calamine, also called cadmia) with powdered coal from earthenware retorts, with the exclusion of air, he pointed the way to an industrially useful process for obtaining zinc. Brass contains zinc. Whenever copper and zinc are present together, brass is formed, as in many metallurgical operations in which zinc is partially liberated.

That iron is present, if in small quantities, in normal limestone, and in the ashes from many plants, he showed by means of the reaction with red prussiate of potash (our potassium ferrocyanide). He observed that the reverse of the precipitation of copper from its solution by iron metal occurs with hot solutions of iron vitriol and copper metal.

Marggraf was as successful in organic as in mineral chemistry. From cedar wood he isolated cedar oil. Although it has a high boiling point itself, it can nevertheless be distilled at much lower temperatures by means of steam; this is also true of many other oils.

The refining of camphor was an art which at that time (and, it seems, again today) was kept strictly secret. Marggraf found that by gradually heating three to four parts of raw camphor with one part of hydrated lime pure camphor was obtained "in the finest, whitest, sparkling crystals."

The distillation of ants furnishes an oil and, additionally, an acid. This acid had been observed by Wray in 1670, but he did not investigate it in detail. It is formic acid, closely related to acetic acid but not identical with it. By freezing it out of its aqueous solution and redistillation it can be purified. It forms well-crystallized salts with the alkalies, ammonia, and with several metals, and reduces mercuric oxide to the metal.

Convinced that as salty tasting plants contain salts in their juices, so sweet-tasting plants must contain something sugary, he studied several such plants like white beet, the sugar root and the common red beet. He discovered that they contain not only something resembling sugar, but real, perfect sugar exactly like that prepared from sugar cane. By triturating those plants and extracting with alcohol, the sugar can be obtained in pure, crystallized form. He described in detail the method for preparing sugar from the sugar root (*sium sisarum*). It is much easier to prepare sugar from beets since their juice is richer in sugar and contains less slimy material. Only the roots are suitable for this purpose, the leaves contain much tartar-like salt. The sugar content of the

198

roots varies with the weather, the temperature, and the degree of ripeness, and it is highest in the completely ripe root. "There should be no doubt by now that this sweet salt, sugar, can be made from our own plants just as well as from sugar cane."

In surveying the work of Marggraf, one is astounded at the number of his discoveries and their importance. He discovered new substances and new reactions. "Care and cleanliness in working" was his motto. He inaugurated attention to the crystallographic appearance of his substances and their examination under the microscope. He laid great stress on the quantitative relationships, as in determining how much silver chloride was formed with a given quantity of silver, how much tin could be dissolved by acids, how much salt of various kinds was present in natural waters. He taught that salts enter the plants from the soil and from the plants into the bodies of animals and men. For the formation of minerals and from the processes of slow poisoning he emphasized the influence of time in chemical reactions. He knew that soluble salts are necessary for fermentation. He denied spontaneous generation of animals from decomposing plant residues, and he rejected the whole scholasticism of assuming occult qualities as "asylum ignorantiae." And finally there is the technological importance of Marggraf's work. Lehmann, the editor of Marggraf's writings, justly said in the introduction:

> With these publications, even a certain kind of people who always ask: cui bono? should be satisfied by demonstrating to these mechanical people what influence these studies had on economy, finances, and other practical sciences.

NOTES AND REFERENCES

O. Köhncke, "Verzeichnis der Abhandlungen von Marggraf," in: *Geschichte der Kgl. Preuss. Ak. der Wissenschaften zu Berlin,* vol. 3, Berlin, 1900.

From: E. O. von Lippmann, "Zeitschrift für angewandte Chemie," Jahrgang 1896, pp. 380–389. (Also in his "Abhandlungen und Vortäge zur Geschichte der Naturwissenschaften," Leipzig, 1906.)
Translated by Eduard Farber.

E. O. VON LIPPMANN

·· 15 ··

Mikhaïl Vasil'evich Lomonosov

1711-1765

AT THE beginning of the eighteenth century, that part of Russia which borders on the White Sea formed almost a cultural island, separated from the rest of the country. It was geographically isolated by swamps and forests; it had never been conquered by the Tartars as so much of southern Russia had been; furthermore, the institution of serfdom had not been established in this region. Although the peasants paid a poll tax and were denied many privileges possessed by the nobility and clergy, they had more independence and wealth than did their counterparts anywhere else in Russia. This was largely because most of the trade with western Europe passed through the port of Archangel and the city of Kholmogory further up the Dvina River. The peasants who lived along the shores of the White Sea were an active and enterprising group who made this trade possible. In the summer they engaged in fishing and in shipping goods as far as Murmansk or even beyond; in the winter they formed large caravans and carried to Moscow the goods which had come from the west. They built ships both for merchants and for the Russian navy. In this active and prosperous area there was even a printing office, rare at that period, and the monasteries were cultural as well as religious centers.

One of the most prosperous of the peasants was Vasiliĭ Dorofeev Lomonosov.[1] He owned a good-sized boat, the "Sea Gull," considerable land, and had enough money to endow in large part the building of a church. It is clear that, although legally a peasant, he was actually a member of what in western Europe was called the middle class. In most of Russia this class did not exist.

He lived in the village of Denisovka, not far from Kholmogory, and here, about November 8, 1711, his only son, Mikhaĭl Vasil'evich was born. Mikhaĭl was raised like all the children of the area, accompanying his father on trading expeditions in the summer and learning the shipbuilding, salt-making, and other industries which occupied much of the peasants' time in the winter. He early showed a great fondness for reading, devouring the re-

203

ligious books that were the only printed materials available to him. When he was about thirteen he obtained a Slavic grammar and an arithmetic. These opened his eyes to a wider knowledge of the world.

In 1725 his father married for the third time. The new stepmother made life at home generally unpleasant for him, since she considered him lazy because of his constant reading. At length, at the age of nineteen, he decided to leave this environment. On December 7, 1730, he joined one of the trade caravans taking goods to Moscow. He reached that city in the middle of January and began to seek a school in which he could obtain the higher education that he felt he must have.

Sons of peasants were not admitted to the better schools. Lomonosov therefore declared that he was the son of a nobleman of Kholmogory. Under this false banner he was admitted to the Slavo-Greco-Latin Academy, a training school for theologians which in its lower classes chiefly taught Latin, and in the later years concentrated on theology and philosophy.

Lomonosov was older than the other students and had almost no money, since his father, angry that the son did not return to help him with his business, refused any aid. In spite of great difficulties, the young man made rapid progress, became an excellent Latin scholar, and seemed destined for a theological career. In 1734, however, the falsity of his claim to nobility was discovered. He could no longer enter the priesthood but, perhaps because of his obvious ability, the authorities allowed him to continue in the school.

Meanwhile the Czar, Peter the Great, after being made a member of the French Academy of Sciences, had decided to found a similar academy in Russia. There were no native scientists available, and Peter sought the aid of Leibniz and of Christian Wolff (1679–1754) of Marburg in securing foreign members for the new academy. Peter died before the Academy opened in 1725, but Wolff had done his work so well that the brilliant band of scholars assembled in St. Petersburg was able to organize and carry on an academy of the first rank. Wolff, a philosopher, mathematician, and physicist of distinction, always retained a great interest in the Imperial Academy of Sciences.

The academicians were granted good salaries and had many privileges. It was only natural that they should wish to preserve these. At first, when only foreigners were available, the members could feel secure in their places, but when native Russians began to qualify for membership, the older members felt threatened and began to form a protective clique. In this way arose the so-called German party, the party of foreigners within the Academy which caused a political split and later seriously hampered the work of the organization.

During its early years the Academy encountered many difficulties. The financial support was at first adequate, but when Czar Peter II moved the capital back to Moscow, funds were withdrawn, and little attention was paid to the administration of the Academy. Under these circumstances full control fell into the hands of the Director of the Chancellery, Johann Daniel Schumacher (1690–1761), an Alsatian who had been the librarian of Peter the Great. He ran the Academy with an autocratic hand and greatly favored the foreign scientists.

In 1734 conditions improved somewhat. The Czarina Anne returned the capital to St. Petersburg, and Baron Korf, an able administrator, became president of the Academy, with which a university was now associated. The members of the Academy served as the university faculty. Korf requested that intelligent students be sent to this university from other Russian schools. Among those who came was Lomonosov. On January 1, 1736, he was enrolled as a student in the University.

At this time the Academy was sending out a series of great expeditions to study the natural resources of the newly opened reaches of Siberia. Although most sciences were represented by Academy members on these expeditions, there was no member trained as a chemist and metallurgist. Korf therefore decided to send three of the university students to western Europe to study these subjects. He naturally wished them to study with Wolff, whose interest in the Academy was still strong. One of the students chosen was Lomonosov. On November 3, 1736, they reached Marburg to begin their work with Wolff.

In the relative freedom given students in Germany the three Russians found a release which resulted in their leading a very gay life and contracting many debts. Fortunately, this did not prevent serious study. Lomonosov for the first time learned the basic scientific theories of the day, particularly in physics. This was essentially a corpuscular science. The idea that the properties of matter depended on particles (or atoms) and their motions stemmed from Galileo and was the dominant theory taught by Wolff, who also stressed the importance of experiment. The corpuscular theory of the early eighteenth century had been systematized by Robert Boyle in the seventeenth. It was not at all the kinetic theory of today, although it was in some respects similar. The motions of the atoms were more limited than they are in modern theory, and the interactions among the atoms themselves were only vaguely understood. The theory was hardly applied at all in chemistry, which Lomonosov also studied at Marburg, for here the phlogiston theory of Stahl was becoming dominant and Boyle's attempt to apply corpuscular mechanisms to chemical reactions was not stressed.

In 1739 Lomonosov went to Freiberg to study metallurgy with Henckel. Although this had been the aim of the whole period of foreign study, Henckel and Lomonosov did not get on well together. In 1740, after secretly marrying a German girl, Elizabeth Zilch, Lomonosov traveled over much of Germany and at last in 1741 he returned to St. Petersburg. It was not until 1744 that his wife was able to join him there.

Lomonosov soon settled into a round of duties connected with the Academy. He seems to have been of a rather quarrelsome disposition and the first years after his return to Russia were enlivened by a series of petty brawls with his neighbors, often leading to physical violence, for he was tall and strong. In 1744 he was forced to make a public apology before the Academy for his behavior. After this his quarrels were on a higher level. Although at first he was on good terms with Schumacher, who ran the Academy with an iron hand, he soon became a bitter enemy of the Director of the Chancellery. The enmity was fully reciprocated. It was enhanced by the fact that Lomonosov represented the rising threat of the native Russians to the power of the German party. His ability was so great that he could not be brushed aside, and as he rose to a position of power almost equal to that of

Schumacher, the latter's hatred increased. Each of the two men almost automatically opposed every policy suggested by the other. In addition, Lomonosov did not hesitate to express his unfavorable opinions of the work of some of the other academicians in very personal terms, and so he had many enemies among his colleagues. The split came to be dramatized mostly by the conflict between the German and the Russian parties. It continued to divide the Academy for a century and a half.

As might have been expected in a student of Wolff, Lomonosov approached the study of chemistry from the standpoint of corpuscular physics. To him atoms were fundamental. He soon began to consider their motions from a viewpoint surprisingly like that of the modern kinetic theory. In this he went far beyond his teacher and the physicists of his day. He recognized that heat was due to molecular motion, that Boyle's idea of fire particles in combustion was incorrect, that phlogiston did not exist, and that matter could neither be created nor destroyed. It can be seen that these ideas, mostly developed in the decade from 1740 to 1750, in large measure anticipated the theories of Lavoisier, announced forty years later. There is some indication that Lavoisier actually knew some of the theories of Lomonosov,[2] but his approach was chemical, while Lomonosov's was physical. The question, however, is why these advanced ideas had such little effect on the progress of science. The answer is to a considerable extent to be found in the personality of Lomonosov himself and in the tremendous variety of his activities.

He was essentially a universal genius. He not only held a modern viewpoint in chemistry and physics, but also in such sciences as geology, geography, mineralogy, and astronomy, to all of which he made contributions. He was absorbed in technological problems.

Early in his career he became interested in mosaics. He tried his hand at making mosaic pictures, found he was successful, and began the attempt to found a mosaic industry in Russia. For this purpose he set up his own glass factory, tested hundred of formulas for different colored glasses, and began to manufacture such glasses so that he could make enormous mosaics. His artistic creations in this field were of a high order, the greatest being his mosaic of the battle of Poltava, showing the victory of Peter the Great over the Swedes. The glass factory and the mosaic business occupied Lomonosov all his life, but they were never a financial success, and in fact kept him in almost constant debt throughout most of his active career.

Besides these activities in theoretical science and in applied chemistry and artistic expression, Lomonosov organized and taught the first known course in physical chemistry. He used this very name more than a hundred years before Ostwald. The course was given for only one year, in 1752–1753, and included laboratory instruction. He designed and supervised the building of the chemical laboratory for the Academy, the first teaching laboratory to be built. He was himself an active experimenter, here again following the precepts of Wolff. He was associated with the first successful freezing of mercury in the great cold of a Russian winter and with many electrical experiments. In the course of a repetition of the Franklin kite experiment with his friend, the physicist, Richmann, the latter was killed by a bolt of lightning, and Lomonosov himself narrowly escaped the same fate.

In addition to his scientific activities, Lomonosov was continually busy composing poetry and in pursuing philological studies on Russian grammar. He is said to have remade the Russian literary language, and he founded modern scientific Russian. It was primarily for his literary work that he remained famous after his death, so much so that Ferdinand Hoefer in his French history of chemistry of 1869 referred to "Lomonosov the chemist who is not to be confused with the poet of the same name."[3]

It was actually his tremendous versatility that was chiefly responsible for preventing Lomonosov from attaining his deserved reputation as a scientist. He was continually planning great comprehensive works which would explain his views on the various sciences, but he was always so busy with so many projects that he never found time to write the books. Some of his ideas were set down in formal papers and published in the "Commentaries" of the Academy of Sciences. The most famous of these was his "Meditationes de caloris et frigoris causa"[4] in which he anticipated many of the ideas of Lavoisier. These papers and the letters that he wrote to his friend Euler probably did influence the thinking of some European scientists. The extent of such influence has never been properly evaluated, however. The greater part of his scientific thinking was expressed in "Orations" before sessions of the Academy or in notes and rough drafts among his own papers. These were not published, but found their way into the archives of the Academy. There they remained until Boris N. Menshutkin unearthed them in the years between 1903 and 1937 and finally gave to the world the full picture of Lomonosov's genius.[5]

Thus Lomonosov appears as a man too busy and too occupied with too many things ever to complete most of them. His constant quarrels with his colleagues, especially with Schumacher, continued unabated throughout his life. As Schumacher grew old, he brought in his son-in-law, I. K. Taubert, to help him; at his death, Taubert took over control of the Academy, thus perpetuating what some academicians bitterly referred to as a hereditary dynasty.[6] Lomonosov fought Taubert as violently as he had Schumacher. It is probable that members of the German party were not sorry that so many of Lomonosov's scientific ideas did not reach a wider scientific audience. Lomonosov himself was much taken up with his quarrels, which in his later years extended to technical disagreements with poets, historians, and grammarians, and so he himself had little time to consider the preservation of his scientific ideas. After 1763 he was ill a large part of the time, and this illness did not make his quarrels any lighter. He died on April 4, 1765.

Chemistry was only one of the manifold interests of Lomonosov, but his ideas in this science were far ahead of his time and it seems likely that they had more influence than has been suspected. This possibility should be more accurately analyzed in the future. In the meanwhile the full extent of the versatile genius of Mikhaïl Lomonosov can now be fully recognized.

NOTES AND REFERENCES

1 Biographical details are taken from B. N. Menshutkin, "Biography of Mikhaïl Vasil'evich Lomonosov," Moscow and Leningrad, 1937. This has been translated as "Russia's Lomonosov, Chemist, Courtier, Physicist, Poet," Princeton University Press, 1952. Further biographical details and information on the early history of the Academy of Sciences can be found

in B. G. Kuznetsov, "Lomonosov, Lobachevskiĭ, Mendeleev," Moscow and Leningrad, 1945.
2 H. M. Leicester, *Chymia*, 5, 138–44 (1958).
3 F. Hoefer, "Histoire de la Chimie," Paris, 1869. VIII, p. 367.
4 *Novi Commentarii Academiae Scientiarum Imperialis Petropolitanae*, 1, 230–44 (1747–1748).
5 T. L. Davis, J. *Chem. Education*, 15, 203–9 (1938).
6 B. G. Kuznetsov, *op. cit.*, p. 34.

HENRY M. LEICESTER

·· 16 ··

Joseph Black

1728-1799

THE story of a philosopher's life is soon told. Black was born, in 1728, at Bordeaux, where his father, a native of Belfast, was settled as a merchant: he was, however, a Scotchman, and his wife too was of a Scottish family, that of Gordon of Hillhead, in Aberdeenshire, settled like Mr. Black at Bordeaux. The latter was a person of extraordinary virtues, and a most amiable disposition, the celebrated Montesquieu honored him with his especial regard; and his son preserved, as titles of honor in his family, the many letters of the President to his parent. In one of them he laments the intended removal of the Black family as a thing he could not reconcile himself to, for his greatest pleasure was seeing them often, and living himself in their society. Although Mr. Black sent his son, at the age of twelve, for some years to a school in Ireland, he was removed to the College of Glasgow in the year 1746, and ever after lived in that which was, properly speaking, his native country. At that college he studied under the celebrated Cullen, then Professor of Anatomy and Lecturer on Chemistry; and, having removed in 1750 to Edinburgh for the benefit of that famous medical school, he took his degree there in 1754. In 1756 he was appointed to succeed Dr. Cullen in the chair of anatomy and chemistry at Glasgow, and he continued to teach there for ten years, when he was appointed to the chemistry professorship at Edinburgh. He then lectured for thirty years to numerous classes, and retiring in 1796 lived till 1799, and died on the twenty-sixth of November in that year. His health never was robust; it was indeed precarious at all times from a weakness in the bronchia and chest, but he prolonged life by a system of the strictest abstinence, frequently subsisting for days together on water gruel and diluted milk. He never was married; but he cherished with unvarying affection his near relatives, who well deserved his care. His favorite niece, Miss Burnet, a person of great sense and amiable temper, was married to his friend and second cousin, Professor Ferguson, the historian and moral philosopher. Dr. Black lived in a select circle of friends, the most illustrious men of the times in science and in letters, Watt, Hutton, Hume, Robertson, Smith, and afterwards with the succeeding generation of Scottish worthies, Robison, Playfair, Stewart. Delighting to commune, to speculate, and to investigate with them, he was careless of the fame which however he could not but be sensible his labors must achieve. He was extremely averse to publication, contemning the impatience with which so many men of science hurry to the press, often while their speculations are crude, and their inquiries not finished. Nor could the reason often urged in defense of this find much favor with one who seemed never to regard the being anticipated by his fellow-laborers as any very serious evil, so the progress of science was secured. Except two papers, one in the "London Philosophical Transactions" for 1775 on the freezing of boiled water; the other, in the second volume of the "Edinburgh Transactions," on the Iceland hot springs; he never published any work after that of which we are now to speak, in 1755, and which, but for the accidental occasion that gave rise to it, would possibly, like his other original speculations, never have been given by himself to the press.

Upon taking his degree at Edinburgh College he wrote and published a Latin Thesis, after the manner of that as well as the foreign universities. The subject was "Magnesia, and the Acid produced by Food in the Stomach" (*De Acido e Cibis orto; et de Magnesia*), and it contained the outline of his discoveries already made. Having sent some copies of this thesis to his father at Bordeaux, one was given to Montesquieu, who at once saw the vast importance of the truths which it unfolded. He called a few days after and said to Mr. Black, "I rejoice with you, my very good friend: your son will be the honor of your name and of your family." But though the discoveries were sketched distinctly enough in this writing, they were only given at large the following year in his celebrated work, "Experiments on Magnesia, Quicklime, and other Alkaline Substances," incontestably the most beautiful example of strict inductive investigation since the "Optics" of Sir Isaac Newton. His fervent admiration of that masterly work was indicated by his giving it to Professor Robison, then a student, and desiring him to "make it the model of all his studies," recommending him at the same time a careful study of the mathematics. It appears that this important inquiry concerning the alkaline

214

earths, the results of which were destined to change the face of chemical science, was suggested by the attempts then making to find a solvent for the stone. I distinctly recollect Dr. Black, in his lectures, prefacing the admirable and most interesting account which he gave of his discoveries, with the statement that the hopes of finding a solvent which should not, like the caustic alkalies, destroy the substance of the bladder in melting the stone, first led him to this investigation. Professor Robison has given a note from his memorandum book indicating that he had at first fallen into the notion of alkalines, when treated with quicklime, deriving from it their caustic quality; the common belief (which gave rise to the term caustic) being that lime obtained from the fire the quality of growing extremely hot, even to ignition when united with water. But experiment soon corrected this idea; for, having exposed the caustic or quicklime to the air till it became mild, he says, "Nothing escapes (meaning no fire or heat); the cup rises considerably by absorbing air." Another observation on the comparative loss of weight sustained by chalk when calcined (in the fire), and when dissolved in an acid, is followed by the account of a medical case, which the professor knew to have occurred in 1752. A third note follows, and proves him to have now become possessed of the true theory of causticity, namely, the expulsion of air, and of mildness, namely, its absorption. The discovery was therefore made as early as 1752—it was published generally in 1754—it was given in its fullest details in 1755. At this time M. Lavoisier was a boy at school—nine years old when the discovery was made—eleven when it was published—twelve when it was as fully given to the world as its author ever delivered it. No possibility therefore existed of that great man finding out when he composed his great work that it was a discovery of his own, as he did not scruple to describe oxygen, though Dr. Priestley had first communicated it to him in the year 1774; or that Black and he discovered it about the same time, as he was in the habit of stating with respect to other gases, with a convenient degree of ambiguity just sufficient for self-defense, should he be charged with unfair appropriation. Who that reflects on the noble part which this great philosopher acted, both in his life and in his death, can avoid lamenting that he did not rest satisfied with the fame really his due, of applying the discoveries of others, in which he had no kind of share, to the investigation of scientific truths, as entirely the result of his extraordinary faculty of generalization, and genius for philosophical research, as those discoveries, the materials of his induction, were the undivided property of others!

The capital discovery of Black, thus early made, and to any share in which no one has ever pretended, was that the causticity, as it was formerly termed upon a false theory, of the alkali and alkaline earths, was owing to the loss of a substance with which they had been combined, and that their reunion with this substance again rendered them mild. But the nature of this substance was likewise ascertained by him, and its detection forms by far the most important part of the discovery, for it laid the foundation of chemical science. He found that it was a permanently elastic fluid, like air in some of its mechanical qualities, those of being transparent or invisible, and incondensable, but differing entirely from the air of our atmosphere in its chemical properties. It was separated from alkaline substances by heat, and by the application of acids, which, having a stronger elective affinity for them, caused it to be precipitated, or to escape in the aëriform state; it was heavier than common air, and it gave a slight acidulous flavor to water on being absorbed by it; hence the inference that it was an acid itself. A short time afterwards (in 1757) he discovered that this peculiar air is the same with that produced by the fermentation of vegetable substances. This he ascertained by the simple experiment of partially emptying in a brewer's vat, where the fermenting process was going on, the contents of a phial filled with limewater. On shaking the liquid that remained with the air that had entered, he found it become turbid, from the lime having entered into union with the air, and became chalk. The same day he discovered by an experiment, equally simple and equally decisive, that the air which comes from burning charcoal is of the same kind. He fixed a piece of charcoal in the broad end of a bellows nozzle, unscrewed; and putting that in the fire, he inserted the other end in a vessel filled with limewater. The air that was driven through the liquid again precipitated the lime in the form of chalk. Finally, he ascertained by breathing through a syphon filled with limewater, and finding the lime again

216

precipitated, that animals, by breathing, evolve air of this description.

The great step was now made, therefore, that the air of the atmosphere is not the only permanently elastic body, but that others exist, having perfectly different qualities from the atmospheric air, and capable of losing their elasticity by entering into chemical union with solid or with liquid substances, from which being afterwards separated, they regain the elastic or aëriform state. He gave to this body the name of *fixed air,* to denote only that it was found fixed in bodies, as well as elastic and separate. He used the term "air" only to denote its mechanical resemblance to the atmospheric air, and not at all to imply that it was of the same nature. No one ever could confound the two substances together; and accordingly M. Morveau, in explaining some years afterwards the reluctance of chemists to adopt the new theory of causticity, gives as their excuse, that although this doctrine "admirably tallies with all the phenomena, yet it ascribes to fixed air properties which really make it a new body or existence" (*"forment réellement un nouvel être"*).[1]

The other discoveries to which Black's led were as slowly disseminated as his own. Oxygen gas had been discovered, in August, 1774, by Priestley, and soon after by Scheele without any knowledge of Priestley's previous discovery; yet in 1777 Morveau, who wrote the chemical articles in the "Supplément," never mentions that discovery, nor the almost equally important discovery of Scheele, chlorine, made in 1774, nor that of azote, discovered by D. Rutherford in 1772, nor hydrogen gas, the properties of which had been fully investigated by Cavendish as early as 1766. Lavoisier's important doctrine, well-entitled to be called a discovery, of the true nature of combustion, had likewise been published in 1774 in his "Opuscules," yet Morveau doggedly adheres to his own absurd theory of the air only being necessary to maintain those oscillations in which he holds combustion to consist; and finding that the increase of weight is always the result of calcination as well as combustion, he satisfies himself with making a gratuitous addition to the hypothesis of phlogiston, and supposes that this imaginary substance is endowed with positive levity; nor does he allude to the experiments of Lavoisier on gases, on combustion,

217

and on oxidation, further than to say that he had for a considerable time been engaged in these inquiries. It was not indeed till 1787 that he became a convert to the sound and rational doctrine, and abandoned the fanciful hypothesis, simple and ingenious though it be, of Stahl. Berthollet, the earliest convert, had come over to the truth two years before. Thus, discoveries had been made which laid the foundation of a new science, and on which the attention of all philosophers was bent; yet the greatest scientific work of the age made no more mention of them than if Black, Cavendish, Priestley, and Scheele had not been. The conjecture may be allowed to us, that if any of these great things had been done in France, M. Morveau would not have been suffered to preserve the same unbroken silence respecting them, even if his invincible prejudices in favor of the doctrine of phlogiston had disposed him to a course so unworthy of a philosopher.

The detail into which I have entered sufficiently proves that the discovery of fixed air laid at once the foundation of the great events in the chemical world to which reference has just been made, because the step was of incalculable importance by which we are led to the fact that atmospheric air is only one of a class of permanently elastic fluids. When D'Alembert wrote the article "Air," in 1751, he gave the doctrine then universally received, that all the other kinds of air were only impure atmospheric air, and that this fluid alone was permanently elastic, all other vapors being only, like steam, temporarily aëriform. Once the truth was made known that there are other gases in nature, only careful observation was required to find them out. Inflammable air was the next which became the subject of examination, because, though it had long been known before Black's discovery, it had been supposed only to be common air mixed with unctuous particles. His discovery at once showed that it was, like fixed air, a separate aëriform fluid, wholly distinct from the air of the atmosphere. The other gases were discovered somewhat later. But it is a very great mistake to suppose that none of these were known to Black, or that he supposed fixed air to be the only gas different from the atmospheric. The nature of hydrogen gas was perfectly known to him, and both its qualities of being inflammable and of being so much lighter than atmospheric air; for as early as 1766 he invented

218

the air balloon, showing a party of his friends the ascent of a bladder filled with inflammable air. Mr. Cavendish only more precisely ascertained its specific gravity, and showed what Black could not have been ignorant of, that it is the same, from whatever substances it is obtained.

But great as was the discovery of fixed air, and important as were its consequences, the world was indebted to its illustrious author for another scarcely less remarkable, both from being so unexpected, and from producing such lasting effects upon physical science. About the year 1763 he meditated closely upon the fact that on the melting of ice more heat seems to disappear than the thermometer indicates, and also that on the condensation of steam an unexpected proportion of heat becomes perceptible. An observation of Fahrenheit, on the cooling of water below the temperature of ice until it is disturbed, when it gives out heat and freezes at once, appears also to have attracted his careful consideration. He contrived a set of simple but decisive experiments to investigate the cause of these appearances, and was led to the discovery of *latent heat,* or the absorption of heat upon bodies passing from the solid to the fluid state, and from the fluid to the aëriform, the heat having no effect on surrounding bodies, and being therefore insensible to the hand or to the thermometer, and only by its absorption maintaining the body in the state which it has assumed, and which it retains until, the absorbed heat being given out, and becoming again sensible, the state of the body is changed back again from fluid to solid, from aëriform to fluid. He never published any account of this discovery, but he explained it fully in his Lectures, both at Glasgow and Edinburgh, and he referred to it in the paper already mentioned, which was printed in the "Philosophical Transactions" for 1775. Well, then, may we marvel that no mention whatever of latent heat is made in the celebrated "Encyclopédie," which owed its chemical contributions to no less a writer and experimentalist than Morveau. The doctrine of latent heat, however, was immediately applied by all philosophers to the production of the different airs which were successively discovered. They were found to owe their permanently elastic state to the heat absorbed in their production from solid or fluid substances, and to regain their fluid or solid state by combining either together or with those substances, and in the act of union giving out in a sensible form the heat which, while absorbed and latent, had kept them in the state of elastic and invisible fluids.[2]

The third great discovery of Black was that which has since been called the doctrine of *specific heat,* but which he called the *capacity* of bodies for heat. Different bodies contain different quantities of heat in the same bulk or weight; and different quantities of heat are required to raise different bodies to the same sensible temperature. Thus, by Black's experiment, it was found that a pound of gold being heated to 150°, and added to a pound of water at 50°, the temperature of both became not 100°, the mean between the two, but 55°, the gold losing 95°, and the water gaining 5°, because the capacity of water for heat is nineteen times that of gold. So twice as much heat is required to raise water to any given point of sensible heat as to raise mercury, the volumes of the two fluids compared being equal.

The true doctrine of combustion, calcination of metals, and respiration of animals, which Lavoisier deduced from the experiments of Priestley and Scheele upon oxygen gas, and of Cavendish on hydrogen gas, and which has changed the whole aspect of chemical science, was founded mainly upon the doctrines of latent and specific heat. It was thus the singular felicity of Black to have furnished both the pillars upon which modern chemistry reposes, and to have furnished them so long before any one attempted to erect the superstructure, that no doubt could by any possibility arise respecting the source of our increased knowledge, the quarter to which our gratitude should be directed. Fixed air was discovered in 1752, and fully explained to the world in 1754 and 1755. Latent heat was yearly, from 1763, explained to numerous classes of students, before whom the experiments that prove it were performed by the author's own hands. Cavendish made his experiments on inflammable air in 1766; Priestley began his in 1768, first publishing in 1772; and he discovered oxygen in 1774, in which year the nature of combustion was first explained by Lavoisier, a boy at school when fixed air was discovered, and having made no experiments nor written any one line upon chemical subjects for seven years after latent heat was discovered. He was but twenty-four years old when he made his first discovery, and thirty-four when his second was added. He lived to nearly fourscore.

It remains to consider him as a teacher; and certainly nothing could be more admirable than the manner in which for forty years he performed this useful and dignified office. His style of lecturing was as nearly perfect as can well be conceived; for it had all the simplicity which is so entirely suited to scientific discourse, while it partook largely of the elegance which characterized all he said or did. The publication of his lectures has conveyed an accurate idea of the purely analytical order in which he deemed it best to handle the subject with a view to instruction, considering this as most likely to draw and to fix the learner's attention, to impress his memory, and to show him both the connection of the theory with the facts, and the steps by which the principles were originally ascertained. The scheme of the lectures may thence be apprehended—the execution imperfectly; for the diction was evidently, in many instances, extemporaneous, the notes before the teacher furnishing him with little more than the substance, especially of those portions which were connected with experiments. But still less can the reader rise from the perusal to any conception of the manner. Nothing could be more suited to the occasion; it was perfect philosophical calmness; there was no effort; it was an easy and a graceful conversation. The voice was low, but perfectly distinct and audible through the whole of a large hall crowded in every part with mutely attentive listeners; it was never forced at all any more than were the motions of the hands, but it was anything rather than monotonous. Perfect elegance as well as repose was the phrase by which every hearer and spectator naturally, and as if by common consent, described the whole delivery. The accidental circumstance of the great teacher's aspect, I hope I may be pardoned for stopping to note, while endeavoring to convey the idea of a philosophical discoverer. His features were singularly graceful, full of intelligence, but calm as suited his manner and his speech. His high forehead and sharp temples were slightly covered, when I knew him, with hair of a snow-white hue, and his mouth gave a kindly as well as most intelligent expression to his whole features. In one department of his lecture he exceeded any I have ever known, the neatness and unvarying success with

221

which all the manipulations of his experiments were performed. His correct eye and steady hand contributed to the one; his admirable precautions, forseeing and providing for every emergency, secured the other. I have seen him pour boiling water or boiling acid from a vessel that had no spout into a tube, holding it at such a distance as made the stream's diameter small, and so vertical that not a drop was spilt. While he poured he would mention this adaptation of the height to the diameter as a necessary condition of success. I have seen him mix two substances in a receiver into which a gas, as chlorine, had been introduced, the effect of the combustion being perhaps to produce a compound inflammable in its nascent state, and the mixture being effected by drawing some string or wire working through the receiver's sides in an airtight socket. The long table on which the different processes had been carried on was as clean at the end of the lecture as it had been before the apparatus was planted upon it. Not a drop of liquid, not a grain of dust remained.

The reader who has known the pleasures of science will forgive me if at the distance of half a century, I love to linger over these recollections, and to dwell on the delight which I will remember thrilled me as we heard this illustrious sage detail, after the manner I have feebly attempted to portray, the steps by which he made his discoveries, illustrating them with anecdotes sometimes recalled to his mind by the passages of the moment, and giving their demonstration by performing before us the many experiments which had revealed to him the most important secrets of nature. Next to the delight of having actually stood by him when his victory was gained, we found the exquisite gratification of hearing him simply, most gracefully, in the most calm spirit of philosophy, with the most perfect modesty, recount his difficulties, and how they were overcome; open to us the steps by which he had successfully advanced from one part to another of his brilliant course; go over the same ground, as it were, in our presence which he had for the first time trod so many long years before; hold up perhaps the very instruments he had then used, and act over again the same part before our eyes which had laid the deep and broad foundations of his imperishable renown. Not a little of this extreme interest certainly belonged to the accident that he had so long survived the period of his success—that we knew there sat in our presence the man now in his old age reposing under the laurels won in his early youth. But take it altogether, the effect was such as cannot well be conceived. I have heard the greatest understandings of the age giving forth their efforts in its most eloquent tongues—have heard the commanding periods of Pitt's majestic oratory—the vehemence of Fox's burning declamation— have followed the close-compacted chain of Grant's pure reasoning—been carried away by the mingled fancy, epigram, and argumentation of Plunket; but I should without hesitation prefer, for mere intellectual gratification (though aware how much of it is derived from association), to be once more allowed the privilege which I in those days enjoyed of being present while the first philosopher of his age was the historian of his own discoveries, and be an eyewitness of those experiments by which he had formerly made them, once more performed with his own hands.

The qualities which distinguished him as an inquirer and as a teacher followed him into all the ordinary affairs of life. He was a person whose opinions on every subject were marked by calmness and sagacity, wholly free from both passion and prejudice, while affectation was only known to him from the comedies he might have read. His temper in all the circumstances of life was unruffled. This was perceived in his lectures when he had occasion to mention any narrow prejudice or any unworthy proceeding of other philosophers. One exception there certainly was, possibly the only one in his life; he seemed to have felt hurt at the objections urged by a German chemist called Meyer to his doctrine of causticity, which that person explained by supposing an acid, called by him *acidum pingue,* to be the cause of alkaline mildness. The unsparing severity of the lecture in which Black exposed the ignorance and dogmatism of this foolish reasoner cannot well be forgotten by his hearers, who both wondered that so ill-matched an antagonist should have succeeded where so many crosses had failed in discomposing the sage, and observed how well fitted he was, should occasion be offered, for a kind of exertion exceedingly different from all the efforts that at other times he was wont to make.

The soundness of his judgment on all matters, whether of literature or of a more ordinary description, was described by Adam Smith, who said, he "had less nonsense in his head than any man living." The elegance of his taste, which has been observed upon as shown in his lectures, was also seen in the efforts of his pencil, which Professor Robison compares to that of Woollett. The neatness of his manipulations was not confined to his experiments when investigating or when lecturing. I have heard one who happened to see him at his toilette describe the operations as performed with exquisite neatness by a number of contrivances happily adapted to the saving of trouble and avoiding uneasiness. His perfect equanimity has been adverted to, and it did not proceed from coldness of disposition, for he was affectionately attached to his friends. Having no family of his own, he may be said to have fallen into those precise and regular habits which sometimes raise in happier individuals a smile, I stop not to inquire whether of envy or contempt, for the single state. It was sometimes said, too, that his habits were penurious. That the expenses of one who had no love of pleasure and no fancy for ostentation to gratify, must have been moderate, is certain; but he lived in the style and manner suited to one possessing an ample income. The ground of the charge was, I believe, that he was said to have a scale by him when he received the fees of his students. I can answer for the truth of this statement, for I well remember the small brass instrument; but I also recollect that he said it became necessary from the quantity of light gold which he used at first to receive unsuspected from one class, particularly, of his pupils. There was certainly no reason why he should pay a sum of forty or fifty pounds yearly out of his income on this account. Both Professor Ferguson and Professor Robison have positively denied the charge of avarice, and have given ample testimony even to his generous nature. While he lived at Glasgow he lost three-fourths of his fortune by the failure of a house in which it was invested; and though he had forseen the catastrophe for two years, he neither attempted to withdraw his funds, nor altered in any respect his kind demeanor toward the head of the firm, whom he knew. At Edinburgh he more than once incurred great risks to help friends in business.

224

GENERAL REFERENCES

Sir William Ramsay, "The Life and Letters of Joseph Black, M. D.," London, 1918.

Henry Guerlac, "Joseph Black and Fixed Air, a bicentenary retrospective," *Isis* 48, pp. 124–151, 433–465 (1957).

NOTES AND REFERENCES

1 Supplement to the 'Encyclopédie,' vol. ii, 1777, p. 274.
2 It is by no means impossible that one day we may be able to reduce the phenomenon of light within the theory of latent heat. It may be that this body when absorbed, that is, fixed in substances, gives out heat; as, while passing through diaphanous substances and remaining unfixed, its heat is not sensible.

From: Henry Lord Brougham, "Lives of Men of Letters and Science who flourished in the time of George III," A. and W. Galignani and Cie., Paris, 1845, pp. 212–227.

HENRY LORD BROUGHAM

·· 17 ··

Henry Cavendish

1731-1810

AMONG the men whom we have honored at these memorial meetings, there are unfortunately too many who have had to struggle against the obstacles that misfortune placed in their path. The man who is the subject of our present discourse had the rare and probably greater merit of not permitting himself to be overcome by the obstacles of prosperity. Neither the accident of his birth, which made fame and honor easily attainable, nor great riches, which offered him the temptation of pleasure, could turn him away from his goal. He did not aspire to glory or distinction; the disinterested love of truth was his motivating force. He cheerfully sacrificed what ordinary men cherish most. For everything that science revealed to him seemed to be sublime and marvelous: he was able to weigh the earth, prepare the means to navigate the air, deprive water of its elemental nature. For the support of these new and controversial doctrines, which were so antithetic to the established concepts of his time, he presented evidence that is even more astonishing than the ideas themselves. His writings are masterpieces of sagacity and precision; the years have not diminished their stature. One can safely predict that his name will endure for all time, for history has taught us that great truths are man's most enduring legacy to posterity.

Assuredly, such geniuses have no need of praise. But they do serve as a splendid example, and that will be our purpose in presenting a summary of the work of Henry Cavendish, member of the Royal Society of London, and foreign associate of the Institute of France.

Cavendish was born in Nice on October 10, 1731, the son of Lord Charles Cavendish, himself a member of the Royal Society and administrator of the British Museum. He was educated in England, but left Cambridge without taking a degree.

His family, descendants of one of William the Conqueror's followers, was one of the most illustrious in Great Britain, and had been a member of the peerage for more than two centuries. In 1694 William III conferred the title of Duke of Devonshire on the head of the family.

229

It has often been noted that more people of rank are seriously concerned with science or literature in England than in other countries. Cavendish's whole career was proof of this predilection, but his natural preference was reinforced by paternal example. His father, Lord Charles, had a scientific bent and carried out some valid experiments in physics. He probably directed his son's first studies, but we have no information about his educational methods nor of young Henry's first scientific attempts. His initial appearance on the scientific scene was most unexpected, but he was obviously well trained. His scientific debut immediately disclosed new vistas and was the signal for a new scientific epoch.

We should like, first of all, to discuss the paper on gases which he presented to the Royal Society in 1766[1]; in it he stated that air is not an element, but that there exist several kinds of air differing essentially from one another.

He tested the elastic fluid extracted from chalk and alkalies, and compared it with air produced by fermentation and putrefaction, and with that found at the bottom of wells, caves, and mines. He found that they all possess the same properties and are, in fact, identical. He called this gas "fixed air" (carbon dioxide). Determining its specific gravity, he found it to be a third higher than ordinary air, which explained why fixed air is found in caves and low places. Furthermore, he discovered that fixed air combines with water and subsequently is capable of dissolving limestone and iron—a property that accounts for the formation of stalagtites and the presence of iron in mineral waters. Finally, he ascertained that it is fixed air that is produced in carbon combustion; it is the presence of carbon dioxide that makes this kind of fuel so dangerous.

His experiments with "inflammable air" (hydrogen) were even more novel and elegant. Before Cavendish, hardly anyone had examined this gas, which was only recognized by the explosions it sometimes caused in mines. He proved, by a series of experiments, that inflammable air is a distinct substance and possesses the same properties, whether it is obtained from the dissolution of iron, zinc, or copper. In particular, he determined that inflammable air is exceedingly light, nearly ten times as light as ordinary air. Since then, our colleague, Charles, has put this knowledge to practical advantage in making navigation in the air safe and easy. In fact, one can say that without Cavendish's discovery and Charles' application of it, de Montgolfier's achievement would scarcely have been feasible, so dangerous and cumbersome for the aeronaut was the fire necessary for keeping ordinary air expanded in the montgolfières (fire balloons).

Cavendish's research on gases had many other far-reaching consequences. Once it was definitely established that several elastic fluids existed, constant in their properties and specifically different in nature, Priestley was able to conduct experiments that led to the elucidation of two of these gases, namely, phlogisticated air and nitrous air. It became apparent how important an influence do the various gases have on the phenomena of nature. It had to be acknowledged that physics and chemistry could have no solid foundation without the recognition of these powerful universal gases.

A few years later, Lavoisier perceived the first inkling of his famous doctrine. By obtaining a large amount of fixed air from the reduction of metals with carbon, Lavoisier concluded that the calcination of metals was the result of nothing but their combination with fixed air. One year later, Bayen reduced mercuric oxide, without carbon, in closed vessels; this marked the initial dissolution of the phlogiston theory. Lavoisier examined the air produced by these reductions in the absence of carbon and found it suitable for respiration; at about the same time, Priestley discovered that this portion of the atmosphere was precisely the part necessary for respiration and combustion. Lavoisier then announced his second step. He declared that respiration, combustion, and calcination of metals were all similar processes of respirable air; fixed air is the particular product of the combustion of carbon.

But no one has as yet found an explanation for the inflammable air that appears when metals are dissolved in acids. Six years later, Cavendish achieved this honor.

Scheele had observed that everything seemed to disappear when inflammable air was burned; neither fixed air nor phlogisticated air remained. Macquer, attempting to catch the steam of the combustion, was astonished to perceive humidity collecting on the sides of the vessels used in the experiments, but he did not pursue his observation further. It remained for Cavendish, who was utilizing inflammable air in his chemical experiments, to predict the importance of the role that hydrogen would play in modern science.[2]

As in his initial experiments, Cavendish applied the precision and originality of his thinking to a subject only vaguely thought about before him. Using a mixture of common air and hydrogen in closed vessels, Cavendish effected combustion with an electric spark. He observed that the hydrogen absorbed a definite proportion of the ordinary air, resulting in a yield of water equal to the combined weights of the two vanished gases.

It took Cavendish three years to verify his findings. He announced his astounding results to the Royal Society on January 14, 1784. Our colleague, Count Monge, who had been struck by the same idea and had performed similar experiments to those of Cavendish, informed Lavoisier and de Laplace of his conclusions at about the same time.

"If the combination of these gases produces water," said de Laplace, "then the decomposition of water should result in these two gases." His group consequently decomposed water into its two constituents, and proved the validity of Laplace's theory. These experiments, in fact, clarified almost everything that had eluded Laplace until then.

One can state with assurance that this new theory, which revolutionized scientific thinking, had its origin in a discovery of Cavendish and its fruition in a subsequent discovery by the same scientist.

A third important contribution, which by itself would have sufficed to bestow immortality upon Cavendish, was the discovery of the composition of nitric acid. This compound, so useful to the arts and so widespread in nature, was thought about in only vague and hypothetical terms before Cavendish.[3]

In his initial experiences with the combustion of inflammable air, Cavendish had observed the concomitant formation of nitric acid; he noted that the amount of nitric acid increased when the mixture contained a larger proportion of the gas, then known as "phlogisticated air," which we call nitrogen.

Later, examining the product of the explosion of niter by carbon, he found it to consist of phlogisticated air and fixed air (nitrogen and carbon dioxide). Since Cavendish knew that it was carbon that produced carbon dioxide, it could only be the niter that was responsible for the production of nitrogen. He promptly proved by direct experiments that his conjecture was correct.

By igniting a mixture of respirable air and phlogisticated air with an electric spark, Cavendish converted it to nitrous air, which changes into an acid with a further addition of ordinary air. The components of nitrous acid were recognized as the same as those in the atmosphere, varying only in their proportions. Consequently, some concept of the universal production of nitrous acid, which until then had been totally incomprehensible, began to evolve.

It is impossible to read about this brilliant epoch of chemistry without enthusiasm. Discovery after discovery followed in quick succession. Cavendish told Berthollet about his research with nitric acid, and learned that Berthollet had succeeded in decomposing ammonia into hydrogen and nitrogen. Cavendish then proceeded to examine the atmosphere itself.

Priestley, who had discovered pure or respirable air, also evolved a method of estimating the respirability of any kind of gas. It was only a question of measuring the portion that was absorbed when mixed with nitrous air; unfortunately, despite Fontana's corrections, Priestley's instruments were inaccurate.

Cavendish, by a slight modification of manual technique, gave greater precision to his instruments.[4] After comparing samples of air taken at different times and in various places, Cavendish formed the not unexpected conclusion that the proportion of respirable air is the same everywhere, and that the odors affecting our senses so perceptibly and the miasmas influencing our economy so cruelly cannot be determined by any chemical means. This conclusion, which at first glance appears very discouraging, opens up an immense perspective and reveals the possibility of as yet nonexistent sciences, which perhaps may solve some of the riddles that now defy solution.

By means of the eudiometer, Humboldt confirmed the findings of Cavendish in the most distant regions of the earth. Biot and Gay-Lussac, ascending in balloons, found these facts as true in the greatest heights as in the lowest layers of the atmosphere. Thus these courageous physicists, by availing themselves of the methods uncovered by Cavendish, verified another of his discoveries.

The spirit of exactness introduced into chemical research by Cavendish's influence benefited science as much as his individual discoveries. It can be stated quite unequivocally that even the discoveries he did not make were made possible by the utilization of his method of scientific investigation. Until about the middle of the eighteenth century, chemistry was a catchall for the arbitrary systems and suppositions that Newton had banished from physics. Cavendish and Bergman fought vigorously against them; they cleaned up this veritable Augean stable, still impeded by the dung of alchemical philosophy. Since then no one has dared to initiate scientific research without using precisely measured quantities, keeping careful account of all the various products. This single feature characterizes modern chemistry more exactly than its theories. For accurate as these theories seem to us today, they may be attacked at some time in the future when scientists are able to master substances that still evade us.

In addition to his knowledge of chemistry, Cavendish was well trained in geometry, and applied the same severe spirit of exactitude to his mathematical calculations—with results that were almost as triumphant as his chemical investigations. In particular, he set about calculating the median density of the earth. These calculations logically led Cavendish to a determination of the earth's weight,[5] a concept which is at first awe-inspiring, but which soon resolves itself to a simple problem of mechanics. Archimedes needed a fulcrum in order to move the earth, but Cavendish needed none to weigh it.

A fellow member of the Royal Society, Michell, who had died some time before, had constructed an apparatus similar to the one our colleague, Coulomb, had used for measuring the force of electricity and of a magnet. A six-foot-long lever, with a small ball of lead attached at either ends, was horizontally suspended at midpoint by a vertical thread. Once the lever was at rest, a great mass of lead of known diameter and weight was brought laterally to each small ball. The attraction of the masses between the balls moved the lever; the twisting thread, obeying a tendency to return to its initial position, made the lever describe small horizontal arcs— similar to the manner in which an ordinary weight, namely, the attraction of the earth, makes a pendulum describe vertical arcs.

By comparing the extension and duration of these oscillations and those of the pendulum, the relationship of the attracting force of the lead masses and that of the earth was ascertained.

But this account gives only a rough idea of the apparatus and of the precautions and calculations needed for the experiment. The mobility of the lever was such that the slightest difference in temperature between the two balls or in portions of the air produced a draft strong enough to make the lever oscillate. Even the attraction exerted by the walls of the wooden cage containing the apparatus had to be calculated. Almost endless was the care required for measuring the extent of the vibrations, and for observing them without affecting them by getting too close. All these difficulties became evident only at the instant of performance; the delicate means for handling them belong entirely to Cavendish. Michell had not even foreseen them.

The result was startling: the median density of the earth was calculated to be 5.48 times as great as that of water. It therefore became apparent that not only was the earth solid, but that the materials that make up its interior must be heavier than those on its surface. Ordinary rocks and stones are about three, rarely four, times as heavy as water; no known rock is five times as heavy. Consequently, one is forced to conclude that heavy metals are predominant toward the center of the earth. Who could have foreseen the new theories about the composition of the earth that resulted from this calculation!

Cavendish was also one of the first scientists who applied calculus to the theory of electricity. Although he did this work before Aepinus, the latter's findings were published before those of Cavendish. Both are based on the same hypothesis, namely, that there exists only one electrical substance, whose molecules repel one another, but which are attracted by other bodies. Cavendish demonstrated more clearly than Aepinus that, granted that this movement occurs at a ratio less than the inverse of the cube of the distance, it can be proved, by means of Newton's theory on the attraction of a sphere, that all the electrical substance of a body of such a shape must lie on the surface.[6]

Since then our late colleague, Coulomb, demonstrated by direct experiments that electrical action is inversely proportional to the

235

square of the distance; he also proved, in a much more general way, the necessity for this distribution on the surface of objects, no matter what their shape.

When Walsh affirmed the analogy of the shock produced by the electric eel with that of the Leyden bottle, objections were raised because the fish does not produce any sparks. Cavendish attempted to explain the difference;[7] he even constructed a kind of artificial electric eel, which demonstrated the same phenomenon when it was electrified. The true cause for animal electricity, however, escaped him. It remained for Volta to invent an apparatus capable of producing this marvelous force continuously. His apparatus, essentially similar to the equipment nature has given to electric fish, could also send an electric current through its inventor without cessation.

From the fertile and imaginative mind of Cavendish came observations on the height of luminous meteors[8] that led to the now well-verified conjectures concerning the fall of stones into the earth's atmosphere. He wrote a paper on the means of perfecting meteorological instruments,[9] and ingenious notes on the effects of chilling mixtures.[10] He concerned himself with the Hindu calendar, and compared the confused cycles of these people with our way of keeping time. Unfortunately, the limits of a public discourse do not permit an analysis of all his efforts. We only cite a few to show that the life of Cavendish is additional proof that great discoveries are effected by men constantly devoted to meditation.

At the end of his life Cavendish busied himself with making astronomical instruments more precise. He pursued his passion for exactitude even in the one science where this quality has been sought most vigilantly.

From this long enumeration of Cavendish's works it is easy to understand that such a productive career could not have been a socially active one. What is not apparent is to what degree his life was ascetic, and how scrupulously he fulfilled his vow to dedicate his life to study. The most austere anchorites were not more faithful to their vows. His way of life was as regularized and precise as his experiments. He particularly disliked wasting either time or words; with that end in view, he worked out a signal system with his servants. Since his demands were very few, the signals were minimal.

However, the interdict of silence applied only to the trivia of life. When his assistance was needed at some new experiment, or when Cavendish was consulted, or sought scientific advice himself, the banns were lifted. In such instances Cavendish enjoyed to the utmost the pleasures of conversation and the interchange of ideas; these Socratic dialogues ended only when all points had been clarified.

As the younger son of a younger son, he was rather impoverished in his youth; it is said his parents treated him as a person who would never be wealthy. However, chance decreed otherwise. One of his uncles, who had returned from the war in India with a huge fortune, developed a great affection for him and made him his sole heir. At first Cavendish did not take his financial responsibilities too seriously. It is told that his bankers pleaded with him to invest his money; they were disturbed because he had permitted almost two million francs to accumulate in an account that drew no interest. Their arguments must have been persuasive, because Cavendish finally left a fortune of some thirty million francs (1,200,000 pounds). Few scholars have been so rich. Cavendish was very generous with his money, and supported many young scholars who showed signs of talent.

He established a large scientific library and collection of physical apparatus for the benefit of the public, reserving no privileges for himself, but borrowing his own books and signing the librarian's register as though he were a total stranger. One day the custodian of the apparatus told him angrily that a young man had broken a very valuable machine. "It is necessary," Cavendish replied, "that young people break machines in order to learn how to use them. Order a new one."

Undoubtedly, Cavendish's regularity of life contributed to his good health and longevity. Until the age of seventy-nine he maintained the activity of his body and the agility of his mind. Unlike most men of genius, neither jealousy nor criticism troubled him. Like Newton, his great compatriot, with whom he had so much in common, he died renowned and famous, beloved by his followers, respected by the generation he had taught, and occupying

237

a unique place in European intellectual circles. He demonstrated to the world a model of what a scholar should be, as well as an example of the happiness he should enjoy.

NOTES AND REFERENCES

1 *Phil. Trans. Roy. Soc. London,* 141 (1766).
2 *Phil. Trans. Roy. Soc. London,* part 1, 119 (1784); *J. phys.,* XXV, 417 (1784).
3 *Phil. Trans. Roy. Soc. London,* 372 (1785); *J. phys.,* XXVII, 107 (1785).
4 *Phil. Trans. Roy. Soc. London,* part 1, 106 (1783).
5 *Phil. Trans. Roy. Soc. London,* part 2, 469–526 (1798), Table XXIII.
6 *Ibid.,* 584 (1771).
7 *Ibid.,* 196 (1776).
8 *Ibid.,* 101 (1790).
9 *Ibid.,* 375 (1776).
10 *Ibid.,* 303 (1783); 241 (1786).
11 *Phil. Trans. Roy. Soc. London,* 383 (1793).

George Wilson, "The Life of the Honourable Henry Cavendish, including abstracts of his more important papers and a critical inquiry into the claims of all alleged discoveries of the composition of water", London, printed for the Cavendish Society, 1851.
The Scientific Papers of the Honourable Henry Cavendish, 2 vols., Cambridge, 1921.

A. G. Berry, "Henry Cavendish, his life and scientific work," Hutchison of London, 1960.

From: "Mémoires de la Classe des Sciences Mathématiques et Physiques de l'Institut Impérial de France," Année 1811, "Histoire de la Classe des Sciences Mathématiques et Physiques de l'Institut Royal de France," Vol. 12, 1811, pp. CXXVI–CXLIV. Translated by Dora S. Farber.

GEORGES CUVIER

·· *18* ··

Joseph Priestley

1733-1804

THE principal source of the materials of the following pages is the work in which the discoveries of Dr. Priestley were originally announced to the public. It consists of six volumes in octavo, which were published by him, at intervals between the years 1774 and 1786; the first three under the title of "Experiments and Observations on different kinds of Air"; and the last three under that of "Experiments and Observations relating to various Branches of Natural Philosophy, with a continuation of the Observations on Air." These volumes were afterwards methodized by himself, and compressed into three octavos, which were printed in 1790. As a record of facts, and as a book of reference, the systematized work is to be preferred. But as affording materials for the history of that department of science, which Dr. Priestley cultivated with such extraordinary success, and, still more, for estimating the value of his discoveries, and adjusting his station as an experimental philosopher, the simple narrative, which he originally gave in the order of time, supplies the amplest and the firmest groundwork.

In every thing that respects the history of this branch of experimental philosophy, the writings and researches of Dr. Priestley, to which I have alluded, are peculiarly instructive. They are distinguished by great merits and by great defects, the latter of which are wholly undisguised by their author. He unveils, with perfect frankness, the whole process of reasoning which led to his discoveries; he pretends to no more sagacity than belonged to him, and sometimes disclaims even that to which he was fairly entitled; he freely acknowledges his mistakes, and candidly confesses when his success was the result of accident rather than of judicious anticipation; and by writing historically and analytically, he exhibits the progressive improvement of his views, from their first dawnings to their final and distinct development. Now, with whatever delight we may contemplate a systematic arrangement, the materials of which have been judiciously selected, and from which every thing has been excluded that is not essential to the harmony of the general design, yet there can be no question that as elucidating the op-

241

erations of the human mind and enabling us to trace and appreciate its powers of invention and discovery, the analytic method of writing has decided advantages.

To estimate justly the extent of Dr. Priestley's claim to philosophical reputation, it is necessary to take into account the state of our knowledge of gaseous chemistry at the time when he began his inquiries. Without underrating what had been already done by Van Helmont, Ray, Hooke, Mayow, Boyle, Hales, MacBride, Black, Cavendish, and some others, Priestley may be safely affirmed to have entered upon a field, which, although not altogether untilled, had yet been very imperfectly prepared to yield the rich harvest which he afterwards gathered from it. The very implements with which he was to work were for the most part to be invented; and of the merits of those which he did invent it is a sufficient proof that they continue in use to this day, with no very important modifications. All his contrivances for collecting, transferring, and preserving different kinds of air, and for submitting those airs to the action of solid and liquid substances, were exceedingly simple, beautiful, and effectual. They were chiefly, too, the work of his own hands, or were constructed under his direction by unskilled persons; for the class of ingenious artists, from whom the chemical philosophers now derive such valuable aid, had not then been called into existence by the demands of the science. With a very limited knowledge of the general principles of chemistry, and almost without practice in its most common manipulations—restricted by a narrow income, and at first with little pecuniary assistance from others—compelled, too, to devote a large portion of his time to other pressing occupations, he nevertheless surmounted all obstacles, and in the career of discovery outstripped many who had long been exclusively devoted to science and were richly provided with all appliances and means for its advancement.

It is well known that the accident of living near a public brewery at Leeds first directed the attention of Dr. Priestley to pneumatic chemistry, by casually presenting to his observation the appearance attending the extinction of lighted chips of wood in the gas which floats over fermenting liquors. He remarked that the smoke formed distinct clouds floating on the surface of the atmosphere of the vessel, and that this mixture of air and smoke, when thrown over the sides of the vat, fell to the ground; from whence he deduced the greater weight of this sort of air than of atmospheric air. He next found that water imbibes the new air, and again abandons it when boiled or frozen. These more obvious properties of fixed air having been ascertained, he extended his inquiries to its other qualities and relations, and was afterward led by analogy to the discovery of various other gases, and to the investigation of their characteristic properties.

It would be inconsistent with the scope of this essay to give a full catalog of Dr. Priestley's discoveries or to enumerate more of them than are necessary to a just estimate of his philosophical habits and character. He was the unquestionable author of our first knowledge of oxygen gas, of nitrous oxide, of muriatic, sulfurous, and fluor acid gases, of ammoniacal gas, and of its condensation into a solid form by the acid gases. Hydrogen gas was known before his time but he greatly extended our acquaintance with its properties. Nitrous gas, barely discovered by Dr. Hales, was first investigated by Priestley, and applied by him to eudiometry. To the chemical history of the acids derived from niter he contributed a vast accession of original and most valuable facts. He seems to have been quite aware that those acids are essentially gaseous substances, and that they might be exhibited as such, provided a fluid could be found that is incapable of absorbing or acting upon them.[1] He obtained and distinctly described[2] the curious crystalline compound of sulfuric acid with the vapor of nitrous acid, or, more correctly, of sulfuric and hyponitrous acids, which, being of rare occurrence, was forgotten, and has since been rediscovered, like many other neglected anticipations of the same author. He greatly enlarged our knowledge of the important class of metals, and traced out their most interesting relations to oxygen and to acids. He unfolded and illustrated by simple and beautiful experiments distinct views of combustion; of the respiration of animals, both of the inferior and higher classes; of the changes produced in organized bodies by putrefaction, and of the causes that accelerate or retard that process; of the importance of azote as the characteristic ingredient of animal substances, obtainable by the action of dilute nitric acid on muscle and tendon; of the functions and economy of living vegetables; and of the relations

243

and subserviency that exist between the animal and vegetable kingdoms. After trying, without effect, a variety of methods, by which he expected to purify air vitiated by the breathing of animals, he discovered that its purity was restored by the growth of living and healthy vegetables freely exposed to the solar light.

It is impossible to account for these, and a variety of other discoveries of less importance singly, but forming altogether a tribute to science—greatly exceeding, in richness and extent, that of any contemporary—without pronouncing that their author must have been furnished by nature with intellectual powers far surpassing the common average of human endowments. If we examine the various faculties with which the mind of Dr. Priestley was most eminently gifted, it will, I believe, be found that it was most remarkable for clearness and quickness of apprehension, and for rapidity and extent of association. On these qualities were founded that apparently intuitive perception of analogies, and that happy facility of tracing and pursuing them through all their consequences, which led to several of his most brilliant discoveries. Of these analogies many were just and legitimate, and have stood the test of examination by the clearer light since reflected upon them from the improved condition of science. But in other cases his analogies were fanciful and unfounded, and led him far astray from the path that might have conducted him directly to truth. It is curious, however, as he himself observes, that in missing one thing, of which he was in search, he often found another of greater value. In such cases, his vigilance seldom failed to put him in full possession of the treasure upon which he had stumbled. Finding by experience how much chance had to do with the success of his investigations, he resolved to multiply experiments, with the view of increasing the numerical probabilities of discovery. We find him confessing, on one occasion, that he "was led on, by a random expectation of some change or other taking place." In other instances, he was influenced by theoretical views of so flimsy a texture that they were dispersed by the first appeal to experiment. "These mistakes," he observes, "it was in my power to have concealed; but I was determined to show how little mystery there is in the business of experimental philosophy; and with

244

how little sagacity, discoveries, which some persons are pleased to consider great and wonderful, have been made." Candid acknowledgements of this kind were, however, turned against him by persons envious of his growing fame; and it was asserted that *all* his discoveries, when not the fruits of plagiarism, were "lucky guesses," or owing to mere chance.[3] Such detractors, however, could not have been aware of the great amount of credit that is due to the philosopher, who at once perceives the value of a casual observation or of an unexpected result, who discriminates what facts are trivial and what are important, and selects the latter to guide him through difficult and perplexed mazes of investigation. In the words of D'Alembert, "Ces hazards ne sont que pour ceux qui jouent bien."

The talents and qualifications, which are here represented as having characterized the mind of Dr. Priestley, although not of the rarest kind nor of the highest dignity, were yet such as admirably adapted him for improving chemical science at the time when he lived. What was then wanted, was a wider field of observation—an enlarged sphere of chemical phenomena—an acquaintance with a far greater number of individual bodies than were then known; from the properties of which, and from those of their combinations, tentative approximations to general principles might at first be deduced—to be confirmed or corrected, enlarged or circumscribed by future experience. It would have retarded the progress of science and put off to a far distant day that affluence of new facts, which Priestley so rapidly accumulated, if he had stopped to investigate, with painful and rigid precision, all the minute circumstances of temperature, of specific gravity, of absolute and relative weights, and of crystalline structure on which the more exact science of our own times is firmly based, and from which its evidences must henceforward be derived. Nor could such refined investigations have then been carried on with any success, because of the imperfection of philosophical instruments. It would have been fruitless, also, at that time, to have indulged in speculations respecting the ultimate constitution of bodies—speculations that have no solid groundwork, except in a class of facts developed within the last thirty-five years, all tending to establish the laws of combination in definite and in multiple proportions, and to support the still more extensive generalization that has been reared by the genius of Dalton.

It was, indeed, by the activity of his intellectual faculties, rather than by their reach or vigor, that Dr. Priestley was enabled to render such important services to natural science. We should look, in vain, in anything that he has achieved, for demonstrations of that powerful and sustained attention, which enables the mind to institute close and accurate comparisons—to trace resemblances that are far from obvious—and to discriminate differences that are recondite and obscure. The analogies that caught his observation, lay near the surface, and were eagerly and hastily pursued; often, indeed, beyond the boundaries, within which they ought to have been circumscribed. Quick as his mind was in the perception of resemblances, it appears (probably for that reason) to have been little adapted for those profound and cautious abstractions that supply the only solid foundations of general laws. In sober, patient, and successful induction, Priestley must yield the palm to many others, who, although far less fertile than himself in new and happy combinations of thought, surpassed him in the use of a searching and rigorous logic, in the art of advancing, by secure steps, from phenomena to general conclusions, and again in the employment of general axioms as the instruments of farther discoveries.

Among the defects of his philosophical habits, it may be remarked that he frequently pursued an object of inquiry too exclusively, neglecting others which were necessarily connected with it, and which, if investigated, would have thrown great light on the main research. As an instance, may be mentioned his omitting to examine the relation of gases to water. This relation, of which he had indistinct glimpses, was a source of perpetual embarrassment to him, and led him to imagine changes in the intimate constitution of gases, which were in fact due to nothing more than an interchange of place between the gas in the water and that above the water, or between the former and the external atmosphere. Thus he erroneously supposed that hydrogen gas was transposed into azotic gas by remaining long confined by the water of a pneumatic cistern. The same eager direction of his mind to a

246

single object caused him, also, to overlook several new substances, which he must necessarily have obtained, and which, by a more watchful care, he might have secured and identified. At a very early period of his inquiries, (viz., before November, 1771), he was in possession of oxygen gas from saltpeter, and had remarked its striking effect on the flame of a candle; but he pursued the subject no further until August, 1774, when he again procured the same kind of gas from the red oxide of mercury, and, in a less pure state, from red lead. Placed thus a second time within his grasp, he did not omit to make prize of this, his greatest, discovery. He must, also, have obtained chlorine by the solution of manganese in spirit of salt; but it escaped his notice, because, being received over mercury, the gas was instantly absorbed.[4] If he had employed a bladder, as Scheele afterwards did, to collect the product of the same materials, he could not have failed to anticipate the Swedish philosopher in a discovery not less important than that of oxygen gas. Carbonic oxide early and repeatedly presented itself to his observation, without his being aware of its true distinctions from other kinds of inflammable air; it was reserved for Mr. Cruickshank of Woolwich to unfold its real nature and characters. It is remarkable, also, that in various parts of his works, Dr. Priestley has stated facts that might have given him a hint of the law, since unfolded by the sagacity of M. Gay-Lussac, "that gaseous substances combine in definite volumes." He shows that:

1 measure of fixed air unites with 1 6/7 measure of alkaline air,
1 measure of sulfurous acid with 2 measures of do.
1 measure of fluor acid with 2 measures of do.
1 measure of oxygen gas with 2 measures nitrous, very nearly;

and that by the decomposition of 1 vol. of ammonia, 3 vol. of hydrogen are evolved.

Let not, however, failures such as these—to reap all that was within his compass—derogate more than their due share from the merits of Dr. Priestley: for they may be traced to that very ardor of temperament, which, though to a certain degree a disqualification for close and correct observation, was the vital and sustaining principle of his zealous devotion to the pursuit of scientific truth. Let it be remembered that philosophers of the loftiest pretensions are chargeable with similar oversights; that even Kepler and Newton overlooked discoveries upon the very confines of which they trod, but which they left to confer glory on the names of less illustrious followers.

Of the general correctness of Dr. Priestley's experiments, it is but justice to him to speak with decided approbation. In some instances, it must be acknowledged, that his results have been rectified, by subsequent inquirers, chiefly as respects quantities and proportions. But of the immense number of new facts originating with him, it is surprising how very few are at variance with recent and correct observations. Even in these few examples, his errors may be traced to causes connected with the actual condition of science at the time; sometimes to the use of impure substances or to the imperfection of his instruments of research, but never to carelessness of inquiry or negligence of truth. Nor was he more remarkable for the zeal with which he sought satisfactory evidence than for the fidelity with which he reported it. In no one instance is he chargeable with misstating or even with straining or coloring a fact to suit a hypothesis. And although this praise may doubtless be conceded to the great majority of experimental philosophers, yet Dr. Priestley was singularly exempt from that disposition to view phenomena through a colored medium, which sometimes steals imperceptibly over minds of the greatest general probity. This security he owed to his freedom from all undue attachment to hypotheses, and to the facility with which he was accustomed to frame and abandon them—a facility resulting not from habit only, but from principle. "Hypotheses," he pronounces, in one place, "to be a cheap commodity"; in another to be "of no value except as the parents of facts"; and so far as he was himself concerned, he exhorts his readers "to consider new facts only as discoveries, and to draw conclusions for themselves." The only exception to this general praise is to be found in the pertinacity with which he adhered, to the last, to the Stahlian hypothesis of phlogiston, and in the anxiety that he evinced to reconcile to it new phenomena, which were considered by almost all other philosophers as proofs of its utter unsoundness. But this anxiety, it must be remembered, was chiefly apparent at a period of life when most men feel a reluctance to change the principle of arrangement by which they have been long accustomed to class the multifarious particulars of their knowledge.

In all those feelings and habits that connect the purest morals with the highest philosophy, (and that there is such a connection no one can doubt), Dr. Priestley is entitled to unqualified esteem and admiration. Attached to science by the most generous motives, he pursued it with an entire disregard to his own peculiar interests. He neither sought, nor accepted when offered, any pecuniary aid in his philosophical pursuits that did not leave him in possession of the most complete independence of thought and of action. Free from all little jealousies of contemporaries or rivals, he earnestly invited other laborers into the field which he was cultivating; gave publicity, in his own volumes, to their experiments; and, with true candor, was as ready to record the evidence which contradicted, as that which confirmed, his own views and results. Every hint that he had derived from the writings or conversation of others was unreservedly acknowledged. As the best way of accelerating the progress of science, he recommended and practiced the early publication of all discoveries; although quite aware that, in his own case, more durable fame would often have resulted from a delayed and more finished performance. "Those persons," he remarks, "are very properly disappointed, who, for the sake of a little more reputation, delay publishing their discoveries, till they are anticipated by others."

In perfect consistency with that liberality of temper which has been ascribed to Dr. Priestley, it may be remarked, also, that he took the most enlarged views of the scope and objects of natural science. In various passages of his works he has enforced, with warm and impressive eloquence, the considerations that flow from the contemplation of those arrangements in the natural world, which are not only perfect in themselves but are essential parts of one grand and harmonious design. He strenuously recommends experimental philosophy as an agreeable relief from employments that excite the feelings or overstrain the attention; and he proposes it to the young, the highborn, and the affluent as a source of pleasure unalloyed with the anxieties and agitations of public life. He regarded the benefits of its investigations not merely as issuing in the acquirement of new facts, however striking and valuable, not yet in the deduction of general principles, however sound and important, but as having a necessary tendency to increase the intellectual power and energy of man, and to exalt human nature to the highest dignity of which it is susceptible. The springs of such inquiries he represents as inexhaustible; and the prospects that may be gained by successive advances in knowledge as in themselves "truly sublime and glorious."

Into our estimate of the intellectual character of an individual, the extent and the comprehensiveness of his studies must always enter as an essential element. Of Dr. Priestley it may be justly affirmed that few men have taken a wider range over the vast and diversified field of human knowledge. In devoting, through the greater part of his life, a large portion of his attention to theological pursuits, he fulfilled what he strongly felt to be his primary duty as a minister of religion. This is not the fit occasion to pronounce an opinion of the fruits of those inquiries, related as they are to topics that still continue to be agitated as matters of earnest controversy. In ethics, in metaphysics, in the philosophy of language, and in that of general history he expatiated largely. He has given particular histories of the sciences of electricity and of optics, characterized by strict impartiality and by great perspicuity of language and arrangement. Of the mathematics he appears to have had only a general or elementary knowledge; nor, perhaps, did the original qualities or acquired habits of his mind fit him to excel in the exact sciences. On the whole, although Dr. Priestley may have been surpassed by many in vigor of understanding and capacity for profound research, yet it would be difficult to produce an instance of a writer more eminent for the variety and versatility of his talents, or more meritorious for their zealous, unwearied, and productive employment.

NOTES AND REFERENCES

1 Series I, vol. ii, p. 175.
2 Series II, vol. i, p. 26.
3 These charges, especially that of plagiarism, which had been unjustly advanced by some friends of Dr. Higgins, were triumphantly repelled by Dr. Priestley, in a pamphlet entitled, "Philosophical Empiricism," published in 1775.

4 Series II, p. 253.

C. Matignon, *Bull. Soc. Chim. France,* sér. 4, *53,* 1313 (1933).
L. C. Nervell, *J. Chem. Educ., 10,* 151 (1933).
E. F. Smith, "Priestley in America," University of Pennsylvania Press, Philadelphia, 1920.

From: *Am. J. Sci., 24,* 28 (1833). Read to the first meeting of the British Association, for the promotion of science, at York, September 28, 1831.

WILLIAM HENRY

·· *19* ··

Carl Wilhelm Scheele

1742-1786

SCHEELE'S merits in chemistry are so great and extended that none of its enlightened friends will mention his name without a feeling of gratitude and veneration. No chemist of the past can be compared to him in the number of unexpected, great and important discoveries; and, I can add, perhaps none of his contemporaries and, I presume, maybe none of his successors. While this is true to my way of thinking, nevertheless I do not wish to be misunderstood as implying that I deem Scheele to be the greatest chemical genius, the most deserving in the art, among all who ever lived. Such a bold decision could perhaps be ventured only by a man like Bergman, who could grasp the whole field of his science and its history by virtue of his gifted intellect—the man who possessed such a philosophical mind as to evaluate the important consequences of the revolutions which the genius produced and with which he influenced his time. And so let me say Scheele was great, extraordinarily great; until now nobody has exceeded him in the number of important discoveries.

Scheele was born on December 19, 1742, at Stralsund, where his father was a merchant. In his early years he enjoyed private schooling; later on he attended the gymnasium. Very early he showed great inclination to learn the art of the pharmacist; his father agreed with his decision. He started his apprenticeship with the apothecary Bauch in Gothenburg and completed it in six years. However, he continued to stay there a few years longer. He laid a good foundation for his science, as testified by the highly skilled apothecary Grunberg from Stralsund, who stopped off at the same apothecary shop with Scheele: "In those years already he was retiring and serious yet very assiduous; he observed all operations very exactly and thought about them nights, read up on them in the writings of Neumann, Lemery, Kunckel, and Stahl. At the same time he tried, without any instructions, designing and painting and succeeded very well, even during his years of apprenticeship. His favorite book was Kunckel's "Laboratorium" [chymicum], and he experimented according to it in secrecy, at night."

After Scheele's departure from Gothenburg, he obtained, in 1765, a position with the apothecary Kalstrom at Malmo. Two years later he went to Stockholm and there directed the apothecary of Mr. Scharenberg. He changed, in 1773, to one at Uppsala, with apothecary Loock. Here he had occasion to enlarge his knowledge through his acquaintance with scholars and the use of the chemical laboratory. In particular he acquired the friendship of Bergmann which always was very important to both men. During his stay, Prince Henry of Prussia in the company of the Duke of Sudermannland visited Uppsala and the academic laboratory there. The Academy asked Scheele to demonstrate some chemical experiments. He complied and performed some bizarre experiments in several ovens. The two royal princes asked him many questions about divers subjects and applauded his explanations.

When the apothecary Pohler died in 1775 at Köping, the *Collegium medicum* proposed Scheele as provisor for the apothecary shop. In the required examination he showed great skill and was appointed. In 1777 Pohler's widow sold him the shop. Here it was that Scheele showed the world how great the man was who occupied such a small position in such a small place.

In Stockholm he had already proved his great chemical knowledge by discovering the new, extremely strange acid in fluorspar.[1]

At Uppsala, a friend assured me, he first carried out the experiments which proved the particularity of aeric acid (oxygen); thus they induced Bergmann to treat this subject further. There, also, he investigated *magnesia nigra* (manganese dioxide) which demonstrated the nature of the compounds of this peculiar substance with acids and, at the same time, started the experiments concerning the dephlogistication by means of *magnesia nigra*.[2] On this occasion he also discovered baryta (barium oxide, 1774).

All this, however, was only preparation for his subsequent achievements at Köping. Here he completed his excellent book on air and fire (Uppsala, 1777) which on its own merits would have gained great applause through the meticulous treatment of such a delicate subject and the number of new findings, had not a man of Bergmann's importance recommended the book so strongly and warmly in the preface. It was read everywhere, was soon out of print, appeared in several new editions and was, as far as I know, translated into French and English (with annotations by R. Kirwan).

He also continued to publish in the volumes of the Stockholm Academy. He found that arsenic, freed of all its combustible element (completely oxidized) by any method, assumes all the properties of a complete acid; it becomes soluble in a small amount of water, reacts like other acids with all substances, and has specific affinities.[3] In his essay on silica, argillaceous earth and alum (vol. 38, p. 36) he explained Baumé's preparation of alum from silica by showing that the earthenware crucible is attacked by the melting (with potash), whereas in an iron crucible the same treatment furnishes no alum at all.

By treating with nitric acid he discovered in *molybdaena nitens* (then often thought to be identical with graphite) a new acid and described its chemical reactions.[4] He invented a beautiful green pigment for water and oil painting by combining dissolved copper vitriol (copper sulfate) with arsenious salt (p. 316) (Scheele's green). He also taught something that would have seemed quite impossible two hundred years before, namely to decompose atmospheric air. He found that it consisted of phlogistic air and 9/33 (*sic!*) of the purest or dephlogisticated air.[5]

With all the art of chemistry, he demonstrated the existence, in milk, of a specific acid which, although it decomposes the acetates of alkalies, is yet closely allied to the plant acids (p. 110). By decomposing milk sugar he observed another acid, not the same as ordinary sugar acid nor lactic acid, from which it differs in the insolubility of its salts with earth alkalies.[6] He achieved the decomposition of tungstone (a tungsten mineral) which had, until then, been greatly misunderstood; by showing that it contained a peculiar acid, he opened the way to Elhujar's reduction to the element.[7]

He showed that the best way to keep vinegar from spoiling for many years, even in the presence of air and in partially filled bottles, consists in boiling it over a strong fire for a quarter of a minute.[8] His research on the coloring matter of Prussian blue, the method of separating it, and of producing it from coal, alkali, and sal ammoniac is one of his most excellent investigations.[9] He found a particular sugar substance (glycerine) in pressed oils and fats when they are boiled with litharge and water. This substance cannot be brought to crystallization, like sugar and honey; it is not only more difficult to destroy by heat but even distills in part without changing, nor can it be fermented.[10] He taught how to crystallize lemon juice by saturating it with chalk and decomposing the precipitate with vitriolic (sulfuric) acid.[11] He found that the substance in rhubarb, which Model took to be selenite and which represents one seventh of the root weight, actually was calcareous salt of sorrel (calcium oxalate).[12] In studying fruit and berry acids he found not only one kind of acid, citric acid, but in addition a different one, malic acid (which is very similar to lactic acid); some plants contain either one or the other; in most plants the acid is a mixture of the two. The same is true of other parts of the plants; with strong nitric acid, a little of the two acids can be obtained even from animal substances, like glue, fish bladder, eggs, blood.[13]

These are the excellent publications of our great chemist which appeared in the volumes of the Royal Academy at Stockholm. Now I am going to add the last of his publications which have not yet come out in the Stockholm journals, at least not in German translation. His experiments showed what the so-called volatile fluorated earth (fluo-silicic acid) actually is, a three-part substance consisting of silica, the acid of fluorspar, and an alkali.[14]

The much-discussed pyrophorus of Homberg had been obtained by heating alum with excrements or, simpler, with vegetable matter or with charcoal. It aroused considerable interest because it ignited upon contact with air. Scheele found that no pyrophorus can be obtained without alkali. When it is produced from alum and coal, this is due to the fact that alum does not crystallize without alkali. Alum really free of alkali does not give off a pyrophorus; however, when it is moistened with a little alkali, this product is obtained.[15]

Scheele's last publication was concerned with the essential salt of galls.[16]

In order to complete the picture of Scheele's standing in chemistry to the best of my ability, I have to add a few items. According to one of his closest friends, the venerable Mr. Ehrhardt, Scheele also was the discoverer of saccharinic acid, derived from sugar and nitric acid. He furthermore gave us our knowledge of tartaric acid. We also owe to him that masterpiece of chemical analysis, the separation of phosphoric acid from bones, as demonstrated by a letter from Scheele to Gahn, who otherwise was held to be the inventor. Under the given circumstances it is not possible to establish exactly when these important findings were made.

In addition to the above publications, most of which adorn my chemical journals, there are some others and several very valuable single remarks in his letters with which he often honored me. Thus, in "Neue Entdeckungen der Chemie" (Part 1, p. 30) there is an essay on the combustible principle in raw lime; here he defends Black's system. In his remarks on air, fire, and the decomposition of water[17] he accepts as true and consistent with his own experience the famous experiment of Cavendish and Lavoisier (that water results from the ignition of flammable air (hydrogen) and vital air (oxygen); he applies to this his own former theory of air and fire (perhaps not quite convincingly throughout).

His moral character was faultless and praiseworthy, as Ehrhardt, Gadolin, Esplihg, and others testify. His appearance gave no hint of his great mind. He rarely took part in the usual social pastimes. He had as-little inclination as time for them, because in addition to his professional work he was always busy with research.

About his chemical-physical apparatus of ovens and vessels I have no precise information. One of his very intelligent compatriots (whom my readers know from the "Annalen") assured me that his apparatus was very simple. A foreigner (a man of great knowledge whose name is also known to my readers) visited Scheele's laboratory after his death and could not praise it highly enough.

His great achievements in science merited general praise, which he actually received; his name was known and valued among all enlightened nations.

Frequently attempts were made to move him from his small dwelling place to more grandiose quarters. Several years ago England wanted to provide him with a position of less work and good income. The negotiations were made difficult by his love of quiet solitude, of his second country of allegiance, and of the monarch who so graciously protected the sciences; a change in the

English government interrupted the negotiations. A year ago the same offer with an annual salary of 300 pounds was renewed; but fate deprived us of him much too soon by his death.

Half a year before that he was plagued by gout. Increasing illness accelerated the intention which he had formed at the time he bought the apothecary shop. He wanted to marry the widow of his predecessor. He kept deferring this step until he acquired more money of his own. Finally, in March, 1786, he publicly announced his engagement. However, his illness worsened, and hope for his recovery diminished every day. In order to fulfill his promise he married on May 19 as he lay on his sickbed. On the twenty-first, he made his wife his sole heir; and on the same day he died. Thus the world lost, in less than two years, two men, Bergmann and Scheele, in whom Sweden (rich as it is in worthy scholars) could take special pride; two chemists who were loved and mourned, and whose memory a grateful world will never cease to venerate.

GENERAL REFERENCES

George Urdang, "Pictorial Life History of the Apothecary Chemist Carl Wilhelm Scheele," Madison, Am. Inst. for the History of Pharm., 1942.
Bengt Hildebrand, "Recherches et documentations sur Carl Wilhelm Scheele," in Lychnos, vol. 1, pp. 76–101, 1936.

NOTES AND REFERENCES

1 Koningl. Svenska Vetenskaps Akademien, Handlingar, 33, 121 (1772).
2 Ibid., 36, 95, 183 (1775).
3 Ibid., 37, 263–294 (1776).
4 Ibid., 40, 238 (1779).
5 Ibid., 40, DB (1779).
6 Ibid., Nya Handlingar, 1, 257 (1780).
7 Ibid., 2, 89 (1781).
8 Ibid., 2, 113 (1781).
9 Ibid., 3, 256 (1782); 4, 32 (1783).
10 Ibid., 4, 316 (1783).
11 Ibid., 5, 105 (1784).
12 Ibid., 5, 182 (1784).
13 Ibid., 6, 16 (1785).
14 Chem. Ann., 1, 3 (1786).
15 Ibid., p. 483.

16 *Chem. Ann.*, 3 (1787).
17 *Chem. Ann.*, *1*, 229, 291 (1783).

From: D. Lorenz Crell's biography in *Chemische Annalen für die Freunde der Naturlehre, Arzneygelahrtheit, Haushaltungskunst und Manufakturen*, vol. 1, Helmstadt und Leipzig, 1787, pp. 175–192. Translated by Eduard Farber.

D. LORENZ CRELL

·· 20 ··

Antoine Laurent Lavoisier

1743-1794

ANTOINE LAURENT LAVOISIER was born in Paris on August 26, 1743. His parents belonged to what would now be described as the upper middle class and were comparatively wealthy. His father was a practicing lawyer and undoubtedly hoped that his son would continue in this profession. The boy attended the *Collège Mazarin* from the age of 11 until 18 years. He was a good student and won a number of prizes in various subjects. Following this well-rounded general basic education Lavoisier spent two years studying for the baccalaureate in law and in 1763 received the degree of Bachelor of Law.

Lavoisier's interest in science was probably first aroused by the astronomer Nicolas Louis de La Caille (1713–1762), who taught the *classe des mathématiques* at the *Collège Mazarin*. For many years Lavoisier was to keep meteorological and barometric observations, although he never published them; this was probably due to La Caille's early training. After La Caille's death Lavoisier came under the influence of the mineralogist Jean Etienne Guettard (1715–1786), a friend of the family who took the young man on numerous field expeditions. Lavoisier's earliest scientific work was concentrated in the fields of geology, mineralogy, and hydrology and patently derived from his connection with Guettard. At this period chemistry and mineralogy were treated in close connection with each other; hence it was natural for Lavoisier to develop an interest in the former subject; this interest was stimulated by his attendance (ca. 1763) at a course of lectures given by the celebrated Guillaume François Rouelle (1703–1770).

Guettard's main interest at the time was the compilation of a projected geological map of France: Lavoisier plunged enthusiastically into collaboration in this venture and carried out extensive and accurate observations. Largely for political reasons the scheme, much to Lavoisier's mortification, was not completed. His results, however, were later used (1784) by Antoine Grimoald Monnet (1734–1817), without proper acknowledgement, when the latter finally published the first geological map of France.[1]

265

In 1765 the Academy of Sciences offered a prize for the worthiest practical essay on the best method for lighting the streets of a large city; Lavoisier decided to compete. He made a thorough investigation, studying both the practical and theoretical aspects of the problem. Lavoisier's paper did not win the prize but was thought so meritorious that the Academy printed it and recommended the award of a special gold medal by the King.[2] The young man showed in this piece of work those outstanding characteristics that were to mark all his writings: clarity of exposition, concise writing, and an unusual understanding of the application of theory and laboratory work to practical problems.

The year 1768 was to see Lavoisier receive striking recognition for so young a scientist; he was elected a member of the Academy of Sciences. The academicians immediately recognized the worth of their new colleague; his wide general knowledge, zeal, and unusual ability in drafting reports were put to good use in the writing up of the findings of the many and varied commissions to which he was appointed. Almost simultaneous with his election to the Academy Lavoisier purchased a one-third interest in a share in the *Ferme-Générale*. This was a financial corporation which leased from the Government the right to collect a number of indirect taxes for consecutive periods of six years. Although the organization contained some honest, progressive, and capable administrators such as Jacques Alexis Paulze (1719–1794), the system was vicious and open to abuse; as a result it involved the members of the company in public opprobrium and hatred. In return for their lease the *Ferme* had to pay a substantial fixed sum in advance and, therefore, acquisition of a share necessitated substantial capital investment although a high return could usually be counted upon. Lavoisier's father helped him, by guarantees, to borrow the necessary money for the purchase. This was not merely an investment for, with his usual energy and competence, Lavoisier threw himself into the administrative details of the company and soon became one of its leading members. For most of his life a considerable part of his time was to be devoted to the *Ferme*— especially the years 1769, 1770, and 1771, when he was kept busy journeying through the country on the company's business. His superior in the company was Paulze; in 1771 he married the latter's daughter who was then only 14 years old—exactly half his own age. Unfortunately the marriage was not blessed with children, but few men have been more happily married than Lavoisier. His wife was an attractive and accomplished hostess and became an essential part of his scientific life. She translated important contemporary scientific works from the English, assisted at most of his important experimental work when she acted as a secretary by taking notes during the course of the experiments, and drew and engraved the thirteen plates for his most important work—the "Traité Elémentaire de Chimie." Lavoisier's connection with the *Ferme* gave him the income that he needed to finance the complicated and delicate apparatus that he required for his work and provided funds for the carrying-out of that work in all its ramifications; unfortunately it was also to lead to his imprisonment and death in May, 1794, when the Farmers-General were all convicted on trumped-up charges and executed.

At the time of his election to the Academy Lavoisier's interests were already veering from geology to chemistry. His earliest two papers of a chemical nature were concerned with gypsum.[3] Using a hydrometer Lavoisier demonstrated that a solution of gypsum was denser than water; from this he was led to a systematic study of hydrometry, during the course of which he devised a novel form of constant-immersion hydrometer. He had a portable model of this instrument made and used it to determine the densities of a large number of naturally occurring mineral waters while on his various journeys through the country. At this time the problem of providing Paris with an adequate and pure supply of water gave Lavoisier the incentive for much of his early work. He strongly supported the scheme of Antoine Deparcieux (1703–1768) for improving the city's water supply; Deparcieux suggested that various waters could profitably be examined by evaporation to dryness. This suggestion was questioned, for the belief that water could be transmuted into earth had not yet been disproved. This question was studied by Jean Baptiste Leroy (1720–1800), who held the view that water could not be obtained free from earth (dissolved salts) by distillation. Lavoisier shared this opinion, at the beginning, and in a paper on hydrometry[4] he even refers to a considerable quantity of earth having passed over with the water during distillation.

267

However, Lavoisier used distilled water as his standard in hydro
metric work and it was not long before the question of the possible
variability arose, for if Leroy was right Lavoisier's standard
might vary, depending on the nature of the water distilled for its
preparation. In order to clear up this point Lavoisier proceeded, in
1768, to determine the exact effect upon water of repeated dis
tillation and to compare the distillate with rainwater.[5] This in
vestigation led him to one of his most important pieces of work in
which he proved conclusively that water could not be transmuted
into earth: he also developed a new technique for testing and
purifying water and thus providing a true standard.

By the end of 1771 Lavoisier had finished his early work in
science and in 1772 began his study of combustion and the cal
cination (oxidation) of metals. The reasons which first led
Lavoisier to study these questions are not clear but it seems likely
that he may have been influenced by the constantly increasing
attention paid to them by his contemporaries. Rozier's "Observations
sur la Physique" for 1772 contains numerous papers on combus
tion and one on the diamond written by Macquer, Cadet and
Lavoisier.[6] The effect of heat on the diamond was not a new
problem, for the phenomenon had previously been studied; it had
been recorded that when strongly heated in air a diamond would
disappear. For the first time, however, Lavoisier and his colleagues
raised the question of whether the same result would occur if the
diamond were heated out of contact with the air. This paper an
swered the question by showing that if tightly packed in charcoal,
so as to exclude the air, and strongly heated, a diamond would not
only fail to disappear but would even come through the ordeal
with its polish almost unaffected. There can be no doubt that
this work on the diamond and the discussion which it caused had
a strong effect on the orientation of Lavoisier's work and led to his
long, complete, and absolutely definitive studies on combustion—
his major work. Further work on combustion of the diamond was
carried out in 1772,[7, 8] and Lavoisier also began experimenting
with phosphorus and sulfur and the conversion of calces into
metals during that year.

Lavoisier's plans for future research on combustion are expertly
summarized in a memorandum that he wrote on February 20,

1773.[9] It reveals a project that was to end by revolutionizing chemistry—an objective he had long intended to achieve. He resolved to work on gases. His work on the subject, together with a history of earlier work by others, is to be found in his "Opuscules Physiques et Chymiques"[10] which appeared in January, 1774, not quite a year from its inception. From Lavoisier's notebooks it is clear that the experimental work was carried out between February 23 and mid-August, 1773: the writing of the "Opuscules" was done during September, October, and November of 1773. The "Opuscules" begins with a lengthy history of gases and shows that he had a wide acquaintance with the subject; this occupies the first half of the book. The second half details Lavoisier's experimental work used in his attacks on the problems of combustion, calcination, and the *fixation* of air. The main problems treated and solved by Lavoisier in this, his first major work were: (1) Is quicklime more complex, or simpler, than chalk? Does quicklime contain an elusive substance, *acidum pingue,* or does chalk contain *fixed* air? (2) Is a metal more complex, or simpler, than it calx? Does the calcination of a metal or the combustion of a substance depend upon the absorption of air?

The book marks an important step in Lavoisier's work. In it Lavoisier broke new ground, made clear the important and controversial questions that needed solving, stated his own convictions regarding them, and obtained an appreciation of the difficulties lying in the way of the work to be undertaken. From the experimental section can be seen the development of his uncanny sense for perceiving and devising decisive experiments. The "Opuscules" was hastily prepared and intended to be the first volume of a series which was not continued. It is, however, a landmark in the history of chemistry.

Lavoisier was convinced that the increase in weight undergone by substances on calcination or combustion was a form of chemical combination with the air. Immediately after the publication of the "Opuscules" he extended his investigations to a study of the calcination of tin and lead in closed vessels. This work was carried out in 1774[11] and led Lavoisier to the conclusion that the atmospheric air consisted essentially of a mixture of two gases, one of which combined with metals during calcination, and another which would support neither life nor combustion. From this time on (March, 1774), Lavoisier broadened the base of his attack on the old theories; his laboratory notebooks show the initiation of work on the formation of nitrous ether, on the products of combustion of hydrogen, and on the composition of niter. The second of these lines of investigation was to lead to results that puzzled him for no less than nine years; his theory predicted an increase in weight when hydrogen, or any other substance, was burnt; but owing to the escape of water vapor Lavoisier actually found a loss in weight. He was also unable to fathom the relationship between fixed air (carbon dioxide) and the gas (oxygen) absorbed from the atmospheric air when metals were calcined (oxydized). This problem was solved early in 1775 when, working with the calx of mercury (red mercury oxide), he compared the gas obtained by heating the calx in the presence of charcoal with the gas given off by heating the calx alone. To his astonishment the gases were quite different—that obtained under the latter conditions was "more respirable, more combustible and therefore purer than common air."[12] This work was reported to the Academy in what has become one of Lavoisier's most famous memoirs; considerable controversy has been caused by speculation regarding the amount of assistance given to Lavoisier by Joseph Priestley (1733–1804) when he visited Lavoisier in Paris in the autumn of 1774. Recent work leads to the conclusion that Priestley's share in the orientation of Lavoisier's work has tended to be exaggerated.[13]

From the publication of this piece of work until September, 1775, Lavoisier's experimental work seems to have been halted, for his laboratory notebooks show no entries for this period. The cause of this slackening in the pace of his researches can be found in his preoccupations in another field of endeavor. This was the newly formed *Régie des Poudres*. Heretofore France's gunpowder requirements had been met by the *Ferme des Poudres,* which was a company of financiers with little incentive other than profit which often ran as high as 30 per cent per annum on the invested capital; the methods of production employed were inefficient and extravagant. When Louis XVI (1754–1793) succeeded to the throne he replaced the Abbé Terray (1715–1778) with the liberal Tur-

270

got (1727–1781) as comptroller-general of finance. Turgot belonged to the school of the *physiocrates,* to whose theories of finance Lavoisier also subscribed, and when he decided to abolish the old *ferme* it was to Lavoisier that he turned for both technical and administrative counsel. To run the newly created *Régie des Poudres* four *régisseurs* were appointed of whom Lavoisier was by far the most active. The new body soon abolished the malpractices of its predecessor and for the first time, as a result of Lavoisier's work, instituted efficient methods of operation.

Lavoisier's work for the new gunpowder commission resulted in his obtaining commodious living quarters and excellent laboratory facilities at the Royal Arsenal where he was to spend many happy and fruitful years (1776–1792). Pierre Samuel Du Pont (1739–1817), a physiocrat and close friend of the Lavoisier's, was later to send his son Irénée to serve his apprenticeship under Lavoisier in the royal gunpowder factory; this young man eventually escaped the French Revolution, fled to America, and founded the great du Pont chemical corporation.

By the end of 1775 Lavoisier had recommenced his research work which he pursued with great zeal through 1776. In the latter year he only published one paper, which was destined to be the first of a long series of memoirs in which Lavoisier developed his ideas following the formulation of his new theory of combustion and calcination. He demonstrated by the analysis of nitric acid that it contained *l'air meilleure que l'air commun* (oxygen) which he believed to be an essential component of all acids.[14] The year was a period of important accomplishment. Lavoisier now felt quite clear about the nature of combustion and respiration and the composition of atmospheric air; for the first time he was ready to launch an open attack on the *phlogistic* theory. Although the phenomenon of combustion had been completely solved, Lavoisier's theory was still incomplete and left a number of questions unanswered. During the next year (1777) Lavoisier presented no less than nine papers[15] to the Academy in which he set out the experimental and theoretical backing for his theory. He showed, in particular, how his own theory of combustion was simpler than the *phlogistic* theory and involved no paradoxical

271

assumptions such as a substance gaining in weight after losing one of its component parts. However, at this time Lavoisier stood alone and his theory had no other adherents.

From Lavoisier's laboratory notebooks it is clear that the five years from 1778 to 1782 did not produce any new or startling discoveries. It must be assumed that his manifold duties in the *Régie des Poudres* and the *Academy of Sciences* occupied much of his time: in addition there is no doubt that his membership of a number of the executive committees that really ran the *Ferme-Générale* absorbed still more of his working day. However, a new interest—agriculture—became evident in 1778 when he started scientific farming work on an estate at Frêchines (near Blois). With his usual methodical mind Lavoisier kept exact, double-entry records regarding every expenditure and receipt for each field under his care. In order to be readily available for consultation he had one set of books at Frêchines and a duplicate set in Paris. He made a habit of being there at least for the sowing and the harvest; he made valuable and practical suggestions for the improvement of agriculture, which was then inefficient in France, and he played an important part in the official *Administration de l'Agriculture* when it was formed in 1785.

A highly important piece of work was accomplished during the winter 1782–1783 in collaboration with the physicist, Pierre Simon de La Place (1749–1827). The results of this work were published in a famous memoir "Sur la Chaleur" which may be considered to have laid the foundation for the science of thermo-chemistry. An ingenious ice calorimeter of their own construction was used to measure specific heats and the heat evolved in combustion and respiration. The work was an extension of the earlier work of Joseph Black (1728–1799) and showed clearly, for the first time, that respiration was in every way a slow combustion process and *animal heat* the visible index of that combustion. The paper has been cited as one of Lavoisier's most brilliant, but it certainly owes much to his collaborator, La Place, who was the first convert to the new theories.

At this period Lavoisier was still greatly puzzled by the nature of the *inflammable air* that he obtained by the solution of metals in acids. On combustion of this gas he expected to obtain an acid

272

and was surprised to find that this was not the case. Other chemists, too, were studying the problem and the English scientist Henry Cavendish (1731–1810) finally solved it by showing that when a mixture of *inflammable air* (hydrogen) was detonated with common air in a closed vessel water was formed as a product of the reaction. Charles Blagden (1742–1820), Secretary of the Royal Society and a friend of Cavendish's, visited Paris in June, 1783, and told Lavoisier of Cavendish's work. Lavoisier and La Place immediately decided to repeat Cavendish's work. In front of Blagden and a number of academicians they burnt inflammable air (hydrogen) and oxygen on a substantial scale in a bell jar over mercury. The experiment had been too hastily prepared for exact quantitative results to be obtained, but Lavoisier at once perceived the importance of this new view of the nature of water and realized that it provided the missing clue to many of his unsolved problems. The very next day he communicated[16] his results to the *Academy,* and he learned that Gaspard Monge (1746–1818) had also made similar experiments. Lavoisier found that his experiments were not readily accepted nor understood, and he therefore took great pains to devise and have made special apparatus for demonstrating the decomposition of water into hydrogen and oxygen and its recomposition from those gases on a large and quantitative scale. These classical and definitive experiments were carried out before a large body of scientific onlookers in February, 1785.[17] Extended and bitter polemics have occurred concerning the amount of credit for priority that can be claimed for Lavoisier in the elucidation of the composition of water; such polemics, as Daumas has pointed out,[18] are fruitless. Irrespective of the apportionment of credit that should actually be made for the discovery, it cannot be denied that Lavoisier was the only one who grasped the import of the fact; he immediately drew the important conclusion that it explained the production of water when an organic substance was burnt and that this discovery could be used for the quantitative analysis of such bodies. He also determined the heat of combustion of hydrogen and deduced that the oxidation of hydrogen from ingested organic foods as well as of carbon explained the fact that more oxygen was used up in respiration than could be accounted for by the amount of carbon dioxide produced and exhaled. This phenomenon also explained why "animal heat" was greater than could be expected from the animal's output of carbon dioxide.

The new chemistry of Lavoisier required for its logical and full development a new chemical nomenclature, since the terminology used by the chemists of the day was antiquated and unsystematic. At this time Lavoisier already had La Place and a number of the younger physicists converted to his views. In 1785 the well-known chemist, Claude Louis Berthollet (1748–1822), came over to his side; he was soon followed by Antoine François Fourcroy (1755–1809) and the best-known French chemist of the day, Louis Bernard Guyton de Morveau (1737–1816). The latter had just found, when editing the chemical sections of the "Encyclopédie Méthodique," that the existing nomenclature prevented him from being able clearly to express a chemical meaning with suitable words. He had already, in 1782, published an attempt[19] to improve the situation, although at the time he was not a follower of Lavoisier. However, de Morveau came to Paris in order to defend the necessity of reforming the nomenclature and became converted to Lavoisier's views. The main result of this visit of de Morveau's was the publication in 1787 of the "Méthode de Nomenclature Chimique"[20] in collaboration with Lavoisier, Berthollet, and Fourcroy. The merits of the new nomenclature are, even today, very evident for it is still the basis of our modern chemistry and has undergone but slight modification since its origin. To place the honor of its inception is difficult, for although it may have originally been de Morveau's idea it was Lavoisier's new chemistry that brought it to fruition: the new chemistry and the new nomenclature were mutually dependent. The "Méthode de Nomenclature Chimique" soon became widely circulated in both French and foreign translations.

During the period 1783–1787 Lavoisier, in addition to his epoch-making work on the composition of water and the elaboration of a new chemistry and its nomenclature, found time to play an active part in such diverse undertakings as a full report on, and an exposure of, the activities of Friedrick Anton Mesmer (1734–1815),[21] a detailed investigation of a project for rehabilitating the public hospital service of Paris,[22] and other less important matters of public interest. At the same time, he actively pursued his scientific attempts to improve farming, zealously directed the royal gunpowder factory, actively participated in the administration of the *Ferme-Générale,* and regularly attended the frequent meetings of the *Academy of Sciences.* It is difficult to understand how he found the time for these manifold activities in a day that did not boast of dictating machines or typewriters.

In 1789 Lavoisier published his most important work, the "Traité Elémentaire de Chimie,"[23] which may well be considered a truly modern text and which certainly laid the foundation of modern chemistry.

The "Traité" was written to fill the need for a complete exposition of his new chemistry. It has been shown[24] that as early as 1778–1780 Lavoisier was already thinking about the need for such a textbook which would break completely with the traditional textbooks of Christoph Glaser (d. 1678), Nicolas Lemery (1645–1715), and others that were still in current use. During the period 1780–1781 he commenced drafting a skeleton of the "Traité"; this outline, which has survived, shows that at this time Lavoisier's ideas on the material which should be included in such a text were still influenced by contemporary customs, but it is a remarkable fact that the "Discours Préliminaire" was drafted in almost the identical form in which it was finally published. In 1788 Lavoisier outlined his textbook in its final form; it was divided into three parts. The first part was concerned with the formation and decomposition of gases, the combustion of simple bodies, and the formation of acids; it thus formed by itself an exposition of the new chemistry. The second part dealt with the combination of acids and salifiable bases, and with the formation of neutral salts. The third section contained a description of the instruments and operations of chemistry; it was illustrated by thirteen beautifully executed plates drawn and engraved by Madame Lavoisier. Of the three parts it was the first that was of the greatest interest, for it was there that details of the new chemistry were discussed, in some cases for he first time. The subjects of heat, the composition of the atmosphere, the analysis of atmospheric air and its parts, a consideration of nomenclature, and the composition of water were but a few of the topics considered.

The second section contained tables showing the reactions between various bases and acids and their resulting compounds. The most revolutionary feature of this section however, was the table of simple substances or elements; this table of 33 elements is one of the mileposts of modern chemistry.

The third and last part detailed the fundamentals of experimental procedure; a subject that was but poorly treated in other books of that period.

The textbook was avidly read by contemporary scientists and widely disseminated. Within sixteen years of its original appearance there were no less than French, English, American, German, Dutch, Spanish, Italian, and Mexican editions. With its publication the phlogistic period came to an end and modern chemistry was born.

After publication of his "Traité" Lavoisier's interests seem to have become modified, and there is a clear swing to physiological chemistry. Already in 1785[25] he had read a penetrating paper to the Société Royale de Médecine in which he gave an account of experimental work, performed on birds and guinea pigs, which demonstrated their ability to live in pure oxygen. He noticed how the animals' distress grew progressively more evident as the concentration of oxygen became less and that of carbon dioxide more. This led him to study the atmosphere in such crowded places as a prison[26] or a theatre[27] and indicated to him how important it was that public places should be adequately ventilated. Arising out of this work came his last experimental investigations—metabolic studies carried out on human subjects and pursued in collaboration with Armand Seguin (1765–1835). These formed the subjects for papers presented to the Academie in 1789[28] and 1790.[29] The work set forth the main factors that influenced the rate of metabolism, i.e., the ambient temperature, digestion of food, and expenditure of work. In addition, and with brilliant perception, Lavoisier deduced the solution to the mysterious way in which the body maintains a constant temperature irrespective of the temperature of its environment or its activities. He made it clear that the thermostatic effect was produced by three counterbalancing factors: transpiration which dissipates heat by the evaporation of water from the skin, adjusting its rate as needed; respiration which generates heat by the combustion (oxidation) of carbon and hydrogen; and

276

digestion which supplies the necessary raw materials for the first two processes.

Subsequent to the "Traité" Lavoisier published no major work. However, by 1792 he had decided to prepare a complete edition of his important memoirs which was to fill eight volumes and was to include the work of those who had supported his new chemistry. The project was interrupted and finally stopped by his arrest and execution, leaving three volumes in various states of readiness. These were subsequently printed for Madame Lavoisier as they stood, and in 1805 she distributed a number of copies under the title of "Mémoires de Physique et de Chimie"[30] to a number of learned institutions and distinguished scientists.

Few Frenchmen can have been more aware of the increasing unrest and mounting dangers that threatened France by 1789. In 1787 Necker had set up the Provincial Assemblies in a belated attempt to stave off disaster. Chosen to represent the Third Estate in the Assembly of Orléans, under whose jurisdiction his country estate fell, Lavoisier soon played a leading part in its deliberations. He produced sound and practical memoranda on the necessity of equitable taxation, savings banks for the poor, the state of agriculture and how to improve it, an old age insurance plan, and the need for freedom of commerce.[31] However, the time was not yet ripe; the majority of the privileged classes was still unprepared to make any real concessions, and nothing was achieved.

Two years later the King was forced to call a meeting of the Estates General (1789) to which Lavoisier was elected an alternate representative. Out of this came the Constituent and National Assemblies in neither of which Lavoisier had any place. A pioneer piece of work on the territorial wealth of France, however, was so well thought of as to be ordered printed by the National Assembly.[32] It was the first reasonably accurate attempt to estimate the total gross national income and thus deduce its taxable potentiality.

The political tide was now running fast; in 1791 the collection of taxes was taken out of the hands of the *Ferme* and in 1792 Lavoisier resigned his post with the gunpowder *Régie* and left his comfortable home and laboratory at the *Arsénal*. In that year the King offered him the post of Minister of Public Funds. In happier times Lavoisier would probably have been glad to accept the challenge, but under the circumstances he must have felt that he would not be able to do anything constructive and refused the post in a touching and dignified letter.

During these disturbed years Lavoisier spent much of his time and energy through his membership of two bodies set up by the National Assembly in 1791. These were the Consultative Committee on Arts and Crafts and the Commission for Weights and Measures. The former was supposed to advise the Government on various technical and scientific questions including useful or allegedly useful inventions; Lavoisier was responsible, as usual, for drafting almost all the reports, by far the most important of which was a lengthy one on a new system of public education and which was entirely his own.[33] The latter was a committee formed by the Academy of Sciences at the instruction of the National Assembly to create a uniform system of weights and measures, as a result of which the metric system was brought into being; Lavoisier's task in this committee was to determine, with the Abbé Haüy, the density of distilled water and he also had full responsibility for the administration of the commission. In addition, the death of the treasurer, Mathieu Tillet (1714–1791) having left the Academy's accounts in much disorder, Lavoisier was appointed his successor; as might be expected the latter soon straightened the finances out and was the most active combatant for the continuation of the Academy's existence until its final suppression in 1793.

Since the early days of the Revolution (1789) the members of *Ferme-Générale* had been under more or less constant attack as bloodsuckers who had fattened on the people, but it was not until 1791 that the National Assembly finally suppressed the body of tax-gatherers and instructed a commission to prepare and submit a detailed statement of accounts by January 1, 1793. Lavoisier was not appointed to this commission which was drawn from among the previous leaseholders, and which by June of 1793 had still been unable to complete the task. On June 5 the National Convention dissolved the commission and shortly after decreed that all the Farmers-General should have their personal files sealed. On September 10 and 11 members of the Revolutionary Committee searched Lavoisier's house but failed to uncover any incrimi-

278

nating material. On September 24 the Convention decreed the lifting of the seals from the Farmers' papers so as to enable them to comply with a new order instructing them to prepare their long-awaited accounts by April 1, 1794. However, the delays in producing their accounts inflamed a number of the extremists, and on November 24 the arrest of all the former tax-gatherers was ordered. Lavoisier heard of the decree for his arrest, and after a few days spent in hiding and fruitless attempts to obtain the reversal of the order for his own arrest on the grounds of his past and present valuable scientific work, he surrendered himself.

At first the conditions under which they were incarcerated rendered it quite impossible for the Farmers to proceed with the preparation of their accounts, but on Christmas Eve (1793) the prisoners were transferred to their former offices which had been fitted with bars on the windows and otherwise rendered escape-proof. Here they were able to have access to all their files and made good progress with the accounting which was ready by the end of January, 1794. These accounts showed quite clearly that the tax-gatherers had acted in complete conformity with the law and gave an entirely adequate refutation of the charges brought against them. At this time they were convinced that, at worst, severe financial reprisals might be levied against them, but that their lives were in no danger.

The Terror, however, was entering upon its most active and extreme phase, and the Farmers were not to escape so easily. In addition to the original charges of financial malpractice new ones were preferred. These new accusations referred in particular to abuse of privilege, excessive rates of interest, and the adulteration of tobacco by the addition of excessive moisture. This latter charge was claimed to be particularly serious, as in addition to hurting the consumer in his pocketbook, it was contended that it had a deleterious effect on his health. The Farmers' accusers brought their report before the National Convention, and in the heated atmosphere of the times had no difficulty in getting a decree passed ordering them brought before the Revolutionary Tribunal which had been established for trying cases of counterrevolutionary activity—of which the Farmers had not been accused. This was tantamount to a death sentence. On the morning of May 7, they were submitted to a routine and meaningless formal interrogation. At one o'clock in the morning of the following night each of the prisoners was handed an almost illegible copy of the charges brought against him, and at dawn they were taken to await their trial before the Tribunal. Here they were allowed fifteen minutes to consult with their officially appointed defense counsel. At ten o'clock they were brought before the Tribunal under the presidency of Coffinhal. A difficulty now arose for the Tribunal had no jurisdiction over the particular offenses listed in the act of accusation drawn up against the defendants. Coffinhal evidently appreciated this and became fearful that some remaining legal or moral scruples in the minds of the jury might allow their prey to escape. In his summing-up, he invited the jury, therefore, to ask itself whether it had been shown that a plot against the people had existed involving unfair exactions, adulteration of tobacco, and supplying the enemies of the Republic with huge sums of money illegally withheld from the Treasury. This last charge had not been mentioned in the accusation nor supported by any evidence presented during the trial; upon conviction such a charge carried the death penalty. The jury unanimously returned a verdict of guilty and the convicted men were duly guillotined on May 8, 1794.

Thus died France's greatest scientist whose labors brought chemistry a new and logical theory, a new and systematic nomenclature, a fresh and scientific outlook, and who had swept away all vestiges of alchemy and superstition. In addition to this remarkable achievement his pioneering work in agriculture, economics, finance, politics, sociology, education, and hygiene all bore the indelible stamp of his impeccable logic, keen practical sense, and strong appreciation of the urgent needs for constructive changes in all these fields.

NOTES AND REFERENCES

1 D. I. Duveen and H. S. Klickstein, "A Bibliography of the Works of Antoine Laurent Lavoisier," London, 1954, pp. 236–244.
2 "Oeuvres de Lavoisier," Paris, 1864, Tome II, pp. 1–70.
3 Duveen and Klickstein, *Op. cit.*, No. 1, p. 14.
4 "Oeuvres de Lavoisier," Tome III, pp. 145–162.

5 Duveen and Klickstein, *Op. cit.*, No. 7, p. 19.
6 *Idem.*, No. 9, p. 21.
7 "Oeuvres de Lavoisier," Tome II, pp. 38–64.
8 *Idem.*, Tome II, pp. 64–88.
9 Duveen and Klickstein, *Op. cit.*, pp. 99–101.
10 *Idem.*, pp. 95–105.
11 *Idem.*, No. 26, pp. 30–31; and No. 28, pp. 32–33.
12 "Oeuvres de Lavoisier," Tome II, pp. 122–128.
13 Duveen and Klickstein, *Op. cit.*, No. 29, pp. 33–38.
14 *Idem.*, No. 33, p. 41.
15 *Idem.*, Nos. 35, 38, 39, 40, 41, 42, 43, 45, and 49.
16 *Idem.*, No. 64, pp. 61–62.
17 *Idem.*, No. 93, pp. 78–79.
18 Maurice Daumas, "Lavoisier, Théoricien et expérimentateur," Paris, 1955, pp. 67–90.
19 "Observations sur la Physique," Vol. 19, pp. 370–382.
20 Duveen and Klickstein, *Op. cit.*, No. 126, pp. 126–130.
21 *Idem.*, Nos. 80 and 81, pp. 71–72.
22 *Idem.*, Nos. 83, 85, and 86, pp. 73–75.
23 *Idem.*, No. 153, pp. 160–172.
24 Maurice Daumas, "Archives internationales d'Histoire des Sciences," July 1950, pp. 570–590.
25 Duveen and Klickstein, *Op. cit.*
26 *Idem.*, No. 56, pp. 56–57.
27 *Idem.*, No. 79, pp. 70–71.
28 *Idem.*, No. 102, pp. 83–84.
29 *Idem.*, No. 106, pp. 85–86.
30 *Idem.*, No. 186, pp. 199–214.
31 *Idem.*, No. 289–298, pp. 321–326.
32 *Idem.*, No. 264, pp. 298–300.
33 *Idem.*, No. 274, pp. 307–310.

DENIS I. DUVEEN

The Chemists' Language

Acier, Fer, ou Mars	Digerer	Poudre
Aimant	Distiller	Precipiter
Air	Eau	Purifier
Alambic	Eau forte	Quinte Essence
Alun	Eau regale	Realgar
Amalgame	Eau de vie	Retorte ou Cornue
Antimoine	Esprit de vin	Sable
Aquarius	Esprit	Safran de Mars
Argent, ou Lune	Estain ou Iupiter	Safran de venus
Argent vif ou Mercure	Feu	Sagittaire
Aries	Feu de Roue	Sauon
Arsenic	Fixer	Scorpion signe celeste
Bain	Farine de Briques	Sel alkali
Bain marie	Filtrer	Sel Ammoniac
Bain vaporeux	Fleurs d'Antimoine	Sel commun
Balance, signe celeste	Gomme	Sel gemme
Borrax	Heure	Soude
Brique	Huille	Soufre
Calciner	Iour	Soufre vif
Camphre	Iumeaux, signe Celeste	Soufre noir
Cancer, ou Ecreuisse	Limaille d'acier	Soufre des Philosophes
Capricorne	Lion, signe Celeste	Subliner
Cendres grauellées	Litharge	Talc
Cendres	Lit sur lit, ou stratum super stratum	Tartre
Ceruse	Luter	Terre
Chaux	Marchasite	Taureau Signe Celeste
Chaux viue	Mercure sublime	Teste morte
Cimenter	Mercure precipité	Tutie
Cinabre	Mois	Verre
Cire	Nitre ou salpetre	Vert de gris
Coaguler	Nuit	Vin
Corne de Cerf	Or	Vinaigre
Creuset	Orpiment	Vinaigre distillé
Cristal	Plomb	Vitriol
Cuiure ou Venus	Poissons, Signe Celeste	Vitriol blanc
Cuiure brulé ou Aes ustum		Vitriol bleu
		Vrine

"Explanation of the most common chemical symbols" from Nicolas Lemery: Cours de Chymie, ed. of 1730, p. 66. The table contains, in alphabetical order, the names and symbols for substances and operations. A few celestial bodies and geological terms are included. The last word is urine with its symbol.

COMMUNICATION is an important part in the work of the scientist. As the vehicle for communication, language has to be adapted for the scientist's purpose because it does not contain the means for expressing his new discoveries. He has to create words, signs, or symbols—an artificial language for his new art of distinguishing things and manipulating them. Yet, while this artificial language is originally designed to facilitate communication, it also has the effect of excluding the uninitiated from the new science. This effect was purposely sought by many alchemists, and they compounded the difficulty by enigmatic expressions. Usually, however, chemists introduced their new language without such evil intent. On the contrary, they tried to use known words by instilling them with new meanings. They called every liquid a "water," and when necessary they designated and distinguished them by normal, descriptive adjectives. Thus "aqua fortis" represented a solution of nitric acid obtained by heating *sal nitrum,* or saltpeter, with vitriol. The name "vitriol," used for glasslike, shiny crystals, could be assumed to be commonly known. The heavy, somewhat viscous liquid derived from it was oil of vitriol; how this became sulfuric acid is connected with a long development which revealed its derivation from sulfur.

Often a common name like vitriol designated different substances. The green variety was recognized as containing iron, the blue vitriol as a copper salt. At least the common part of the name had a chemical significance, both are sulfates. It was different with a term like plumbago, under which lead and graphite were combined. We still talk of lead pencils, although they are made with graphite, not lead. *Magnesia nigra* and *magnesia alba* are not the black and the white forms of the same basic substance; the first is an oxide of the ironlike metal, manganese, the other the carbonate of the light, calciumlike metal, magnesium.

An effective way of designating a chemical was to indicate the method of its production. *Magnesia usta* is produced by burning; the name is distinctive, although it does not say much about the composition or properties. For a time, any precipitate, like the deposit in wine casks, was called a tartar; faintly persistent original reference to *tartarus,* meaning hell, remained.

Paracelsus, that revolutionizing spirit, needed a number of new words for his new concepts, such as *archeus* for the life power or the alchemical property in organisms that digests food; *mumia* for "the inner doctor;" *iliaster* for the constructive principle; *cagaster* for the destructive force; and *protoplastus* for man in a biological consideration. Only the last of these terms has survived—the word, protoplasm, as a designation for "living" protein.

Some of the names in this category follow the pattern which a historian of psychology described in these words: "Men have always accepted readily such contentions as that imitation is explained by referring it to an instinct of imitation, or a good memory depends on having a good faculty of memory. Such naming is word magic."[1]

This magic is impressive because of its past, connected with ancient feelings and concepts; its force resides in the application to the future, thus carrying with it the truly scientific function of predicting future events.

A different use of the past in naming new discoveries is exemplified in Faraday's work. He found that parts of the chemical molecule migrate under the influence of an electrical potential. Following the advice of William Whewell (1794–1866) Faraday (p. 465) called those parts *ions,* which is the ancient Greek word for wanderers. He could not very well have used the English equivalent, because its connotations were too much alive and in common use. He could, however, have used any symbol. In fact, this was done somewhat later when it was agreed to designate a negative ion by a minus sign or simply a prime sign, a positive one by a plus or a point, connected with the symbol for the particular element or group: Cl^- or Cl' thus became the symbol for the chlorine ion, Na^+ or $Na^{\cdot}$ for sodium ion. Such signs and symbols recall the use of signs for designating the pitch and duration of musical notes and their interesting history (see, e.g., the article "Notation" in *Harvard Dictionary of Music* by Willi Apel, Harvard University Press, Cambridge, 1950).

286

ATOMIC SYMBOLS

John Dalton *D.C.L, F.R.S. &c.*

explanatory of a

LECTURE

given by him to the MEMBERS of the

Manchester Mechanics' Institution.

October 19th 1835.

ELEMENTS.

Hydrogen	⊙	Oxygen	○	Azote		Chlorine	
Carbon	●	Phosphorus		Sulphur	⊕	Lead	
Zinc	Ⓩ	Iron		Tin		Copper	Ⓒ

OXIDES.

SULPHURETS.

COMPOUNDS.

Binary.

Water ....

Nitrous gas ....

Carbonic oxide ....

Sulphuretted hydrogen ....

Phosphuretted hydrogen ....

Olefiant gas ....

Cyanogen ....

Ternary.

Deutoxide of hydrogen ....

Sulphurous acid ....

Acetic acid ....

Nitrous oxide ....

Carbonic acid ....

Phosphoric acid ....

Nitrous vapour ....

Carburetted hydrogen ....

Prussic acid ....

Bicarburetted hydrogen ....

Tan ....

Quaternary.

Sulphuric acid ....

Binolefiant gas ....

Pyroxylic spirit ....

Quinquenary.

Ammonia ....

Nitrous acid ....

Prussic acid ....

Sexenary.

Alcohol ....

Pyroacetic spirit ....

Septenary.

Nitric acid ....

Decenary.

Ether ....

FIG. 6.

The symbols for the chemical elements and compounds had their own long history before they developed into their present simple and expressive form. The chart on page 284 from a once famous textbook, the "Cours de Chymie" (first edition: 1675) by Nicolas Lemery (1645–1715) shows symbols, still used in the eighteenth century, which express a very old tradition. In ancient times, gold was really thought to have a direct connection with the sun, silver with the moon, and other metals with the then-known planets. The convictions about these associations vanished, but the symbols for them remained and formed the models for other symbols in Lemery's chart designating newly recognized chemicals.

After Lavoisier (p. 264) introduced a new system of chemistry, he collaborated with three other outstanding scientists on developing a new nomenclature. New symbols, based on Lavoisier's system, were proposed by Adet and Hassenfratz. Dalton (p. 334) imagined a pictorial representation of the atoms; the pictures reproduced here are from a late period of much greater restraint than the earlier (1808) ones (see page 287). Others proposed circles inscribed with the initial of the names for the elements. Finally, any reference to an imagined form of the atoms was omitted. The initials proved sufficient for designating the elements. Numbers attached to these initials indicated the relative proportions in compounds. Berzelius (p. 386) saw the advantage of such symbols in "facilitating the expression of chemical proportions and enabling us to point out the number of the elementary atoms in each composite substance without lengthy circumscription and without difficulty" (1819).

In all their simplicity, the new symbols expressed a wealth of chemical knowledge. The work of many chemists, such as the ideas of Cannizzaro, (p. 662) Couper (p. 704), and Kekulé (p. 698), were necessary to abandon the previous hooks and special brackets for indicating atomic connections in a molecule. A straight line now proved sufficient and effective. Kekulé's benzene "ring" thus took the form of a hexagon, with the six carbon atoms at the corners, simple lines for single bonds and double lines for double bonds between the atoms:

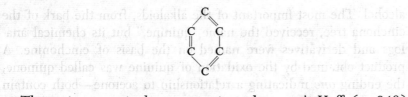

These signs acquired new meaning when van't Hoff (p. 948) extended the formulas from the plane into three dimensions. He took the symbols seriously and developed the consequences of distributing the four valances of carbon regularly around it. The regular tetrahedron thus became the steric symbol of the carbon atom. Stereochemistry, the study of the situation of atoms of a molecule in three dimensions, became a highly important new field of study. Emil Fischer's (p. 982) chemistry of the carbohydrates was completely and successfully based on this foundation. It remained so even after Rutherford (p. 1344) introduced a new model of the atom, a heavy nucleus surrounded by almost weightless electrons. Such deep insight into the nature of matter led to electronic representations of atomic bonds and molecular reactions. New symbols were added to the old ones without rendering them essentially obsolete. (Rutherford, "The Nuclear Constitution of Atoms," 1920).

Nomenclature found a new basis in the system devised by Lavoisier and his colleagues. However, this meant only a new start. The discoverers of new elements had the privilege of introducing new names, selected to indicate a most striking property, as in the name "iodine" for the violet color of its vapors, or references to earth (tellurium), moon (selenium), or a planet (uranium), even to an ancient goddess (cerium)—arbitrary references that seemed appealing because in some way they continued very ancient practices, although their mysterious allusions were gone.

Old names continued in use beside the scientific names, such as Glauber's salt (p. 116) for sodium sulfate; others, like lactic and tartaric acid, were completely adopted by science, and their previous connotations helped in memorizing these names by reference to their origin. Sugar is still used for carbohydrates, even for those that are neither digestible nor sweet. *An* alcohol may have little in common with *the* alcohol except the group —OH connected with a carbon atom. Phytol, from chlorophyll, thus is *an* alcohol, although quite different in appearance and properties from *the* ethyl

289

alcohol. The most important of the alkaloids, from the bark of the cinchona tree, received the name "quinine," but its chemical analogs and derivatives were named on the basis of cinchonine. A product obtained by the oxidation of quinine was called quinone, the ending *one* indicating a relationship to acetone—both contain

$\overset{|}{\underset{|}{C}}{=}O$, the ketone group. Acetone, the *one* first made from acetic

acid (or rather its calcium salt) is a low-boiling, colorless liquid, quinone is yellow and a crystallized solid at room temperature.

Thus, the ketone function, for which chemically specific reagents were found, does not characterize all the main properties of qui-

none. This quinine derivative contains two $\overset{|}{\underset{|}{C}}{=}O$ groups in a par-

ticular setting, derived from a benzene ring:

Acetone

Quinone

Similar structures were produced from napthalene. Their name: naphthoquinones, related to the chemical structure of quinone, but not to quinine in any other way. Instead of one quinone, many quinones and quinoids became established.

As similar processes continued, the advantages of the "common" names dwindled. "Lengthy circumscription," to use the Berzelian expression, became necessary. Chemical science needed a better kind of nomenclature.

Efforts in this direction were initiated with especial vigor in the twentieth century. Many of the great chemists were also name givers. The great textbook writers, among them Fourcroy, Gmelin (p. 454), Berzelius, Wurtz (p. 522), Dumas (p. 522), Wöhler (p. 506), Mendeleev (p. 718), and Beilstein (p. 522), had to consolidate chemical language and enlarge it by new terms. Systematic work on a chemical nomenclature was beset with initial

290

difficulties. Ciamician (p. 1086) and some of his colleagues complained about the lack of response to their efforts. Nomenclature is still the continued topic of international chemical congresses.

New names for chemical compounds are now mostly formed by agreed symbols for the atomic groups and by figures specifying the number and relative position in the molecule. Willstätter's (p. 1366) new substance was thus called cyclooctatetraene, because eight (*octa*) carbon atoms are in a ring (*cyclo*) and have four (*tetra*) ethylenic bonds (*ene*). Steric isomers are characterized by syllables like *syn* and *anti* for the relative positions in three dimensions. Optical isomers receive the small capitals D or L before their names to indicate whether they turn polarized light to the right or to the left, or whether their parent substances do.

International convention also extends to the letters and symbols used for work, heat, free energy, and energy functions used in thermodynamics, the field in which Willard Gibbs (p. 784) did so much pioneering work.

The foregoing observations about a vast and complex topic have been written mainly with reference to some of the subjects that occur prominently in the present biographies. Large dictionaries of the chemists' language are available. Even they are insufficient for those parts of chemistry in which mathematics is used extensively. At a faculty meeting in 1884, Willard Gibbs said: "Mathematics is a language!" In an address of 1937, Nevil Vincent Sidgwick (p. 1376) referred to the difficult mathematical expression of wave mechanics when he said: "It makes the non-mathematical reader think that as he can't understand the language he can't understand the conclusions either, which is quite untrue; and not uncommonly, I think, it leads the non-mathematical writer to believe that if he knows the technical terms he must understand their meaning, which is by no means always the case." It was well said by Clerk Maxwell: "For the sake of persons of different types of mind scientific truth should be presented in different forms, and should be regarded as equally scientific whether it appears in the robust form and colouring of a physical illustration, or in the tenuity and paleness of a symbolical expression."

The old symbols were loaded with meanings and emotions; the new symbols appear tenuous and pale.

291

Yet these new symbols have their peculiar fascination for those who are prepared for them. In his autobiography Amé Pictet (1857–1937, professor of chemistry at the University of Geneva) tells of a decisive incident that occurred in 1877, in Bonn, where he studied under Kekulé and Anschütz. He looked into the show window of a bookstore and saw a booklet by Koenigs, opened at the page containing the new symbolic formula for pyridine. It was

$$
\begin{array}{ccc}
 & H & \\
 & | & \\
H & C & H \\
\backslash & / \backslash & / \\
C & & C \\
\| & & \| \\
C & & C \\
/ & & \backslash \\
H & N & H
\end{array}
$$

the formula of "benzol in which nitrogen functions in place of the triatomic residue $\overset{\cdots}{C}H$ and thus may be represented as a closed chain," in the words of James Dewar (1842–1923). It impressed Amé Pictet so deeply that he promised himself to work henceforth on this type of compound—and he did.

NOTES AND REFERENCES

1 Edwin G. Boring, "A History of Experimental Psychology," 2nd ed., Appleton-Century-Crofts, New York, 1950, p. 207.
"Chemical Nomenclature," *Ind. Eng. Chem.*, No. 6, in *Advances in Chemistry Series*, American Chemical Society, Washington, D.C. See also: *J. Am. Chem. Soc.*, 55, 3915 (1933).

EDUARD FARBER

292

·· 22 ··

Martin Klaproth

1743-1817

LIKE so many of the prominent chemists of that era, Klaproth came to chemistry from pharmacy. Born at Wernigerode on December 1, 1743, he finished his local schooling and at 15 he became an apprentice at an apothecary shop in nearby Quedlinburg. His master was Friedrich Victor Bollmann, a competent pharmacist, but obviously not an efficient teacher. Later Klaproth wrote: "I cannot praise the instruction I received from one of my teachers, but in accord with the fashion of that time I had to content myself with what I could learn by observing the operations carried on by my older associates and from my reading in one or the other of the out-of-date apothecary books for which, however, I was given little leisure." In 1766 he took a position in an apothecary shop in Hannover, and from 1768 to 1770 he worked in the Wendland Apothecary in Berlin. From 1770 he was prescriptionist in the Ratsapotheke at Danzig. At the beginning of 1771 he was back in Berlin, at the well-known Schwanenapotheke belonging to the Rose family. During his first stay in Berlin, Klaproth had extended his chemical knowledge under Johann Heinrich Pott and Andreas Sigismund Marggraf; now Valentin Rose, the elder (1736–1771), became his teacher and fatherly friend. When Rose died, Klaproth took over the independent direction of the pharmacy and also assumed the bringing up of the two minor sons of the deceased. In that year he moved into a house belonging to the Academy of Sciences, "behind the Observatory," and lived there until his death on January 1, 1817.

In 1780 he set up his own laboratory and was able, especially after he had given up pharmacy as his profession (1787), to devote himself intensively to the chemical researches which soon made his name well-known. The usual honors came to him: he became a member of the Sanitary Board, of the Academy of Sciences in Berlin, and of numerous other scientific bodies at home and abroad. In 1792 he was appointed to teach chemistry at the Artillery School, and in 1810 he was called to be the first Professor of Chemistry at the newly founded University of Berlin with the title of Obermedizinal-und-Sanitätsrat.

Klaproth's contributions were chiefly in two areas of chemistry. Although he had been brought up on the Stahlian doctrines, he was one of the first German chemists to work consciously and effectively in favor of the "new" antiphlogistic theory. His own laboratory studies made analytical chemistry one of the most important foundations of chemical research.

Although the phlogistic hypothesis had put down particularly deep roots in Germany, so that the antiphlogistian views made but slow progress there, this was partly due, as Kopp wrote, "to a certain national feeling, which made the German chemists resist the replacement of the system of Stahl, their countryman, by the modern 'chimie française' " (H. Kopp, Geschichte der Chemie I, 345, 1843). Entirely devoid of such prejudices, Klaproth subjected the question at issue to a scientific test and in 1792 proposed to the Berlin Academy that the experiments of Lavoisier on combustion and calcination be officially repeated. When the findings confirmed the results and conclusions reached by Lavoisier, Klaproth did not hesitate to announce that he was an adherent of the new system, and he began to advocate its adoption by his professional colleagues. His example did much to bring about the abandonment of the out-of-date views in Germany and to cause the further development of chemical research in that country to be in harmony with the modern theory. His editing, together with Formey, of the "Prussian Pharmacopeia" (1799) which now for the first time was composed on antiphlogistic foundations, made significant contributions to the spread of the newer ideas, including the introduction of the new nomenclature.

As an analyst, Klaproth was distinguished above all by his scrupulous exactness and reliability. Much of what is now taken for granted in chemical analytical studies was made the common property of analytical methodology by Klaproth's example. His services in this field can be properly appreciated only after considering the conditions prevailing in analytical chemistry at that time. Kopp has given us a clear description of the state of things:

The loss or the excess, which almost always appears in an analysis, was previously always balanced out by the chemist himself according to his best estimate, but often also according to preconceived notions, and the result of the observation was not reported as the findings of the experiment itself, but almost always only the conclusions were given which the operator considered, with more or less justification, he could deduce from the experiments. . . . This is why so many basically incorrect statements regarding the quantitative composition were held to be correct on the mere authority of the observer. . . . Klaproth was the first to introduce the custom of reporting not only his own conclusions concerning the composition of a compound, but also of giving complete details of the investigation; the agreement between the weight of the substances obtained with the weight of the substance taken for study now provided a measure of the accuracy of the investigation and of the reliability of the methods employed. And because the errors committed were no longer concealed, more attention was directed to their sources and to the means of avoiding them.

Many other fundamental principles and methods of analytical chemistry go back to Klaproth. He was the first to point out the necessity of bringing the precipitates obtained in the course of an analysis to constant weight by drying at definite temperatures or by ignition. The accuracy of his work was characterized by the necessity to take into account even the influence which the material of the equipment used in the analysis might exert on the course and the result of the procedure—as, for instance, the mortars used for grinding the sample. Klaproth devised the method of decomposing silicates by evaporation with caustic potash and fusion in a silver crucible. He introduced many other qualitative and quantitative processes relative to the analysis of inorganic materials and actually used and tested them in hundreds of analyses of minerals.

Only the most important of his experimental investigations will be mentioned here. In 1789 he reported to the Berlin Academy on the results of a study of pitchblende, in which he proved the presence of a new element that he called uranium. The new material isolated by him from pitchblende was not uranium itself, but instead, as was pointed out by Péligot in 1841, uranous oxide. In his translation of Macquer's chemical dictionary, Leonhardi proposed

297

that the new element be named "Klaprothium." Klaproth, however, stated that the name uranium had been chosen in honor of the planet, Uranus, discovered in 1781 by William Herschel. "Up to the present, seventeen individual metallic substances have been acknowledged. However it is the purpose of the present paper to increase this number with a new one." In the same year Klaproth was able to announce the discovery of a new earth, zirconia, in zircon from Ceylon; this substance had been studied only a short time before by Johann Friedrich Wiegleb (1732–1800), an apothecary in Langensalza, without noting anything about the presence of an unknown earth. In 1793 Klaproth published a detailed study of strontianite, in which he, at about the same time as Hope, described the properties of strontia, whose existence had been conjectured several years previously by Crawford and by Cruikshank. In 1795 Klaproth was again favored by the discovery of a new element through his investigation of rutile, the so-called Hungarian red schorl, which at that time was regarded as a kind of tourmaline or garnet. On the basis of the analysis and the reactions of the "white earth" finally obtained, he came to the conclusion that an oxide of a hitherto unknown metal must be present; he named it titanium. In justifying this name he stated:

> When no name can be found which indicates the characteristic properties of a new material dug from the earth . . . I believe it is better to choose a name that *per se* says nothing and consequently can occasion no incorrect ideas. Accordingly, I will take the name for the present metallic substance, as was done in the case of uranium, from mythology, and in fact from the primeval sons of Earth, the Titans, and consequently I name this new species of metal titanium.

In 1797, Vauquelin had analyzed Siberian red lead spar (crocoisite) and discovered that the lead was combined with a peculiar acid which proved to be the oxide of a new element. Because of the color of its compounds it was named chromium. Near the end of 1797, i.e., almost at the same time, Klaproth likewise announced that he had discovered the new element in this Siberian mineral. Franz Müller von Reichenstein, director of the mines in Tran-

298

sylvania, in 1792 suspected that a new element was present in the gold ores of Abrudbanya. Bergmann confirmed this suspicion to the extent that he showed the material not to be antimony. But only Klaproth, in 1798, was able to render these observations more definite. The new element, which he also found in sylvanite, was named tellurium, "a name taken from old mother Earth."[1]

In 1800, Klaproth made a study of gadolinite. This mineral, originally called ytterbite from the site of its occurrence, Ytterby, Sweden, had been investigated (1794) by Johann Gadolin, professor of chemistry, at Abo, Finland. He isolated one of its components, which in 1797 was named yttria by Ekeberg, and which later was found to be a mixture of the oxides of several metals. Klaproth described the properties of yttria in a manner that was very exact for the period. Not long after this (1803), Klaproth—at about the same time as Berzelius and Hisinger—found ceria in cerite. The name cerium—from the planet Ceres—was given to the new element by Berzelius. Klaproth gave the name ochroite to the light-brown substance he had isolated.

In a paper "On the True Nature of Proust's So-Called Pearl Salt" (1795), Klaproth pointed out that the "fusible urine salt" obtained from evaporated urine, namely, sodium ammonium phosphate, as well as the "salt of pearl" (sodium phosphate) which separates on further evaporation, are not salts of a special "pearl acid" but rather of phosphoric acid. He elucidated the composition of spathic iron ore, found sodium to be an essential constituent of cryolite along with alumina and hydrofluoric acid, showed that apatite contains phosphoric acid, and analyzed red copper ore (cuprite), yellow lead ore (wulfenite), red silver ore, aragonite, lepidolite, dolomite, emerald, topaz, garnet, and many other minerals. In leucite taken from many regions he found silicic acid, alumina and "vegetable alkali" and thus—surely for the first time —definitely pointed out potassium as an essential constituent of a mineral. His study of honeystone led him to conclude that this mineral is the hydrated salt of a special plant acid, which he called "honeystone acid" (mellitic or benzene hexacarboxylic acid in modern terms). He showed that nickel is present in meteoric stones and meteoric iron masses. He studied the natural products which

299

von Humboldt brought back from his journeys, such as moya (a vulcanic product) from Quito and guano from the islands off the Peruvian coast. Other such specimens included mineral waters from various places, water from the Dead Sea, Egyptian *natrum*. "heavenly manna" from Sicily, and also Greek, Roman, and Chinese coins, ancient weapons and tools, Chinese gongs, glasses from a villa of Tiberius on Capri, fossil elephant teeth, and other rarities.

From among his pharmaceutical activities, a word is in order regarding "The History of the Bestuscheff Nerve Tincture" (Neue Beiträge zur Natur- und Arzneiwissenschaft, 1792). This secret remedy was put out by the Russian Field Marshal, Count Bestuscheff (1686–1760), in large amounts. There were two varieties, a yellow and a white tincture. Later, it is reported, one of the general's aides sold the secret formula to the French General, La Motte, who then marketed the tincture under the name "Gold Drops of General de La Motte." "The widespread reputation of the Bestuscheff and the Lamotte drops in curing or alleviating stubborn diseases as well as the phenomenon, which was still quite new in chemistry, that the yellow drops lost their color entirely in sunshine and regained it in the dark, soon attracted the attention of physicians, natural philosophers, and chemists. Efforts were made to analyze these tinctures and to discover their ingredients, but with varying success." As an example of the great respect enjoyed by this medicament it may be pointed out that, in 1731, Louis XV sent 200 vials of the La Motte drops by special messenger to Rome for the Pope who was suffering from the gout. In France it was believed that the secret tincture had been found to contain gold, and the wily maker had done nothing to dispel this belief. However, in the meantime several chemists had solved the secret of the "gold drops" by analysis; it was found that the yellow drops were nothing but a dilute solution of iron and hydrochloric acid, while the white tincture contained in addition to the alcohol only a trace of a "sweetened acid." Klaproth had made a critical analysis of the numerous formulations which had been published for the preparation of the drops and had himself proposed an improved method of preparation. His method was to extract the iron from its concentrated solution in hydrochloric acid and to treat the ether extract with alcohol.

Klaproth published some of his many papers in various periodicals such as Crell's "Chemische Annalen." A collected edition appeared in six volumes from 1795 to 1815, as "Beiträge zur chemischen Kenntnis der Mineralkörper." The title of the sixth volume is: "Chemische Abhandlungen gemischten Inhalts." In addition he prepared a revision of Gren's "Handbuch der Chemie" (1760–1798), and in association with Friedrich Wolff, he published a chemical dictionary which gave an encyclopedic presentation of the entire chemical knowledge of the time: "Chemisches Wörterbuch," Berlin, 1807–1810 (5 volumes). Supplements: Berlin 1815–1819 (4 volumes). This work appeared in French as "Dictionnaire de chimie, traduit de l'allemand, avec des notes, par E. J. B. Bouillon-Lagrange et par H. A. Vogel," Paris 1810–1811 (4 volumes).

Not much is known of Klaproth as a man. Essentially he was an uncomplicated personality, engrossed in his profession. His character corresponded completely to the type of his research activity, whose outstanding features were reliability and honesty. Whenever, as frequently happened, his chemical studies made it necessary for him to correct the errors and inaccuracies of other scientists, this was always done in a courteous tone with no trace of pretence or superiority. A. W. Hofmann suitably characterized Klaproth in these words:

> Possessed of a modesty devoid of all conceit, filled with appreciation of the merits of others, though mindful of their weaknesses, but implacably strict in the appraisal of his own work, Klaproth has given us for all times the model of a true natural scientist.

NOTES AND REFERENCES

1 Paul Diergart, *Zeitschrift für angewandte Chemie*, 33, 299 (1920), regarding the history of the discovery of tellurium. See also M. E. Weeks, "The Discovery of the Elements," who stresses that despite the mistaken notion of many writers that Klaproth was the discoverer, the latter always credited the discovery to von Müller.

George Edmund Dann, "Martin Heinrich Klaproth," Akademie-Verlag
Berlin, 1958.

From: Bugge, "Buch der Grossen Chemiker," vol. I (1929), pp.
334–341, slightly abbreviated. Translated by Ralph E. Oesper.

GÜNTHER BUGGE

·· 23 ··

Benjamin Rush

1745-1813

IN THE exhibition hall of the National Archives, sealed in a display case in an atmosphere of helium, is the Declaration of Independence of the United States of America. Below and to the right of the oversized signature of John Hancock stands another name, Benjamin Rush.

The act of signing this piece of parchment was alone sufficient to immortalize Rush, but even if he had not served in the Continental Congress he would be remembered as one of the greatest of colonial physicians and one of America's earliest professors of chemistry.

Rush was born on a farm near Philadelphia, December 24, 1745. He attended the College of New Jersey (Princeton University), and then went into the pharmacy of Dr. John Redman in Philadelphia, intending eventually to become a physician. Redman's pharmacy was an important step in Rush's chemical career. There, by his diligence and ambition, he impressed the patrons, one of whom was John Morgan, a physician who had recently persuaded the College of Philadelphia to open a medical school, the first in the colonies. Morgan's title was Professor of the Theory and Practice of Physick, but he also acted as professor of chemistry because there was no one else in town who knew enough about chemistry to teach it. When Morgan learned of Rush's ambition to study at the University of Edinburgh, then the favorite medical school of Americans, the thought came to Morgan that here, possibly, was a future chemistry teacher for Philadelphia's medical school. So he made a bargain with Rush. He offered to support Rush as a candidate for the professorship of chemistry if Rush would concentrate on chemistry at Edinburgh and come home with a good record. Rush jumped at the opportunity. He took Joseph Black's course twice, and after graduation in 1768 visited Baumé, Macquer, and other French chemists on the continent and inspected plants using chemical processes in England. When he returned to Philadelphia in 1769 he applied to the trustees of the

305

College for the professorship of chemistry and was elected unanimously.

Rush was only 23 years old, and he knew little about the science outside of what he had learned in Europe. Quite naturally he based his course on that of his teacher, a fact easily confirmed by comparing Rush's "Syllabus" and the lecture notes left by his students with Black's "Lectures on the Elements of Chemistry," as published by John Robison, Edinburgh, 1803. This was good fortune for the students since they learned what was probably the best system of chemistry devised up to that time. Rush, however, did not follow Black servilely; he recommended the works of Fourcroy, Macquer, Marggraf, Kirwan, Home, Lewis, Bancroft, Boyle, and other chemists to his students and he wove new information from abroad into his lectures.

Black never went to the trouble of publishing his lectures. Rush, therefore, could not refer his students to a text of the master, but he could help them in obtaining an over-all view of the course by drawing up an outline that he published in 1770 under the title, "Syllabus of a Course of Lectures on Chemistry." This was the first chemistry text printed in the colonies. Rush brought out a second edition in the 1770's and a third in 1783.

Like Black, Rush performed lecture demonstrations for his students, but he was hampered by the lack of chemicals and apparatus. James Cutbush, an early American chemist who knew Rush, said that he showed only four or five demonstrations, but "so little was this science pursued at that time in the United States, that this simple exhibition occasioned a numerous assemblage of medical students."

The professorship of chemistry gave Rush a steady income, and, by publicizing his name, a profitable medical practice. He worked incessantly. In speaking of his life at this time he said:

> Medicine is my wife; science is my mistress; books are my companions; my study is my grave; there I lie buried, the world 'forgetting, by the world forgot'. . . .

He wrote articles for the layman and the scientist—his first article, "An Account of the Effects of the Strammonium or Thorn-Apple" appeared in *Transactions of the American Philosophical Society,* 1771.

Handicapped by the lack of a laboratory and equipment Rush did little in chemical research, but in 1773 he carried out an investigation of mineral waters, a favorite study of those times. In the vicinity of Philadelphia were several springs noted for their medical virtues. Rush obtained samples from the Abington and Bristol wells, and from a well within the city. He evaporated the samples to dryness, and estimated the relative quantities of iron oxide, earth, and salt in the residues. He combined his report with directions for the medical use of the waters, and published the information in a pamphlet, "Experiments and Observations on the Mineral Waters of Philadelphia, Abington, and Bristol, in the Province of Pennsylvania."

This study was no great contribution to science, but it is of interest as one of the earliest quantitative analyses that was made in the colonies. Furthermore it illustrates one of Rush's characteristics as a chemist, his tendency to apply science to practical problems rather than to concern himself with theory.

Busy as Rush was he found time for what historians call "humanitarian movements," one of which, education, is of particular interest to us because Rush set out to teach chemistry to adults and girls, two groups of people then generally ignored by educators. The adult course he prepared in the autumn of 1774 by skimming the main topics from his collegiate course, and then advertising his wares in the *Pennsylvania Packet:*

> At the request of a number of his fellow-citizens, Doctor Rush will deliver eight lectures on such parts of chemistry as abound with the greatest variety of the most useful and entertaining facts and experiments, in the College of this city. The subjects of these lectures will be as follows:
>
> Of the effects of heat upon all bodies. Of the history of cold. Of climates. Of the structure of thermometers, &c. Of the phenomena of mixture, and of the laws of chemical attraction. Of the chemical apparatus. Of the objects of chemistry. Of simple and compound salts. Of the manufactories of salt-petre and gun powder. Of the irregularity in the arrangement of the strata of earths on the surface of the globe. Of the manufactories of glass and porcelane. Of in-

flammable bodies. Of phosphorus. Of aether. Of the causes of meteors, fire damps, &c. Of the metals. Of the art of alchemy, or the philosopher's stone. Of the causes of earthquakes and volcanoes. Of mineral waters. Of the nature, origin and uses of fixed air. Of the chemical history of vegetables. Of fermentation. Of wines, beer, &c. Of the chemical history of animal bodies. Of the elements or principles of agriculture.

These lectures will begin on Monday the 9th of January, at six o'clock in the evening, and will be continued three times a week until the whole are delivered. Tickets at one guinea each may be had of Mr. John Dunlap, Mr. Robert Aitken, and at the London Coffee House.

We do not know how the townspeople greeted Rush's lectures. The times were bad. The dark clouds that preceded the storm of the revolution were gathering on the horizon, and Rush's pupils had more stirring matters to think about than "the chemical history of vegetables," or "chemical apparatus." Many years passed before the country was back to normal, and by then Rush had other things on his mind. Had it not been for the interruption, his evening public lectures might have grown into an annual event, and might have stimulated the study and application of chemistry in Philadelphia. As it is, Rush's course remains one of the earliest series of public lectures on science given in America and perhaps the first on the subject of chemistry.

The public lectures and the college class of 1774–75 ended the first phase of Rush's career in chemical education. The medical school closed its doors to ride out the revolutionary storm. The Pennsylvania Convention elected him to Congress on July 20, 1776, and on August 2 he signed the Declaration of Independence. He went into the Continental Army as a physician and, shocked by the deplorable status of the medical services, tried to indict his superior officers, but only succeeded in bringing about his own resignation. In the midst of these political and military activities he also turned his knowledge of chemistry to the assistance of the revolutionists, who needed gunpowder.

Rush had actually begun to worry about the supply of munitions some years earlier, particularly after the British government had forbidden the colonists to import saltpeter, the major ingredient of gunpowder. He had written an article on the preparation of saltpeter for the November 28, 1774 issue of the newspaper "Pennsylvania Packet." He followed this by another article in the January 25, 1775 issue of the "Pennsylvania Journal," explaining the methods given by Glauber and Cramer. In June, 1775, he combined these articles into an essay for the "Pennsylvania Magazine." Congress took his magazine article, added an essay by Benjamin Franklin on the German practice, and published it as a pamphlet, "Several Methods of Making Salt-Petre; Recommended to the Inhabitants of the United Colonies, by Their Representatives in Congress." Dispatch riders carried copies to the colonies. Massachusetts Bay and New York reprinted it, and John Nathan Hutchins placed extracts in his "Almanack and Ephemeris."

The following year Congress appointed Rush to a committee to improve the quality of gunpowder made in colonial mills. The Committee of Safety in Philadelphia placed him on a committee to superintend the manufacture of saltpeter at a small factory. On the basis of their experience, Rush and his co-workers drew up a report, "The Process for Extracting and Refining Salt-Petre, According to the Method Practiced at the Provincial Works in Philadelphia," for the assistance of other munitions makers.

We have no way of telling how much dependence Revolutionary manufacturers placed on Rush's essays, but country-wide circulation certainly gave his writings some significance in the American search for gunpowder.

The College of Philadelphia reopened in 1778. Shortly thereafter a quarrel born during the Revolution caused the political party in power to charter a new institution, the University of the State of Pennsylvania, in place of the College. This angered Rush; nevertheless he agreed to continue his courses. Subsequently the trustees of the University ordered professors to take an oath of loyalty to the radical state government, which Rush refused to do, and they hired William Shippen who, Rush felt, had been responsible for poor management of Army hospitals. So Rush turned his back and refused to teach again until 1783.

During these years Rush practiced medicine and carried on his civic interests. In 1781 one of his former pupils, Dr. Hugh Martin, returned from Fort Pitt and opened the door for one of Rush's

309

most interesting experiences in chemistry. Martin claimed that he had discovered a cancer medicine used by Indians in the forests of western Pennsylvania. He advertised his medicine in newspapers, wrote a pamphlet, "Narrative of a Discovery of a Sovereign Specific, for the Cure of Cancers," and soon had a profitable clientele. Rush was suspicious of Martin and tried to ascertain the nature of the drug, but Martin evaded his old teacher.

In 1784 Martin died. Rush hurried to the executors of the estate, obtained a sample of the medicine, took it home and analyzed it. It turned out to be arsenic oxide, a substance used occasionally by physicians in the treatment of skin cancer.

Rush's exposure of Martin's fraud, published in the *Transactions of the American Philosophical Society,* in the popular magazine *American Museum* and in Rush's *Medical Inquiries and Observations,* gave Rush publicity, and doubtless boosted his medical practice. Aside from its value to the medical profession, the analysis showed Americans the usefulness of chemistry at a time when the practical value of the science had not come to be widely realized.

In yet another way Rush showed his countrymen the utility of chemistry, by teaching girls how science entered into homemaking. This came about in 1787 when he helped organize the Young Ladies' Academy of Philadelphia. His philosophy of female education was simple and practical: in a pioneer country, girls should learn useful, rather than entertaining, subjects. Chemistry and physics were constantly applied to the management of the home, and therefore they should be taught.

During the autumn of the year Rush put his theory into practice by drawing up a course of twelve lectures designed to acquaint girls with the chemical and physical principles behind cooking and housekeeping. This, so far as we are aware, was the first course in chemistry ever given to girls in America. In the course seven lectures were devoted to the principles of chemistry. This material was an abridgment of Rush's course in the medical school. The final five lectures pointed out the applications. Rush prepared an outline of his course for the girls and had it published under the title, "Syllabus of Lectures, Containing the Application of the

Principles of Natural Philosophy, and Chemistry, to Domestic and Culinary Purposes."

Rush explained to the girls the rationale behind extinguishing fires in chimneys, removing wine or cherry stains from linen, choosing materials of construction for the home, washing, bleaching, dyeing, and even "preserving female beauty." In thus applying chemistry to home economics, Rush scored another "first" in American education.

Rush's course, based on the old phlogiston theory ("By adding a body which abounds with phlogiston to this calx and melting, it may be restored to metal again: thus grease melted with calx of lead reduces it to lead") and filled with odd ideas ("Heat passes slowly through white bodies. Hence, the use of white hats and clothes in summer and hence the goodness of Providence in covering the heads of old people with white hair") strikes us today as being quaintly humorous. But withal Rush deserves much credit for his originality and foresight in drawing up a type of course that colleges adopted more than a century later.

Two years after his course at the Young Ladies' Academy, Rush switched from the professorship of medicine in the medical school to the professorship of theory and practice of physic. These two years are of interest to us because during this period the ideas of Lavoisier were sailing across the Atlantic to America. We should like to know in what spirit Rush received and transmitted the new French chemistry. We know that he had been in the habit of varying his course to meet changes in chemistry, introducing the discoveries of Ingenhouz, Priestley, and others to his classes, but this is no guarantee that he was receptive to such radical ideas as those of Lavoisier. Since almost all of his chemical career lay in the phlogiston period, he could be excused if he were slow in adopting the new theories. The question of Rush's feelings toward antiphlogistic chemistry cannot be determined definitely.

In 1789 Rush left chemistry and thereafter confined himself almost solely to the teaching and practice of medicine. Still, he continued to exert an influence on chemistry through his students and through men whom he guided into professorships. We have no exact figure of the number of students who attended his courses between 1769 and 1789, but an estimate would be between 1000 and 1500. He taught chemistry to more men than any other American up to the end of the eighteenth century, probably more than all other eighteenth century American chemistry professors combined. One of his students, John Penington, wrote "Chemical and Economical Essays" (Philadelphia, 1790), one of the earliest American chemistry books.

He was succeeded as professor of chemistry by one of his students, Caspar Wistar, who in 1791 gave way to another of his students, James Hutchinson. In 1794 when the chair of chemistry was again vacant, Rush led the campaign to obtain Joseph Priestley. The trustees elected Priestley, only to have him decline, after considerable vacillation. Rush then suggested James Woodhouse, one of his favorite pupils, who won the election and went on to become the first internationally known American chemist. When Woodhouse died in 1809 Rush championed another of his former students, John Redman Coxe. Coxe won the election, but had Rush lived long enough he might have regretted this victory, for Coxe turned out to be the one conspicious failure in the university's long line of competent chemistry professors. In the same year, 1809, Rush tried to persuade the trustees of the university to create a professorship of natural philosophy in the medical school and to place Robert Hare in the position. The trustees refused to open a new chair, but the soundness of Rush's judgment of Hare is shown by the fact that Hare later (1818) was elected professor of chemistry and went on to become the country's greatest chemist in the pre-Civil War era.

Joseph Priestley had high regard for Rush. In discussing his thoughts about the vacant chair of chemistry at the university, Priestley wrote to Rush: "The Professorship of Chemistry in your College has, I own, some attractions for me, and one of the principal is the opportunity it would give me of having the advantage of your society, the loss of which I often speak of with regret." The two men talked over their ideas on chemistry, and Rush, when Priestley was in town, acted as Priestley's physician. Priestley, who lived away from the world in Northumberland, longed, occasionally, for the intellectual atmosphere of the big city, and on one occasion he wrote to Rush: "I frequently think with much pleasure and regret on the many happy hours I spent in your company, and wish we were not at so great distance. Such society would be the balm of life to me."

Rush's students respected and admired him. Thomas Duché Mitchell, a member of Rush's class, a founder of the Columbian Chemical Society, and later professor of chemistry at Transylvania University and Ohio Medical College, wrote in his student notebook a "Eulogium on Rush":

> While Empires totter and in ruin lie,
> And monarchs fall and all their glories die,
> Thy name, O! Rush, shall brave the wreck of time,
> And live revered in ev'ry distant clime;
> Shall cheer the sons of science on their way,
> And beam around them with the light of day;
> Thy fame shall burn, when dazzling lights expire,
> And unborn ages feel the glowing fire.

Even outside of the university Rush's influence was felt. In 1795, upon his advice, a young Scottish emigrant named John Maclean settled at Princeton, where he demonstrated his knowledge of chemistry so well that the college elected him its first professor of chemistry and natural history.

Samuel Miller, of New York, wrote in his "Brief Retrospect of the Eighteenth Century" (1803), a two-volume history of American culture, that Rush had done "more in his capacity as teacher than all other physicians in the United States, collectively, to diffuse a taste for medical inquiries, and to excite a spirit of observation, and of laudable ambition, among the students of medicine in our country."

Chemistry and Rush met for the last time in the Columbian Chemical Society, organized in August, 1811, to which his admirers elected him an honorary member. He died on April 19, 1813, and was interred in the burial ground of Christ Church, not far from the graves of two other Americans who had signed the Declaration of Independence, Benjamin Franklin and Francis Hopkinson. After his death his services to his country and to medicine were remembered and magnified while his part in the story of early American chemistry was almost forgotten.

Rush was the prototype of early American chemists, of the men who earned their living directly or indirectly from medicine or some other endeavor and who followed chemistry because they liked it. He was not a notable researcher or practicing chemist like some of his contemporaries in Europe, but he was a first-class teacher. He stimulated his student's interest in science, taught them to be observant, and by his own example instilled in them the virtues of diligence and thoughtfulness. James Cutbush, himself a professor of chemistry, and one of the earliest American historians of chemistry, called Rush "the father of chemistry in America."

NOTES AND REFERENCES

Scores of articles have been written about Rush's activities and contributions to American medicine and culture. Nathan G. Goodman has published a full-length biography, "Benjamin Rush, Physician and Citizen, 1746–1813," University of Pennsylvania Press, Philadelphia, 1934.

George W. Corner edited "The Autobiography of Benjamin Rush," Princeton University Press, Princeton, 1948.

Lyman H. Butterfield compiled and edited two volumes of "Letters of Benjamin Rush," Princeton University Press, Princeton, 1951.

For Rush's career in chemistry see Wyndham D. Miles, "Benjamin Rush, Chemist," *Chymia, 4,* 37–77 (1953).

WYNDHAM D. MILES

·· 24 ··

Claude-Louis Berthollet

1748-1822

BERTHOLLET belongs to the great chemists of all times, by virtue of his thoughtful interpretation of chemical facts, the comprehensiveness of their compilation, and the concepts and laws which he discovered.

Claude-Louis Berthollet was born November 9, 1748, in the small town of Talloire near Lake Annecy. At 22 he was a doctor of medicine in Turin; two years later, in Paris, he devoted himself to further studies. Boerhaave's student, Tronchin, recommended him to the Duke of Orléans, and through the generosity of the latter Berthollet was able to carry out chemical researches in his own laboratory. Along with medicochemical researches which had no very important outcome, he touched various facets of the then existing field of chemistry. Greater things were going on in laboratories and in scientific institutions around him. Lavoisier had begun his publications on oxygen and the overthrow of the phlogiston theory; from England, Germany, and Sweden came new discoveries. Berthollet was especially interested in the discovery of muriatic acid by Scheele, the untiring experimenter. Experiments with this acid caused Berthollet to become one of the first important chemists to abandon the phlogiston theory and to accept the new system of oxygen completely. The year 1784 was a turning point in his life and his thinking. In that year he obtained a government appointment and began the series of publications that extend beyond their actual special field. They deal with the chemistry of chlorine and its practical application, the chemistry of prussic acid and of ammonia. He was active in developing the new nomenclature of chemistry together with Lavoisier, Fourcroy, and Guyton de Morveau.

The second important event in his life was the journey to Egypt in 1798 which he undertook at the request of the government. He met Napoleon, and from then on a close friendship existed between these two dissimilar men. It was at this time that he began his great work, "Research on Affinities." After ten years, when he concluded this work, his health began to fail. Death released him from a long period of suffering on November 7, 1822.

In 1774 Scheele had published his researches on oxidized muriatic (hydrochloric) acid. He heated it with manganese dioxide and obtained a gaslike substance which is yellow-green in color, very reactive, and sparingly soluble in water. The manganese dioxide is simultaneously converted into the ordinary chalk of manganese. Since it was furthermore known that in this change the mineral gave off "vital air," it was clear that it also did this during the operation which produced the yellow-green gas. But since the absorption of vital air into a substance, on the basis of the phlogiston theory, was described as a loss of phlogiston, this gas had to be called dephlogisticated muriatic acid. From the standpoint of the oxygen theory the explanation was quite different. Manganese dioxide gives off oxygen; at the same time this new gas is formed by the muriatic acid, and therefore the gas is an oxidized hydrochloric acid. We give to this acid the formula HCl, and the reaction is explained as an oxidation. However, the oxygen does not appear in that end product on which at that time all attention was focused; rather it combines with the hydrogen while the other ingredient of hydrochloric acid, chlorine, is set free as an element. The composition of the acid was at that time not known. The new system of chemistry led to a mistaken idea which was held for decades. As analogous to nitric, sulfuric, and phosphoric acids, one saw muriatic acid as connected with the substance which was thought to be that which generally made acids. Therefore it seemed clear that muriatic acid was an oxide, even if the base was unknown. Thus arose the concept that chlorine gas was a higher step in the oxidation of this base, in which it was combined with even more oxygen.

Berthollet thought he could prove that oxidized hydrochloric acid contained oxygen and is not just the result of the elimination of hydrogen. A watery solution of chlorine develops oxygen in the light and hydrochloric acid remains in the solution. The simplest explanation seemed to be this: the chlorine loses its oxygen and thereby forms hydrochloric acid. Berthollet was even able to determine quantitatively the amount of oxygen in the chlorine: 87 parts by weight of acid were combined with 13 of oxygen. Two

318

salts are formed upon introducing chlorine into caustic potash solutions, the known chloride, and a new salt which Higgins already knew, but which he had identified erroneously as saltpeter. That this second salt had a high oxygen content is shown by its great effect on inflammable materials when heated.

It took about thirty years until the true nature of hydrochloric acid and chlorine were known, but even then it was not generally recognized. The discussions and disputes over this subject demonstrate the difficulties of experiment and thought in identifying an element. Even after the thorough researches of Gay-Lussac and Davy, Berzelius in 1815 cited many experiments against the elemental nature of chlorine and for the former concept of chlorine as the second oxide of the unknown base of hydrochloric acid, called murium. As late as 1865, Schönbein, still upheld the murium theory. All this is reminiscent of the time, then just ended, of the phlogiston theory; just as in the latter the role of air was not recognized, so in this case it was the function of water that caused difficulties. The combination of error and truth is shown by a conclusion drawn by Berthollet from the behavior of chlorine which became important to the theory of acids—it dissolves metals (iron and zinc) without formation of hydrogen, which in other cases is formed by the solution of metals in acids. But in both cases chlorides form; therefore, Berthollet argued, the idea which was prevalent until that time was false—that the metals in acid solution lose their hydrogen by reaction with acids. When metals react with chlorine directly to form the known salts of hydrochloric acid, then they have combined with the oxygen in chlorine. They behave in a similar manner when dissolved in ordinary acid: they combine with the oxygen, take the oxygen out of the water and thus liberate its other component, hydrogen. This erroneous theory was not easily disproved.

Scheele had already found that chlorine bleaches plant colors and thereby forms hydrochloric acid. Oxygen, too, has a bleaching action, therefore chlorine must give off oxygen when it becomes hydrochloric acid. As commissar for the directorship of dyeing plants, Berthollet had a special incentive for his interest in this phenomenon. He found a new technical application for it. The yellowish color of fabrics was ordinarily destroyed by bleaching in the sun. This took months, necessitated various treatments with alkaline lyes, several washings, and plenty of good weather. With the use of chlorine water the bleaching process was speeded up considerably. Berthollet applied solutions of chlorine of varying diminishing strengths, rinses with potash lyes and dilute sulfuric acid followed, varied according to the differences of weaves and yarns. The use of chlorine in dyeing very soon penetrated industry. It is noteworthy that even at that time a new substance gained industrial significance not much later than ten years after its discovery.

Berthollet's trip to Egypt in 1798 lead to numerous experiments in the field of dyeing, which of course were also connected with his public office. The existing French practice of appointing scientists to posts in state manufactures again proved fruitful in this instance. Berthollet realized that many dyestuffs have a strong affinity to earthen and metallic bases. Similarly, there are attractive forces between the dyestuff and the fiber. He applied the "pneumatic doctrine," i.e., the knowledge of the nature of gases, particularly oxygen, to the explanation of the chemistry of dyestuffs. In the process of developing indigo and setting it free from its naturally occurring compound by a fermentation, hydrogen is liberated so that the remaining substance gains a higher carbon content. To this he attributed the deep color of indigo, which approximates the black of coal. Although rather vague and confined to loosely woven analogies, this is the beginning of a chemical theory of dyestuffs.

According to Scheele, ammonia gas consists of nitrogen and phlogiston, that is, nitrogen and hydrogen, as Priestley found. Berthollet discovered (1785) that ammonia reacts violently with chlorine, as hydrogen does with chlorine, and that nitrogen is thereby liberated. According to Priestley's method, he analyzed ammonia by means of electrical sparks and then burned the hydrogen with oxygen, and found the first quantitative result: 80 parts of nitrogen are combined with 20 parts of hydrogen. Davy later confirmed this result which is only approximately correct.

Again according to Scheele, prussic acid is formed by heating coal, potash, and sal ammoniac (ammonium chloride). Prussic acid itself does not contain ammonia, as Bergmann and Scheele believed, and it contains no oxygen, even though it reacts very definitely as an acid. Lavoisier's theory claimed that all acids must contain oxygen; but again in hydrogen sulfide Berthollet found no sign of the presence of this acidifying principle. With the exposition of such results he prepared the way for the later theory of acids. When he participated in developing a nomenclature for the new system of chemistry, either he himself was not clear about it or else he compromised, so that oxygen is still described there as the general acidifying element.

Explanations for the causes of chemical change had been sought in concepts of hate and love between the elements. Such concepts were close enough to human feelings to recur in many chemical ideas for hundreds of years. The atomists sought and found a mechanical explanation: the form of atoms and certain attachments to them determine whether the various components of a substance fit together and how they adhere. Boerhaave spoke of the friendship and relationship of combining substances. But is it not rather the unrelated, the opposites that strive to come together? When different substances strive toward each other with varying degrees of strength, then one can perhaps make them quantitatively comparable and assign them definite numbers. This is what Geoffrey the Elder attempted to do in his "Tables of Relationships." But are the relationships so constant that one numerical relationship is sufficient? There were examples enough to show that the effect differs according to temperature, concentration, and impurities. There was more promise in the attempt of Carl Friedrich Wenzel to find the strength of affinities, under exactly controlled conditions, from the intensity of the reactions. To him the chemical effect seemed stronger the higher the concentration of the effective substance was in their solutions.

Among the many other contemporaries who explored the connection between affinity and mass only Jeremias Benjamin Richter had some success with his "Tables of Relationships" (1792–1802). They gave a survey of the saturation ratios of a great number of acids and bases and were limited to reactions of neutralization. Many experiments had been made in measuring relationships; the works of the Count de Buffon (1775), of Macquer (1766), and of Guyton de Morveau (1780) had contributed considerably to the knowledge of various types of affinities. Berthollet carried the problem one important step further by conceiving of chemical relationship as a force of equal importance with the other known forces. If the compression of a gas requires force in a physical sense, then affinity must likewise exert force in overcoming elasticity when a gaseous substance is transformed into a solid chemical compound, for instance, when a metal condenses gaseous oxygen into a solid oxide. When, on the other hand, a solid body can be formed from two substances brought together in a dilute solution, then it is formed by the force of cohesion. The possibility of forming a volatile gas or of a solid precipitate is decisive in the formation of the products of reaction. The effect of the affinity is proportional to the effective quantity, for the reason that affinity is a physical, not an elective, force. Berthollet expressed this very boldly near the end of the first volume of his "Essay":

> I have been led, through these various observations, to conclude that chemical affinity does not follow any special laws, but rather that all phenomena which depend on the reciprocal effects of the bodies are effects of the same qualities which physics seeks to encompass: that, therefore, in this respect one should not differentiate between physics and chemistry, and that the affinity of various substances which causes their combination is not selective but variable according to the effective quantity and the conditions which contribute to these operations.

Heat has the property of expanding bodies; it is because of this that it influences chemical operations. The then prevalent assumption that heat, light, and electricity were substances prevented him from seeing their influences more clearly.

Thus we have three physical conditions on which the course of the chemical reactions depends: (1) elasticity—the endeavor of gases to fill up a large space; (2) cohesion—the firm clinging together of parts of some substances, which causes their insolubility; (3) the mass of participants in a reaction which can be influenced when gases and insoluble substances leave the system.

322

From this Berthollet gathers several general laws dealing with chemical compounds, including alloys and solutions.

> When an obstacle hinders a continued progression of combination and demands a gathering of force, then the combination at the moment that this accumulated force is overcome suddenly assumes the complete quantity and all characteristics which it would have gained had the progression been continuous, in the manner in which water at the boiling point takes on all the heat which corresponds to the vaporous state. In compounds which separate because they are insoluble, the force of cohesion is the obstacle; but they do not always take on the proportions of the greatest degree of insolubility; they may have a surplus of one or another element, according to the quantities which can exert their influence, so that only a small number of compounds exists whose proportions would be constant.

In chemistry the concept of discontinuities had predominated. Here is the attempt to assert the principle of continuity in chemistry, illustrated by the striking example of the heat of evaporation. Of course, the result is immediately dimmed, if not destroyed, by the conclusion that the combining weights change at random. This rests on the arbitrary assumption of an analogy which later forms the basis of the explanation of the experiments. In the biography of Proust (Chapter 25) more is said on this subject. But it is greatly to Berthollet's credit that he carried through an energetic concept of affinity with as much clarity as the existing state of chemistry permitted. His vision included the chemical processes in living organisms, for which Berzelius was not the last who could not proceed without the assumption of a life force.

> It seems to me too, that the combinations which constantly go on in living animals are also an effect of affinity which is changed through circumstances as in other chemical phenomena, but these circumstances are more numerous; organic action can change them further by contractions and movements which are subject to organic sympathy and living influences.

It took almost one hundred years and, after many preparations, the combined efforts of Wilhelm Ostwald and his contemporaries to show that an energetic concept of chemical events is possible.

NOTES AND REFERENCES

Pierre Lemay, "Berthollet," *Rev. hist. pharmacie, 145,* 80–83 (1955).

From: Bugge, "Buch der Grossen Chemiker," vol. I, pp. 342–349.
Translated by Dora S. Farber.

EDUARD FARBER

·· *25* ··

Joseph Louis Proust

1754-1826

PROUST's most outstanding and, for the development of chemistry, most significant achievement was the experimental proof of the law that chemical substances combine to form chemical compounds in constant proportions by weight. In any particular quantity of zinc oxide, zinc and oxygen are present in the same proportionate amounts; when other metals form two different oxides or chlorides, then each of these is characterized by the relative weights of the components. There is, then, a lower and a higher oxide. The relative content of oxygen in one is sharply and constantly different from that in the other. Therefore, the proportions of the combining weights can change discontinuously.

His many other chemical researches were determined by Proust's studies with Rouelle and the tasks set for him by his teacher, such as the inorganic components of urine and urea. Also they were occasioned by the interest which, in time of war, is often directed at substitute substances and materials of war (grape sugar to replace cane sugar, camphor, black powder for cannons). As Berthollet's outward circumstances determined his chemical tasks—his position as commissioner of dye works, his studies on travel to Egypt—so the circumstances of the country in which Proust lived for a long time influenced his field of work—the raw materials and manufactures peculiar to Spain. A skilled experimenter and observer, a sharp and eloquent disputant, independent and able to rise above misfortune—thus he appears in the reports of his contemporaries and in his scientific papers. This man, thin and of medium height, had not only outwardly a *physiognomie voltairienne.*

He was born September 26, 1754, in Angers. He followed the occupation of his father, an apothecary, with great success and was later the favorite student of Rouelle. From 1777 to 1780 he was professor of chemistry at the Real Seminario de Vergara. His lectures at the Musée, later the Lycée du Palais Royal, attained great fame. Recalled by the Spanish king, a laboratory was put at his disposal (1791) in Madrid. Its appointments were considered

327

magnificent by his own countrymen. With modest means he continued his researches in France. In 1817 he returned to his native town and died there on July 5, 1826.

That Nature deals with the composition of substances with scales in her hand, as it were, was clear to him from the beginning. Actually, this is of course the presupposition for all quantitative analysis: that it deals not only with the substance that happens to be used at the time, but one that may be produced again and again. If it is qualitatively the same, it must also have the same composition quantitatively. That exactly definable substances are also always qualitatively the same, that a particular vitriol always has the same properties—this was not at all to be taken for granted. It was the conclusion reached after hundreds of years of experimental chemistry. To this constancy of properties the quantitative era of chemistry now brought the recognition of the constancy of the components. For scientific chemistry a pure substance must be the same in all its parts, including the dimensions of atoms and molecules. In equal parts of a substance the proportions of the component elements are always constant. Proust saw proof of this in the fact that natural copper carbonate had the same components as copper carbonate made synthetically in the laboratory.

These never changing proportions, these constant characteristics, which define the compounds of art or nature, in one word this 'pondus naturae' that Stahl saw so clearly, all this, I say, is no more in the power of chemists than the law of specificity which rules all compounds.

In the year in which Proust wrote this, Berthollet began his lectures at the Egyptian Institute where he set forth the opposite contention, namely, that constant combining proportions are brought about only through chance by influential circumstances. Thus, a dispute, lasting many years, began between these two very different men, both great thinkers, a dispute which neither then nor today could be solved by assuming that the successful experiments were on one side and the unsuccessful ones on the other.

328

Proust's studies actually originated in technology. He explored what went on in the distillations of quicksilver from cinnabar, as they were carried out very frequently in Almadén. In the oxidation of quicksilver he found the idea and the proof of constant proportions. He had gained the background for this work with his teacher, Rouelle, who, in 1754, had already determined the constant and discontinually changing proportions of the elements in salts, at least insofar as he differentiated between salts with a minimum and salts with a maximum surplus of acidity. In iron Proust first found the significant generalization of these relationships. There are two sets of iron compounds, for instance, a green and a red vitriol. They can be sharply differentiated by their chemical behavior. Only the red vitriol forms Prussian blue or gives a black compound with pyrogallol. With alkali, the solutions of the salts form a greenish precipitate from the green vitriol, from the red vitriol a brown precipitate. These colors, too, mark the difference of the compound. To be sure, when exposed to air, the green precipitate gradually turns brown; but the substances formed in the intermediary stages are not pure, they are mixtures of the two extremes. Only these extremes exist as true compounds. They correspond to two oxides with greatly differing oxygen content. Of course, the quantitative determinations which Proust performed on them are quite far from the proportions later recognized as correct; Klaproth was already able to make much more exact analyses. It also should be pointed out that Proust did not yet see (indeed, from the figures obtained through his experiments, was not able to see) that the discontinuously differing combining weights are simple multiples.

He proved that for iron, tin, lead, copper, antimony, nickel, and cobalt there are two distinctly separate oxides. Two sets of salts should also be present. The chloride, sulfate, and nitrate of these metals should exist in two sets, which, however, could not yet be unequivocally determined.

Mixtures and solutions should be sharply distinguished from true compounds. The boundary line could not then be exactly defined; yet Proust was very sure of its existence. "The solution of ammonia in water can, in my eyes, not be the same as that of hydrogen in nitrogen which produces ammonia. The solution of

329

silver sulphide in antimony sulphide, which produces 'red silver,' is not the same as the solution of silver in sulphur, which produces the sulphide of this metal." Proust felt that the combination between iron and oxygen, or zinc and sulfur, stops at two different levels; the color change led him to this conclusion. To be sure, we do not see the discontinuous change of weight proportions itself, "but although we cannot intuitively see what happens in a true calcination, the only way we can judge this clearly is with the help of the countless analogies with which the field of compounds supplies us."

The difference between Berthollet and Proust was so marked because they used such different kinds of "countless analogies." For Berthollet they are connected with general thoughts and physical forces; for Proust with specific experimental methods of chemical separation. These he considered appropriate and proved successful. To Berthollet they appeared artificial, to Proust they followed Nature's own rules.

Of the analytical methods which Proust developed, the use of hydrogen sulfide to precipitate heavy metals from solutions of their salts is especially important. This method has since become part of the basis of analytical chemical procedures.

Proust's investigations of combining proportions are the only ones which had a purely scientific goal and outcome. In his other work he aimed at practical applications—improving living conditions, finding new means of nourishment, applying new methods for manufacturing gunpowder and detonating fuses. Occasional investigations were concerned with the possibility of making camphor from indigenous plants, others with uric acid and kidney stones.

Marggraf and Achard had attempted to make sugar from beets, but, according to Proust, they were still far from developing a good substitute for colonial cane sugar. He found it possible to obtain sugar from grapes, especially abundant in France and Spain. The methods for cane sugar devised mainly by Dutronne proved very helpful. Some of the calcium salt of malic acid remained in this grape sugar, but only ignorant people would object to this. On the contrary, the refining is carried unnecessarily far; at least for the poor, the "liquid" sugars in the molasses should not be discarded.

The publication on grape sugar, which appeared about four years after the experiments had first been performed, aroused great interest and controversy over plagiarism and priority. Actually, Tobias Lowitz (1757–1804) had, in 1792, isolated a sugar from honey which crystallized in cauliflowerlike aggregates, and he had described many of its chemical aspects. Proust published his work at the time when sugar imports were cut off by England, and Napoleon offered him 100,000 francs to start the manufacture of grape sugar. Proust declined; it is not known for what reason.

Also of interest are Proust's studies on vegetable gluten, "the sticky mass which remains after the starch is removed by kneading wheat flour with water." The fermentation of this gluten to a kind of cheese had been observed long before Proust; carbon dioxide, ammonia, and vinegar had been found in the substance. More characteristic substances were obtained by washing the cheese; cheese acid, which is soluble in alcohol, and the insoluble white powder contained therein, the cheese oxide. Both were examined as to their behavior to the usual reagents and especially in distillation. The cheese oxide sublimes first; at higher temperature it decomposes with a strange odor, from which Proust concluded that this substance belongs on the one hand to the fats and on the other hand to the animal oxides. "And in fact, its more fatty than powdery texture, its volatility, its combustability and its white flame, the abundance of oil, the small amount of water and still less of ammonia, all this seems to belong to the oily or superhydrogenated substances." On the other hand, its solubility and the ease with which it changes to oxalic acid would make it akin to oxides. Proust concluded that it must be, on the whole, an oxide in which Nature had been sparing with oxygen and nitrogen. In this connection the manufacture of cheese itself was discussed; this led to the kumiss of the Tatars. "All this brings me, I don't know how, to the potatoes." But he really did know how: through his doubting the formation of alcohol from starch. What he had found was later called leucin.

From barley flour, instead of gluten another similar substance was obtained. Proust called it hordein. After the germination of barley much less hordein is found. Proust concluded from his researches on this raw material for making beer that this must be a good food. He tried to make a vegetable from the lichen of Iceland (*lichen islandiscus*) after removing from it a bitter "extractable principle." Through this, he came to speak of scorbute (scurvy), against which grape sugar is also supposed to be effective. He recommended that soup tablets made from bones and meat be given to soldiers as concentrated nourishment. His studies on gunpowder were very comprehensive. He prepared mixtures of coals, determined the distance of the shot, the duration of the burning of the powders with a short pendulum, weighed the residues, and analyzed the combustion gases. These systematic measurements, however, lead only to the conclusion that the "old" proportions of mixing saltpeter were the best.

From: Bugge, "Buch der Grossen Chemiker," vol. I, pp. 350–355. Translated by Dora S. Farber.

EDUARD FARBER

·· 26 ··

John Dalton

1766-1844

J OHN DALTON, the founder of the chemical atomic theory of the constitution of matter, was born about the fifth of September, 1766, in the village of Eaglesfield, near Cockermouth, in Cumberland. He was the son of a poor hand-loom weaver, and always lived in relatively humble circumstances. Throughout his life he was solely dependent on his own exertions, yet he rose to be one of the most famous of men. His career illustrates in a remarkable manner the fact that independence of character may lead a powerful mind to conclusions of the greatest importance, notwithstanding deficiencies resulting from imperfect education and rural environment.

His parents, Joseph and Deborah Dalton, came of an old Cumbrian Quaker stock, and had six children. Three of these children, Jonathan, John, and Mary, lived to a good old age, three others died early. John, like his brothers and sisters, was brought up in the necessarily hard conditions of life imposed by the poverty of the family, and to a large extent was self-taught. He had the good fortune, however, to be sent to the village school at Eaglesfield carried on by Mr. Fletcher, a Cumbrian Quaker schoolmaster of much ability, and attended there "till eleven years of age, at which period he had gone through a course of mensuration, surveying, navigation, etc." Dalton in his early years not only attracted the attention of his Quaker schoolmaster, but also that of another remarkable Eaglesfield man, Mr. Elihu Robinson, who became his patron and then his fast friend for life. Mr. Elihu Robinson was a capable meteorologist and also a skilled instrument maker, and young Dalton was particularly fortunate to have so good a coach in those days to assist him in his studies.

The progress which young Dalton made under these stimulating influences was very great, for, in his own words, he "began about twelve to teach the village school, and continued it two years." As the emoluments coming to the "head" of the school were not large, young Dalton had to increase his earnings by working as a laborer on a small patch of land which his father farmed.

335

When Dalton was fifteen, in 1781, he left Eaglesfield to become an assistant in a school for "Friends" of both sexes at Kendal, where he "remained in that capacity for three or four years, then undertook the same school as principal and continued it for eight years."

During the twelve years that John Dalton kept school at Kendal he was unceasingly engaged in self-improvement. He contributed frequently to a semieducational periodical entitled the *Ladies' and Gentlemen's Diary and Woman's Almanac,* edited by Dr. C. Hutton of the Royal Military Academy, and on more than one occasion received a prize for the solution of problems in mathematics and philosophy.

In Kendal, as at Eaglesfield, Dalton was singularly fortunate in securing the friendship of persons of similar tastes and character. In this instance it was to a blind man (Mr. John Gough) that young Dalton was indebted for a close and valuable friendship. Gough had unfortunately been rendered quite blind by smallpox when about two years old, but in spite of this drawback he was a most competent scholar and investigator. Dalton often gratefully recognized his indebtedness to Gough for the assistance the latter gave him in his studies and investigations.

Following the lead of Elihu Robinson in Eaglesfield, and of John Gough in Kendal, Dalton's first attempts of scientific investigation were daily observations of temperature, barometric pressure, rainfall, dew point, and other meteorological subjects with his homemade instruments. From these early days to the day before his death Dalton continued to make daily observations on the weather, the number of observations which he made and registered during his long life amounting to 200,000. We gain a clue to his motive in these studies from a letter written in his twenty-second year, in which he speaks of "the advantages that might accrue to the husbandman, the mariner, and to mankind in general if we were able to predict the state of the weather with tolerable precision."

In 1787 Dalton tried his hand at public lecturing, as in October of that year he began a course of twelve lectures on natural philosophy at the school in Kendal. In the subsequent years of his life, Dalton repeated his public lectures both in Kendal and elsewhere, but, as would appear, with scanty success, as he was never a really popular exponent of science even in after years when at the height of his fame.

In 1793 Dalton left Kendal and henceforward took up his permanent residence in Manchester, where he had obtained the post of tutor in mathematics and natural philosophy at the New College, an institution which had been established in 1786 by the Presbyterians of Manchester. In Manchester, Dalton soon found a much wider sphere for his great powers than in Kendal, and judging by his letters to his old friends in the North he seems to have been very happy in his new post. He soon found, however, that his time was so much taken up with tuition at the college and with private tuition at home that he had scarcely time to turn to any mathematical or philosophical pursuit. And so as time went on he began to consider the advantages to his freedom which would result from his giving up the tutorship at the college and gaining his living as a private tutor. Accordingly in 1799 he resigned his tutorship at the college, and henceforward devoted his life to scientific inquiry, but earning his bread as a private teacher, principally in mathematics and natural philosophy, to such as might come to him at a charge of two shillings a lesson.

When he arrived in Manchester from Kendal, Dalton brought with him the manuscript of a volume entitled "Meteorological Observations and Essays," and this was printed and published in 1793, and appeared in a second and enlarged edition forty-one years later. These observations were made and the book written at Kendal. The work begins with descriptions of the barometer, thermometer, hygrometer, and rain gauges, and connected with these are tables of observations made at Kendal and Keswick. The book also contains essays on the barometer, on the thermometer and their variations, on the formation of cloud, on evaporation, on the distribution and character of atmospheric moisture, and on the aurora borealis, which if they had been written at the present day might well be considered as remarkable productions from the pen of a well-trained and experienced philosopher. How much more remarkable must they appear when we remember that they were written at the end of the eighteenth century by a young Kendal schoolmaster ignorant, to a great extent, of what had been written by others, and out of reach of libraries and of books of reference.

On October 3, 1794, Dalton was elected a member of the Literary and Philosophical Society of Manchester. In May, 1800, he was elected Secretary of the Society, which office he held until 1808, when he was made a Vice-President. In 1817, he was raised to the dignity of the Presidential Chair, and continued in this high office for the rest of his life. During his long connection with the Society he contributed to it 116 memoirs and essays on various subjects, the more important of which were his first communication read on October 31, 1794, dealing with the "Color Blindness" of himself and his brother, and his communication read on October 21, 1803, introducing his "Chemical Atomic Theory" and his "First Table of the Relative Weights of the Ultimate Particles of Bodies."

The ancient Greek philosophers had long ago taught that matter is made up of small indivisible particles, and the idea of the atomic constitution of matter, and even the belief that chemical combination consists in the approximation of unlike particles, had been already expressed by Kirwan in 1783, as well as by Higgins in 1789. Dalton was, however, the first to propound a truly *chemical atomic theory,* the only one hitherto proposed which explains the facts of chemical combination in a satisfactory manner. The cardinal point upon which Dalton's atomic theory rests, and in which it differs from all previous suggestions, is that it is a *quantitative* theory respecting the constitution of matter, whereas all others are simply *qualitative* views. For while all previous upholders of an atomic theory, including even William Higgins, had supposed that the relative weights of the atoms of the various elements are the same, Dalton at once declared that "the atoms of the different elements are not of the same weight; and that the relative atomic weights of the elements are the proportions by weight in which the elements combine or simple multiples or submultiples of them."

"The atomic theory," wrote Sir William A. Tilden in 1921, "has undergone modification in every direction since Dalton's day. But to the original conception we owe to a large extent the development of chemistry as a department of science. Without it chemistry would have continued to consist of a mass of heterogeneous observations and recipes for performing experiments or for manufacturing metals, salts and all kinds of compounds, but without the law and order by which the whole becomes intelligible."

Dalton was never a good popular lecturer on scientific subjects, but the originality of his ideas and the importance of the facts which he had discovered placed him in the forefront of the scientific men of the age, so that we need not wonder to find that the Royal Institution in London wanted Dalton to give a course of lectures; and he first appeared before that critical audience on December 22, 1803, lecturing not merely on chemistry, but on mechanics and physics, repeating the course again in the winter 1809–10. In 1807 Dalton gave a course of lectures in Edinburgh and in Glasgow, similar to those he had given in London.

It was not until the year 1815 that Dalton came to be known as a man of mark in the scientific world, or rather it was not until then that his merits were fully appreciated by those who were in authority at that time. One of the first marks of this appreciation was the offer to Dalton in 1818 of the post of scientific expert to the expedition which the Government was about to dispatch to the Polar regions under the command of Sir John Ross, but Dalton characteristically refused the offer, preferring to stay at home and carry on his researches in his laboratory rather than to voyage in the cold Polar Seas.

Honors first came to Dalton from abroad. In 1816 he received the first mark of distinction when he was elected a corresponding member of the French Academy of Sciences, and this honor he prized highly.

In 1822 Dalton visited Paris and made the personal acquaintance of the leading French scientists of that time. He attended a meeting of the Academy of Sciences, and also visited the laboratories of some of the great French savants.

In 1810 Sir Humphry Davy proposed to Dalton to offer himself as candidate for election to the Royal Society, London, but for some unknown reason Dalton refused to put in a nomination, and it was not until 1822 that Dalton was proposed (without his knowledge) and duly elected a Fellow of the foremost of English scientific societies.

In 1826 the Royal Society of London awarded the first of the Royal Medals given by the King (William IV) to Dalton "for the development of the chemical theory of definite proportions, usually called the atomic theory, and for his various other labors and discoveries in physical and chemical science." This afforded to Sir Humphrey Davy, as president of the Society, the opportunity of testifying to the high position held by Dalton in the esteem of the world of science.

Honors both from his own country and from abroad, poured in upon Dalton in later life. Davy's death had caused a vacancy among the seats of the eight foreign associates of the French Academy, and to this—one of the highest honors which a man of science can receive—John Dalton was elected in 1830. Other foreign academies—notably those of Berlin, Moscow, and Munich—placed his name on their roll of foreign members.

Dalton was one of the founders of the British Association for the Advancement of Science, and he took part in the early meetings of the Association at York (1831), Oxford (1832), and Cambridge (1833). At the Oxford gathering, in 1832, the degree of D.C.L., was conferred upon him. Probably that ancient university never distributed its honors to four more distinguished men than on that occasion. They were John Dalton, Michael Faraday, David Brewster, and Robert Brown. Dalton evidently seemed proud of his scarlet gown; nor did this color strike him as anything out of keeping with his Quaker habit, for to him both that and the green of the Oxford gardens appeared as a dull drab.

In 1833 Lord Grey's Government granted Dalton a pension of £150 a year and this was increased to £300 a year in 1836. The announcement of the first grant was communicated to Dalton by Professor Sedgwick, the eminent geologist, in his address as President of the British Association for the Advancement of Science delivered in the Senate House of the University of Cambridge, the announcement being received, by the members present, with prolonged applause.

While the Government and the nation were thus testifying to the value of Dalton's work, Manchester was not unmindful that she had a prophet within her walls, and his friends and admirers

340

far and wide were induced to take steps to secure a suitable and lasting memorial of the great citizen in the town where he had so long labored. The question as to whether this should take the shape of a building devoted to scientific research, or of a more personal memorial such as a statue, was at length decided in favor of the second alternative. In 1834, Dalton therefore sat to Chantrey, the sculptor, in London, for the statue destined to stand in the grand entrance of Manchester Town Hall, and opposite to it is the fine statue of James Prescott Joule, Dalton's greatest pupil and follower. Thus is Dalton's memory kept green among the citizens of Manchester.

In 1834 Jonathan Dalton died, and the manner of his decline from paralysis seemed to foreshadow the end of his distinguished brother, for both survived the first seizure several years. The first attack, in the case of John Dalton, occurred in April, 1837. From this he partly recovered but on July 27, 1844, the malady recurred and was followed by a peaceful death a few hours later.

The feeling in Manchester on the death of Dalton was so deep that a public funeral was decided upon. His remains were placed in the darkened Town Hall, and they were visited by no less than 40,000 persons. On August twelfth the funeral took place. A procession of more than one hundred carriages accompanied the body to the Ardwick Cemetery, and many hundreds of persons went on foot to the grave. All the shops and warehouses on the route, and many others, were closed. And thus the body of the simple-minded "Friend" was brought to mother earth.

But Manchester did more than this to honor Dalton. On January 26, 1853, a town meeting was held for the purpose of founding a scholarship for the encouragement of original research in chemistry, to be held in the then newly established Owens College, now the headquarters of Manchester University. A sum of £4000 was raised by public subscription, and a more fitting testimonial could not have been proposed. The establishment of a scholarship for scientific research was at that time a circumstance without a parallel; but, in spite of the novelty of the experiment, the experience of seventy years has fully borne out the wisdom of the course which its originators adopted, and today there exists a long list of "Dalton

Scholars" who have contributed to the progress of chemical science, many of whom hold high and responsible positions in scientific, manufacturing, and official life.

NOTES AND REFERENCES

J. R. Partington, *Ann. Sci.*, 4, 245 (1939).
F. Soddy and J. R. Partington, *Nature*, 167, 734 (1951).
From: *J. Chem. Educ.*, 3, 485 (1926).

ARTHUR HOPWOOD

·· 27 ··

Louis Jacques Thenard

1777-1857

THE story is told us that a boyish herdsman one day exclaimed, "Were I Emperor, I would tend my cows on horseback." "And I," rejoined his comrade, "would eat meat three times a week." "For my part," cried the third and youngest, "if such a thing should happen to me, I would be paid thirty farthings a day, that I might give twenty of them to my mother." Animated by some of these primitive and better inspirations, which find no echo in our large cities, three vigorous lads of Champagne were traversing, on a fine morning in spring, one of the great routes which led to the capital of France. With swelling hearts and light purses they had quitted the paternal roof and the village of La Louptière, near Nogent sur Seine, and had turned their faces toward Paris, not with a view to make their fortunes there, but from an ambition to add something to the stock of knowledge which they had gathered from the lessons of his Reverence, the curate, and Father Bardin, then the oracle of the department. One of the three looked forward to nothing less than being physician of his parish; the others proposed to occupy the same field, as apothecaries; the most enterprising of the three thought of adding something to the profits of the laboratory by a small trade in groceries. What justified the more avaricious projects of the latter was the circumstance that his parents, honest tillers of the soil, had lost some moderate resource through the undistinguishing violence of the revolution, and were burdened besides with the support of five other children. The one now departing, moreover, had been ever the ambitious hope of his mother; what more natural than that he should form plans for her gratification.

As our young adventurers neared the great city, the center of so many illusions, it occurred to the most circumspect of the party that it would not be amiss to scrutinize the resources of their budget. Scrupulously told, the contents could by no dexterity of computation be brought to authorize an outlay of more than sixteen sols (eightpence) a day for each of them. This consideration determined them to direct their steps to the furthest recesses of the

345

Latin Quarter, and even there it was only in the highest story of one of the buildings that they found the refuge of a common chamber. Under the same roof there happened to be then domiciled a family of those hardy natives of Auvergne, who, that they may some day possess a rood or two of land and be enabled to die among their mountains, distribute for thirty years water and charcoal among the inhabitants of the capital. With the maternal head of this family the young financier, whose thoughtful foresight has been already signalized, opened negotiations for himself and his comrades, and although the difficulties of the situation were avowed with the ingenuousness of seventeen, and the worthy dame could not but feel the risk she incurred in undertaking to provide for the demands of three young stomachs on such scanty resources; although it was now the epoch of "ninety-four," and she a mother, or rather perhaps for that very reason, she agreed to receive them as boarders. Thus were physical needs provided for; food and a shelter; who could ask for more?

It remains to say that the conductor of this negotiation, one of the most critical of his life, who thereby secured himself a footing in Paris, was Louis Jacques Thenard, born May 4, 1777. Once or twice in the beginning of this engagement it happened to him to be too late for the culinary arrangements of mother Bateau. The trying abstinence which such a lapse of attention imposed left its lesson. "I acquired from it," he said in after life, "a habit of punctuality from which I have never deviated, and which adds to the claims of that excellent woman to my grateful remembrance."

Two eminent men were then engaged in teaching chemistry. Fourcroy, by the clearness of his intellect and a ready and learned method, had achieved a success which secured him universal reputation. Vauquelin, less brilliant but more experimentative, had amassed by incessant labor the materials with which he has enriched science. Our young Champagnard, all eyes and ears, lost not one of their lessons; he listened and still listened; at length conscientious self-examination satisfied him that he comprehended nothing. At this mortifying discovery, one which the incapable never make, he arrived on a sincere scrutiny of the obstacle at the conclusion, that in a science not purely speculative it is necessary to begin by a practical initiation. Vauquelin, who was then poor,

346

gave admission into his laboratory to such of his scholars as could pay a fee of twenty francs a month, but with such a condition Thenard had no means of complying. Yet here alone could he see any resource, and therefore, taking courage, he presented himself before the professor, candidly disclosed to him at once his penury and his inclination to labor, and entreated to be received, if even on the terms of a domestic assistant. Vauquelin had, however reluctantly, before discarded such offers; the analogy of his own situation at one period did not prevent him from beginning to frame a refusal, when happily the interposing voices of his own sisters, who had entered at the moment and were touched by the mortification, the intelligence and even, through sympathy, by the provincial accent of the young candidate, came to his succor. "Ah, do not send him away; observe how modest, how docile he is; he would not only be useful in the laboratory, but would mind our pot of soup, which most of your dawdlers suffer to spoil by overboiling." Thanks to this lesson in practical chemistry, Thenard was accepted. "I have never been so ungrateful," he used afterward to say, "as to forget that a pot which is allowed to boil can make but indifferent soup." His rapid intelligence and accommodating nature soon made him a favorite with the youth who frequented the laboratory and procured him at the same time the means of extending the circle of his studies and developing his singular dexterity.

Three years now passed by without bringing any marked alleviation of his condition, but without any abatement on his part of heart or hope. Vauquelin at length procured him a tutorship in an institution, and Thenard, though looking but remotely to the exigencies of a lecturer's chair, felt the necessity of reforming an accent and gesture which reflected the impressions of his native province. For this purpose, as well as from a very decided taste, he attended the theatre as often as his stomach would compromise for an abstinence sufficiently long to justify an expenditure of thirty sols. One morning Vauquelin said to him: "I am summoned to Rouen; my course has commenced; you must occupy my place." Unavoidable deficiencies could not but make themselves perceptible, at the first lecture, to the new professor as well as to his audience, but each succeeding one was marked by so much improvement that, at the fifth, Thenard ventured to cast his eye over the throng and discovered Vauquelin and Fourcroy, in a corner, smiling at his efforts. At the sight he precipitately abdicated the chair. But from that time those eminent men labored in concert for his advancement, and succeeded in securing him an assistant professorship at the Polytechnic School. The earliest accession of a little ease and leisure was but a signal to Thenard for the institution of original researches. Beginning with 1799, when his first Memoir was presented to the Academy, that body has known him, for more than half a century, to lay before it, several times in each year, the results of inquiries which have formed the basis of striking improvements in science, the arts, and industry. Summoned, one day, unexpectedly and not a little surprised, into the presence of the minister of the interior, the latter said to him: "There is a deficiency in the supply of ultramarine blue, which is, besides, always scarce and very dear, and Sèvres stands in need of a material which can resist an intense fire. Here are fifteen hundred francs; go and find me a blue which will answer the required conditions." Thenard began to stammer an excuse. "I have no time to lose," said Chaptal, the minister in question, in a petulant one. "Go and bring me my blue as soon as possible." In a month from that time the rich tints of the beautiful fabrics of Sèvres bore witness to the success of the chemist.

In 1803, Thenard had shown that the supposed zoonic acid was but an impure acetous acid, and although Berthollet, then in the zenith of his reputation, was the discoverer of this acid, the circumstance produced no change in the generous appreciation which the latter always manifested for his young competitor. Nor was this the only occasion on which Thenard, firm in the expression of his own convictions, was called upon to contravene so imposing an authority. When occupied with the oxidation of metals, he unhesitatingly maintained the idea of oxides in fixed proportions in opposition to Berthollet, who denied it.

Thenard devoted much attention to organic chemistry, and although later inquirers have advanced beyond him, there still remains to his share the merit of having clearly conceived and indicated the relations which connect chemistry with physiology. This science of life rests on an art in which chemistry is pre-eminent, on the high and delicate art of analysis. It was this art which, in its higher and more subtle applications. Condillac first introduced into philosophy, and Lavoisier tells us that he himself derived it from that acute thinker.

In 1807 appeared researches of great interest on ethers. These, it was known, are formed by distilling certain acids with alcohol, and this was all that was known. Thenard announced several new ethers; and, yet more, laid a foundation for the theory of these agents, which have already revealed to us some of their surprising effects on life, and doubtless hold in reserve others more surprising still.

During this period of engrossing application, Thenard was, early one morning, surprised by a visit from Vauquelin. "Up, in all haste," cried the visitor, "and apparel yourself handsomely." Thenard, scarcely awake, asks an explanation. "The law respecting pluralities forces me to resign my chair at the College of France, and I require you to go at once and apply for it." Thenard feels a delicacy. "Come, come," rejoins the professor; "be quick; I have taken the cabriolet by the hour and you ruin me with these delays." The necessary visits being made, Thenard readily secured the position which conduced so much in the end to his extraordinary popularity. The students seemed to attach themselves with peculiar enthusiasm to one raised by toil from their own ranks and wholly unchanged by his elevation. Vauquelin, who continued to watch over his interests, and who greatly admired in Fourcroy the charms of delivery which he himself neglected, would fain have invested his favorite pupil with this additional attraction, and Thenard readily lent himself to the attempt. It was perhaps the only experiment in which he ever failed. In vain did he seek for models in society counsels from his friends, instructions from our great actors, Molé and Talma; the Champagnard was destined to bear to the end the original impress, somewhat rough perhaps, but thoroughly French, which definitely consigned him to a type well-recognized and not a little vaunted by our national self-esteem.

About this period a great sensation was produced in the scientific world. Berzelius had just revealed the power of decomposition exerted by the voltaic pile upon compound bodies. Davy, availing

349

himself of more powerful apparatus, had succeeded in decomposing the two fixed alkalies, which till then had been considered simple bodies: in potash and soda he found, united with oxygen, two metals to which he gave the names of potassium and sodium. He afterward undertook the analysis of the alkaline earths, each of which afforded a peculiar metal, while in all, oxygen presented itself as a common principle. Proceeding still further, he disclosed, in a paper full of original views, some of the profound relations which connect chemical with electric forces, affinities with electricity. With generous enthusiasm, the Institute of France awarded to this paper the grand prize founded for the progress of galvanism; and although war was raging between the two countries, the English savant was invited to come and receive it in person. This was an act of justice nobly accorded.

"Will you tolerate this triumph of the English?" impatiently demanded Napoleon of Berthollet. A gigantic pile was forthwith constructed by the Emperor's order, and confided to Thenard and Gay-Lussac, who soon after were able to announce to the Academy that by means of the ordinary affinities they had succeeded in obtaining new substances more abundantly than by the pile. By employing potassium and sodium, they effected the isolation of a new and simple substance, which they named boron.

Davy recognized the superiority of the chemical method for the extraction of metals; but he claimed this boron as an element which had come to light through his own investigations. This Thenard and Gay-Lussac would by no means concede, and they were right; but they maintained at the same time that sodium and potassium, so far from being simple bodies, were combinations of alkalies with hydrogen, or hydrurets. Their English rival justly answered that, if they adhered to this theory, it would follow of course that their simple principle of boron was but a *hydruret of boric acid*—an argument which remained unanswered. This, however, was the commencement of a discussion which, with profit to science and credit to both countries, continued for not less than five years, and which marks the epoch at which the basis of existing ideas respecting simple bodies was definitely fixed.

In one of the memoirs in which they rendered an account of the

350

different aspects of their controversy with the English savant, Thenard and Gay-Lussac had said: "The conjecture is not inadmissible that oxygenated muriatic acid is a simple body." It was not without having first tested this acid with potassium, and strenuously sought to extort some evidence of oxygen, that they gave expression to such an opinion. For, if oxygenated muriatic acid were admitted to be a simple body, a new principle of acidification would be disclosed, and a serious breach be thus made in the theory of Lavoisier. Recoiling from this consequence, and restrained moreover by the immovable opposition of Berthollet, they hesitated to pronounce more decidedly. Hence the recognition which they evaded passed to the credit of England. Davy admitted the oxygenated muriatic acid as a simple substance, giving it the name of *chlorine* or *chlorium,* but at the same time he generously resigned to his two rivals the first indication of the new principle. Thus the grand theory of Lavoisier was subjected to modification, though without forfeiting its title to be considered one of the noblest contributions of French genius to science.

The two friends, whose resources and reputation had been constantly increasing with their labors, had, during this whole controversy, been so completely identified in effort and responsibility, that the learned abroad were disposed to confound them in a single individuality; and indeed the part borne by each remains to this day undetermined. When, in 1809, a course of instruction was opened at the Sorbonne, both were called to participate. Here Thenard proposed to conduct an elementary course, without discontinuing, however, his more abstruse labors at the College of France. So great was the concourse of pupils that space for accommodation was often deficient, and many who had waited long were forced to retire. This suggested to Thenard the propriety of publishing his lectures. They appeared accordingly in four volumes, the first edition in 1813, the sixth in 1836, each edition costing much labor, as the author continued to intercalate the discoveries and doctrines of successive periods. This work maintained an exclusive ascendency in the schools for more than a quarter of a century, so that it may be said that almost all Europe has learned chemistry of Thenard, and doubtless most of the great chemists of the present day, French or foreign, would take pleasure in acknowledging their obligations to his clear and comprehensive method.

When the Institute lost Fourcroy, numerous competitors disputed with Thenard the honor of succeeding him. His friend Gay-Lussac had the satisfaction of completing, by his first vote, the unanimity of voices with which his comrade was called to a chair. On this occasion the first impulse of Thenard was one which sprang from his heart. "When I once felt assured of success," he said, "I immediately set out for Louptière, full of the joy which I should communicate to my mother. To crown my good fortune, I carried with me a book which she had asked me for: "The Imitation of Jesus Christ," in large letters, such as she could read without spectacles. When this copy, so rarely to be met with, fell into my hands, I had regarded it as the happiest of my discoveries." At the maternal fireside, the simple habits of his childhood were resumed and old associations cordially refreshed. Here he again listened to the tender counsels of his mother, who, at the moment of parting, said to him: "It is now time for you to marry."

This admonition fell on no unwilling ears. From the time when he first received the patronage of Vauquelin, Thenard had formed the acquaintance of a young chemist, named Humblot, to whom birth and fortune had opened a path as smooth as his own was rugged. In order to sustain the courage of Thenard, Humblot had often cited to him the instance of his own father-in-law, who, at first simply a laborer in a convent garden, had contrived to evince his talent as a painter, and by the opportune development of other talents in the service of his country during the Revolution, had achieved for himself both distinction and fortune; so that it was said of him by a great man, whose confidence he had won: "Conté is capable of creating the arts of France in the midst of the deserts of Arabia." Received into the intimacy of this family, Thenard, whose origin and mediocrity of fortune were well known to them, met with warm sympathy in all his successes; yet was it left to the sagacity of Madame Humblot to divine, which as a daughter of Conté she was well qualified to do, that he was silently waiting for some still greater success in order to acquire the boldness to ask for her daughter—whom Thenard confessed to be for him only

352

too fair and too rich. This obstacle not proving insurmountable, our savant married; and as he was a man who ordered affairs with judgment, and knew how to enter into the details of practical life, he began from that time to build up the large fortune in which were blended the results of his labor, his alliance, and his skillful management.

The constantly increasing success of his lectures had become, with Thenard, the most sensitive test of his self-love. At each of them he seemed to put forth all the ardor of a general on the battlefield; leaving nothing unprovided for, and making but a limited number of experiments, he required them to be exact and striking, and to be presented at the precise moment. The slightest inadvertence or misapprehension on the part of his assistants drew upon them sharp reproofs, and they must have had a hard time of it but for the prompt return of good nature and the acknowledgements which followed. "In a lecture-room," insisted Thenard, "it is the students alone who have a right to be considered; professor, assistants, laboratory, ought all to be sacrificed to them." Before an auditory which had witnessed one of his outbursts, he soothed the not unreasonable susceptibility of him he had maltreated by saying, "Fourcroy has often done the like to me! It produces promptness of apprehension."

It was this same promptness of apprehension which supplied Thenard with one of those penetrating insights which open new horizons to science. The discovery of oxygenated water is recounted by himself in the following terms: "In 1818 I was delivering my first lecture on the salts at the Sorbonne: 'in order that the metals should unite with acids,' I was saying, 'it is necessary that they should be oxidized, and that they should be so only to a certain point; when the quantity of oxygen is too great, the oxide loses a part of its affinity.' As an example I was about to cite the deutoxide of barium, when the thought suddenly crossed my mind that the experiment had not been made. As soon as I re-entered the laboratory I called for oxygenated barytes; I diluted chlorhydric acid with ice, adding it in such a manner as to have a liquid at zero. I hydrogenized the barytes and reduced it to the state of paste. I then made the mixture; when, to my great surprise, the barytes dissolved without sensible effervescence. So anomalous a fact could

353

not fail to arrest attention. When I returned for my following lecture, I perceived small globules attached to the sides of the vessel, like those which are seen in a glass filled with champagne wine; bubbles of gas were escaping from the liquid, though quite slowly. I then took a tube closed with the lamp at one of its extremities, and, pouring in some of the liquid, heated it. The bubbles were now rapidly disengaged and gas accumulated in the part of the tube which remained free; I introduced a match and it kindled—there was oxygen present. The hour for my lecture had arrived and I went through with it, but the preoccupation of my mind must have been deplorably apparent."

Thenard had fallen on the traces of a new fact; at first he was disposed to believe that he had made the discovery of suroxygenated acids, but he soon satisfied himself that these acids had no existence. Was it, then, water itself, simple water, which was oxygenized? The idea had scarcely entered his mind before it was proved by experiment, and oxygenated water was thus added to the acquisitions of chemistry.

A new and suggestive fact had been reached by Thenard, the report of which soon spread through scientific Europe. Foreign chemists came to assist in the experiments, and the arrival of Berzelius, at this time, in the French capital, seemed appropriately to welcome the recent discovery. Calling without form on Thenard, the Scandinavian philosopher saw him for the first time; yet these eminent men at once recognize each other, and find themselves, as if in virtue of the law of affinities, converted on the instant into old friends. "I come," said Berzelius, "to gather ideas in the domain of French chemistry, which you have so much aggrandized and enriched. You will, of course, let me see the oxygenated water." The conversation turned on Gay-Lussac and his iodine, the new element which that chemist had so distinctly identified; as well as on his cyanogen, a compound substance which affects, in its combinations, all the characters of simple bodies. "We must not forget," said Thenard, "the admirable theory of definite proportions which we owe to you, and which, revealing the immutable laws by which bodies combine, has become the torch of chemistry." "I admit," rejoined Berzelius, "that I have been fortunate. Do you know," he added, "that your recent labors and those of your friend have given Davy occasion to say, 'Thenard and Gay-Lussac apart are stronger than Thenard and Gay-Lussac united?' " From this conference Thenard proceeded directly to the Sorbonne, and was conducting his lecture with his usual facility, when his eyes casually wandered to a corner of the apartment, and he immediately showed signs of discomposure. The audience, in turn, became uneasy, but Thenard, promptly recovering himself, exclaims: "Gentlemen, you have a right to know the cause of my embarrassment;" and, pointing to a remote part of the amphitheatre, "Gentlemen, there is Berzelius." At once the crowd rises, and a respectful circle surrounds the illustrious stranger with long and rapturous applause. Moved by such proofs of enthusiasm, and forgetting his usual phlegm, the Swede exclaims, as he is borne unresistingly to a seat near the chair: "With such pupils it is impossible to be other than a good professor." He afterwards observed to Thenard, "I had promised myself to verify, in entire secrecy, whether all that fame had taught me respecting your talents as a professor were exact. I find it even below your real merit."

Appointed counsellor of the University in 1830, "Thenard," says M. Girardin, "not only rendered to science the great services expected of him, but proved himself an admirable man of business. Severe against abuses and negligence, no one lent himself with more lavish facility to all true reforms. Much as he had to be proud of in this world, I have never known him prouder and happier about anything than the right conduct of the state colleges." For four years he occupied a seat in the Chamber of Deputies, and as he had accepted it with reluctance, so he left it without regret, saying, as he repaired to the scene of rejoicing for the election of his successor, "I am going to assist in celebrating the restoration of my own liberty." His declaration that "he did not meddle with anything but what he thoroughly understood," may be held to have been the rule of his public life. When a member of the higher chamber, he moved a revision of the laws of instruction, a reimpression of the works of Laplace, and the national protection of the widows of learned men; he gave also a profound consideration to some of the questions relating to public industry. The spirit of party exercised no dominion over him. Swayed by reason, he set no value on administrative parade, preferring to all other authority

355

that which he exercised as an undoubted master in the domain of science.

During an academic career of forty-seven years, he constantly yielded a zealous support to whatever views or undertakings appeared to envelope a germ of progress, and there was scarcely one of his colleagues who was not indebted to him for the suffrage of an applauding voice. It was natural that he should cherish a profound regard for the Academy where his fame, his services, and, above all, his habits of conciliation, assured the highest authority to all his expressions of opinion. In private life he cheerfully accepted the obligations of his eminent scientific position, and his house, open to merit of every description, was the abode of amenity and grace. A certain vestige of its rustic origin, a simplicity which recalled the character of our central populations, gave to this amiable household only a new and peculiar charm. In person Thenard was large and vigorous, bearing erect a head covered with a redundance of black hair, with features well marked and animated by an eye of lively intelligence. It was impossible not to recognize in him one of those organizations on which nature has lavished all the elements of a complete existence. That attachments, both of a public and private nature, should gather about one thus constituted, was inevitable; complaisant and just, to him all was easy and simple; neither reproach nor ill-will ever troubled a heart which, more than once, was agitated by the expressions of grateful acknowledgment.

During his lectures at the Polytechnic School, it happened, on one occasion, that something essential to the demonstration was wanting. Thenard impatiently calls for it, and while the attendant runs to seek it, lays his hand, as if to gain time, on a glass, and carries it, without examination, to his lips. Having swallowed two mouthfuls, he replaces it, and with entire self-possession observes, "Gentlemen, I have poisoned myself; what I have drunk is corrosive sublimate, and the remedy is the white of eggs; bring me some." The students, to whom his first words had conveyed an electric shudder, precipitate themselves through doors and windows, ransack the neighboring stores and kitchens, and, as each one brings his contribution, soon an immense heap of eggs rises before the professor. In the meantime, one of the students has flown to the Faculty of Medicine, and, interrupting an examination, exclaims, "Quick, a physician! Thenard has poisoned himself at the school in delivering a lecture." Dupuytren rises, seizes a cabriolet on his passage, and rushes with breathless haste to the scene of the accident. But, already, thanks to the albumen, the life of Thenard was saved. Dupuytren, however, insists on the use of a probe, in order to be sure that none of the corrosive substance is absorbed by the stomach. An inflammation of the organ is thereby produced, and Thenard, saved from the poison, is put in danger by the remedy.

During his illness, the students of all the schools manifested the most poignant anxiety; with affectionate zeal they watched around his house night and day, in order to avert every possible cause of disturbance, and listened in uneasy silence for tidings from the interior. Every morning exact bulletins were posted in all the principal establishments, without its being known who were the authors. When Thenard reappeared in his chair at the Sorbonne, the delight manifested was proportionately great. Every one sprang to his feet without seeming to know in what way to express his joy, and the professor for once confessed himself overwhelmed by a torrent of profound and grateful emotions.

Thenard expired June 21, 1857.

NOTES AND REFERENCES

Georges Bouchard, ed., "Un Grand Français, le Chimiste Thenard 1777–1857," par son fils, Paul Thenard, Jobard, Dijon, 1950 (at the expense of the present Baron Thenard, grand-grandson of Jacques).

From the biography by Pierre Jean Marie Flourens, *Mémoires de l'Academie des Sciences, 32,* I–XXXV (1864). Translated for the Smithsonian Institution by C. A. Alexander and published in *Annual Reports of the Smithsonian Institution 1862,* pp. 373–383.

PIERRE JEAN MARIE FLOURENS

357

·· 28 ··

Gay-Lussac

1778-1850

J OSEPH-LOUIS GAY-LUSSAC, one of the greatest scholars of France, was born September 6, 1778 at Saint-Léonard, a small town of the ancient Limousin, located near the border of the Auvergne. His grandfather was a physician and his father *procureur du roi* and judge at the Pont de Noblac.

Gay-Lussac was one of the best students at the École Polytechnique; later on he became one of its most famous and beloved professors.

In 1800, Berthollet returned with General Bonaparte from Egypt and asked for a student of the École Polytechnique to become his laboratory assistant. Gay-Lussac was selected for the job. The work that Berthollet suggested to him had results which were diametrically opposed to what Berthollet expected. I would not venture to affirm that Berthollet was not a little upset when he saw his predictions fail, but contrary to the attitude of many other scientists whom I could name, Berthollet appreciated the independence of the young experimenter and told him: "Young friend, your destiny is to make discoveries, from now on you shall eat at my table; I want to be your father in scientific matters, and I know that I shall have reason to be proud of it some day."

Before Alexander von Humboldt started on his memorable voyage to America (1799–1804) he had prepared himself for it by diligent studies. One of these was concerned with the eudiometric methods for determining the constituents of air. This work, carried out in a hurry and with faulty procedures, was rather inexact. Gay-Lussac noticed this and pointed out the error with a liveliness for which I would have to reproach him if the youth of the author had not rendered it excusable.

One day, von Humboldt noticed among those assembled in the salon of the country house at Arcueil a young man of high stature and modest but firm manners. "This is Gay-Lussac," Humboldt was told, "the physicist who recently ascended [in a Montgolfière] to the greatest height that men have reached so far, in order to solve important scientific questions." This is, added Humboldt to himself, also the author of that bitter critique of my eudiometric work. Quickly, however, he overcame the feeling of repulsion, approached Gay-Lussac, and after a few flattering words about ascensions, he affectionately offered him his friendship. That was the beginning of an attachment which never failed in the future and soon brought welcome fruits. In fact, the two new friends immediately carried out an important eudiometric study.

This study, presented before the Académie des Sciences, the first of Pluviose in the year XII (January 1805), had as its main objective the determination of the accuracy of Volta's eudiometer for the analysis of air, but the authors also illuminated or speculated, very ingeniously, on a number of questions of chemistry and the physics of the earth. In this memoir is to be found the remark, which Gay-Lussac later developed to such an important extent that, when oxygen and hydrogen combine, their volumes are in the precise proportions of 100 oxygen to 200 hydrogen.

Through Berthollet's friendship and effort Gay-Lussac, who was now repetitor in Fourcroy's lecture course, received a year's leave of absence in order to accompany Humboldt on a voyage to Italy and Germany. Before leaving Paris, the two friends had equipped themselves with meteorological instruments and apparatus for determining the inclination of the magnetic needle and the variable force acting on magnetic needles at different latitudes. They left Paris on March 12, 1805. Gay-Lussac left from Berlin in the spring of 1806 rather suddenly when he learned that the death of Brisson left a vacant place at the Institut and that he might be called upon to replace the old physicist.

Shortly after he had become a member of the Institut, Gay-Lussac began to study how the elasticity of gases changes with the dependence on temperature, and the formation and diffusion of vapors—the same field that was investigated in England by Dalton, who became one of the eight associates of the Académie. Although his genius was recognized by all his compatriots, Dalton held (in the small town of Dumphries) the very humble and unlucrative position of a special professor of mathematics, and in his experiments he could use only imperfect instruments. It should, therefore, have been easy to submit his results to careful verifications. Gay-Lussac, however, did not know the work of the illustrious English physicist and never mentioned it in the elaborate and very instructive history of physicists who preceded him.

In 1807 Berthollet founded a particular scientific society composed of a very small number of persons, the Société d'Arcueil, named after the community near Paris where Berthollet's country house was. Gay-Lussac, as could be foreseen, was one of the first members of the new society.

The first volume of the journal published by the Société d'Arcueil begins with a memoir in which Gay-Lussac united the results of all the magnetic measurements made with von Humboldt during their travels in France, Italy, and Germany.

In the second volume we find, among other interesting articles, a memoir on the combination of gaseous substances with each other; this memoir contains results so remarkable and important that they have been called the laws of Gay-Lussac. These laws can be expressed as follows:

> When gases react with each other, the volumes in which they combine are in the simplest numerical relationships: either 1 and 1, or 1 and 2, or 2 and 3. Not only do they combine only in these relationships, but the apparent contraction in volume which sometimes occurs also has a simple relationship to the volume of one of the combined gases.

Now we have arrived at the time when Humphry Davy, following the way so auspiciously opened by Nicholson and Carlisle and continued by Berzelius and Hisinger, succeeded in converting potassium hydroxide and sodium hydroxide into metals which soften between the fingers, like wax, which float on the surface of water because they are lighter than water, and which spontaneously catch fire with this liquid with the most vivid light.

The announcement of this brilliant discovery, toward the end of 1807, produced a great stir in the scientific world. The Emperor Napoleon joined in it and put at the disposal of the École Polytechnique the funds necessary for the construction of a colossal pile. While this was constructed for Gay-Lussac and Thenard, they imagined that the well-directed ordinary affinities should suffice for the production of potassium and sodium. They tried various dangerous experiments and succeeded beyond their expectations. Their discovery was published on March 7, 1808. From this moment on, the two new metals, which are obtained in only very small quantities with the pile, could be produced in great abundance and thus become a common means of chemical analysis.

Towards the middle of 1811, Bernard Courtois, a saltpeter worker in Paris, discovered in the ashes of varec (seaweed) a solid substance which corroded his kettles, and which since the proposal of Gay-Lussac has been called iodine because of the very impressive violet color of its vapor. Courtois gave samples of this substance to Desormes and Clément, who studied it. Clément did not publish Courtois' discovery and the results obtained together with Desormes until the Institut session of December 6, 1813.

At that time, Sir Humphry Davy was in Paris, having obtained the exceptional permission from the Emperor to travel in France. Shortly after his arrival he received several samples of the mysterious substance from Clément. Gay-Lussac, hearing about this, judged immediately how much it would hurt the honor of the French experimenters and academies that a foreign chemist had thus been given priority by chance and a little thoughtlessness. He went to Courtois, obtained from him a small quantity of the substance he had found, started to work, and produced, in a few days, results of great variety, importance, and novelty. Under his searching eyes iodine became an element which furnishes one particular acid by combining with hydrogen, and another one by uniting with oxygen. The first of these acids was a new example for the fact that oxygen was not the only acid-producing principle, as had long been believed. The author particularly emphasized the analogy which he had established between chlorine, sulfur, and iodine.

Prussian blue, well-known by manufacturers and painters, had been studied by many scientists, among them Macquer, Guyton de Morveau, Bergman, Scheele, Berthollet, Proust, and Porrett. Gay-Lussac joined them; his results were contained in a memoir of September 18, 1815. Here the author first gives an exact analysis of the acid present in Prussian blue and which Guyton de Morveau had called prussic acid, but which had never before been obtained in pure form, free of water. Gay-Lussac explained how he had isolated the radical of prussic acid which has since been named cyanogen. He established that cyanogen is a compound of nitrogen and carbon, that prussic acid is definitely formed from this radical and hydrogen, and that its name should be hydrocyanic acid, today often replaced by cyanohydric acid.

Chemists never fail to say what taste their new product has. Who does not think with horror that if Gay-Lussac had not departed from that general habit, if he had placed a single drop of this liquid on his tongue, he would have collapsed at the same instant as if struck by lightning!

As fertile in the invention of industrial processes as in the discovery of scientific truths, Gay-Lussac created in marvelous succession chlorometry, exact methods for measuring the concentration of commercial alkalies, ingenious means for more economical production of sulfuric acid, and crowned this series of important work by discovering a process which has replaced, in all civilized countries, the old and defective method of analyzing alloys of silver and copper by cupellation.

Gay-Lussac's knowledge of foreign languages—Italian, English, and German—permitted him to enrich his lectures by thorough erudition from original sources. Upon entering his laboratory, one was immediately struck by the intelligent order everywhere. The machines and utensils which one saw were mostly made by his own hands and were distinguished by their conception and execution. Since Buffon said "le style c'est l'homme" (the style is the man), I might add with not less reason that the great chemist and the good physicist can be recognized by the arrangement of the equipment they use.

During his long and glorious scientific campaigns Gay-Lussac was severely wounded on several occasions. The first time was on June 3, 1808—by potassium he had prepared in large quantity by a new method.

One might have thought that Gay-Lussac felt only that calm satisfaction naturally produced by some new discoveries; that would be erroneous. For protection against the humidity of the laboratories located in basements, Gay-Lussac ordinarily put sabots over his shoes. Pelouze, one of his favorite students, told me that after the success of a decisive experiment he had often seen him, through the half-open door of his room, giving signs of most vivid joy, even dancing in spite of his inconvenient footgear.

Besides all the furnaces, retorts, and apparatus of all kinds, Gay-Lussac's laboratory had a table of white wood on which our friend marked down the results of his experiments as they progressed. On this table he also outlined the articles on general laws and questions of priority.

Berthollet died in 1822. At that time it was known that he had willed his sword, the integral part of his uniform as *Pair de France*, to Gay-Lussac. But this act of enlightened justice was not carried out as promptly as could have been hoped for. "Why," said Gay-Lussac's friends to the dispensers of royal favors, "why make him wait so long for a reward which must sooner or later be his? Do you find him not sufficiently outstanding?" "You do us an injustice," they replied. "Do you have something to object to his relatives?" "We know they all are honorable and most distinguished." "Or could it be a question of his fortunes?" "We know that Gay-Lussac is very well off as the fruit of his work." "Then what stops you?" And then they would whisper ever so faintly, as if they were ashamed of such a fact, that the great chemist worked every morning in his laboratory with his hands— which seemed utterly incompatible with the dignity of a *Pair de France*. This was the pitiful reason which for several years prevented the fulfillment of Berthollet's ingenious prediction.

Gay-Lussac saw his end coming with the resignation inspired by a pure conscience; he looked calmly not only on death, but on dying, as Montaigne would have said. The dropsy which suddenly attacked him made rapid progress, and our friend expired without boast or weakness on May 9, 1850.

NOTES AND REFERENCES

Edmond Blanc and Léon Delhoume, "La Vie Émouvante et Noble de Gay-Lussac," Gauthier-Villars, Paris, 1950.

Hans Schimank, "J. L. Gay-Lussac und seine Leistungen auf dem Gabiete der allgemeinen und physikalischen Chemie," *Naturwissenschaften*, 38, 265 (1951).

From: the biography by François Arago, "Oeuvres Complètes de François Arago," published under the direction of J.-A. Barral, vol. III, Paris and Leipzig, 1855, pp. 1–112. Translated by Eduard Farber.

FRANÇOIS ARAGO

·· 29 ··

Humphry Davy

1778-1829

THE chemical revolution, dominated by the figure and work of Lavoisier, was essentially completed by 1789 with the appearance of that great man's book, "Traité Elementaire de Chimie." The fight for the new system had been won on the battlefield of combustion, with Lavoisier's material oxygen the winner over metaphysical phlogiston. But the nature of the victory and the problems it brought were often more clearly discerned by those who came after than by those who fought it. The young men who first learned their chemistry in the last decade of the eighteenth century were in a position to take advantage of the accident of a well-timed birth. Humphry Davy, born in 1778, was in his own time the most brilliant of this outstanding group which included Amedeo Avogadro, L. J. Thenard, J. L. Gay-Lussac, and J. J. Berzelius, all born within three years of one another.

During the early years of the nineteenth century, these men and others began to have critical thoughts on the validity of the oxygen theory of combustion and acids and of the nature of the chemical element. A new and powerful tool, that of voltaic electricity, was widely applied to chemical investigations, and the new atomic theory of John Dalton made its appearance. It was characteristic of Davy that he seized upon the new experimental method, but subscribed to none of the theories. Amid all this he threaded his sometimes brilliant and always solitary way to experimental certainties and philosophic doubts.

Humphry Davy was born on December 17, 1778, in Penzance, Cornwall, near the southwestern tip of England. Davy's ancestors had been, for a number of years, possessors of a small freeholding called Varfell near Penzance. His father had been trained as a woodcarver in London, but on unexpectedly inheriting the holding, largely abandoned his trade as means of livelihood and practiced it as an art for the enjoyment it gave him. In later years Humphry Davy was to show a similar attitude, for though he never lacked adequate funds, he deliberately passed up several opportunities for large financial gain from his discoveries. He preferred to work for

371

the enjoyment it gave him, and to let mankind share whatever benefits might come from his discoveries.

In the case of Davy's father, however, art for art's sake was apparently overdone, for upon his death in 1794, the family finances were in a precarious state. Davy's mother sold Varfel and opened a millinery shop in Penzance. With the income from this and a later inheritance of her own, she successfully raised the family of two sons and three daughters. Davy's mother lived a long life, witnessed the scientific and popular success of her eldest son, and died only a few years before Humphry's own fatal illness.

Davy early showed some of the talents and abilities for which he later became so famous. He learned to read some time near his fifth birthday and always read with a rapidity and comprehension which astonished those who knew him. His first teacher was so impressed with his progress that he recommended that the boy be placed in a better school. Later teachers, however, were not so strongly impressed, and recalled chiefly his great imaginative powers. Davy began writing poetry at an early age and continued the practice throughout his life.

The inspiration for his poetry as well as for his devotion to science came principally from his love of nature. As a boy he explored the wild and rocky coasts of Cornwall, noting the geological features of the area, and became familiar with the old tin mines dating back to Roman times. He acquired what amounted to a passion for fishing which he never relinquished until his final illness made its pursuit impossible. Typically, Davy studied the feeding and spawning habits of the different species of fish, not only for the sake of becoming a better fisherman, but also because it was his nature to do thoroughly whatever task was worth doing. He took great pride in his fishing ability and disliked being out-fished by any of his companions.

Even before his father's death, Humphry had moved to Penzance for his schooling. He lived with a John Tonkin who had raised Humphry's orphaned mother many years before. It was in Mr. Tonkin's garret that Davy began his first serious chemical experiments. Possibly because of his independence of mind and his internal resources, he was left pretty much alone in his later schooling, a fact for which Davy expressed some gratitude.

After the death of Davy's father and the removal of the family to Penzance, Humphry was apprenticed to John Borlase, a surgeon and apothecary who later obtained his medical diploma. It was the intention of all concerned that young Davy would ultimately attend the University of Edinburgh and obtain his medical degree. In view of the professional opportunities of the time for a boy interested in science, this was a reasonable choice and the arrangement was agreeable to Davy. Only after several years of success in the Royal Institution did he finally relinquish this plan.

Davy's formal education was over. But during his apprenticeship to Mr. Borlase, he continued his self-education which he had carefully planned. Self-education, admirable as it is, often leaves conspicuous gaps. In Davy's case the weakness was that of too much self-reliance, and a corresponding reluctance to assimilate the work of others.

It was during this apprenticeship that he began to narrow his interests to chemistry, finding his sources of information, if not his inspiration which he must have provided for himself, in Lavoisier's "Elementary Treatise," and Nicholson's "Dictionary of Chemistry." Very shortly Davy was making experiments of a sort far removed from the childish manufacture of fireworks some years earlier.

In 1798, there came a change in the plans for Davy's career. Dr. Thomas Beddoes, an intelligent but rather erratic physician, organized the establishment of a Pneumatic Institution at Clifton near Bristol for the purpose of providing medical treatment through the use of various recently discovered gases. The knowledge of the role of oxygen in animal life suggested the idea that other gases might also have positive physiological properties. Beddoes needed someone to conduct the chemical investigations, and Davy was recommended by Davies Gilbert. Gilbert, older than Davy, had some time before recognized the abilities of the young man who was "fond of making chemical experiments," and undertook to promote his career. Gilbert later (1828) succeeded Davy as president of the Royal Society, partly through the influence of the retiring Davy. Arrangements for Davy's employment at Clifton were finally completed and Davy left Penzance in October, 1798, to take up his new duties.

Even before his move to Clifton, Davy had written two long papers on chemical theory, and Beddoes had agreed to publish them as part of a collection he was gathering from the west of England. Davy's contributions occupied nearly the first half of the volume, which appeared in 1799. Davy had begun these essays shortly after undertaking the serious study of chemistry; fired by his youthful enthusiasm and abundant self-confidence he set out to reform the science of chemistry as he had found it in Lavoisier.

In the first paper, "Essay on Heat and Light," he took exception to Lavoisier's concept of heat as a fluid, preferring to think of it as a mode of molecular motion. Whereas Lavoisier had identified oxygen gas as a combination of caloric and the chemical atoms of oxygen, Davy chose to think of it as a combination of light and the oxygen atoms. In the paper that followed Davy attempted to explain the colors of "organic beings" by means of his "phosoxygen," as he called oxygen gas. These papers were the product of an immature Davy, more illustrative of his active imagination than of his later experimental rigor. Although there was much ingenuity in his arguments, they were supported by insufficient and sometimes irrelevant evidence, and written with an assurance that could only be called presumptive. These papers were not well received and Davy soon regretted their publication. But he had learned a lesson; science must be based firmly on experimental evidence and speculation must be kept separate and distinctly indicated as such. This became the pattern for Davy's subsequent writings.

Davy's first scientific success came soon after. He began a systematic investigation of the properties of the various gaseous compounds of nitrogen, prompted by the theory of Samuel Latham Mitchill, an American physician and naturalist, that nitrous oxide was the principle of contagion. Davy quickly satisfied himself that this gas was quite harmless, whether breathed or exposed to an open wound. The discovery of its semi-intoxicating powers followed soon after, and Dr. Beddoes was ecstatic, for this discovery seemed to justify the principle upon which his Pneumatic Institution was founded. The results of these investigations were published as a separate paper in 1800. This paper was in sharp contrast to the previous ones; rigorous in gathering and presenting of evidence and cautious in drawing conclusions. It did much to establish Davy's scientific reputation.

Meanwhile Davy was making another kind of reputation, this one in literary circles. Dr. Beddoes' wife was a sister to the novelist, Maria Edgeworth, and at the Beddoes' home Davy met many of the young writers who came to talk with Maria during her frequent visits. Davy was more than just accepted in this literary company; he formed deep and lasting friendships with Samuel Taylor Coleridge and Robert Southey. Davy was a poet, too, and some of his verse was published by Wordsworth and Coleridge in their annual anthology.

At that time, Count Rumford, that peculiar combination of genius and opportunist, was working with notable men in London toward the founding of an institution for the "promotion of science and the diffusion and extension of useful knowledge." Other arrangements being completed, a staff was needed. Davy was recommended for the position of assistant in chemistry, and early in 1801 was appointed to that post. Count Rumford had not been favorably impressed by Davy's personal appearance, being fearful that the rough appearance and Davy's less than polished manners were a true reflection of the man inside. A single trial lecture convinced the Count of the contrary. Davy's success as a lecturer was so apparent from the beginning that within six weeks the conditional nature of his appointment was changed by the removal of the word assistant from his title. By the end of another year, he was promoted to professor of chemistry.

Davy's success was not confined to the opinion of his employers. His audiences were enthralled by his youthful enthusiasm and clarity of exposition, and flocked loyally to lectures which certainly they did not always understand. The auditorium of the Royal Institution became a gathering place for the fashionable people of London, particularly the young and feminine. Humphry Davy received in return almost more invitations to dinners and social gatherings than he could accept. His transition from the rough Cornishman to a social lion of London was rapid indeed.

But Davy's success had more significant consequences than his pleasant social life. The financial success of the Institution became largely dependent upon Davy. Hence his influence was dominant in determining what the Royal Institution became. By the success of his example, he set the pattern for his illustrious successors, Faraday, Tyndall, Dewar, and Bragg.

In keeping with one of the original purposes of the Royal Institution, Davy was required to conduct experiments and give lectures in fields of applied chemistry. Beginning in 1802, he was successively engaged in the investigation of tanning, mineralogy and metallurgy, and agriculture. Even though these requirements postponed his pursuit of more fundamental science, Davy attacked these areas with great diligence and enthusiasm, although with varying success. Davy's vigor in these efforts was not prompted only by his sense of professional obligation, for one of his principal motivations throughout his life was his belief that science could serve no better cause than to provide a real improvement of the unhappy lot of the majority of mankind.

But he also recognized that practical application of scientific knowledge to social needs must rest on an understanding of the fundamental knowledge of the behavior of natural things. Unfortunately, the fundamental knowledge necessary to a significant improvement in the art of tanning lay far beyond the scope of the chemical theory and practice of his time. Consequently, Davy's efforts in this area were only moderately successful.

Davy's failure to contribute significantly to mineralogical knowledge can be attributed largely to his own temperament and the limitations of his self-education. The meticulous analytical techniques required for mineralogical and metallurgical investigations, Davy did not possess, nor did he have the sustained patience to acquire them. Even so, he knew the worth of careful analytical skills and respected such abilities in his contemporaries, William H. Wollaston and J. J. Berzelius.

It was in agricultural chemistry that Davy's independent attitude became an asset rather than a liability. Early in the nineteenth century there was no well-developed body of knowledge and technique in this area as there was in mineralogy. When Davy first began his agricultural investigation, Sir Thomas Bernard, who had been one of the principal founders and patrons of the Royal Institution, offered for Davy's use a piece of ground near his villa

376

at Roehampton. Under Davy's direction numerous experiments were carried out there over several years. The results of these experiments were included in his lectures to the Board of Agriculture. The Board was sufficiently impressed with his efforts; Davy was given a permanent appointment as professor of chemistry and for ten years he delivered an annual series of lectures to them. In 1813, he published these lectures in book form under the title, "Elements of Agricultural Chemistry." This book appeared in a total of four editions, the last in 1827, just before Davy's death.

The chief contribution Davy made to the improvement of agricultural came from his insistence that agriculture must depend upon the methods and knowledge of the basic sciences, chemistry and geology in particular. His book was the first significant attempt to present a systematic treatment of the scientific knowledge fundamental to agriculture. He treated the organization of plants, the chemistry and geological origins of soils, the nature of the atmosphere, and the uses of natural and artificial manures. The breadth of Davy's book necessitated a dependence upon other writers, particularly for the chapter on the organization of plants. But much of what he presented was based on his own experiments, or those of his many landed friends who willingly cooperated with him. Not everything in the book was correct, for Davy subscribed to the humus theory, which held that the source of carbon for plant growth was the humus in the soil. Nevertheless, Davy's insistence that improvements in agricultural practice must come from an increased knowledge of basic science marks the beginning of a fruitful tradition.

Just prior to his leaving Bristol and the Pneumatic Institution, Davy had begun some experimentation on the effects of voltaic electricity on chemical compounds. This had been inspired by the discovery of Nicholson and Carlisle in 1800 that water could be decomposed by the current from a voltaic pile. Davy began his experimentation with the apparatus made for Dr. Beddoes at the Pneumatic Institution, and by the time of his move to London had published several papers on the effects of galvanic electricity. After his move to London, he presented in the Royal Institution a course of lectures on galvanic phenomena, but the press of other duties forced him to abandon further investigations in this field.

By 1806, he had his professional obligation under sufficient control to resume this work. The results were spectacular.

In his earlier work, Davy had experimented widely in the identification of conducting materials, arrangements of apparatus, and other largely technical aspects of the new field. In his first Bakerian Lecture before the Royal Society in 1806, "On some Chemical Agencies of Electricity," Davy had proceeded well beyond his earlier work, providing an excellent summary of what was then known of electrochemistry.

For this paper, Davy was awarded a prize established by Napoleon to be given to the person who contributed most to the advancement of electricity. To the suggestion that he should not accept the prize because England and France were at war, Davy replied, ". . . if the two countries or governments are at war, the men of science are not. That would, indeed, be a civil war of the worst description." Davy was held in sufficient regard in France that, when he desired to visit there in 1813, he received special permission from Napoleon himself.

Perhaps the most significant section of this paper was that on the relations between electrical energies of bodies and their chemical affinities. A logical extension of the idea that chemical affinity is the result of natural electrification of the elements is the use of electricity for the reversal of these natural charges, which should bring about a decomposition of the compound into its elements. This, of course, had already been done in some cases, but Davy saw it now as a general principle to be tried on some of the more reluctant compounds whose composition was only suspected.

His success in verifying his suspicions was reported in his second Bakerian Lecture in 1807. He not only was able to report the decomposition of the fixed alkalies, soda and potash, but also to indicate their composition as the oxides of two new metals. The strange properties of sodium and potassium, metals which not only floated on water but would also react with it in a violent and spectacular fashion, were ideally suited for illustrating his public lectures. These demonstrations to his loyal audiences confirmed again their opinion that Humphry Davy was the most brilliant scientist alive. A serious illness interrupted Davy's career at this point, but after his recovery he took up where he had left off.

The isolation of calcium, magnesium, strontium, and barium (as amalgams, a method suggested by Berzelius) soon followed.

But Davy had lost time and his papers of these next years (1808–1811) show signs of haste and uncertainty. Davy was puzzled by the results of much of his work. The application of simple analogies, the nearest thing he had to a chemical philosophy, yielded no clarifying results. By analogy with the volatile alkali, ammonia, the newly discovered sodium and potassium might also be thought to contain hydrogen. By reverse analogy, since potash and soda contain oxygen ("seemingly a principle of alkalinity as well as acidity"), so might ammonia contain oxygen. If so the oxygen would have to be part of the nitrogen. Davy, persistently but unsuccessfully, attempted to find conclusive evidence relevant to this hypothesis.

Unfortunately, he "discovered" hydrogen to be an ingredient of sulfur and phosphorus, which strongly suggested to him and others that maybe hydrogen was phlogiston. Other workers too were "discovering" hydrogen in previously considered elementary bodies, and the fundamental question of what substances were or were not elements became a serious one.

To Davy there was "no reason to suppose that any real *indestructible principle*" had yet been discovered. But hydrogen, for many reasons, was the most likely candidate, an idea William Prout made explicit some years later. Davy's uncertainties about the compound or simple nature of bodies applied to his views on oxymuriatic acid gas, which he later named chlorine. The cause of his investigations of this material was the fact that carbon, which took oxygen away from so many substances, could not take it away from the oxymuriatic acid gas. In a series of papers, beginning in 1810, he established to his own satisfaction that oxymuriatic acid gas contained no oxygen and indeed should be placed in the list of the undecompounded bodies. He suggested the name, chlorine, as one based on a property independent of its composition. Although many chemists quickly interpreted Davy's brilliant work as demonstrating the elementary nature of chlorine, Davy was always more cautious; he would only assert that as yet it had not been decomposed, and contained no oxygen.

But even this conditional conclusion had great significance for the oxygen theory of Lavoisier, and Davy embodied these and other views in his "Elements of Chemical Philosophy," published in 1812. One of the obvious properties of chlorine was its ability to react with certain materials, producing flame and light. This had previously been attributed to the oxygen in the chlorine, but that explanation was no longer tenable. Davy recognized that chlorine must take its place beside oxygen as a supporter of combustion and the unique role of oxygen in chemical theory was thereby lost. In addition, hydrochloric acid could no longer be held to contain oxygen, and oxygen as a principle of acidity had likewise to be abandoned. The book offered no system to replace the one of Lavoisier now made unsatisfactory by Davy's work and, as the title suggests, it contained only the elements of information which any chemical system must take into account.

The year 1812 was a memorable one for Davy, for on the eighth of April he was knighted by the Prince Regent, and two days later was married. His "Elements of Chemical Philosophy," published later in the year, was dedicated to the new Lady Davy. That year also marks the end of his full association with the Royal Institution, for at the time of his marriage and knighthood he requested that he no longer be required to give the lectures. He was retained in an advisory capacity.

His partial separation from the Institution did not halt his chemical investigation, for he still had the use of the laboratories. In addition, he had constructed a portable laboratory which he took with him on his travels. A few months prior to his departure in 1813 for an extended trip on the continent, he and the Royal Institution had the good fortune of hiring Michael Faraday as his assistant. Faraday, Lady Davy and her maid, and the portable laboratory all accompanied Davy to the continent.

While in France, Davy received a small quantity of substance X, recently discovered there. This substance, later named iodine, Davy quickly showed to be analogous to chlorine and a member of the group of electronegative elements headed by oxygen. This work tended to confirm Davy's suspicion that the fluorates also contained an undecompounded body of this same class.

Shortly after his return from the continent in 1815, Davy was offered the problem of devising a safety lamp for use in gas-filled mines. Explosions in the mines caused by the use of open flames in miners' lamps had become a problem recognized even by the mine owners as demanding some solution. A particularly tragic disaster in 1812 led to the organization of a group of mine owners actively seeking some solution. After nearly three years of failure to find any cure, they had largely abandoned hope. Davy's great fame and recognition as the outstanding scientist of his time made it almost inevitable that he would be asked for help. Three months after his return to London Davy's help was sought by "A Society for Preventing Accidents in Coal Mines." Davy of course acceded.

After obtaining adequate samples of the fire damp, Davy undertook a systematic investigation of its properties. He determined its composition, confirming earlier work, studied its explosive properties with various mixtures of air and other gases, and studied the speed of propagation of the flame in tubes of different sizes and materials. From this work he discovered that tubes of small enough diameter would not allow the flame to pass at all. Hence his first model of a safety lamp allowed air to enter and exhaust gases to leave only through small tubes. Further investigation showed that metal tubes need not be as small as glass ones, and he correctly concluded that the superior heat conducting property of the metal was responsible. The use of wire gauze instead of tubes was the final outcome of this information. By January, 1816, he had constructed the lamp entirely of wire gauze, thus eliminating any need for glass in the lamp at all.

Manufacture of his lamps was arranged for and their success was quickly demonstrated in the mines. The speed with which Davy had accomplished his task and the complete success of his efforts made this episode one of the most dramatic in the history of science. But this work was typical of Davy at his magnificent best. His incisive mind and systematic acquisition of the relevant information quickly gave him the idea that his able hands placed in physical form. Already famous among his colleagues and popular with the more leisured class who had crowded his lectures in the Royal Institution, he now in the space of a few months became the benefactor of thousands of unfortunate laborers. Davy himself was proud of his work and he valued it ". . . more than anything I ever did." He refused to take out a patent on the invention, preferring to let it be the property of those who benefited from its use.

But Davy, in spite of some claims to priority on the part of others, received rewards other than satisfaction. The Royal Society awarded him the Rumford medal for the best work in the preceding two years dealing with heat and light, and in 1818 he was created a baronet.

One honor was yet left to Davy, and this he received in 1820, when he was elected to the presidency of the Royal Society. Davy's chief hope for the Royal Society was that it should increase its effectiveness through a closer association with the government. It should be the coordinator and director of science for the nation. From his own experience with the Royal Institution, he knew what could be accomplished with even limited funds if they were free from commitments. However, the only increase in governmental support during his tenure in office came with the creation of the Royal medal. But even for this, the actual funds were not given until after some ten awards had been made.

The first award of the Royal medal was made in 1826 to John Dalton. Davy had not yet resigned the presidency of the Royal Society because of ill health, and it was he who made the presentation and the accompanying speech. According to Davy, the award was made to Dalton for his "development of the chemical theory of definite proportions, usually called the atomic theory." This speech and its title reveal much of Davy, the man, as well as of Davy, the scientist. Davy was never known for his tact in his personal relations with his professional colleagues, as this example illustrates. The award speech itself was only partly complimentary to Dalton, for it is full of Davy's reservations and personal interpretations of the worth of Dalton's work. To Davy the atomic theory was too conjectural, and as such not to be trusted. He had his own unhappy experience with phosoxygen, which taught him the danger of speculation, and he had also seen the abandonment of the uniqueness of oxygen largely as a result of his own work. In the award speech he neatly separated the facts of definite proportion from the hypothesis of Dalton's atoms, seeing much value in the former and great danger in the latter.

It was not just the atomic hypothesis he distrusted; he subscribed to no theory and indeed had no understanding of the essential role of theory in the development of scientific thought. It was for this reason that, in spite of his ability, he made no significant contribution to the logical structure of science. He was brilliant at perceiving and defining new areas of knowledge to be explored, and unexcelled in bringing order to problems of limited scope. But he was impatient of larger tasks which would have forced him to assimilate data not his own and compile them in a unified form. Davy's mind, quick and brilliant though it was, showed itself in his writings as somewhat undisciplined, possessing a kind of intellectual impatience.

Davy was a self-educated man and his knowledge of chemistry was almost confined to that which he had discovered or repeated for himself. Although this was a formidable body of knowledge, it left him without adequate perspective in his own field. He appeared jealous of the more able of his colleagues, and frequently offended them with his lack of tact. Gay-Lussac, Berzelius, and Faraday are examples. His professional fame had come early and he may never have felt secure in his position of scientific prominence. He was not on intimate terms with any of his scientific equals.

He had risen fast from the rather crude country boy from Cornwall to the idol of social London. Although he desired position in that society, and indeed married into it, he apparently never felt at home there. He was highly self-sufficient in his activities and his favorite recreation was fishing, either alone or with a carefully chosen companion. His marriage was not a particularly happy one, although there was no cause for public talk. Increasingly during his last years of failing health, he traveled without Lady Davy, she finding her satisfactions in the social life of London, and he his consolations in travel. But when his last days approached and he gently hoped to Lady Davy that she come to him, she did so without delay. His brother John came, also, and both were with him when he died in Geneva, May 29, 1829.

GENERAL REFERENCES

J. Davy, "Memoirs of the Life of Sir Humphry Davy," Vol. I of "The Collected Works of Sir Humphry Davy," London, 1839–40.

J. Davy, ed., "Fragmentary Remains, Literary and Scientific, of Sir Humphry Davy, bart," London, 1858.

J. Paris, "The Life of Sir Humphry Davy, bart., LL.D.," London, 1831.

J. E. Thorpe, "Humphry Davy, Poet and Philosopher," New York, 1896.

J. C. Gregory, "The Scientific Achievements of Sir Humphry Davy," London, 1930.

ROBERT SIEGFRIED

·· 30 ··

Jöns Jacob Berzelius

1779-1848

CHEMISTRY, during the first half of the nineteenth century, was dominated by the figure of Berzelius despite the fact that, as a Swede, he was geographically isolated from the major centers of chemical activity. He reached maturity just at the moment that chemistry had thrown off the shackles of alchemical thought. Not only did he recognize the importance of the point of view developed by Lavoisier, but he was among the first to recognize the significance of the atomic hypothesis of Dalton. In fact, once Dalton had pointed the way, it was Berzelius who performed the accurate but tedious analytical work that ultimately won acceptance for the atomic doctrine.

During the years 1815 to 1835 Berzelius was virtually the supreme authority with respect to chemical matters. His textbook, his *Jahres-Bericht,* his dualistic theory, and his atomic weight tables gained him a position of respect which fell off only slowly with the decline of his powers during his later years. Regardless of the obstacles that he placed in the path of the developing organic chemistry of this time, he raised chemistry to a higher level as the result of his careful experimental work and sound criticism.

Jöns Jacob Berzelius was born on August 20, 1779, at Wäfversunda, the son of a school principal in East Gothland. As the result of the early death of his father and the remarriage and subsequent early death of his mother, his education was completed with difficulty. Financial problems, coupled with a certain independence of mind, forced him to abandon his studies several times for interludes of tutoring. An interest in nature directed his ambitions toward medicine, the field which was at the time most satisfactory for one interested in scientific studies. His medical examinations at Upsala were passed without distinction and he was granted, in 1802, the doctorate in medicine. As a thesis, he presented some analytical work on mineral waters which he had carried out earlier while employed as a physician's assistant.

His interest in physical science was well developed by this time. With a half-brother, he had carried out experiments on electricity.

Following news of Volta's experiments, he constructed a pile with 60 pairs of copper coins and zinc plates to be used for medical experiments. While at Upsala he studied Girtanner's *Anfangs-Gründe der antiphlogistischen Chemie* and obtained Professor Johan Afzelius' somewhat reluctant permission to carry out experiments in his laboratory. Studies on nitrous oxide led to a paper which the Swedish Academy of Sciences refused to publish because of objections to his use of the new antiphlogistic nomenclature.

Following receipt of the doctorate, Berzelius was appointed to an unpaid position in the School of Surgery in Stockholm, where he also took on other medical duties. He lived at the house of Wilhelm Hisinger, a mine owner with an active interest in chemistry. Berzelius and Hisinger collaborated on several researches, one of which clarified the nature of the decompositions that take place when aqueous solutions are subjected to an electric current, another of which led to the discovery of ceria and its recognition as the oxide of a new metal. The discoverers of ceria were unsuccessful in reducing the oxide to the metal and it was many years later that Mosander succeeded in preparing the element in impure form. (Klaproth discovered ceria independently shortly before the work of Berzelius and Hisinger.)

These early years in Stockholm were marred by two unsuccessful commercial ventures. The one of lesser importance involved collaboration in a series of scientific lectures which failed to gain sufficient subscribers. More serious was his partnership in a firm marketing mineral water, the failure of which left him heavily in debt. However, from 1806, salaried academic appointments began coming his way in Stockholm and his fortunes improved as his scientific reputation grew. Consolidation and reorganization of the local medical schools in 1810 led to his appointment to the chair of chemistry and pharmacy in the Karolinischen Medico-Chirurgischen Institut.

In view of his growing scientific reputation it was natural that he should be called upon for public service. He was made a member of the Academy of Science in 1808 and served as its president from February to August in 1810. In 1807 he was engaged as a writer for the Academy's newly-founded *Economiska Annaler* and served as virtual editor before its abandonment in 1809. With the founding of the Academy of Agriculture in 1811, Berzelius was made manager, a post which was soon made a lifetime one. That same year saw his appointment to a Commission on Gunpowder. This commission was to study and make recommendations for the improvement of Swedish powder. The commission was dissolved in 1818 after a period of little accomplishment, because of little governmental support for its activities.

By 1812 Berzelius was well known in the chemical world and was in correspondence with such figures as Berthollet and Davy. In that year financial support for a trip to France was tendered by a member of the royal family but war broke out between Sweden and France before the trip could begin. England was an acceptable alternative and the period from July through October was spent there. He not only met Davy, who received him coolly at first, but made valuable contacts with William Wollaston, Smithson Tennant, Alexander Marcet, Frederick Accum, Thomas Young, James Watt, and William Herschel. Dr. Marcet was particularly kind. Berzelius attended his lectures on chemistry at Guy's Hospital and learned much about organization and demonstrations which he was to incorporate into his own teaching in Stockholm. On returning to Sweden he brought with him from England an air pump and various other pieces of scientific equipment for use in his teaching and research.

The following decade was a busy one. Besides his work on atomic weights, dualistic theory, and chemical symbols, all of which will be discussed in detail later, he began his studies on mineralogy, embarked on another commercial venture, declined Klaproth's vacant chair in Berlin, and suffered a breakdown in health which led to a year of travel.

Berzelius' interest in minerals was passive until 1813, when he was visited by the English physician, William MacMichael, who spent some time with him receiving practical instruction in chemistry. While there, the heirs of Anders Gustaf Ekeberg (1767–1813) offered his mineral collection for sale. Ekeberg, along with Afzelius, had taught Berzelius chemistry at Upsala, and was the discoverer of tantalum. MacMichael, who wished to supply the

British Museum with samples of rare Swedish minerals, bought the collection, took those samples which he desired, and gave the remainder to Berzelius.

When Berzelius began to arrange the collection he found the classification systems of such mineralogists as Haüy, Werner, Karstens, and Hausman inadequate to his purposes. All of them, depending as they did on physical characteristics, brought together chemically unrelated substances. Berzelius determined that classification must be on a chemical basis and set out to devise such a system. Study of numerous minerals revealed to him that silica was a common constituent and that the silica, in fact, served as the acid component, combined with some form of basic earth. The silicate rocks might therefore be looked upon as salts of silicic acids. From a study of recorded analyses he found that the acid portion of silicates was to the basic portion as 3, 2, or 1 is to 1. From this knowledge he devised a purely chemical system of mineral classification. This was privately published in 1814. Blake translated the work into English, Gehlen into German.

Berzelius' work in mineralogy was continued, through the invitation of the now elderly Gahn, toward the investigation of an unusual quartz vein near a mine at Fahlun. New minerals were discovered and analyzed in Gahn's well-equipped laboratory. Johan Gottlieb Gahn (1745–1818), the discoverer of manganese, was a mine owner and was assessor at the College of Mines. He was an expert analyst with the blowpipe and during this period taught Berzelius his techniques.

During this study Berzelius isolated a substance which he believed to be the oxide of a new metal that he named thorium, after the god, Thor. A decade later he learned that the substance was yttrium phosphate. However, the name, thorium, was retained for a new element, discovered in 1829 in a Norwegian mineral that had been submitted to him for analysis. An impure sample of the metal was prepared by Berzelius by heating potassium with potassium thorium fluoride.

In 1816 Berzelius joined Gahn in the purchase of a bankrupt factory manufacturing sulfuric acid, vinegar, white lead, and other chemicals. The plant operated successfully until it was lost in a fire in 1826. As in his earlier experiences, Berzelius ended up with

390

a financial loss. However, soon after purchasing the plant he discovered the element selenium in certain wastes from sulfuric acid manufacture.

In 1818, following an intensive period of work on his textbook, Berzelius suffered badly from migraine headaches and became greatly depressed. For the sake of his health he undertook a trip to Paris, visiting England en route. He was away from Stockholm an entire year, returning greatly refreshed. In Paris he spent much time with Berthollet, who introduced him to Laplace, Cuvier, Gay-Lussac, Thenard, Chaptal, Dulong, Chevreul, Arago, Biot, Vauquelin, Ampère, and Humboldt. Haüy spent much time showing Berzelius his mineral collection and presented him with rare specimens. He attended the lectures of Gay-Lussac, Vauquelin, Thenard, Haüy, Brongniart, and Biot with great benefit to his own lecture techniques. Gay-Lussac, in particular, he found to excel in art of presentation and grace of diction. His own work on electrochemical theory and definite proportions he found little known in Paris. This led him to publish while there. He also prepared a French edition of his mineral classification and gave instruction in the use of the blowpipe. With Dulong he carried out experiments toward the improvement of the atomic weights of hydrogen, nitrogen, and carbon, and studied the density of oxygen, nitrogen, and carbon dioxide. Before leaving Paris he purchased instruments and materials which would make his own laboratory more nearly the equivalent of those he had visited.

Following some geological sightseeing in rural France he went to Geneva where he renewed his friendship with Marcet and met Theodore de Saussure, the elder de la Rive, Pictet, Prevost, and others. At Tübingen he visited his former student, C. G. Gmelin, before proceeding to Freiburg where the famous mining school attracted his attention. At Berlin he was asked to name one of his students for Klaproth's still vacant chair; but since he did not consider any of them qualified, he proposed that the promising young Eilhard Mitscherlich, who had just discovered the law of isomorphism, spend a year in preparation in his laboratory in Stockholm at the expense of the Prussian state. This proposal was approved.

Berzelius did not offer laboratory work as a routine part of his chemical instruction. However, he did on occasion open his laboratory to advanced students who spent a period of time with him learning analytical techniques and carrying out various studies. Not only Swedes, but men of other nationalities were accepted. When Mitscherlich arrived in 1820 he was accompanied by Heinrich Rose of the famous family of German apothecaries. Soon thereafter they were joined by Rose's brother, Gustav, who later became professor in mineralogy in the University of Berlin where Heinrich Rose and Mitscherlich held chairs in chemistry. Friedrich Wöhler spent time with Berzelius in 1823–24. Others who studied with Berzelius and left their mark on science were Gustav Magnus (1827–28), later professor of physics and technology in Berlin, Germain Henri Hess (1828), who became professor of chemistry at St. Petersburg, W. Johnston (1832), who became professor of chemistry at Durham, and A. Sobero (1839–40), Sardinian general of artillery. His most important Swedish students were J. A. Arfwedson, Nils G. Sefström, and Carl Gustav Mosander.

The return of his headaches in 1821 led to a trip to the mineral water springs at Karlsbad in Bohemia. While there he visited the mines of Joachimsthal, examined mineral waters on the estate of Prince Metternich and volcanic remains with Goethe. In the latter case Berzelius was successful in demonstrating to Goethe that the poet's theory of volcanic origin was not in accord with the facts. The success of the Karlsbad waters led Berzelius to assist several countrymen in the founding of an establishment for treatment with artificial Karlsbad water. The venture was an immediate success. It was soon purchased and operated by Mosander.

In 1826 Berzelius was appointed to a committee for the reorganization of public instruction. He proposed a greater amount of science in the curriculum, arguing that everyone should know the reason for the increase and waning of the moon, the operation of the syphon and the barometer, the floating of ice on water, and similar matters. However, his proposal was voted down and the traditional curriculum was continued.

The last two decades of his life were characterized by periods of concentrated experimental work and writing, severe illnesses, trips to foreign countries in search of restored health, all somewhat cyclical. He retired from his teaching duties in 1832, his chair being assigned to Mosander. Berzelius was now one of the leading chemists of the world and was eagerly welcomed by chemists and geologists wherever he went. Former students held chairs in important universities and his writings were quickly published in translation.

Only as old age approached did he give serious thought to marriage. He had been so busy with scientific matters during his earlier years that he seemed not to have found time nor desire for family life. His faithful servant, Anna Blank, had not only seen to the housekeeping duties for eighteen years but had served as a laboratory helper as well, cleaning apparatus, keeping things in order, and even assisting with preparations. In 1835, as the loneliness of advancing years became apparent, he sought the hand of Johanna Elizabeth Poppius, twenty-four-year-old daughter of his old friend, the counsellor of state. The proposal was received with approval by the parents and the daughter. Thereupon he decided, since his health was poor, to make a visit to Paris and attend the meeting of German scientists at Bonn on the return journey. Following a trip of three months, during which he renewed many friendships and received various honors, he returned to Stockholm for his wedding. At that same time King Charles (John Bernadotte) who had knighted him in 1818, made him a baron. During his remaining years he continued his scientific writing and participated in educational activities in Sweden. His death occurred on the seventh of August, 1848.

Berzelius' contributions to chemistry fall into three categories: (1) dissemination of chemical knowledge; (2) theoretical contributions; and (3) experimental studies, particularly those dealing with electrochemistry and atomic weight determinations. Actually, these activities were outgrowths of one another and are not easily separated. Also, it would hardly be fair to imply that his scientific activities were solely chemical. His training was in medicine and his interest in this field was never lost. His studies of minerals made him a leading mineralogist and geologist. It would not be stretching the truth badly to consider him among the last of the great chemists who could embrace and contribute to the whole field of chemistry. Following his death no one figure gained so much importance in so many areas of the subject.

DISSEMINATION OF CHEMICAL KNOWLEDGE

From the beginning, Berzelius was a fluent writer. His first published paper, dealing with electrochemical studies, appeared in 1802. All together, he published around 250 papers besides his books and the *Jahres-Bericht*.

The lack of Swedish texts on medical chemistry spurred him on to the production of a book on physiological chemistry, *Föreläsinger i Djurkemien* (Lessons in Animal Chemistry) the first volume of which was published in 1806, the second two years later. These volumes did more than review the status of animal chemistry; they contained the results of the author's original investigations on milk, bile, blood, bone, and other tissues. He once remarked that animal chemistry would have been a permanent interest if the need of his students for a general textbook had not turned him in this direction.

Since all of the German texts available in Sweden were considered inadequate, Berzelius brought out the first volume of his *Lärbok i Kemien* in 1808. The projected second volume did not appear until nearly a decade later. The original volume, which contained his earliest studies on combining proportions, was published just when Davy's isolation of alkali and alkaline earth metals was completed and Dalton's atomic theory was publicized. It was clear that a second volume must deal with these matters. But Berzelius became deeply involved in study and volume two was not forthcoming. The need for a new edition of the text in 1816 led to the completion of the second and third volumes of his textbook along with revision of the first. The textbook was very popular. By the time of his death it had gone through five editions and was widely used in German and French translations.

The manual on the blowpipe has already been mentioned. The *Afhandlingar i fysik, kemi och mineralogi* was founded in 1806 to serve as a Swedish outlet for papers in these fields. It was published at irregular intervals until 1818. In 1821 Berzelius began the preparation of an annual review, at the request of the Swedish Academy of Sciences, of which he had become secretary in 1818.

This annual review was continued up to the time of his death. The first volume covered the year 1820. It was translated from the Swedish into German as the *Jahres-Bericht über die Forschritte der physischen Wissenschaften*. The translation of the *Jahres-Bericht* was carried on after the first year by Wöhler. A French translation by Plantamour covered the years 1841–1848.

The *Jahres-Bericht* was a review of major influence. Berzelius not only pursued the literature to learn of new findings but kept in touch with a large circle of correspondents. He reported new discoveries as he heard of them and added his own remarks regarding their significance. Since he now carried great weight as a scientific authority his evaluation of the work of other scientists frequently had the effect of gaining them rapid recognition when he approved, or of throwing serious obstacles in their path when he disappeared. Major figures in the field might be able to bear up under his disapproval but younger men were not so fortunate. In certain cases, as for example the slipshod atomic weight reports of Thomas Thomson, the criticisms were of great benefit to chemistry. In other cases, they represented the holding action of a man no longer able to keep up with the new ideas in a rapidly developing field.

ORGANIZATION AND THEORIZING

Berzelius' capacity for organization is seen not only in his classification of minerals but in his work on chemical nomenclature. Taking the French nomenclature devised by Guyton de Morveau, Fourcroy, Lavoisier, and Berthollet, he refined and extended it in the light of the new knowledge of analytical chemistry. His work also served to adapt the French system to the Germanic languages.

Of equal importance was the introduction of modern symbolism. The use of symbols for chemical substances has a long history but usage before the nineteenth century was unsystematic and cumbersome. Dalton, while developing his atomic theory, made use of symbols representing atoms of various elements. The idea of definite symbols for definite elements was a good one but Dalton's circle symbols were tedious to write; furthermore, they were not a standard item in a printer's type font. Berzelius, in papers appearing in Thomson's *Annals of Philosophy* in 1813 and 1814, proposed that the initial letter of the Latin name be used to represent each element. Of course, there were a number of cases where several elements had names starting with the same letter. Here Berzelius suggested that the initial letter be assigned to nonmetals in preference to metals. Where a second letter was necessary, as in the case of many metals and some nonmetals, this was to include the second letter of the name or, when necessary, the initial letter with the first consonant not held in common with another element. It was further suggested that the symbol stand for one volume (equal to one atom) in chemical formulas. The convenience and logic of the symbols led to their gradual acceptance; Dalton and Thomas Thomson were the only die-hard opponents to their use.

Berzelius also recognized the usefulness of symbols for expressing the atomic composition of compounds in the form of formulas. Here, however, he undid the usefulness of his early proposal, which involved the use of superscripts to represent the number of atoms (i.e., H^2O), in favor of an arbitrary oversimplification which introduced the need for special type faces. Double atoms in a compound were represented by a barred symbol (i.e., H, Cl) and oxygen came to be symbolized by a dot above the accompanying element. Thus, the formula for water became H, and that for sulfur trioxide, S. Berzelius' formulas were not highly popular and, in fact, formulas were not widely used in chemical circles until mid-century.

In the *Jahres-Bericht* for 1832 Berzelius examined the phenomenon of different compounds with the same formulas. Up to this time there was a general assumption that only one compound could have a certain composition. However, there were a number of cases where compounds showed the same analyses, yet had different properties. Berzelius had encountered two different oxides of tin with the same formula. Liebig's studies on the fulminates and Wöhler's studies on the cyanates showed the same formulas for fulminic and cyanic acids. Faraday had discovered a gas (butylene) with the same formula as olefiant gas (ethylene). In the latter instance, the specific gravity of butylene proved twice that of olefiant gas so the molecule of one was twice that of the other.

In the other cases, however, it was not possible to demonstrate any difference in molecular sizes. Berzelius proposed that such compounds be called *isomers,* meaning "composed of equal parts."

In a paper published in the *Annales de chimie et de physique* in 1836 Berzelius examined a new force involved in certain chemical reactions. He pointed out a number of cases where a certain agent brought about chemical changes without being decomposed in the process. For such an agent he suggested the name *catalyst.*

The development of the dualistic, or electrochemical, theory was an outgrowth of Berzelius' early experiments on electrochemistry. He and Hisinger had at the beginning of the century made careful studies of the behavior of electrolytes during the electrolytic process. They observed that acids, bases, and salts represented compounds which decomposed in solutions exposed to the current from a voltaic pile and reported that hydrogen and metals were liberated at the negative pole while oxygen was liberated at the positive pole. They also observed that the solutions around the positive and negative poles became progressively more acidic and basic, respectively. Similar results were observed independently by Davy, whose reports gained much wider attention than the Swedish paper of Berzelius and Hisinger.

The dualistic notion was not entirely original with Berzelius since Lavoisier had believed oxygen to be a universal constituent of acids. Davy had shown that bases also contain oxygen. Berzelius combined these observations into a system that held salts to be combinations of an acid (nonmetal + oxygen) and a base (metal + oxygen). Since a similar dualism exists in electricity and since the electric current decomposes salts into basic and acidic constituents, Berzelius believed that the chemical combination could be explained by supposing atoms to show an electrical polarity. Oxygen was most negative, potassium the most positive, with other elements ranging in between. The theory permitted opposite polarities to reside within the same kind of atom in order to account for elements showing varying modes of combination. In general, metals were primarily electropositive and even when combined with oxygen the oxide showed a residual positive char-

397

acter. Nonmetals might be positive toward oxygen but negative toward metals. Nonmetal oxides always showed negative character. Salts were a natural result of the combination of positive metallic oxides and negative nonmetallic oxides. Salts themselves were not necessarily neutral, for double salts like the alums were explained as the combination of a positive and negative salt.

The electrochemical theory first appeared in de la Métherie's *Journal de Physique* in 1811. It was further developed through the years and held a position of great importance in chemistry for two decades. In the mineralogical field it was particularly effective in explaining chemical composition and it remained popular with geologists long after it had outlived its usefulness to chemists. In the field of inorganic analysis the influence of Berzelius' thought is still apparent in the tendency to report analyses of many of the elements in terms of the oxide.

It was in the field of organic chemistry that the electrochemical theory ran into serious troubles. Berzelius was a participant in the speculations of the 1830's regarding organic radicals and types, but he was never able to fit his dualistic ideas into the growing science in a convincing manner. The phenomenon of substitution was a major blow to him since he could not accept the idea that an electronegative element like chlorine could be substituted for electropositive hydrogen without altering the type of compound involved. As a consequence of his reluctance to face the facts of the rapidly developing organic field his prestige began to diminish. He mercilessly condemned Laurent's nucleus theory but this did not deter Dumas from rejecting dualism in favor of unitary ideas in organic formulation. Berzelius denied the similarity between acetic and trichloracetic acids until 1842 when Melsens converted the chlorinated acid back to ordinary acetic acid, whereupon Berzelius devised the copula theory to permit of substitution within only a part of the acetic acid molecule. This device for keeping the molecule dualistic was received without enthusiasm and failed to halt the development of unitary ideas.

Berzelius saw further defeat of his ideas regarding the importance of oxygen in acids in the work of Graham and Liebig on polybasic acids. His last decade of life was truly plagued by the rise of a new school of chemical thought.

EXPERIMENTAL STUDIES

Frequent allusion has been made above to Berzelius' experimental work. In addition, reference may be made to the isolation of silicon, titanium, and zirconium, studies on the oxides of nitrogen, examination of compounds of vanadium and molybdenum, the halides of boron and silicon, the ferrocyanides, carbon disulfide, and various investigations on organic compounds. He introduced the use of filter paper into analytical chemistry, developing procedures for preparing it free of soluble matter and for correcting for ash content. He also introduced rubber tubing into laboratory operations.

Berzelius' greatest work lay in the analytical investigations leading to accurate knowledge of combining weights and through them, to atomic weights. In preparing the first volume of his textbook he became deeply interested in the work of Richter on chemical equivalents. He immediately recognized that analytical knowledge of certain compounds might be extended to the composition of other compounds. Upon learning of Dalton's atomic theory he became a convert to atomism. He recognized, however, that analytical values of greater accuracy than those used by Richter and Dalton were needed before the concepts could safely be extended and he set for himself the task of providing such data.

During the decade following 1807 he carried out studies on the composition of compounds of 43 elements. More than 2000 compounds were prepared, purified, and analyzed. It was frequently necessary to devise new methods of gravimetric analysis and nearly all reagents had to be prepared and purified. Out of these studies came values for combining weights which in many cases compare very well with modern results. In some cases the agreement is due to compensating errors in the methods used by Berzelius but very frequently the agreement can be attributed to his painstaking attention to analytical details. A by-product of the work was verification of the laws of definite and multiple proportions.

Berzelius recognized that such combining weights, or equivalents, did not necessarily represent atomic weights and set out to unravel the proper atomic weights for the known elements. The problem was a formidable one since there was at that time no cer-

399

tainty regarding the formulas of any chemical compounds. Dalton had faced the same problem but resolved it by assuming that formulas must be simple. For example, he held that such common compounds as water, ammonia, and nitric oxide contained one atom of each of the component elements. Berzelius recognized the dangers in such an assumption and sought for more sophisticated criteria.

In Gay-Lussac's law of combining volumes Berzelius not only recognized support for the atomic theory but detected an approach toward the establishment of formulas. The concept that equal volumes of gases at the same conditions contained the same number of atoms was a reasonable and useful principle when applied to elemental gases, although Berzelius could never bring himself to apply the concept to molecules of compound gases and persistently refused to accept Avogadro's idea of diatomic molecules of elemental gases.

If equal volumes of elemental gases contained equal numbers of atoms, then atomic weights must be proportional to the weights of equal volumes. This approach was only of limited usefulness, however, since the only elemental gases then known were hydrogen, oxygen, nitrogen, and chlorine.

Gay-Lussac's law also served as a clue to the correct formulas for water, ammonia, and several other substances. Thus Berzelius, at an early date, set the atomic weight ratio of oxygen to hydrogen at 16 to 1 as against the value of 7 (*sic*) to 1 set by Dalton, who looked upon water as HO.

Berzelius used oxygen from the beginning as the reference element, its atomic weight being taken as 100. With him, as with Lavoisier before him, oxygen was the most important of all of the elements and occupied a central position in chemical philosophy. It formed oxides with all of the known elements, hence lent itself to the direct determination of combining weights. Once the combining weight of an element toward oxygen was known, there remained the most difficult problem, namely, deduction of the formula so that the atomic weight might be calculated. Here Berzelius made extensive use of analogies, besides setting up certain arbitrary rules of operation. After 1819 he also made use of the law of Petit and Dulong relating to atomic heats and the law of isomorphism enunciated by Mitscherlich as the result of his study of the crystals of phosphates and arsenates.

Berzelius published a preliminary table of atomic weights in 1814. This was followed by a more comprehensive one in 1818 and a revised table in 1826.

Since he looked upon salts as combinations of basic and acidic oxides he set up the rule that the amount of oxygen in the basic portion of the salt must be to the oxygen in the acidic portion as 1 is to 1, 2, or 3. In his early period he believed than an atom of oxygen must be combined with at least an atom of metal. Then the lower oxide of mercury and copper must be HgO and CuO, making the higher oxide HgO^2 and CuO^2. Since more of the metal oxides appeared to correspond to the higher than to the lower oxides, the accepted formulas became ZnO^2, MgO^2, CaO^2, etc. In the case of the two oxides of iron, lead, and manganese he noticed that the oxygen in the two compounds varied as 1 to 1½, hence 2 to 3, and the formulas became FeO^2 and FeO^3, for example. Chromium and aluminum oxides were considered analogous to ferric oxide and became CrO^3 and AlO^3.

The case of chromic oxide required reconsideration and correction before the 1826 table was published and resulted in a readjustment of the formulas of all of the metallic oxides with corresponding halving of the atomic weights. Berzelius knew that chromium formed an acidic oxide with twice as much oxygen in it as the ordinary oxide held. This oxide he first formulated CrO^6. However, he recognized the relationship of the chromates to the sulfates (containing the acidic oxide, SO^3), and he decided that the acidic chromium oxide must be CrO^3. Therefore the other oxide must become Cr^2O^3. Then, since ferric and aluminum oxides were isomorphous with Cr^2O^3, their formulas must be changed to Fe^2O^3 and Al^2O^3 and the lower oxide of iron must become FeO. This led to changing other metallic oxides to the monoxide form (ZnO, CaO, MgO, etc.), a change that was clearly consistent with results obtained by applying the law of Petit and Dulong (except for cobalt and silver). In the case of silver, sodium, and potassium he continued to believe their oxides similar to those of divalent

401

metals and used the formulas AgO, NaO, and KO in his 1826 table, giving their atomic weights twice the correct value. On the whole, the Berzelius' atomic weights were well conceived. Those of silver, sodium, and potassium had to be halved. That of carbon was found by Dumas to be too high. Most of the remaining ones were found in subsequent years not to require correction but merely refinement. His work was well done and the fact that many of his contemporaries favored equivalent to atomic weights was not a reflection on Berzelius, but revealed rather the lesser stature of these contemporaries.

NOTES AND REFERENCES

J. Carriere, ed., "Berzelius und Liebig, Ihre Briefe von 1831–1845," Munich u. Leipzig, Verlag von J. F. Lehmann, 1893.

B. Duschnitz, "Jöns Jacob Berzelius und die Elektrochemie," Z. Elektrochem., 36, 57–63 (1930).

Georg W. A. Kahlbaum, "Jöns Jacob Berzelius und Humphry Davy," Mitt. Gesch. Med. Naturw., 3, 277–290 (1904).

Wilhelm Ostwald, "Berzelius' 'Jahresbericht' and the International Organization of Chemists," J. Chem. Educ., 32, 373–375 (1955).

W. Prandtl, "Humphry Davy. Jöns Jacob Berzelius," Stuttgart, Wissenschaftliche Verlagsgesellschaft, 1948.

H. Rose, "Nachruf," Am. J. Sci., Series 2, 16, 1–15, 173–186, 305–313 (1853). Ibid., 17, 103–113 (1854).

H. G. Soderbaum, "Jöns Jacob Berzelius, Autobiographical Notes," Baltimore, Williams & Wilkins, 1934 (translated by Olaf Larsell).

H. G. Soderbaum, "Berzelius," in G. Bugge, "Das Buch der Grossen Chemiker," vol. 1, 428–449, Berlin, Verlag Chemie, 1929.

George Urdang, "Berzelius and Pharmacy," J. Am. Phar. Assoc., Scientific ed., 37, 481–85 (1948).

P. Walden, "Berzelius und Wir," Z. angew. Chem., 43, 325–329, 351–354, 366–370 (1930).

O. Wallach, ed., "Briefwechsel zwischen J. Berzelius und F. Wöhler," Leipzig, Verlag von W. Engelmann, 1902.

R. Winderlich, "Berzelius und Davy," Z. angew. Chem., 42, 607 (1929).

F. Wöhler, "Early Recollections of a Chemist," Ber., 8, 838–852 (1875); Am. Chemist, 6, 131–136 (1875).

AARON J. IHDE

·· *31* ··

Benjamin Silliman

1779-1864

ONE warm July morning in 1801 on the campus of Yale University President Timothy Dwight stopped a young lawyer named Benjamin Silliman and offered to make him Yale's first professor of chemistry. Since then Yale has recruited her chemistry professors in a more orthodox manner and has chosen men with a scientific background, but none of them has surpassed in fame or in color the young man who did not attend a chemistry lecture until he was twenty-three years old.

Stepping into a professorship of chemistry without warning or training was not the first nor the last unusual act in the life of Benjamin Silliman. At the time of his birth in Trumbull, Connecticut, August 8, 1779, his father, Brigadier General Gold Selleck Silliman, was in a British prison, having been captured in the Silliman home at Fairfield by a midnight raiding party. Benjamin grew up in Fairfield, swam and fished in Long Island Sound, and attended country school before entering Yale at the age of thirteen. For four years he studied industriously, attended chapel regularly, and in general behaved so gentlemanly—unlike the typical collegian of the times—that his classmates teased him with the nickname "Sober Ben." After graduating in 1796 he labored for two years on his widowed mother's farm. Bored by the intellectual stillness of rural life he turned to school teaching at Wethersfield. Finally he decided on a profession, law, and in October, 1798, he started his studies in Judge Simeon Baldwin's office at New Haven. This proved a lucky move for Sober Ben, for it brought him back under the eye of President Dwight of Yale, who promptly appointed the young man to the office of tutor in the college.

Dividing his time between classroom and mock court, Silliman pressed forward toward a legal career. Shortly before he passed his bar examination friends offered him a tempting position in Georgia. This he might have accepted, and thereby missed becoming the best-known American science teacher of his time, had not President Dwight countered with the amazing offer of a professorship of chemistry and natural history! Silliman did not know what to do. He had never so much as heard a lecture on chemistry. "During my novitiate," he wrote later, "chemistry was scarcely ever named. I well remember when I received my earliest impressions in relation to chemistry. Professor Josiah Meigs—1794–1801–delivered lectures on natural philosophy from the pulpit of the College Chapel. He was a gentleman of great intelligence, and had read Chaptal, Lavoisier, and other chemical writers of the French School. From these, and perhaps other sources, he occasionally introduced chemical facts and principals in common with those of natural philosophy." This was Silliman's only acquaintance with chemistry on the day when Dwight proffered the professorship.

Silliman saw many obstacles, but Dwight skillfully disposed of these. Law, Dwight pointed out, was crowded, but chemistry was a new, wide-open field in which an ambitious man could make his mark. Further, Silliman was only twenty-one, young enough to change from one profession to another. Finally, Dwight offered Silliman leave of absence to attend chemistry lectures and prepare himself for the new job. Silliman surrendered; but, being a shrewd Yankee he went on to pass his bar examination in 1802 and so could have returned to law had the career that Dwight held out to him proved to be dross.

Why, we may wonder, did Dwight choose a prospective lawyer to introduce chemistry into Yale? First, because chemists were so scarce in America that Dwight did not know where he could lay his hands on one. Second, he feared that a foreign chemist might not fit into the Yale system and might not get along with the other teachers. And finally, one suspects that Silliman's conscientiousness, seriousness, and piety appealed to the Reverend Dr. Dwight.

To assist Silliman in getting off to the right start, Dwight wrote for advice to Princeton where Professor John Maclean taught one of the few chemistry courses in America. Maclean recommended the works of Scheele, Priestley, Kirwan, Lavoisier, and Chaptal, but he also stated that it was impossible for Silliman to become a teacher through books alone, and recommended that Silliman journey to the University of Pennsylvania and attend the chemical lectures of James Woodhouse, the best chemist in the United States.

406

Philadelphia became Silliman's home for several months in the winters of 1802–03 and 1803–04. There he met Benjamin Rush; Joseph Priestley, who came down to the city occasionally from his home in Northumberland; Henry Seybert, the country's best mineralogist; and most important, a youthful chemical genius who turned out to be his lifelong friend, Robert Hare.

"The chemical lectures," he recalled, "were important to me, who had as yet seen few chemical experiments. Those performed by Dr. Woodhouse were valuable, because every fact, with its proof, was an acquisition to me. The apparatus was humble, but it answered to exhibit some of the most important facts in the science; and our instructor delighted, although he did not excel, in the performance of experiments. He had no proper assistant, and the work was imperfectly done; but still it was a treasure to me . . . and I soon began to interpret phenomena for myself and to anticipate the explanations."

As revealing as Woodhouse's lectures were to Silliman, the young learner was missing one of the important phases of chemical education, the experience of handling chemicals and apparatus in a laboratory. This, of course, was no fault of Woodhouse or of Silliman, since student laboratories were unknown in those days, but luckily for Benjamin, his classmate Robert Hare liked to experiment. Hare had already gained a reputation for his invention of the oxyhydrogen blowtorch, and he invited Silliman to work along with him in, of all places, their landlady's cellar-kitchen. "Hare was desirous," wrote Silliman, "of making it [the blowtorch flame] still more intense by deriving a pure oxygen from chlorate of potassa, then called oxy-muriate of potassa. Chemists were then ignorant of the fact that, by mixing a little oxide of manganese with the chlorate, the oxygen can be evolved by the heat of a lamp applied to a glass retort. Hare thought it necessary to use stone retorts with a furnace-heat; the retorts were purchased by me at a dollar each, and, as they were usually broken in the experiment, the research was rather costly; but my friend furnished experience, and, as I was daily acquiring it, I was rewarded, both for labor and expense, by the brilliant results of our experiments."

During the winter of 1803–04, while he attended Woodhouse's lectures the second time, Silliman began to write lectures for his future courses. In addition to the notes that he took during lecture, he drew material from Joseph Black's *Lectures on the Elements of Chemistry* (Edinburgh, 1803), and from Thomas Thomson's four-volume *System of Chemistry* (Edinburgh, 1802).

Back home in New Haven in April, 1804, the lawyer-turned-chemist, now twenty-four years old, began his teaching career in a room hired for him by the college. This temporary arrangement lasted only one year since Yale was already erecting a building with a laboratory and lecture room for the new chemistry course. But laboratories were something beyond the ken of an architect of those days, and when Silliman visited the half-completed laboratory for the first time he found himself in a gloomy cavern fifteen feet underground. "How did it happen? I suppose that Mr. Bonner, an able civil architect. . . . had received only some vague impressions of chemistry—perhaps a confused and terrific dream of alchemy, with its black arts, its explosions, and its weird-like mysteries. He appears, therefore, to have imagined, that the deeper down in mother earth the dangerous chemists could be buried, so much the better. . . ." It was too late for Bonner to change the plans of the building, so Silliman had to stay underground. But he persuaded the college to make his quarters more livable by tearing out stone pillars and arches, and digging a wide trench along the outside of the building to admit light and air through subterranean windows. "The room was now paved with flag-stones; a false floor of boards was constructed, rising the lowest level as high as the ground-sill of the outer door, and thus affording an elevation— an inclined plane—sufficient to prevent the vision of the rear from being obstructed by the front rows of hearers. A gallery was erected on the side of the room opposite to the windows, access being made from the front of the tower or steeple through the intervening cellar, over a paved walk. Tables were established on the floor of the laboratory, in a line with a large hydro-pneumatic cistern or gas-tub, and a marble cistern for a mercurial bath. . . . Arrangements were made for furnaces, and for the introduction of water from a neighboring well. The tables were covered with green cloth, the stone floor was sprinkled with white beach-sand; the walls and ceiling were white-washed; the backs and writing-tables of the benches, and the front and end of the gallery, were

408

painted of a light lead color; and the glass of the windows being washed clean, the laboratory now made a very decent and rather inviting appearance, like the offices, storerooms, and kitchens that are seen almost underground in cities."

In this underground laboratory, so damp that iron rusted rapidly, and "all preparations that attracted water became moist or even deliquesced," Silliman spent the next fifteen years of his life teaching Yale men the facts of geology and chemistry. Silliman's total equipment consisted of a few things that he had purchased in Philadelphia, some apparatus for natural philosophy that Yale had imported from England many years before, and an old blacksmith's forge. "At that time," Silliman wrote, "there were very few chemical instruments of glass to be obtained in this country. I had picked up a few glass retorts in Philadelphia, and I made application to Mr. Mather, a manufacturer of glass in East Hartford, a few years later, to make some for me. On stating my wish, he said he had never seen a retort, but if I would send him one as a pattern, he did not doubt he could make them. I had a retort the neck or tube of which was broken off near the ball—but as no portion was missing, and the two parts exactly fitted each other, I sent this retort and its neck in a box, never dreaming that there could be any blunder. In due time, however, my dozen of green glass retorts, of East Hartford manufacture, arrived, carefully boxed and all sound, except that they were all cracked off in the neck exactly where the pattern was fractured; and broken neck and ball lay in state like decapitated kings in their coffins."

The scarcity of apparatus in the United States was turned to Silliman's advantage. Yale decided to spend $10,000 for scientific apparatus and library books in Europe, dealing through commission merchants. When Silliman heard of this he hurried to President Dwight and asked that Yale send him to purchase the items, paying him the same commission and allowing him time to attend scientific lectures. This was a shrewd Yankee move if ever there was one. It gave Silliman a year abroad and the opportunity of learning chemistry from the best European chemists, with expenses paid by Yale.

In London he studied analytical chemistry in Frederick Accum's laboratory, and attended the chemical lectures of George Pearson.

In Edinburgh he listened to Thomas Hope and John Murray. He met the leading British scientists, among them Watt, Dalton, Davy, and Banks. He inspected factories, visited Parliament, attended meetings of scientific societies, and even went to a few plays. He witnessed the first gas lights in London, and saw Admiral Nelson at Portsmouth embarking for the battle of Trafalgar. He tried to visit France, but was turned back at Antwerp on suspicion that he was a British spy.

Silliman was an inveterate diarist. In Europe he kept a journal, and after returning to New Haven he distributed the manuscript among his friends. Several of them suggested that he publish it, and one offered to assume any financial responsibility. This led to *A Journal of Travel in England, Holland and Scotland, and of Two Passages over the Atlantic, in the Years 1805 and 1806,* whose three editions were widely read, here and in Europe, and which gave Silliman's name considerable publicity among literate Americans.

Silliman's year in Europe marked the end of his formal education. His training was mediocre compared to the training that chemists receive now, but in his day it made him one of the best informed chemists in the country. If we run our minds eye over his contemporaries—Maclean, Mitchill, Woodhouse, Seybert, Dexter, and the others—we see only two other chemists, Woodhouse and Seybert, whose background rivaled Silliman's. The European trip was one of the circumstances responsible for Silliman's outstanding attainments as a teacher and for the success of chemistry at Yale.

Silliman's voyage had one other effect on science at Yale. The lectures that he had attended in Scotland had emphasized geology and mineralogy, two subjects that Silliman did not know very much about. His appetite whetted, Silliman took up those subjects and soon became a respectable amateur. In New Haven lived George Gibbs, a wealthy amateur mineralogist who had collected some 10,000 specimens, mostly in Europe. Silliman tickled Gibbs' pride and persuaded him to exhibit the collection in the college. With this first-class teaching tool at hand, Silliman split mineralogy and geology from the chemistry course and taught them as individual subjects—the first time, it is said, that geology was taught as a separate subject in an American college.

Up to this point Silliman, despite his hard work, had done nothing that would raise him above other American chemistry professors, but in 1817 his friend George Gibbs showed him the way to immortality. Gibbs had been a strong supporter of Archibald Bruce's *American Mineralogical Journal,* and when Bruce, because of ill-health, stopped publishing, Gibbs persuaded Silliman to start a new journal. In July of 1818 there appeared the first issue of the *American Journal of Science,* generally referred to as *Silliman's Journal.*

Silliman's training gave him a wider and deeper understanding of science than most other American editors of his time, enabling him to maintain the journal on a high plane. His how-to-win-friends-and-influence-people attitude brought him the friendship of a wide circle of American scientists who offered him their articles. In the pages of the *Journal* appeared communications on natural history from pioneers in the West, and formal research reports from professional men in the East. European scientists read the journal to keep up with American discoveries, and even sent appropriate articles for its pages. It made Silliman's name more familiar in Europe than perhaps that of any other American scientist.

It was not an easy thing to keep a scientific periodical alive in early nineteenth century America, but Silliman had just the proper amount of Yankee tenacity to hold on through years of small subscription lists while other journals folded up. In his old age Silliman surrendered the editorship to his son, Benjamin Jr., and his son-in-law, James Dwight Dana, and the *Journal* still appears regularly, a century and a half after its founding. It is the oldest continuously published scientific journal in America, with the exception of the publications of a few organizations such as the American Philosophical Society. If Silliman had done nothing else, his journal would have given him a place of honor in the history of American science.

Shortly after Silliman sent forth his periodical, tragedy struck his family. First his mother, then his five-year-old son, and then an infant son died, leaving him broken-hearted. Sorrow and overwork headed him for a breakdown. To cheer his spirits his brother-in-law suggested a trip to Canada. Even in travail Silliman could not refrain from taking notes of historical and scientific sights along the way, and in 1820 he turned these into a book, *Remarks, Made on a Short Tour, between Hartford and Quebec, in the Autumn of 1819.* This volume proved to be as popular as his earlier European travel book. It went into a second American edition and a London edition, and Silliman could have run it into a third edition had he desired.

Silliman's success with his travel books unfortunately did not extend to his one chemistry text. Early in his career he had favored William Henry's *Elements of Experimental Chemistry* and had seen three American editions through the press. Each year Silliman modified his course slightly to fit the new discoveries in chemistry and of his own changing ideas; as the course changed it became more and more difficult for him to find a suitable text. So in 1830 he brought out his own two-volume *Elements of Chemistry, in the order of the lectures given in Yale College.* So far as students were concerned the book was a failure. It contained far too many details for young men, almost all of whom had never attended a chemistry course before and never would again. The style was ponderous and dull. Silliman had overshot his mark and turned out a tome that could almost be classified as a reference book, that appealed almost solely to other teachers rather than to students. Why did Silliman fail with the written word when he was so successful with the spoken? He attributed his failure to overwork; he had so many irons in the fire that he could not give his manuscript the thought and revisions that might have turned it into a popular, long-lived text.

Silliman's influence during his first quarter of a century as a professor was confined almost entirely to collegiate circles. Then in 1834 he embarked upon the career of a public lecturer and carried science to many sections of the United States. He delivered his first series of lectures at Hartford on the subject of geology, sprinkled liberally with chemistry and mineralogy. An audience of more than 300 people turned out to hear him, netting him $350, a handsome fee in those times when working men earned a dollar or two a day. Later that year the citizens of Lowell invited him to their town. In 1835 he lectured in Boston to audiences varying from 1000 to 1500, at a fee of $1500, then at Salem, at New Haven, and finally at Nantucket where former President John Quincy Adams came to listen. In 1836 he addressed 1300 people in New York, and then went up to Boston, where his evening lectures on chemistry were completely sold out and he had to deliver duplicate lectures in the afternoons to accommodate the crowds. In 1837 he again spoke on geology in New York, and followed this in 1838 with chemistry. In 1840 John Lowell invited him to deliver the first course of lectures for the new Lowell Institute in Boston. People showed up for tickets three hours before lecture time, and when Silliman stepped on the stage to begin his talk on geology there was not a vacant seat in the house. Silliman lectured for two hours, but Mrs. Lowell was so engrossed that she was willing to sit for two hours more. In 1841 he returned to the Institute to deliver the first lectures on chemistry. Ten thousand people requested tickets. In 1842 he returned again. "I was told," he wrote, "that on the day of applying for tickets, Federal Street . . . was entirely filled for a long distance with a dense mass of people, waiting for hours for a chance, and content to advance slowly as the front melted away. The tickets at once commanded two or three or more dollars, and they are often drawn by servants and others for the purpose of selling them again for money." In 1843 he gave his final series at the Institute. Later that year he lectured upon geology to audiences of 1000 at Pittsburgh. At Baltimore in 1844 audiences of 600 attended his geology lectures. New Orleans, Mobile, Natchez, Rodney, and other southern towns heard him in 1845. In succeeding years he visited other cities. In 1852 he spoke at the Smithsonian Institution in Washington. In 1855, after repeated requests, he went west to St. Louis. He was eighty years old in 1857 when he appeared on the platform for the last time.

Why was Silliman so sucessful in attracting listeners wherever he went? One reason was a set of three principles that he followed: "The first requisite in a public speaker is that he himself understands the subject which he proposes to explain; the second, that a transparent perspicuity shall enable every intelligent and at-

413

tentive hearer to comprehend his teachings; and a third, that a vivid animation should excite the speaker, and thus warm the hearer." Another reason was, that he carried along, even to the farthest cities, charts, chemicals, and equipment with which to illustrate his remarks or to show experiments. After the Boston lectures he wrote his wife, "I made a very liberal use of potassium and sodium, which are not only splendid subjects of experiment but are highly illustrative of chemical principles." From Salem he wrote, "our chemical experiments have given us much employment, and all of them, especially those with the calorimotor and compound blowpipe have been very successful. The people are astonished to see intense ignition coming out of cold fluids, and the rocks themselves melting under a stream of burning gases." The large geological drawings that he hung in halls cost him several hundred dollars. The deflagrator (a battery with very large, movable plates) that he had made for his Boston lectures on chemistry cost him $1000. As a result of his principles and his conscientious preparations Silliman caught and held the interest of his listeners from the moment he appeared on the platform until he bowed good night. "As a popular lecturer," wrote Joseph Henry, "he was . . . one of the best I have ever heard."

Silliman through his public lectures did more to spread a knowledge of science and to stimulate people to study science than any other teacher of his generation. He was the first person to bring science to some areas, and some of his young listeners decided to follow in Silliman's footsteps. Josiah P. Cooke, later professor of chemistry at Harvard, wrote, concerning Silliman's talks at the Lowell Institute: "At those lectures I was an attentive listener. Although a mere boy—one of the youngest of those present —I then acquired my taste for the science which has since become the business of my life."

At Yale, for his first forty years, Silliman taught chemistry by the same methods that he used in his public lectures, that is, by lecture and by the demonstration of experiments. This situation was not confined to Yale; it was the same in other American colleges and in Europe, and it was so because chemistry, as a profession, scarcely existed. The only people whom Silliman permitted to come into his laboratory and learn how to handle chemicals and apparatus were a few young men who intended to teach chemistry. In 1842 his son, Benjamin, Jr., began to give laboratory instruction to a small group of students. The course was optional, and carried no credit in the college. But Silliman had begun to realize that industry and agriculture were reaching a point where professional chemists were needed.

In 1846 he asked Yale to set up an official school of science. The trustees agreed and in 1847 opened the new school, with John P. Norton as professor of agricultural chemistry and Benjamin Silliman, Jr., as professor of technical chemistry. The accuracy of Silliman's foresight was shown by the rapid growth of the new department, later known as the Sheffield Scientific School in honor of Joseph E. Sheffield, an early benefactor.

By this time Silliman was well along in years, and he began to take life a bit easier. He visited Europe again, this time for pleasure. As on his tour of fifty years before he kept a journal that he published upon his return. This two-volume *Visit to Europe in 1851,* filled with chatty information about people and places, was the American Baedeker of its day, and attained five editions.

In 1853, after a term of fifty years on the Yale faculty, Silliman resigned. Chemistry had expanded tremendously since that day in 1804 when he had delivered his first lecture, and no longer could one man be expected to teach chemistry, mineralogy, and geology on the college level. Yale split Silliman's professorship in two, appointing his son, Benjamin, Jr., to the chair of chemistry and his son-in-law, James Dwight Dana, to the chair of mineralogy and geology.

In retirement Silliman kept himself busy lecturing to the public and editing his *Journal.* He had always been the antithesis of the ivory tower scientist, and had played the part of the good citizen in the political issues, the church, and other aspects of community life. When Kansas was thrown open to slavery, upsetting the Missouri Compromise of 1820, he spoke and wrote vigorously in opposition. If he had been of less stature his words might have gone unheeded, but the public had its eye upon him, and Southern senators reviled him and Northern senators defended him in senate speeches. He helped compose a petition to President Buchanan protesting against the use of Federal troops in Kansas, and he was one of the targets of the President's reply. In some quarters he came to be regarded as one of the leaders against the President's pro-slavery policies. He voted for Lincoln and favored his policies, although there was little that he, a man of eighty-one at the time of the bombardment of Fort Sumter, could do actively to aid the North. But the government did not forget that he was one of the nation's most distinguished scientists, and when Congress created the National Academy of Sciences in 1863 for the purpose of providing technical advice, it chose Silliman as one of the fifty charter members. Silliman did not live to see the end of the war. On Thanksgiving morning, 1864, he passed away quietly in his home.

If we judge Benjamin Silliman solely by his accomplishments as an experimental chemist he would not be in this volume. That is not to say that he lacked talent—his paper in the *Transactions of the American Philosophical Society* on the analysis of the Weston meteor aroused interest here and abroad, he was perhaps the first American to prepare potassium by Gay-Lussac's method, he extended Hare's experiments on the fusion of materials in the oxy-hydrogen flame—but the quality and quantity of his work would not place in the front rank of chemists. He is here because, in the words of George P. Fisher, he was "the most eminent of American teachers of natural science." He had perhaps more influence than any other teacher of his time in spreading chemistry throughout the United States. Thousands of young men from every section of the country attended his classes over a period of half a century, and thousands more attended his public lectures. His students taught at University of Nashville (George T. Bowen), Yale (Benjamin Silliman, Jr., James D. Dana, Denison Olmsted, George J. Brush, William H. Brewer, John P. Norton), Laval, McGill and Massachusetts Institute of Technology (Thomas S. Hunt), Amherst (Edward Hitchcock, William C. Fowler), Rensselaer Polytechnic Institute (Amos Eaton), Burlington College (Gamaliel Olds), Harvard (Josiah Dwight Whitney), Dartmouth (Oliver P. Hubbard), Williams (Chester Dewey), University of Louisville (Benjamin Silliman, Jr.), and at other colleges.

More than a century has passed since Silliman put away his lecture notes and closed his laboratory, but his name still lives on in Silliman College of Yale University, and in the *American*

Journal of Science; and his influence is still felt in American chemical education through the hundreds of teachers who have descended from his chemical family tree.

NOTES AND REFERENCES

The "Life of Benjamin Silliman," Charles Scribner, New York, 1866, 2 vols., edited by George P. Fisher, contains some of Silliman's correspondence and reminiscences, and although quite old and poorly arranged, is indispensable.

A more recent biography, containing a useful bibliography, is "Benjamin Silliman," Schuman, New York, 1947, by John F. Fulton and Elizabeth H. Thomson.

WYNDHAM D. MILES

·· 32 ··

Robert Hare

1781-1858

THIS is the story of a man who made his mark in chemistry while still in his 'teens, but then had to work in a brewery half his life before he obtained employment as a chemist.

We know little of Robert Hare's early years or of his life away from chemistry, despite the fact that he was one of America's first great scientists. He was born in Philadelphia to Robert Hare, Sr., a brewer, on January 17, 1781, at a time when Americans were fighting the Revolutionary War. He grew up in Philadelphia when that city was the seat of the Continental Congress, the capital of the United States, and the official home of George Washington. Washington was his boyhood hero, and Hare remained, at heart, a Washingtonian Federalist for the rest of his life. On the anniversary of Washington's birthday, thirteen years after the President's death, the memory of the man inspired Hare to a poem that started:

Hail, glorious day, which gave Washington birth,
  To Columbia and liberty dear,
When a guardian angel descended on earth
  To shed blessings o'er many a year.

Though heroes and statesman, by glory enshrined
  May be seen in the temple of fame,
No hero or statesman, unblemished we find,
  Save one, bearing Washington's name.

Robert seems to have been a normal boy in every respect except that he liked chemistry as much as present-day youths like baseball and football. Philadelphia was then the scientific center of the country, and Hare had opportunities of learning chemistry in public lectures and at school. He attended the Academy of the University of Pennsylvania, where Caspar Wistar, Benjamin Rush, James Hutchinson, Benjamin Smith Barton, and Robert Patterson, all members of the University's faculty and all, at one time or another, teachers of chemistry, may have stimulated him.

He did not go to the University, perhaps because his father's brewery demanded too much of his time, but during the winters from 1798 to 1803 he attended the chemistry lectures of James Woodhouse at the Medical School of the University. When school was in session, Hare boarded close by. The University, in common with other schools, did not have a laboratory for students, but Hare made up for this by experimenting in his landlady's cellar-kitchen. Professor Woodhouse, the best American chemist of his generation, "entertained the highest respect for Hare's attainments, and often regretted that a genius so well adopted to chymistry could not be applied altogether to its improvement."

In the course of his experiments, or as a result of something Woodhouse said in the lectures, Hare grew interested in finding a method of reaching higher temperatures than chemists could ordinarily attain with furnaces and burning glasses. Reasoning that the combustion of hydrogen would give a hotter flame than any other reaction, he set out to try his ideas. With the mechanical skill that later helped him become a great researcher he turned a keg from his father's brewery into an ingenious, two-compartment gas holder, from which he could force oxygen and hydrogen by pumping in water. From sheet tin he rolled two long, slender, and somewhat flexible tubes. From two blowpipes he constructed a device that faintly resembled our present-day welding torch. Finally he connected one end of his tubes to the gas holder, the other end to his torch, and had the first oxyhydrogen blowtorch, the ancestor of our welding- and metal-cutting torches.

It sounds simple. So simple, perhaps, that you are wondering, why does the author spend so many words on this? Well, Hare's invention, like many others, was simple once it had been constructed. But remember these things: new methods of attaining high temperatures had been interesting chemists for a third of a century; oxygen and hydrogen had been known for a quarter of a century; and Hare lived in an age of giants. Lavoisier, Priestley, Black, and others had the facts needed to construct an oxyhydrogen blowtorch, but none of them experienced the flash of genius that came to Hare.

The Chemical Society of Philadelphia, of which Hare was corresponding secretary, published an account of his work in a pamphlet entitled *Memoir of the Supply and Application of the Blow-Pipe* (1802). Tilloch's *Philosophical Magazine* and the *Annales de chimie* recognized the value of Hare's *Memoir* and reprinted it for European chemists. In 1839, when Hare was in the twilight of his career, the American Academy of Arts and Sciences honored him with the Rumford Medal for this invention that he had made almost forty years before in the morning of his career.

With the oxyhydrogen torch Hare was able to melt sizable quantities of platinum for the first time, and to fuse hitherto refractory materials. Many years later one of his assistants, Joaquin Bishop, saw the industrial possibilities of working platinum and founded the Bishop Platinum Company. In addition to its value in the laboratory, Hare's torch led to a new type of illumination. Thomas Drummond conceived the idea of mounting an oxyhydrogen torch in a lighthouse, playing the flame upon a block of calcium oxide, and condensing the light through a lens. The intensity and whiteness of the Drummond light made it a significant advance in navigational safety. The theatre borrowed the Drummond light to cast a sharp beam on the actors, from whence is derived our expression, "in the limelight."

After the winter of 1803–1804 Hare was forced to spend almost all of his time helping his father manage the brewery, and he was unable to follow his inclination toward chemistry. These years contributed to his future in an unusual manner. He constructed a tighter keg than those on the market, and devised a new cock to tap casks. "Without having become a mechanick I never could have succeeded," he wrote in speaking of his inventions. Actually, Hare became a very expert mechanic, an acquirement that later enabled him to devise ingenious apparatus, and thus contributed in no small measure to his success as a researcher.

In 1809 when Professor James Woodhouse died, Hare tried to break away from business and into the academic world by applying for the vacant professorship of chemistry in the Medical School of the University. He had many supporters. Professor Benjamin Silliman of Yale recommended him as "one of the fairest hopes of science of this country." Robert Patterson, Director of the Mint, and Joseph Cloud, chemist of the Mint, wrote that "we have no hesitation in declaring, that we believe him qualified to supply the vacancy occasioned by the death of the late Professor of Chymistry." Other important men added their recommendations. But the medical faculty opposed any candidate who did not have a regular medical degree, and Hare, who had only an honorary medical degree bestowed by Yale in 1806, lost the election to John Redman Coxe, M.D.

Benjamin Rush supported Coxe in the election, probably because he and Coxe were bound by ties of comradeship that had existed since the yellow fever epidemic of 1793 when Coxe had assisted Rush. But friendship did not blind Rush to Hare's ability, and a few months later he tried to persuade the trustees to add a professorship of natural philosophy to the medical faculty and to elect Hare to the post. Perhaps as a result of Rush's prompting, the trustees did this in 1810.

The influential medical professors were not able to bar Hare this time, but they placed insurmountable obstacles in his path. His course was not to be compulsory for the medical degree, he could not mention any subject touched upon by another professor, and he had no voting privileges in faculty matters. These restrictions prevented Hare from discussing chemistry, which was customary in natural philosophy courses, and they practically deprived him of any listeners, since medical students would not pay an extra fee or spend their time on a nonrequired subject.

Hare offered his course, but he found that he had no audience. Since his only remuneration was student fees, he could not afford to continue. After two years of frustration it became clear to him that the conditions surrounding the professorship of natural philosophy doomed it to failure and he resigned the post.

For several years misfortune dogged Hare. The death of his father threw the management of the brewery entirely upon Robert. The War of 1812 sapped and finally killed the business. He went to New York and tried unsuccessfully to become a manufacturer of illuminating gas. He went to Providence and considered opening a drug store. And then fortune struck. Early in 1818 the College of William and Mary elected him professor of natural philosophy. It happened so unexpectedly that Hare had no time to ready a series of lectures. But with his extensive knowledge of science he was able to give a fine performance.

"I am enabled to say," wrote Ferdinand Campbell, professor of mathematics, who attended the chemistry lectures out of curiosity, "that speaking extempore with little time for preparation, he has satisfactorily explained the principles of chymistry, and illustrated them by a great number of experiments . . . he has never appeared to be at a loss in expounding the most difficult phenomena which the science presents, and by the force of a talent which seems peculiar to himself, he is enabled to attract and rivet the attention in discussing the most ordinary and familiar topicks. His success in the manipulations, in my opinion, is not owing more to the care with which he selects his agents, than to the mechanical skill with which he prepares his apparatus, or supplies it where it is found wanting." Robert Nelson, professor of law, who also listened to Hare's chemistry lectures, said he "found his experiments, and the explanation of them very satisfactory." President Smith recalled that Hare had "used exertions almost unparalleled, amidst difficulties the most perplexing and harassing." A number of students signed a testimonial stating that Hare had "explained the principles of Chymistry to his class, with perspicuity and ability," and that they were indebted to him "not only for the fidelity with which he has discharged his duties in the lecture room, but more especially for his laborious and unparalleled exertions which he made for the class in the laboratory, in renovating and preparing the apparatus so as to ensure as far as possible the success of the experiments and to enlarge their sphere."

For ten years Hare had sought an academic appointment without success. Now a half year after William and Mary acquired him, a second offer suddenly appeared. The Chair of Chemistry in the Medical School of the University of Pennsylvania was again vacant. This time Hare's friends proved irresistible, and he was elected. The Chair at Pennsylvania was more lucrative, the facilities at the University were better, and Philadelphia had more to offer, scientifically and culturally, than Williamsburg. So Hare accepted the post and returned to his home town. He was thirty-seven years old. Now for the first time in his life he could forget

425

business and devote all of his time to science. He accomplished much during the next three decades, but what might he have done had he been able to enter chemistry ten or fifteen years earlier?

During the first decade of Hare's career at the University he used the same small laboratory that had served his predecessors for two decades. Here he constructed apparatus, conducted research and started a steady flow of articles to American and European journals. In 1827 the University moved to a location near the center of town. In the new building the trustees fitted out a spacious (for that time) laboratory and chemical lecture hall at a cost of $4750—a large proportion of the total cost ($23,750) of the building. So proud was Hare of his new facilities that he published an engraving and description in *Silliman's Journal,* and as the frontispiece of the fourth edition (1840) of his *Compendium of the Course of Chemical Instruction in the Medical Department of the University of Pennsylvania.*

The laboratory was set off from Hare's lecture room by a long lecture table, and the entire hall measured sixty feet square. Since descriptions of early American laboratories are rare, Hare's own word picture of his "working place" is of considerable interest:

The hearth, behind the table, is thirty-six feet wide and twenty feet deep. On the left, which is to the south, is a scullery supplied with river water by a communication with pipes proceeding from the public water works, and furnished with a sink and a boiler. Over the scullery is a small room of about twelve feet square, used as a study. In front of the scullery and study are glass cases for apparatus. On the right of the hearth two other similar cases, one above the other, may be observed. Behind the lower one of these is the forge room, about twelve feet square; and north of the forge room, are two fire proof rooms communicating with each other, eleven feet square each: the one for a lathe, the other for a carpenter's bench, and a vice bench. The two last mentioned rooms, are surmounted by groined arches, in order to render them secure against fire; and the whole suite of rooms which I have described, together with the hearth, are supported by seven arches of masonry, about twelve feet each in span. Over the forge room is a store room, and over the lathe and bench rooms, is one room of about twenty by twelve feet. In this room there is a fine lathe, and tools.

426

The space partially visible to the right, is divided by a floor into two apartments, lighted by four windows. The lower one is employed to hold galvanic apparatus, the upper one for shelves, and tables, for apparatus, and agents, not in daily use. In front of the door just alluded to, is a gallery for visitors.

The canopy over the hearth is nearly covered with shelves for apparatus, which will bear exposure to air and dust, especially glass. In the center of the hearth is a stack of brick work for a blast furnace, the blast being produced by means of a large bellows situated under one of the arches supporting the hearth. The bellows are wrought by means of the lever represented in the engraving, and a rod descending from it through a circular opening in the masonry. There are two other stacks of brick work on the hearth against the wall. In one there is a coal grate which heats a flat sand bath, in the other there is a similar grate for heating two circular sand baths, or an alembic. In this stack there is likewise a powerful air furnace. In both of the stacks last mentioned, there are evaporating ovens.

The Laboratory is heated not only by one or both of the grates already mentioned, but also by stoves in the arches beneath the hearth, one of these is included in a chamber of brick work. The chamber receives a supply of fresh air through a flue terminating in an aperture in the external wall of the building, and the air after being heated passes into the laboratory at fifteen apertures, distributed over a space of thirty feet. Twelve of these apertures are in front of the table, being four inches square, covered by punched sheet iron. In the hearth there is one large aperture of about twelve by eighteen, covered by a cast iron plate full of holes, the rest are under the table. By these means the hot air is, at its entrance, so much diluted with the air of the room, that an unusually equable temperature is produced, there being rarely more than two degrees of Fahrenheit difference between the temperature in the upper and in the lower part of the lecture room. There are some smaller windows to the south, besides those represented in the engraving. One of these is in the upper story, from which the rays enter at the square aperture in the ceiling over the table on the right. Besides these, are the windows represented in the engraving back of the hearth, and four others in the apartments to the north of the gallery. All the windows have shutters, so constructed as to be closed and opened with facility. Those which belong to the principal windows are hung like sashes with weights, so that they ascend as soon as loosened, and when the light is again to be admitted, are easily pulled

427

down by cords and fastened. In addition to the accommodation already mentioned, there is a large irregular room under the floor of the lecture room on the eastern side. This is used as a place to stow a number of cumbrous and unsightly articles which are, nevertheless, of a nature to be very useful at times. Also for such purposes, and for containing fuel, there is a spacious cellar under the lecture room and laboratory.

This room, so quaint when compared to the present-day efficient industrial and university laboratories, served the professors and students of the Medical School for half a century. George Wood, a student and later a colleague of Hare, praised the laboratory equipment highly:

> The chemical apparatus is, by the admission of all who have inspected it, unequalled in extent, variety, and splendour. Individuals who have visited the schools of Germany, France, and Great Britain, agree in the statement, that they have no where met with a laboratory so amply furnished with all that is calculated to illustrate the science of chemistry as that of Dr. Hare. Some idea may be formed of its extent, and at the same time of the liberality which presides over the experimental course of chemistry in this school, from the fact that the expenditures of the professor, connected with his lectures, have amounted, on an average, to fifteen hundred dollars annually from the period of his election to the chair, in the year 1818.

In 1826 Hare issued a work in two volumes, each of fifty-two pages, entitled *Engravings, and Descriptions of a Great Part of the Apparatus used in the Chemical Course of the University of Pennsylvania.*

The small rooms in the laboratory, which were fitted out with lathes, a carpenter's bench, a vise bench and tools, served as Hare's workshop where he devised and developed the equipment which he used in his research. So proficient was Hare as a craftsman that he acted as an instrument maker for Benjamin Silliman, William J. Macneven, Eliphalet Nott, and other American chemists. Hare continued to add to his collection of apparatus until 1847.

428

when he resigned his professorship. He took his apparatus with him when he left the school, as his predecessors back to the days of Benjamin Rush had done. Joseph Henry, secretary of the Smithsonian Institution, recognized the historical value of the apparatus and asked that it be deposited in Washington. Hare agreed to present to the Institution all the apparatus which Henry judged to be worthy of preservation, and in 1849 the equipment was shipped. It was placed in cases in the east wing of the museum where it remained until it was almost totally destroyed by fire many years later. Today all that remains of Hare's splendid collection are a few miscellaneous pieces of equipment in the University of Pennsylvania.

Hare placed great reliance upon the use of demonstrations as a teaching aid. In his own words, "from the time that I became a lecturer, I applied myself so to improve and multiply the means and methods of experimental illustration, as to render manipulation easier and the result more interesting and instructive." He found, in time, that some students did not grasp the minutia of the experiments and apparatus, others were not interested, and still others wished to know every detail. A consideration of these varied tastes led him to prepare a pamphlet in which he explained his technique and apparatus, *Minutes of the Course of Chemical Instruction in the Medical Department of the University of Pennsylvania* (Philadelphia, 1822). This small text was bound with alternate blank pages upon which the student could jot notes. It went through several revisions, growing in size each time, and in 1828 became a text of 350 pages, *Compendium of the Course of Chemical Instruction in the Medical Department of the University of Pennsylvania*. The *Compendium* contained more than 200 copper plate engravings of apparatus, many of which had been modified or devised by Hare. The subject matter included physics, inorganic chemistry, animal chemistry, and vegetable chemistry. Six years later a second edition appeared, enlarged to more than 400 pages. In 1838 the third edition, now increased to 518 pages, was published. The fourth and last edition, with 605 pages, came from the press in 1840. The *Compendium* was the best and most complete text written by an American up to this time. It never became popular beyond the borders of the University, probably being too comprehensive for chemistry courses in other American colleges.

Evidence of Hare's ability as a teacher is mirrored in the students who studied under his direction. John D'Wolf, who was elected professor of chemistry at Brown University in 1827, acquired his knowledge from Hare. Another student, Robert Bridges, held the professorship of chemistry at the Philadelphia College of Pharmacy and Science from 1842 to 1862, and for several years was lecturer on chemistry at Franklin Medical College. George T. Bowen, who started his career under Silliman at Yale, came to Philadelphia to profit by Hare's instruction, and later became professor of chemistry at the University of Tennessee. Martin Hans Boyé, a Swede, took the degree of Doctor of Medicine at the University (1844), but thereafter turned to chemistry. He assisted Hare, taught in academies of Philadelphia, and found time to write a score of experimental papers. Robert Empie Rogers, one of the four famous Rogers brothers, studied chemistry under Hare and finally succeeded his teacher when the latter retired in 1847. Wolcott Gibbs studied at the University from 1841 to 1845, and assisted Hare in the laboratory. He later became professor of chemistry in the College of the City of New York (1849–1863), and finally Rumford Professor at Harvard. Josiah Dwight Whitney, later a famous geologist, after graduating from Yale arrived in Philadelphia in 1839 to study under Hare. He soon found himself "head over ears in pots and kettles, retorts and alembics, and all the paraphernalia of a well-stocked laboratory." Joaquin Bishop, founder of the Bishop Platinum Company, the first American platinum works (1842), learned the background for his business while collaborating in research with Hare. While this list of students does not compare with the number of Americans trained by some of the famous European teachers, such as Liebig, Wöhler, Dumas, and Rose, it indicates the wide respect in which Hare was held by his contemporaries.

Hare was by far the most versatile and prodigious experimenter in American chemistry during his day. The articles that came from his laboratory are entirely too many to be discussed in detail here, but certain subjects serve to illustrate his ability.

430

Hare's interest in electricity led him to electrolysis. Eventually he used mercury as the cathode in the electrolysis of aqueous solutions of metallic salts. By this means he obtained calcium amalgam from which he isolated calcium metal. This was the first time the element had been prepared in this country. In 1829 he constructed a covered electric furnace in which he converted charcoal into graphite, and also made calcium carbide, phosphorus, and calcium. In this work he was half a century ahead of the commercial application of the electric furnace. He devised new processes for the isolation of a number of elements, including boron and silicon. He synthesized ammonia by directing a jet of a gaseous mixture of two volumes of nitric oxide and five volumes of hydrogen against a heated platinum sponge. He was a master in the art of gas analysis, and devised several ingenious eudiometers.

Two interesting anecdotes which throw light on Hare as an experimenter and theoretician came from Ira Remsen and Michael Faraday. Remsen wrote the following concerning his research on double salts:

> I became interested in double halides and published an article giving my views regarding the nature of these compounds. Soon after the appearance of my article I received a letter from Dr. Wolcott Gibbs telling me that Robert Hare had expressed similar views in 1821. He sent me his copy of Hare's Chemistry and I was astonished to read the chapter that had been written fifty or sixty years before my article. The line of thought was practically identical with mine, and it was expressed beautifully. . . . Hare was both investigator and scientific philosopher.

Faraday, during the course of his experiments in electricity, devised a battery. Then he discovered he had been anticipated by Hare:

> Guided by these principles I was led to the construction of a voltaic trough. . . . On examining, however, what had been done before, I found the new trough was in all essential respects the same as that invented and described by Robert Hare.

431

Hare labored under the disadvantage of working in America where he was out of the main current of scientific activity. Consequently, his researches did not become as widely known as they would if he had been a European and published in European journals. As a result of this lack of publicity Hare has less of a reputation than many contemporary European chemists who actually were inferior to him as chemists.

Hare labored at the University for almost three decades before age forced him to retire. The remaining eleven years of his life were as active as the first sixty-five. One of his first acts was to write a novel entitled *Standish the Puritan,* a story based on the American Revolution. He took great interest in meteorology and observed the effect of several tornados which he attributed to an electric current of air. An explosion in a warehouse filled with niter in New York engaged his attention, and he conducted a variety of experiments with mixtures of niter and organic matter in an effort to explain the catastrophe. In the early 1850's he was caught up in the spiritualism movement. He invented a "spiritoscope" which would prevent fraud by mediums, and enable a person to communicate directly with the spirits. In 1854 he collected the results of all of his investigations on spiritualism and published them in New York in a 460 page book, *Experimental Investigation of the Spirit Manifestations.* The following year in an effort to convince his Episcopalian brethren of the validity of spiritualism he published a 24 page pamphlet, *Dr. Hare's Letter to the Episcopal Clergy, offering to Submit New & Irrefragible Evidence of Human Immortality.* Hare was never shaken in his faith in spiritualism, and he died on May 15, 1858, believing in the existence of a world of spirits.

Hare was an experimentalist of high order and was ahead of other American chemists in his ability to attack a problem. His knowledge of chemistry, grasp of technique, dexterity as a mechanic, and conscientiousness made him the best teacher of advanced students that the United States could offer. It was not until specialists returned from German universities that men of Hare's stature appeared in American chemistry, and there were few of them who were his equal in the nineteenth century.

NOTES AND REFERENCES

The "Life of Robert Hare, an American Chemist (1781–1858)," Philadelphia, J. B. Lippincott, 1917, is the only full length biography of Hare, but it is unhandy for the serious student because it does not give any references to the sources used by the author, Edgar Fahs Smith.

WYNDHAM D. MILES

·· 33 ··

Michel-Eugène Chevreul

1786-1889

ON APRIL 9, 1889, the life of the great French chemist, Michel-Eugène Chevreul, came to a peaceful close shortly before his one hundred and third birthday. For nearly eighty years he had contributed article after article to the scientific journals. Both his parents had lived past the age of ninety years,[1, 2] and one of his works was dedicated "to the memory of Michel Chevreul and of Etinnette-Madeleine Bachelier, respectful homage from their son in recognition of the moral sense and good health they transmitted to him."[1]

Chevreul was born at Angers on August 31, 1786, and at the age of seven years he looked through the window, with childlike curiosity, to watch the guillotining of two young girls. In later life, however, his bright outlook was not marred by the dark scenes of his childhood.[2] He received his early training at the Central School in Angers. At the age of seventeen years he went to Paris to study under the great pharmacist and chemist, Nicolas-Louis Vauquelin, assistant to A.-F. de Fourcroy at the Collège de France, and three years later he took charge of the laboratory. His first scientific memoir,[3] a chemical examination of some fossil bones, was published in 1806, and in the same year he assisted Vauquelin in analyzing some human hair.[4]

Since Vauquelin was greatly interested in the purple vapor evolved when indigo is heated, he asked Chevreul to investigate it.[5] Chevreul found that indigo purified by successive treatments with water, alcohol, and hydrochloric acid gave off "a vapor of a superb purple, much more intense than that produced by an equal quantity of the same indigo when not purified; from which it follows that this phenomenon is produced by the indigo and not by foreign bodies to which it is united." He showed that this vapor is the indigo itself, most of which volatilizes without decomposition; that indigo can be purified by sublimation or by recrystallization; that pure indigo is purple and not blue; and that the intensity of the color increases as the molecules are brought closer together. He also demonstrated the presence of indigo in its white, reduced form in pastel, or woad. Four years later he published a paper on the preparation of natural indigo.[5] He also examined Brazilwood and logwood[6] and discovered brazilin and hematoxylin.

In 1823 he published the results of eleven years of research on the hardness of soaps.[7] He found that the sodium soap of a given fat is harder (less soluble in cold water) than the corresponding potassium soap but that the fat as well as the alkali is a determining factor. He determined the solubility in cold water of the sodium and potassium soaps of stearic, "margaric," and oleic acids, and showed that the hard soaps lose water on exposure to air. He also proved that the hardest soaps are obtained from the fats in which the stearates are high in proportion to the "margarates" and oleates and that the soaps from natural oils can be imitated by mixing the fats to be saponified.

Chevreul found that when soaps are used as detergents, they are hydrolyzed to form free alkali and an acid salt, such as potassium bistearate of the approximate composition $C_{18}H_{35}O_2K \cdot C_{18}H_{36}O_2$ His work was confirmed by Krafft and Stern in 1894, who concluded that it would be difficult to add anything essentially new to "the simple and clear views of Chevreul, Berzelius and Persoz."[8]

In 1809 a specimen of soft soap used in fulling cloth was sent to Chevreul for analysis.[9, 10] When he dissolved some of it in a large volume of water, he observed some shining crystals. "When one places some soap formed from pork fat and potash in a large volume of water," said he, "part of it dissolves, while another part precipitates in the form of little shining spangles, which I shall call nacreous matter. After having decanted off the liquor, one washes the deposit repeatedly with cold water and then throws it on a filter." He then washed the pearly scales with alcohol and, upon treating them with hydrochloric acid, liberated a new fatty acid which he named "margaric acid" because of its mother-of-pearl luster. He also prepared the same substance from other soaps and used it in separating the solid acids ("margaric," palmitic, and stearic) from the liquid oleic acid, the potassium salt of which remained in solution. Although Chevreul's "margaric acid" was merely an intimate mixture of palmitic and stearic acids, a compound $C_{17}H_{34}O_2$, intermediate between palmitic and stearic acids is now known by the same name.

Chevreul gave the name phocenic acid to the principal odorant (trivaleric acid) of the soaps of dolphin oil, "hircic acid" to that of mutton fat and butyric acid to the odorant of butter fat, and stated that the latter "contains two other acids which I name capric and caproic."[7, 11] His "hircic acid" is now known to be a mixture of homologous fatty acids present in mutton suet. Chevreul made ultimate analyses of butyric, phocenic, and "hircic" acids and emphasized the practical value of a knowledge of the odorous organic acids in the manufacture of cheese.

When C. M. d'Ohsson, a friend of Berzelius, and the physiologist François Magendie visited Chevreul, he showed them some of his new products, including butyric acid, "which smelled horribly bad . . . I tried in vain," said d'Ohsson in a letter to Berzelius "to discover some new instruments in his and Gay-Lussac's laboratories. I found, on the contrary, that everything there was of the greatest simplicity, and your laboratory certainly does not suffer by comparison."[12]

Even in his early thirties, Chevreul was already at the height of his powers. In 1819 Berzelius wrote to W. von Hisinger, "The greatest chemists now in France are Gay-Lussac, Dulong, Chevreul and Thenard."[12] During his visit to Paris in the summer of 1819 Berzelius wrote, "With Thenard, Gay-Lussac, Dulong and Chevreul I lived on the same footing as among my old schoolmates at Upsala."[13] Berzelius often watched the experiments on saponification, and once said of Chevreul, "He is the most excellent observer of details; none of them are too small for his notice; and the services he has rendered to the science, which are by no means small, result merely from his study of details. However, he is not so fortunate in the presentation of general theoretical concepts."[12, 14] Chevreul believed that "elementary and professional education should be confined to that which is true and easily demonstrated to be true."[15]

In 1813 he began to lecture on fats and their saponification products before the French Academy of Sciences, and ten years later these discourses were published under the title "Chemical researches on fatty substances of animal origin."[16, 17] Fats had formerly been regarded as acid substances which could unite directly with a base to form a soap, which was thus believed to be a binary salt of fat and alkali. In 1741 Claude-Joseph Geoffroy (Geoffroy the Younger), a member of a famous family of French apothecaries, showed that, when a soap solution is neutralized with a mineral acid, the resulting fatty substance differs from the original one by dissolving readily in alcohol.

"When olive oil," said he, "is separated, by means of an acid, from the soap which has been dissolved in spirits, it becomes similar to an essential oil; it is more flammable, gives less soot, and combines immediately with spirit of wine. On distillation, however, it does not, like the true essential oils, pass over with the water."[19]

In 1783 C. W. Scheele, in his quiet pharmacy, heated a mixture of olive oil and litharge and obtained a "sweet principle," which is now known as glycerol.[18] He also obtained the same substance from other vegetable and animal fats and clearly distinguished it from sugar and honey.

In 1816 Chevreul quantitatively saponified the fats of man, the sheep, the cow, the jaguar, and the goose, and found that, in each case, about ninety-five per cent of the fat had been saponified. He computed by difference that there must be about five per cent of soluble matter in each of these fats, and observed that "the sirupy liquid which contained the sweet principle produced by saponification (glycerol), although evaporated until it began to volatilize, always weighed much more than the fat had lost of soluble matter."[20] He believed at first that he had merely been unable to remove all the water and "saline matter." When in 1818 he discovered phocenin (glyceryl valerate) and butyrin, he realized that they were compounds of the volatile acids and anhydrous glycerol[20] and that the excess weight represented the quantity of water fixed by the fat to form the glycerol in saponification. He knew, too, that the fatty acids and the glycerol were not merely mixed in the fats; for if that were true, it would be possible to leach out the glycerine with water. Moreover, alcohol, which dissolves both fatty acids and glycerin, does not dissolve the fat. He compared the fats in this respect with ethyl acetate and postulated that they must be formed of fatty acids and a substance which adds on water to form glycerol.

In the first book of his treatise on fats Chevreul showed that the

440

classification, according to melting point, into waxes, fats, butters, and oils was unscientific, and described methods for the ultimate analysis of fatty substances. Book Two describes many fats and the saponification products obtained from them with different alkalies; an investigation of the fatty acids and their physical and chemical properties; a study of the metallic salts of oleic acid; and descriptions of cholesterin, ethal (cetyl alcohol), cetin, olein, phocenin, butyrin, and "hircin."[17]

In the third book he discussed the saponification of cetin, a crystalline fat obtained from spermaceti. He obtained no glycerol from the cetin, but ethal (cetyl alcohol) instead. In Book Four he gave comparative results of the saponification of various fats, including those from dolphins and porpoises, from edible fish, and from cadavers. Although Fourcroy had not distinguished clearly between the adipocere he discovered in dead bodies, the spermaceti from the sperm whale, and the crystalline substance, cholesterin, obtained from biliary calculi, Chevreul proved that these are three distinct substances.[21-24] He was led to this discovery by his careful investigation of some crystals which had formed, after several months, on the surface of a fatty material that had been brought from Rouen for analysis.

In Book Five Chevreul discussed contemporary views on saponification and proved that acetic acid and carbon dioxide are not produced and that gaseous oxygen is not necessary for the saponification reaction. He also determined the weight of fat which can be saponified by a given weight of potash, i.e., the saponification number of the fat.[17, 20] Book Six contains a résumé of the researches and their applications, and discusses the properties of the stearates, "margarates," and oleates of sodium and potassium and their solubility in alcohol, acids and alkalies.

In 1825 Chevreul and Gay-Lussac obtained a patent for the production of fatty acids for the manufacture of candles by treating tallow and oils with potash, soda, or other alkali and then decomposing the resulting soap with hydrochloric acid. Since the glycerol could be recovered from the aqueous solution, it, too, could be produced on a large scale.

Although the first candles made by the Chevreul–Gay-Lussac method were greasy and unsatisfactory, the engineer, Jules de

441

Cambacérès, improved them by his invention of the plaited wick, and in 1831 Adolphe de Milly, one of Chevreul's former students, and M. Motard introduced the use of lime instead of caustic soda and began to manufacture excellent stearin candles near the Barrière de l'Étoile, which became known as "star, or adamantine" candles. They had been made possible by Chevreul's discovery that the removal of glycerol from fats enormously increases their hardness and illuminating power.[21, 25, 26]

To appreciate the importance of this improvement, one must view it through the eyes of Chevreul's contemporaries. "The stearic candle industry," said A. W. von Hofmann, ". . . opens a new era in the history of illumination. In the present generation only the oldest still recall the tallow candle, soft and dripping, disagreeable in color, giving off a sickening odor, requiring constant care as it burned and giving only a dim, smoky flame. Suddenly the tallow candle was replaced by the stearic candle of brilliant whiteness, odorless, hard and sonorous, burning without the slightest aid and with a bright flame. It is your hands which have opened to the grateful world a source of light in no way inferior to that of wax candles, capable of competing with gas light, the use of which was already widespread, and which does not seem menaced by the illumination of the future, by the electric light."[16, 27]

In 1824 Chevreul published his great work entitled "General considerations on organic analysis and its applications,"[28] the first part of which is devoted to proximate organic analysis and the second to its applications. Like the naturalists, Chevreul used to classify everything into families, genera, and species. Among the immediate, or proximate, principles he included the sugar, gum, starch, and lignin of a plant; the fibrin and albumin of the cellular tissue of an animal. In the term *species* he included these immediate principles and compounds of two or more of them according to definite proportions. He applied the term *variety* to specimens of a given organic species which differ in secondary crystalline form or other minor properties from the substance considered as typical of the species. By *genus* he meant a collection of organic species which possess one or more important properties in common. He conceived of each specimen of a given species as an aggre-

442

gation of identical individuals and realized that the true individuals are the compound atoms (molecules).

Berzelius had stated that blood fibrin, albumin, and gelatin are partly converted by the action of alcohol and ether into a fatty substance similar to adipocere. Chevreul, realizing that if alcohol and ether were to be used in proximate organic analysis, this point must be settled, proved quantitatively that the fatty substances contained in alcohol and ether placed in contact with tendons, fibrin, etc., had merely been extracted from those substances. On treating elephant tendons with alcohol, he obtained stearin and olein. When he treated the same tendons with dilute potash, he produced a quantity of stearic, "margaric," and oleic acids equivalent to the stearin and olein previously obtained by means of alcohol. Berzelius later extracted fat from the fibrin of ox blood and acknowledged that Chevreul's statements were correct.[29]

Chevreul's book on organic analysis discusses, among other things, the effect of heat and of oxygen on organic compounds; solvents used in organic analysis; saponification as a method of analysis; and the applications of proximate organic analysis to the arts and industries and to medicine, pharmacy, toxicology, and the biological sciences.

In the section on pharmacy he wrote: "If in medicine, in a given case, one is in doubt as to the dose of medicaments such as the sulfates of soda and of magnesia, the subphosphate (sousphosphate) of soda, the bitartrate of potassium or of emetic, the composition of which is rigorously defined, there is all the more reason for being so when it is a matter of prescribing such medicaments as extract of opium, cinchona barks, ipecacuanha roots, etc., which contain unknown proportions of the active principles. Proximate organic analysis, which gives the methods of isolating these principles from the foreign substances with which they are united or mixed in the extracts, barks, roots, etc., and which, by defining them as *species* possessed of constant properties, brings them to the condition of the first medicaments of which I spoke, renders eminent services to pharmacology by destroying a cause of uncertainty which the use of many of the most important remedies of the healing art used to present. Physicians, then, should lend full

443

support to researches such as those of MM. Sertürner, Robiquet, Boullay, Gomes, Magendie, Pelletier, etc., to whom we owe the discovery of morphine, of the vesicant principle of cantharides, of picrotoxin, of cinchonine, of quinine, of emetine, of strychnine, of brucine. Researches of this nature are well suited to change the opinions of those who believe with Descartes in the danger of *the remedies of chemistry.*"[28]

Chevreul was evidently referring here to F. W. Sertürner's discovery of morphine in 1805–1817; P.-J. Robiquet's analysis of cantharides in 1810; P.-F.-G. Boullay's discovery of picrotoxin in 1811; B. A. Gomes' memoir on the gray ipecacuanha of Brazil (Lisbon, 1801); the researches of Joseph Pelletier and F. Magendie on ipecacuanha in 1817; and the discovery of strychnine in 1818, of brucine in 1819, and of quinine and of cinchonine in 1821 by Joseph Pelletier and J.-B. Caventou. In his eulogy at the funeral of Robiquet, Chevreul said:

> His examination of cantharides informs us of the presence of uric acid in insects which feed on leaves and also of the existence of a principle to which they owe the property of acting as a vesicatory, a discovery which is remarkable in that, by demonstrating as early as 1810 the possibility of extracting the active principle of a complex medicinal substance, it can be considered as the point of departure for numerous researches on this subject . . .

Chevreul also pointed out in his treatise that when the medicinal property of a root, bark, or extract is due to a combination of several principles and not to any one of them alone, such "active combinations" may be separated from the foreign materials which weaken their essential properties and make correct dosage difficult.

At the close of the book he discusses the origin of life. Although he did not believe that the phenomena of life and those of inorganic matter have identical causes, he added that "it must not be concluded that I share the opinion of those scientists who claim to explain the mysteries of organization by one or more forces which they call vital." Even before Wöhler's synthesis of urea had been announced, Chevreul stated that "it would be contrary to the spirit of chemistry to base a classification on the impossibility which

444

has hitherto existed of completely forming an organic compound absolutely identical with one which formed part of an organized being; and according to what we know today, there are more reasons for hoping that this formation will be accomplished than there are for believing the contrary."[28]

On September 9, 1824, Chevreul became director of the dye plant at the Gobelin Tapestry Works.[30] "On entering the Gobelins," said he, "I found neither barometer nor thermometer nor accurate balances nor platinum ware nor mercury trough nor reagents; the laboratory was a sort of stable or kitchen, paved and damp." He devoted the years from 1828 to 1864 to a study of colors and the technique of dyeing. His first published work on color appeared in 1830 under the title "Memoir on the influence that two colors can have on each other when seen separately."[31] In 1829 and 1830 Chevreul published his lectures on chemistry applied to dyeing[32] and in 1832 he discovered creatine as a normal constituent of muscular tissue.[21, 33]

In 1828, soon after his work on fats and organic analysis had opened up two great fields of research, Chevreul broke ground in a third new field, the psychology of color, and in 1839 he published his great work on "The principles of harmony and contrast of colors and their application to the arts."[35] He showed that the chemical composition of the colors had nothing to do with the effects of their simultaneous contrasts; distinguished between simultaneous, successive, and mixed contrast of colors; showed how to imitate colored objects with the coloring materials in a state of very small division and how to produce given effects with colored threads; and applied his results to the production of Gobelin tapestries, Beauvais furniture tapestries and Savonnerie carpets, to color-printing on cloth and paper, to horticulture, and to the making of maps, mosaics, glass windows, engravings, and clothing. He himself stated that his work on contrast of colors was just "as experimental and as exact" as his previous treatises on fatty bodies and organic analysis.[35]

Feeling the need for a definite standard with which colors could be compared, Chevreul constructed a chromatic circle, using as his fundamental points of comparison certain rays of red, yellow, and blue, each of which was marked by a well-defined Fraunhofer

445

line. He placed these three colors at equidistant points on the circle and interpolated twenty-three definite color mixtures in each of the three intervening sectors. In addition to this "normal" circle, he prepared eight others, in which the colors were toned down with definite known proportions of black. He thought that official standards of color ought to be preserved like standards of weights and measures, but realized the difficulty of obtaining enough dyes which would be sufficiently permanent. In his lectures at the Gobelins, he used to construct a mammoth circle of skeins of worsted on the floor of the great exhibition hall.[36]

In 1854 he published an exposé of the divining-rod and other psychic and spiritualistic phenomena which were then creating a furor on both sides of the Atlantic.[37] Professor Joseph Jastrow has recently published an interesting account of these psychological researches.[38]

Chevreul also made notable contributions to the history of chemistry, including an "Histoire des connaissances chimiques," and a more extensive work "Résumé d'une histoire de la matière depuis les philosophes grecs jusqu'à Lavoisier inclusivement," only a portion of which was published.[39, 40] Mme. Metzger has emphasized the fact that these works are well worthy of study by historians of chemistry.[41]

When he was about ninety years old Chevreul made a detailed psychological study of the changes which accompany old age.[42] In 1883, at the suggestion of J.-B.-A. Dumas, Chevreul, then ninety-seven years old, was appointed "director of advanced studies for the observation and analysis of the colors of dyes."[30] Chevreul had been publishing scientific memoirs for twenty-nine years before the *Comptes rendus* was founded, yet among its great volumes from the years 1836 to 1888, inclusive, there are scarcely any which do not contain one or more of his articles or critical discussions or notices of his appointment to important committees.

Since B.-B. de Fontenelle had died a month before his one-hundredth birthday, and since Chevreul's birthday comes in the summer, when most scientists are away from Paris, the observance of the Chevreul centenary began three months ahead of time. On May 17, 1886, the Academy of Sciences had a ceremony in his

446

honor, and on August 30 and 31 the Society of Agriculture paid homage to him. According to tradition, Chevreul had been elected president of this society every alternate year, and he had fulfilled these duties "with a punctuality one would never expect from a centenarian."[2] When he arrived at two o'clock, he was greeted by the eleven presidents of the sections of the society, each carrying a large bouquet of roses.

The third celebration was that of the city of Paris and the Museum of Natural History, aided by the press. An exhibition of industrial products which had been improved through Chevreul's researches, which had been suggested, had to be abandoned for lack of space to display all the materials which were submitted.[36] When the statue of Chevreul was unveiled, the entire Museum was decorated with red velvet, flowers, and the finest tapestries, ancient and modern, that had ever been made at the Gobelin plant, and more than two thousand delegates from learned societies, schools, museums, and workshops came marching in with banners.

The informal dinner at six-thrity was illuminated by thousands of candles presented by the stearin manufacturers of Paris.

After the centenary, Chevreul lived very quietly and drove daily to watch the construction of the Eiffel Tower. M. Gaston Tissandier, the editor of *La Nature,* has left us the following picture of Chevreul the centenarian: "M. Chevreul is tall of stature and is, even today, slender and erect. Elegant of manner, of incomparable affability, he rarely greets you without a smile on his lips. His head is wonderfully expressive, the forehead large and powerful, covered with white hair. A few years ago he still used to attend the winter ball at the Élysée, and we recall seeing him there at midnight, fresh and smiling, surrounded by ladies, whom he was gallantly entertaining, with exquisite and charming grace."[2] To a new assistant he once said, "You must have courage to accept a position as my preparateur; I have already killed off four of them."[2]

The monograph on the national manufactures of France, which was published in 1889, shortly before Chevreul's death, states that "Thanks to the resolute vigor of his intellect, accumulating discovery after discovery, M. Chevreul has pursued these great researches at the Gobelins up to the present. The famous scientist

447

whose centenary all Paris celebrated two years ago still discharges in an honorary capacity the duties with which he was entrusted in 1824."[30] Only a few days before his death, Chevreul suffered the loss of his only son, Henri, a bibliophile like himself. The introduction of the "Law of simultaneous contrast of colors" was written by M. Henri Chevreul, and he had also intended to prepare a preface for the reprint of the "Chemical researches on fatty bodies" which was issued in 1889.

NOTES AND REFERENCES

1 Anon., "Le centenaire de M. Chevreul," *Moniteur Scientifique* (Quesneville), 1193–1200 (October 1886). Signed: Dr. Q.

2 Tissandier, G., "M.-E. Chevreul," *La Nature,* 14 (2), 197–202 (August 28, 1886).

3 Chevreul, M.-E., "Examen chimique des os fossiles trouvés dans le département de Maine-et-Loire," *Ann. chim. phys.,* (1), 57, 45–50 (1806).

4 "Abstract of a memoir on human hair read at the National Institute on the 3rd of March by M. Vauquelin," *Nicholson's J.,* (2), 15, 141 (October 1806). *Ann. chim. phys.,* 58, (1806), 41.

5 Chevreul, M.-E., "Expériences chimiques sur l'indigo. Expériences chimiques sur le pastel," *Ann. chim. phys.,* (1), 66, 5–53 (April 30, 1808); *Nicholson's J.,* (2), 32, 211–216 (July 1812); "Sur la préparation de l'indigo," *J. de physique,* 74, 471–473) (1812).

6 Chevreul, M.-E., "Expériences chimiques sur les bois de Brésil et de Campèche," *Ann. chim. phys.,* (1), 66, 225–265 (June 30, 1808).

7 Chevreul, M.-E., "Sur les causes des différences que l'on observe dans les savons, sous le rapport de leur degré de dureté ou de mollesse, et sous celui de leur odeur; et sur un nouveau groupe d'acides organiques," *Ann. chim. phys.,* (2), 23, 16–32 (1823).

8 Krafft, F., and Stern, A., "Ueber das Verhalten der fettsauren Alkalien und der Seifen in Gegenwart von Wasser," *Ber. d. deutschen chem. Ges.,* 27, 1747–1761 (June 25, 1894).

9 Simon, L.-J., "Chevreul. Les corps gras d'origine animale. L'Analyse immédiate et l'espèce chimique. L'Atome composé," *La Nature,* 53 (2) 235–238 (1925).

10 Chevreul, M.-E., "Researches on various fatty bodies . . . ," *Annals of Philos.,* 12 (September 1818), 186–199; 12 (October 1818), 257–290; *Ann. chim. phys.* (1), 88 (December 31, 1813), 225–261; *Ibid.,* (1), 94 (April 30, 1815), 80–107.

11 Chevreul, M.-E., "On newly discovered animal acids," *Annals of Philos.,* 22 (September 1823), 209–210; *Ann. chim. phys.* (2), 23 (1823), 16–32.

12 Söderbaum, H. G., "Jac. Berzelius levnadsteckning," Almqvist & Wiksells Boktryckeri A.-B., Upsala, 2 (1929–1931), 76. Letter of d'Ohsson to Berzelius, July 4, 1817; *Ibid.*, Vol. 2, page 159. Berzelius to Hisinger, June 6, 1819; *Ibid.*, Vol. 3, pages 542–543. Berzelius to Philippe Plantamour, June 11, 1847.

13 Söderbaum, H. G., "Jac. Berzelius reseanteckningar," P. A. Norstedt & Söner, Stockholm (1903), page 196.

14 Söderbaum, H. G., "Jac. Berzelius Själfbiografiska anteckningar," P. A. Norstedt & Söner, Stockholm (1901), page 75; English translation by Olof Larsell, Williams and Wilkins Co., Baltimore (1934), page 101.

15 Armstrong, H. E., "M.-E. Chevreul, 1786–1889," *Nature*, 116 (November 21, 1925), 750–754.

16 Malloizel, G., "Oeuvres scientifiques de Michel-Eugène Chevreul," Comité du Centenaire, Paris (1886), 298 pages.

17 Chevreul, M.-E., "Recherches chimiques sur les corps gras d'origine animale," Levrault, Paris (1823), 484 pages; *Imprimerie Nationale, Paris* (1889), 425 pages, folio.

18 Dobbin, L., "The collected papers of C. W. Scheele," G. Bell and Sons, Ltd., London (1931), pages 255–258; Scheele, C. W., *K. Vet. Acad. Nya Handl.*, 4 (1783), 324–329.

19 Geoffroy, C.-J., "Mittel, den Weingeist gefrieren zu machen, und den fetten Oelen einige Eigenschaften der wesentlichen Oele zu geben," *Crell's Neues chem. Archiv*, 4 (1785), 229–232; *Hist. de l'acad. roy. des Sciences* (Paris) (1741).

20 Chevreul, M.-E., "Recherches chimiques sur les corps gras," *Ann. chim. phys.* (1), 94 (May 31, 1815), 113–144; *Ibid.* (1), 94 (June 30, 1815), 225–280; *Ibid.* (1) 95 (July 31, 1815), 5–50; *Ibid.* (2), 2 (August 1816), 339–372; *Ibid.* (2), 7 (1818), 155–181, 264–275, 367–382.

21 Matagrin, A., "Chevreul et la bougie stéarique," *L'Industrie Chimique*, 12 (1925), 400–402.

22 Thomson, Thomas, "Account of the improvements in physical science during the year 1815," *Annals of Philos.*, 7 (January 1816), 58–59.

23 Cuvier, M. le Chevalier, "Royal Institute of France. Chemistry," *Ibid.* 7 (March 1816), 232.

24 Fourcroy, A.-F., "Système des connaissances chimiques," Baudouin, Paris Brumaire, An IX), 9 (1801), pages 33, 61, 250, 255, 296; Vol. 10, pp. 43, 56, 83, 302.

25 Carpenter, W. L., "A treatise on the manufacture of soap and candles," E. and F. N. Spon, London (1885), pages 253–4.

26 Riemer, H., "Hundert Jahre Fettsäure-Industrie," *Z. deutschen Öl- und Fett-Industrie*, 45 (1925), 576–578, 590–592.

27 Hofmann, A. W. von, "M.-E. Chevreul," *Ber. d. deutschen chem. Ges.*, 22 (May 13, 1889), 1163–1169.

28 Chevreul, M.-E., "Considérations générales sur l'analyse organique et sur ses applications," F. G. Levrault, Paris, 256 pages (1824).

29 Berzelius, J. J., "Lehrbuch der Chemie," Arnoldische Buchhandlung, Dresden and Leipzig, 4th Edition, 9 (1840), 87–88.

30 Havard and Vachon, "Les manufactures nationales. Les Gobelins, la Savonnerie, Sèvres, Beauvais," Georges Decaux, Paris (1889), pages 291–304.

31 Chevreul, M.-E., "Mémoire sur l'influence que deux couleurs peuvent avoir l'une sur l'autre quand on les voit séparément," *Quarterly J. Sci.*, 1 (1830), 409–410; *Mém. Acad. Sci.* (Paris), 11 (1832), 447–520.

32 Chevreul, M.-E., "Leçons de chimie appliquée à la teinture," *Pichon et Didier, Paris,* 3 Vols. (1829–1830).

33 "Creatin, eine neue im Muskelfleisch enthaltene Substanz," *Liebig's Annalen,* 4 (1832), 293–294.

34 Chevreul, M.-E., "Recherches sur la teinture," *Compt. rend.,* 2 (1836), 20–22, 292–296; 4 (1837), 2–12; 5 (1837), 167–177, 881–892; 10 (1840), 121–124, 631–640; 14 (1842), 783–785; 23 (1846), 954–956; 36 (1853), 981–987; 52 (1861), 327–332, 762–771, 825–833, 885–890, 937–942; 53 (1861), 981–985; 54 (1862), 877–880; 57 (1863), 133–141, 173–181.

35 Chevreul, M.-E., "De la loi du contraste simultané des couleurs, et de l'assortiment des objets colorés . . . ," Pitois-Levrault, Paris (1839), 735 pages; "The principles of harmony and contrast of colours and their applications to the arts," George Bell and Sons, London, 3rd Edition (1889), 450 pages.

36 Anon., "Foreign honorary members. M.-E. Chevreul," Proc. Am. Acad. Arts and Sciences, 24 (1889), 452–457.

37 Chevreul, M.-E., "Traité de la baguette divinatoire, due pendule dit explorateur et des tables tournantes," Mallet-Bachelier, Paris (1854), 258 pages; "Sur une classe particulière de mouvements musculaires," *Compt. rend.,* 23 (December 14, 1846), 1093–1096.

38 Jastrow, J., "Chevreul as a psychologist," *Sci. Mo.,* 46 (June 1937), 487–496.

39 Chevreul, M.-E., "Histoire des connaissances chimiques," Gide et Guerin, Paris (1866), 479 pages.

40 Chevreul, M.-E., "Résumé d'une histoire de la matière depuis les philosophes grecs jusqu'a Lavoisier inclusivement," Didot, Paris (1878); *Mém. Acad. Sci.* (Paris), 39 (1877), 322–757.

41 Metzger, Hélène, "Eugène Chevreul. Historien de la chimie," *Archeion,* 14 (January-March 1932), 6–11.

42 Chevreul, M.-E., "Sur l'explication de nombreux phénomènes qui sont une conséquence de la vieillesse," *Compt. rend.,* 80 (June 14, 1875), 1414–1419; *Ibid.,* 80, 1542–6 (June 28, 1875); 81, 5 (July 5, 1875); 81 (July 12, 1875), 61–64.

Georges Bouchard, "Chevreul," Paris, ed. de la Madelaine, 1932.

MICHEL EUGÈNE CHEVREUL

Pierre Lemay and Ralph Oesper, "Chevreul," in *J. Chem. Ed.*, 25, 62–70 (1948).

George Sarton, "Hoefer and Chevreul," in *Bull. Hist. of Medicine*, 8, 419–445 (1940).

From: *J. Am. Pharm. Assoc., Scientific ed.*, 29, 89–96 (1940).

MARY ELVIRA WEEKS
LYLE O. AMBERG

·· 34 ··

Leopold Gmelin

1788-1853

LEOPOLD GMELIN (born August 2, 1788, in Göttingen), was the third son of Johann Friedrich Gmelin, later professor of botany and chemistry. His grandfather was a member of the Royal Society, and both he and his great-grandfather were professors at the University of Tübingen.

In his autobiography Leopold Gmelin mentions that, besides attending the Gymnasium in Göttingen from 1799 to 1804, he had a private tutor. In the summer of 1804 he also attended the lectures on chemistry by his father, who died on November 1, 1804. In the summer of that same year, his father had sent him to Tübingen to keep up the family tradition and work in the family pharmacy as well as to register for courses at the university. He studied materia medica and pharmacology with Ferdinand Gmelin, his cousin, and medicine with K. Fr. Kielmeyer, the husband of his cousin Lotte Gmelin. Then he returned to Göttingen and worked there with his father's successor, F. X. Stromeyer. Aware of its significance for the chemical profession, he also studied mathematics with Thibaut. According to his teacher, he was the second-best student of medicine among his numerous pupils. After passing his examination in 1809, Gmelin went again to Tübingen to study chemistry until Easter, 1811, with his former teachers and to start his thesis on the black pigment of eyes. This he completed with experiments at the Jacquin laboratory in Vienna. In 1812 he got his degree in Göttingen.

In 1813, under the leadership of Stromeyer, he undertook the analysis of the mineral haüyne, and in the fall of the same year established himself at Heidelberg. The following year he was made associate professor. Together with his cousin, Christian Gottlob, he went to Paris until the spring of 1815 to finish his studies and, at the same time, to meet the authorities in the field of chemical research: Gay-Lussac, Thenard, Hauy, and Vauquelin. After the death of his teacher and friend Fourcroy, Vauquelin had taken over the management of the laboratory of the medical faculty. Leopold Gmelin now joined its staff. It was one of the most excel-

455

lent places of learning. Thenard and Chevreul had worked there. Vauquelin himself had just isolated chromium from the Siberian leadspar; shortly before Gmelin's arrival, Vauquelin had done research on the separation of the platinum metals.

GMELIN AND HIS GREAT BOOK

After his return from Paris, Gmelin resumed his teaching job in Heidelberg. In 1817 he declined an offer to succeed Klaproth in Berlin, and consequently he was made a full professor. Thus, for the first time, chemistry got a chair of its own as part of the medical faculty. During these years he was working on the preliminaries for a reference book on chemistry which later determined the entire course of his activities. We do not exactly know when he decided on this plan and when he started to work for it. More important than the time are the conditions which prompted him to undertake this far-reaching enterprise. There had been attempts, at the turn of the nineteenth century, to collect the known chemical facts; but they did not meet with any lasting success, although they took into account the whole material according to Lavoisier's findings. It is true that there existed, beginning with the year 1808, the textbook in several volumes by Berzelius, who was one of the most prominent scholars in the field of chemistry. But the aim of a textbook differs from that of the archive; as Berzelius himself says, it has to lead the student step by step and has to develop and build up things according to their dependence upon each other. But Leopold Gmelin was concerned with something different—with the complete and objective collection of the whole state of chemical knowledge. He saw the accumulation of unorganized facts which, during the antiphlogistic time after Lavoisier, had not yet undergone the all-encompassing evaluation and rating which were to become a pressing necessity for chemistry because of the steadily increasing variety of the experimental material. Leopold Gmelin was steeped in a family tradition of scholarship and erudition and, therefore, was able to accomplish his self-appointed task successfully. The striving after objective clarification began early and with great intensity in this young university professor, and liberated within him the forces that made him the

456

Linnaeus of chemistry. When Leopold's father, Johann Friedrich Gmelin, in 1780 wrote his introduction to chemistry for the use at universities, he said in the preface:

> There are few sciences which since their first formation can show so many textbooks for the use in lectures than chemistry, but also few which have undergone so many changes and still are daily being altered, improved, and enlarged. This, and the difference in intentions which each author has when planning his textbook, seem to be the causes to which we owe the frequent appearance of chemical textbooks in our time.

And when, in view of these facts, we ask ourselves what has given Leopold Gmelin's book its lasting value, we can safely state as the reason that, when writing his book, he did not envision any individual, subjective aim, but that it was the incorruptible, forever valid law of scientific objectivity that guided him during his report of the contemporary state of knowledge. To strive after truth was his motto—and for him this meant the objective presentation of the prevailing experimental state of science.

When Gmelin was twenty-nine years old, the first volume of his *Handbuch der Chemie* was published. He clearly and solidly followed Lavoisier. Already the first edition got a friendly reception. In 1819 Trommsdorf wrote in his *Neues Journal der Pharmacie*: "The present textbook of chemistry is distinguished by the fact that the author has arranged matters according to modern viewpoints. The presentation is enlightening, neither too short nor too detailed, and yet very complete."

In 1815 Leopold Gmelin became director of the Chemical Institute which at that time was located, together with the Physical Institute, in the cameral building at the Karlstor. In 1818, after having declined to succeed Klaproth in Berlin, an ardent wish of his was realized and fulfilled: The scientific institutes were transferred to the former Dominican Monastery, in which he also got an apartment. This move effected a decisive change in his laboratory situation. On February 28, 1818, he wrote to his mother:

> Now, by the way, my laboratory is almost entirely installed, and there is an immense improvement concerning the locality. The

457

auditorium is close by and is spacious and has railed benches, so that everybody can see the experiments clearly. There is running water in the laboratory. Adjacent to the laboratory there are three rooms, and besides I have a large one for the minerals. . . . In chemistry I have 30 in attendance. I would have more, if I did not collide with Leonhard, who lectures on mineralogy at the same hour. In pharmacology, which is taught by two others besides, I have only 4.

He always kept trying to improve the state of his laboratory, especially during the first years of his activities at the university, when his work on the book had not yet absorbed him entirely.

Leopold Gmelin worked in Heidelberg until the year 1851, without any other interruption than official trips and little vacations with the family at the home of the Gmelins or at health resorts, as the applications for leave of absence in the records of the university show. Thus he was active in the laboratory, with his lectures, with the book, and during a number of years as "pulp miller," i.e., as proprietor of a paper mill in the valley of Schriesheim which belonged to the family. Unfortunately, this activity brought him more trouble than satisfaction.

GMELIN AS A TEACHER

Kussmaul, in his *Jugenderinnerungen eines alten Arztes* (Diary of the early years of an old doctor), described Gmelin as the magnificent picture by C. l'Allemand of 1837 depicts him:

His appearance was extraordinarily charming, the beautiful head with the clever and friendly face surrounded by abundant curly, snowy white hair; his friends compare him accurately with a blossoming cherry tree. Strangely enough, Gmelin, in his lectures, seemed embarrassed like a beginner, he pronounced the words hesitatingly and hastily, but the numerous experiments which accompanied the words never failed.

We must not forget to mention Wöhler, Gmelin's most outstanding pupil. It is true that the teacher advised him not to attend his lectures, since he would find little new to learn there. But besides his main studies in medicine, Wöhler worked with Gmelin in the laboratory. It was Gmelin who advised Wöhler to give up practical medicine, in accord with Gmelin's own example, and devote himself entirely to chemistry; he recommended Wöhler to Berzelius. Wöhler wrote Berzelius July 17, 1823:

> I venture therefore, especially encouraged through the advice of Mr. Leopold Gmelin, under whose guidance I have studied chemistry until now, to inquire, whether I could have the good fortune to be able to work in your laboratory this coming winter.

And on August 1, Berzelius answered:

> Anyone who has studied chemistry under the guidance of Mr. Leopold Gmelin, will certainly find very little to learn with me. In spite of this, I do not want to deny myself the lucky occasion to make your personal acquaintance, and I will therefore accept you with all my heart as my working companion.

GMELIN AS AN EXPERIMENTER

Most of Gmelin's researches were done between 1814 and 1843. The beginnings of his work give a good insight into the state of analytical methods at the start of his research activities; they are extremely primitive in the field of organic chemistry, only uncertainly groping in the field of inorganic chemistry; on the other hand, relatively far-developed and absolutely satisfactory in quantitative chemistry especially in the analysis of minerals. But it would be wrong to say that his further work reflected the progress in chemistry, that, like Liebig and Wöhler, he arrived at more refined and improved methods, and like these two scholars, achieved more and more brilliant results. On the contrary, his best and, to the present day, valuable researches, which would have secured him a place of honor in the history of chemical research even without his great book, he carried out as a young professor between 1820 and 1826. In the 1830's his publications became shorter and shorter, and in the year 1843, ten years before his death, his experimental work ended entirely.

When we know and celebrate Leopold Gmelin as the creator of the *Handbuch der anorganischen Chemie*, we involuntarily have the idea that he was an "inorganic" chemist, or at least preferred to

459

occupy himself with inorganic problems. That this is not so we learn from a letter that Wöhler wrote to Berzelius in 1824, where he says of Gmelin: "His main occupation is organic chemistry, especially in relation to physiology." In fact his most voluminous researches were made in this field and brought results which are still valuable.

One can divide Gmelin's researches into five groups: (1) organic-physiological; (2) organic-chemical; (3) inorganic-chemical; (4) mineralogic-analytical; and (5) theoretical-systematical. In numbers the publications in all five subjects are almost equal, except for the last.

His Göttingen thesis, "Chemical Researches of the Black Pigment in the Eyes of Oxen and Calves"—published 1814—lies in the physiological realm. His next physiological work was published in 1820, together with Tiedemann, who from then on collaborated in researches of this kind. The title is "Experiments on the Ways in Which Substances Get from the Digestive Tract into the Blood." When, in 1823, the French Academy put the prize question to explore: "Quel sont les phénomènes qui se succèdent dans les organes digestifs durant l'acte de la digestion" (What are the phenomena which succeed one another in the digestive organs during the act of digestion), Gmelin and Tiedemann did not hesitate to undertake the difficult study of digestion in mammals, birds, fish, and amphibians. In the course of two years they accumulated material; not only a series of organic substances unknown until then, but they also stated with satisfaction that they had brought some light into the dark happenings inside the digestive organs. Therefore their disappointment was great when the French Academy did not give the prize to their work, which they had sent in anonymously, but only rated it equal to a much less complete work by Lassaigne and Leuret. In spite of this judgment by the Academy, their work made a great sensation in chemical and medical professional circles and was applauded with enthusiasm. In his annual reports Berzelius devoted to it a review of 34 pages for the first volume alone: "Animal chemistry has been enriched with a very important and detailed work by Fr. Tiedemann and Leopold Gmelin." Liebig, too, devoted some favorable comments to this work.

460

Through this research Gmelin and Tiedemann could be classed among the founders of physiological chemistry. Among some prominent details in this work, I should like to mention the reaction with dyestuffs of the bile, which Leopold Gmelin found and which was named after him; it is still used today. They discovered a series of organic substances, especially cholic acid, called by them "Cholsäure," to differentiate it from the gallic acid, taurine in the gallbladder of oxen, pancreatine. Besides they proved the presence of potassium rhodanite in human saliva.

In 1834 Gmelin, together with Tiedemann, published another physiological-chemical work, in which E. Mitscherlich took part. The subjects were the changes in the blood as well as the form in which carbonic acid is absorbed in the blood.

In the introduction to the organic part of the first edition of his book, Gmelin defines organic substances as follows:

In their most complete state, the substances of organisms differ from those of inorganic nature: 1) in the inherent force of life, 2) in the individual inner and outer structures, 3) in that for the greater and most important part, they are composed of special chemical compounds which are not specific, but only as remnants of organic substances in the inorganic.

Others already did not believe any more in the *vis vitalis* as necessary for building up organic substances, but they were still inclined to agree that organic substances originate in living beings and could not be manufactured from inorganic substances. This was still the conviction of Wöhler, in spite of his statement, in 1828, that very much to his surprise, he obtained urea instead of ammonium cyanate from cyanic acid and ammonia. In 1825, Gmelin himself succeeded in discovering the synthesis of a then unknown organic acid when he heated, according to Brunner's method, potassium carbonate with coal in order to recover pure potassium by distillation. He separated the free acid and, because of its safron-yellow color, called it croconic acid. One could speculate whether the discovery of organic synthesis would not have been connected with Gmelin's name if croconic acid had been a known substance at that time and not relatively unimportant, even

461

today. We can assume with certainty that Gmelin himself would not have reached this insight. Neither Gmelin in 1825, nor Wöhler in 1828, has drawn the conclusion that the synthesis of an organic substance could actually take place without the action of *vis vitalis*, the life force.

In his work on cyanides of iron Gmelin made an interesting discovery in 1822. Berzelius comments on it as follows:

> Gmelin discovered a double cyanide which, in my opinion, is more interesting . . . it is obtained when chlorine (oxidized muriatic gas) is introduced into a solution of crystallized prussiate of potassium until the solution does no longer precipitate iron-oxide salts with a blue color.

Gmelin obtained crystals from the solution which he called red iron-potassium cyanide, also called "Gmelin's salt."

Gmelin as a systematizer also tried to formulate theories. In this, however, he was not very successful; he lacked the great vision and the creative idea, and he became enmeshed in a thousand little details.

In surveying Gmelin's scientific work we have to return to his *Handbuch*: In the first edition (1817) Gmelin reported on 48 elements, in the fourth (1843) there were 55. Nevertheless, the inorganic part of the book did not increase much since the first edition. This edition consisted of two inorganic volumes and one, of moderate size, for organic chemistry. In the second edition (1822), the number of organic substances was noticeably increased. In the third edition, the inorganic part comprises only one volume, the organic two of equal size. In the fourth edition three volumes of the inorganic part are combined with six organic volumes. When Gmelin began to prepare this edition the subdivision and presentation of organic chemistry proved to be a great headache. The content of the previous editions had become entirely useless, particularly the old division into acids and oxides. He had to look for a new classification; for this he had to study the several theories of the younger chemists and to form his opinion about them. The concepts of atoms, molecules, and equivalents had not yet been clearly distinguished and were used indiscriminately. Gmelin tried to replace the concept of atoms, which had caused so much confusion, by "mixing weight." Liebig enthusiastically accepted this proposal and attempted to convince Berzelius, but he declined on principle. Gmelin for a time remained faithful to his "mixing weights," but in the foreword to the fourth edition he declared: "Furthermore I have decided to adopt the atomic hypothesis, and I have, therefore, replaced the mixing weights by the atoms."

In 1851 a decline in health forced him to request his resignation from the Heidelberg chair. He exerted all his influence to obtain Bunsen as his successor in Heidelberg.

In 1852, his desires were fulfilled and Bunsen became his successor. In the same year he published one volume of the organic part of his book in spite of several strokes. On April 13, 1853, a life rich in exhausting and indefatigable work came to its end.

From the biography by Emil Pietsch in collaboration with E. Beyer, *Ber. deut. chem. Ges.,* 72, part A, 5–33, (1939). Translated by Dora S. Farber.

EMIL PIETSCH
E. BEYER

·· *35* ··

Michael Faraday

1791-1867

IT IS clearly in the field of electrical researches that Faraday's reputation is most profound but his interests were sufficiently broad so that he ranks high among the investigators of chemistry as well.

Michael Faraday, the son of a blacksmith and a farmer's daughter, was born on September 22, 1791, at Newington, in Surrey, a town which has by now become a part of Greater London. The family was poor and there were three other children. At age thirteen, Michael became errand boy for George Riebau, bookbinder and stationer. A year later he began a seven-year term as an apprentice in the firm. In 1812 he became journeyman bookbinder to one de la Roche, a French immigrant of fiery temper. This, coupled with a distaste for the pedestrian career of bookbinder, soon caused him to seek other employment.

Faraday's formal education was limited to a few years in elementary school. He showed, however, a deep-seated desire for self-improvement. As an apprentice he read extensively in items left for binding, becoming particularly excited by Mrs. Marcet's "Conversations in Chemistry," and the electrical sections of the "Encyclopaedia Britannica." When he could afford materials he performed simple chemical experiments and built an electrical machine. He also became a member of the City Philosophical Society, an organization founded by a Mr. Tatum who gave evening lectures on natural philosophy.

In the spring of 1812 a Mr. Dance, one of Riebau's customers, took Faraday to the Royal Institution to hear the last four of Davy's lectures. Faraday took careful notes, added drawings, and sent them to Sir Joseph Banks, president of the Royal Society, in the naive hope that this might pave the way toward work in the scientific field. Some time later, after receiving no reply from Banks, Faraday wrote to Davy, enclosing his notes and drawings, and asking for a job. Davy granted an interview and attempted to dissuade Faraday from a scientific career. Some days later Davy offered him a position as assistant at the Royal Institution at a salary of 25 shillings per week and the use of two rooms for living quarters. His earliest work involved assisting Davy with experiments on nitrogen trichloride after Davy's vision had been harmed by an explosion of the unstable compound.

Davy was at the height of his scientific career when Faraday joined him. His discovery of the alkali and alkaline earth metals, his studies on the elemental nature of chlorine, and various other researches had established his reputation as an experimentalist. His lectures at the Royal Institution had been attended by capacity audiences. He had been knighted by George III in April, 1812, and in that month was married to a wealthy widow. He resigned his professorship of chemistry at that time but was appointed honorary professor for the remainder of his life and continued to use the laboratory of the Institution for experimental studies.

In October of 1813 the Davys left London for a Continental tour. Faraday was taken along as a secretary and scientific assistant to Davy but, when Davy's valet quit before the trip began, Faraday was drafted into this service as well. In the daily journal kept during the trip and from letters to friends in London it is apparent that Faraday enjoyed his association with Sir Humphry but found Lady Davy a woman of violent temper who was unreasonable in her demands and treated him as a lackey.

The trip occupied eighteen months and saw the party through Paris, Montpellier, Florence, Rome, Naples, Milan, the Rhineland, and the Low Countries. Faraday assisted Davy with the burning of a diamond in the great lens of the Duke of Tuscany. They visited Mt. Vesuvius, saw Volta in Milan, and met various other important figures in Continental science.

Upon his return to London, Faraday was again engaged at the Royal Institution as laboratory assistant and superintendent of apparatus. Davy continued to do experimental work at the institution although William Thomas Brande (1788–1866) had been appointed professor of chemistry. Faraday's first publication, dealing with the analysis of Tuscany lime, appeared in 1816. In reprinting the paper in the collected "Experimental Researches in Chemistry and Physics," Faraday noted, "Sir Humphry Davy gave me the analysis to make as a first attempt in chemistry at a time when my fear was greater than my confidence, and both far greater than my knowledge; at a time also when I had no thought of ever writing an original paper on science" (p. 1).

During the next year six more papers came from his pen. His confidence apparently grew rapidly, for his scientific productivity during the next two decades was high. Several of his early papers dealt with the escape of gases through capillaries. In observing that the mobility of gases decreased as their specific gravities increased, Faraday was laying background for the law of gaseous diffusion later recognized by Graham. These diffusion experiments were made at the time that Davy was making his experiments on flames which led to the development of the safety lamp.

The period between 1815 and 1825 was a busy one. Faraday was still feeling his way into science, becoming more venturesome as he saw his early efforts favorably received. The period was one of broad interests, with Faraday probing into a number of unrelated problems. A few of his studies were to have lasting significance, others were merely a part of his training in science. His abilities began to be recognized as research problems were suggested to him and greater responsibilities were given to him. In 1821 he was made superintendent of the laboratory at the Royal Institution.

His improved circumstances led him to embark upon marriage with Sarah Barnard, the daughter of a silversmith who was an elder of the Sandemanian Church in London. Faraday had himself grown up in this sect and continued to be a faithful adherent to the end of his days. The Sandemanians were followers of Robert Sandeman and his father-in-law, Rev. John Glas, a Scotch Presbyterian who dissented from the main church. Several congregations were formed in England during the eighteenth century. They failed to gain in popularity but maintained their own strength for a considerable period. There was no formal clergy, the church being governed by elders chosen from among the members. The Sandemanians believed that the Bible contained all that was necessary for salvation.

Faraday and his wife faithfully adhered to the tenets of the sect which demanded rigorous attendance at services, heavy charitable contributions, and abstention from frivolous activities such as smoking and drinking. Faraday became an elder in 1840 and was responsible for conducting services on alternate Sundays. He once fell from favor when he missed church to attend a royal dinner at the request of Queen Victoria, but this appears to have been his only transgression. He avoided discussion of religion and considered religion to be of a different order of truth than natural truth.

The Faradays lived in the rooms provided by the Royal Institution until 1858, when the Queen, at the suggestion of Prince Consort Albert, provided a spacious house on Hampton Court Green. Here they lived until Faraday's death on August 25, 1867. Their needs were always simple ones and they took no part in social affairs. Their marriage was childless.

In 1824, on the nomination of Wollaston, Wm. Herschel, and several others, Faraday was elected to membership in the Royal Society. For some reason which has never been satisfactorily explained, Davy, president of the Society, opposed the election. A year later the cause of Davy's animosity must have disappeared, for he proposed to the managers of the Royal Institution Faraday's promotion to the directorship of the laboratory. Soon thereafter he inaugurated the Friday evening lectures on science. These were open to the public and were very popular over the years. Faraday was an able lecturer and demonstrator with a talent for popularizing difficult subjects.

Faraday's earliest research of a systematic nature was that dealing with alloys of steel. This was carried out between 1819 and 1824, partly in collaboration with James Stodart, an English instrument maker. Their purpose was the improvement of steel in the direction of producing better cutting instruments with resistance to corrosion. The work was carried out on an extensive basis involving not only the preparation of small samples in the furnace in the basement of the Royal Institution, but the preparation of commercial batches by Green, Pickslay and Co. of Sheffield.

Faraday analyzed "Wootz," a crucible steel made in India by fusing magnetic ore with carbonaceous matter, in order to learn why it was particularly suitable for razors and cutlery. He also made studies of meteoric iron and prepared iron and steel alloyed with nickel in an attempt to imitate meteoric iron. He reported that the presence of nickel reduced rusting in iron but accelerated it in steel. In all, Faraday studied twelve metals and the non-

470

metals silicon and sulfur for their effects on the properties of steel. The metals used were platinum, rhodium, palladium, osmium, iridium, copper, silver, gold, nickel, chromium, tin, and titanium. The platinum metals, which formed by far the largest group of tests, were supplied by Wollaston, who was a manufacturer of malleable platinum and who had done extensive research on the metals of the group. Faraday's results showed that these elements gave the best results; but, except for platinum, they were too rare to be practical.

For some reason which is not clearly understood, the researches were terminated in 1824 without leading to really practical results. The death of Stodart in 1823 may have removed from the scene the person who was encouraging the studies. In addition, there was no large demand at the time for superior steel, particularly if this steel contained rare and expensive metals. Facilities for steelmaking also were not well developed before mid-century, Faraday's own facilities for steel research were primitive, and interest in other problems no doubt caused him to abandon the studies, particularly since his empirical methods necessitated a great deal of tedious work to study the effect of even a single metal in a variety of proportions. Seventy-nine of the specimens were placed in a wooden box for storage. Faraday never touched them again and many years later could not even recollect what had become of them.

In 1930 the box and its contents came to the attention of Sir Robert Hadfield, a leading English metallurgist who had been responsible for the development of manganese steel. Hadfield, on the basis of metallographic, spectroscopic, hardness, electrical, and magnetic tests carried out on the specimens, concluded that Faraday had made significant progress toward the understanding of alloy steels. Actually, his work had not been a significant factor in the development of practical steel alloys toward the end of the century, although his work was extended in France by Boussingault, Berthier, and Bréant, and was also influential upon Russian experimenters.

In a study dealing with the hydrate of chlorine, discovered in 1785 by Berthollet and shown to be the hydrate in 1810 by Davy, Faraday succeeded in obtaining chlorine itself in liquid form.

When the solid hydrate was heated in a sealed tube it melted and separated into two layers, the upper simply a solution of chlorine in water, the heavier proving to be liquid chlorine. He next found that chlorine could be liquefied by placing it under a pressure of about four atmospheres, such as might be obtained by forcing air into a tube of chlorine gas with a syringe, and cooling.

Davy, who had suggested part of this investigation, now reported the condensation of hydrogen chloride gas. He sealed ammonium chloride and sulfuric acid in a glass tube and mixed the chemicals. The hydrogen chloride that formed partially condensed in the other end of the tube. Faraday continued the experiments under Davy's guidance. By generating gases in sealed, bent tubes that could be heated at one end and cooled at the other, Faraday succeeded in liquefying sulfur dioxide, hydrogen sulfide, carbon dioxide, euchlorine ($Cl_2 + ClO_2$), nitrous oxide, cyanogen, and ammonia. Considerable danger was encountered in the work with carbon dioxide and nitrous oxide where even strong tubes frequently exploded. Attempts to liquefy hydrogen, oxygen, phosphine, silicon tetrafluoride, and boron trifluoride ended in failure.

These studies were not pursued further at the time but were resumed in 1844. Thilorier had succeeded in solidifying carbon dioxide in 1835 through the use of high pressure and low temperature. By the use of solid carbon dioxide and ether (Thilorier's mixture), extremely low temperatures could be produced. Faraday built pressure equipment that made it possible to work at up to 50 atmospheres. It now became possible to liquefy a number of additional gases—arsine, hydrogen iodide, hydrogen bromide, phosphine, boron trifluoride, silicon tetrafluoride, and ethylene. He succeeded in solidifying hydrogen iodide and bromide, sulfur dioxide, hydrogen sulfide, nitrous oxide, cyanogen, and ammonia, but not chlorine, ether, alcohol, carbon disulfide, or oil of turpentine. He also failed in all attempts to liquefy hydrogen, oxygen, nitrogen, nitric oxide, carbon monoxide, and methane. In the case of nitrous acid gas ($2NO_2 \rightleftharpoons N_2O_4$) he observed that, upon cooling, it lost the greater part of its color and turned into a white solid.

In 1825 his investigation of an oily by-product of the illuminating gas industry led to the discovery of benzene and butylene.

The Portable Gas Co., which produced illuminating gas by dropping whale or cod oil into a hot furnace, called his attention to an oily liquid that separated out when the gas was compressed for introduction into the portable cylinders in which it was supplied to commercial and private consumers. Faraday subjected this oil to distillation and obtained, after extensive fractionation, a main portion boiling in the neighborhood of 85°C. This was purified by crystallization and subjected to extensive study. The vapor density was reported to be "nearly 40" ($H_2 = 1$). It was analyzed by passing the vapor over hot copper oxide and measuring the carbon dioxide and water formed, and also by detonating the vapor with oxygen. The results indicated a ratio of nearly 12 to 1 for carbon to hydrogen. Since Faraday considered the "proportional" (atomic) weight of carbon to be 6 he named the compound "bicarburet of hydrogen." The name "benzin" was introduced by Mitscherlich in 1833 after he prepared the same compound from benzoic acid.

Faraday also studied the reactions of various reagents with benzene. Chlorine showed little action until placed in sunlight, whereupon dense fumes of hydrochloric acid were evolved and a crystalline solid and a dense fluid were formed. These were not investigated further but undoubtedly were para- and orthodichlorobenzene. Derivatives were also observed when nitric acid and sulfuric acid were added to benzene.

The butylene occurring with benzene in the original oily residue was removed by gentle heating, followed by condensing the vapors through a tube cooled to −18°C. Faraday determined the composition by detonation and obtained a value in agreement with the composition of olefiant gas (ethylene). The vapor density, however, was found to be twice that of ethylene. He found that chlorine combined with the new hydrocarbon volume for volume, as did ethylene, but produced a compound of different composition.

Various other studies of organic compounds were made during this decade. As early as 1820 he analyzed a compound which Hugo Müller subsequently showed to be hexachlorobenzene. In 1821 he obtained a white, crystalline substance by treating Dutch liquid (ethylene chloride) with chlorine. Analysis showed the compound to be "perchloride of carbon," a compound containing

473

no hydrogen and corresponding to hexachloroethane. By passing this compound through a hot tube he obtained a liquid which, according to his analysis, must have been tetrachloroethylene. While studying the chlorination of ethylene he also encountered an iodide ($C_2H_4I_2$) which formed when ethylene and iodine vapor were exposed to sunlight.

A paper in 1826 reported on the reactions of sulfuric acid and naphthalene to produce a new acid. He actually had obtained the two isomeric napthalene monosulfonic acids but he did not distinguish them as separate compounds. Fifteen salts of the acid were prepared and studied.

Still another facet of his work from 1824 dealt with the improvement of optical glass. He was placed on a committee set up by the Royal Society and was closely associated with the instrument maker, George Dollond, and the astronomer, John Herschel. Faraday dealt with chemical composition and manufacture of the glass, Dollond supervised the grinding of lenses, and Herschel studied the physical properties of the lenses.

The studies resulted in production of "heavy" borosilicate glass. As an optical glass it proved satisfactory but without special virtue. The collaborators gradually lost interest in the project and it was abandoned in 1830. The glass found some use in microscopes and prisms, but the great hopes for it were largely unwarranted. However, the glass took on importance two decades later in connection with Faraday's magneto-optical researches.

Faraday's greatest fame lies in his electrical researches. They were begun early in his career, when he was busy with chemical and metallurgical studies, and resumed from time to time. In 1820, on the day that he and Davy learned of Oersted's discovery that an electric current caused deflection of a magnetic needle, they repeated the experiments and verified the results. In the autumn of 1821, Faraday started another series of experiments which were finished on Christmas Day. He realized that the direction of the deflecting force in a wire was at right angles to the direction of current flow and he succeeded in devising an apparatus in which a wire carrying a current could be made to revolve about a stationary magnet, and conversely, in which a magnet would revolve about a fixed wire. These were primitive forms of the electric motor, but Faraday made no attempts to extend the experiments in the direction of a practical device.

Soon after publication of his experiments Faraday found himself charged with having appropriated ideas of Wollaston. Faraday now explained that, while it was true that Wollaston had visited the Royal Institution to perform experiments on electrical and magnetic relationships in April, 1821, he (Faraday) had gained the impression that Wollaston expected the wire to rotate axially. Wollaston himself never entered into the recriminations and remained a friendly supporter of the rising scientist.

Although Faraday made no electrical discoveries during the next ten years, the subject had not lost interest for him. In his commonplace book for 1822 there was penned the entry, "Convert magnetism into electricity." The production of magnetic effects by a current had suggested the opposite relationship, but all attempts toward the demonstration of this resulted in failure.

In August, 1831, Faraday put aside all other researches and resumed serious work on the problem of electricity from magnetism. He soon observed that when two insulated wires were wrapped around an iron ring, a current was induced in the secondary wire whenever the current in the primary wire was started or stopped. This discovery was the principle of the transformer. A few weeks later he observed a flow of electricity when a magnet was plunged into or withdrawn from a coil of wire—the principle of the dynamo. Thus the production of electricity from magnetism was realized. It had eluded Faraday so long because he had neglected to move magnets across conductors. Once this need for motion was recognized he succeeded in producing current by moving a copper disc between the poles of the large magnet owned by the Royal Institution, but he failed to carry the work farther toward the production of a practical dynamo. His electrical researches were continued, however, toward the direction of understanding the phenomena themselves.

From 1844, Faraday undertook to deal with electromagnetic induction from a theoretical standpoint. Since iron filings in a magnetic field tend to orient themselves in lines, Faraday introduced the concept of magnetic lines of force. Electricity was produced when lines of force were cut by a conductor. Thus, matter itself

475

was not so important as the lines which filled the space between material objects and which were disturbed by the motion of matter. This was the beginning of the "field" concept that was extended into a useful mathematical system by James Clerk Maxwell.

Faraday himself had little understanding of mathematics and always sought to explain physical phenomena in nonmathematical terms. In his later years he expressed regret that Maxwell was unable to explain electromagnetic phenomena in nonmathematical fashion. Throughout his life Faraday was to utilize the simplest possible equipment in his researches and avoid any sort of mathematical treatment.

Faraday's electrochemical contributions grew out of experiments in which he demonstrated that electricity produced from static and galvanic sources was identical. By subjecting paper wetted with potassium iodide solution to the action of a current he observed that the spot of iodine, formed where the positive electrode touched the paper, was proportional in diameter to the number of turns taken on the electrical machine or to the number of seconds that current flowed from his cell. In following up this observation, he decomposed water in a variety of ways and became convinced that, in his own words, "The chemical power of a current of electricity is in direct proportion to the absolute quantity of electricity which passes."

Out of this conviction was developed the "Volta-electrometer," a gas coulometer which measured quantity of current from the volume of hydrogen and oxygen obtained by the decomposition of water. By using this device he went on to establish the second law of electrochemistry. He observed that in electrolytic decompositions the amounts of various elements produced by a given quantity of electricity were in proportion to their chemical equivalents.

The discovery of this relationship served to strengthen the position of those chemists who chose to think in terms of equivalent weights rather than atomic weights. Faraday himself, like his master, Davy, never placed much weight on atomic ideas. Berzelius, who might easily have incorporated the electrochemical equivalents into atomic philosophy, refused to recognize their validity when he blindly confused current intensity with quantity.

Early in his electrochemical studies Faraday introduced a new

476

nomenclature intended to clarify thinking about the subject. With the assistance of the Reverend William Whewell, classical scholar and historian of science, he introduced the terms *electrolysis, electrode, electrolyte, ion, cation, anion, cathode,* and *anode.* It must not be supposed, as a result of this, that he held advanced views regarding ionization in solution. He was inclined to avoid theorizing with regard to the nature of electrolysis except for a very confused statement in one of his papers. He strongly opposed the Grotthuss chain theory which was popular at the time.

Following the electrochemical researches, which were vigorously pursued in 1833 and 1834, Faraday began to suffer from fatigue and rheumatism. He spent a part of the next year in Switzerland in an effort to regain his health. The following years saw a further decline in health, accompanied by periods of failing memory. This distressed him a great deal since he was accustomed to concentrate on his research problems and had established a reputation as a brilliant lecturer. His Friday evening lectures at the Royal Institution had always been well attended. Following elevation to the Fullerian professorship of chemistry in 1833, a chair without lecture obligations, he continued to make public appearances from time to time. Now it became necessary to curtail his public appearances as well as his researches.

In the mid-forties his health had improved somewhat although the failing memory was to plague him the rest of his life. He now inaugurated his Juvenile Lectures which became an annual series at the Royal Institution during the Christmas season. He also took part in certain public services such as the investigation of the Haswell Colliery disaster with the geologist Lyell, and took certain consulting activities for the military services and the admiralty. The researches on liquefaction and solidification of gases were extended at this time and his ideas on lines of force were developed.

He was motivated throughout his career by a belief in the unity of nature. This had repeatedly caused him to return to the efforts to produce electricity from magnetism, and it now stimulated his thinking in connection with magnetic and electrical forces. He sought further to bring gravitational forces into the system, but without success.

During this period he learned that certain substances were attracted toward a magnetic field (paramagnetic) while others were repelled (diamagnetic). Also, with the aid of the great magnet of of the Institution and through use of his borosilicate glass, he discovered magneto-optical rotation. It was found that substances which ordinarily transmitted plane-polarized light without effect, rotated such light when in a powerful magnetic field. This appeared to suggest a relationship between light and magnetism, but it was not possible to unravel this further.

The years from 1847 onward were years of decline. Faraday suffered from mental confusion and spells of giddiness. His doctors advised him to give up work; which he did. In subsequent years there were intervals during which his experiments were resumed but never with the success of earlier years. In 1852, when there was a great deal of interest in submarine cables, he carried out experiments on submerged wires for the Electric Telegraph Company. He was called upon for advisory work from time to time by government and industry. In 1862 he urged the government to place more emphasis on science in the educational curriculum but his advice was largely ignored.

In retrospect, Faraday, through his powerful mental ability, was able to rise above the lack of an extensive formal education, coupled with a late start in scientific activity, to reach the heights of scientific brilliance. Using simple equipment and neglecting mathematical analysis, he was nevertheless able to uncover important truths in a broad area of physical science. His penchant for working on significant problems is revealed in the frequency with which he made discoveries which were simultaneously being made elsewhere, i.e., the discoveries of Joseph Henry on electromagnetic induction in America, or those on electrochemical equivalence by Carlo Matteucci in Italy.

Faraday represents the supreme example of the lone worker. After careful training and encouragement under the discerning eye of Humphry Davy he worked on alone. Under primitive laboratory conditions he made one important discovery after another, but since he worked without assistants he left no school of successors as did such contemporaries as Gay-Lussac, Dumas, Liebig, Wöhler, and Bunsen.

NOTES AND REFERENCES

1 Rollo Appleyard, "A Tribute to Michael Faraday," Constable, London, 1931.

2 E. W. Ashcroft, "Faraday," Brit. Mfgs. Assoc., London, 1931.

3 T. W. Chalmers, "Historic Researches," Scribner, New York, 1952, pp. 49–63, 169–180, 185–195.

4 W. Cramp, "Michael Faraday and Some of His Contemporaries," Pitman & Sons, London, 1931.

5 J. A. Crowther, "The Life and Discoveries of Michael Faraday," Society for Promoting Christian Knowledge, London, 1918.

6 Rosemary G. Ehl and A. J. Ihde, "Faraday's Electrochemical Laws and the Determination of Equivalent Weights," *J. Chem. Educ., 31,* 226–232 (1954).

7 M. Faraday, "Chemical Manipulations," J. Murray, London, 1827.

8 M. Faraday, "Experimental Researches in Electricity," 3 vols., R. and J. E. Taylor, London, 1839–55.

9 M. Faraday, "Experimental Researches in Chemistry and Physics," R. and J. E. Taylor, London, 1859.

10 M. Faraday, "The Chemical History of a Candle," Chatto and Windies, London, 1861.

11 J. H. Gladstone, "Michael Faraday," Macmillan, London, 1872.

12 Robert A. Hadfield, "Faraday and His Metallurgical Researches," Chapman & Hall, London, 1931.

13. W. Jerrold, "Michael Faraday: Man of Science," Macmillan, London, 1891.

14 H. Bence Jones, "The Life and Letters of Faraday," 2 vols., Longmans, Green, London, 1870.

15 H. Kondo, "Michael Faraday," *Scientific American, 189,* no. 4, 90–98 (1953).

16 Thomas Martin, "Faraday's Diary, Being the Various Philosophical Notes of Experimental Investigation Made by Michael Faraday," G. Bell & Sons, London, 1932–1936, 7 vols. and index.

17 T. Martin, "Faraday," Duckworth, London, 1934.

18 T. Martin, "Faraday's Discovery of Electro-Magnetic Induction," Arnold, London, 1949.

19 L. C. Newell, "Faraday's Discovery of Benzene," *J. Chem. Educ., 3,* 1248 (1926).

20 L. C. Newell, "Faraday's Contributions to Chemistry," *ibid., 8,* 1493 (1931).

21 W. Ostwald, in G. Bugge, Das Buch der grossen Chemiker, Verlag Chemie, Berlin, 1929, vol. 1, pp. 417–427.

22 W. L. Randall, "Michael Faraday (1791–1863)," Small Maynard, Boston, 1925.

23 Sylvanus P. Thompson, "Michael Faraday, His Life and Work," Macmillan, London, 1898.
24 Wm. A. Tilden, "Faraday, 1791–1867," in *Famous Chemists,* G. Routledge & Sons, London, 1921, pp. 152–169.
25 John Tyndall, "Faraday as a Discoverer," Longmans, Green, New York, 1874, London, 1868.

AARON J. IHDE

·· 36 ··

Eilhardt Mitscherlich

1794-1863

EILHARDT MITSCHERLICH was born on the seventh of January, 1794, in the village of Jever in Oldenburg. His father was pastor of Neuende; his uncle, the well-known philologer, was professor in Göttingen. He was educated at the Gymnasium of Jever, under the historian Schlosser. Following the example of his uncle, and encouraged by Schlosser, he devoted himself to the study of history, philology, and especially the Persian language. In order to prosecute these studies, he went in 1811 to the University of Heidelberg, and in 1813 to Paris. He had hoped to be allowed to accompany an embassy to Persia, but was prevented by the fall of Napoleon. In 1814, on his return to Germany, he commenced writing a history of the Ghurides and Kara-Chitayens, compiled from manuscripts in the Göttingen Library, and of which a specimen was published in 1815 under the title "Mirchondi historia Thaheridarum." Unwilling to renounce his favorite project of travelling in Persia, he determined to accomplish it without any extraneous assistance. The only way in which it appeared possible to travel was in the character of a physician; accordingly he resolved to study medicine. He went to Göttingen for this purpose, and first applied himself to the introductory sciences, especially to chemistry, which so fascinated him that he gave up philology and his intention to visit Persia. In 1818 he went to Berlin for the purpose of obtaining license to lecture. Link allowed him to carry on his researches in the laboratory of the University. Here he undertook the examination of the phosphates and arsenates, and confirmed the accuracy of the latest conclusion arrived at by Berzelius, viz., that phosphoric and arsenic acid each contain five equivalents of oxygen, while phosphorous and arsenious acid contain three equivalents. He noticed at the same time that the similarly constituted phosphates and arsenates crystallized in similar forms. Up to this period he had never paid any especial attention to crystallography, but the conviction that he was on the eve of a great discovery allowed him no rest. He studied the laws of crystallography, learned the method of measuring the angles of crystals, and soon satisfied himself that the phosphates and arsenates are not merely similar but identical in form, and that, consequently, bodies exist of dissimilar composition having the same crystalline form, and that these bodies are compounds containing respectively the same number of equivalents. Many minerals appeared to confirm this law, viz., the carbonates, dolomite, chalybite, diallogite, and calcite, and the sulfates, baryte, celestine, and Anglesite. In confirmation, however, of this discovery he considered it necessary to appeal to artificial salts which crystallize readily and distinctly, and are easily obtained of sufficient purity, so that his conclusions might be confirmed by any one without difficulty. The neutral sulfates of protoxide of iron, oxide of copper, oxide of zinc, and magnesia, which all contain water, mostly in different proportions, appeared peculiarly well-fitted for this purpose. He found that the following were similar in form: (1) sulfate of copper and sulfate of protoxide of manganese; (2) sulfate of protoxide of iron and sulfate of oxide of cobalt; (3) sulfate of magnesia, sulfate of oxide of zinc, and sulfate of oxide of nickel. He also found that the salts which had dissimilar forms contained a different number of equivalents of water, and that those which had similar forms contained the same number. He then mixed the solutions of the different sulfates, and found that the resulting crystals had the form and the same number of equivalents of water as some one of the unmixed sulfates. Lastly, he examined the combinations of these sulfates with sulfate of potash, and showed that the double salts had all similar forms belonging to the oblique system, and that they were composed of one equivalent of the earthy or metallic sulfate, one equivalent of sulfate of potash, and six equivalents of water. The memoir in which these observations are recorded was presented to the Berlin Academy on the ninth of December, 1819. In the course of the preceding August Berzelius came to Berlin, on his way from Paris to Stockholm. He became acquainted with Mitscherlich, and conceived such an opinion of his talents, that he suggested him to the Minister Altenstein as the most fitting successor to Klaproth in the chair of chemistry in the University of Berlin. Altenstein did not at the moment act upon this suggestion, but consented to the proposal that Mitscherlich should perfect his chemical education by working for some time under the guidance of Berzelius. In Stockholm he continued and extended his researches on the phosphates and arsenates, and wrote a memoir on the subject, which appeared in the Transactions of the Swedish Academy. In it he described with great care the forms of the acid and neutral phosphates and arsenates of potash, soda, and ammonia, the neutral double salts of potash and soda, and of ammonia and soda, and the phosphates and arsenates of oxide of lead. He showed in every case that the phosphates and arsenates have similar forms and analogous compositions. Urged by Berzelius to give a name to this newly detected property of the chemical elements, he designated it by the term *isomorphism*. This discovery was of the highest importance for the theory of chemical equivalents, inasmuch as it explained the exceptions to the law of definite proportions in the mineral system of Berzelius. It appeared moreover, from the crystallization of the mixtures of the different sulfates, that isomorphous substances combine in all proportions; and that they replace one another in indefinite proportions in the composition of minerals was proved by Mitscherlich's fellow students, Heinrich Rose and Bonsdorff, in the cases of augite and amphibole.

The doctrine of isomorphism, moreover, was an admirable test of the determination of the equivalents of the different elements, whilst the smallness of the number of changes in the equivalents of the simple substances that followed the discovery of isomorphism, is an indication of the admirable sagacity with which they had been determined by Berzelius. Mineralogists and chemists had long been occupied with researches on the relation between chemical composition and crystalline form; they had discovered a number of important facts bearing upon the subject, but no one had discovered the basis upon which the phenomena rested. Fuchs had already observed that some of the constituents of a mineral might be replaced by others without any change of form, and had called these constituents *vicarious,* but by adducing the sesquioxide of iron and lime as vicarious constituents in gehlenite, he showed that the true explanation had eluded his grasp. Fuchs had moreover

485

remarked the close resemblance of the mineral sulfates to one another, as well as that of the rhombohedral carbonates. He also showed that strontianite was not rhombohedral as Haüy supposed, but prismatic, and that it resembled aragonite in form. The small percentage of strontian detected in aragonite by Stromeyer was regarded by Fuchs as the cause of the resemblance of the forms of the two minerals, as the very small quantity of carbonate of lime in chalybite had been supposed the cause of its resemblance to calcite. The only conclusion which Fuchs drew from the resemblances of these minerals was, that certain substances possess such an overpowering force of crystallization, that, even when present in small quantity, they constrain other substances to assume their form.

In November 1821 Mitscherlich returned to Berlin, was elected a member of the Academy of Sciences and appointed professor extraordinary in the University, and remained in that position till 1825, when he became professor in ordinary. In the summer of 1822 he gave his first lecture on chemistry to a large audience. He also continued his researches on isomorphism, and those which he had commenced in Stockholm, especially those which bore upon the artificial formation of minerals. He exhibited to the Academy a collection of about forty crystallized substances, which he had found in the slag heaps surrounding the copper-smelting furnaces of Fahlun during a visit he paid to that place in 1820, in the company of Berzelius. Of these, however, he described only two, a silicate of protoxide of iron isomorphous with olivine, and a mica, the composition of which approximates closely to that of a black mica of Siberia. He resumed these researches along with Berthier in the winter of 1823 and 1824, which he passed in Paris, and by fusing the mineral constituents together in proper proportions, succeeded in producing diopside, idocrase, and garnet.

In the course of his examination of the phosphates and arsenates he had observed that the acid phosphate of soda crystallizes in two totally different forms, both of which belong to the prismatic system, but cannot be referred to the same parameters. From this he inferred that the ultimate atoms of crystallized bodies by change of circumstances may admit of a change in their arrangement, and hazarded the opinion that, as aragonite resembles strontianite and cerussite in form, and calcite resembles dolomite, chalybite, and diallogite, it is possible for the substances isomorphous with aragonite to crystallize in the form of calcite, and the substances isomorphous with calcite to crystallize in the form of aragonite, and so greatly enlarge each group of isomorphous bodies. This opinion was looked upon with great distrust by chemists and mineralogists. All the examples he had brought forward were taken from compound bodies, which possibly might have contained admixtures that analysis had failed to detect, and the substances assumed to have the same composition might after all be different. These doubts were suggested by the analyses of aragonite, which had been pronounced by some of the most eminent chemists of the time to be pure carbonate of lime; then Stromeyer detected strontia in it, which, notwithstanding that its amount was very small, and different in aragonite from different localities, was immediately regarded as the cause of the difference of its form from that of calcite; lastly, Bucholz proved the existence of a variety of aragonite absolutely free from any admixture of strontia, to which, therefore, the difference of form could not by any possibility be due. At this conjuncture Mitscherlich made the remarkable discovery that sulfur also takes different forms under different circumstances. The crystals obtained from solutions belong to the prismatic system, and are identical in form with those which occur in nature; but when sulfur is fused and allowed to cool, with proper management distinct crystals are obtained, but they are entirely different from the former, inasmuch as they belong to the oblique system. This observation was of great importance, because sulfur being a simple substance crystallizable at pleasure in either of its two forms, the difference of form could not be attributed to a difference of composition. He had already proved that the acid phosphate of soda and carbonate of lime possessed the same property of crystallization in two different forms, which he now considered as appertaining to all simple substances and their chemical combinations, and to which he gave the name of *dimorphism*. He regarded it, moreover, as affording an explanation of the fact that bodies possessing analogous chemical constitutions are not

487

always isomorphous. The memoir on the dimorphism of sulfur was presented to the Academy on July 26, 1826.

It was found that the forms of isomorphous substances are not absolutely identical, except, of course, when they belong to the cubic system, but exhibit some differences, showing that the chemical nature of the substance is not altogether without influence on the form. In order to determine the difference between the angles of isomorphous bodies with greater accuracy than was attainable by the use of the ordinary Wollaston's goniometer, he caused a goniometer to be constructed by Pistor, provided with four verniers, each reading to 10″, and with a telescope magnifying twenty times for viewing the reflexions of the signal in the faces of the crystal. With this instrument, in the summer of 1823 he began to measure the angles of calcite from Iceland, and was surprised to find differences in the angle between the same pair of cleavages amounting to 20″, a difference which, though small, was too large to be attributed to errors of pointing or reading. The observations were made in the morning and in the afternoon in a room facing the south. The morning observations differed from those made in the afternoon, but the observations made at the same period of the day agreed well with one another; also the temperature of the room in the afternoon was nearly 4°C. higher than in the morning. He therefore concluded that the variation of the angle could only be due to the unequal expansion of the crystal in different directions. He increased the difference of temperature by immersing the crystal in a bath of heated mercury, and found that the cleavages became more nearly at right angles to one another, by 8′ 34″, for an increase of temperature of 100°C. In dolomite from Traversella, breunnerite from Pfitsch, chalybite from Ehrenfriedersdorff similar changes occurred amounting to 4′6″, 3′29″, and 2′22″ respectively, for a change of temperature of 100°C. A large number of other crystals examined by him afforded like results. In the winter of 1823–1824, during his stay in Paris, he measured the expansion of calcite in volume by Dulong's method, and found it equal to 0.001961 for 100°C. Hence it appears that by an increase of temperature of 100°C. the crystal expands 0.00288 in the direction of its axis, and contracts 0.00056 in a direction at right angles to its axis. He confirmed the accuracy of this most unexpected result by comparing, at different temperatures, the thickness of two plates of calcite of nearly equal thickness, bounded by planes parallel and at right angles to the axis respectively, and the thickness of a plate bounded by planes parallel to the axis with that of a plate of glass of nearly the same thickness, the expansion of which was known. His memoir on this important discovery was presented to the Academy on March 10, 1825.

The large goniometer which he employed in these observations being too cumbersome, and also too costly to be used by mineralogists in measuring the angles of crystals, he contrived an instrument more convenient for ordinary use, reading to half a minute, and provided with a telescope having a magnifying power of not more than three. The signal consists of cross wires in the focus of a collimator, as in the goniometers of Rudberg and Babinet. The adjustment of the crystal is effected by a very ingenious contrivance due to M. Oertling, by whom many of these instruments have been constructed. By the invention of this goniometer, which has come into general use under the name of Mitscherlich's goniometer, he conferred a great boon on mineralogists. A minute description of it appeared in the Memoirs of the Berlin Academy for 1843, a considerable time after it was originally contrived, and not till its value had been tested by long use.

Of his observations on the effect of heat on the double refraction of crystals, little is known beyond a notice in Poggendorff's "Annalen" of the remarkable changes which occur in gypsum when heated. At the ordinary temperature of the atmosphere the optic axes lie in a plane at right angles to the plane of symmetry, and make angles of about 60° with a normal to the plane of symmetry. On warming the crystal the optic axes approach the plane of symmetry, and at about 92°C. they coincide, exhibiting the phenomena of a uniaxal crystal, and on further increasing the temperature they open out in the plane of symmetry.

In 1827 Mitscherlich discovered selenic acid, and the isomorphism of selenate of potash with sulfate of potash, and afterwards of other selenates with the corresponding sulfates. In 1830 he observed the isomorphism of manganate of potash with sulfate of potash. This led him to a further examination of manganese, and to the discovery of the isomorphism of the permanganates with the perchlorates, and to the isolation of the hydrate of permanganic acid. At a later period (1860) he repeated, by new and more accurate methods, the analysis of permanganate of potash, which had been called in question, confirming the exactness of the earlier analysis; he succeeded at the same time in isolating the anhydrous permanganic acid.

The crystallographic researches he carried on about the time of the discovery of the new acids were extremely numerous, yet very little has been made known respecting them. He prepared a large number of salts in his laboratory, determined the systems to which they belonged, measured some of the angles, and drew by hand the figures of their principal combinations. But this, though it satisfied his own curiosity, was manifestly insufficient for publication, and the new discoveries that presented themselves were much more attractive than the wearisome and time-consuming task of preparing his researches for the press. He made, however, an attempt to carry out his intention of describing the forms of the most important simple and compound bodies. He commenced with the sulfates, selenates, and chromates, because these salts present almost all the phenomena on which the laws of crystalline form and chemical composition are founded. He described the sulfates and selenates of soda and of oxide of silver; the sulfate, selenate, and chromate of oxide of silver and ammonia; the sulfate and selenate of oxide of nickel, and the selenate of oxide of zinc; the anhydrous and hydrous chloride of sodium; iodide of sodium and bromide of sodium; sulfate, selenate, and chromate of potash, and sulfate of ammonia. Unfortunately these were his last regular contributions to crystallographic chemistry. Long afterwards he described the forms of the chloride and iodide of mercury, the latter of which is dimorphous, and the forms of phosphorus, iodine, and selenium crystallized from solution in bisulfide of carbon, which proved to be in an isomeric state differing in density from fused selenium.

In 1833 his crystallographic labors were interrupted by the publication of his "Treatise on Chemistry." For this work he had been long preparing himself by original researches, by associating with the most eminent chemists of Europe, by visiting their laboratories,

490

and the most important manufactures and smelting-furnaces. A large number of original observations of his own are embodied in this work, which had never appeared in any scientific journal. A fifth edition was commenced in 1855, but left unfinished. In this year he commenced his important labors on the density of the vapor of bromine, sulfur, phosphorus, arsenic, and mercury, nitrous acid, nitric acid, sulfuric acid, etc., and on the relation of the density of vapors to their chemical equivalents. In the same year he commenced his researches on benzoyl, which suggested to him a simple theory of the constitution of those organic combinations in which compound radicals are assumed to exist. His experiments on the formation of ether led him to the doctrine of chemical combinations and decompositions by contact, whereby dormant affinities in mixtures, or compounds held together by feeble affinities, become active by mere contact with a substance chemically inactive. These labors in the domain of organic chemistry wholly occupied him for nearly twelve years. At the conclusion of this period he turned his attention to geology. Indeed, ever since he had engaged in researches on the artificial production of minerals, he used to theorize on the formation of rocks, and on the existence of mineral springs and volcanoes. In his earlier travels, while his main object was the examination of chemical manufactures and smelting-furnaces, his attention was also directed to the geology of the countries through which he passed. He frequently devoted the concluding lectures of each half-year's course to a sketch of the geological structure of the earth, and the changes which its surface had undergone. Year after year he made systematic journeys in the Eifel, with the intention of publishing a complete description of the extinct volcanoes of that district, and connecting it with a theory of volcanic action. And, as the study of this region made a comparison with the volcanoes of other countries desirable, he visited in succession the principal volcanic districts of Italy, France, and Germany. But, notwithstanding all this preparation, the description of the Eifel was never printed, with the exception of some pages distributed among the hearers of lectures of a popular character given by him in the winter of 1838 and 1839. In these he states the views of the nature of volcanic processes which he then entertained. They appear to have been founded on a very careful study of volcanic phenomena. He sup-

491

poses the explosive action to be caused by the vapor of water. The only hypothesis, however, by which the presence of water in an active volcano could at that time be accounted for, was beset by serious difficulties. These have since been removed by the beautiful experiment made by Daubrée, which shows that when one side of a stratum of porous rock is heated, water in contact with the opposite side makes its way through it, in the direction of the heated part, notwithstanding the high pressure of the vapor generated on that side.

During the autumnal vacation of 1861 he made his last geological excursion in the Eifel. In December of that year he began to suffer from heart disease; the complaint increased in severity in the summer of 1862, and he had much difficulty in completing his course of lectures. In the autumn of this year he went again to the Rhine, but only to stay in a country house near Bonn, the home of his son-in-law, Professor Busch. Here his health appeared to revive, and he returned to Berlin feeling so much better that he commenced his winter lectures; a fortnight before Christmas, however, he was obliged to give them up, never again to be resumed. In the spring of 1863 he retired to a country house at Schöneberg, near Berlin, and here, on the morning of August 28, his valuable life was closed by a painless death. His name will ever be cherished in the annals of that science which he had so greatly enriched. Few philosophers have ever united such a versatility of genius with a mind so severely disciplined, or who, possessing such a talent for observing, were able to deduce such important results from their observations.

He was a member of probably every Academy in Europe. He was elected foreign member of the Royal Society in 1828; the Royal Medal was awarded to him in 1829, "for his Discoveries relating to the Laws of Crystallization, and the Properties of Crystals."

In 1852 he was elected foreign associate of the French Institute, in the place of Œrsted.

NOTES AND REFERENCES

"The greater part of the preceding notice is extracted from an Address to the German Geological Society by Professor G. Rose, Mitscherlich's successor as president of the Society."

W. Prandtl, "Deutsche Chemiker in der ersten Hälfte des 19. Jahrhunderts,"
Verlag Chemie, Weinheim/Bergstrasse, 1956.

From: *Proc. Roy. Soc.* (*London*), *13*, IX (1864).

GUSTAV ROSE

·· 37 ··

Anselme Payen

1795-1871

PAYEN was the first to attempt a separation of wood into its component parts. He treated wood with nitric acid and obtained a fibrous substance, which was relatively resistant to this reagent. This substance Payen called "cellulose," a term that he coined and introduced into chemical literature [*Compt. Rend.*, Acad. Sci. Paris 8,51 (1839)]. He showed that cellulose had the same percentage composition as starch, and was apparently isomeric with it. He found that irrespective of its origin, cellulose had the same chemical composition, which could be represented by the formula $C_6H_{10}O_5$ and was apparently the identical substance in all plants. Payen also found that in isolating the cellulose he had to remove a substance or a group of substances, which had a higher percentage of carbon than cellulose. These substances Payen called "incrusting materials" (*les matières encrustantes*), and he considered that the cellulose was mechanically incrusted or impregnated by them. These incrusting materials were later (1857) designated by Schulze as lignin, a term previously used by the botanist and plant physiologist de Candolle. The "incrustation hypothesis" of Payen was in the main supported by Schulze, although other investigators, among them Erdmann, opposed Payen's views. It is of interest, however, to point out that Payen's "incrustation hypothesis" has in more recent years been vigorously supported by Wislicenus and by Freudenberg.

Anselme Payen was born in Paris, France, on January 6, 1795. He was the son of Jean Baptiste Pierre Payen and Marie François Jeanson de Courtenay. The elder Payen was educated at the Collège de Navarre in Paris, where he distinguished himself especially in philosophy and in the sciences. Through the insistence of his parents, however, he studied law and was for a time assistant to the procurator of the King for the city of Paris. This legal work, however, did not prove to his liking and in 1792 he established a factory at Grenelle, a suburb of Paris, for the production of various chemicals, chiefly sal ammoniac. This enterprise proved to be quite successful, and we soon find him engaged in the production of other

497

chemical substances, such as sulfuric acid, hydrochloric acid, borax, refined sulfur, soda, and gelatin. He also established at Vaugirard a factory for the production of sugar from sugar beets. This was then a new industry in France, and during the continental blockade of the Napoleonic wars the cultivation of sugar beets and the extraction and refining of sugar therefrom were greatly encouraged by the French Government.

Anselme Payen received his early education from his father, who was a strict disciplinarian and very early inculcated in his son the habit of systematic study, a characteristic he retained for the rest of his life. However, in order to get a thorough grounding in the sciences his father sent him to the École Polytechnique in Paris where he studied chemistry under Vauquelin, physics under Fourcroy, and mathematics under Tremery.

When young Payen was barely twenty years of age his father placed him in charge of a plant for the refining of borax. This was then a relatively new industry in France, for the Dutch virtually had a monopoly of the production of refined borax in Europe. The crude borax containing material was imported by the Dutch from the Orient and then refined by them. Young Payen conceived the idea of preparing borax synthetically from soda and boric acid, which was then obtained almost entirely from the hot springs and lakes of Tuscany. Payen's efforts were crowned with success, and in 1820 he placed on the market synthetic borax at one-third of the then prevailing price and thus succeeded in establishing a new industry in France.

In 1820 Payen's father died, and at the age of twenty-five years the young man had to assume full responsibility for the management of several factories established by his father, including the factory for the production of sugar from beets. For the clarification of the sugar solutions vegetable charcoal, principally wood charcoal, was employed. This peculiar property of wood charcoal was first brought to the attention of chemists in 1785 by an apothecary by the name of Lowitz of St. Petersburg, Russia, although according to E. O. von Lippmann the decolorizing property of wood charcoal was known as early as the fifteenth century to some of the German alum and saltpeter producers. However, this observation was apparently entirely forgotten. As already mentioned, among the chem-

498

icals made by Payen in his factory at Grenelle was sal ammoniac. This was prepared from the complex mixture of volatile substances obtained by the destructive distillation of bones and other products of animal origin. In the retort there remained a charred mass known as animal charcoal or bone char, which was then largely a useless by-product. Although Figuier of Montpellier in 1811 called attention to the decolorizing property of animal charcoal, no application was made of this discovery until Payen got interested in this problem. Payen was motivated in this study by the double objective of improving the process of sugar refining, and of utilizing the animal charcoal. In a paper published in 1822, entitled "Theory of the Action of Animal Charcoal and Its Application to the Refining of Sugar," Payen gave results of a thorough study of the decolorizing properties of animal charcoal and pointed out that it owes its activity to the peculiar shape and state of aggregation of the carbon in this material. He also showed that it had the capacity of removing certain salts from solution and thus facilitated the crystallization of the sugar. He also developed an apparatus, called a "decolorimeter," for the determination of the decolorizing ability of various lots of animal charcoal. This may be considered the first important scientific paper published by Payen.

The credit for first using animal charcoal industrially for the refining of sugar clearly belongs to Payen. It was as a result of his zeal and industry that the popular prejudice against the application of animal charcoal to the refining of substances used for human consumption, such as sirup and sugar, was overcome. In addition to thus improving the process of sugar refining, Payen's work resulted in establishing an important new industry, namely, that of animal charcoal production. We thus see that a product which had heretofore been entirely useless became the basis of an important new industry. Few sugar technologists are today aware of the fact that when they decolorize their sugar solutions by means of animal charcoal they are making use of a method of sugar refining introduced more than a century ago by the French chemist Payen, now all but forgotten.

Because of his work on sugar beets, Payen very early in his life became interested in agricultural chemistry, and in the application of science in general to the improvement of agricultural practices, an interest he retained throughout his long and useful life. In these days when we hear so much about the industrial utilization of agricultural products, it may be of interest to point out that Payen more than one hundred years ago not only advocated this very thing, but also made important contributions toward its realization. In a book he published in 1826 together with Chevalier, entitled "Traité de la pomme de terre" (Treatise on the Potato), he described in considerable detail not only the preparation of various foods and feeding stuffs for human and animal consumption, including the production of sugar and sirup, but also the methods for the preparation of starch and alcohol from potatoes. Part of the results contained in this book were published in the Proceedings of the Central Agricultural Society of France in the year 1823, and in recognition of this work Payen was given a gold medal by that society.

In the early part of the nineteenth century the need arose in France for the development of more economical methods of disposal of the carcasses of domestic animals that died of accident or of diseases of an epidemic character. Accordingly, in 1825 the Central Agricultural Society of France offered a first prize of 1000 francs for the most practical and economical method for the utilization of the carcasses of these animals. In 1830 the first prize was awarded to Payen for his 132-page memoir, which was published in the proceedings of the society for that year. There is a great deal of analytical data in this paper, which in many cases were obtained by methods devised by Payen. The method developed by him for the determination of nitrogen consisted in heating the sample to red heat and collecting the gaseous products in dilute sulfuric acid. While this did not, of course, give him all the nitrogen in the sample in the form of ammonia, it is nevertheless of interest from the historical standpoint as it was the forerunner of the Will and Varrentrapp method, where it is recalled the sample is heated with soda-lime and the ammonia collected. This was later superseded by the now well-known Kjeldahl method.

The methods that Payen described for the utilization in industry and in agriculture of various products of animal origin have proved to be practical, and many of the processes now in use for the utilization of the by-products of the meat-packing industry can

500

be traced to those described by Payen in his paper published more than one hundred years ago.

In 1835, at the age of forty, Payen gave up all active participation in the various manufacturing enterprises that he was interested in and accepted the position of professor of industrial and agricultural chemistry at the École Centrale des Arts et Manufactures in order that he might devote all his time to teaching and scientific research. In 1839 in addition to his duties at the École Centrale he also accepted the professorship of applied chemistry at the Conservatoire des Arts et Métiers. These two positions he held until the time of his death.

The next thirty-six years of Payen's life were undoubtedly the most fruitful of his entire career, judged from the many contributions of a fundamental character he made to chemistry. He published about two hundred scientific papers in various scientific journals, such as the Comptes Rendus, Bulletin de la Société d'Encouragement pour l'Industrie National, Annales du Conservatoire des Arts et Métiers, Annales de Chimie et de Physique, Annales d'Histoire Naturelle, Bulletin de la Société Chimique, Journal de Chimie et Médecine, Mémoires de la Société Centrale d'Agriculture de France, Annales des Mines, and others. These papers covered a wide field of investigation and included such subjects as starch, dextrin, sugar, lignin, cellulose, bitumen, and various phases of agricultural chemistry including studies on plant and animal nutrition, the latter studies being conducted in cooperation with the famous agricultural chemist Boussingault. He also published papers in the field of inorganic chemistry. It was in connection with his studies on starch that Payen together with Persoz discovered the enzyme diastase. The paper on starch that he published in 1836 is remarkable for its clearness and precision. He showed that starches obtained from different sources differed as to size, shape, and state of aggregation, but that they all had the same chemical composition.

Payen had a practical turn of mind, and in the midst of his work on the purely scientific phases of chemistry he was always interested in the application of chemistry to industry, agriculture, hygiene, and medicine.

Payen was a prolific writer of books on industrial, agricultural, and food chemistry, and many of his books became standard works of reference and were translated into English and into several other European languages. Special mention should be made in this connection of his "Traité de Chimie Industrielle," in which Payen describes in great detail the various processes then used in chemical industry. Even the superficial reader of this book can see at once that its author was not a mere compiler, but rather one who has actually had many years of practical experience in the operation of the several processes described by him. In fact many of the processes there described were developed and improved by Payen. From the titles of the various books published by Payen one may get some idea of his extensive knowledge and interests.

The following is a list of his more important books (for a complete list of Payen's books the reader is referred to H. C. Bolton's "A Select Bibliography of Chemistry," Washington, 1893):

1. Traité de la pomme de terre; sa culture, ses divers emplois dans les préparations ailmentaires, les arts économiques, la fabrication du sirop, de l'eau-de-vie, de la potasse, etc. Paris, 1826. (Published with Chevalier.)

2. Traité de la fabrication et du raffinage des sucres. Paris, 1832.

3. Des engrais. Théorie actuelle de leur action sur les plantes principaux, moyens d'en obtenir le plus d'effet utile. Paris, 1839.

4. Mémoire sur l'amidon, la dextrine et la diastase considérées sous les points de vue anatomique, chimique, et physiologique. Paris, 1839.

5. Précis de chimie industrielle à l'usage des écoles préparatoires, aux professions industrielles, des fabricants et des agriculteurs. Paris, 1849.

6. Précis d'agriculture théorique et pratique a l'usage des écoles d'agriculture, des propriétaires et des fermiers. Paris, 1851. (Published with A. Richard.)

7. Traité de la distillation betteraves. Paris, 1854.

8. Traité complet de la distillation des principales substances

qui peuvent fournir de l'alcool; vins, grains, betteraves, fécule, tiges, fruits, racines, tubercules, bulbes, etc. Paris, 1857.

9. Précis théorique et pratique des substances alimentaires et des moyens de les améliorer, de les conserver et d'en reconnaitre les alterations, 4th ed., Paris, 1865.

Payen was a member of many scientific societies. He was elected a member of the Central Agricultural Society of France (La Société Centrale d'Agriculture de France) in 1833 and was its permanent secretary for 26 years. He was elected a member of the French Academy of Sciences in 1842. Among the other societies to which he belonged may be mentioned l'Académie de Médecine, Société d'Encouragement pour l'Industrie Nationale, Société d'Horticulture de la Seine, and of the Council of Hygiene and Public Health.

Payen served the French Government in diverse capacities, particularly as a member of various governmental commissions. He was made a Knight of the Legion of Honor by Charles X in 1828. Louis Philippe made him an officer of the Legion of Honor in 1847, and in 1863 Napoleon III elevated him to the rank of commander.

One of the characteristics of Payen was his intense patriotism, and for 40 years he served as commander of the battalion of National Guard of the town of Grenelle, where he made his home.

In 1821 Payen married Zelie Charlotte Mélanie Thomas, which proved to be a very happy union. There were five children in the family, four of which, however, died in childhood and only one child, a daughter, survived him.

Payen's last days were greatly saddened by the disasters that France suffered as a result of the Franco–Prussian War. In spite of his advanced age he refused to leave the city of Paris on the approach of the Prussian army and displayed a great zeal in the study of all problems relating to the feeding of the besieged and famished city. On May 9, 1871, while attending one of the sessions of the Academy of Medicine he became ill and died three days later (May 12). Few of his friends and comrades were able to pay their last respects to this distinguished savant, for those were the days preceding the establishment of the Paris Commune and civil war raged on the streets of Paris. He was buried in the cemetery at Grenelle.

NOTES AND REFERENCES

1 *Amer. Journ. Pharm.* (ser. 4) *1*, 432 (1871). (Anon. obituary notice.)
2 "Éloge biographique de M. Anselme Payen," J. A. Barral, in *Memoires Publies par la Société Centrale d'Agriculture de France*, pp. 67–87, 1873.
3 "Éloge de M. Payen, by Aimé Girard," in *Annales du Conservatoire Impérial des Arts et Métiers*, 9, 317–331, 1873.
A complete list of the scientific papers published by Payen can be found in the Catalogue of Scientific Papers, compiled by the Royal Society of London.

From *Journal of the Washington Academy of Sciences*, 30, 65–71 (1940).

MAX PHILLIPS

504

·· 38 ··

Friedrich Wöhler

1800-1882

FRIEDRICH WÖHLER was born on July 31, 1800, in the village of Eschersheim near Frankfurt-on-the-Main, at the home of the parson, who was his mother's brother-in-law. All reports about Wöhler's childhood agree that he showed pleasure in experimenting and collecting at an early age. In the year 1814, Friedrich Wöhler entered the Gymnasium in Frankfurt, where he remained until he entered the university. He attended school regularly and was promoted to higher grades after the usual time intervals, but distinguished himself—as he himself honestly confessed later—neither by exceptional zeal nor outstanding knowledge. The reason for this was, at least in part, that he occupied himself constantly and passionately with chemical experiments and with the collecting of minerals. As a result of these distractions, his homework was often disregarded; what he neglected most was mathematics, for which he had the least feeling and talent to begin with, and in which he later had to receive private instruction.

Young Wöhler now began to know chemical processes with ever better understanding; for, while he was limited in his experiments in the beginning to Hagen's old "Experimental Chemistry," the only chemical work which he owned, and from which his father had already studied chemistry, he now had the ample library of Dr. Buch at his disposal. Chemical experiments became a real passion with him, and filled his mind completely. He gradually transformed his room into a laboratory full of glasses, retorts, mortars, and pestles, everything in great disorder. He performed incandescence experiments in the kitchen, where he took possession of all the coal ovens. He also built a small Volta column from large Russian copper coins and zinc plates, and became familiar with its ability to decompose water and to produce contractions in the arms. To be sure, its strength was not sufficient for the reduction of potassium; but his eagerness to see and own this strange metal, which he knew only from its description, was so great that he undertook its production by chemical means. At that time, the metal was usually obtained according to the method of Gay-Lussac and Thenard, with the aid of iron at high temperature. But Curaudau had already demonstrated that potassium hydroxide is also decomposed by coal at incandescence. It was Curaudau's process that he carried out. A large old graphite crucible served as an oven; it had been given to him by mint master Bunsen, from whom he had also borrowed a bellows, which his sister operated. The task was successful beyond all expectation, and the pleasure of all concerned when they viewed the first little potassium globules was gratifying.

In the spring of 1820, when he was almost in his twentieth year, Wöhler graduated and entered the university. He spent his first year of study in Marburg, where his father had also been a student and where old friends who were to guide and supervise the inexperienced student still remained. Much to the displeasure of his Marburg landlord, our friend again turned his living quarters into a laboratory and began to experiment with thiocyanic acid and other cyanide compounds. Through Dr. Buch's sponsorship, the small investigations carried out in Marburg were published, in 1821, in Gilbert's *Annalen*. In the treatise on thiocyanic acid, we find an interesting and exact description of the behavior of thiocyanate of mercury at elevated temperatures. We have all, at some time, admired Pharaoh's serpent; however, few people know that it occurred for the first time in the improvised laboratory of medical student, Friedrich Wöhler, in Marburg.

After one year, Wöhler entered Heidelberg University, already filled with enthusiasm for Leopold Gmelin, who indeed was his favorite teacher and most benevolent friend and advisor during his entire period at the university. He wanted most of all to attend Gmelin's chemistry lectures. However, Gmelin considered it unnecessary; thus, strange as it may seem, Wöhler never heard any lectures on chemistry. But he benefited greatly from his personal contact with Gmelin and from the opportunity of working in his laboratory. Here he began the experiments with cyanic acid, the results of which are recorded in two papers, published in 1822 and 1823. In these treatises, which in a sense represent the prelude to the famous investigation of urea, the formation of cyanic acid by means of the action of cyanogen on barite is described. A special influence was exerted on Wöhler's development by the fact that Gmelin and Tiedemann were occupied at this time with their joint chemicophysiological investigations. He enjoyed the special favor of Tiedemann, an outstanding man who aroused in him a very lively interest in physiology. Perhaps it was partly at his suggestion that he undertook the solution of a question, posed by the medical faculty, about the transition of materials in urine, on which he did a large number of experiments, partly on himself, but mostly on dogs. He was fortunate enough to receive the prize for his work. Although he could have used this as a dissertation, he preferred to have it included in Tiedemann's *Zeitschrift für Physiologie* (1824).

On September 2, 1823, Wöhler and G. Spiess passed the examination by the faculty and graduated as doctors of medicine, surgery, and obstetrics *insigni cum laude*. At this point, Gmelin changed the course of his life by advising him to follow his own example in giving up practical medicine and devoting himself entirely to chemistry. Without thinking this over at length, and feeling certain in advance of his father's approval, he gladly agreed to Gmelin's proposal. On the latter's further advice, and encouraged by the favorable manner with which Berzelius had discussed Wöhler's first investigations in his "Annual Report," he inquired of Berzelius whether he might be permitted to work with him. After Wöhler received a friendly and affirmative reply, he immediately began the trip to Stockholm.

Wöhler was at that time the only person working in Berzelius' private laboratory; before him, Christian Gottlob Gmelin, Eilhardt Mitscherlich, and Heinrich and Gustav Rose had been there; Gustav Magnus followed him. Wöhler had the good fortune to work with Berzelius at a time when he was at the height of his career and was occupied with the magnificent investigations on fluorine compounds, silicon, boron, etc. It was very instructive for him to follow the specific course of these investigations, thereby getting to know all the ingenious means and methods which were characteristic of Berzelius. Berzelius did not give any systematic instruction; he endorsed independent investigations, but questions

509

and discussions on one's research project were encouraged. Wöhler resumed his investigations on cyanic acid; Berzelius was very much interested in them since they appeared to be important in solving the question of the nature of chlorine.

On September 17, 1824, Wöhler took leave of Berzelius and began the trip back with the two Brongniarts, arriving at his parents' home in Frankfurt in October.

He immediately began preparations for an inaugural thesis in Heidelberg. This strenuous work did not prevent him from resuming his relationship with his father's friend, Dr. Buch, and also frequently meeting the kindly old Sömmerling, who at that time was occupied with the observation of sun spots and with experiments on the concentration of ethyl alcohol through membranes. He also had no hesitation about undertaking the translation of Berzelius' "Annual Reports," at Gmelin's request.

In March, 1825, Wöhler traveled to Berlin. There he was immediately employed as teacher of chemistry and mineralogy under the director, Klöden, initially for one year on "mutual approval," with a salary of 400 Thaler and a modest free apartment. At the same time, he was committed to give chemistry lectures, for a salary, on certain evenings during the winter, for manufacturers and for older business people in general.

In possession of a laboratory of his own, Wöhler began a number of investigations. The production of chromium oxide by igniting a mixture of potassium bichromate and ammonium chloride was performed in accordance with the corresponding preparation of tungsten oxide which he had already carried out in Sweden. During Wöhler's stay in Stockholm, Berzeluis had succeeded in isolating silicon; using this work as a basis, Wöhler prepared aluminum by utilizing the action of potassium on aluminum chloride. The new metal, precipitated as a grey powder, turns greyish white when treated with polishing steel, is soluble in acids and alkali, and combines directly with phosphorus, sulfur, selenium, and tellurium. One can recognize that Wöhler's method for the separation of this interesting metal is the same one he employed twenty years later for larger quantities, and which, soon afterwards, Sainte-Claire Deville made available for industry.

Using the same process, Wöhler succeeded in isolating the rare metals, beryllium and yttrium, which proved to be elements similar to aluminum.

In the field of organic chemistry, one should mention first a paper on the production of malate of lead from unripe mountain ash berries, and a treatise on the nature of picric acid, which at that time had the name of carbazotic acid. The explosive nature of this substance seemed to him to indicate a content of nitric acid. In fact, he obtained nitric acid from it through the action of pyrolusite, sulfuric acid, and barite. But he did not by any means regard this as proof that nitric acid itself is the cause of the explosive character of the acid; "this could also be nitrous acid or only nitrous oxide."

The work that towers over all the others during the Berlin period is the artificial production of urea, discovered by Wöhler in the year 1828. The formula for cyanic acid, which had been derived from his earlier experiments, had been attacked by Liebig but had been successfully defended by Wöhler. In the course of his investigations, he again isolated the peculiar white crystallized substance which he had obtained in the reaction of cyanogen and aqueous ammonia, and which now revealed itself as "urea." "The unexpected result," says Wöhler in the same treatise, "is also a remarkable fact inasmuch as it presents an example of the artificial production of an organic, and so-called animal, substance from inorganic substances."

Approximately at the time of Wöhler's research on cyanic acid, Liebig, and Gay-Lussac in Paris, had undertaken the memorable work, on the fulminating metallic compounds of Howard and Brugnatelli, and had established the remarkable fact that, in fulminate of silver, regardless of the greatest difference in properties, the substance combined with the metal has the same elementary composition as that in cyanate of silver. Liebig, doubting the correctness of Wöhler's analyses, believed that he had proved the assumption of a different composition, by means of an analysis which, it became evident later, was made with impure cyanate of silver. Liebig therefore declared that cyanic acid was cyanous acid, and fulminic acid the true cyanic acid (1824). This caused

Wöhler to undertake new analyses, which entirely confirmed his earlier results.

In the course of the winter during which Wöhler was occupied with preparations for establishing himself in Heidelberg, Liebig, who at that time already was a professor in Giessen, came to Frankfurt, and the two young chemists became acquainted at the home of a mutual friend. Their association in Frankfurt was only of short duration, but when they parted, each was convinced that he had found a lifelong friend.

Among the many scientific contributions of the two co-workers, there is probably none as important as their investigation of benzoyl compounds. At the time when the joint investigators opened their campaign, oil of bitter almonds and benzoic acid were among the most familiar substances. It was also known that a drop of oil of bitter almonds which stands exposed to air for several hours is transformed into a rosette of benzoic acid; however, this transformation was completely incomprehensible if the formula for benzoic acid considered valid at that time, which Berzelius had deduced from the analysis of lead salt, was the correct one. Thus, the first step to be taken had to be a repetition of Berzelius' analysis. By burning silver salt in place of lead salt, they soon arrived at our present-day expression for benzoic acid, and thus the transformation of oil of bitter almonds was labled a simple oxidation process. They now assumed that both substances contain a ternary radical, for which they proposed the name benzoyl.

One might think that the great success of the work on benzoyl compounds would have directed Wöhler's interest toward the field of organic chemistry. But this was not at all the case. Mineral chemistry did not lose its attraction; in fact, there is a whole series, albeit of smaller works, to be enumerated in the field of inorganic chemistry, which belong to the Cassel period (1831–1836).

At this point we must also recall an industrial episode in Wöhler's career. During his stay in Cassel, the large supply of nickel arsenide (cobalt speiss) which had accumulated at the Hessian bluing works of Schwarzenfels induced him to carry out experiments on the technical production of nickel. These succeeded so well that he, together with several friends, was able to found a nickel factory, from which thousands of pounds were sold each year, especially to Birmingham. He already had the idea that nickel could be used successfully for coins, but this concept was not accepted.

The year 1836 introduced a profound change in Wöhler's living conditions. Professor Friedrich Stromeyer had died in Göttingen in August of the previous year. During the conference concerning a replacement for the vacant teaching post, Leopold Gmelin in Heidelberg was suggested as first choice. As he declined the position, the votes were divided: some wanted to appoint Liebig, others Wöhler. In the end, the latter was the victor; the goal of his ambition, a professorship at a German school of higher learning, has finally been attained. In the spring of 1836, under the rectorship of Dahlmann, he entered his new post in Göttingen.

In the beginning, he had little time for his own work. However, the winter semester of that same year found him completely at home in Göttingen, equipped for research and with one discovery after another emerging from his laboratory. At first, the experiments with oil of bitter almonds were of fundamental significance; he suggested to his friend Liebig that they be made the subject for a joint paper. Hardly any of the many other investigations which he carried on, in part alone, in part with Liebig, show so clearly the remarkable investigative ability, the incomparable gift of observation of the man. In October, he communicated for the first time on the subject with his collaborator:

Göttingen, October 26, 1836.

Dear Friend:
    I feel like a chicken that has laid an egg and thereupon starts to cackle noisily. I discovered this morning how one can make oil of bitter almonds containing hydrocyanic acid, from amygdalin, and wanted to propose to you the further pursuit of this matter as a joint work, since the subject is connected too closely with the benzoyl investigation, and since it thus would look strange if one of us would reenter this field by himself. For one cannot imagine how far it will extend, and I am certain that it will be fruitful if it is fertilized with your dung.

From the letter dated Göttingen, October 28, 1836:

513

Dear Friend:

I hope that you have received my letter of two days ago. Since then, I have made a very remarkable discovery in regard to amygdalin. Since it was a fact that oil of bitter almonds can again be obtained from amygdalin, I thought that the latter could be produced from the former, in the usual distillation of almonds with water, by means of an effect like that of ferment on sugar, which here most probably would be ascribable to the albumin in the almonds. And this idea seems to be completely confirmed. The facts are as follows:

1. Amygdalin, dissolved in water and digested with a crushed sweet almond, begins at once to have the odor of oil of bitter almonds, which later can be distilled off in such a quantity that all the amygdalin appears to have been transformed into it.

2. The same effect is produced by a strained emulsion of sweet almonds.

3. A boiled emulsion of sweet almonds, in which, thus, the albumin is coagulated, does not produce the slightest trace of oil with amygdalin.

4. Crushed sweet almonds, covered with alcohol and then freed of it by means of compressing, produce oil of bitter almonds as before with amygdalin.

5. Crushed peas (i.e., their albumin) produce no oil with amygdalin.

Now, to begin with, three points must be ascertained:

a. Which substance in the bitter or sweet almonds is it which produces the oil of bitter almonds when in contact with amygdalin and water?

b. Is the effect one of mutual disintegration or, like the ferment, one of catalysis?

c. What is the other product which probably is created besides the hydrocyanic acid-containing oil?

From Liebig:

Giessen, December 31, 1836.

It has been determined definitely that sugar is produced in the decomposition of amygdalin. I had emulsion be prepared by washing sweet almonds with ether until all oil had been removed, and dissolved the residue in water.

In this solution a certain quantity of amygdalin was dissolved and allowed to stand in a warm place at 35°, until the odor was com-

514

pletely gone. This took six days; the mass had assumed a syrup-like consistency, tasted quite sweet and, when mixed with yeast, began to ferment violently. This should decide the matter, but I shall repeat the experiment with the emulsion which I obtained from you today.

(*Signed*) Liebig.

It would be difficult to find a more striking example to show how happily the two friends supplemented each other in their entire being.

The investigations on the nature of uric acid appear in the course of the year 1838.

Early in 1839, Friedrich Wöhler wrote to Justus Liebig:

Göttingen, February 2, 1839.

I have entered a new path to get at uric acid. I heated it with water in a sealed tube up to 200°. This took place in the container of the oil bath. At 200°, it had dissolved into a completely clear, yellow liquid. When cooled to about 20°, it became cloudy and gradually coagulated into a yellowish, transparent jelly. When the tube was opened, it was apparent that no gaseous substances had been formed, and that, on the whole, the contents behaved like ammonia salt of mycomelinic acid. As you can see, this does not agree with our formula for mycomelinic acid.

In a second experiment, the tube exploded with great violence, so that the upper wall of the thick copper oil bath was bent into a completely concave shape. I am now considering having a piece of metal apparatus made for such experiments.

On this occasion I had the idea of treating other substances, also, in this manner. Indigo did not change at 200°, neither did oil of turpentine; however, morphine dissolved completely while giving off an almost vermilion-colored substance, and upon cooling, fairly large red crystals formed. This must be studied more closely.

Among the compounds of silicon, our special interest is directed to the spontaneously igniting silicon hydride gas, discovered jointly with H. Buff.

On June 25, 1863, he wrote to Liebig:

515

I live entirely at the laboratory, occupied with the new silicon substance which is derived from silico-calcium, and which, in its pure state, has a deep orange-yellow color. I am becoming more and more convinced that it is constituted in the manner of organic substances in which the carbon is replaced by silicon. Its entire behavior, also, is analogous. In darkness, even in water, it remains entirely unchanged, but in sunlight it develops hydrogen gas, just as in fermentation, and becomes snow white. This white material then behaves entirely like the previously described silicon oxide, which, however, certainly cannot be a hydrated oxide. Under dry distillation the yellow silicon, as I want to call it, behaves like an organic substance. One obtains hydrogen gas, silicon-hydride gas, brown amorphous silicon (corresponding to carbon), and silicic acid (corresponding to carbonic acid).

The work in the field of inorganic chemistry was again followed by a large number of chemicomineralogical investigations. The observation that the quinic acid contained in cinchona bark yields a crystallizing volatile substance with a strange odor when oxidized with potassium bichromate or pyrolusite and sulfuric acid had already been made a few years earlier by Woskresensky, who had analyzed the substance and designated it by the name of quinoyl, which later was changed to quinone. Wöhler repeated the experiments of the Russian chemist; first of all he found that, in dry distillation of quinic acid, a partially solidifying distillate is obtained from which, in addition to a tarlike substance, there can be isolated benzoic acid, carbolic acid, salicylic acid, benzene, and, as the chief constituent, a new crystallizing material which, because of its relationships to the quinone discovered by Woskresensky, was given the name of hydroquinone. Oxidation with pyrolusite and sulfuric acid was recognized as the best method for the production of quinone from quinic acid.

Wöhler's extensive work on narcotine and its decomposition prdoucts took place in the same period as his research on quinone. It was specifically the decomposition of this alkaloid, found by Robiquet in opium, by pyrolusite and sulfuric acid that formed the subject of these studies.

A much later investigation by Wöhler concerned cocaine, the alkaloid contained in the coca leaves of the erythroxylon varieties

516

native to South America and which exerts a narcotic effect. This substance is obtained from the coca leaves by digestion with water at 60 to 80° C., by precipitating the watery extract with lead acetate, removing the lead from the filtrate by sodium sulfate, and shaking the solution, which has been mixed with soda, with ether. The cocaine, which crystallizes in prisms, decomposes, when heated with hydrochloric acid to 100°, into benzoic acid and a new organic base, ecgonin. As is well known, the investigation on cocaine was later continued successfully by Lossen.

Experiments on the effect of hydrochloric acid on amygdalin, whose by-products are mandelic acid, a humic substance, and sal ammoniac, led Wöhler to the concept that amygdalin contains as further constituents oil of bitter almonds (1 eq.), hydrocyanic acid (1 eq.), and sugar (2 eq.).

Some of Wöhler's observations on physical phenomena should be mentioned briefly. He ascertained that the crystalline and the amorphous modifications of certain substances (a lithofellinic acid, sugar, amygdalin, sylvic acid, sulfur) are distinguished by their melting point as well as in their behavior in other respects.

Wöhler enriched the knowledge of electricity by the construction of new galvanic elements. As Poggendorff had successfully replaced the expensive platinum with iron in the Grove battery, so Wöhler succeeded in substituting iron for zinc and constructing a battery made up of iron and dilute sulfuric acid, and iron and concentrated nitric acid. Wöhler's battery delivered a strong current at a low cost.

The last treatise, written shortly before his death, is concerned with the same field, and deals with a voltaic element of aluminum, using concentrated nitric acid as the contact fluid.

The magnificent achievements in the field of research, which have been presented to the reader in their bare outlines, did not kept Wöhler from enjoying simultaneously varied literary pursuits. During his stay in Sweden, he had translated Hisinger's "Introduction to the Mineralogical Geography of Sweden" into German; and after his return, he had taken over the publication of Berzelius' "Annual Reports" from 1825 on. We find Wöhler's name on the title page of this journal from its fourth to its twentieth year of publication.

Almost simultaneously with the first "Annual Report" handled by Wöhler, there appeared the first volume of Berzelius' large "Lehrbuch der Chemie," which he likewise translated; the last volume was completed in the year 1831. The first edition was rapidly followed by three others. A fifth, written in German by Berzelius himself, was begun in the year 1843, but was never completed because of Berzelius' death in 1848. This last edition, also, probably did not appear without Wohler's collaboration.

Wöhler's "Foundations of Inorganic and Organic Chemistry" had an enormous success. The first edition of this little book appeared in 1831, and the fifteenth, with the collaboration of Hermann Kopp, in the year 1873. It was translated into many other languages.

The first edition of the "Foundation of Organic Chemistry" appeared in the year 1840, the fifth, still written by Wöhler alone, in 1854; since then, five further editions, the last in 1877, have been published under the title, "Wöhler's Foundation of Chemistry by Dr. R. Fittig." This book, also, has been translated many times.

Wöhler gave us a book from which generations of chemists have learned the art of analysis, namely, his "Examples for Practice in Analytical Chemistry." These appeared at first without his name. How modest he felt in regard to this little book becomes clear in a letter to Liebig. On April 26, 1849, he wrote: "I send you herewith some selenium slime and vanadium-containing iron ore. For the simplest way to work on these, you will find recipes in the enclosed cook book, which I recently smeared together. It is designed for my laboratory students and is to serve the purpose of sparing me the enormous boredom of having to preach one and the same thing a thousand times."

Similarly, on May 5, 1853: "I have entirely rewritten the little book. It is again to appear without my name, for after all, everybody can write such a book."

Wöhler further edited, together with Liebig and Poggendorff, the first six volumes of the large "Dictionary of Pure and Applied Chemistry," whose publication began in the year 1842. The book was published in irregular installments.

Last, but not least, Wöhler's participation, over many years, in the publication of Liebig's *Annalen* deserves to be remembered.

Since its founding in the year 1832, Wöhler had published the majority of his works in Liebig's journal, which then had the name *Annalen der Pharmacie*. In the year 1838, he became its coeditor; the twenty-seventh volume was the first to carry his name. Before the end of the year, Wöhler called attention to the fact that the title of the journal no longer corresponded to its contents. "For the Annals of Pharmacy," he wrote to Liebig on October 18, 1838, "you must, in the future, introduce the title, 'Annals of Chemistry and Pharmacy.' The present title certainly does not fit our uric acid investigation, for example, at all. The publisher will have no objections, and the number of subscribers will only increase." However, not until the year 1840, with the thirty-third volume, did the journal begin to appear under the changed title which, in the year 1874, took on its present form: "Liebig's Annalen der Chemie." Wöhler was a member of the editorial staff until his death. His name graces almost 200 volumes of the Annalen.

Besides his unceasing activity in the field of research and his comprehensive literary works, Wöhler carried on an astonishing amount of teaching. Over a period of many years, indeed, teaching was his favorite occupation.

Liebig expressed in a letter to his friend what he thought of this magnificent didactic ability. Wöhler had asked Liebig to provide a place in the laboratory at Giessen for a student from Göttingen. "Those are rather stupid fellows," Liebig replied, "who go from Göttingen to Giessen for the sake of chemistry—like going from a horse to a donkey."

Both friends were heavy smokers, especially Wöhler, who once made this comforting remark to a nonsmoking colleague: "There are examples of non-smokers who also became bearable chemists; however, this occurs only rarely."

Probably no one will doubt that the outward recognition by his contemporaries was not lacking for the conqueror in the field of research. There was hardly an academy of sciences, hardly a learned society which would not have regarded it as an honor to enter Wöhler's name in its membership list. In the year 1872, he received from the Royal Society the Copley medal, the highest scientific distinction it bestows.

519

Before this event, Wöhler had received an interesting medal made of aluminum, to which, with full right, he attached great value. It is well known that Deville, in his experiments begun in 1845 to obtain aluminum in large quantities, finally applied the same method by means of which Wöhler, in the year 1827, first had produced the metal. For industrial production, extraordinary obstacles had to be overcome; specifically, a sodium industry had to be created first. No one recognized more sincerely than Wöhler the merit which Deville earned with the manufacture of aluminum; and just because of this, he must have been especially happy that Deville did not let any opportunity pass to honor him as the discoverer of aluminum. We thus recall with pleasure that the great-hearted French investigator had a medal coined from the first bar of aluminum which he had obtained; on one side it had the picture of the emperor Napoleon III, on the other the name of Wöhler with the year 1827.

Half in earnest, half in jest, he suggested to the friends who congratulated him on his eighty-second birthday that they should only celebrate his ninetieth. However, the time remaining to him was to be measured only in weeks.

He passed away on September 23, 1882, in the tenth hour of the morning.

NOTES AND REFERENCES

H. S. van Klooster, *J. Chem. Educ.*, 21, 158 (1944).

J. Valentin, "Friedrich Wöhler," Wiss. Verlagsgesellschaft, Stuttgart, 1949.

Selections from the biography by August Wilhelm von Hofmann in "Zur Erinnerung an Vorangegangene Freunde," Vol. 2, Vieweg, Braunschweig, 1888, pp. 1–205. Translated by Elisabeth F. Lanzl.

AUGUST WILHELM VON HOFMANN

·· 39 ··

Jean-Baptiste Dumas

1800-1884

and

Charles-Adolphe Wurtz

1817-1884

DUMAS

WURTZ

In THE perpetual future which is our science, there are decisive moments when the evolution of ideas takes a revolutionary turn. These moments occur when certain forms of thinking have become overly traditional and are in danger of losing their creative force. At such times there always arise bold reformers who set up new principles and syntheses—to the detriment of the established rules and for the benefit of the future.

In France, a century ago, chemistry knew such a moment and such men. This was the moment when the electrochemical dualism of Berzelius saw its original fecundity weakening. The men were those to whom chemical science owed the renaissance of that atomism which, awakened from half a century of sleep, became the living and lasting basis through Dalton's conception of the fundamental stoichiometric laws and through Avogadro's aphorism.

Among these men, Jean-Baptiste Dumas and his pupil, Charles-Adolphe Wurtz, were among the greatest. Forcefully, and in very different ways, they helped to build the ingenious synthesis that made Laurent, Gerhardt, and Kekulé famous.

One of them brought the old Berzelius edifice down with one stroke: the theory of substitutions. The other furnished the full and definite order for the monument which Dumas, Laurent, Gerhardt, and Kekulé constructed on the ruins of the old one. This new edifice, which received the name of "atomistic theory," dominates this science today.

Dumas came from the Gard, Alais, and Wurtz from the Bas-Rhin, Strassbourg. Born in two extreme places of France, they differed as much as their provinces had marked them with different virtues and characters. But their great country gave them common qualities, among them that clarity which has usually been recognized as one of the characteristics of the French mind, and that taste for logical and elegant constructions which they received as much from their heritage as from their Latin culture. Finally, their relationship of teacher to pupil gave them that intimate union of thought by which the members of the same scientific family can be recognized.

Both men were wonderfully eloquent. They also were endowed with the geometrical spirit of precision and of finesse, an extraordinary ability for work, an exceptional experimental skill, and robust health. Living in the brilliant period of romanticism, they did not escape its influence. Dumas was the Victor Hugo of chemistry and Wurtz its Sainte-Beuve.

Jean-Baptiste Dumas discerned families among the elements, and he compared them with the families of homologs in organic chemistry which he had been the first to establish; the fundamental concept of homology was introduced by him. Thus, he saw the elements as compositions that can be arranged in series, just like the hydrocarbon compounds, the alcohols, acids, nitriles. The aliphatic hydrocarbons, for example, form an arithmetically progressing series on the basis of $CH_2 = 14$. With a designating the first term, and d its progression, every series of this kind is represented by $a + n.d$. Dumas represented the families of elements by relations of this kind. His ideas remind us of those of Curie, Rutherford, Aston, and the followers of these great discoverers of our time. Did not Dumas say that the atomic weights of many elements differ from each other by 4 units, or a multiple of 4, the relative mass of the alpha particle? The importance of the atomic weight of helium is evident in the following relations which Dumas indicated:

$$
\begin{array}{lll}
\text{Li} & = 7 & \quad \text{Te} = 128 = 16 + 7 \times 16 \\
\text{Na} = 23 = 7 + 1 \times 16 & \quad \text{Mg} = 24 \\
\text{K} = 39 = 7 + 2 \times 16 & \quad \text{Ca} = 40 = 24 + 1 \times 16 \\
\text{O} = 16 & \quad \text{Sr} = 88 = 24 + 4 \times 16 \\
\text{Se} = 80 = 16 + 4 \times 16 & \quad \text{Ba} = 136 = 24 + 7 \times 16
\end{array}
$$

The figures have since changed somewhat, but we know that in questions of this kind precision plays a secondary role. Intuition suggested to him that Prout's hypothesis was justified, and on this basis he opened the era of precise determinations of atomic weights. He founded a whole line of scientists, chemists, and physicists— J.-B. Stas, Richards, who concentrated on specifically chemical measurements, Leduc, and Ph.-A. Guye, who specialized in measuring gas densities. Dumas was the inventor of these two great methods which have been in constant, exclusive, and fruitful use during a century.

This part of Dumas' work, although considerable and remarkably original, has been strangely neglected by biographers and historians who were mostly specialists in organic chemistry and thus directed their attention to those of his studies which are concerned with this discipline. As I have tried to show, it was because Dumas directed that discipline, in the light of new principles, toward then unknown ways, that he was led to rigorous determinations of atomic weights and consequently became interested in Prout's hypothesis.

In organic chemistry, nothing was as serious as the absence of good, quantitative analytical methods. Such a need had to impress a Dumas. He decided to fill it. At that time carbon was measured by volumes of carbonic acid, and this method was harassed by errors. Dumas transformed this volumetric measurement into a gravimetric one, a reliable method that has remained classic. Assisted by his pupil, Jean Servais Stas, he used this method for fixing the atomic weight of carbon, which was then assumed to be 12.24. In the hands of these skilled experimenters, it fell suddenly to 12.00, and it has not been changed since.

However, it was not enough to know the atomic weight of carbon; that of oxygen required precise determinations which Dumas and his student Boussingault carried out. I refer to that admirable synthesis of water which has since been repeated so often, using an incredible number of new precautions, but without much change in the results of our originators.

Turning from organic to general chemistry, Dumas carried out two hundred precision measurements for determining the atomic weights of thirty elements, half of all that were then known.

An accurate means for determining nitrogen in organic substances was needed. Dumas invented the one which carries his name and which has remained in use since his day. In Dumas' method nitrogen is determined by volume, as is generally known; it is less well known that Dumas also measured nitrogen in amines or amides in the form of ammonia. This method has been attributed to Will and Varrentrapp after they applied some convenient improvements of details.

Beyond the precise facts he described, the many substances he discovered, the practical rules he pronounced (and to which his biographers have clung too tightly), a great and profound thought dominated his work and was to dominate all future work. When one finds in the publications of a chemist the first natural classification of the elements, when it is true that the same chemist has been the first to bring out the facts of the concept of chemical function and has classified organic compounds according to their reactive groups, that he has in all respects created the fundamental notion of homology and applied that of isology without specifically naming it, what else can one conclude except that he is the inventor of the comparative method—the most powerful of the methods in chemical science?

On several occasions Dumas' work expresses that comparative chemistry which he, thinking perhaps of Cuvier, introduced into chemical literature.

I cannot analyze here in detail the more than eight hundred reports, notes, or memoirs of Dumas. Everything is there—politics, physiology, medicine, botany, mineralogy, biological and analytical chemistry, and especially organic chemistry. Dumas was the last of the essentially encyclopedic men; this accounts for his broad views.

At a time when no other alcohol was known than that obtained from wine, there could not be a concept of alcoholic groups. Such a concept could only result from a generalization of the chemical properties of wine alcohol. Without any possible guidance by previous ideas, Dumas, while still very young, undertook to study wood alcohol. He extracted from it pure methyl alcohol which he recognized as closely analogous with the alcohol from wine. He determined its composition and pointed out that it differs from ethyl alcohol by a CH_2 group. To do this he had to know the relative molecular weights of the two compounds. No difficulty there: he compared their vapor densities. Was not this a most surprising initiative so many years before Gerhardt?

With his student Péligot he studied ethal (cetyl alcohol)

(1836) which he suspected to be an alcohol because Chevreul had obtained it by saponifying spermaceti. He was impressed by the fact that its composition differs from that of wine alcohol by a multiple of CH_2, which also distinguished wine alcohol from wood. One of his pupils, Cahours, then extracted amyl alcohol made from potatoes. From these several studies, and with only four members of a long series, Dumas developed the notions of function and homology.

In his study of the aliphatic acids he let himself be guided by those principles of which he intuitively conceived the general validity. Between formic acid and the former margarinic acid he affirmed (1842) the existence of fifteen intermediates, so that only six of them remained to be found. And the discoveries from his hands multiply rapidly, among them the amides (1830) and the urethanes (1833). For the ethers, the nitrides, or the previously mentioned compounds, he determined their essential constitution. Not satisfied with having found the concepts of functional groups and homologous series, he did not cease to add examples for them, and he thereby established the main principle of the future constitutional formulas.

Most noteworthy in all this is the new method which he inaugurated and which proves his pioneering originality. His predecessors and his contemporaries directed their work to the heavy molecules; his preference was the light molecules. You will recognize the principle that assumed predominance as the interest in synthesis progressed. The idea of synthesis could not have impressed itself as strongly as we know it did in Berthelot if Dumas' concepts had not preceded Berthelot.

Dumas was only thirty years old when he presented to the scientific world the theory to which he mainly owes his fame. It was an exceedingly bold theory because it contradicted nothing less than the great doctrine which dominated all of chemistry and which was not only endorsed by the eminent Berzelius but, in addition, was considered to be an indispensable corollary to the reform views of Lavoisier. Dumas attacking the dualism of Berzelius is like Lavoisier confronting the phlogiston theory of Stahl, a David defying Goliath. "When a hydrogen-containing substance," he said in 1835, "is submitted to the dehydrogenating action of

527

chlorine, bromine, iodine, oxygen, etc., it gains one atom of chlorine, bromine, iodine, or a half-atom of oxygen." We see in this pronouncement only a law confirming the generality of indisputable facts. Lavoisier also had only brought together facts and their legitimate generalization, but this had not prevented his contemporaries—the greatest among them—from accusing him of opposing the most general and solidly established facts with risky hypotheses. Dumas in his turn experienced the powerful reaction which the unanimous chemists of the preceding period had raised against Lavoisier. It was a universal clamor in which the voices of Liebig and of Berzelius himself predominated. Dumas affirmed that the molecular building of every chemical species is a unitarian block in which each element can be replaced by another without modifying the structure. Berzelius, who felt that such a stroke could fell dualism, maintained that it is *impossible* that a negative atom, such as chlorine, could take the place of a hydrogen atom, which is positive. Dumas' counterattack consisted in letting the facts speak, and in multiplying them. This is the greatly reduced picture of that great discovery and the violent polemic it aroused.

If circumstances had permitted me to give a complete survey of Dumas' work—comparable only to Lavoisier's—I would have discussed many of his other chemical studies, for example, those concerning silicon and the acids of phosphorus. I would have reported more about his research in organic chemistry and analyzed his work in biological chemistry. After the scholar I would have described the professor, but I shall limit myself to saying that in this function he was equaled only by his disciple Wurtz, his living replica and worthy follower.

We would have followed Dumas to the Atheneum, to the School of Medicine, to the École Polytechnique, the École Centrale, the Sorbonne, and even to the Collège de France, because he taught in all the establishments of higher education in Paris. We would have seen him creating a school of chemistry, the École Centrale des Arts et Manufactures, and influencing Duruy officially to recognize the importance of scientific laboratories by endowing them and by uniting them administratively under the name of École Pratique des Hautes études (Practical Institute for Advanced Studies).

At the Institut we would have studied his work as a much appreciated member of the Académie Française. I would also have attempted to analyze his achievements as a member of the municipal council of Paris and as its president; and finally those which made him outstanding as a senator and brought him the honor of participating in the government of France.

In the histories of science Dumas is presented as a reformer. He was—and that is much greater—an innovator, one of the most powerful. He did not, as is frequently said, open a new era for organic chemistry. That science did not yet exist. He created it, just as Lavoisier created the unity of chemical science.

While Dumas was so fertile in ideas that he could not develop them himself and, having started so much, could not complete everything, Wurtz gave to each of his studies—limited as they are in number—the character of finished works which neither time nor innovations could attack. Perfection, to a degree which is perhaps unique in the history of science, was the dominant aspect of this creative genius. In more than half a century no error, not even an expression which should be modified, has been found in his original writing. This gives us the measure of the highly critical scholar who never used this quality except for himself.

However, Wurtz was not less of an enthusiast than Dumas, although in his work Wurtz did not show the same ardent splendor. In this respect they differed as only a southern Frenchman can differ from an Alsatian.

Charles Friedel (to whom I was assistant), J. A. Le Bel, and Lecoq de Boisbaudran, who have kindly honored me with their friendship, taught me to admire Wurtz because they themselves overflowed with great admiration for their teacher. I have heard it said by my teacher Hanriot, in one of the talks in which his malicious and refined nature took pleasure, that Wurtz was suspected of taking lessons in declamation so as to assure the success of his lectures. He entered the lecture room calm, all buttoned up, with a well-knotted necktie; he became more lively as the lecture proceeded, to end up in a tempest, beside himself in enthusiasm after having torn off his cuffs, rumpled his necktie, and burst the buttons from his robe in the exuberance of his gestures and the heat of his words. At that time of pomp the lectures at the Facultés were invariably given in robes.

At the laboratory, Wurtz was in daily contact with his students. "He was," said Friedel, "the most accessible, the gayest and the most active of teachers." It must have been an engrossing spectacle, this young science which broke down the barriers of the unknown with bewildering speed. In a field in which the roads had just been traced, those who started on their way needed models which the great numbers could imitate and which the best could use for inspiration. It was up to Wurtz to create these models; we know that they are admirable.

After Davy, Liebig had suggested that all acids should be considered as compounds of hydrogen. Wurtz accepted this idea and showed, in accord with previous work by Dumas, and against the protests by Berzelius and Rose, that hydrogen enters into the constitution of hypophosphorous acid. He wrote its formula, $PH_2 O_2H$, and that of its anhydride, $P_2H_4O_3$.

Wurtz then took up phosphorus and phosphoric acid and their esters. He showed that in the three acids the quantity of hydrogen remains constant and their acidity increases with the proportion of oxygen:

PH_3O_2	PH_3O_3	PH_3O_4
Hypophosphorous	Phosphorous	Phosphoric

On this occasion he discovered the oxychloride of phosphorus which Gerhardt later used for preparing chlorides and anhydrides of acids.

By the action of chlorine on urea Wurtz prepared cyanuric acid and proved that this compound had a triple acidic function. He studied its esters; by reaction with ammonia and water he transformed isocyanic esters into substituted ureas, and by reaction with potassium hydroxide into new ammonia compounds. Treatment with acids furnished substituted amides which function as acid and as alcohol. In his research on glycol, glycerine, cyanuric acid, aldol, etc., Wurtz promoted the knowledge of organic compounds with multiple functions.

Under conditions similar to those in which Cahours had obtained amyl alcohol, Wurtz discovered butyl alcohol. He did this under the direct influence of Dumas. However, an original mind never fails to add something personal to what he imitates. Wurtz added nothing less than the general method of preparing ethers by reacting silver salts with the iodides of alcohols. This classical method has rendered many services, and Wurtz himself used it for the synthesis of glycols, glycerines, and pseudo-alcohols.

As an inventor of original syntheses Wurtz can be compared only with Berthelot Synthesis is and remains the order of the day. Synthesis was the way to answer questions of theory while continuing to speculate about the substitution in radicals.

But these radicals themselves, methyl, ethyl and so on, do they really exist? Can they exist in the free state or not? The question was to be pursued for half a century, waiting to be reopened. Frankland and Kolbe had announced the isolation of methyl and ethyl. Dumas, who had not forgotten Avogadro's viewpoint and knew that the molecule of hydrogen should be presented as H_2, thought that the methyl and ethyl of Frankland and Kolbe must be dimers of these radicals, that is ethane and butane. Later on, Hofmann gave arguments for this interpretation, but since they referred to the temperatures of boiling, they could not convince the chemists of that time. Wurtz thought that if they were dimers, there should be hydrocarbons which result from the union of different radicals. He treated the mixture of two hydroethers with sodium and thus obtained ethyl-butyl and butyl-amyl. Besides, he showed that his method is general. It has become classical and one of the most successful means of synthesis.

The simple types of Laurent and Gerhardt, which were then accepted, suggested to Wurtz that the atoms of hydrogen, oxygen, nitrogen, and carbon differed from each other by their capacity for substitutions. We are touching here on a most important historical point which seems to have escaped the attention of most historians. Read that beautiful book Wurtz wrote about atomic theory (La Théorie Atomique, posthumously published by Felix Alcan, Paris, 1886). You will see that he there defined valency, which he first called atomicity, as the capacity for substitution of the diverse atoms. By thus giving a rejuvenated form to the old concept of equivalence he not only invented what later on was called valency,

531

but he also gave a clear definition, the only one to withstand the influence of time, and one which his successors had the imprudence not to heed because they were more metaphysically inclined than he, although Wurtz had prophetically warned against the danger inherent in considering valence as a force.

I have already indicated the importance which Wurtz attributed to the multiple functions. This idea dominated the major part of his work. It established a second stage in the development of the new organic chemistry. The multiplicity of the same function can grow according to the sequence of the numbers. Between the monoalcohols and the trialcohols like glycerine, there must be dialcohols. He synthesized these by the processes:

$$C_2H_4I_2 \rightarrow C_2H_4(C_2H_3O_2)_2 \rightarrow C_2H_4(OH)_2.$$

The fecundity and importance of the discovery of the glycols were not less than those of the amines. In studying them he discovered ethylene oxide, which he compared with the oxides of metals, because he endeavored to extend the new results of organic chemistry to all of chemistry.

Where Wurtz had sown new seeds, he also harvested: compounds of polylactic acid, poly ethylene, derivatives of ethylene oxide and ammonia, choline identical with the nevrine of the biochemist—these are consequences he produced from his preceding research. The work of Wurtz is a splendid symphony in which it is easy to recognize the themes.

We encounter them in his study of chloral which Dumas had considered as a substitution product of aldehyde. But the substitution is not real, because from the action of chlorine on aldehyde Wurtz directly obtained acetyl chloride. He recognized that this is irregular, and he attributed this irregularity to the reactivity of the hydrogen included in the aldehyde group. Therefore, in collaboration with his student Vogt, he blocked the aldehyde function, which permits the subsequent reaction with chlorine to proceed as foreseen by the theory of substitutions and Dumas' views. How many young organic chemists today block the indiscrete functions for similar purposes, without even suspecting that the method was invented by Wurtz?

532

During his research on chloral, Wurtz discovered aldol, the first aldehyde-alcohol, then dialdane, with the same strange property of being coagulated by heat as albumin, and finally paraldol, which has the same relation to aldol as paraldehyde to aldehyde.

In between he gave attention to the halogen-ethers of amylene hydrate which he had discovered, and to the anomalous vapor densities of these ethers. The question of anomalous vapor densities was then quite new, and the adversaries of atomism has forged it into a weapon. Cahours had explained the case of phosphorus pentachloride by dissociation which H. Sainte-Claire Deville had just discovered. For the ethers of amylene hydrate Wurtz had recourse to the same explanation. He removed any doubt by showing that the combination between amylene and hydrobromic acid develops less heat the higher the temperature, and that this heat ceases when the vapor density of the mixture reaches half of the valency theoretically ascribed to the bromohydrate of amylene. In this manner Wurtz contributed to building the theory of chemical equilibria, the historical and necessary preface to our present chemical thermodynamics.

We also owe to him that bibliographic monument called Dictionnaire de Wurtz which was the chemical bible of the oldest among us.

Born seventeen years after Dumas, Wurtz passed away in the same year as his teacher. Although very ill, he could at least give him a supreme adieu into which he put all his fervor as disciple and in which he gave free rein to his great soul of man and scholar.

From G. Urbain's "Conférence" at the Société Chimique de France, May 8, 1934; see *Bulletin de la Société Chimique de France,* 5th series, vol. 1, pp. 1425–1447, 1934. Translated and abbreviated by Eduard Farber.

GEORGES URBAIN

·· 40 ··

Justus von Liebig

1803-1873

TODAY we enter the renovated house in which, 125 years ago, as the church register says, a son was born as the second child to Georg Liebig and his wife Marie Karoline, nee Moserin. Underneath it says in the church register, entered by a later hand: "died 1873 in Munich as a world-famous chemist."

Truly, the church register is right. With unheard-of splendor Liebig's name had risen to world fame three generations ago. From the threshold of manhood until biblical age Liebig stood among men as a leader in a fierce struggle, full of tremendous power. Misunderstandings hung over him like thunderclouds, torn by flashes of lightning from his genius, after which applause and criticism rolled like thunder through the human atmosphere. He felt in himself the call for an accomplishment for which no man's strength and life span could be sufficient. He meant to build up chemistry, of which there was nothing in Germany, and outside of Germany only a modest knowledge in the realm of inanimate nature, so richly and splendidly that there would be order, light, coherence, and system. Through his example and his teaching he meant to show the direction and pave the way for young people, the path which led to an understanding of the events in animate nature, and a new flourishing of industry. What he wanted has become in our day the common will of a great branch of science that he created. What we have gained was accomplished because the succeeding generations stood on his shoulders. What does it matter that in some cases he was too hasty and succumbed to error? The error of the mediocre person entangles the threads and curbs advancement in the knowledge of nature; he does not dare to make a definite statement, and still cannot make up his mind to admit his doubts frankly. Not so Liebig. When he erred, he had the courage and the distinctness of the creative error. In the hands of his successors, the method of exact research that he introduced, the respect for experiment that he put above the authority of any teacher, corrected his errors. Thus he fulfilled his tremendous

537

mission in a higher sense even when he, in the narrower sense of the specialist, did not find the final truth.

Of Liebig's early days we do not know much, and the best we know comes from himself. His youth was spent at a time when obedience in a child was considered more important than his individuality. It is certain that as a boy he felt the one-sided passion for chemistry that guided him through his entire life. The little laboratory that was connected with his father's pharmacy developed and nourished this drive toward chemistry. There he learned to make lac, varnish, and paint according to a prescription. He watched the neighbors make soap. He was at home at the dyer's and the tanner's, and from the itinerant magician he learned how to make toy torpedoes. He devoured whatever chemical literature was to be found in his native town and he repeated each experiment until he had memorized every detail.

Through these passionate and persistent activities he gained two things that were decisive for the direction and the success of his life. He learned to see chemical phenomena with precision, and to keep them in mind with a certainty which surpassed the ability of average people. A typical example of his special precision of mind has been handed down from the days when he was a professor in Giessen. His friend Wöhler sent him a new preparation in the form of a white crystalline powder, of which there were a great many at that time. Liebig looked at this white powder, which to any other eye did not differ from other white powders, and defined it as the same allantoin which Gmelin had sent him seven years previously and which he had analyzed at that time. He ordered the anaylsis to be repeated with the new powder. But the composition was found different from the one he had formerly ascertained for allantoin. Which scholar of normal acuity of observation and of average memory would not have distrusted his recollection? Not so Liebig. The mislaid vial with the old preparation was sought for and found, and the renewed examination of its contents showed that it really was identical with Wöhler's new substance, and that the old analysis differed because of an accidental impurity. Pettenkofer reported in his Liebig memorial paper a second similar case, which he himself has observed during Liebig's stay in Munich.

538

Let us pause for a moment in order to make clear what an extremely strange and peculiar young man we are studying. He learned to watch, he learned the scientific evaluation of an observation, and he learned both without a teacher. The solid old German schooling which gave the boys a uniform education in the philological manner had neither interest, advancement, nor even tolerance for young scientific geniuses. But the most noteworthy fact is that the book which could have given the right leadership was lacking. How many of us have not obtained an important part of our training autodidactically! But in Liebig's time where were the clear and well-arranged descriptions of chemistry? The German chemical literature contained at that time some beautiful experiments and single great observations embedded in a thick tangle of false statements, mystic imaginations, worthless analogies, and wrong philsophical considerations; in short, a dreadful conglomeration of much worthless trash with isolated gems, difficult, as one would imagine, for an experienced man to isolate, but totally unfit and misleading for a boy who had to rely on himself.

But young people have their special guiding star and protection in their one-sidedness. Obsessed by their idea, everything is unreal to them that does not fit into this idea, and glides off. In Liebig's world of ideas, throughout his whole life, only those chemical things are real that one can make and see. And the abstract connection into which one can and must bring them has only reality and significance insofar as it arranges, orders, and thus makes understandable the similarities and differences which the real things reveal through experiments. In this manner he discarded superstition and mysticism and all those philosophies of nature which later he called the plague and the black death of the century, and he picked out of the literary trash the verities that made him a chemist without a teacher.

But what a heavy task this young man had to accomplish, and how could he manage to get ahead in school, and learn the grammar of the ancient languages which do not have any connection with his goal? Finally, what answer should he give the principal, who admonished him in school, and who asked him reproachfully what he wants to become! He answered what to him was the most self-evident and natural ambition in the world, and what was the

539

most puzzling for his teacher and his schoolfellows, namely, that he wanted to become a chemist. His answer provoked loud laughter; under this ill-humored gayety his career as a pupil came to an end. But what were his parents to do with such a son in Darmstadt in the second decade of the past century? They tried the pharmacy in Heppenheim, where he stayed for ten months and, as can easily be assumed, became familiar with the work. But then it lost its attraction for young Liebig; although an apothecary might be a chemist, quite obviously the apothecary in Heppenheim was not. He returned to his parents in Darmstadt, seventeen years old, having amounted to nothing in school, unwilling to persevere at the pharmacy, and declared that he intended to study a subject which really was not available in Germany, namely, chemistry.

There is hardly anything more impressive in the world than the passionate will of an outstanding young man who directs his life toward a strange ideal goal. When people feel that he wants the one and only thing with the full and unbending strength of youth, they step aside and let him have his way. There is a special light emanating from such a young man that we cannot match with our dim experience of life. Therefore, father Liebig gave in, although not overly blessed with the gifts of fortune, and sent the son to Bonn to study with Kastner, an outstanding chemist who at that time was teaching in Germany. With Kastner, Liebig went from Bonn to Erlangen, graduated there after finishing two experimental tasks, one of which refers to the firecrackers of the itinerant magician. After three semesters he returned to his father's house as a Ph.D., richer by far, but not instructed by the celebrated teacher.

When Liebig, then nineteen years old, came back to Darmstadt from Erlangen, he had a letter of recommendation from Kastner to the Hessian government. He needed financial assistance since he intended to go to Paris where there were such great chemists as Gay-Lussac, Thenard, and Dulong. Since paternal means were not sufficient, the Hessian government arranged for his trip. He remained in Paris for two and a half years and experienced days of glory, a glory that was to shine in his heart until the later years of his old age. For the first time he listened to lectures about chemistry that revealed not a welter of knowledge and pretended sagacity, but clear and orderly insight into a growing science. In the laboratory he continued, probably without much instruction, the work on the fulminic salts, and with such success that Gay-Lussac presented the results to the Paris *Académie* on July 28, 1823. Alexander von Humboldt, who was present at the meeting, became interested in Liebig and finally, through Humboldt's intervention, Gay-Lussac accepted him as assistant in his laboratory in order to give him the opportunity to continue his work. The short time of this cooperation from the summer of 1823 to the spring of 1824 gave to science the final formula of the fulminic acid salts, and to Liebig all the enrichment that a researcher in his formative years can gain from another great researcher in the period of his maturing and greatest development.

In the spring of 1824 Liebig returned to Darmstadt, taking along such a recommendation from Alexander von Humboldt and Gay-Lussac that the Hessian government, without asking the faculty, made him assistant professor and, after a very short time, full professor at the state university of Giessen.

The formative years were over. There are three periods in the life of a scholar—one during which he develops into someone; the second, during which he is someone; and the third, during which he is important. For Liebig the second period had started. He passed it in Giessen where he stayed for twenty-eight years, taking over the leadership in the chemistry of organic substances.

In the history of chemistry there was a period of ninety years (1776–1865), from Lavoisier's explanation of the process of burning to Kekulé's benzene theory, during which a struggle about the fundamental viewpoints concerning the theory of reactions took place. The struggle revolved around the concept of the formation of chemical compounds from the elements, so that their chemical changes could be uniformly understood.

During the first half of this 90-year period the number of outstanding men devoted to the task was very small. The amount of knowledge calling for a uniform presentation was small. But around the turn of the century the interest began to spread. Liebig's contemporaries turned toward the new field in noticeably greater numbers than their fathers, and discovered an abundance of new chemical phenomena. The next generation conceived the image of a great new blossoming branch of science.

But how could this new thriving subject come into existence? How did the young people dedicated to it learn about chemical science? Did every one of them take the autodidactic route which Liebig had taken until he was mature enough to get the ultimate polish through Gay-Lussac? At all times there are outstanding men who, in this autodidactic way, become the founders of new disciplines, but a new discipline comes into being only where a well-regulated course of instruction has been created.

Beginning the establishment of this instruction in the winter of 1824 to 1825 was Liebig's first deed in Giessen. The model of the lecture he brought along from Paris. His own work with Gay-Lussac showed him the way for the continuation of studies for mature young colleagues. But how could one become a mature young chemist? For this there were neither tools nor methods. Liebig wrought the most indispensable financial support from the Hessian government. During his first years in Giessen he worked out a schedule system and courses for training in experimental work. They have remained fundamentally the same for one hundred years. In order to understand the magnitude of this accomplishment one must pay attention to particular matters, i.e., to his building up qualitative and quantitative analysis, following this with the preparation of chemical substances, and finishing with independent scientific work. The greater idea and the more forceful deed consisted in excluding from his teachig the boiling of soap, the distilling of spirits, the making of sulfuric acid, and what else there was of highly estimated chemical industry. What could have helped him more to get government support than an indication that such obviously useful subjects were treated in his laboratory? Who came to study with him if not the practically inclined sons of families that were somehow connected with one of the chemical trades? But, with the force and insight of a prophet, he knew that chemical technology could grow only with young people who had learned how purely scientific problems can and must be solved. In 1840, in his paper about the study of science and the status of chemistry in Prussia, he wrote, we assume, with justifiable pride:

> "I know many who now are at the head of soda and sulfuric acid factories, of sugar plants and plants for manufacturing red prussiate of potassium, of dye-works and other industries, without ever having had anything to do with the process before. While they were familiar with the method of manufacturing during the first half hour, the next one already brought many most efficient improvements."

Built on this principle, Liebig's teaching has been the cause for the creation of chemistry as a branch of science, and, during the following two generations, for the worldwide fame of German chemistry.

This is his service to the people who work in this field. But what about its substance, about the doctrine of chemical compounds?

The first information to acquire about chemical compounds in order to explore their nature was about the elements which composed them, and the proportions of the quantities in which these elements are present in the compounds. With this problem chemical analysis became the focus of interest during the time of the evolution of chemistry. The scales became the most important tool of the chemist. Besides the definition of weight, the measuring of volume, temperature, and pressure became essential.

In the realm of minerals, analysis kept pace with the specifically chemical, quantitative knowledge of the behavior of substances, especially promoted by the great Swedish chemist Berzelius who, twenty-four years older than Liebig, came to well-earned great fame and worked in his field as a powerful man until his death in 1848. Until Wöhler's revolutionary preparation of urea from mineral substances in 1828, producing organic matter had seemed to be Nature's privilege. The progress in analytical skill did not keep pace with the progress of knowledge in the realm of organic matter.

Not that it was impossible to identify according to their quantitative composition those substances which contain mainly carbon, hydrogen, oxygen and nitrogen. But innumerable identifications came out wrong, and Berzelius, as Liebig stresses, needed eighteen months for the exact analysis of seven substances, while the faculty demanded the same result in one week. Liebig did not invent a fundamentally new method, but he changed and improved the available suggestions and tools until, with some practice, the desired fast and reliable result could be guaranteed. His method has been used until the present day. It was, really, the key to organic chemistry.

But after the gate has been opened, what awaits us? A confusing abundance of reciprocal actions between organic substances and with organic substances! According to what points of view does this multitude of materials have to be arranged—this plethora of material that is swelling every year with new discoveries? This is the big topic around which, in the second half of the previously mentioned ninety years, the best minds concentrated their efforts. Twice Liebig encroached upon the development of these ideas with special success. The first time he gave science a theory of the polybasic acids. Almost 20 years later Kekulé said about this theory: "A large part of the present opinion is nothing more than a further extension and more consequential carrying through of the concepts used in the theory of the poly-basic acids." The second time Liebig, in cooperation with his friend, Wöhler, established the theory of the organic radicals. These two great men showed that, in the intricately arranged organic substances, there are groups of atoms which, during many different chemical rearrangements, hold together like a uniform element. They showed this with so many proofs and with such overwhelming force that Berzelius saluted the experiments as the dawn of a new era, and the chemists accepted the new doctrine with unanimous consent. For the vast array of Liebig's other accomplisments for the systematic chemistry during the 1830's there is no room in this survey. There are important substances like the cyan compounds and acetaldehyde, there is chloroform, and chloral, which later were largely used in medicine. Surrounded with special splendor is the group of urea derivatives which Liebig and Wöhler explored together. There are numberless analyses, many special experimental

544

results, contributions to theories, and an abundance of critical comments to foreign research.

There was scarcely a subject in the chemistry of those days that he did not investigate. The stupid devil who published some sheer nonsense as a chemical accomplishment was not too unimportant for a knock over the head, and nobody was so high up that Liebig would keep quiet about his mistakes. Shortly after joining the editorial staff of a pharmacological journal, at the age of twenty-eight, Liebig inserted on the title page the addition: "in connection with an experimental criticism." Where possible, though, he made his own experiments the basis for his criticism. But soon it was not possible any more, because the task was too much for him. Thus it happens that he was mistaken occasionally in his criticism and used sharp, nasty expressions when he was wrong. But when the facts taught him otherwise, he admitted his errors without restraint. His friend Wöhler warned him not to make enemies. But how could a high level and a general reliability come into being in this young branch of science if our Liebig did not underline what was good and repudiate what was bad? Truly, an unusual way of behavior, but—in Carlyle's expression—very heroic, and especially suitable to explain the feeling of leadership and a leader's responsibility with which Liebig faced chemistry Certainly, too, a behavior which was destined to bring about many hours of bitterness during his lifetime! Who has hit will be hit back by others when he shows a weak spot, and with the increasing years the blows always hurt more.

But still our hero is at the age of greatest strength, full of incomparable knowledge, sparkling with ideas and, as it seems, called to lead the development of the systematic chemistry of organic compounds to a height which, like his methods of analysis and of teaching, was to remain definite for a whole century. Then, during the fourth decade of his life, he turned aside. His interest in systems subsided. The deflection which led him toward agricultural and physiological chemistry and to the summit of his fame took place.

Liebig's starting point was one of the most beautiful and most general perceptions we have. With grandiose vision he understood that green plants, and only they, build their complicated, organic substances from the inorganic elements of air and soil, under the influence of sunlight, and that during this process they emit oxygen into the surrounding atmosphere. The animals live off of the plants and, using the oxygen, decompose in their bodies what the plant has built up.

In pursuit of this grand idea, it obviously is necessary to open up a kind of scientific account book for the plants. What single substances do they get to live on and to grow? There is, in the first place, water, about which there is nothing new to say. There is the carbon of the air which is conveyed to the plant by the wind, very diluted it is true, but in large quantities, and there is, as it seems, also as part of the atmosphere, ammonia in sufficient quantity. Its nitrogen, together with the carbon of carbon dioxide and with the elements of water, is used in the formation of protein in the plant. But are these elements sufficient? Let us examine the ashes of the plant! In hundreds of analyses they show half a dozen other chemical elements in the form of their compounds, elements which cannot have come from the air, because they are not contained in it, and which necessarily must have been taken from the soil in which the plant grows, because there is no third source. This way the scientific account book gets a new page, a debit and credit account of the soil. For if we take the harvest out of the soil, do we not take along all the mineral substances which the chemical analysis shows in the plant ashes? Thus the soil will get poorer, now of one substance, then of a different one, according to what it can yield out of its composition, and to what mineral substances the different kinds of plants extract from it. This impoverishment is counteracted by the continuous erosion, which decomposes new rocky material and brings it into a chemical form which the plant can utilize. The remaining deficit we may cover by supplying fertilizer; and we have to cover it this way if we do not want the soil to become barren. And now let us study the methods of agriculture, its teachings and its success, and see in detail how far they conform with the new knowledge and what will have to be understood better and be done better!

The foregoing is approximately the new insight that Liebig proclaimed to the listening world with overwhelming force of thought and presentation!

546

The impression was extremely great. A few years before, his contribution to the theory of radicals had been received with universal acknowledgment by his colleagues. It was not so this time. On the contrary, one critic doubted the accuracy, another the novelty; besides, it was felt that not much had been proved and much remained to be examined. The dangerous applause of the masses of professional agriculturists overcame these doubts. But the applause could not persist against the contradictory experiences which could not be avoided, because, in fact, one or the other part of the great creation had been built up in a hurry without a sufficient experimental basis.

With the objections that he has repeated something known before, he can deal. According to his own words he has tried to put a light into a dark room. All pieces of furniture were in it, as well as tools and objects of convenience and pleasure, but all these things were not clearly and distinctly visible for the people who were using this room for their profit and advantage. "Now, after each object had received a part of the, probably, faint light, many claim that the light has not changed anything essential in the room. One person had already known and used this thing, the other that one, and together they all had felt and touched what was on hand."

Not quite so successfully did he cope with those who argued by means of experiments which they cannot bring into accord with his doctrine. Indeed, he could not lend enough weight to this theory because the role of microorganisms in the soil was still unknown at that time. Later it was to clarify many points, especially those dealing with nitrogen.

But the worst trouble for him was that there was a point at which his own observation confirmed the objections of his adversaries. He himself started agricultural experiments, and tried out the patent fertilizer which he had recommended. It was smelted together from phosphates and potash, according to his directions, in such a way that it contained the phosphoric acid and the alkali in a relatively insoluble state, so that they could be dissolved and washed away by rainwater. This patent fertilizer failed, and for many years he could not find the cause. Certainly difficult years for our hero, as long as this hole was not filled and thus a pillar of the edifice of his ideas remained hollow. But finally he succeeded in solving the problem. The fundamental idea of the need of potassium and phosphoric acid in the soil was right. Wrong was the additional reasoning that one must supply the soil with both substances in an insoluble state. The soil has a force for retaining these substances. Even in an easily soluble state they are not quickly washed out, and the less soluble form only deters needlessly and without profit their absorption by the soil.

In special matters, a new generation finds many things to do by way of additions and alterations. But in general Liebig enjoyed the pleasure that all over the world a common respect for his work as a great achievement prevailed, and this respect has stayed. A tremendous development of the fertilizer industry obtained its impetus through his doctrines. He is responsible for the fact that millions of people live on the increased production of the soil. Whoever measures his accomplishment by its effect on the general way of living will award him the greatest honor for his agricultural chemistry.

The other steps he took in the science of life did not carry him equally far. Physiology obtained the greatest stimulation from them, and one or the other of his ideas became a lasting possession of science. Still, in view of the whole, the subject proved too complicated and nature too rich to arrive at an understanding of the isolated life processes with the knowledge of his day. We are closer to the goal today. But we only have climbed a mountain in order to see how far the sky is.

In August, 1852, Liebig moved to the University of Munich and worked there, highly honored, until on April 18, 1873, death claimed him. Tremendous work, enough to consume the strength of many people, and yet done by him alone, had not entirely worn out this giant during his years in Giessen, but had made him tired. The creative achievement came more slowly. He no longer accepted any students, and most of his strength was devoted to the insight which, in his days in Giessen, he gained from living and inanimate nature. His days were filled with lectures, academic speeches, new editions of his books and publications, especially the formulation of his chemical letters with which he undertook to bring this branch of science and his achievement closer to all educated and broad-minded people. In between there are new sparks, partly of organic-chemical, partly biochemical, partly technical nature. The last organic chemical compound that he prepared and described, fulminuric acid, returned him to the realm of phenomena from which he had started in his schooldays. There was the broth for sick people, the reduction of acidity and improvement of rye bread, the baking powder and the malt soup, and before all the meat extract, which as a nourishment of great value became the object of an important industry. Finally there were the silver mirrors with which he occupied himself, until after long endeavors he was able to demonstrate how they could be manufactured on a mass production scale. The connection with the development of chemical systems was gradually lost. Other hands cultivated the soil which he had made arable in his early years. But his work in Munich raised chemistry out of the quiet usefulness of a special field to the position and significance of one of the great realms of human culture.

NOTES AND REFERENCES

F. R. Moulton, ed., "Liebig and After Liebig," American Association for the Advancement of Science, Washington, D. C., 1942.

Ludwig Thudichum, "The discoveries and philosophy of Liebig, with special reference to their influence upon the advancement of the arts, manufactures and commerce," Journal of the Society of Arts, 24, 80, 95, 101, 125, 141, London, 1875–6. (Five Cantor Lectures.)

From the address at the dedication of the Liebig-Haus in Darmstadt, July 7, 1928. See: *Zeitschrift für Angewandte Chemie, 41,* 891–897 (1928). Translated by Dora S. Farber.

FRITZ HABER

·· *41* ··

Thomas Graham

1805-1869

THE simple story of Mr. Graham's life, though not without its measure of interest, and certainly not without its lessons, is referred to in the following pages only in illustration of the grander story of his work. Thomas Graham was born in Glasgow, on December 21, 1805. He entered as a student at the University of Glasgow, in 1819, with a view to becoming ultimately a minister of the Established Church of Scotland. At that time the university chair of chemistry was filled by Dr. Thomas Thomson, a man of very considerable mark, and one of the most erudite and thoughtful chemists of his day. The chair of natural philosophy was also filled by a man of much learning, Dr. Meikleham, who appears to have taken a warm personal interest in the progress of his since distinguished pupil. Under these masters, Mr. Graham acquired a strong liking for experimental science, and a dislike to the profession chosen for him by his father; who, for a time at least, seems to have exerted the authority of a parent somewhat harshly, but quite unavailingly, to effect the fulfillment of his own earnest wishes in the matter.

After taking his degree of Master of Arts at Glasgow, in 1826, Mr. Graham worked for nearly two years in the laboratory of the University of Edinburgh, under Dr. Hope. He then returned to Glasgow; and, while supporting himself by teaching, at first mathematics and afterward chemistry, yet found time to follow up the path of experimental inquiry, on which he had already entered.

His first original paper appeared in the *Annals of Philosophy* for 1826, its author being at that time in his twenty-first year. It is interesting to note that the subject of this communication, "On the absorption of gases by liquids," forms part and parcel of that large subject of spontaneous gas movement with which Mr. Graham's name is now so inseparably associated; and that, in a paper communicated to the Royal Society just forty years later, he speaks of the liquefiability of gases by chemical means, in language almost identical with that used in this earliest of his published memoirs.

Having, in the interval, contributed several other papers to the

553

scientific journals, in the year 1829 he published in the *Quarterly Journal of Science*—the journal, that is to say, of the Royal Institution—the first of his papers relating specifically to the subject of gas diffusion. It was entitled "A short account of experimental researches on the diffusion of gases through each other, and their separation by mechanical means." In the same year, he became lecturer on chemistry at the Mechanics' Institute, Glasgow; and in the next year, 1830, achieved the yet more decisive step of being appointed professor of chemistry at the Andersonian University. By this appointment he was relieved from anxiety on the score of living, and afforded, in a modest way, the means of carrying out his experimental work.

In 1831, he read, before the Royal Society of Edinburgh, a paper "On the law of the diffusion of gases," for which the Keith prize of the society was shortly afterward awarded him. Although several of his earlier papers, and especially that "On the diffusion of gases," published in the *Quarterly Journal of Science,* had given evidence of considerable power, it was this paper—in which he established the now well-recognized law that the velocities of diffusion of different gases are inversely as the square roots of their specific gravities—that constituted the first of what may properly be considered his great contributions to the progress of chemical science.

In 1833 he communicated a paper of scarcely less importance, to the Royal Society of London, entitled "Researches on the arseniates, phosphates, and modifications of phosphoric acid." It afforded further evidence of Mr. Graham's quiet, steady power of investigating phenomena, and of his skill in interpreting results; or rather of his skill in setting forth the results in all their simplicity, undistorted by the gloss of preconceived notions, so as to make them render up their own interpretation. It is difficult nowadays to realize the independence of mind involved in Mr. Graham's simple interpretation of the facts presented to him in this research, by the light of the facts themselves, irrespective of all traditional modes of viewing them. Their investigation let in a flood of light upon the chemistry of that day, and formed a starting point from which many of our most recent advances may be directly traced. In this paper, Mr. Graham established the existence of two new, and, at that time, wholly unanticipated classes of bodies, namely, the class of polybasic acids and salts, and the class of so-called anhydro acids and salts. The views of Graham on the polybasicity of phosphoric acid were soon afterward applied by Liebig to tartaric acid, and by Gerhardt to polybasic acids in general, as we now recognize them. After a long interval, the idea of polybasicity was next extended to radicals and to metals by Williamson and myself successively; afterward to alcohols by Wurtz, and to ammonias by Hofmann. The notion of anhydro-salts was extended by myself to the different classes of silicates; by Wurtz to the compounds intermediate between oxide of ethylene and glycol; and by other chemists to many different series of organic bodies.

The next most important of the researches completed by Mr. Graham while at Glasgow was the subject of a paper communicated to the Royal Society of Edinburgh, in 1835, "On water as a constituent of salts," and of a second paper communicated to the Royal Society of London, in 1836, entitled "Inquiries respecting the constitution of salts, &c.," for which latter a royal medal of the society was afterward awarded. The subject of hydration had yielded him such a harvest of results in the case of phosphoric acid, that it was only natural he should wish to pursue the inquiry further. Indeed, it is a curious illustration of the persistency of the man that he never seems to have left out of sight the subjects of his early labors. Almost all his subsequent original work is but a development, in different directions, of his youthful researches on gas diffusion and water of hydration; and so completely did he bridge over the space intervening between these widely remote subjects, that, with regard to several of his later investigations, it is difficult to say whether they are most directly traceable to his primitive work on the one subject or on the other.

In 1837, on the death of Dr. Edward Turner, Mr. Graham was appointed professor of chemistry at University College, London, then called the University of London. On his acceptance of this appointment he began the publication of his well-known "Elements of Chemistry," which appeared in parts, at irregular intervals, between 1837 and 1841. Elementary works, written for the use of students, have necessarily much in common; but the treatise of

Mr. Graham, while giving an admirably digested account of the most important individual substances, was specially distinguished by the character of the introductory chapters, devoted to chemical physics, wherein was set forth one of the most original and masterly statements of the first principles of chemistry that has ever been placed before the English student. "The theory of the voltaic circle" had formed the subject of a paper communicated by Mr. Graham to the British Association in 1839; and the account of the working of the battery, given in his "Elements of Chemistry," and based on the above paper, will long be regarded as a model of lucid scientific exposition.

In 1841 the now flourishing Chemical Society of London was founded; and though Mr. Graham had been, at that time, but four years in London, such was the estimation in which he was held by his brother chemists, that he was unanimously chosen as the first president of the society. The year 1844 is noticeable in another way. Wollaston and Davy had been dead for some years. Faraday's attention had been diverted from chemistry to those other branches of experimental inquiry in which his highest distinctions were achieved; and, by the death of Dalton in this year, Mr. Graham was left as the acknowledged first of English chemists, as the not unworthy successor to the position of Black, Priestley, Cavendish, Wollaston, Davy, and Dalton.

From the period of his appointment at University College, in 1837, Mr. Graham's time was fully occupied in teaching, in writing, in advising on chemical manufactures, in investigating fiscal and other questions for the Government, and in the publication of various scientific memoirs, several of them possessing a high degree of interest; but it was not till 1846 that he produced a research of any considerable magnitude. In that year he presented to the Royal Society the first part of a paper "On the motion of gases," the second part of which he supplied in 1849. For this research Mr. Graham was awarded a second royal medal of the society in 1850. The preliminary portion of the first part of the paper related to an experimental demonstration of the law of the effusion of gases, deduced from Toricelli's theorem on the efflux of liquids—a demonstration that was achieved by Mr. Graham with much ingenuity, and without his encountering any formidable difficulty. But the greater portion of the first part, and whole of the second part, of this most laborious paper were devoted to an investigation of the velocities of transpiration of different gases through capillary tubes, with a view to discover some general law by which their observed transpiration rates might be associated with one another. Again and again, with characteristic pertinacity, Mr. Graham returned to the investigation; but, although much valuable information of an entirely novel character was acquired— information having an important bearing on his subsequent work —the problem itself remained, and yet remains, unsolved. Why, for example, under an equal pressure, oxygen gas should pass through a capillary tube at a slower rate than any other gas is a matter that still awaits interpretation.

Near the end of the same year, 1849, Mr. Graham communicated, also to the Royal Society, a second less laborious, but in the novelty and interest of its results more successful, paper "On the diffusion of liquids." It was made the Bakerian lecture for 1850, and was supplemented by further observations communicated to the society in 1850 and 1851. In his investigation of this subject, Mr. Graham applied to liquids the exact method of inquiry which he had applied to gases just twenty years before, in that earliest of his papers on the subject of gas diffusion published in the *Quarterly Journal of Science;* and he succeeded in placing the subject of liquid diffusion on about the same footing as that to which he had raised the subject of gas diffusion prior to the discovery of his numerical law.

In 1854 Mr. Graham communicated another paper to the Royal Society, "On osmotic force," a subject intimately connected with that of his last previous communication. This paper was also made the Bakerian lecture for the year; but, altogether, the conclusions arrived at were hardly in proportion to the very great labor expended on the inquiry. In the next year, 1855, just five-and-twenty years after his appointment at the Andersonian University, Mr. Graham was made master of the mint; and, as a consequence, resigned his professorship at University College. During the next five years he published no original work.

Thus, at the beginning of the year 1861, Mr. Graham, then fifty-six years of age, had produced, in addition to many less important communications, five principal memoirs; three of them in the highest degree successful; the other two less successful in proportion to the expenditure of time and labor on them, but, nevertheless, of great originality and value. The most brilliant period, however, of his scientific career was to come. In the year 1861, and between then and his death in 1869, Mr. Graham communicated four elaborate papers to the Royal Society, three of them far exceeding in novelty, interest, and philosophic power anything that he had before produced; and the other of them, relating to a certain physical effect of that hydration of compounds, from the consideration of which his attention could never wholly be withdrawn. This least important paper, "On liquid transpiration in relation to chemical composition," was communicated to the Royal Society in 1861. Of the three greater papers, that "On liquid diffusion applied to analysis" was communicated also in 1861. For this paper more especially, as well as for his Bakerian lectures "On the diffusion of liquids" and "On osmotic force," Mr. Graham received, in 1862, the Copley medal of the Royal Society; and, in the same year, was also awarded the Jecker prize of the Institute of France. Following in quick succession, his paper "On the molecular mobility of gases" was presented to the Royal Society in 1863; and that "On the absorption and dialytic separation of gases by colloid septa," in 1866. With regard to these three great papers, two of them were each supplemented by a communication to the Chemical Society; while the third was supplemented by four successive notes to the Royal Society, containing an account of further discoveries on the same subject, hardly less remarkable than those recorded in the original paper. The last of these supplementary notes was communicated on June 10, 1869, but a few months before the death, on September 13, of the indefatigable but physically broken-down man.

In considering Mr. Graham as a chemical philosopher and lawgiver, we find him characterized by a pertinacity of purpose peculiarly his own. Wanting the more striking qualities by which his immediate predecessors, Davy, Dalton, and Faraday, were severally distinguished, he displayed a positive zeal for tedious quantitative work, and a wonderful keen-sightedness in seizing the points which his innumerable determinations of various kinds, conducted almost incessantly for a period of forty years, successively unfolded. His work itself was essentially that of detail, original in conception, simple in execution, laborious by its quantity, and brilliant in the marvelous results to which it led. As regards its simplicity of execution, scarcely any investigator of recent times has been less a friend to the instrument-maker than Mr. Graham. While availing himself, with much advantage, of appliances devised by Bunsen, Poiseuille, Sprengel, and others, all the apparatus introduced by himself was of the simplest character, and for the most part of laboratory construction.

Essentially inductive in his mode of thought, Mr. Graham developed his leading ideas, one after another, directly from experiment, scarcely, if at all, from the prevailing ideas of the time. As well observed by Dr. Angus Smith, "he seemed to feel his way by his work." His records of work are usually, in a manner almost characteristic, preceded each by a statement of the interpretation or conclusion which he formed; but the records themselves are expressed in the most unbiased matter-of-fact language. Singularly cautious in drawing his conclusions, he announces them from the first with boldness, making no attempt to convince, but leaving the reader to adopt them or not as he pleases. Accordingly, in giving an account of his various researches, Mr. Graham rarely, if ever, deals with argument; but he states succinctly the experiments he has made, the conclusions he has himself drawn, and not infrequently the almost daring speculations and generalizations on which he has ventured. Some of these speculations, on the constitution of matter, are reproduced in his own words further on.

Mr. Graham was elected a fellow of the Royal Society in 1837; corresponding member of the Institute of France in 1847; and doctor of civil law of Oxford in 1855.

The remaining pages of this abstract are devoted to an account of his principal discoveries—the generalizations they suggested to him, and the relations in which they stood to precedent knowledge.

MODIFICATIONS OF PHOSPHORIC ACID

At the date of Mr. Graham's investigation of this subject, when oxy-salts were usually represented as compounds of anhydrous base with anhydrous acid, the point of greatest importance, with regard to each class of salts, was held to be the ratio borne by the oxygen of the base to the oxygen of the acid. Thus, in the carbonates, this ratio was as 1 to 2; in the sulfates, as 1 to 3; and in the nitrates, as 1 to 5. But with regard to the phosphates, taking common phosphate of soda at a type of phosphates in general, there was a difficulty. Dr. Thomson maintained that, in this salt, the ratio of the oxygen of the base to the oxygen of the acid was as 1 to 2; and his view was substantially supported by Sir Humphry Davy. Berzelius contended, however, that the ratio was as 1 to 2½, or, to avoid the use of fractions, as 2 to 5; but, notwithstanding the excellence of the Swedish chemist's proof, and its corroboration by the researches of others, the simpler and, as it seemed, more harmonious view of Dr. Thomson prevailed very generally in this country. Anyhow, those phosphates in which the oxygen ratio was the same as that in phosphate of soda were taken as the neutral salts. But phosphate of soda was found to have the peculiar and quite inexplicable property of reacting with nitrate of silver to throw down, as a yellow precipitate, a phosphate of silver, in which the proportion of metallic base exceeded that in the original phosphate of soda—the precipitation of the basic salt being accompanied correlatively by the formation of a strongly acid liquid. According to Berzelius, the ratio of the oxygen of the base to that of the acid, in this yellow precipitate, was as 3 to 5.

In 1821 Mitscherlich, then working in Berzelius' laboratory, obtained, by treating ordinary phosphate of soda with aqueous phosphoric acid, a new crystallizable phosphate of soda, in which the ratio of acid to base was twice as great as that in the ordinary phosphate. This new salt, which had a strongly acid reaction to test paper, he called the biphosphate of soda. He observed that it was a hydrated salt, and that while the ratio in it of the oxygen of the base to the oxygen of the acid, was as 1 to 5, the ratio of the oxygen of the base to the oxygen of the water was 1 to 2.

In 1827 Mr. Graham's fellow-townsman, and predecessor at the Mechanics' Institute, Dr. Clark, discovered another new phosphate of soda, in which the ratio of the oxygen of the base to the oxygen of the acid was identical with that in the ordinary phosphate, namely, as 2 to 5. But whereas the ordinary phosphate crystallized with 25 proportions of water, the new phosphate crystallized with only 10; and whereas the ordinary phosphate gave a yellow precipitate with nitrate of silver and a strongly acid supernatant liquid, the new phosphate gave a chalk-white precipitate with nitrate of silver and a perfectly neutral supernatant liquid. This new phosphate, being formed by heating the common phosphate to redness, was accordingly designated the pyrophosphate.

Other anomalies with regard to phosphoric acid and the phosphates were also known to chemists; and, on referring now to standard chemical works written before the year 1833, the whole subject of the phosphates will be seen to be in the greatest confusion. It was in this year that Mr. Graham communicated his paper, entitled "Researches on the arseniates, phosphates, and modifications of phosphoric acid," to the Royal Society.[1]

In the course of these researches he established the existence of a class of soluble subphosphates analogous to the yellow insoluble phosphate of silver; and he showed, with great clearness, that in the three classes of phosphates, namely, the subphosphates, the common phosphates, and the biphosphates, the ratio borne to the oxygen of the acid by the other oxygen of the salt is the same, namely, as 3 to 5; only that, in the three classes of salts, the nonacid oxygen is divided between different proportions of metallic base and water, thus:

Subphosphate of soda .... $3NaO \cdot PO_5$.
Common phosphate of soda .... $HO \cdot 2NaO \cdot PO_5$.
Biphosphate of soda .... $2HO \cdot NaO \cdot PO_5$.

He further pointed out that, to these three series of salts, there corresponded a definite phosphate of water, or,

Hydrated phosphoric acid .... $3HO \cdot PO_5$.

Compounds of one and the same anhydrous acid with one and the same anhydrous base, in different proportions, had long been known; but it was thus that Mr. Graham first established the notion of polybasic compounds—the notion of a class of hydrated acids having more than one proportion of water replaceable by metallic oxide, and that successively, so as to furnish more and more basic salts, all preserving, as we should now say, the same type.

Mr. Graham further showed that Dr. Clark's pyrophosphate of soda, like the common phosphate, yielded an acid salt or biphosphate; and that these two compounds were related to a hydrated phosphoric acid differing in composition and properties from the above-mentioned hydrate, and yielding, after neutralization with alkali, a white instead of a yellow precipitate with nitrate of silver. This series of compounds he expressed by the following formulæ:

Clark's pyrophosphate of soda .... $2NaO.PO_5$.
Acid or bipyrophosphate of soda ...... $HO.NaO.PO_5$.
Hydrated pyrophosphoric acid .... $2HO.PO_5$.

Lastly, Mr. Graham showed that when the biphosphate or bipyrophosphate of soda was ignited, there was left a new variety of phosphate, which he called the metaphosphate, having the same proportions of soda and anhydrous phosphate acid as the original compound, but differing from it in several properties, more particularly in its inability to furnish any acid salt. From this new phosphate he obtained the corresponding hydrated acid, and found it to be identical with that variety of phosphoric acid then, and still, known as glacial phosphoric acid, which had previously been noticed to possess the distinctive property of causing a precipitate in solutions of albumen. This salt and acid he represented as follows:

Metaphosphate of soda .... $NaO.PO_5$.
Metaphosphoric acid .... $HO.PO_5$.

Speaking of the acid obtainable from, and by its neutralization reconverted into, the phosphate, pyrophosphate, and metaphosphate of soda respectively, Mr. Graham remarked: "The acid, when separated from the base, will possess and retain for some time the characters of its peculiar modification. . . . But I suspect that the modifications of phosphoric acid, when in what we would call a free state, are still in combination with their usual proportion of base, and that that base is water. Thus the three modifications of phosphoric evidence may be composed as follows:

Phosphoric acid .... $3HO.PO_5$.
Pyrophosphoric acid .... $2HO.PO_5$.
Metaphosphoric acid .... $HO.PO_5$;

or they are respectively a triphosphate, a biphosphate, and phosphate of water." These remarks he followed up by analytical evidence, showing the existence of the three hydrates, each in its isolated state.

Just as in his demonstration of the relationship to one another of subphosphate of soda, phosphate of soda, bi-phosphate of soda, and common phosphoric acid, Mr. Graham originated the notion of polybasic compounds, so, in his demonstration of the nature of the pyrophosphates and metaphosphates, as bodies differing from the normal compounds by an abstraction of water or metallic base, did he originate the notion of anhydro compounds—so did he discover, for the first time, an instance of that relationship between bodies which is now known to prevail most extensively among products of organic as well as of mineral origin.

The different properties manifested by phosphoric acid, in its different reputedly isomeric states, having been shown by Mr. Graham to be dependent on a difference of hydration; that is to say, on a difference of chemical composition, he was inclined to view the difference of properties observed in the case of other reputedly isomeric bodies as being also dependent on a difference of composition, the difference occasionally consisting in the presence of some minute disregarded impurity. Accordingly he communicated to the Royal Society of Edinburgh in 1834[2] a paper "On phosphureted hydrogen," in which he showed that the spontaneously inflammable and nonspontaneously inflammable varieties of the gas "are not isomeric bodies, but that the peculiarities of the spontaneously inflammable species depend upon the presence of adventitious matter," removable in various ways, and existing but in very minute proportion.[3] He further showed that the vapor of some acid of nitrogen, apparently "nitrous acid, is capable of rendering phosphureted hydrogen spontaneously inflammable when present to the extent of one ten-thousandth part of the volume of the gas." In connection with this research may be mentioned Mr. Graham's earlier experiments on the influence of minute impurities in modifying the chemical behavior of different substances. In some "Observations on the oxidation of phosphorus," published in the *Quarterly Journal of Science*[4] for 1829, he showed that the presence of 1/450 of olefiant gas, and even 1/4400, by

563

volume, of turpentine vapor, in air under ordinary pressure, rendered it incapable of effecting the slow oxidation of phosphorus. He also observed and recorded the influence upon the oxidation of phosphorus of various additions of gas and vapor to air, under different circumstances of pressure and temperature.

In addition to the memoirs cited above, the question of hydration formed an express or incidental subject of many other of Mr. Graham's investigations. It is noteworthy that, for him, osmosis became a mechanical effect of the hydration of the septum; that the interest attaching to liquid transpiration was the alteration in rate of passage consequent on an altered hydration of the liquid; that the dialytic difference between crystalloids and colloids depended on the dehydration of the dialytic membrane by the former class of bodies only; and similarly in many other instances.

Lastly, in comparing highly diffusive substances on the one hand, with feebly diffusive substances on the other, one broad dissimilarity became apparent, namely, that highly diffusible substances affected the crystalline state, while feebly diffusive substances were amorphous, and characterized, in particular, by a capability of forming gelatinous hydrates. Hence the distinction established by Mr. Graham between highly diffusive bodies, or *crystalloids,* and feebly diffusive bodies, or *colloids.* Compounds capable of existing both in the crystalline and gelatinous states he found to be possessed of two distinct diffusive rates corresponding respectively each to each.

DIALYSIS AND OSMOSE

The subject of dialysis was included in the paper "On liquid diffusion applied to analysis," referred to in the preceding section; and some further results were communicated in 1864 to the Chemical Society, in a paper "On the properties of silicic acid and other analogous colloidal substances."[5]

In the course of his experiments on diffusion, Mr. Graham made the curious discovery that highly diffusible crystalloid bodies were able to diffuse readily, not only into free water, but also into water that was already in a low form of combination, as in the substance of a soft solid, such as jelly or membrane. Common salt, for instance, was found to diffuse into a semisolid mass of jelly almost as easily and as extensively as into a similar bulk of free water; but the introduction of a gelatinous substance, though not interfering in any appreciable degree with the diffusion of a crystalloid, was found to arrest almost entirely the diffusion of a colloid. The colloid, of but little tendency to diffuse into free water, proved quite incapable of diffusing into water that was already in a state of combination, however feeble. Hence, although the partial separation of a highly diffusible from a feebly diffusible substance might be effected by the process of free diffusion into water, a much better result was obtained by allowing the diffusion to take place into, or through, the combined water of a soft solid such as a piece of membrane or parchment-paper. In the process of dialysis, then, crystalloid and colloid bodies, existing in solution together, are separated from one another by pouring the mixed solution into a shallow tray of membrane or parchment paper, and letting the tray rest on the surface of a considerable excess of water, once or twice renewed. By this means the crystalloid, in process of time, diffuses completely away through the membranous septum into the free water; but the colloid, being quite incapable of permeating the membrane, however thin, is retained completely on the tray, unable to reach the free water on the other side.

By means of the process of dialysis, Mr. Graham succeeded in obtaining various colloid organic substances, such as tannin, albumen, gum, caramel, &c, in a very pure state; some of them, indeed, in a state of purity exceeding any in which they had before been met with. But the most curious results were obtained with different mineral substances, usually thrown down from their dissolved salts in the state of gelatinous or colloid precipitates. Most of these precipitates being soluble in some or other crystalloid liquid, on submitting the so-produced solutions to dialysis, the crystalloid constituents diffuse away, leaving the colloid substances in pure aqueous solution. By proceeding in this manner, Mr. Graham was able to obtain certain hydrated forms of silica, ferric oxide, alumina, chrome, prussian blue, stannic acid, titanic acid, tungstic acid, molybdic acid, &c., in the state of aqueous solution

565

—these bodies having never before been obtained in solution, save
in presence of strongly acid or alkaline compounds serving to dissolve them. Altogether, the production of these colloid solutions
of substances, such as silica and alumina—in their crystalline
state, as quartz and corundum, completely insoluble—threw an
entirely new light upon the conditions of aqueous solution.

The colloidal solutions, obtained as above, of substances usually crystalline, were found to be exceedingly unstable. Either
spontaneously, or on the addition of some or other crystalloid reagent, even in very minute quantity, they pectized or became converted into solid jellies. Hence Mr. Graham was led to speak of
two colloidal states; the peptous or dissolved, and the pectous or
gelatinized. In addition to their power of gelatinizing, their muta-
bility, their noncrystalline habit, and their low diffusibility, substances in the colloid state were found to be further characterized
by their chemical inertness and by their high combining weights.
Thus the saturating power of colloid silica was only about 1/36
of that of the ordinary acid.

In his supplementary paper communicated to the Chemical Society, Mr. Graham showed how the pectous forms of different mineral colloids could, in many cases, be reconverted into their peptous forms. He further showed how the water of different peptous
and pectous colloids could be mechanically displaced by other
liquids, as alcohol, glycerine, sulfuric acid, &c. To the different
classes of compounds so formed, he gave distinctive names. Thus,
the alcoholic solution and jelly, of silicic acid, for instance, he designated as the alcosol and alcogel, respectively.

Closely associated with the passage of different liquids through
membranes is the action known as endosmose, discovered by
Dutrochet. Mr. Graham's principal results on this subject are recorded in a very elaborate paper "On osmotic force," communicated to the Royal Society in 1854;[6] but a few further results and
a statement of his final views are contained in the paper, referred
to immediately above, "On liquid diffusion applied to analysis."
When the solution of a saline or other compound is separated
from an adjacent mass of water by a membranous septum, a
greater or less quantity of the water very commonly passes through

the septum into the solution; and if the solution be contained in a vessel of suitable construction, having a broad membranous base and a narrow upright stem, the water, in some cases, flows into the vessel through the membrane, with a force sufficient to raise and sustain a column of 20 inches or more of liquid in the stem. The problem is to account for this flow; which, with acid fluids more particularly, takes place in the reverse direction—i.e., from the solution into the water.

In the course of his experiments Mr. Graham examined the osmotic movement produced with liquids of most diverse character, employing osmometers of animal membrane, albuminated calico, and baked earthenware. His results were, moreover, observed and recorded in very great detail. As an illustration of these results, it may be mentioned that with 1 per cent solutions in the membranous osmometer, the liquid rose in the stem 2 millimeters in the case of common salt, 20 millimeters with chloride of calcium, 88 millimeters with chloride of nickel, 121 millimeters with chloride of mercury, 289 millimeters with protochloride of tin, 351 millimeters with chloride of copper, and 540 millimeters with chloride of aluminum. Mr. Graham showed, further, in opposition to the views of Dutrochet, that the velocity of the osmotic flow was not proportional to the quantity of salt or other substance originally contained in the solution; and that the flow did not depend on capillarity, as Dutrochet had inferred; or yet on diffusion, as some of his own experiments might be thought to indicate. Eventually he was led to the conclusion that osmose was essentially dependent on a chemical action taking place between one or other of the separated liquids and the material of the septum. He appears to have held somewhat different views of the nature of this chemical action at different times, and not to have considered it as being in all cases of the same character.

OCCLUSION OF GASES BY METALS

The experiments of Deville and Troost having made known the curious fact of the permeability of ignited homogeneous platinum and ignited homogeneous iron to hydrogen gas, and given some indication also of the permeability of ignited iron to carbonic oxide gas, Mr. Graham, in 1866, corroborated the results of the French chemists in reference to platinum; but, modifying their method by letting the hydrogen pass into a space kept vacuous by the Sprengel pump, instead of into an atmosphere of other gas, assimilated the process to that which he had employed in his India-rubber experiments. The results he obtained were communicated to the Royal Society, partly in the paper already referred to "On the absorption and separation of gases by colloid septa," and partly in four supplementary notices published in the proceedings of the society. In carrying out the investigation forming the subject of these several communications, Mr. Graham had the advantage of being admirably seconded by his assistant, Mr. W. Chandler Roberts, whose able and zealous cooperation he repeatedly acknowledged in the warmest terms.

In the course of experiments made on the transmission of gases through ignited metallic septa, a particular platinum tube, being rendered vacuous, was found at all temperatures below redness to be quite impermeable to hydrogen; whereas, at a red heat, it transmitted 100 cubic centimeters of hydrogen in half an hour, the quantities of oxygen, nitrogen, marsh gas, and carbonic gas, transmitted under the same conditions, not amounting to .01 cubic centimeter each in half an hour. It was ascertained further that, with an ignited vacuous tube of platinum surrounded by a current of ordinary coal-gas, (a variable mixture of gases containing on the average about 45 per cent of marsh gas, 40 per cent of hydrogen, and 15 per cent of other gases and vapors,) a transmission of pure hydrogen alone took place through the heated metal. This property of selective transmission, manifested by platinum, was so far analogous to the property of selective transmission manifested by India rubber, that whereas a septum of India rubber transmitted the nitrogen of the air in a much smaller ratio than the oxygen, the septum of ignited platinum transmitted the other constituents of coal gas in an infinitely smaller ratio than the hydrogen. Hence the knowledge of the absorption by India rubber of the gases which it most freely transmitted, suggested to Mr. Graham an inquiry as to the possible absorption of hydrogen gas by platinum.

But it was with palladium that Mr. Graham obtained his most

568

extraordinary results. This metal he found to have the property of transmitting hydrogen with extreme facility, even at temperatures very far short of redness. Coincidentally, at temperatures even below those requisite for transmission, palladium was found capable of absorbing many hundred times its volume of hydrogen. Thus a piece of palladium-foil maintained at a temperature of 90°–97° for three hours, and then allowed to cool down during an hour and a half, while surrounded by a continuous current of hydrogen gas, gave off, on being afterward heated *in vacuo,* 643 times its volume of the gas, measured cold; and even at ordinary temperatures, it absorbed 376 times its volume of the gas, provided it had first been recently ignited *in vacuo.* In another experiment, palladium sponge, heated to 200° in a current of hydrogen and allowed to cool slowly therein, afterward yielded 686 times its volume of the gas; while a piece of electrolytically deposited palladium heated only to 100° in hydrogen, afterward yielded, upon ignition *in vacuo,* no less than 982 times its volume of the gas. The lowness of the temperature at which, under favorable circumstances, the absorption of hydrogen by palladium could thus be effected, soon suggested other means of bringing about the result. For example, a piece of palladium foil was placed in contact with a quantity of zinc undergoing solution in dilute sulfuric acid; and, on subsequent examination, was found to have absorbed 173 times its volume of hydrogen. Again, palladium, in the forms of wire and foil, was made to act as the negative pole of a Bunsen battery effecting the electrolysis of acidulated water; and in this manner was found to absorb from 800 to 950 times its volume of hydrogen in different experiments.

Palladium being thus chargeable with hydrogen in three different ways—namely, by being heated and cooled in an atmosphere of the gas; by being placed in contact with zinc dissolving in acid, i.e., with hydrogen in the act of evolution; and, lastly, by being made the negative electrode of a battery—correlatively, the charged metal could be freed from its occluded hydrogen by exposing it to an increase of temperature in air or vacuo; by acting on it with different feebly oxidizing mixtures; and by making it the positive electrode of a battery.

569

That hydrogen is the vapor of a highly volatile metal has frequently been maintained on chemical grounds; and from a consideration of the physical properties of his hydrogenized palladium, Mr. Graham was led to regard it as a true alloy of palladium with hydrogen, or rather hydrogenium, in which the volatility of the latter metal was restrained by the fixity of the former, and of which the metallic aspect was equally due to both of its constituents. Although, indeed, the occlusion of upward of 900 times its volume of hydrogen was found to lower the tenacity and electric conductivity of palladium appreciably, still the hydrogenized palladium remained possessed of a most characteristically metallic tenacity and conductivity. Thus, the tenacity of the original wire being taken as 100, the tenacity of the fully charged wire was found to be 81.29; and the electric conductivity of the original wire being 8.10, that of the hydrogenized wire was found to be 5.99. In further support of the conclusion arrived at by Mr. Graham, as to the metallic condition of the hydrogen occluded in palladium, he adduced his singular discovery of its being possessed of magnetic properties, more decided than those of palladium itself, a metal which Mr. Faraday had shown to be "feebly but truly magnetic." Operating with an electromagnet of very moderate strength, Mr. Graham found that while an oblong fragment of electrolytically deposited palladium was deflected from the equatorial by 10° only, the same fragment of metal, charged with 604.6 times its volume of hydrogen, was deflected through 48°. Thus did Mr. Graham supplement the idea of hydrogen as an invisible incondensable gas, by the idea of hydrogen as an opaque, lustrous, white metal, having a specific gravity between 0.7 and 0.8, a well-marked tenacity and conductivity, and a very decided magnetism.

NOTES AND REFERENCES

1 *Philosophical Transactions,* 1833, 253.
2 *Edinburgh Royal Society Transactions,* xiii, 88 (1836).
3 It was afterward isolated by P. Thenard.
4 *Quarterly Journal Science,* ii, 83 (1829).
5 *Chemical Society Journal,* xvii, 318.
6 *Philosophical Transactions,* 177 (1854).
   R. A. Gortner *J. Chem. Educ.,* 11, 279 (1934).

570

Selections from the biography by William Odling in the *Proceedings of the Royal Institution*, London, reprinted in *Annual Reports* of the Board of Directors of The Smithsonian Institution, 177–216 (1871).

WILLIAM ODLING

·· *42* ··

Robert Wilhelm Bunsen

1811-1899

$\mathbf{R}$OBERT BUNSEN was born March 31, 1811, in Göttingen. His father's family resided in Arolsen, and many of its members had been mint masters. The best known of these direct forebears is Jeremias Bunsen, 1688–1752, who was court painter, master of the mint, and mayor in Arolsen. This many-sided man obviously was a great admirer of science, as indicated by his books on thunder and lightning, and on his "Explanations of magnetic and electric forces."

Little is known about Bunsen's childhood and early youth. He was the youngest of four sons. The father was librarian and professor of linguistics at the University, with a great sense of humor and very sociable. The mother, the daughter of a British-Hanoverian officer named Quensel, is reported to have been very serious-minded and deeply sensitive.

In later years, Robert Bunsen accused himself of having been so extremely opinionated in his childhood that he drove parents and teachers to despair. During such attacks only his mother could influence him. Such difficulties obviously were the cause for his moving from Göttingen to Holzminden, where he finished school in 1828.

He returned to Göttingen and spent all his student years there, mainly occupied with chemistry, physics, and mineralogy, with some mathematics besides. At the age of nineteen he won his doctor's degree with a physical thesis "Enumeratio ac descriptio hygrometrorum."

Two years later we find Bunsen engaged in extended travels for which he had received stipends. In May, 1832, he visited Henschel's machinery manufacturing plant where he saw "a new small steam engine." He continued to Berlin, visiting factories and studying the geognostic and mineralogic collections of Weiss. He met Heinrich and Gustav Rose and worked in Heinrich's laboratory for a while. He also had contact with Runge, the discoverer of aniline.

He visited Liebig in Giessen, met Mitscherlich in Bonn for a

575

geological trip through the Eifel mountains, and arrived in Paris toward the end of September. In Paris the cholera epidemic was on the decline. In a session of the Academy which Bunsen attended October 22, Chevreul, then at the height of his fame, presented a paper on cholera and its treatment by sulfurous acid. At the same session it was reported that Ampère had found an external application of fluoric acid as a remedy against the scourge.

In Paris Bunsen met the outstanding chemists and visited the porcelain works at Sèvres. In May, 1833, he started from Paris to Vienna where he arrived in July. From there he visited many industrial establishments.

Full of these new experiences Bunsen started as lecturer at Göttingen. During three semesters he gave public lectures. His experimental studies on the insolubility of metal salts of arsenious acid led him to an antidote against arsenic poisoning, the hydrate of iron oxide. This was the only time that Bunsen touched on physiological chemistry. Even today there is no better antidote against arsenic than the one discovered by Bunsen.

On April 2, 1836, Bunsen received the nomination as successor to Wöhler at the Higher Trade School at Kassel. There he remained only two years and then changed to the University of Marburg where he became a full professor in 1841. In Kassel, Bunsen started his only extensive and highly important work in pure chemistry, half inorganic, half organic, which made him immediately famous. It is the study of alkarsine, or, to use the title of his later publications: "Studies in the cacodyl series, 1837–1842."

"Cadet's liquid" had long been known as a product obtained when arsenic is distilled with potassium acetate. The chemical composition of this liquid was entirely unknown. Bunsen was not deterred by the nauseating, almost indestructibly clinging odor of this poisonous substance which, in addition, is highly inflammable. With great experimental skill Bunsen mastered these difficulties. One of the arsenical compounds exploded in a closed glass tube (Nov. 9, 1836), and Bunsen lost the vision of one eye through a glass splinter. The consequence of the poisonous vapors and the wound brought him near to death.

The experiments showed alkarsine to be the oxide of an arsenic-containing radical. This radical can undergo chemical combinations, yet it remains as a unit and can be isolated as such, a "real" radical.

Such a real radical had been isolated by Gay-Lussac in 1815, the radical cyan, which in its compounds behaves like chlorine. Liebig and Wöhler had given support to a radical theory in their publication "On the radical of benzoic acid," in 1832. Now, through Bunsen's researches, the theory of radicals reached a new height. However, Bunsen did not take part in the violent discussion on theoretical subjects going on at that time.

Between 1837 and 1842 he published five papers on cacodyl, but he also studied the process of the blast furnaces. By careful analysis of the gases developed in these furnaces, he showed that at least 42% of the heat value is wasted, and he pointed out how to utilize this heat. He also started technical experiments on the generation of galvanic currents in batteries. For the highly expensive platinum used in Grove's battery he substituted a carbon electrode which he made himself. Bunsen's battery found large-scale use in industry for the production of light and in electroplating (galvano-plastics).

The most memorable and delightful episode in Bunsen's Marburg period is the scientific journey to Iceland in 1846. The publications during the last years at Marburg and the one year Bunsen spent in Breslau are almost exclusively devoted to the scientific discoveries he made in Iceland; the exception is a study on the process of raw iron production in England which he undertook in collaboration with Playfair in 1847. He wrote to Berzelius: "I am in possession of more than a hundred gas samples, enclosed in glass tubes, which I have collected in the new lava stream, in the great crater of Hekla, in several springs and fumaroles in the North and South of the country."

In 1852 Bunsen accepted the call to succeed Leopold Gmelin in Heidelberg. From all over the world students, and chemists with completed education, came to Heidelberg in order to learn or to do research in Bunsen's institute. After the end of the 1860's, chemists came only to study inorganic and, particularly, analytical chemistry under Bunsen. Organic chemistry developed mightily in theory and practice, but Bunsen declined to follow the trend in his institute.

We have to visualize this complete disregard for a great development in chemistry in order to understand how much that was entirely new and outstanding he achieved in the fields of his preference, physical and analytical chemistry. We may perhaps say that he needed to retire into himself in order to create and develop what his demon told him. Until the 1870's, he frequently had students participate in elaborating his ideas; from then on, he retired more and more into himself. As a counterweight, he taught indefatigably until the very last years of his activities. His courses were those which other teachers often consider especially thorny, namely, to introduce students to the beginnings of science through the theory and practice of analytical chemistry.

His first discoveries in Heidelberg developed out of his former (1842) construction of electric batteries, the carbon-zinc element which he further improved by eliminating nitric acid and using chromic acid instead. With these sources of energy he prepared pure chromium and manganese from the solutions of their chlorides, and from their molten chlorides the light metals: magnesium (1852), aluminum (1854), sodium, barium, calcium, lithium (until 1855). Thus Bunsen drew attention to electricity as an important help in producing metals by decomposing their salts. He searched for explanations of the electrolytic decomposition. In order to find the true atomic weights of these metals he measured their specific heats, and for this purpose he constructed a special apparatus, the ice calorimeter.

It was perhaps the splendid light that magnesium shows on burning that caused Bunsen to devote considerable attention to photochemical studies, carried out with H. E. Roscoe from 1852 to 1862. For measuring the chemical effects of sunlight Bunsen and Roscoe used hydrogen and chlorine, mixed in equal volumes. The mixture is converted into hydrochloric acid in a certain relationship to the light. From their measurements the authors concluded that the light radiated by the sun in one minute is equivalent to the chemical energy connected with the conversion of 25 times 10^{12} cubic miles of the hydrogen-chlorine mixture into hydrochloric acid.

In 1860 Bunsen published his first paper in cooperation with Gustav Kirchhoff: "Chemical analysis through observation of the

578

spectrum." Bunsen was the first to prepare analytically pure compounds of potassium, sodium, lithium, barium, strontium, and calcium. The Bunsen burner he had constructed in 1855 gave the "nonluminous" gas flame in which the pure compounds were heated. The spectrum was produced with a spectroscope which, at first, consisted of a prism, a cigar box, and two ends of otherwise unusable old telescopes.

Bunsen and Kirchhoff predicted that spectrum analysis would be the means for discovering new elements which either occurred in very small quantities and were therefore overlooked, or which the usual analytical tools were not able to distinguish from other elements. The prediction was splendidly fulfilled. Only one year later, two new elements, rubidium and caesium, were discovered and separated from the spring water at Dürkheim. From 44,000 kilograms of the water, 17 grams of rubidium and caesium chlorides were obtained. This led Bunsen to penetrating studies of other mineral waters. He worked out special methods for the analysis of such waters by "flame reactions" about which he published a separate booklet in 1880.

The volumetric analysis of gases had interested him for a long time. In 1857 he published his "gasometric methods" which became a classic, full of chemical, physical, and mechanical instructions that elevated gas analysis to equal rank with gravimetric and titrimetric methods.

Bunsen continued to work on the nature of gases; his last three studies, published 1883–1885, are concerned with the condensation of carbon dioxide on polished glass surfaces, and with capillary gas absorptions. In 1887 he described a steam calorimeter and determined the specific heats of platinum, glass, and water with this instrument.

Between all these investigations are hundreds of little observations and tricks which became known only to those who really were Bunsen's pupils in the laboratory. Twenty years ago, when I myself had the good fortune of studying under him, he was scarcely working any longer on his own projects in the laboratory, and he did not assign scientific topics to students. I was actually the last one to whom he gave a purely scientific, not only analytical, task, which was to find out whether the so-called pentathionic acid

579

really existed. From the moment that I began my independent work Bunsen lost all personal interest in me. When I later published the results of this work, which was fully appreciated by the chemists concerned with this topic, Bunsen never lost a word about this subject which he had suggested. I would not mention all this if it had not been very typical of Bunsen, even in much earlier times, to work with his students only as long as they did not gain some independence. Bunsen was not in sympathy with the method which Liebig practiced in Giessen before going to Munich in 1852, the method which is now generally adopted and in which the teacher continues to help his advanced students in scientific thinking and working. At the height of his activities, Bunsen permitted a few exceptional and older students to participate in work he was developing, as, for example, Roscoe in the photochemical studies.

A very important factor in preparing the student for learning in the laboratory was Bunsen's lecture. In precisely one hundred hours he presented regularly, each semester, a course in "Experimental Chemistry"—with the exclusion of organic chemistry. Bunsen carried out a tremendous amount of experiments. In addition he laid great stress on summaries in tables which covered the blackboards. During these hundred hours Bunsen mentioned, at the appropriate times, his own discoveries in condensed and greatly simplified form. He never said: "I have discovered," or "I found;" that would have been against his innermost feelings. He was characterized by extraordinary, distinguished modesty. That does not mean that he was not conscious of his own value. He knew how to use it at the right time and in the right company; he even had a considerable degree of very sound egotism.

When he was seventy-eight, Bunsen retired from his chair. Professor Brühl took over his lectures until Victor Meyer became Bunsen's successor. Bunsen did not show any interest in the changes which the progress in chemistry demanded in his institute. He passed the last decade of his life in contemplative leisure. Although he showed no more interest in chemistry, he returned to his first love, geology, and never tired hearing the lastest news about it from his expert friends.

Bunsen never interfered with any personal developments, not

580

even in small details, except rarely and reluctantly. He founded no family. His work was his life. His recreation were travels which extended almost all over Europe. During his travels, alone or with close friends, he felt happy and relaxed.

NOTES AND REFERENCES

Georg Lockemann, "Robert Wilhelm Bunsen," Wissenschaftliche Verlagsgesellschaft, Stuttgart, 1949.

Selected from "Address at the Academic Memorial Service for R. W. Bunsen," Nov. 11, 1899, at the University of Heidelberg. See: *Journal für praktische Chemie, 169,* 381–407 (1900). Translated by Eduard Farber.

THEODOR CURTIUS

·· *43* ··

Hermann Kopp

1817-1892

THE history of an epoch is the history of its leading men. They are the centers and sources of intellectual energy. In them the ever-widening waves of mental progress have their origin, and it is under their vivifying influence that science and learning grow and spread.

Hence, therefore, we do well, from time to time, to gauge our gain in knowledge by contemplating the life work of the men who have influenced it, and who have stamped it with the marks of their power and individuality. It is this consideration that has induced your Council to see in the occasions which the stern act of death compels us to notice, opportunities, not only of recording our sense of reverence, esteem, and admiration for those who have so faithfully tended the lamp of learning, but also of tracing the immediate outcome of their labours, and of measuring its influence on contemporary science.

By the wish of your Council I appear this evening, on this, the first anniversary of the death of Kopp, to discharge what is to me a pious duty. Five-and-twenty years ago it was my good fortune as a student in Heidelberg to come into contact with Kopp, and to be influenced by his work and teaching.

To know Kopp was to love him, and to love him was, as Steele wrote of another, a liberal education. For to his friends he was ever ready to display the ample treasures of a mind rich not only in the lore of an ancient learning, but stored with the knowledge of a time of great achievement and of profound historical interest—the time which stretches from the closing years of Berzelius down to the final decade of the century; which covers the period of the grand movement that had its inception in the little laboratory on the banks of the Lahn, and which witnessed those memorable intellectual combats between the champions of opposing schools of chemical thought, the echoes of which are only faintly heard, if heard at all, by the student of today. Kopp's colloquial powers were admirable; like the Great Lexicographer, he loved to fold his legs and have his talk out. His strong common sense; his vigorous,

585

incisive thought; the range of his information of men and letters; his quick, retentive memory; his felicity of expression; his fund of anecdote; his ready wit and genial humour—all made him delightful to listen to. To watch the play of his features as he talked was in itself a recreation. Every line in the quaint impressive face was instinct with intelligence, the outward and visible sign of the active restless *geist* behind it. Not that there was any sense of unrest about the man. When I first knew him, a quarter of a century ago, he may be said to have passed the noontide of his intellectual career; he was living the quiet, contemplative, postmeridian life of a philosopher whose period of active service as a researcher was well nigh spent, happy in his surroundings and in his occupation; his social sympathies satisfied by his relations with colleagues like Bunsen, Kirchoff, Helmholtz, Renaud, Königsberger, and Zeller; and his mental activity finding scope for itself in his lectures, in the exercise of the various offices connected with the management of the University which he was called upon to fill, and in his literary labors. His life, like that of the greater number of men of science, had not been what the world calls eventful; the successive steps in his preferment as a teacher and the appearance of his books and memoirs were the main incidents which marked the even tenor of his way. Born October 30, 1817, at Hanau, he was early attracted toward the study of natural science. His father, Johann Heinrich Kopp, a distinguished physician, seems to have occasionally occupied himself with experimental chemistry, and Leonhard's *Taschenbuch* and Gehlen's *Journal* contain papers by him on mineral analysis, and on investigations relating to physiological chemical products. The younger Kopp received his school training at the gymnasium of his native town, where he acquired that knowledge of Latin and Greek, and that love for classical learning, which he turned to such signal account in the preparation of his great work on the history of chemistry. When eighteen, he proceeded to Heidelberg, to the University which eventually claimed him as professor, where he studied chemistry under Leopold Gmelin, and physics under Wilhelm Muncke. Gmelin, who became ordinary professor of medicine and chemistry in the University in the year in which Kopp was born, is mainly known by his *Handbuch der Chemie,* of which an English translation by the

586

late Henry Watts, the first editor of our Journal, was published by the Cavendish Society. Muncke is chiefly remembered on account of his share in the production of Gehler's *Physikalisches Wörterbuch,* and by his work on the thermal expansion of liquids. Wöhler has told us something of the conditions under which practical chemistry was studied in Heidelberg during the first quarter of the century, from which we may gather that Kopp could have had but few opportunities of gaining experience of manipulative work in the old cloisters which at that time did duty as the University laboratory. He left Heidelberg, for Marburg, where he graduated in 1838, presenting to the Philosophical Faculty as his thesis an essay entitled, *De oxydorum densitatis calculo reperiendœ modo,* from which it is evident that he had already, whilst barely twenty-one years of age, been attracted by those problems which were to constitute the chief experimental labours of his life. From Marburg he passed to Giessen, drawn thither by the influence which has made the Giessen laboratory famous in the annals of chemistry. At Liebig's instigation, and under his direction, he studied the mode of decomposition of mercaptan by nitric acid. This, which was for the most part a repetition of the work of Löwig and Weidmann on ethylsulfonic acid and its salts, is, practically the only investigation in pure chemistry that Kopp ever published. Work of this kind had evidently few attractions for him, and he quickly returned to those studies which, as his inaugural dissertation shows, he felt that he was most fitted to pursue.

In 1841 Kopp became a *privat-docent* in the Giessen University, lecturing alternately on theoretical chemistry, crystallography, meteorology, and physical geography. At about this time, that is, when twenty-four years of age, he began his *History of Chemistry,* and, as his material accumulated, he added this subject to the list of his lecture courses. In 1843 he became extraordinary professor, and on the removal of Liebig to Munich in 1852, he and Heinrich Will were together made ordinary professors, and were entrusted with the charge of the Giessen laboratory. But to a man like Kopp such a position was certain to prove uncongenial; he was not fitted, either by temperament or by training, to carry on the traditions of a place so indissolubly associated with the name and fame and field of work of another, and after a year he resigned the sole con-

587

trol to his friend and colleague. Kopp remained in Giessen nearly five-and-twenty years, and all his most important experimental work was done there. In 1863 he received a call from Heidelberg, which he accepted; here, as has been said, he remained until his death, occupying himself latterly with lectures on the history of chemistry and on chemical crystallography. He was repeatedly solicited to accept a position in some one of the larger universities, notably in Leipzig and in Berlin; but all attempts to draw him from his dear Ruperto-Carolina were unavailing. "Even Bunsen alone," he was wont to say, "keeps me fast in Heidelberg." And by no one is Kopp's departure more keenly felt than by Bunsen, his friend and colleague for more than a quarter of a century. The strollers on the Anlage still miss the quaint figure on its way to the daily visit to the old veteran, who, rich in honor and in years, is now the last of that famous group which has made Heidelberg renowned as a center of intellectual life and scientific activity.

Kopp is best known to the literary world by his *History of Chemistry*. The first volume of this work, a monument of learning and of patient labour, of constructive skill and sagacious criticism, appeared in 1843, and the fourth and final volume in 1847. His life-long friend Hofmann, who was with him at Giessen, has told us that, by the publication of this classical work, Kopp, then barely thirty years old, suddenly found himself famous: —"With one accord his contemporaries recognised that here was a production which, whether they regarded the thoroughness of research that it displayed, or the manner in which the material resulting from that research was sifted and arranged, was without a parallel in the literature of any other country. And even today, after the lapse of nearly half a century, there is no historical work on chemistry that can be even remotely compared with it. Numbers of books relating to the same subject, some of considerable merit, have since been published in Germany and France, but it is not difficult to perceive that they are all grounded on Kopp's great work." For upwards of forty years Kopp had it in contemplation to bring out a new edition, and much of the later historical work he published, such as his *Beiträge zur Geschichte der Chemie,* which appeared between 1869 and 1875, and the *Entwicklung der Chemie in der neueren Zeit,* printed under the auspices of the Historical Commission of the Bavarian Academy in 1873, together with the two volumes on *Die Alchemie in älterer und neuerer Zeit,* grew out of the materials he had gathered together. "But," again to quote Hofmann, "the better is here the enemy of the good. Kopp postponed the 'vermehrte und verbesserte Auflage' year after year, in the hope of being able to make a fuller study of certain special periods. Whoever is familiar with the mass of profoundly interesting matter he had accumulated, or who has had the opportunity of seeing the bulky note-books in which it was stored, must deeply lament that the hand which could alone arrange these treasures is now stiffened in death."

On the death of Berzelius, in 1848, the leaders of the Giessen school determined to carry on the work which had mainly occupied the closing years of the illustrious Swedish chemist. Berzelius' *Year Book* had become a power in the chemical world, mainly on account of the authority wielded by the greatest chemical critic of his time. The *Jahresbericht* of Liebig and Kopp differed, however, fundamentally, both in plan and execution, from its Swedish prototype. It was to be a review of the year's progress, not only in chemistry, but also in all those sciences which were associated with chemistry, or were, in any definite sense, ancillary to it; it was to be done impartially, and with no special reference to any set of dogmas or particular school of chemical thought. Practically the whole of the more active members of the scientific side of the philosophical faculty of the University were concerned in its production. To Kopp fell the greater share of the arrangement, and of the general editorial management; in addition, he undertook the summaries relating to theoretical, physical, and inorganic chemistry. To Buff and Zamminer were entrusted pure physics; to Heinrich Will, organic chemistry; to Knapp, technical chemistry; to Ettling, mineralogy; and to Dieffenbach, chemical geology. The first volume appeared towards the close of 1849, and consisted of a review of the work of 1847 and 1848. Liebig continued to be associated with Kopp as editor for some years after his removal to Munich, but in 1857 his place was taken by Will, who acted as co-editor until 1862, when Kopp resigned his share in the responsible direction of the publication just prior to his removal to Heidelberg.

In 1851 Kopp joined Liebig and Wöhler in the production of

589

the *Annalen der Chemie und Pharmacie,* and for many years he continued to take the responsible share in its management. His name as editor appears on the title-page of no fewer than 190 volumes of this famous periodical, which, under its present designation of *Justus Liebig's Annalen der Chemie,* constitutes an abiding monument to the influence and power of its great progenitor.

Kopp's services to the literature of our science were, however, by no means confined to its journalism. Engrossing and arduous as his duties as an editor must have been, he yet found time to write the admirable *Introduction to Crystallography,* and to prepare the section on "Theoretical Chemistry" in that well-known text book, Graham-Otto's *Lehrbuch der Chemie.* These works enjoyed great popularity in Germany, and have exercised no inconsiderable influence on the education of the present generation of chemists in that country. The *Introduction to Crystallography* was indeed written specially for chemists with a view of interesting them in a study which is still too frequently neglected by them; and the "Theoretical Chemistry" proved of signal service in disseminating the doctrines which constituted the "new chemistry" of thirty years ago.

No record of Kopp's literary activity would be complete without a reference to his occasional writings, some of which are among the most typical and most characteristic of his productions; as, for example, his *Aus der Molecularwelt,* written for Bunsen's seventieth birthday, and the *Aurea catena Homeri,* with which he greeted Wöhler when fourscore years of age. In the *Molecularwelt,* Kopp's delicate fancy and quaint humor are seen at their best; the book attracted considerable attention even beyond chemical circles, and rapidly ran through a number of editions. His lecture *Sonst und Jetzt in der Chemie,* which appeared in 1867, may still be read with interest as an historical account of the changes which have conduced to the present development of chemical theory. His pen, indeed, in spite of frequent illness and waning strength, was busy to the last, and he closed a long half century of literary labour in preparing for Ostwald's "Chemical Classics," an annotated edition of Liebig and Wöhler's famous memoir on the radicle of benzoic acid—the memoir which, it will be remembered, Berzelius hailed as the dawn of a new day.

Kopp occupies an almost unique position as an investigator. The one consistent purpose of his work was to establish a connection between the physical and chemical nature of substances; to prove, in fact, that all physical constants are to be regarded as functions of the chemical nature of molecules. It is not implied, of course, that the conception of such an intradependence originated with him. As a matter of fact, almost immediately after the publication of Dalton's *New System of Chemical Philosophy,* in which the doctrine of atoms was revived to account for the fundamental facts of chemical union, the endeavour was made to connect the chemical attributes of a substance with one of its best defined physical constants, viz., its atomic mass. Prout's hypothesis is, in reality, the generalized expression of such an attempt; it is an adumbration of Mendeleeff's great discovery of the law of periodicity. But it may be justly claimed for Kopp that no one before him made any systematic effort to connect such of the physical qualities of substances as admit of quantitative statement with the stochiometrical values of such bodies. The sporadic attempts made prior to 1840 were practically fruitless on acount of the imperfect nature of the physical data up to that time extant.

When Kopp began his inquiries, very few boiling points were known, even approximately; and he had, as a preliminary step, to ascertain the conditions under which such observations must be made in order that accurate and comparable results be obtained. The thermal expansions of barely half a dozen liquids had been measured, and the very methods of making such measurements with precision had to be worked out.

At the outset of his investigations, Kopp found the physical constants with which he was more immediately concerned very much as Berzelius found Dalton's values of the relative weights of the atoms; at the close of his work, they were hardly less accurately known than were those stochiometric numbers to the ascertainment of which the great Swedish chemist had dedicated his life.

Kopp's more important memoirs readily and naturally fall into comparatively few groups:—viz., (1) those concerning the relations between the specific gravities of substances and their molecular weights; (2) those treating of the relations between boiling point and chemical composition; and (3) the papers relating to the

591

specific heats of solids and liquids. As regards the other papers, only the briefest notice is here possible.

In the paper on Solubility (*Annalen*, 34, 260 (1840)), Kopp seeks to determine the behavior of a solvent towards a mixture, in excess, of two soluble salts, or, in other words, to ascertain how far the solubility of one substance is affected by the presence of another when the conditions are such that chemical change is *a priori* impossible. Are the salts, he asks, dissolved in the ratios of their specific solubilities; or is the solubility of the one salt unaffected by the presence of the other; or can the aggregate amount of the dissolved saline matter be deduced from the specific solubilities of the constituents? He finds, as regards the solubility of two salts possessing a common basic radical, that they are never present in the saturated solution in the exact amount required by their specific solubilities. In the case of two salts containing an acid radical in common, it was observed that the salt having the "stronger" base preserved its specific solubility, and that the other salt dissolved in the solution to an extent depending on its particular character, the quantity being sometimes greater and sometimes less than the calculated amount. He also shows how such determinations afford a method of recognizing the existence of double salts in solution, but which, as in the well known case of carnallite, are more or less decomposed on crystallization. Lastly, he points out how the temperature corresponding to the change of hydration, or some other condition, in a salt, either in the dissolved or undissolved portion, as, for example, in the case of sodium sulfate, may be deduced from the formulas expressing the relation of solubility to temperature, where, as in that salt, we have to do with two solubility curves.

In 1818 Dulong and Petit found that when the atomic weights of the elements are multiplied by their respective specific heats approximately the same number is obtained. This fact was subsequently embodied by them in the statement that: "The atoms of all simple bodies have exactly the same capacity for heat." In 1831 this generalization was extended by Neumann (*Pogg. Ann.*, 23, 1) so as to include compounds, and what is now known as Neumann's law was thus expressed by its discoverer: "In bodies of analogous chemical composition the specific heats are inversely as the stochiometrical quantities, or, what is the same, stochiometrical quantities of bodies of analogous chemical composition have the same capacity for heat."

Subsequent observers, among whom may be named Avogadro, Hermann, and especially Regnault, Person, and Pape, added greatly to the experimental material on which the validity of Neumann's law is founded. The whole question was, however, reopened by Kopp in 1864. By means of a simple modification of the method of mixtures, Kopp determined the specific heats of a large number of substances, for the most part compound in their nature. He concluded that each solid substance, at a sufficient distance from its melting point, has a specific heat which may vary somewhat with physical conditions (temperature, greater or less density, amorphous or crystalline nature, &c.); but the variations are never so great as must be the case if a variation in the specific heat of a substance is to be held as a reason for explaining why the determinations of the specific heats of solid elements do not even approximately obey Dulong and Petit's law, nor those of solid compounds of analogous chemical constitution Neumann's law. Neither law is universally valid, although Kopp found that Neumann's law applies in the case of many compounds of analogous composition to which, on account of their totally different chemical deportment, different formulas are assigned; and even in cases in which these laws have hitherto been considered as essentially true the divergences from them are material. Each element has the same specific heat in its solid free state as in its solid compounds. From the specific heats to be assigned to the elements, either directly from experimental determination, or indirectly by calculation on the basis of the law just stated, the specific heats of their compounds may be calculated.

Kopp concludes his memoir with certain suggestive considerations as to the nature of the chemical elements. What substances, he asks, are to be regarded as chemical elements? Does the mere fact that they are nondecomposable determine this? Or may a body be nondecomposable in point of fact, and yet from reasons of analogy be regarded not as an element but as a compound? He reminds us that the history of chemistry furnishes numerous examples of cases in which sometimes one and sometimes another

593

mode of view led to results which at present are regarded as accurate. The earths were nondecomposable in point of fact in 1789, when Lavoisier expressed the opinion that they were compounds, oxides of unknown metals. Lavoisier's argument was based on the fact that the earths enter as bases into salts, and that it was to be assumed in regard to all salts, that they contained an oxygen acid and an oxygen base. But the view, founded on the same basis, that common salt contains oxygen, and the subsequent view that what is now called chlorine contained a further quantity of oxygen besides the elements of an oxygen acid, did not find an equally permanent recognition. On the basis of the actual nondecomposability of chlorine, Davy, about 1810, maintained its elementary character; and this view became general when Berzelius adopted it, more, Kopp thinks, because he was outvoted than because he was convinced.

In a very great number of compounds the molecular heat gives more or less accurately a measure of the complexity of their composition, and this is also the case with those compounds which, from their chemical deportment, are comparable with the undecomposed bodies.

If ammonium or cyanogen had not been decomposed, or could not be so by the chemical means at present available, the greater molecular heats of their compounds, compared with those of analogous chlorine or potassium compounds, and the greater molecular heats of ammonium and cyanogen obtained by indirect determination, as compared with those of potassium and chlorine, would indicate the compound nature of these so-called compound radicals. The conclusion appears legitimate that, for the so-called elements, the directly or indirectly determined atomic heats are a measure of the complexity of their composition (*Phil. Trans.,* 1865, 155).

These conclusions are, it should be stated, largely based upon the fact of the abnormally low atomic heats of bodies of low atomic weight, such as carbon, silicon, boron, glucinum, &c., when taken at comparatively low temperatures. Kopp would regard bodies of low atomic weight as of a low order of complexity. But since it has been recognised that the specific heat of such bodies is very largely affected by temperature, and in such manner that their atomic heats at high temperatures more and more closely approximate to the value required by Dulong and Petit's law, the force of Kopp's argument is materially weakened.

In 1841, Kopp, from observations on methyl and ethyl derivatives, drew attention to the fact that in many analogous chemical compounds the same difference in composition frequently occasions the same difference in boiling point (*Annalen, 41, 87, et seq.*). He also pointed out that in many other similar compounds, mostly alcohols, acids, and esters of the fatty series, a difference of xCH$_2$ apparently corresponds to a difference of about x19° in the boiling point; that an acid boils 40° higher than the corresponding alcohol; and that an ester boils 82° lower than the isomeric acid. On comparing analogous compounds differing only in the number of C atoms, he further concluded that the boiling point of the compound having xC atoms more than the other was $x \times 29°$ higher, and that a compound having xH atoms more than the other boiled $x \times 5°$ lower. He subsequently found that this difference of 19°, corresponding to an increment of CH$_2$, is not observed in all homologous series. Thus, in the benzene hydrocarbon xCH$_2 = x24°$; in the fatty ketones and aldehydes it is 22°; in the alkyl chlorides it is 31°; and in the fatty anhydrides it is 12.5°. Isomeric compounds of the same type and of the same chemical character have the same boiling point; if of the same type but of different character, or if of different type, their boiling points are different. Hence Kopp concluded that the boiling point of a liquid was a function partly of molecular weight and partly of chemical constitution. The influence of molecular weight, alone, may be studied by comparing bodies of strictly analogous constitution, e.g., the normal fatty acids. If Kopp's main contention is valid, the relations should hold good at other temperatures than that of the boiling point under atmospheric pressure, and by observations on the vapor pressures of the normal fatty acids, Landolt concluded that such was the case.

Further and more accurate observations showed, however, that Kopp's original propositions must be materially modified.

Kopp's first memoir on the subject of specific volume appeared in *Poggendorff's Annalen* for 1839 under the title of "Ueber die Vorausbestimmung des specifischen Gewichts einiger Klassen chemischer Verbindungen" (*Pogg. Ann., 47, 133*). In this paper he discusses the specific gravities of a number of compounds of metals and nonmetals, and by means of certain assumptions, he deduces general formulas from which he is able to calculate the specific gravities of certain oxides and haloïd salts with results which show, in general, a fair agreement with the observed values. In the same manner he calculates formulæ for other anhydrous salts, such as sulfates, carbonates, and nitrates, on the supposition that such salts consist of combinations of oxides and acids, or that they are made up of a radical, acid, *plus* oxygen. By means of these formulas he infers that it is possible to draw conclusions concerning the specific gravity of metals for which this constant is unknown. Kopp here uses the term *specific volume* for the first time, and he defines it as the molecular weight (*Mischungsgewicht*) of a body divided by its specific gravity. He finds that the specific volumes of similarly reactive elements, as, for example, chlorine, bromine, and iodine; tungsten, molybdenum, chromium, iron, manganese, nickel, cobalt, &c., are respectively equal or nearly equal. In other cases, as silver and gold, potassium and sodium, the specific volumes stand to each other in simple relations. Elements which, like barium and strontium, form isomorphous compounds show identity in specific volume, and Kopp sees in this fact an argument for the validity of the theory of hydrogen-acids; for, if we conceive that baryta replaces the strontia in an isomorphous strontium salt, it follows that the baryta will occupy a wholly different volume from the strontia; whereas, if barium replaces strontium in equivalent proportions, then since each element occupies practically the same volume, there is no *a priori* reason for any sensible change in crystalline form, which is in accordance with observation.

The conception of specific volume is still further expanded in a lecture given by Kopp to the Chemical Section of the "Naturforscher Versammlung"—the equivalent of our British Association for the Advancement of Science—at Erlangen, in 1840 (*Annalen,* 36, 1 (1840)). He first attempts to prove that the specific weight of isomorphous substances is proportional to their atomic weight; or that isomorphous bodies possess the same atomic volume. Strictly speaking, this law can hold only for those substances which are perfectly isomorphous. The bodies termed isomorphous are, in general, only approximately so, for we find the angles of their crystals deviating several degrees from one another; and the relations between the axes of bodies thus denominated isomorphous are not perfectly equal. The more nearly the crystalline forms of isomorphous substances are identical, the more nearly will their atomic volumes be the same.

Kopp's memoir, which gave to the specific gravity of a solid and liquid substance a new and important significance, attracted much attention and occasioned no little controversy. Schröder (*Pogg. Ann.*, 553 (1840)), starting from the observation of Ammermüller, that equal volumes of the two oxides of copper contain the same amounts of copper and multiple amounts of oxygen, assumed that the volume of the copper, as of the oxygen, is equal in the two substances, but that the amount of the oxygen in the cuprous oxide stands to that in the cupric oxide as 1 to 2. Hence Schröder drew the general conclusion that the same element can have different specific volumes in different compounds, but that the several values for the specific volumes stand in simple relations to each other. He saw in this hypothesis not only an explanation of the condensation which accompanies chemical union, but also a rational basis for the belief that the volume of a compound is equal to the sum of the volumes of its components.

Schröder's ideas, to begin with, had something in common with those of Kopp, but they underwent frequent modifications during the next 30 years. The characteristic manner in which the two philosophers presented their views was thus sketched by Berzelius:—"Schröder is invariably of opinion that he has discovered what is right: to his thinking, the proofs he cites are evident; he is always convinced and insists that his reader is equally so . . . Kopp, on the other hand, draws attention not only to that which supports a statement but also to that which is adverse to it . . . He searches for truth, but he indicates, without reserve, what he provisionally regards as only probable."—(Quoted by Ostwald, *Stöchiometrie,* p. 620).

Kopp's conceptions on the subject at this time took more formal shape in the small book he published in 1841, at Frankfort, *On the Specific Gravity of Chemical Compounds.* A summary of this work appeared in the *Phil. Mag.* for 1842, from which the following abstract is made:—The atomic volume of a compound is seldom equal to the sum of the atomic volumes of its elements, that is, the "primitive atomic volumes" calculated from the specific gravity of the elements in the isolated state. If the atomic volume of a compound is greater than the primitive atomic volumes of either of its components, it is impossible, *a priori,* to say whether one or both of the elements are contained in it with an atomic volume different from the primitive value; but it is certain that one element in a compound does not possess its primitive atomic volume if the atomic volume of the compound is smaller than the primitive atomic volume of that element. It is not as yet possible to state for every compound which element enters into it with its primitive atomic volume, or whether both acquire different ones. It is only possible to infer this with any degree of probability in the case of analogous compounds which have *one* element in common.

Kopp continued to the last to interest himself in the problem which had been the mainspring of his scientific activity. Shortly before his death, he gave to the world, through the *Annalen* (250, 1889, 1), a critical account, written with the dignity and calm that befits the well-earned leisure of a veteran controversialist, of the many strivings which had been made to solve it since the tentative efforts put forth in his thesis of 1838.

We rise from the perusal of this memoir with the conviction that, after all, the work thus summarized takes us but little beyond the threshold of the fundamental truth of which its author was the first to perceive the indication.

As yet we see through a glass darkly, and know only in part; but with the fuller light of a rapidly advancing knowledge, we shall most certainly get an insight into the causes which affect the universality of Kopp's conclusions. The discrepancies, if we could only read them aright, contain within them the clues to a broader generalisation which will more clearly connect the chemical nature of molecules with their physical attributes. Our experimental material will soon be sufficient for the basis of this generalisation, even if it is not so already. What is wanted is another Kopp to interpret it correctly.

NOTES AND REFERENCES

Julius Ruska, "Hermann Kopp, Historian of Chemistry," *J. Chem. Educ.*,
   14, 3 (1937).
Max Speter, "Vater Kopp," *Osiris*, V, 392–460 (1938).

Selections from *J. Chem. Soc.*, *63*, 776–815 (1893).

THOMAS EDWARD THORPE

·· *44* ··

Henri Sainte-Claire Deville

1818-1881

THE records of the Deville family go back a long way. At the close of the sixteenth century, they left their ancestral home at Périgueux and at Bergerac found refuge from the religious disturbances. About one hundred years later, one of the sons emigrated to the Antilles. He became a prosperous shipowner and a leading citizen, always generous of his time, advice, and money. Even though he never gave up his French citizenship, he took over the functions of the Danish governor of the Virgin Islands when the latter was away in Europe. His children were born on St. Thomas, and when they reached the proper age, the boys were sent to Paris to be educated. The brothers, Charles (b. February 26, 1814) and (Étienne) Henri (b. March 2, 1818) were enrolled in the same class at the Institution Sante Barbe (the later Collège Rollin) and there received a solid foundation in the traditional classical curriculum. They decided to go into science; Charles entered the École des Mines; his younger brother chose medicine. Eventually, they both became eminent scientists, and hence are among the relatively few men of West Indian origin who have attained leadership in fields other than art and literature. In fact, Henri is said to have hesitated between music and science when he completed his collegiate studies.

His time was far from fully occupied by his medical studies, and he became an enthusiastic attendant at the science lectures delivered at the various schools. Thenard's lectures on chemistry at the Sorbonne[1] attracted him especially, and having ample funds, the young medical student set up a laboratory in the garret of a house on the Rue de la Harpe. Here he not only repeated the demonstration experiments he had witnessed, but soon he was making original investigations. He was essentially self-taught in laboratory manipulations, but by patient repetition he acquired manual dexterity. This independent method of learning made him self-reliant, and throughout his career he seldom called for outside help in handling or devising new types of equipment. He worked incessantly all his life.

603

His first paper, "Études sur l'essence de terebenthine," was written before he was twenty-one. He submitted it to the Academie, and the examiners (Thenard, Pelouze, Dumas) reported: The difficulties of the subject taken up by the author, the conscientious care that he has given to all of his experiments, and the novelty of some of his results, determined the committee to recommend that his paper be included in *Recueil des savants étrangers*.[2] With this commendation, Deville continued his work, and the next year published further papers on turpentine[3] and in 1841 reported his findings on the essence of elemi and balsam of tolu.[4] From the latter material he obtained a hydrocarbon, which, because of its resemblance to benzene, he named benzoene. This compound had been isolated in 1837 by Pelletier and Walter, who called it retinnapthe, but Deville believed his product was isomeric with the latter. Glenard and Boudault obtained it by destructive distillation of "dragon's blood"; hence they proposed the name "dracyle." Eventually the identity of the three products was established; the compound is now called toluene.[5] Deville studied the action of various reagents on his product, including nitric and sulfuric acid, and isolated the corresponding derivatives, although not always in pure form. He obtained methyl benzoate from tolu, the earliest instance of an ester derived from a natural product. His studies of oil of lemon, creosote, rosin, and guiacum led to publishable results. Therefore, it is not surprising that his degree of *Docteur en Médecine* (1843) was soon followed by *Docteur ès Sciences*. He now definitely decided to devote himself to science, even though the financial prospects were less than those in a medical career. He found it easy to accept the changed situation when he learned that his father's estate amounted to practically nothing. His tastes had always been simple, his needs modest. He was quite prepared to make his own way, relying on hard work coupled with an active mind.

Education, particularly at the higher levels, was being reorganized throughout France, and the Council of the University of Paris was empowered to make the necessary changes in curricula and faculties. Thenard, a power in this body, firmly believed in the policy of appointing young men of promise. Accordingly, Henri Deville, although only twenty-six, was sent in February, 1845, to

604

Besançon not only to be professor of chemistry but also dean of the newly created scientific faculty. He soon showed that Thenard's confidence in him was justified. The city authorities were worried about the salubrity of the drinking water taken from the Doubs, and they asked Deville to examine this river and its tributaries. All of his previous experience had been in organic chemistry, but he attacked this apparently dull analytical problem with his customary ease and thoroughness. He learned the methods then in use, improved them, and devised others. Characteristically, he did not restrict his study to the local waters, but had samples sent from many important sources. The results were summed up in two remarkable papers.[6] He showed that river waters invariably contain silica and nitrates, results later confirmed by Boussingault and shown to have an important bearing on agriculture. In his eulogy, Pasteur said:

> This extraordinary analytical talent which was a feature of Deville's genius never left him thereafter; if you review the whole of his perserving labor you will find it marked at every step by evidences of a passionate striving for the most perfect analytical methods. This rigor in analysis, which is the integrity of the chemist, was communicated by Deville to all of his students It shines through the work of all those whom he has inspired.[7]

The next year brought a really brilliant success. Acid anhydrides (then called water-free acids) had been prepared only in the case of polybasic acids. One group of chemists, headed by Gerhardt, even maintained the nonexistence of anhydrides of monobasic acids. Deville, characteristically, did not allow this *a priori* dictum to divert him from an actual trial. He placed dry silver nitrate in a U tube, heated it to $60°C$., and passed in dry chlorine. The volatile product was condensed in a tube immersed in a freezing mixture. Analysis proved the beautifully crystalline material to be N_2O_5.[8] The sensational new product and its discoverer were exhibited by Dumas. Many years later he wrote:

> I still seem to hear the applause with which the intelligent and appreciative audience at the Sorbonne hailed both the container lined with beautiful crystals of anhydrous nitric acid and the youth-

ful dean of the faculty of Besançon, who was rendering to them the first report of this new product.[9]

Deville's competency was now well recognized, and consequently, when Balard was made professor at the Collège de France, Deville was appointed his successor (January 22, 1851) at the École normale supérieure. The salary was 3000 francs per year. The purpose of this institution was the training of teachers for the secondary schools; there were no facilities for advanced work.[10]

There was ample laboratory space but practically no equipment or scientific library. The annual laboratory fund was 1800 francs. Deville accepted these circumstances and set about improving the facilities. Because of Deville's success as a teacher, Dumas appointed him as his substitute lecturer at the Sorbonne. This arrangement lasted from 1853 until 1866, when Deville was given a titular professorship. His lectures at the Sorbonne were long remembered as being filled with spirit and embellished with unexpected figures of speech and analogies.[11] Deville throughout his career kept away from disputes over theoretical matters; he taught his students to hold in contempt wordy scientific notions in which high-flown verbiage is used to conceal the lack of sound ideas.

Deville taught in the École normale for thirty years. Of necessity he had to deal with beginners, but he never seemed to lose patience with them or to regret the time spent in elementary instruction. Perhaps the reason lay in the simplicity and fundamental kindness of the man, but he also balanced this unexciting type of usefulness by a constant program of research. The abundant distractions which Paris offers were renounced; he resolved early in his life to devote his days to physical tasks, his evenings to study and reflection. Referring to Deville, Dumas said:

> There is no need of discussing the directorship of a school of fine arts or the headship of a laboratory of experimental science, if the chief needs to do nothing beyond surrounding himself with intelligent, industrious students and to aid them with advice drawn from kindly experience. However, things do not happen that way. The head of the laboratory must himself be a model of diligence, devoted

completely to his work, patient, working with his own hands, the first to set to work, the last to stop. The students must be able to be proud of their teacher or feel honored that their school is brought to the attention of the scientific world or men of discretion by remarkable discoveries, by new ideas set forth there, or by achievements that win applause. Their school spirit unites under such influences, their creative faculties are awakened, the generations animated by this same spirit march together to the attainment of truth in science. . . . It is only at this price that a man can found a school in which he is the master and beloved teacher, if to the gifts of intelligence, inspiring confidence and respect, he adds that sovereign kindness of heart, which is the ineffable source of affection.

From the moment he entered the laboratory at the École normale to the day he was kept away from it by the illness to which he was to succumb, Deville was the most assiduous, the most unassuming, the happiest of those whom the love of science had brought together there.

Deville started by putting his scanty equipment in order and organizing his courses. As soon as things were going smoothly, he began his private research. The first two years were spent on a study of carbonates[12] and particularly of a number of analytical problems. At Besançon he had become acquainted with both the dry and wet methods of mineral analysis and knew their merits and defects. He skillfully combined them into his *voie moyenne,* which was characterized not only by its wide range of applicability but by the extensive use of readily volatilized reagents, whose excess accordingly could be easily removed. The method was well adapted to the analysis of natural silicates. The sample was heated to redness with pure lime, the resulting mass pulverized, and then treated with nitric acid. The insoluble silica was separated from the soluble nitrates; the latter were thermally decomposed to the corresponding bases, which could then be treated by the conventional procedures. The method,[13] although constantly used in Deville's laboratory, was not widely adopted. However, it gave its originator a clearer insight into inorganic reactions and demonstrated to him that the properties ascribed to certain metals were actually due to impurities. Consequently, it was imperative to devise methods of isolating or purifying these metals, some of them quite rare at that time. His first efforts in this direction dealt with aluminum.

The use of alum (L. *alumen*) goes back to at least the fifth century B.C. This name was applied to a variety of products containing varying percentages of aluminum sulfate. The ancients were totally ignorant of its composition, but the alchemists of the Middle Ages showed that it consists of vitriolic acid combined with an earthy material whose identity remained uncertain until well into the eighteenth century. In 1727, Geoffroy the Younger showed that the same earth was likewise a constituent of clay, a finding that was confirmed by Macquer, Bergman, Scheele, and others. It was generally believed that this earth was a simple substance, but Baron and then Lavoisier (1782) declared it was an oxide of a metal which holds the oxygen so tenaciously that the latter cannot be removed by heating with carbon. In 1808 Davy exposed red hot alumina to potassium vapor without effect, nor was he, or Berzelius, or Oersted able to secure the metal from the oxide by means of the voltaic current. In 1824 Oersted found that aluminum chloride can be prepared by passing chlorine over a hot mixture of alumina and carbon, and he tried the action of potassium amalgam on his new preparation. The mercury was distilled away from the reaction product, and specimens of the residue, which resembled tin, were exhibited, in March and April, 1825, to the Copenhagen Academy. Being occupied with other matters, Oersted urged his good friend Wöhler, who visited him in 1827, to try to improve the process. Wöhler found that Oersted's product consisted chiefly of potassium. When (1827) he heated a mixture of potassium and aluminum chloride in a crucible, the action was so violent that the cover had to be wired down. The reaction mass was treated with water to remove potassium chloride, and there remained a gray powder "which on closer examination, especially in sunshine, appeared to consist of tiny metallic spangles."[14] Wöhler then dropped the subject for eighteen years. In 1845 he utilized a procedure suggested by Liebig in 1836 to reduce the violence of the reaction, namely, to pass the vapor of the aluminum chloride over heated potassium. The reaction was carried out in a platinum tube, since glass tubes invariably broke. Wöhler thus

608

obtained not only powder but also globules the size of a pinhead. He was able to determine some of the physical and chemical properties of the new metal, but the quantities available were so small that actually aluminum remained a rarity. This work caused no great stir in chemical circles, and industrial applications were not even dreamed of.

Deville had no thought of isolating the metal when he began his work on aluminum. Reasoning from the general similarity of ferric and aluminum compounds, he thought it might be possible to prepare a lower aluminum oxide analogous to ferrous oxide via the corresponding but unknown aluminum dichloride. Accordingly he sought to prepare the latter by reducing aluminum trichloride by means of metallic potassium. He used essentially the method of Wöhler, but because potassium had become more plentiful he operated on a larger scale than was possible to his German predecessor. Beautiful bright metallic globules were obtained and the product showed all the characteristics that are now typical of aluminum. He proved that Wöhler's preparation were contaminated with platinum. Three reports of his progress were sent to the Académie in 1854.[15]

The excellent physical properties of aluminum, coupled with its resistance to air, water, etc., led Deville to give serious consideration to its technical possibilities, provided the cost would be brought down. He proved that sodium could be used in place of potassium, which was quite dangerous to handle, and that the substitution would be further advantageous because of the much lower equivalent weight (23:39). However, sodium at that time was a chemical rarity and sold at 7 francs per gram as against 900 francs per kilogram for potassium. By 1855 Deville brought the price of sodium down to 2000 francs per kilogram and in 1859 to 10 francs. The process which he developed to factory scale had been originated by Gay-Lussac, Thenard and Brunner; it involved the reduction of sodium carbonate by carbon in the presence of lime. He found that this alkali metal could be cast into ingots and handled with comparative safety. These studies preliminary to large-scale production of sodium, aluminum chloride, and aluminum were carried out at the École normale, and their cost was met in part by a grant from the Académie. When they showed sufficient promise, Dumas, in 1855, brought the matter to the attention of the Emperor, who was interested in the development of new industries. Deville was summoned and exhibited specimens of aluminum to the monarch, who was intrigued with the idea of fitting out his troops with cuirasses and helmets of the new metal. Hence, Deville was given a government grant to defray the costs of pilot plant operations at Javel, and technical success was soon assured.[16]

Though Deville had proclaimed "clay is the ore of aluminum," his raw material was bauxite, so-named because beds of this hydrated alumina occur at Baux, a town near Arles. After being freed of iron, the pure alumina, produced via aluminate, was mixed with carbon, heated, and treated with chlorine to form the chloride. A succession of pans charged with about 500 grams of sodium each was placed in an iron tube, heated to 200–300°, and an excess of aluminum chloride vapors was then passed over the molten metal. The reaction mass was transferred to iron or clay crucibles and heated to complete the reaction. The tiny beads of aluminum were tediously collected and then melted together. Later it was found that it is much better to use the double sodium aluminum chloride. The reaction proceeds much more quietly so that the double chloride and the sodium may be mixed and then heated together. Part of the aluminum at least is thus obtained in larger plates and globules. Still later cryolite was included in the charge and because of the increased fluidity, the metal collected still more readily.

The preliminary work at Javel was followed by technical installations at Rouen and at Nanterre. Deville was assisted especially by his colleagues Debray and Morin, and when more capital was needed, they and other chemists subscribed 50,000 francs. Through cooperative labors they brought the method definitely to the point where it had no competition until the perfection of the electrolytic process.[17] The latter of course was not technically feasible so long as dynamic current was not available at a low price.

The first ingot produced at Javel was presented to the Académie on June 18, 1855.[18] Eventually, pieces weighing 6–8 kilograms were produced in one operation. Hence by 1856 Deville could state: "I now have no doubt that sooner or later aluminum will

610

become an everyday metal." The first kilogram cost more than 30,000 francs, but by 1859 the metal could be sold for 300 francs. Massive bars of this handsome metal, which previously had scarcely been seen in a pure state, were displayed at the Exposition of 1855, and it was clear that the new material would render inestimable service in many directions. Used at first for jewelry, it quickly outgrew this limited application, where nonoxidizability was valued more highly than lightness. Deville soon prepared aluminum bronzes, which were quickly employed in the manufacture of tableware, art objects, household utensils, marine instruments, etc.[19] It has been said: "The study of this metal and its metallurgical production, as well as the various compounds of aluminum, carried out during a series of years, forms one of the most remarkable and complete contributions made to inorganic chemistry."[20]

Deville was primarily a teacher and research man, and not an industrialist.[21] Hence when the aluminum process was well launched, he left its future technical development to others and returned to his laboratory. With sodium and aluminum now readily available, he soon used them in important new discoveries. Silicon, which is associated with aluminum in clay, had been isolated by Berzelius in 1823 as a gray powder. Deville obtained this element as shiny platelets in 1854 by electrolyzing impure sodium aluminum chloride and then dissolving away the aluminum with hydrochloric acid. In 1856 he passed a slow stream of silicon chloride vapor over pure aluminum and so produced octahedral crystals of adamantine silicon. In collaboration with H. Caron, he developed (1863) a more rapid procedure for obtaining crystalline silicon. Potassium fluosilicate was heated with a mixture of sodium and zinc. The sodium reduced the salt and the zinc dissolved the resulting silicon, which was then isolated by distilling away the zinc.[22]

In 1808, Gay-Lussac and Thenard isolated a new element, boron, by reducing boric acid with potassium. Their product was a greenish powder. When, in 1856, Wöhler and Deville substituted sodium for the potassium, the yield was much better and so they could make a close study of the properties of the element. They found, among other new facts, that amorphous boron burns in nitrogen to produce a nitride. By reducing boric oxide with alumi-

611

num, they obtained beautiful crystals of adamantine boron, whose hardness, refractive powers, and brilliance were rivaled only by those of the diamond.[23]

Bussy in 1831 isolated magnesium by means of the Wöhler reaction, but, as in the case of aluminum, the yield was scanty, and the product contained considerable potassium. Consequently the properties of metallic magnesium were not well established. In 1857, Deville and Caron reduced fused magnesium chloride with sodium, in the presence of calcium fluoride as a flux. The yield was 75 per cent of the theoretical, and considerable amounts of quite pure magnesium were obtained. They distilled the metal in carbon vessels in an atmosphere of hydrogen and then made an extensive study of the pure metal. The wealth of chemical radiation in its brilliant flame was particularly emphasized.[24]

The collaboration of Deville and Wöhler was continued in their work on titanium. They were the first to isolate this metal in a state of high purity. Wöhler was well aware of the exceptional affinity of titanium for nitrogen, and hence they prepared the element, in an atmosphere of hydrogen, by passing sodium vapor over potassium fluorotitanate.[25]

The difficulties encountered in some of the researches forcibly impressed Deville with the inadequacy of the available means of producing high temperatures. As early as 1852 and 1853, he devised laboratory furnaces, heated by coke, oil carbon, or hydrocarbons (including turpentine) burned under forced draft.[26] In 1856, he published an extensive discussion of the production of very high temperatures by means of illuminating gas fed with oxygen.[27] This procedure was quickly adopted by industry and it led eventually to autogenous welding. Deville then went on to prepare good sized specimens of a number of metals with a hitherto unattained degree of purity. For example, oxides of chromium and manganese were reduced by means of sugar charcoal; nickel and cobalt were similarly obtained from their oxalates. The lime or magnesia crucibles, which he had to use because of their refractory qualities, had the advantage of absorbing the silica and other acidic impurities. In this way, he and Debray were able to write a new chapter in the history of the high-melting metals (including platinum), because their highly pure preparations exhibited the actual properties of these elements.[28] Aided by Debray, he further improved his furnaces and then studied the properties of platinum and the methods of freeing it from palladium, rhodium, ruthenium, iridium, and osmium.[29] This work was put on a large scale at the request and expense of the Russian government. The latter had tremendous stocks of demonetized platinum, manufacturing residues, and rich ores for which the available methods were totally inadequate. Deville and Debray were entrusted with 56 kilograms of this material. After three and one-half months of incessant toil, day and night, 42 kilograms of platinum and an ingot of iridium (1.8 kilogram) were delivered to the Russian agent. The actual loss of platinum was only 120 grams. It was now possible to make reliable studies of platinum-iridium alloys and Deville and Debray became the recognized authorities in the field of the platinum metals. Hence in 1872, the International Commission on Weights and Measures commissioned Deville to prepare the alloy (90% Pt, 10% Ir) from which the standard kilogram and meter were to be manufactured. The conscientious and meticulous Deville devoted his entire care and time to this most important assignment and later to the analogous task relative to the international geodetic standard of length. These strenuous labors on the chemistry and metallurgy of the platinum metals extended over a period of about ten years; they probably shortened his life.[30]

The artificial production of minerals began with Gay-Lussac, who, in 1821, reproduced crystals of iron oxide similar to specimens collected at Mt. Vesuvius. Berthier, Ebelmen, and de Senarmont, in turn, had varying success in such endeavors. Deville's equipment for producing high temperatures and his discovery of dissociation (see p. 615) led him into this field. Caron was again his collaborator. For example, they subjected metal fluorides to the action of boric anhydride at high temperatures and obtained boron fluoride and the crystalline metal oxide. Mixtures of an amorphous phosphate with a metal fluoride or chloride were fused; apatite and other crystalline phosphates resulted.[31] By such procedures they reproduced rubies, sapphires, zircons, and other gem stones. They employed an old idea of Élie de Beaumont, namely to use gases or volatile reagents as mineralizers. When dry hydrogen was passed over hot amorphous zinc oxide (or sulfide)

613

the compound volatilized and was redeposited in crystalline form at the cooler end of the porcelain tube. Since the hydrogen which issued from the tube was pure, the gas seemingly acted merely as a mechanical carrier, or, as some thought, its mere presence had brought about the result. Deville showed that actually the effect was due to what is now known as an intermediate reaction catalysis. The amorphous zinc compound was reduced, and the resulting zinc vapor reacted, at the region of lower temperature, with the steam (or hydrogen sulfide) to produce hydrogen and regenerate the zinc compound which thereupon deposited in crystalline form. Hydrogen chloride gas gives analogous results. By this method of apparent sublimation, he prepared many crystalline sulfides and oxides. The products closely resembled such natural crystalline materials as pyrites, etc., which may have been produced in nature by a similar series of reactions, since gaseous reactants (hydrogen chloride, steam, carbon dioxide, hydrogen sulfide) are quite common in volcanic regions. This fact was demonstrated by explorations carried on, sometimes at great peril, by Charles Deville. A number of slightly soluble carbonates, sulfides, etc. were transformed into crystals at temperatures not above 100°C. In these cases, Deville and Debray took advantage of solubility variations.[32]

The opening of the Pennsylvania oil fields and the consequent rapid extension of the use of petroleum products as sources of heat and light had a marked repercussion in Europe. The Emperor, in 1867, engaged Deville to make a study of mineral oils with a view to their safe and efficient adoption in industry, especially transportation. He ran numerous fractionations to learn how to eliminate the dangerous volatile components, and he also determined the coefficients of expansion to discover the amount of free space necessary to avoid rupture of the containers. He determined the calorific value of these oils in equipment that simulated industrial conditions. He designed ingenious apparatus for use in oil-burning locomotives and steamboats, and also constructed an oil furnace for laboratory and jewelers' use that gave temperatures sufficient to melt porcelain.[33]

Characteristically, Henri Deville refused to allow his name to be presented for election to the Académie before his brother had been chosen. They were made members of the Section of Mineralogy and Geology on December 28, 1857, and November 25, 1861, respectively. Similar honors from other learned societies came in deserved measure. The laboratory at the École normale became one of the outstanding research centers of the Continent. Open house was held regularly. After a week of full activity, there was a brisk clean-up, early Sunday morning, and then the doors were opened to all. Students, alumni, friends, philosophers, mathematicians, industrialists, naturalists, and scientists of all varieties found these informal gatherings pleasant and instructive. Deville demonstrated his new findings or discussed scientific topics. Dumas wrote:

> You came away at ease with others and with a feeling of contentment with yourself. You had learned something, you had furnished your bit to progress; there you were surrounded by great talents and eminent minds, who did not haggle over crumbs of praise, but who were prompt to express admiration, were strangers to envy, ignoring jealousy, and practicing the utmost tolerance. These memories will be the eternal honor of the École normale.

Scientists from other countries came to see Deville. From 1855 on, he and Faraday visited back and forth.[34]

With the collaboration of L. Troost, an extended study of vapor densities was begun in 1857. The Gay-Lussac method was limited to quite volatile substances, while the Dumas method could not be used at temperatures approaching the softening point of glass. Deville employed porcelain bulbs and so made successful measurements at 1000–1200°C. He also proved the advantage of surrounding the bulb with the vapors of boiling liquids (Hg, Cd, S, Zn) which gave constant temperatures, as opposed to the fluctuations attending the use of hot oils or alloys that had been employed by previous workers.[35]

Deville's measurements increased the growing number of "abnormal" vapor densities, and in due time these data contributed not only to universal applicability of Avogadro's hypothesis but also to the establishment of the fact that certain materials (e.g., aluminum chloride) exhibit different molecular weights at say 500°C. (Al_2Cl_6) as compared with 1000°C. ($AlCl_3$). In other words, thermal dissociation is closely interwoven with problems

615

of molecular weights of gases, and this phenomenon constituted one of the most important of Deville's larger fields of research. He explained the abnormal densities as being the densities of mixtures of dissociation products and not of single substances, and his postulate was confirmed by experiment.

This important series opened with a paper: "Sur la dissociation ou décomposition spontanée des corps sous l'influence de la chaleur."[36] The passage of a material from the liquid to the gaseous state is not abrupt and is governed by the quantity of heat available. The two states can exist side by side, and an equilibrium is established which is characterized by the vapor tension. These facts were accepted, but matters were assumed to be quite different when the application of heat resulted in decomposition rather than a mere change of state. It was believed that for each material there is a particular temperature below which the constituents remain completely combined, whereas there is complete dissociation when it is exceeded. Deville's work was initiated by Grove's observation that platinum, near its melting point, partially decomposes water vapor into its elements. This action by the metal was ascribed to a mysterious force which enabled the metal to accomplish this decomposition by its mere presence. Deville had a horror of invoking occult forces to cover up ignorance of real causes.

In our studies, it is imperative to take no notice of such unknown forces, to which recourse is had only because their effects cannot be measured. Instead, our attention should be fixed solely on observation and quantitative measurements of those effects as are within our reach. We can thus determine their differences and analogies, and new light will be shed by these comparisons and measurements.

A new light did indeed come to him when he compared simple changes of state and partial thermal decompositions. Just as heat converts water into steam, it likewise is capable of decomposing the latter into its constituent elements. Deville showed that steam is partially decomposed not only at the melting point of platinum (1750°C.) but even at the melting point of silver (960°C.). When he passed carbon dioxide charged with water vapor through a red hot tube packed with porcelain, and collected the issuing gas over strong potash, an explosive mixture of hydrogen and oxygen

616

was obtained. Or, when steam was passed through a porous earth-enware tube, which was inclosed by an impervious tube, the inter-vening space being flushed out continuously with carbon dioxide, the latter contained significant amounts of hydrogen when the ap-paratus was heated to 1100–1300°C. The lighter hydrogen had diffused more rapidly than the oxygen, and thus the liberated ele-ments were fairly well separated from each other before thy had a chance to reunite. He was thus able to demonstrate "the phenome-non of the spontaneous decomposition of water, a phenomenon which I propose to call *dissociation*." This term has now been uni-versally adopted, though few who use it are aware of its coiner.

The crux of Deville's demonstration lay in a rapid cooling of the dissociation products or in providing an efficient means of separat-ing them from each other. By ingenious and varied experiments he proved that certain compounds, which were regarded as extremely stable, readily dissociate at high temperatures (1200–1500°C.) and that a chemical equilibrium is established, which is governed by the same factors (temperature, pressure, removal of products) that are significant in the evaporation of a liquid, where physical equilibria are set up. The separation of gases by diffusion through the walls of tubes led him to an intensive study of the permeability of metals to gases at high temperatures.[37] Since many gaseous compounds are decomposed by the passage of electric sparks, and since the effect is probably due to thermal decomposition followed by immediate cooling of the products, Deville reasoned that the ef-fect of high temperatures could be greatly magnified by introducing a cold surface into the reaction vessel. On this basis, he developed his famous hot-cold tube, in which a stream of cold water is passed through the inner tube that takes the place of the porous tube in the dissociation apparatus previously discussed. The results were excellent, and the thermal dissociations of CO_2, SO_2, and HCl were readily demonstrated.

Deville's students also worked in this field. For example, Isam-bert (1868) studied the dissociation of ammonium chloride, and Gernez (1867) demonstrated the influence of a stream of gas on the thermal decomposition of calcium and barium bicarbonates. Deville and his school provided explanations for many natural events, such as the incrustations produced by waters that are perfectly limpid when they issue from the earth; the constant proportion of carbon dioxide in the earth's atmosphere, which is regulated by its equilibrium with the calcium bicarbonate in the waters of the rivers and oceans; the continuous decomposition in the lungs of the bicarbonates carried by the blood and their re-formation in the tissues. The mineralizing action of hot gases (p. 614) was also reconsidered in the light of the new knowledge.

His students Troost and Hautefeuille showed that allotropic transformations and polymerizations proceed according to the laws of dissociation and Deville discussed their results at considerable length.[38] He believed that all compounds would dissociate at sufficiently high temperatures, and the fact that solar spectra revealed the presence of nothing but elements supported this idea. In fact, he seriously considered the possibility of the thermal decomposition of the elements themselves. "What assurance have we that hydrogen is a simple substance, and that at temperatures of millions of degrees it will not be split into two elements which combined to produce the hydrogen?"

Deville not only published many papers on dissociation but gave by invitation important comprehensive lectures, at Geneva in 1859 and 1860, before the Société de Physique et d'Histoire naturelle.[39] His lectures before the Société chimique de Paris on March 18 and April 1, 1864, were published in book form in 1866 with the title "Leçons sur la dissociation." Though attacked by some, notably Berthelot and in Holland, his theory of dissociation was accepted as of prime importance. Dumas wrote:

> The views of Newton on affinity have received unexpected and considerable support in the beautiful and important researches that Henri Ste. Claire Deville has devoted to the phenomenon of dissociation, which is one of the greatest acquisitions not only of chemistry but of natural philosophy (physics). Through his discovery of this capital phenomenon he has opened a new road to the science, by closely relating chemical decompositions to the purely physical phenomenon of the formation of vapors.

Only the more extensive of Deville's research projects could be discussed here, but many other problems received his able attention. More than two hundred books, pamphlets, and papers make

618

up the record of his indefatigable toil.[40] Understandably, he suffered from acute fatigue at times. He confessed to a friend: "Perhaps this work with aluminum, which has taken my money and the best of my time, is getting the best of me. I am very tired and bored with life." However, a short period of relaxation sufficed to bring him back to his laboratory with renewed vigor and enthusiasm.

The leading learned societies were proud to count him among their members, and from time to time he was invited to give addresses on topics of fundamental interest. He was beloved by his students, to whom he also acted as a wise counsellor. He never sought honors or advancement for himself. He used his influence solely to secure improvements in his laboratory, so that he could still further contribute to the progress of his beloved France by developing her resources and providing her with able chemists and teachers.

The ties between him and his brother Charles were extraordinarily close, and the bond was further strengthened by the marriage of one of his five sons to Charles' daughter. The death (October 10, 1876) of his brother dealt Henri a blow from which he never recovered. "It was as though half of himself had been lowered into the grave, and he seemed to have a presentiment that his own end was on the way." His thoughts, so decided, so calm, became hesitant, disturbed. The future of his loved ones occupied much of his thoughts. The desire to finish the researches he had under way took on an impatient character which might have been regarded as merely an attack of nerves, if it had not been recognized as the manifestation of a profound internal malady. His health declined steadily, and despite the best of care he expired in his modest summer home at Boulogne sur Seine on July 1, 1881.

The funeral was delayed to permit Deville's many students and friends to assemble from all parts of France. The main address was given by his dear friend Pasteur, who since 1857 had been his colleague at the École normale supérieure. This was in fulfillment of a promise made in 1868, when Pasteur had felt himself to be mortally ill and in need of comfort. Deville visited him and said: "You will survive me, I am older than you; give me your word that you will pronounce my funeral oration." Midway in his remark,[7] Pasteur had to stop to wipe away his tears. Thereafter, he kept a picture of Deville in his study. As was fitting. Henri was laid to rest next to his brother.

The Académie paid Henri Sainte-Claire Deville the signal honor of the posthumous award of its Prix Jean Reynaud (10,000 francs) which was given each five years for the most meritorious work relating to each class of the Institut. The committee report[41] reviews the development of the work on dissociation which was termed "one of the purest gems in the crown of French science." The eulogy of the Deville brothers for the Académie was composed by its permanent secretary, Dumas. This flowery recital of their accomplishments was read to the Académie on May 5, 1884 by Dumas' successor, J. Bertrand, for the author had died on April 11.[42]

NOTES AND REFERENCES

1 The great Swedish chemist Berzelius came out of one of Thenard's lectures and said: "I have been a teacher of chemistry for twenty years, but not until now have I seen how it should be taught."

2 *Compt. rend., 9*, 704 (1839).

3 *Compt. rend., 10*, 106 (1840); *11*, 444 (1840); *Ann. chim. et phys.* [2], *75*, 37 (1840).

4 *Compt. rend., 12*, 184 (1841); *13*, 476 (1841); *Ann. chim. et phys.* [3], *3*, 151 (1841).

5 A. Cahours, *Compt. rend., 30*, 320 (1850); *Jahresber. Fortschr. Chem. Mineral., 22*, 354 (1843); *Ann., 54*, 9 (1845).

6 *Compt. rend., 24*, 693 (1847); *Ann. chim. et phys.* [3], *23*, 32 (1848).

7 L. Pasteur, *Compt. rend., 93*, 8 (1881).

8 *Compt. rend., 28*, 257 (1849); *Ann. chim. et phys.* [3], *28*, 241 (1850). The reaction is $4 \, AgNO_3 + 2 \, Cl_2 = 4 \, AgCl + O_2 + 2 \, N_2O_5$.

9 J. B. Dumas, "Discours et éloges académiques," Paris, 1885, p. 305. Deville's finding led Gerhardt to modify his ideas concerning acid anhydrides; he then postulated that they resulted from the union of two molecules of acid accompanied by the loss of water. On this basis, he developed a general method of preparation and, eventually, at the expense of his health, produced anhydrides of monobasic organic acids. See E. Grimaux and C. Gerhardt, "Charles Gerhardt," Paris, 1900, pp. 407 ff.

10 There were no teaching laboratories in Paris until 1832, when Dumas set up one at his own expense, first in the École polytechnique, and later (1839) on the Rue Cuvier. Here he carried out many of his most famous

researches with the collaboration of promising young men. The political upheavals of 1848 made it necessary to close this training center because he could not meet the expenses. Consequently, when Deville took up his duties at the École normale there were no public facilities for training gifted young men to become future university professors of chemistry.

11 Henry Le Chatelier, who heard Deville regularly, was fond of quoting him and his original teaching aids. "If, after 35 years, these memories have remained so vivid in our memory, it is because they produced an impression on our minds, subconscious perhaps, but nevertheless deep and deliberately so planned by Deville."

12 *Compt. rend.*, 32, 875 (1851); 34, 330, 880 (1852).

13 *Ann. chim. et phys.* [3], 38, 5 (1853).

14 For the early history of the isolation of metallic aluminum see K. Goldschmidt, *Z. angew. Chem.*, 38, 1057 (1925); 39, 375 (1926); C. Matignon and C. Fourholt, *Chimie & industrie*, 13, 9 (1925); 14, 368 (1926); 15, 702 (1926); N. Bjerrum, *Z. angew. Chem.*, 39, 316 (1926); J. Edwards, F. Frary and Z. Jeffries, "The Aluminum Industry," New York, 1930, Vol. 1.

15 *Compt. rend.*, 38, 279 (1854); 39, 321, 535 (1854).

16 Detailed accounts of the development of the process are given with diagrams of the equipment in *Ann. chim. et phys.* [3], 43, 5 (1855); 46, 415 (1856).

17 Deville and Bunsen, in 1854, prepared aluminum by electrolyzing the fused double chloride. Bunsen claimed that his territory had been violated, an opinion shared by Leibig, who wrote to Wöhler (May 15, 1854): "I was in Paris two days, and saw Deville and his aluminum. Just think, he prepares it by Bunsen's method with the galvanic current. The only thing really new is the large pieces." For details of the Bunsen-Deville polemic see *Compt. rend.*, 39, 325, 771, 905 (1854). See H. N. Holmes, *J. Chem. Educ.*, 7, 233 (1930), for account of Lyman B. Hall's discovery at Oberlin College, Ohio. Hall's teacher, Frank F. Jewett, had studied at Göttingen during Wöhler's lifetime.

18 *Compt. rend.*, 40, 1296 (1855).

19 See Deville's detailed account in his "De l'aluminium, ses propriétés, sa fabrication et ses applications," Paris, 1859. See also the early volumes of *Rev. aluminium* (1924–1926).

20 Deville never denied his debt to Wöhler and as soon as enough metal was available had a medal made bearing the latter's bust and the date 1827. Wöhler never doubted his own priority. On April 7, 1873 he wrote to Liebig: "In response to my inquiry, Lepsius tells me that the eagles on the captured French flags really are made of gilded aluminum—a metal which was first prepared at Berlin in 1827. *Sic eunt fata.*" Claims in Wöhler's behalf were pushed by outsiders and without his knowledge. See *Compt. rend.*, 38, 339, 555, 557 (1854). Oersted is now generally

given credit for the earliest isolation of aluminum. Cf. footnote 14. See, however, H. Rheinboldt's valuable "Hundert Jahre Aluminium," Bonn, 1928, where Wöhler's claims are defended.

21 For some years he was on the board of directors of the Paris Gas Company and also the Eastern Railroad of France.

22 *Compt. rend.*, *39*, 321 (1854); *45*, 163 (1856); *Ann. chim. et phys.* [3], *43*, 5 (1855); *45*, 163 (1856).

23 *Compt. rend.*, *43*, 1088 (1856); *44*, 342 (1857); *45*, 888 (1857); *46*, 185 (1858); *Ann. chim. et phys.* [3], *52*, 63 (1858); *Ann.*, *105*, 67 (1857). Most of this work was done in Wöhler's laboratory at Göttingen. The first publication was hurried because Dumas warned them that others were working in this field. Through Dumas' influence, Napoleon III made Deville and Wöhler officers of the Legion of Honor at the same time.

24 *Compt. rend.*, *44*, 394 (1857); *Ann. chim. et phys.* [3], *67*, 340 (1863). In 1852, Bunsen prepared magnesium by electrolyzing the fused chloride, and this method quickly replaced the chemical method when current became relatively inexpensive. However, Deville had an important part in bringing the magnesium industry into being.

25 *Compt. rend.*, *45*, 480 (1857); *Ann. chim. et phys.* [3], *52*, 92 (1858).

26 *Compt. rend.*, *35*, 796 (1852); *37*, 1003 (1853).

27 *Ann. chim. et phys.* [3], *46*, 182 (1856).

28 *Compt. rend.*, *44*, 673, 1101 (1857). It should be noted that as early as 1782, Lavoisier melted platinum on hot carbon with the aid of compressed oxygen. "Oeuvres," Paris, 1862, Vol. 2, pp. 423, 451.

29 *Compt. rend.*, *48*, 731 (1859); *50*, 1038 (1860); *54*, 1139 (1862); *Ann. chim. et phys.* [3], *56*, 385 (1859); *61*, 5 (1860).

30 *Compt. rend.*, *75*, 849 (1862); *78*, 1502 (1874); *76*, 839 (1875); *78*, 1091, 1509 (1876); *88*, 210, 558 (1879); *Ann. chim. et phys.* [5], *16*, 506 (1879); *23*, 120 (1881); *Ann. sci. Éc. norm. sup.* [2], *8*, 9, 41 (1879); *9*, 9 (1879).

31 *Compt. rend.*, *46*, 764 (1858); *47*, 985 (1858); *52*, 780 (1861); *Ann. chim. et phys.* [3], *67*, 443 (1863).

32 Most of Deville's many papers on the laboratory preparation of minerals will be found in Vols. 52, 53, 54 of *Compt. rend.* See also *Ann. chim. et phys.* [4], *5*, 104, 118 (1865); H. Debray, *Agenda du chimiste*, 343 (1882).

33 *Compt. rend.*, *66*, 442 (1868); *67*, 1089 (1868); *68*, 349, 485, 686 (1869); *69*, 933 (1869); *72*, 191 (1871).

34 A charming permanent souvenir of this friendship was Deville's translation (published 1865) of Faraday's classic "History of a Candle," to which the translator added complementary notes and a biographical sketch of the author.

35 *Compt. rend.*, *45*, 821 (1857); *49*, 239 (1859); *56*, 891, 977 (1863); *57*, 897 (1863); *62*, 1157 (1866).

36 *Compt. rend.*, *45*, 857 (1857).
37 *Compt. rend.*, *57*, 965 (1863); *58*, 328 (1864); *59*, 102 (1864); *66*, 83 (1868).
38 *Compt. rend.*, *76*, 1175 (1873).
39 *Archives*, *6*, 266 (1859); *9*, 51 (1860).
40 A complete bibliography of Deville's publications is given by J. Gay, "Henri Sainte-Claire Deville, sa vie et ses travaux," Paris, 1889.
41 *Compt. rend.*, *94*, 326 (1882).
42 Biographical essays on Henri Deville, in addition to those already cited, have been published in *Nature*, *24*, 219 (1881); *Popular Science*, *20*, 543 (1881), and especially by D. Gernez, *Ann. sci. Éc. norm. sup.* [3], *11*; Supplement, pp. 1–70 (1894).

From: *Chymia*, *3*, 205–221, University of Pennsylvania Press, Philadelphia, 1950.

RALPH E. OESPER
PIERRE LEMAY

·· 45 ··

August Wilhelm Von Hofmann

1818-1892

THE childhood and adolescence of Hofmann present a picture of an extremely happy development of a young man. Born at Giessen on April 8, 1818, he grew up in the scientific atmosphere of the small university. His father, who was in the service of the Grandduke of Hesse-Darmstadt, had come to Giessen in 1817 as provincial architect and had built his own house there. He was filled with serious ambitions and transmitted his noble aspirations to his son. The trips which they took together to France and Italy aroused in the boy a lasting enthusiasm for the beauties of art and nature.

Wilhelm entered the University at Giessen in 1836, intending to study law. He also attended lectures on mathematics and sciences, and he was especially attracted by Liebig's course in analytical chemistry. Once under the spell of that already world-famous teacher, he never again left this science and soon became Liebig's enthusiastic student. The latter cordially received the gifted young man, all the more so because his father, as university building superintendent, was overseeing the construction of the chemical laboratory.

It is a remarkable coincidence that Hofmann's first independent research dealt with the same topic that was later to bring him fame, namely, aniline, a basic material present in coal tar. Endowed with an unsuspecting power of varied chemical reactivity, it became in Hofmann's hands the starting point of the modern dye industry.

He was awarded the doctorate *summa cum laude* on April 9, 1841. His thesis was published two years later in Liebig's Annalen with the title: "Chemical investigation of the organic bases in coal tar." The accidental instigation for this study came from one of Liebig's former pupils, Ernst Sell, who had built a tar distillery and had proudly sent his former teacher a sample of coal tar oil as his first product. Liebig turned this material over to his private assistant for investigation. It was already known that this liquid contained small amounts of acidic and basic substances. Laurent had

627

studied the former, carbolic acid, and had recognized it as phenyl hydrate. Hofmann turned his attention to the basic components. However, he needed larger quantities and so he went to Sell, whom his family knew. At the factory at Offenbach he himself extracted 1200 pounds of tar oil with hydrochloric acid and after eight days returned to Giessen with two pounds of a precious mixture of bases. Hofmann's study showed that the main portion of this mixture was identical with a base obtained by C. J. Fritzsche of St. Petersburg, who had prepared it from anthranilic acid and had named it anilin from the Portuguese anil (blue), because the Berlin chemist Otto Unverdorben had first obtained it (1826) by distilling indigo. Hofmann immediately adopted this name. However, he found this pyrolytic method extremely cumbersome for preparing considerable quantities of this interesting material. The situation was altered in 1845 when he discovered a procedure for preparing aniline from benzene. The latter was treated with strong nitric acid and the resulting nitrobenzene then reduced by means of a mixture evolving hydrogen. Up to then, benzene had been prepared exclusively from benzoin resin, but now with the aid of this reaction Hofmann made the surprising discovery that benzene is the chief constituent of the low-boiling fractions of coal tar. At that time, only the scientific importance of his discovery was significant. Happy in the possession of a ready means of securing adequate raw material, Hofmann turned his whole attention to the study of aniline.

Stimulated by papers on indigo, which as Liebig's assistant it was his duty to abstract for the *Annalen,* he subjected the chlorinated derivatives of indigo to the Unverdorben process of dry distillation and obtained the corresponding chlorinated anilines. These studies were of great importance to the development, then in progress, of the chemical theories because they made it possible to mediate between two irreconcilable viewpoints, namely, the electrochemical theory of Berzelius and the substitution theory of Dumas. According to the former, the character of a compound is determined solely by the nature of the elements it contains; while Dumas, who had found that the positive hydrogen in compounds could be replaced by negative chlorine without an essential change in the chemical character of the compounds, believed that the latter depended not only on the nature of the elements making up the compounds but on the position of the elements. In possession of mono-, di-, and trichlorinated aniline, Hofmann demonstrated that in fact negative chlorine can take the place of a hydrogen atom without destroying the positive character of the base. This was a brilliant confirmation of the Dumas theory, but there remained the other equally important finding that the negative constituent undoubtedly exerts an effect on the over-all nature of the compound. The basicity of aniline is somewhat diminished even in the mono derivative, the decrease is more marked in the dichloro compound, and "in the neutral trichloraniline the electronegative properties of the entering chlorine atoms have brought about an equilibrium with the electropositive character of the original system." Hofmann had thus reconciled two seemingly incompatible theories; while substantiating the Dumas concept he also confirmed the views of Berzelius. This research made Hofmann's name known in the scientific world and he was awarded the gold medal of the Société de Pharmacie de Paris with a value of 200 francs.

By this time Hofmann had moved to Bonn. Exceedingly responsive to feminine beauty, he had become engaged to Helene Moldenhauer, the charming niece of Liebig's wife. Since there was no chance of securing an independent position at Giessen, he had accepted the post of Privatdozent at Bonn. He started his teaching career with a course of lectures on agricultural chemistry, but soon found other fields to cultivate.

Liebig had introduced the Baconian inductive method into scientific research. The famous Giessen laboratory had attracted eager young men from all parts of the civilized world. This new system of chemical education also had attracted the attention of discerning Englishmen and had pointed up the grave defects of the teaching methods in use in England.[1] A committee had been formed, under the chairmanship of Prince Albert to found a "College of Chemistry" and it was planned to secure one of Liebig's students to head this school. Hofmann, along with Heinrich Will and C. W. Fresenius, was suggested by Liebig.

The celebration (1845) honoring the seventy-fifth anniversary of Beethoven's birth brought Queen Victoria and Prince Albert

629

to Bonn, the birthplace of the great musician. By chance, Hofmann was living in the apartment that Albert had occupied while he was a student, and arrangements were made for the prince to visit his former lodgings. Hofmann had fitted up a laboratory in these rooms and performed some experiments for the eminent visitors who were charmed by the gracious manner with which he entertained them. All his life, Hofmann had the ability of making both high- and low-born casual visitors and acquaintances feel at home in his presence. The royal couple urged his speedy appointment to the London post; in fact the Prince appealed to Friedrich Wilhelm, King of Prussia, who was then in Bonn, to secure from the Minister of Education a two-year leave for Hofmann, since the position in England was not a state appointment and was being guaranteed only by a private committee. England never had any reason to regret this choice. Instead of two years, Hofmann stayed in England for twenty years. During this period he worked as researcher, teacher, and intellectual leader in many chemical enterprises; all of these activities were extremely fruitful.

Many important people were among his students. They included: Sir Frederick Abel, the director of the powder factory at Woolwich, who "tamed" guncotton and introduced it into warfare; Warren de la Rue, the head of the Government Printing Office and the largest paper factory in London; E. C. Nicholson, the director of one of the largest chemical plants in Great Britain; the gifted Charles Blackford Mansfield (1819–1855), the first to fractionate the light tar oil into benzene and toluene, and who lost his life in a fire during the operation of his process; the renowned Sir William Crookes (1832–1919) who discovered thallium in the chamber slime of the sulfuric acid plants; John Stenhouse (1809–80) the investigator of archil dyeing. Many chairs of chemistry were occupied by Hofmann's British students. It is interesting to note that German students also came to be taught by Hofmann. Among these were: Peter Griess (1829–1888), who in addition to his activity as chemist of the great Alsopp brewery at Burton-on-Trent found time to make remarkable contributions to the chemistry of dyes, especially through his discovery of the diazo reaction; Georg Merck (1825–73) a member of the famous chemical family of Darmstadt; C. A. Martius (1838–1920) the founder of the great

Agfa chemical concern; Jacob Volhard (1834–1910) who was destined to write the detailed biographies of Liebig and Hofmann.

Hofmann's scientific accomplishments were largely the extension of his early researches. The multiplicity and variety of reactions of aniline opened an unlimited field for his labors. In the reports, which he regularly submitted to the founders of the college concerning his activities, there are ten papers by him bearing the title: "Contributions to the knowledge of the volatile organic bases." The guiding principle of these studies was to lay bare the analogies which the new bases (aniline, toluidine, cumidine, etc.) exhibit with respect to ammonia. Intensive studies were made of the action of cyanogen, chlorcyanogen, carbonyl chloride, carbon disulfide, iodine, and many other agents on these bases. There resulted the fundamental studies of cyanoaniline and its decomposition products, oxanilide and oxanilic acid, also investigations on melaniline (diphenylguanidine), which leads to phenylisocyanic acid, on phenylurea from aniline cyanate, on carbanilide, which is the diphenylurea prepared from aniline and phosgene, on sulfocarbanilide and its desulfurized products, and many more. The important result of these investigations was the recognition that the Berzelius theory is not capable of explaining the relationships between all of these findings and that aniline is not to be regarded as an additional product of ammonia, as demanded by this theory, but rather as a substitution product of ammonia.

At its start, the Royal College had to be content with rented quarters but in due time it moved into a house of its own on Oxford Street, where laboratories and an auditorium had been erected according to Hofmann's plans. However, despite the generosity of its patrons, the organization of a private institution was not favorable to an unhampered development. There were financial difficulties, which at times even extended to the nonpayment of Hofmann's salary. The situation changed radically in 1853 when the government, which had no doubts about the usefulness of the college, took it over and attached it to the Royal School of Mines as the chemical division. Lyon Playfair (1819–1898) the head of the school, had accepted a call to Edinburgh and Hofmann was given the professorship in the combined schools. He thus was assured of a stable government position, which was made even more attractive when, at Graham's suggestion, he was appointed the latter's successor as master of the mint, a well-paying post which did not markedly encroach on his time.

Although Hofmann's researches had thus far been concerned chiefly with theoretical topics, they now took a turn which was to have significant consequences for the development of the chemical industry. His laboratory became the cradle of the coal tar dye industry. The ability of aniline to yield dyes had long been known, ever since F. F. Runge (1794–1867) had used its oxidation to a blue by bleaching powder as a means of detecting this base. Realizing the complicated nature of the organic dyes, Hofmann had turned his attention first to the simpler reactions. Only after his student and assistant, William Henry Perkin (1838–1907), recognized the technical value of the violet dye, which he had discovered in 1856 and had called mauve (from the color of the mallow blossom) did Hofmann begin to occupy himself with the colored derivatives of aniline. The first dye was so costly that it could be used only for dying silk threads which were then incorporated into expensive fabrics. However, intelligent technology soon mastered this lucrative business. Other dyes came on the market, including a fine red, called fuchsin (from the fuchsia flower) and made by oxidizing aniline by various means. Hofmann demonstrated that it could not be obtained from pure aniline but only from a mixture of aniline and toluidine. He found that rosaniline, which he prepared from aniline and carbon tetrachloride, and which is the parent compound of all aniline dyes, contains three substitutable hydrogens. He found that the brilliant aniline blue, discovered by Charles Girard (1837–1918) and Georges de Laire (1837–1909), and prepared by heating rosaniline with aniline, has three phenyl groups in place of the three hydrogens; in other words, a triphenylaniline has resulted. On the basis of this knowledge, he attempted to introduce other radicals and after many unsuccessful trials he was able to produce, with the aid of ethyl and methyl iodide, a triethylrosaniline and trimethylrosaniline. These exceedingly beautiful violet dyes, known as Hofmann violets, dominated the fashions for some years and brought him notable financial success. A magnificent aniline green proved to be the iodomethylate of trimethylrosaniline, and was placed on the market under the name "iodine green" or "methyl green." After only a few years, the coal tar dyes celebrated an unparalleled triumph at the London World Fair of 1862. The wondrous splendor of their colors, the brilliance of their shades, and the variety of their nuances aroused general admiration and spread the fame of their scientific discoverer and promoter. To the extent that the state of chemistry permitted at that time, Hofmann's researches explained the formation and constitution of these dyes. A decade passed before Emil and Otto Fischer finally proved the constitution of the rosaniline dyes.

Although his scientific career was marked by these great triumphs, his private life was touched with sorrow. After six years of happiness, he lost his wife Helene in 1852. Four years later, he married Rosamund Wilson. In the meantime, his position became more and more secure. His highly intelligent companionship, his winning amiability, his bubbling humor, and his quick but never caustic wit made him a favorite in London society. It need hardly be said that his advice was sought not only by his industrialist friends but also by the governmental authorities. His judgment was asked on questions of tariffs, the control of foodstuffs, on hygiene, education, and difficult court cases. He was often a member of the jury at international exhibitions. His accomplishments brought him the "Grand Prix" (100,000 francs) at the Paris exhibition of 1867; Napoleon III made him an officer of the Legion of Honor. From 1867 on, Hofmann was foreign secretary of the London Chemical Society, and in 1861 was elected its president.

By 1865 he had spent twenty years in England; he was at the peak of his fame. He had seemingly adopted a new home, although he had not cut himself off from his native land. His vacations were frequently spent in Germany and many of his friends would have liked to see him come back permanently. It appeared unlikely that he would exchange his brilliant position in London for a chair in a German university. And yet, when the Prussian ministry made him an offer to take over the chair at Bonn, which had become vacant because of the retirement of C. G. Bischoff (1792–1870), and again, a little later, when the death of Eilhard Mitscherlich (1794–1863) left a similar vacancy at Berlin, he was

633

seized by "a severe homesickness for the mental plateau of a German university." which did not permit him to delay much longer the return to his homeland. While still in London, he directed the construction of the new chemical building in Bonn. He never occupied it but left it to his successor August Kekulé. In May, 1865, he moved to Berlin, where an elaborate laboratory and a fine auditorium were built according to his plans. The latter was connected, through a spacious private laboratory, with his official residence.

The wide circle of friends that Hofmann had acquired in London —the brilliant farewell dinner, which they gave him, was attended by seventy-one friends and admirers—was in sharp contrast to the number of intimate acquaintances he had in Berlin. But he soon was on a friendly footing with his colleagues in the faculty and the Academy of Sciences, and his winning personality exerted such marked influence on his professional colleagues that he quickly became the center of the intellectual life of everyone associated with chemistry. He was well aware of the favorable effect of the London Chemical Society on English science and technology, and even before the new laboratory was finished, he, together with A. Baeyer, C. A. Martius, C. Scheibler, E. Schering, H. Wichelhaus, and others, founded the Deutsche Chemische Gesellschaft, whose membership soon included all of the eminent chemists of Germany and many foreigners. Hofmann was the soul of the organization. In twenty-three years, he served as president no less than fourteen times. With incomparable skill he conducted the meetings at which the members read their papers. These and other publications appeared in the *Berichte,* which was begun in 1868 and is still appearing and is regarded as one of the leading periodicals, especially of organic chemistry. The Hofmann laboratory issued 899 papers, 150 from his own pen. Including those which appeared in other periodicals, the total number was 277.

Hofmann was one of the most zealous members of the Prussian Academy of Sciences. He made it a practice to present there the results of his investigations and was a master of the art of captivating the members—as well as those of other faculties—by the elegant and spirited manner of his delivery. The death of his second wife, Rosamund, in 1860, after only four years of happiness, possibly had contributed to his willingness to leave London. His third wife, Elise Moldenhauer, was the cousin of his first wife and the sister of the wife of the physicist Heinrich Buff (1805–1879), whose first wife was Hofmann's sister. Unfortunately, this marriage also was comparatively short-lived (1866–1871), since she died after a long illness. However, his companionable nature required domesticity; in 1873 he married Bertha Tiemann, the sister of his assistant and friend of long standing, Ferdinand Tiemann (1848–1899). This fourth marriage lasted almost nineteen years. In all, Hofmann had eleven children, and was survived by five sons and three daughters.

The struggle for German supremacy in dye chemistry dates back to the 1860's. At the London Exhibition of 1862 there were virtually only English and French firms among the thirteen prize winners. However, as early as 1860, the Sell tar distillation had passed into the hands of K. Oehler who, in addition to mauvein and fuchsin, had placed on the market a splendid aniline blue, which was unexcelled for a long time. At the same time, the dye company, Friedrich Bayer, erected a fuchsin factory at Elberfeld. In 1863, Meister, Lucius, and Brüning at Höchst, a.M. manufactured this same product "with the help of one chemist and a 3-horse power steam engine." Fuchsin sold for 60 marks per pound but after a year the price fell to 24 marks. A color factory was built at this time by W. Kalle in Biebrich and in 1865 the Badische Anilin und Sodafabrik was started at Mannheim but soon moved to Ludwigshafen. In 1867, C. A. Martius, who had been Hofmann's assistant in London, and Paul Mendelssohn-Bartholdy put up an aniline factory at Rummelsberg near Berlin; this was united in 1873 with the Jordan dye factory in Treptow to form the Aktiengellschaft für Anilinfabrikation (AGFA). Finally, the dye dealers, Leopold Cassella & Cie., who had been in business at Frankfurt a.M. since the beginning of the century, in 1870 founded a dye factory in the Electorate of Main.

It was not easy to overcome the lead enjoyed by other countries. The vast development of the British acid and alkali industry provided cheap auxiliary materials, and the advanced gas industry in England and France yielded copious amounts of such raw materials as tar and its distillation products. In contrast, Germany for many years was dependent on foreign sellers and had to pay high prices for the materials required for dye manufacture. However, Germany had a considerable advantage in the large number of young chemists who had been trained in the German universities along the lines introduced and practiced by Liebig, and they were eager to make practical use of their scientific tutelage. Consequently, there began a heated struggle with the foreign countries and among the German manufacturers themselves, which led to constantly mounting accomplisments.[2]

The steadily increasing demand of the dye manufacturers for raw materials and chemicals of all kinds also energized the organic chemical industry and hastened its large-scale development in Germany. Just as Hofmann was closely associated with dyestuff industry through his friend Martius (q.v.) he now came into close contact with the inorganic industry through his friend Hugo Kunheim (1838–1897), whose father had built a sulfuric acid plant as early as 1834, which had been moved to the Upper Spree by the son in the 1870's and greatly enlarged. Hofmann was likewise in close contact with the pharmaceutical industry through Ernst Schering, who had started as proprietor of the "Grüne Apotheke" and then established a chemical preparations business in Berlin, which was converted into a stock company in 1871. Schering (1824–1889) was one of the founders of the German Chemical Society and as its treasurer was in close association with Hofmann. When Schering relinquished this post after twelve years he was succeeded by his faithful collaborator in the Schering business, Julius Holtz (1836–1911) who carried on for twenty-five years.

Hofmann made notable contributions to physical, biochemical, technical, and engineering chemistry. His favorite creation, the rosaniline dyes, were joined by other classes of coloring matters, which like the indulines and safranines belonged to those of the Perkin mauvein class, and the quinoline dyes, which yield a beautiful cyan blue, and quinoline red and yellow. He was especially interested in the dyes cedriret and pittacal, which had been obtained thirty years earlier by Carl Reichenbach (1788–1869) from beech wood tar, and which Hofmann now found to be closely related to the rosanilines. He repeatedly investigated the nitrogenous compounds used as raw materials in dye manufacture. He found phenylene and tolulyldiamine in the high-boiling fractions of technical aniline. The discovery of hydrazobenzene and its remarkable intramolecular transformation into benzidine, the investigation of the xylidines, the beautiful researches on the migration of the methyl group of methylated amines into the benzene nucleus, which led to pentamethylaniline and eventually to hexamethylbenzene, and many other equally important discoveries were quickly added to the weapons of the industrial chemists.

Again and again he turned his attention to the amines of the alcohol series. There was no general method of passing from a hydrocarbon series to the next lower series. Hofmann discovered a surprising reaction which permitted this, by treating the acid amides of the fatty acids with bromine and alkali. By means of this elegant method, he was able to degrade the monamines from the ninth to the first member, i.e., to go from nonylamine to methylamine, and to obtain pure products. This Hofmann degradation reaction became of great practical importance, especially in the technical synthesis of indigo. These studies of the amine bases were followed by the laborious investigations of the ethylene bases, then by studies of the amidines and guanidines, cyanic acid and its numerous derivatives, and finally the isonitriles. The overpowering stench of the latter compounds made their investigation an act of scientific heroism, but these studies led to the physiologically important discovery of the synthesis of the mustard oils, which proved to be sulfur derivatives of the isonitriles, and which are not inferior to the latter in their assault on the olfactory organs.

On other occasions Hofmann also dealt with plant chemistry. He devoted an intensive study to the alkaloids of the water hemlock, coniine and conhydrine, which led to the synthesis of inactive coniine and cleared up the relation of this base to piperidine and pyridine, thus discovering an important method for the degradation of cyclic bases through the elimination of nitrogen.

The tenacity with which Hofmann pursued his ideas until he had reached his expected objective is illustrated by the synthesis of formaldehyde. He was convinced of its possibility but strove in vain for twenty years before he hit upon the elegant and simple method of passing a current of air charged with methyl alcohol over a slightly heated platinum spiral.

He was a brilliant speaker and his pedagogical lectures were

637

masterpieces not only in content but in their experimental embellishment which he developed to an exceptional degree. Frequently he interjected humorous remarks and anecdotes. When discussing smokeless powder, he commiserated the painters of battle scenes who had now been deprived of their prime stage property, powder smoke. On arriving at the subject of benzene, he smilingly remarked: "Benzene has a characteristic odor; a lady once told me it smells like cleaned gloves." Once, when a bumptious student, who already knew this description, called out "like cleaned gloves" from the upper row of seats, before Hofmann had a chance to do so, the lecturer inquired with feigned seriousness: "Did you also know this lady?"

After twenty years in England, Hofmann had become accustomed to use the romantic style of scientific expressions and employed it even when speaking German. Accordingly, stilted sentences such as "Gentlemen, the experiment demonstrates most evidently the verification of our anticipation" were not uncommon. But this was not unusual in those times when the use of foreign words and phrases was still the hallmark of a scientific lecture. Furthermore, he limited this usage to his formal lectures; in the printed versions of his papers and other writings, he placed great weight on a classic form of expression. His ability to devise new and striking lecture experiments was inexhaustible. He repeatedly invited the members of the Chemische Gesellschaft to a lecture on demonstration experiments. Much of the equipment which he devised for these tasks has become part of the stock in trade of chemical lectures, particularly the "Hofmann eudiometer" for showing the volume relations of gas reactions. He was in great demand as a speaker on all sorts of occasions. At international meetings, he spoke fluently in four languages.

He produced an enormous literary output. Besides his many papers, he published a number of books. His "Einleitung in die moderne Chemie" was heartily applauded and translated into several languages. He showed a marked predilection for the history of his science. As fascinating as they are instructive are his historical sketches of the past: "Berliner Alchemisten und Chemiker" and "Ein Jahrhundert chemischer Forschung unter dem Schirm der Hohenzollern" (1881–82) in which he relates the history of chemistry in Brandenburg: from the goldmakers Leonhard Thurneysser (1531–1596), who attempted this feat in the "Grauen Kloster" and Johann Kunckel (1630–1703), who instead of making gold discovered the hitherto unsurpassed ruby glass, to the scholarly investigators Friedrich Hoffmann (1660–1712) to whom we owe "Hoffmann's drops" and the first artificial mineral waters, G. E. Stahl (1660–1734) the creator of the phlogiston theory, J. T. Eller (1689–1760), to whom Prussia owes the beginning of its medical establishments, J. H. Pott (1692–1777) the founder of ceramics, who in 30,000 trials exposed all possible mixtures of clays to various temperatures, Marggraf (1709–1782) and F. C. Achard (1753–1821), the founders of the beet sugar industry, and to his own predecessors at the University of Berlin, namely, M. H. Klaproth, S. F. Hermbstädt, H. Rose, and G. Magnus.

Chemistry is in debt to him for the incomparable treasure of historical material contained in his memorial addresses which he customarily delivered in his capacity as president of the German Chemical Society. The personal relations in which he stood with all the prominent chemists of the nineteenth century, his wide general culture, his astonishing fund of knowledge acquired by reading, combined with a superb memory, his acquaintance with many quite foreign provinces of learning, his artistic organizing talent, his command of languages, his frequent journeys which extended to all European countries, the Orient, Africa, and North America—all these contributed to make his "Erinnerungen an vorangegangenen Freunde" veritable masterpieces in content and form. These detailed biographies of eminent scholars, such as Liebig, Wöhler, Graham, Magnus, Buff, J. B. Dumas, Quintino, Sella, Griess, von Fehling, and Wurtz fill three large volumes (1889).

However, Hofmann did not leave merely literary monuments to the heroes of science. He did not rest until in conjunction with colleagues he had secured the erection of statues to Liebig in Munich and Giessen, and to Wöhler in Göttingen. He also took an effective part in the publication of the correspondence of these two great chemists (two volumes, 1888, reissued 1958).

To the last days of his busy life he enjoyed complete mental freshness and good bodily health. On May 5, 1892, he held his usual morning lecture. In the late afternoon he attended a faculty meeting and participated in two doctorate examinations. About 9 o'clock he reached home in excellent spirits, where as usual he found several supper guests. Suddenly he complained of not feeling well. He was put to bed, but before the physicians arrived he was already breathing his last. Sensing that the end was near, he bade his dear ones farewell in touching phrases. His last paper was found ready for the printer on his writing desk.

In 1900, the Hofmann Haus was dedicated in his memory. For many years it served as the headquarters of the Chemische Gesellschaft and of the Beilstein and Gmelin treatises on organic and inorganic chemistry, respectively. A statue of the great man stood before this center of German chemistry. This structure was a prey to the bombings of World War II. However, Hofmann had erected his own best memorials: in the hearts of his students, in the annals of the science and the Deutsche Chemische Gesellschaft, in which his name and spirit will endure for many years to come.

NOTES AND REFERENCES

1 See George Haines, "German Influence upon English education and science 1800–1866," 1957.
2 John J. Beer, "The Emergence of the German Dye Industry," (Illinois Studies in the Social Sciences, 44). University of Illinois Press, Urbana, 1959.

From Bugge, "Buch der Grossen Chemiker," 2, 136–153. Translated by Ralph E. Oesper.

BERNHARD LEPSIUS

·· *46* ··

Louis Pasteur

1822-1895

LOUIS PASTEUR was one of those great men who are not limited by the bounds of a single science but who range through several fields and create new disciplines. He also belongs to that company of scientists who do not consider it necessary to exhaust a subject once it has been attacked, who have the rare ability of being aroused only by really significant relationships and discoveries, who are always ready to break off an investigation when it reaches the stage at which only minor advances are still to be expected, but who, on the other hand, doggedly persist despite temporary failures until the great objective which they anticipated has been attained. Such men leave much work for their associates and successors. Finally, Pasteur was one of those whose entire sum of work, no matter how diversified it may seem at a casual glance, is not an unrelated array of research, discoveries, and ideas, but rather a cohesive succession guided by basic concepts. The labors of such are held together not by the artificial limits of a particular science but by limits which result from the magnitude of their scientific power.

Pasteur was a chemist by profession and undeniably a great one. He not only unveiled the secret of stereoisomerism, which in itself would have made him lastingly famous, but he also made fundamental contributions to the solution of the problems of fermentation and putrefaction. He thus discovered the bridge from chemistry to biology. He delivered the death blow to the ancient doctrine of spontaneous generation. Along with Robert Koch[1] he was one of the pre-eminent pioneers in the field of infectious human diseases. He discovered the protective inoculation of animals against anthrax and of humans against rabies. He was one of the greatest benefactors the human race has produced. Although his most significant accomplishments were in medicine, he never studied this field in a formal manner. His greatest success came only after Koch had made his signal advances with regard to infectious diseases. He was spared such catastrophes as came to Koch when the latter witnessed the failure of his tuberculin, but

643

neither of them was able to place the theory of infectious diseases on a clear scientific basis. Koch thought and created systematically, whereas Pasteur, although master of his subject, was still dependent on the impulses of his wildly vacillating genius.

Imbued with positivism, Pasteur penetrated deeply into the problems of our life in his experiments on spontaneous generation. The fermentation industries, the culture of the silkworm, and the food preservation industries owe him as much as they do any of the practical and technical men who worked in these fields. In medicine he founded the modern method of combating contagious and infectious diseases, and was also the originator of many biological cures which came after he had passed from the scene. He can likewise be regarded as the intellectual discoverer of antiseptic and aseptic surgery in that the methods of Joseph Lister (1829–1913) evolved as a direct consequence of Pasteur's discoveries. Even though Semmelweiss[2] had previously and correctly recognized the essence of infectious diseases, the Listerian ideas and procedures actually contributed much more to antisepsis. Consequently, without the work of Pasteur, surgery could not have celebrated its triumph so soon. The fruits of Pasteur's researches add up to a tremendous and significant sum.

Louis Pasteur was born at Dôle, a small town in the Department of Jura. His father, a tanner, came back from the Napoleonic campaigns with decorations but no money. He married a simple working girl who, like the mothers of many other eminent men, had a keen mind. She made the modest home a place of a certain amount of intellectuality and filled its atmosphere with ambitious plans for her son. The little house now bears a marble tablet with the inscription in gilt letters: "Ici est né Louis Pasteur, le 27 Decembre, 1822."

The family moved to Arbois in 1825, and here the boy received his first contact with industrial chemistry in the tannery which his father set up on the banks of the Cuissance. When he, the smallest in the class, appeared at the elementary school for the first time, he brought an armload of thick dictionaries. Although they were obviously unsuitable for his needs at that early age, this incident shows that he was aiming high and was being encouraged at home. His father, although weary after a hard day, was always glad to help him in the evening. However, Louis was not an especially good student at first. Like many boys, he flitted from one interest to another. He was particularly talented in art. There still exist pastel portraits of his friends, which are said to be remarkably good for a thirteen-year-old. As soon as he realized that his parents were making sacrifices for his education, he turned over a new leaf and began to show some of the energy and industry which characterized all the rest of his life. The school principal predicted: "He will go far." To the boy, he said: "Begin to think about the great École normale in Paris." The educational resources at Arbois were limited, and so Pasteur transferred to the neighboring city of Besançon, where he graduated *Bachelier és Lettres* and was appointed *maître répétiteur* (tutor) in the college. He continued to prepare himself for the École normale, and during the vacations took the requisite courses in mathematics.

Both at Arbois and Besançon he was an outstanding student, but he often was a thorn in the flesh of the venerable old chemistry instructor because of his incessant habit of asking difficult questions in the presence of the class. The professor, who was rather limited in his knowledge of the subject, bluntly told the young man that it was the prerogative of the teacher to question the students and not vice versa. Pasteur took the hint and went to an apothecary who had something of a reputation in Besançon because he had once published a paper in the *Annales de chimie et de physique*. From him he secretly took a few lessons, but his enthusiasm unfortunately was not matched by his success in the entrance examination for the École normale. He ranked only fourteenth and wisely decided to spend another year on improving his qualifications. He remained in Paris, under the tutelage of Father Barbet, who remitted one third of his room and board. In October, 1843, Pasteur again took the entrance examinations and this time ranked third.

Founded in 1794, at the close of the Reign of Terror, the École normale supérieure served to train teachers for the state secondary schools, the lycées. It has had many famous graduates and is still located on the Rue d'Ulm; later Pasteur made many of his famous discoveries there. Even as a student he was extremely interested in chemistry, an enthusiasm that was furthered by the lectures of

645

Balard[3] at the École normale and of J. B. Dumas at the Sorbonne. The students at the École enjoyed a large measure of personal freedom; consequently the conditions were favorable for the development of intelligent young men like Pasteur. One of his teachers, Gabriel Delafosse (1796–1878), who had been an associate of the great crystallographer René Haüy (1743–1822), interested Pasteur in molecular physics. He thus indirectly led Pasteur to his first great chemical discovery, the theory of the asymmetric carbon atom. In 1844, Mitscherlich had reported that the salts of paratartaric acid (racemic acid) and tartaric acid have the same chemical composition and are identical with respect to crystal form, specific gravity, and double refraction. However, they differ in that the tartarates rotate the plane of polarized light to the right, whereas the paratartrates are optically inactive, as was proved by Biot[4] even though "here the nature and the number of atoms, their arrangement and their distances from each other in the two compounds being compared are the same." Pasteur realized almost at once that something had been overlooked; it was impossible for molecules to behave differently toward polarized light if they were truly identical both chemically and physically.

An external event almost distracted Pasteur's interest from this problem. When he began the experimental study of this topic at the end of his third year, he was an instructor in physics. Unexpectedly, he was appointed professor of physics at the Lycée of Tournon. By personal intercession, Balard persuaded the Ministry to allow Pasteur to remain at the École normale. Consequently he was now free to pursue another project he had embarked upon to improve his competence in crystallography, namely, a repetition and continuation of a study by de la Provostaye on the crystalline form of the tartrates. Years later, Pasteur told a friend that this research had been of prime importance in shaping his scientific career. These studies of tartaric acids led him to the problems of fermentation and they in turn to the study of diseases.

Pasteur confirmed the findings of his more skilled predecessor but found what had escaped the latter, namely, the presence of hemihedral facets on tartaric acid itself as well as on its salts. These facets also occurred on the double salts of racemic acid, but in these instances some were oriented to the right, some to the left.

By hand-picking he divided the crystals into two groups and found that the solutions of one lot behaved optically like' those of the dextrorotatory tartaric acid, while the solution prepared from the second group rotated the plane of polarization to the left. The acids themselves showed the same difference. Pasteur prepared no less than nineteen different tartrates and found that all exhibited hemihedral faces. He demonstrated that the racemic acid could be decomposed into two optically active antipodes through crystallization of the double salts, and that one of the antipodes is the ordinary dextrorotatory acid. In addition, racemic acid can be regenerated by mixing equal amounts of the solutions of the two varieties of tartaric acid.

These findings aroused tremendous interest at the Académie des Sciences. Biot was commissioned to arrange for a repetition of the experiment under his own scrupulous supervision. He furnished Pasteur with a sample of racemic acid, which had been found to be inactive to polarized light, as well as samples of sodium carbonate and ammonia water, and requested him to prepare the sodium ammonium double salt. This was done in Biot's presence in one of the rooms at the Collège. Ten days later, when the solution had deposited 30–40 grams of crystals, Pasteur was again summoned to Biot's laboratory to select the dextro-and levorotatory crystals, placing them to Biot's right and left, respectively. Biot then prepared the carefully weighed solutions and called Pasteur back into the laboratory just before making the examination in the polarimeter. The more interesting solution, which was to cause rotation to the left, was tried first. The rotation was to the left. Visibly moved, the illustrious old man embraced Pasteur and in a trembling voice said: "My dear boy, I have loved the sciences so much all my life that this makes my heart pound."

Pasteur recognized that the cause of the remarkable phenomena must reside in the molecular structure of the molecules. By extending his observations and ideas concerning the asymmetric structure of the crystals to the chemical molecule itself, he evolved the theory of the asymmetric carbon atom. He may legitimately be regarded as the founder of modern stereochemistry, since, to quote Wislicenus: "Stereochemistry, in the restricted sense of the word, comprises chemical phenomena which demand a consideration of

647

the grouping of atoms in space." Pasteur's researches on asymmetry included other notable successes. He discovered a second method of resolving racemic tartaric acid into its optically active decomponents. By forming salts with optically active alkaloids, he found a second inactive form of tartaric acid (mesotartaric acid) which could not be resolved into active components; he prepared an optically active and an optically inactive alcohol from ordinary (racemoid) amyl alcohol; he converted quinine and cinchonine into the isomeric quinidine and cinchonidine; he found that galactose is a fission product of milk sugar.[5]

Pasteur was appointed professor of physics in the Lycée at Dijon in 1848, but only three months later he was transferred to the University of Strasbourg as deputy-professor of chemistry. He succeeded to the chair in 1852. Here he married the daughter of the rector in 1850. Little did Mlle. Laurent realize what she was likely to face when she married a young scientist so engrossed in his work that it is said he had to be fetched from his laboratory for the wedding ceremony because he had forgotten the day. From the first she sympathized with his work and understandingly accepted the circumstances when he returned home tired and irritable. She protected him from the petty annoyances of the household so that he might keep his mind clear for the problems that were engaging his attention. There was little recreation for either of them. In the evenings she took down his dictation, interrupting him from time to time to ask for explanations because she knew that ideas become clearer when expounded, particularly to nonprofessionals. It has been truly said that Mme. Pasteur was a perfect companion to her husband and also his best assistant.

In 1854, he was called to Lille, and at thirty-two was named dean to organize the faculty of science which had just been created. During all these years he had continued, almost without interruption, his chemical studies on asymmetry. It is of great interest with respect to the type of his mind, and also with regard to the spirit of the time, that Pasteur advanced and doggedly maintained the theory that all higher molecules which are built up by the living organism are asymmetric, whereas those prepared in the laboratory are without asymmetry. Only the lower atomic complexes of the living organism, such as urea, which participate

648

merely externally in its origin and growth, possess symmetry. Exceptions are apparent, not real. Here is a distinct vitalistic theory, put forth in a period in which, as it now appears, there was already a pronounced effort to substitute purely mechanistic theories for the metaphysical tendencies of the first half of the nineteenth century. This vitalistic theory can no longer be upheld with respect to accepting asymmetry as a criterion of life.

Pasteur made extensive experiments in his efforts to advance in this direction. He subjected materials to powerful magnetic fields, with the intent to introduce dissymmetric influences during the formation of crystals, and to rapid and violent rotary motion, but with no effect. However, the subsequent development of the science has shown that his intuition was fundamentally correct. The complete discordance of his time is symbolized in the fact that Pasteur, who eventually became the annihilator of the doctrine of spontaneous generation, was at the time seriously accepting ideas which had as their ultimate goal the generation of life in the laboratory.

His studies of tartaric acids led directly to his investigations of fermentation. Proceeding from an industrial experience, he attempted to ferment the dextrorotating ammonium tartarate. He added protein materials to the chemically pure solution of the salt and found that it fermented in a vat. At first the solution became cloudy and the turbidity was proved to be due to a microorganism, a yeast fungus. A solution of ammonium racemate behaved similarly, but with the striking difference that the initially optically inactive solution gradually became more and more levorotatory. After reaching a maximum optical rotation, the fermentation ceased. Obviously, the dextrorotatory acid had been consumed; levorotating crystals of ammonium tartrate were isolated from the fermented liquor. Pasteur continued his studies in this direction; attempts that in later decades would have been termed mystical but which to him appeared respectable from the scientific standpoint. This was equally true of all of his earlier attempts along these lines which, except in the last instance, are now known to have been fundamentally hopeless. In addition, he showed that *Penicillium glaucum* feeds preferentially on dextrorotating tartaric acid with comparison to its consumption of the levorotatory acid, a finding that must be dependent on the molecular structure of this

649

fungus. Although he did not carry the experiments beyond this point he thus provided another means of resolving a racemic compound into at least one of its enantiomorphs. Perhaps he realized the sterility of this line of research. However, it actually was an outside event that led him to pursue the problem of fermentation along another line.

The chief industry of Lille was the manufacture of alcohol from sugar beets and grain. The business men of the city were anxious to see something practical accomplished by their new chemistry professor. Pasteur saw the validity of this desire and decided to study the fermentation industry. He had long considered fermentation to be a chemical phenomenon, and he saw in it innummerable possibilities of application to daily life, applications that might possibly be conducted on a manufacturing scale. Liebig had advanced the theory that fermentation, putrefaction, the decay of nitrogenous materials, etc., resulted from reaction with the oxygen of the air. The French physicist, Charles Cagniard-Latour (or de la Tour) (1777–1859), and the German anatomist, T. S. Schwann (1810–1882), the founder of animal cytology, had recognized that the yeast which separates during alcohol fermentation consists of fungi. The former also considered the possibility that yeast is the causative agent of fermentation. Other fermentation theories had been advanced. Liebig conceded the participation of yeast in the fermentation process but believed the active agent to be the dead, decomposing yeast cell which had come into contact with the air.[6]

Pasteur observed the schizomycetes in lactic fermentation and believed that this organism caused the fermentation, just as the yeast did in the production of alcohol. He also discovered the bacillus of the butyric fermentation, an organism which was anaerobic, i.e., it had the characteristic of living only in the absence of oxygen and of being killed by air. He furthermore explained putrefaction as a kind of fermentation, assuming incorrectly that the putrefactive organisms belonged among the anaerobia.

Doubtless many problems were brought to Pasteur by the Lille spirit manufacturers; he diligently collected experimental material in their factories, and through him this industry was brought into close relation with science. This was the start of a movement which constantly grew in pace and extent, a movement that proved most lucrative to the whole French national economy and gave science an impulse such as it had never before experienced. The vinegar makers of Orléans soon invited Pasteur to lecture to them. He showed that if the acetifying agent is not removed after the wine has turned to vinegar, the acetic acid may be further oxidized and decomposed. The process which he proposed to stop this action likewise served to destroy the vinegar "eels" which rendered the vinegar cloudy. The period around 1870 was marked by a polemical controversy with Liebig, whose views on fermentation have long since been relegated to the graveyard of discarded theories. However, it is important to note that it was possible at that time for a scientist of Liebig's stature to regard questions of microbiological chemistry as of little or no importance.

Pasteur's studies of fermentation closed a period of research that may still be termed chemical. He was approaching fifty, but his most important findings were still to come. He had endowed pure chemistry with contributions of the first rank; he had laid the foundations of chemical biology, i.e., reactions that proceed with the participation of living organisms. He furthermore made a notable advance by demonstrating the monetary return to industry when it makes intelligent use of the powers of science.

In 1857, Pasteur was recalled to the École normale supérieure in Paris as director of scientific studies. Here, at his own expense, he fitted up a laboratory, primitive in the modern sense, in which he worked for ten years on topics more biological than chemical. He dealt with the old problem of spontaneous generation, a subject that necessarily was of prime interest for determining the origin of the active fermenting and putrefying agents. He showed that spontaneous generation had never been irrefutably demonstrated. The famed statement by William Harvey (1619) *"omne vivum ex ovo,"* as well as the dictum by Rudolf Virchow (1821–1902), the eminent contemporary Prussian pathologist, *"omnis cellula e cellula,"* were unsubstantiated declarations. It was Pasteur who converted them into laws of biology.

Pasteur applied his theory of fermentation to practical problems in three more instances. First he used it in connection with the aging of wine and the so-called wine diseases. He showed that young wine does not change if it is hermetically sealed against the air, and that its various maladies correspond to definite infections with particular organisms, each one leading to a particular disease, such as becoming sour or bitter. Likewise, each type of clouding has its individual organism. He found that all clouding could be prevented in wines by a brief heating to 45–60°C. Thus began "pasteurization," the process of partial sterilization. Henceforth it was possible to protect foods against spoilage without radically changing them by boiling, etc. However, this technique had fore-runners.

November 16, 1865, has become famous as the date of his great and somewhat theatrical wine test. He had noted that the tasters had a prejudice against wines which they knew had been heated; therefore he asked the commission in charge to omit stating which samples had undergone this treatment. He offered the tasters identical samples from the same bottle; they gave one glass a slight but nevertheless distinct preference. The commission, which had to render a decision, then admitted that the difference, if any, between heated and unheated wines was insignificant. Pasteur thus showed the wine-makers the causes of the wine diseases, and taught them that heating their wines in the casks would give protection without injury to the taste.

A second translation of Pasteur's researches into practice concerned the infectious diseases that were seriously threatening the French silkworm industry. Epidemics among the worms became so bad that the growers, in 1853, became convinced that the plagues were carried by the native eggs or "seed," and accordingly they imported eggs from abroad. The initial results were excellent, but in 1854, when attempts were made to use the eggs from the moths hatched from the imported seed, another epidemic appeared. Eggs were brought in from all possible sources, but by 1864 all European eggs produced diseased worms and only those from Japan were healthy. In 1863, the government contracted to pay an Italian grower 500,000 francs if his alleged cure proved effective. Nothing helped. Four million cocoons were harvested in all France in 1865 as contrasted with 26 million in 1853. The loss was 100 million francs. A plea for help, signed by 3600 mayors, councilmen, and growers, was sent to the Senate. A committee was appointed, with J. B. Dumas as chairman, to study the matter. Only when he was composing his report did he think of Pasteur in this connection, a rather remarkable choice for a problem which seemed to demand a zoologist, entomologist, or one trained in the biological sciences. At the time, Pasteur was immersed in his studies of spontaneous generation, wine diseases, and the manufacture of vinegar. However, his revered teacher overcame the objections of the former student, who declared that he knew nothing about the subject and hardly knew what a silkworm looked like. To this Dumas replied: "So much the better. As ideas you will have only those which shall come to you as a result of your observations."

In July, 1865, Pasteur went to Alais. During each of the next five years he spent several months there, hoping to clear up the confusion. His wife, daughter, and assistants became enthusiastic silk-growers along with him. In the beginning it was not even known whether the disease was infectious, and Pasteur proved this as an initial step. The cause was the microscopic corpuscle, which had been discovered by Italian scientists. Pasteur found it to be a species of parasite. Having arrived at an insight into the nature and means of preventing the "pepper disease," he was confronted with his discovery that it was not the sole reason for the decline of the silkworm culture in France. A second malady was raging, known as "flachérie" to which the worms often succumbed within 24 hours.[7] It too was elucidated. Pasteur now knew enough to tell growers how the silkworm culture in the south of France could be revitalized. It was a matter of using only healthy seed. Accordingly, after the eggs were laid, the female moths were to be examined under the microscope for the causative organisms. If found, the tainted eggs must be ruthlessly destroyed. This method of egg selection proved efficacious. When some growers objected to the use of the technique, he replied: "If you tell me that the microscope frightens you, and that its manipulation seems not easy to you, I reply that there is in my laboratory a little girl of eight who knows how to do it very well."

In 1868, at forty-six, Pasteur had a stroke which paralyzed his left side and persisted partially to the end of his life. It was of great importance that he neverthelesss carried on, because for almost thirty years longer he continued to turn out significant studies and obtain capital results. The painful sensations in the lamed part of his body, which are common among semiparaylzed persons, probably were the reason for certain of his eccentricities in this later period. Possibly he had been afflicted with a heart condition long before the stroke; there may have been arterial disturbances of the brain, or a metabolic toxicity, which made him sometimes cross and irritable. An accurate history of Pasteur's physical condition would be highly instructive with respect to a study of the foundations of genius. The physical ailments of exceptional men might teach us much about metaphysical matters. At the time, he believed that he had not much longer to live. He was totally paralyzed in all his limbs for two months, but he refused to capitulate to his invalidism. He dictated to his wife the plans for the studies he had in mind. In the period of relative convalescence, which directly preceded the Franco-Prussian War, in a period when he, like many other scientists on both sides, had become rabidly chauvinistic, he took up a study of the diseases of beer. He needed only to apply what he had learned from his earlier researches. He thus realized his ambition to free France from its dependence on Germany, and he taught the French brewers how to make a product that not only had the proper taste but also, in contrast to earlier brews, would keep well even in contact with the air. Such beers, prepared with scrupulous attention to the exclusion of foreign yeasts and other microscopic organisms, have been called "pasteurized beer" because one of the steps advocated by him was to heat the wort to a fairly high temperature but below boiling. It is interesting to note that Pasteur had no liking for beer; he did not appreciate its subtle taste qualities, and those studies were taken up simply to occupy the leisure forced on him by the siege of Paris.

Pasteur's monumental medical discoveries date from this war period. About 1860 he had begun to realize that processes of fermentation and putrescence are identical with those operating in communicable diseases. Similar ideas had been held by physicians as early as the sixteenth century but had made no headway. The notion of a *contagium vivum,* of living infectious substances, was directly opposed to the accepted theory, deeply rooted in the Hippocratic-Galenic Greek medicine, a theory which had been stubbornly retained during the medical reformation in the Renaissance, and which persisted until well into the nineteenth century. According to this doctrine, diseases were the consequences of putrefaction, which was held to be a spontaneous poisoning of the organism through contact with substances it had produced because of contact with foul air. Moreover, in some pestilences the emphasis was placed on autointoxication, i.e., the poisoning of the normal body fluids, which had been formed in excess or had escaped the bounds of their natural mixture. The prevailing theory of infection, the theory of blood poisoning, was dominated by the notion that the organism alone was responsible for its own toxicity. The thought that an infection could enter the body from outside was of very minor importance. The essentials of the theory went back to the basic concepts of Greek medicine. A frontal attack on this long-established theory was a heresy that flew into the face of medical convictions and beliefs, a heresy that shook the very foundations of medicine. Its overthrow would go far beyond the field of infectious diseases, the very elements of pathology would be shattered. Basic ideas that had held sway for centuries, theories that had been tested by the best minds, would suddenly be outmoded and discarded.

This historical introduction is essential to an understanding of the resistance encountered by a theory which stated positively that infection is not essentially an internal process but enters the organism from outside. Certain eminent physicians of the early years of the second half of the nineteenth century viewed the modern theory of infection as scientific barbarism and regarded it as the fruit of wild flights of imagination, somewhat as though it were seriously contended today that disease processes could be explained without anatomy or biochemistry. This scoffing attitude persisted even long after Jacob Henle (1809–1885) had deductively anticipated (1840) the parasitic theory of infection processes, after Ludwig Traube (1818–1876) had attributed the ammoniacal decomposition of urine to the infiltration of germs (1864), after Ignaz Semmelweiss (1818–1865) had shown that puerperal fever is due to the introduction of a poison into the uterus from the external environment (1861); after Felix Guyon (1831–1920) had successfully used boric acid for treating an in-

655

flammation of the urinary bladder in line with Pasteur's studies; and even after Lister had started to work out an antiseptic treatment of the wound in surgical procedures. Even the eminent Rudolf Virchow opposed the infection theory with all his might.

In 1860, Pasteur stated that he was planning to extend the range of his studies to medicine. Others before him had discovered parasitic causes in certain infectious diseases. In 1860, Pasteur showed that chickens which had recovered from fowl cholera had become immune to the disease. He was able to weaken the virus by transplanting it from one nutrient medium to another so that eventually the injection of a large quantity of the attenuated culture was still able to protect a chicken without danger. In this prophylactic inoculation of chickens, Pasteur had in mind the protection against smallpox which Edward Jenner (1749–1823) had achieved in 1796 by vaccination with cowpox lymph.

In the spring of 1881, Pasteur made his famous, somewhat theatrical, demonstration in which he protectively inoculated 25 sheep against anthrax in the presence of the Society of Agriculture of Melun. His method was analogous to the procedure he had employed against chicken cholera, but in this instance he had to overcome the additional obstacle that the anthrax spores could not be attenuated. He solved this problem by culturing the anthrax bacillae at a temperature at which they form no spores. The fine success of finding a feasible method of combating anthrax brought him the Grand Order of the Legion of Honor and did much to inculcate in the public mind a real faith in microbial science. However, some of the inoculated animals died, there were some failures, and there followed a devastating attack from Robert Koch, who showed that the action of the vaccine was uncertain, and furthermore that it contained also streptococci, staphylococci, and other harmful bacteria. Nevertheless, Pasteur was now the pride of the French people, and in 1882 he was elected to the *Académie Française.* That same year he embarked on his studies of sepsis and discovered a method for vaccinating against pig erysipelas, using a culture in which the virus was passed from animal to animal.

He had been interested in rabies since 1880. It was well known that these researches culminated in the Pasteur treatment, i.e.,

656

with the development of an inoculation which, when used in time, protects those who have been bitten by a rabid animal.

Pasteur was now sixty-four; he was at the threshold of old age. Throughout his scientific career he had steadily achieved triumphs of the first order, but his restless spirit was still not satisfied. A considerable portion of chemistry, important parts of chemical industry, and much of the medicine of his time had been radically altered because of his work. A glance at economic and population statistics showed him the vast gains that had been realized from his researches, and the mortality tables demonstrated how many human and animal lives had been extended because of his accomplishments. His creative period was over; his students throughout the world continued along the lines he had laid down. He was now sick and aging, yet he knew precisely how he could best utilize the time left to him. It was essential to ensure the continued progress of his medical advances through organizations. The discovery of the prophylaxis for rabies aroused everywhere great enthusiasm. It increased the popularity of Pasteur more than all his former works. In return for such a benefaction the great public desired to manifest its gratitude in a manner worthy of itself and of the man it wished to honor. It was then that the subscription was started which has made possible the founding of the Pasteur Institute.[8] This was an answer to his desire to found a research organization for the study of infectious diseases. As a fervent patriot and chauvinist, he hoped to make France the center of such activities. The Académie placed its intellectual resources at his disposal; large French financial interests cooperated; voluntary gifts came from every direction.

Toward the end of 1886, his physicians sent Pasteur to Bordighera, where he partly regained his strength. During this last period of his life he turned once more to purely theoretical topics. He had assumed in the beginning that the attenuated viruses act by consuming certain materials that are requisite for the production of toxins. As soon as the latter are regenerated in the body, the immunity is lost. Somewhat later, he came to believe that the attenuated parasite, especially that of rabies, does not confer immunity directly. He thought that in addition to the active rabies toxin there must also be present a soluble material which spreads

657

through the whole body and because of its speed, precedes the toxin itself. He hoped to carry out experiments to find the material which prevents the action of the toxin, i.e., to find the actual immunizing agent. He discussed at considerable length the methods which might lead to this goal. Accordingly, he came rather close to becoming a chemist once more. He planned to filter the poisoned nerve tissue through a porcelain filter out of contact with the air to prevent any destructive oxidation. He also planned to determine the lowest temperature at which the rabies toxin could be destroyed. There would supposedly be no destruction of the toxin below this temperature and accordingly the activity of the vaccine would be preserved. In this manner, the virus and the vaccine would remain completely separated, and only the latter would be needed. He did not return to these ideas later, perhaps because the side-chain theory took sole possession of the field.

The erection of the Institut Pasteur made satisfactory progress. The architect refused to take a fee for his services; the contractors accepted only their actual outlays; and the workmen, contrary to their usual custom, even worked on Mondays. The structure at 25 rue Dutot, near the Boulevard Vaugirard, was strictly functional; there was little or no ornamentation but plenty of light and air. The workers in the cramped quarters in the École normale had merely to move their balances and microscopes into the new building. The ceremonial dedication was held on November 14, 1888; the President of the Republic was present. The subscription lists were displayed on a table; up to then the total was 2,286,680 francs. The auditorium was inadequate to accommodate the throng. Pasteur was so affected that his son had to read his speech. In this address Pasteur lauded the French system of education from the lowest grades to the learned academies. Modesty was not one of his virtues, but on that great day he told the audience that he could not have reached this pinnacle of his success if he had not been given everything he had ever needed for his work. Although he was physically able to move into the Institut, Pasteur never really worked there. The actual administration was put into the hands of Emile Duclaux (1840–1904) who held the title of director from Pasteur's death until his own.

Pasteur's strength had been waning for years. He spent much of the time at Villeneuve-L'Étang, a small place not far from Paris, and succumbed to a uremic condition there on September 28, 1905. Despite his constant preoccupation with things of the world, this genius and benefactor of mankind died fortified with the sacraments of his church. He had always been a pious man; his science had not removed God from his world; skepticism had not been the price of his deep knowledge of Nature.

Fittingly, his remains are entombed in the chapel of the Institut. The murals of his resting place picture his main scientific triumphs. "The sacred fire kindled by the grand maître is still burning. Long may this flame be fed within the temple where now rests in eternal sleep that hero of science whose greatest ambition was to be able in his last hour to pronounce the words, so simple in their form, so boundless in their aspiration:

"J'ai fait ce que j'ai pu."[9]

GENERAL REFERENCES

René Vallery Radot, "The Life of Pasteur," translated by R. L. Devonshire, New York, 1923.

Emile Duclaux, "Pasteur, The History of a Mind," translated by E. F. Smith and F. Hedges, Philadelphia, 1920.

Piers Compton, "The Genius of Louis Pasteur," New York, 1932.

J. W. Moseley, "Pasteur the Chemist," J. Chem. Ed. 5, 50 (1928).

René J. Dubois, "Louis Pasteur," Little, Brown & Co., Boston, 1950.

NOTES AND REFERENCES

1 Robert Koch (1843–1910), creator of the classic methodology of micropathology. In 1882, he discovered the tubercle bacillus, in 1884 the bacillus of cholera, and in 1890, because of outside pressure, prematurely published the earliest results on tuberculin.

2 Ignaz P. Semmelweiss (1818–1865), professor of obstetrics in Budapest, demonstrated in the General Hospital in Vienna the transfer of the cause of puerperal fever from the hands of the physicians and midwives and thus became the founder of antiseptic treatment of wounds. He was attacked bitterly and died at odds with most of his professional colleagues.

3 A. J. Balard (1802–1876), born in Montpellier, came to Paris as assistant to Thenard and Pelouze. He discovered bromine in 1826.

4 J. B. Biot (1774–1862), professor of physics at the Collège de France.

5 Pasteur's researches on optical isomerism and related topics were summed up in the two lectures he delivered to the Académie des Sciences early in 1860. These texts are available in English translation as *Researches on Molecular Asymmetry,* Alembic Club Reprints, No. 14.

6 In 1897, Eduard Buchner (1860–1917) showed that even the cell-free extract of the yeast can ferment appropriate substrates.

7 *Flachérie* or *morts-flats* proved to be a hereditary disease, more complicated than *pébrine,* and more nearly related to human diseases. It is also contagious.

8 P. Roux, "L'Oeuvre médicale de Pasteur," *Agenda du chimiste,* 1896, p. 543.

9 Percy Frankland, Pasteur Memorial Lecture, delivered March 25, 1897. J. Chem. Soc. 1897, Transactions, p. 683.

From Bugge: "Buch der Grossen Chemiker," 2, 154–172, abbreviated. Translated by Ralph E. Oesper.

RICHARD KOCH

·· 47 ··

Stanislao Cannizzaro

1826-1910

THE aspects and events of Cannizzaro's life are of such varied complexity that although we may pronounce him a genius in science and a true Italian when needed by his country, the facts and events of his life do not admit of a uniform treatment, and each of them must be considered in its time and by itself. He appears to us as an ardent youth in the study of physiological problems, or as a mind entirely speculative; mature in reflection and gifted with keen political vision, or as an instructor of comparable effectiveness; as a fiery and logical orator, or an experimenter of precision; as a fighter or a soul inspired by the sentiments of tender lyricism.

As an adolescent, he gave proof of the superior quality of his mind and soul; he rose swiftly above his competitors with vast and penetrating vision; not with vain words reaching only for the ephemeral triumph of monetary victory, but by the affirmative proposition of ideas and facts which give others pause, compel them to follow him, which make him a universal genius.

Canizzaro's fame is the treasure of Sicily, of Italy, and of all mankind; a fame that received recognition in his lifetime. Italians and foreigners bowed before him with that sentiment of sincere deference which only the great can inspire, and which engraved his name alongside those of Galileo, Torricelli, Volta, and Galvani.

In the year 1826 Stanislao Cannizzaro opened his eyes to the resplendent light of July in Palermo, on a day auguring good luck— the thirteenth. We can say that he inherited from his father, an illustrious magistrate, the serious conception of life which influenced all his conduct; but we would also like to think that his earliest scholastic triumphs came from the recognition of his lively mind rather than as prizes awarded to the studious and hard-working scholar.

In those days the political situation in Sicily was tragic. It had become a province of the Kingdom of Naples which the treaty of Vienna in 1815 had reconstituted for the hated Bourbon dynasty.

Cannizzaro was dedicated to the idea of liberation, despite the fact that his father, Mariano, was chief of police at just that particular period when the most furious reaction against the liberals occurred, and one of his sisters, who had become Marchesa Ruffo, was lady-in-waiting to the Queen. Yet we must not forget that three brothers of his mother, née Di Benedetto, died as heroes for the liberation and unity of their native country: two on the barricades of Palermo, in 1860, and the third at Mentana, in 1867.

Shortly after he reached the age of fifteen, he matriculated at the university for the study of medicine; but he followed with in-interest a wide variety of courses, among them literature and mathematics. In the end he took his examinations only at the medical school, not ever taking "either this prize or that," as he wrote himself in a short autobiography. His love for all that could be known led to the profound affection, born of admiration, for those exceptional men with whom he eventually associated himself as perfect disciple, dedicating himself to the discipline in which the master chosen by him excelled.

The first of these encounters was with the physiologist Michele Foderà. For three years Stanislao Cannizzaro dedicated himself to biological studies. For lack of laboratories at the university, the experimental work was carried out at Foderà's or Cannizzaro's home; we do not know with what scant equipment!

The Seventh Congress of Italian Scientists was held at Naples in 1845. The nineteen-year old Cannizzaro participated, presenting a paper that aroused great interest but also the inevitable opposition.

It was a doctrinaire dissertation on a thorny and complex subject, the possibility of a distinction between centrifugal and the centripetal nerves. The line of argumentation was founded on experimental data and interpretations of the greatest physiologists of the period, not without the support of numerous experiments completed by Foderà and Cannizzaro. I do not exaggerate in affirming that the Congress of Naples was of decisive influence on the life of Cannizzaro. A second experience, one that was of the greatest importance for Cannizzaro, made a lasting impression upon his work and his entire life. From his experiments he had intuitively recognized the existence of a chemical causation in physiological processes and now desired to pursue the study of chemistry. He mentioned this to the physicist Macedonio Melloni, and it occurred to Melloni to introduce Cannizzaro to a chemist, young yet already famous, one Raffaele Piria, and to ask him to take the young Palermitan into his laboratory at Pisa. What a great fortune this meeting proved for Italian chemistry!

Cannizzaro dedicated himself henceforth exclusively to chemistry, because of the attraction exerted on him by the great personality of the man who was to become his revered master. It matters little that events soon terminated this close community of life in Pisa. The important thing is that this association was carried on through very frequent exchanges of letters and less frequent meetings, until the premature death of the great Calabrian master in 1865.

Thus it was only two years that Cannizzaro was able to live in that peaceful and austere Tuscan city, but they were years fruitful of results, replete with instruction for the young assistant who swiftly assimilated the technique of organic chemistry in which Piria was and remained Italy's unsurpassed master.

Cannizzaro himself wrote:

During these two academic years—1845/46 and 1846/47—I received all of my chemical education, interrupted only by the summer vacations, which I spent in Sicily.

As laboratory assistant I followed attentively the lectures in inorganic and organic chemistry during these two years, carrying out the experiments designated by the professor; the rest of the days was spent in the laboratory in the company of Piria who during those years devoted over eight hours daily to the most important of his investigations on salicin, populin, asparagin, and some naphthalene derivatives, as well as a number of mineral analyses.

Most of the time I was a mere bystander, watching with concentration and in silence that unsurpassable paragon of orderly procedure, precision and adroitness that was Piria in experimentation and analysis.

From time to time he delegated to me the task of continuing some experiment or analysis which he had started, or of preparing material which he needed, in the completion of which tasks it was my duty to attend faithfully to the precise instructions which I received from him.

In the morning hours, before Piria descended from his living quarters to the laboratory, or when he was away from it, I attended to the experimental demonstrations for the lectures, working alone or in the company of Bertagnini; that again was a task to which the greatest care had to be devoted in order to meet the standards set by Piria, who demanded not merely exactness but also elegance of form.

Often the evenings were passed in highly gratifying talks with Piria, and it was only at such times that he explained to me his investigations which I had witnesses during the day as bystander; only then did we have discussions as equals.

These latter words, which could easily be taken to be those of conceit, although they are not, spring from a most unusual knack of bringing out the close, proud, but just and kindly character of this son of Calabria, and in describing how life unfolded among these three great men: for there shall not be forgotten the gentle figure of Cesare Bertagnini, who was tied by the same filial devotion to the common master, and by brotherly affection to Cannizzaro—that Cesare Bertagnini who had to succumb to in insidious malady at the age of thirty when his name already gave a definite promise to science.

For too many years the spirit of revolt against the Bourbonic betrayal of 1815 had been seething in the best minds, waiting for the day of its unrestrained explosion. And so came the twelfth of January, 1848, with its lightninglike revolution, the flight of the Bourbons, the establishment of the "Kingdom of Sicily," which, however, had a president in the person of Ruggiero Settimo.

Cannizzaro had arrived in the summer of 1847 to spend the vacations in Palermo, intending to return to Pisa at the opening of the new academic year. Instead, he joined up with the Liberals who were then preparing the revolution and was at their side on the day of struggle and victory.

He received a commission as an officer in the artillery of the new Sicilian state; eventually, only twenty-two years old, he was elected as representative of Francavilla in the so-called Chamber of Commons; he attended the sessions of the parliament and also took the floor on several occasions.

The end of 1848 and the early months of 1849 found Cannizzaro, the artillery officer, between Messina and Taormina, engaged in the defense of the fatherland threatened by the Bourbonic reaction which was eventually to triumph. Cannizzaro, included in the list of those barred from returning to the Royal domains, had to take refuge in exile; on April 23, 1849, he boarded the frigate "In'depenza" for Marseilles.

He remained at Paris for a part of 1849, through 1850 and a part of 1851, working in Chevreul's laboratory. There he was associated with Cloez, with whom he published his first study on cyanamide, which he prepared by causing the halogens of cyanogen to react with ammonia. Cannizzaro and Cloez also studied the action of heat on cyanamide, and the polymerization induced by it.

The year 1851 saw the end of his exile. He was offered the chair of chemistry and physics at the Collegio Nazionale at Alessandria. The post was anything but outstanding, and Cannizzaro hesitated, until a warm letter from his teacher prompted him to make an affirmative decision. "I urge you to accept," wrote Piria, "because while it is only a mediocre position, you could later on obtain a chair at Turin or Genova. Besides, some thought must also be given to this unhappy land, which one can serve with the retort equally well as with the musket; for until such time that people begin to realize that what counts are concrete things and words are chaff, nothing of value will be achieved. We are still far from such a time; hence the blight, past and present!"

A grand reception was extended to him by the authorities at Alessandria; eventually a proclamation was published inviting workers and students to hasten to the lectures to be given by our hero. Cannizzaro now was full of enthusiasm and wrote to his friend Bertagnini to order an elaborate list of apparatus: "The laboratory is in operation: it is the most poetic laboratory in all of Italy."

This marks the resumption of the collaboration among these three most outstanding chemists. It is not merely the laboratory of Alessandria, it is in fact the Italian school of chemistry that begins to function here, as is evidenced by the numerous letters exchanged among these three.

Here in Alessandria, Cannizzaro rediscovered himself. Born for scientific research, he now dedicated himself to its pursuit forever, putting behind the episode of political activity and the hardships of exile, which nevertheless had been filled with productive labor. He finally succeeded in overcoming the prevailing disposition toward theoretical and abstract investigation; this, in fact, was to lay the foundation of his future greatness. For experiment is the great teacher who reveals to us the laws of life, which otherwise remain veiled from our inquiring minds. The greatest genius of the Renaissance, Leonardo da Vinci, put it in these words: "Nature is full of infinite reasons which have never yet been revealed in experiments." And Cannizzaro carried on his experiments and worked, all on the granite foundation of reality, to make his laboratory the hearth where the flame of science must forever be kept burning.

And so, in 1853, he was able to publish his memoir on benzyl alcohol, in which he described the reaction between benzaldehyde and potash, known to the chemical world as "Cannizzaro's reaction." It is a most peculiar process whereby, while one portion of the benzaldehyde is oxidized and passes into benzoic acid, the remainder is reduced and transformed into benzyl alcohol, the first alcohol of the aromatic series to be isolated and characterized. Cannizzaro's reaction is relied upon today for the explanation of several biological phenomena of oxidoreduction.

Together with Bertagnini he studied anisic alcohol and converted benzyl chloride, a derivative of benzyl alcohol, into phenylacetic acid. These investigations were to a large extent carried to their conclusion at Genoa, where Cannizzaro, as had been foreseen by Piria, was appointed professor at the University in 1855.

"In Genoa," he wrote, "I found my laboratory to be a miserable room, damp and dark, and no equipment for even the most elementary experimental demonstrations for the lectures, as a result of which I was unable throughout the whole of 1855 to continue the studies begun at Alessandria, not to speak of undertaking any new ones. The following year I was assigned new premises on the top floor of the university building, which I was able to adapt efficiently for work with an assistant and a couple of students, but regular practical courses were out of the question."

Raffaele Piria was meanwhile called to the University of Torino. The closeness of the teacher, who had played a conspicuous part in his appointment to Genoa, was a source of great happiness to Cannizzaro, who did not allow the meagerness of his physical facilities to deter him from the accomplishment of rewarding studies.

The year 1858 marks a milestone in the history of chemistry, by the publication of his *Sunto di un corso di filosofia chimica* which Cannizzaro published in *Nuovo Cimento,* that admirable scientific periodical edited in Pisa.

This compendium is the achievement that established Cannizzaro's claim to fame. Through it modern chemistry, freed from the chains of artificial and contradictory theories, was able to pursue a course that has brought it such glory.

There is no pretense in my cursory remarks to establish any absolute claims, but I shall say that Dalton's atomic hypothesis and Cannizzaro's atomic theory constitute the two pillars of modern chemistry, the keystone of which is Avogadro's law.

The investigation of substances in the gaseous state had enabled Amedeo Avogadro to determine and establish the numerical relationships between molecules that react and the products of such reactions. This was accomplished by a most ingenious and daring interpretation of Gay-Lussac's law of volumes, as the outcome of which Avogadro enunciated the law that "under the same conditions of temperature and pressure equal volumes of all gases contain the same number of smallest particles." Consequently, the ratio of the weights of equal volumes of gases is equal to the ratio of the weights of the single particles of each individual gas. When these gases react with one another, e.g., one volume of gas A becoming associated with two volumes of gas B produces two volumes of gas C, it becomes obvious that one particle of C is constituted of one particle of B and one-half particle of A. Acknowledging the existence of the one-half particle of A either meant acknowledging that each particle was constituted of at least two atoms, or the absurd proposition of adopting a divisible atom. The questionable point of Avogadro's law, as enunciated by him, was therefore the meaning of the term "particle." The general disposition was to agree that the elements had monoatomic molecules, and so Avogadro's law was amended by substituting for the cautious term "particle" the term "atom," overcharged with meanings.

It was only through the influence of Stanislao Cannizzaro that light was finally thrown upon the matter. In his *Sunto,* he acknowl-

669

edged without reservation the applicability of Avogadro's law, namely, that under identical environmental conditions equal volumes of gases contain the same number of smallest particles; but he stated positively that these particles are the *molecules* and not the atoms, since even the elementary substances were made up of molecules, each consisting of two or more atoms.

Hence, if one simple substance reacts with another, each molecule opens up and its atoms, with the atoms of the other substance, proceed to form compound substances which are the product of the reaction.

Cannizzaro successfully demonstrated in his *Sunto* that the clear distinction between atom and molecule causes all apparent contradictions to vanish and cleared up all the uncertainties which even after so many years of experimentation were still persisting in many areas of chemical science. The foundation of his exposition is provided by his definition of the relative atomic weight, on which our modern chemistry depends: The "smallest quantity" of an element capable of entering into the molecule of a compound is precisely *the atomic weight of the element.*

This atomic theory was presented by Cannizzaro at the Carlsruhe Congress in 1860; notwithstanding the inevitable doubts and skepticisms of some, it met with a very favorable reception.

It has been told how the German chemist Lothar Meyer, having received a copy of the communication from Cannizzaro, barely thirty-four years old and little known abroad, frankly stated that he felt "as if a veil had been drawn from his eyes," such was the light that illuminated his mind. However, the fervor of applause did not lack the contrasting note expressed by those who either by inherent opposition to anything new, or by anxious adherence to their own notions, or because some corner of the veil of Maja still left something of the occult, adopted an attitude of resistance to the coordinating power of Cannizzaro's theory.

Among the most dogged adversaries of the theory was the great Marcelin Berthelot, who could never agree that matter, even in the gaseous state, could obey such simple laws as those enunciated by Avogadro; he would never recognize the validity of these laws even when, in his late age, he was constrained to adopt the system of atomic notation.

670

Another opponent was no less a luminary than Sainte-Claire Deville; but the objections which he raised were based on some apparent anomalies in the behavior of matter in the gaseous state. Cannizzaro was able to show, however, that all of this was due to phenomena of molecular dissociation; a prolonged series of experiments, his own and those of others, eventually established the definite and incontestable victory of his theory.

But general chemistry has yet another debt to Cannizzaro. I am referring here to the doctrine of valency, a subject in connection with which the textbooks only too often mention big names alien to it, while the name of our illustrious chemist is passed over in silence. Credit must go to Raffaello Nasini for having reclaimed from them the outstanding part which Cannizzaro played in the working out of the theory. It was presented, with all desirable clarity and extension in his *"Lezione sulla teoria atomica" fatta nella R. Universita di Genova 1858,* which was published, in the famous *Sunto* in such completeness that very little could be found to change in it even today. The fact that Cannizzaro's work on this subject of such capital importance was ignored, or nearly so, is due to the circumstance, as Nasini explains, that those engaged in research were interested only in what appeared to be directly related to the *Sunto,* that is to say, in achieving a system of atomic and molecular weights that would agree with all physical constants and with the law of Avogadro, with a view to arriving at securely established atomic and molecular weights. Consequently they remained unaware that all of this implicitly connoted what, besides, was also explicitly stated, namely, the theory of valence.

Cannizzaro is for this reason one of the founders, and perhaps the principal one, of the above theory; it is comforting to see that in 1924 an important English text "Chemistry and Atomic Structure," by A. Main Smith, gives the credit to Cannizzaro.

The *Sunto* and the Congress of Carlsruhe, where he was the center of attraction among the greatest scientists of his time, introduced him to the scientific world, and the Italian universities began to compete with each other for him. The first invitations came from Naples and Pisa, but he preferred to return to his beloved Palermo in 1861. The previous year, when Garibaldi entered Palermo, Cannizzaro had hurried to this city to see his old mother and his sisters whom he had left in 1849 and, according to his own statement, to offer his help for the consolidation of the revolution.

In Palermo he was appointed professor of inorganic and organic chemistry and director of the laboratory annex which had not changed since the days he was there; the laboratory was only a small room attached to the lecture hall.

During the academic year 1862–63 he had to save money in order to make a few changes to the first of the university buildings to obtain working space. In the meantime, before starting his experimental work he manifested in many speeches that his thinking was clear and concise.

In 1863, in the inaugural speech of the academic year at the University of Palermo he presented an exact definition of the philosophy that governed his thinking. This philsophy resembled partially the philosophy which Stuart Mill called the physico-concrete deductive theory to distinguish it from the deductive theory of the classics which was only based on unproved theories; the physico-concrete deductive theory is based on observations and results that originate from the crucible of experience. This speech vibrated with the patriotic passion of the revolutionary of 1848 that inspired all Italians to make Rome the capital of their country.

The reputation of the master brought to the laboratory at Palermo Italians as well as foreigners anxious to learn; among them Lieben, Körner, and Naquet; among the Italians his successor, Emanuele Paternò. Palermo became at that time, particularly after the death of Piria in 1865, the center of chemical education in Italy.

In spite of his many political and administrative activities, Cannizzaro found time to undertake many studies on the field of organic chemistry. Among other things Cannizzaro proposed to give the name hydroxyl to the —OH group, a nomenclature which has been accepted since then, and he defined the reactions of the alcoholic, phenolic, and acidic "ossidriles."

In 1871 Cannizzaro was called to Rome, capital of united Italy. As much as he loved his Palermo he could not resist the great name of Rome. While in Rome he transformed the old Convent of San Lorenzo (in Panisperna) into the first Italian Institute of Chemistry.

Here he commenced his work on monobenzil-urea and other researches which constituted the continuation and the conclusion of his previous works. But the Roman period is mainly the period of his work on santonin. With only the use of primitive means available at that time, Cannizzaro obtained results which permitted him to determine the constitution of santonin; later researches recognized his conclusions as correct. While some corrections and modifications had to be made in the details, the main discovery of Cannizzaro remains valid.

He exhibited a great ardor in his work. The laboratory was for him the temple in which the flame of science was never extinguished. Every day he discussed his ideas with his collaborators and stimulated great enthusiasm for research. He always had a word of encouragement for everybody, a kind tolerance for mistakes, and a comforting word for the unsuccessful. He gave everybody that complete freedom of initiative necessary for the development of scientific research.

He took great care in the preparation of his lectures. Piero Giacosa described Cannizzaro's lectures as "unforgetful and marvellous." Cannizzaro treated his subjects not in a dogmatic but in an evolutionary way. The development of chemical science, in his courses, was traced from its past in order to demonstrate how it was formed step by step.

During the lectures his whole body became a part of his intellectual activity and one could often observe him becoming inflamed by the idea, stop suddenly, become agitated and lose himself in thought. He would write new formulas on the blackboard, change them, or erase them with dramatic gestures. When this happened, he used everything he had at hand to demonstrate his thoughts. He crumbled up the chalk in his hands and covered the blackboard with all kinds of scribblings. He used his sleeves and coat-tails to clear the blackboard, and finally, when he was finished and exhausted he sat down absent-mindedly on the chair on which he had put his hat, holding his head in his hands.

His head was that of a lion, with a convex forehead radiating flashing intelligence; his eyes were penetrating and bright. He had a strong voice, was impetuous in his affections, excitable, humble with the humble but arrogant with the arrogant. At the age of eighty-four Stanislao Cannizzaro was still possessed with the admiration for science and the love for his country. He died in 1910.

In May 1926, on the occasion of the centennary of his birth, Cannizzaro's mortal remains were transferred to our Pantheon and now repose near the remains of the other great with whom he had in common the flame of science and faith.

From: Domenico Marotta's address at Palermo, October 1, 1939; *Gazetta Chimica Italiana*, 69, 689–717 (1939). Translated by Alfred A. Bacher.

DOMENICO MAROTTA

·· *48* ··

Marcelin Berthelot

1827-1907

IT IS the end of the year 1845. In the narrow room of a pension in Paris, rue de l'Abbé-de l'Epée, two young men sit together studying and talking. The first is the twenty-two-year-old Ernest Renan. He has just left the theological seminary and does not know whether to devote his life to the church or to free scientific pursuits. His friend is four years younger, and of the two he is the more ambitious, the less sure. He is preparing for the final examination of his school career. Not many months later the name of Marcelin Berthelot will for the first time make Paris take notice; for in the competition among all the lycées of France he will win the highest prize in philosophy.

Questions of science are the center of their discussions and, as is fitting for young people, it is not one subject but rather all of knowledge which is their concern. The book of Renan, "The Future of Science," published much later, had its origins in these discussions. It contains results of Berthelot's systematic attempt to assimilate the fundamentals of all sciences. This task, in spite of assiduous devotion and mental mobility, was never completed.

The political discussions between the two friends would have lent themselves less easily to the compilation of a book; the differences were too basic. The theologically trained Breton, Renan, could not value democracy and social and economic progress as highly as Berthelot. Born October 27, 1827, the son of a Parisian doctor, Berthelot learned from his father deep insight into the lives of the poor in a large city. Such insight does not make one cheerful. The memory of a sickly childhood re-enforced his impressions of the economic and biological uncertainty of individual life, and these feelings remained so strong that the seventy-one-year-old Berthelot, toward the end of a life crowned with success and recognition, wrote the shattering phrase *"Je n'ai jamais fait plain crédit à la vie"* (I have never trusted life completely).

Short autobiographical sketches about his youth, which Berthelot wrote for the publication of letters exchanged between him and his friend, reveal many facets of his character. The striving after a complete system of science continued to lead him even when he

677

had to limit his activity to the field of chemistry; there he completed experimental research into the systems of mechanics, chemical synthesis, and thermochemistry. And because of this he attempted to see it grow out of alchemy and develop away from it. If today it sometimes seems to us that in doing this he often placed his own achievement in the foreground more strongly than we would wish it of one so versatile and accomplished, we must always remember his feeling of the uncertainty of life. Insofar as it sprang from the early impressions of his father's worries over the precarious health of others, it was always subjective. Therefrom came the urge to form at least factual certainties, and to build up his own ego.

Connected with this was the goal of fame, emphasized in a peculiarly French manner. Berthelot himself, on a trip through Germany and its universities, often deplored their poverty and narrowness of scope, but pointed out the one definite advantage: *"L'absence des préoccupations ambitieuses, qui perdent tous nos savants dès qu'ils arrivent à l'âge mur"* (The absence of ambitious strivings which ruin all our scholars as soon as they reach a mature age). Living in uncertainty is difficult. If life itself does not seem to offer certainty, the creative person in compensation builds his certainties elsewhere, and the rationalist chooses science for this. Berthelot, the "successor of the Encyclopedists of the eighteenth century," became known as a positivist in his philosophical convictions. This attitude probably came about because he only believed in scientifically gained insights and trusted them more than "life." The paradox is old, the problem it encompasses leads back to the Socratic saying that virtue is knowledge. It is not for us to solve it here, especially since it has value in life only as tension. Here we shall only try to find the roots from which Berthelot's scientific work received nourishment. These show up more easily in general tasks than in the purely experimental part. Berthelot, who already with his thesis "On compounds of glycerine with acids and the synthesis of the bases of animal fats" (April 1854), undertook a big step into unknown regions of chemistry, who was made apothecary of the first order for his work "On compounds analogous to cane sugar" (November 1858), for whom the government in 1864 created a new chair in chemistry at the Collège de France, after

678

1870 took a more vigorous and direct part in the political life of his country. From 1881 on he was senator for life, from December, 1886, to May, 1887, minister (we would say: secretary) of education, and for four months (November 1895 to March, 1896), even Secretary of State. In this way he had the opportunity to proclaim from a position of authority his ideas on natural sciences as the foundation of education, and to plead for peace and international arbitration. For those to whom it may seem limited to put life after science it may now become clearer how Berthelot tried to formulate life from scientifically acquired certainty. He arived at principles which are now even more vital and applicable than then: the division of higher education into a philological and a natural science branch, physical education, direction of the international affairs through sensible guidance rather than ambitious diplomacy and emotional slogans. He may have been ambitious, he may have thought less of the works of his predecessors and colleagues than their accomplishments deserved—if he used the position he gained through unbelievably hard work to serve mankind in this way, then all reproaches must lose their sting and become merely historical facts. Also, he freely gave all the results of his scientific work to industry, which found in them great stimulation.

Berthelot's chemical achievements can be divided into five major categories:

1. *Syntheses of Organic Chemical Compounds.* Chimie Organique fondée sur la Synthèse (1860). Leçons sur méthodes générales de synthèse en chimie organique (1864). La Synthèse Chimique (1876). Les Carbures d'Hydrogène (1851–1901), Recherches experimentales (1901).

2. *Chemical Equilibria and Reaction Mechanisms.* Essai de Mécanique Chimique (1879). Traité Pratique de l'Analyse des Gaz (1906).

3. *Thermochemistry.* Sur la Force des Matières Explosives d'après la Thermochimie (1883). Thermochimie, Données et Lois numériques (1897). Traité Pratique de Calorimetrie (1893).

4. *Physiological Chemistry.* Chimie Végétale et Agricole (1899). Chimie Animale (1899).

679

5. *History of Chemistry.* Les Origines de l'Alchimie (1885). Collection des Anciens Alchimistes Grecs (1887–1888). Introduction a l'Étude de la Chimie des Anciens et du Moyen-âge 1893). Archéologie et Histoire des Sciences (1906).

In addition there are many lectures and publications about more general subjects, necrologues, etc.: Science et Philosophie (1886). Science et Morale (1897). Science et Education (1901). Science et Libre-Pensée (1905). Necrologues on: Balard, Victor Regnault, H. Sainte-Claire Deville, Ad. Wurtz, Pasteur, Claude Bernard, Joseph Bertrand, Renan, Chevreul, and others.

Berthelot was not the first to conduct organic-chemical syntheses. The purely algebraical concept of a "first" may rarely be used in historical events without further research bringing correction. But Berthelot used existing beginnings for new possibilities, to make new realities from them. Faraday already had believed he could make alcohol synthetically. Berthelot not only evolved the production of ethyl alcohol from ethylene, but also made methyl alcohol out of methane, which in its turn was made from synthetic barium formate, and finally propyl alcohol was produced in a similar way. Hermann Kolbe (1845) synthesized acetic acid; Berthelot made it in a different way, he added the synthesis of formic acid, which later gained industrial significance, and after this many new chemical developments followed that are syntheses and not just analyses. Chevreul recognized the components of many animal fats by exact analyses, fractional crystallizations, and critical observation of the influence of air and water. Berthelot concluded from these analyses what one must do for a synthesis of fats; he actually produced several fats made of glycerin and fatty acids. He obtained acetylene after many attempts by introducing hydrogen into an electric arc between carbon electrodes. The new substance found by him, and whose outstanding properties he described, combines with many other substances and polymerizes to form benzene.

When, in 1860, his book appeared in which all organic chemistry is presented in the new light of synthesis, Berthelot complained about the narrow-minded criticism of Chevreul who saw

680

the principles which he had set up forty years before as unchangingly definitive. Biot, more pleased with Berthelot's experiments, could not agree with the more general points of view of the work. Berthelot intended to declare a new era, that of synthetic organic chemistry.

Berthelot felt the strain of this work for many months; in November, 1860, he slowly recovered. One and a half years later the first part of his great work, "Experiments on Affinities, On the Formation and Decomposition of Ethers" (actually: esters) appeared. He published this together with L. Péan de Saint-Gilles. Its general significance Berthelot summarizes in the second volume of his *Essai de Mécanique chimique:*

> One can justly say that before my work on the synthesis of neutral fats, 1854, and the generalization of the method of sealed glass tubes, the theoretical importance of time in chemical mechanics was little known. Péan de Saint-Gilles and I performed the first systematic researches on this point in our experiments on the formation of ethers.

Certainly Wilhelmy had studied speeds of reactions in his experiments on the inversion of sugar (saccharose) in 1850. And the method of the sealed glass tubes does not appear here for the first time. Wöhler in his *Untersuchungen über die Harnsäure* (uric acid) had used them many years previously. And yet Berthelot's work brought not only new material but new points of view. The neutralization between acid and base takes place in an electrically conducting system; the formation of esters is dependent on diffusion processes. The systematic method of the experimental examinations and the discussions of the results make this work of Berthelot one of the finest and most instructive. Guldberg and Waage carried these experiments further to quantitative laws. Berthelot said, increase in volume slows down the reaction; according to Guldberg and Waage "when the same masses of active substances are present in different volumes, then the reactivity of these masses is in inverse proportion to the volumes." Berthelot acknowledged the existence of a borderline between combination and decomposition, an equilibrium which can be approached from both sides.

In 1864 I started to concern myself with thermochemistry. The work which I had pursued up to that time, I mean the synthesis of organic compounds, was completed at least as far as the formation of all parts of fundamental compounds, hydrocarbons and alcohols, and where the defining of general methods is concerned.

From 1869 on, he devoted himself almost exclusively to thermochemistry.

Truly the basic principles for ordering individual results were clear to me from the beginning: they are those which I now call the three principles of thermochemistry, especially the third, which was most particularly mine: I refer to the principle of maximum work.

He wanted to base all of chemistry, i.e., the formation and reaction of the organic and inorganic substances, on the same mechanical principles which govern the various branches of physics. Claude Louis Berthollet had similar ideas about fifty years previously. Berthollet is also just about the only one whom Berthelot recognized as a predecessor, although with many reservations. The relationship between the two can be seen in a closer consideration of the famous *"principe du travail maximum"* (principle of maximum work):

Every chemical change occurring without the action of an outside energy aims at producing the compound (or system of compounds) which liberate(s) the maximum of heat.

According to Berthollet the physical removal of a reaction product from the solution determines the direction in which the reaction will continue; for Berthelot it is the release of heat from the system which determines the result. But it is just this principle, which he himself designated as unequivocally his, that was immediately attacked from many sides. Berthelot attempted to demonstrate his principle with various auxiliary assumptions. Finally he declared that in dissociations and where equilibrium is reached from both sides, the principle of maximum work in its original form might not be sufficiently far-reaching. The work of Gibbs and Helmholtz contributed much that was new, he said, and yet the principle itself remained. Berthelot's third principle could not be saved. The two other principles, however, had already been formulated by G. H. Hess in 1840, although certainly Berthelot had no knowledge of them until 1879.

Really Berthelot's own is the law of distribution, which states that a substance in the presence of two different nonmiscible solvents divides itself between them in a constant relation. Here it is not the law of mass action which operates, rather everything depends upon the influence of the contacting surfaces. Exceptions exist and were later explained by Walther Nernst as due to the change of the molecular association of a substance when dissolved in various solvents.

For six years Berthelot worked almost exclusively on his *Essai de Mécanique Chimique*. But his researches in thermochemistry continued to occupy him for a long time. With many co-workers, most of whom later attained outstanding heights in the field of chemistry (Sabatier, Matignon, Delépine, Stohmann, Thomsen, and many others took part in his work) he expanded the measurements more and more. The book is a compilation of these experiments and contains a great number of specific data which for the most part are still fundamental. They are governed by one method and one thought—combustion in the calorimetric bomb, and the determination of the heat of formations from the heat of combustion. In the same way in which, thirty years before, he had added synthesis to the analysis of Chevreul, he now completed the measurement of heat of combustion as a whole, by concluding the heat of formation from it. The designation of exothermic and endothermic reactions stems from him. He searched for individual rules and pointed out, for example, the following differences between inorganic and organic compounds: The specific heats for the chlorides of alkalies and earth alkalies differ from each other only within narrow limits; in organic compounds the specific heats between homologs rise very sharply; for every new adition of CH_2 the increase is, however, not constant as it is for the heats of combustion. But, he finds, one must not exaggerate these differences, for what we now call elements may, with new methods, be yet decomposed. "Besides, nothing hinders us from assuming that a discovery such as that of the voltaic current may enable chemists of the future to go beyond the limits set for us."

The thermochemical researches were fruitfully expanded in two special directions—research into explosives, and application to animal physiology. The first is distinguished through the development of new experimental methods for which Vieille deserves special credit. The speed of explosion became measurable under the most varied conditions, and examination of the gases formed by these explosions pointed to the possibilities of finding new and better explosives. In this way Berthelot made scientifically fruitful the war of 1870, which had affected him deeply. The expansion of his interests into the field of animal physiology, for which Lavoisier more than Liebig set the example, held him until his death. As late as April 3, 1907, he delivered to the Academy a discourse on heats of formation and combustion of blood and bile pigments. His book on animal heat is remarkable for its clarity. Of earlier work in this field he cites only his own.

Although the experiments with explosives were undertaken in the framework of a great organization, Berthelot, after they were concluded in 1883, set up a large plant-chemical research station in Meudon. The results, won through long years of labor have, however, remained only contributions to specific problems; even what is perhaps the most important result, the recognition of the action of nitrifiying bacteria in the soil, represents really a confirmation and expansion of experiments begun by others (Schloesing and Muntz, 1877) rather than a new discovery.

The only way in which Berthelot was able to pursue his work in the history of chemistry in such an outstanding manner was by securing the cooperation of outstanding philologists and the support of the Académie Française. One must not underestimate the value of these organizational achievements, even if in specific instances certain objections may be raised.

During his lifetime Berthelot received the highest recognition for his achievements. France gave him all the scientific honors which were hers to give. The fiftieth anniversary of his doctor's degree, in 1901, was celebrated the world over. Germany sent

Emil Fischer, Engler, and Harries to the celebration. On this occasion Fischer praised Berthelot as the only one who still embraced the entire field of chemistry.

Berthelot's death aroused the greatest sympathy. He had experienced the uncertainty of life in a most horrible way through the sudden death of his son in a railway acident in 1904. His wife, who since that time had suffered from a heart ailment, died March 27, 1907, and a few hours later he too died. Both were buried with great solemnity in the Pantheon. On his one hundredth birthday the cornerstone of the Maison de Chimie at the Place d'Iena was laid with great ceremony. It had been established through international contributions.

His spirit was perhaps best expressed by himself in a sentence of one of his letters to his great friend, Renan, in 1892. *"Je serai dupe jusqu'au bout de ce désir du progres, que vous reléguez si sagement parmi les illusions"* (I shall continue until the end to let myself be fooled by that desire of progress which you so wisely consider an illusion).

NOTES AND REFERENCES

Paul Sabatier, *J. Chem. Educ.*, 3, 1099 (1926).
Albert Ranc, "La pensée de M. Berthelot," Paris, Bordas, 1948.

From: Bugge, "Buch der Grossen Chemiker," 2, 190–199. Translated by Dora S. Farber.

EDUARD FARBER

·· *49* ··

Alexander Mikhailovich Butlerov

1828-1886

UNTIL the beginning of the nineteenth century almost all Russian scientific work was carried on by foreigners. Nearly every investigation was performed at or directed by the Imperial Academy of Sciences at St. Petersburg. This Academy had been controlled almost from its opening in 1725 by its German members, and even when Russians were admitted they had little to say as to its functioning. They naturally resented this and formed a group which opposed the foreigners. Thus the Academy was split during most of its existence into a "German" and a "Russian" party, a split which later extended into most phases of Russian science.[1]

A number of provincial universities were founded in Russia in the opening years of the nineteenth century. At first these institutions carried on little or no research. They offered a training ground in which young Russians could learn the basic scientific ideas of western Europe. Many of these young scientists were inspired to study abroad, and when they returned to their universities they brought back not only western ideas, but also the desire to continue their laboratory investigations. Thus as the century advanced a progressively broader outlook developed among Russian scientists.

The University of Kazan, founded in 1805, played a leading role in the history of Russian chemistry. By 1840 it had two outstanding chemists on its faculty. These were Karl Karlovich Klaus (1796–1864), a student of Berzelius and the discoverer in 1844 of ruthenium, and Nikolaï Nikolaevich Zinin (1812–1880), who had studied with Liebig. He first reduced nitrobenzene to aniline in 1843. Zinin was the more progressive of the two, as his studies in organic chemistry kept him abreast of the latest developments in what was then the fastest growing branch of chemistry. Klaus devoted himself to inorganic chemistry and retained the dualistic ideas of Berzelius all his life. Both men were inspiring teachers and first-class research chemists.

Alexander Mikhaïlovich Butlerov came to this university at a period of its great chemical activity in 1844.[2] He was born on August 25, 1828, in the small town of Chistopol, near Kazan. His father, a retired army officer, was a landlord in the district. His mother died when he was eleven days old, and he was raised in the home of his maternal grandfather. During his years in the Kazan gymnasium he developed a great interest in insects, spending much time on collecting expeditions. His father wished him to become a mathematician, but he felt that he had no ability for "calculation" and preferred the observational sciences. During his first year at the University of Kazan he spent more time on botany and zoology than he did on chemistry.

At the same time, he was attracted by the work of Klaus and Zinin. He began to perform chemical experiments, at first under their guidance, and later in his rooms, somewhat to the disgust of the other residents who did not enjoy the resulting odors. He wrote his thesis for the degree of candidate on the butterflies of the Ural-Volga region, but after this he turned to chemistry. In 1851 he received the degree of Master of Chemistry with a thesis on "The Oxidation of Organic Compounds." This was a general review of the literature rather than the result of a specific investigation, but it gave evidences of insight into chemical problems that foreshadowed his later work.

Butlerov had been inspired to take up chemistry by the examples of both Klaus and Zinin. In 1847 Zinin was called to the Medico-Surgical Academy in St. Petersburg, and so it was Klaus who was responsible for most of Butlerov's training. Klaus was able to give excellent laboratory instruction, but his theoretical ideas were out of date and he could not guide the young student along the new paths opening in mid-century organic chemistry. A visit to Zinin in the capital in 1854 first introduced Butlerov to the work of Gerhardt and Laurent and began his acquaintance with western chemistry. Meanwhile, in 1851 he had become assistant to Klaus, and when the latter was called to Dorpat in 1852, Butlerov took over most of the teaching of chemistry at Kazan.

His academic career progressed rapidly. In June, 1854 he received the degree of Doctor of Chemistry and Physics from the University of Moscow. He had written his thesis, which concerned the ethereal oil of certain plants, at Kazan. The physics professor there refused to accept it, and so he presented it at Moscow and received the degree. In September, 1854, he was appointed ex-

690

traordinary professor of chemistry at Kazan, and in March, 1857, he became ordinary professor. In 1851 he married Nadezhda Mikhaïlovna Glumilina, and his sons, Mikhaïl and Vladimir, were born in 1853 and 1864.

Until 1857 Butlerov carried on little experimental work and developed no theoretical ideas. When he was appointed full professor he had an opportunity to travel in the west, and this gave him the chance to discover his full talents. He went first to Berlin to visit Mitscherlich, then to Fresenius at Wiesbaden and Mohr at Koblenz. He spent some time at Heidelberg where he met Bunsen and Kekulé. The winter of 1857–1858 he spent in the laboratory of Wurtz in Paris, working on methylene iodide. After this he returned to Heidelberg for a short visit, and later met Liebig, Kolbe, and Wöhler. He learned the value of gas for laboratory use from Pettenkoffer. When he returned to Kazan in August, 1858, he had changed, in his own words, "from a student to a scholar."[3]

Now the most active and important period of his life began. During his foreign travel Kekulé and Couper established the tetravalence of carbon. Butlerov met Kekulé in Heidelberg and Couper in Paris. He knew of their ideas before these were published. As he taught his chemistry courses at Kazan, he began to develop his concept of the relation of tetravalent carbon to the problem of isomerism in organic compounds. He invented the term "chemical structure" and went on to see its implications. He started from the idea of Gerhardt that formulas represented only reactions: a given compound could have various formulas to express the different reactions in which it took part. He soon came to the realization that a full and unique structural formula could be written for each compound, and that each formula corresponded to one definite substance. These ideas were greatly in advance of the speculations of Kekulé himself, who in his textbook of organic chemistry, published 1861–1866, still used many of the ideas of Gerhardt. The experimental work and the series of papers by Butlerov which followed in the early 1860's constitute his greatest claim to fame, for they develop clearly the implications of the structural theory. This work led Butlerov to such outstanding discoveries as that of the tertiary alcohols in 1864 and the nature of tautomerism in 1876.

Butlerov first presented his ideas to the western chemists at a scientific meeting in Speyer in 1861. He read a paper entitled "The Chemical Structure of Compounds," the first general use of this term, although Lomonosov had used the expression in some of his unpublished work. The ideas which Butlerov developed there, and which he expanded in his subsequent studies, were summed up in his textbook, "Introduction to the Full Study of Organic Compounds," published in Russian in 1864 and in German in 1867. This was the first text to use structural ideas throughout.

Besides his experimental and theoretical work, Butlerov was forced to engage in several polemical exchanges with such men as Lothar Meyer, who questioned his priority in the structural theory. His friendship with Kekulé was not disturbed by these discussions. His student, Vladimir Vasil'evich Markovnikov (1838–1904), who extended his ideas by considering the effects of position and substitution of radicals on the course of chemical reactions, ably defended him on many occasions.

While Butlerov was fighting his scientific battles and establishing his reputation abroad, he was engaged in political struggles in his own university. The division of Russian scientists into German and Russian parties existed in Kazan as well as in St. Petersburg. In general the German party was conservative and had the support of the government, while the Russian party was liberal and was supported by most of the students. Since the government appointed the rector of the university and maintained an inspector there who made the final decisions in academic matters, the German party usually held the upper hand, though student dissatisfaction and unrest occurred constantly.

When Butlerov returned to his post in Kazan in 1858 he found a full-scale upheaval in progress. The students disliked the lectures of the professor of physiology and demanded that he "leave the university and give place to new scientific strength." The university authorities hesitated for some time, but they finally permitted the professor to resign, at the same time informing the students that in the future no demonstrations of any kind would be allowed in the lecture rooms. When the students insisted on applauding a popular professor, the authorities expelled 18 of them. At this, 137 students prepared to leave the university. Since the student body numbered only about 300,[4] such a move would have been disastrous. For the moment it was a stalemate, and when a report was sent to the Czar, his only reply was, "It is a great pity, but do nothing." The inspector and the popular professor were both finally dismissed, and the rector was also removed from his post because he could not control the students. In this crisis the government turned to Butlerov, even though he was a member of the liberal party, because he was popular with the students. He was appointed rector in 1860. His position was very difficult, since the conservative party was dominant in the University Senate and continually fought his policies.

New student troubles broke out at the end of 1860. The students demanded the resignation of the professor of Latin, "a very poor and tedious lecturer."[5] When he tried to continue his lectures, he was shouted down. The inspector demanded the names of the offending students, and more students than the auditorium held admitted their guilt. Butlerov attempted to quiet both sides of the dispute, but without success. In mid-1861 the struggle ended with the dismissal of two students, the Latin professor, and the resignation of Butlerov, who in any case wished to go abroad to present his ideas to his fellow chemists.

With his resignation he submitted the recommendation that the university faculty be permitted to name its own rector. This was granted in 1862, and the Senate promptly chose Butlerov to become rector once more. He accepted, and immediately became involved in a struggle with the conservative professors, led by the Dean of the Medical Faculty. Student riots occurred, and a special government commission found "discord among the professors and highhandedness and dissension among the students." The resignation of Butlerov was demanded secretly by the government authorities. When he presented his resignation to the faculty without explaining the reason, the Senate refused to accept it. He was forced to explain that his resignation was *expected* by the higher officials. In July, 1863, he at length resigned, probably with a sense of great relief, for he did not enjoy political struggles. Nevertheless, he was fully in sympathy with the Russian party and remained so all his life. His own diplomatic ability prevented any open break with the government authorities, and even allowed

693

him to oppose them openly at times without himself suffering such consequences to his career as Mendeleev later endured.[6]

During the remaining years which Butlerov spent at Kazan he continued his chemical work and also developed his outside interests. His early enthusiasm for insects led him to a deep interest in bee-keeping. He made numerous scientific studies and published a number of papers on the life of bees. His country estate, Butlerovka, absorbed much of his attention. He studied methods of improved agriculture for the peasants there.

In 1867 Butlerov made another trip abroad. This was partly intended for the defense of his priority in the structural theory, although he visited many points of interest as a tourist and was nearly shipwrecked in a heavy storm while traveling from Marseilles to Algiers. While on this trip he received word that he had been appointed professor of chemistry at the University of St. Petersburg. The enthusiastic personal recommendation of Mendeleev played a large part in his securing this appointment.[7]

The high regard in which Butlerov was held at Kazan was shown when he left, officially by his appointment as honorary member of the university, and unofficially by the statement often made later when difficulties arose, "If Butlerov had been here, this would not have happened." This high regard was justified by the fact that he had founded at Kazan a school of organic chemists which lasted almost until the present.[8] The most famous of his own students was Markovnikov, who succeeded him at Kazan and later became professor of chemistry at Odessa and Moscow.[9] At first Markovnikov carried on studies initiated by Butlerov, and was led by these to the well-known Markovnikov rule. At Moscow he turned his attention to the Russian petroleum industry and isolated and synthesized many compounds present in petroleum. He won international recognition in this field. A second student of Butlerov was Alexander Zaĭtsev (1841–1910), who later took over the teaching of chemistry at Kazan. Many of Zaĭtsev's students afterwards staffed other Russian universities. The best known of these was S. N. Reformatskiĭ (1860–1934).[10]

Butlerov delivered his first lecture in St. Petersburg in January, 1869. He soon became one of the most popular professors in the university. In 1870 he was made an adjunct in the Academy of

694

Sciences, in 1871 an extraordinary member, and in 1874 the ordinary member in chemistry. The Academy was still divided into the German and Russian parties, and Butlerov at once allied himself with the latter. He quickly came into conflict with the permanent secretary of the Academy, Veselovskii, who spoke for the most conservative members. The feeling between the two men was heightened by the fact that Veselovskii was jealous of the increasing scientific importance of the University of St. Petersburg.

The struggle came to a head in 1880 when Zinin died and his place in the Academy was to be filled. Butlerov took a leading part in the attempt to elect Mendeleev to the vacancy. This attempt failed, as did a somewhat later effort to exclude from the Academy a candidate who had never learned Russian. As a result of these failures Butlerov published a vehement letter in the public newspapers in which he questioned whether it was the "Russian" or only the "Imperial" Academy in St. Petersburg. Although these attempts to overcome the German party did not in themselves succeed, they brought the issue into the open and greatly weakened the power of Veselovskii and his friends.

In St. Petersburg Butlerov carried on his former activities as an apiarist and presented papers on bees before the Imperial Free Economic Society. He was active in popularizing chemistry by lectures to the public and by writing popular books on the subject. Until the end of his life he lectured on chemistry in the higher schools for women.

At this time he became deeply interested in spiritualism and attended many séances. The scientific community in St. Petersburg was divided on the truth of spiritualistic phenomena. A committee of leading scientists was appointed to investigate the reality of the effects produced in séances. Mendeleev took an active part in the work of this committee, which could not produce any evidence in favor of the spiritualists. Mendeleev was an outspoken skeptic, but this neither shook the faith of Butlerov nor altered his friendship with Mendeleev.

In 1880, tired of lecturing, Butlerov retired from the University, although he retained a laboratory in the Academy of Sciences. He conceived the idea that the atomic weights of the elements might not be constant, but might vary because of some change in the

695

"chemical energy" of the atom. He spent the last years of his life in an attempt to prove this theory and left much unpublished work in this field at his death. Some have seen in these ideas a hint of the later recognition of isotopes. It is doubtful if this analogy can be carried very far.

In 1885 Butlerov visited the Caucasus to study the bees of the region. He became interested in the possibility of growing tea in this area. He planned to return to this study in the following summer, but in June of 1886 he became ill and was forced to go to his estate of Butlerovka instead. A thrombosis of the leg caused his sudden death there on August 5, 1886.

NOTES AND REFERENCES

1 Leicester, H. M., *J. Chem. Educ.*, 24, 438–43 (1947).
2 Most of the details of Butlerov's life are taken from L. Gumilevskiĭ "Alexander Mikhaĭlovich Butlerov 1828–1886," Moscow, 1952. See also Leicester, H. M., *J. Chem. Educ.*, 17, 203–9 (1940).
3 Borodin, A. I. and Butlerov, A. M., *J. Russ. Phys. Chem. Soc.*, 12, 215–52 (1880).
4 Markovnikov, V. V., *J. Russ. Phys. Chem. Soc.*, 19, Butlerov Memorial Number, 69–95 (1887).
5 Gumilevskiĭ, *op. cit.*, p. 142.
6 Leicester, H. M., *J. Chem. Educ.*, 25, 439–41 (1948).
7 Tishchenko, V. E., *J. Russ. Phys. Chem. Soc.*, 61, 641–51 (1929).
8 Gustavsen, G., *J. Russ. Phys. Chem. Soc.*, 19, Butlerov Memorial Number, 58–68 (1887); Arbuzov, A. E., *Uspekhi Khim.*, 9, 1378–94 (1940).
9 Leicester, H. M., *J. Chem. Educ.*, 18, 53–7 (1941).
10 Sementsov, A., *J. Chem. Educ.*, 34, 530–2 (1957).

HENRY M. LEICESTER

·· 50 ··

August Kekulé

1829-1896

AUGUST KEKULÉ was born on September 7, 1829, in Darmstadt, where his father was Grand-ducal Hessian Head Councillor in the War Office. After August Kekulé graduated from the gymnasium at Darmstadt, he went to the University of Giessen in order to study architecture as his father desired. At school, August had excelled in mathematics and drawing, but of science, in which later on he was to achieve greatness, he had learned almost nothing. Liebig's lectures won him over to chemistry which he ardently studied under Will and Fleitmann.

A stepbrother who had become rich as a businessman in London afforded the means for August to study for a time in Paris. Distinguished by the beauty of youth, by a natural ease of meeting people, and a vivid eloquence, he gained the friendship of Charles Gerhardt, from whose theory of types Kekulé's theory of valency later developed.

For one and a half years, he was private assistant to von Planta at Schloss Reichenau near Chur, a time during which he followed up the stimulations received in Paris from Dumas, Wurtz, and particularly from Charles Gerhardt. Aided by his great perceptive faculty and an unfailing memory, Kekulé during this period familiarized himself with the total available knowledge of the chemistry of carbon compounds.

A sojourn in London as assistant of John Stenhouse followed. In London he became attached to Alexander Williams Williamson (1824–1904). He met William Odling and was on friendliest terms with Reinhold Hoffmann, an assistant of Williamson's, and Hugo Müller, assistant of Warren de la Rue (1815–1889). The Royal Society published Kekulé's study of thioacetic acid which contains the principle of his theory of atomic valence.

His years of apprenticeship were now over. He became a lecturer at the University of Heidelberg. With extremely modest means he established a private laboratory. As his principal field of work he selected organic chemistry which Bunsen had completely abandoned at that time, and was joined by Adolf Baeyer.

In Heidelberg, Kekulé published his famous paper on fulminating mercury in which he recognized carbon as a tetravalent element, that is, an element in which one atom combines with four atoms of a monovalent element, for example, hydrogen.

In his paper "On the constitution and the metamorphoses of chemical compounds and the chemical nature of carbon" (Liebig's *Annalen*, 106, 1858), Kekulé developed the theory of the interlinking between atoms of polyvalent elements. He explained the immeasurable diversity of carbon compounds by the faculty carbon atoms have of combining with each other, through part of their valences, to form carbon chains. Valences not utilized for combining with carbon atoms are employed for binding the atoms of other elements or groups of atoms.

In order to promote his ideas Kekulé started a comprehensive textbook of organic chemistry (3 volumes, 2165 pp., published 1861 to 1862).

Through the efforts of Jean Servais Stas (1813–1891), August Kekulé became full professor of pure chemistry at the Belgian State University of Gent (1858). He soon became proficient in the French language. His laboratory attracted students from Germany, England, and Belgium. His *Lehrbuch* began to be published. The results of his research on succinic acid, tartaric acid, and unsaturated dicarboxylic acids were published.

In 1865 he brought a dream to life and completed the benzol theory. Here is his own account of the dream:

> There I sat and wrote my Lehrbuch, but it did not proceed well, my mind was elsewhere. I turned the chair to the fireplace and fell half asleep. Again the atoms gamboled before my eyes. Smaller groups this time kept modestly to the background. My mind's eyes, trained by repeated visions of a similar kind, now distinguished larger formations of various shapes. Long rows, in many ways more densely joined; everything in movement, winding and turning like snakes. And look, what was that? One snake grabbed its own tail, and mockingly the shape whirled before my eyes. As if struck by lightning I awoke; this time again I spent the rest of the night to work out the consequences.

Kekulé had hit upon the idea to assume the six carbon atoms of benzene, which is composed of six carbon and six hydrogen

700

atoms, arranged in a ring. He compared the benzene ring with the snake biting its own tail. Through this idea a field of unlimited extension was theoretically opened up; it comprises all those substances which can be assumed as derived from benzene by substituting its hydrogen atoms by other elements, the substances which at Kekulé's suggestion are called benzene derivatives, or aromatic substances. On the basis of the benzene theory new kinds of isomeric relationships could be foreseen and these, together with the structure of natural and synthetic compounds, became accessible to directed experimental research.

In order to present the valence theory and the concept of chains and rings of carbon atoms to his students, Kekulé invented atomic models. The models for the elementary atoms were wooden spheres of equal size and different colors, e.g., hydrogen, a white sphere with one brass socket; carbon, a black sphere with four brass rods of equal lengths, directed toward the corners of a regular tetrahedron. The brass sockets permit the connection of such carbon-atom models and, thus, the construction of complex carbon compounds. An excellent scientific tool was thereby provided for teacher and student.

During almost thirty years of teaching at Bonn Kekulé lived to see the spectacular rise of organic chemistry and chemical industry in Germany. The number of his students rose from year to year. Many of them occupied prominent positions as professors or directors of plants and their scientific laboratories.

During his first years at Bonn Kekulé endeavored to establish a mechanistic concept of valency. By means of excellent experimental work, carried out under his direction, he refuted objections against his benzene theory. He loved to study the historical development of his science. In important patent suits between large chemical organizations he acted as arbiter and influenced the development of our patent law by his thorough expert opinions.

He continued lecturing until the last; it was not a strain for him but a source of relaxation and pure joy. Clearly organized and succinctly presented, his lectures were unsurpassed in the way in which elegant experiments were integrated with the words.

He was one of the greatest promoters of chemistry, with the gift of penetrating discernment, rich in creative intuition, combining the abilities of an ingenious researcher with those of an impressive speaker.

NOTES AND REFERENCES

F. R. Japp, *J. Chem. Soc.*, London, 73, 97 (1898).
Richard Anschütz, "August Kekulé," Berlin, 1929 (2 volumes).

From the address by Richard Anschütz on the occasion of dedicating the Kekulé monument in Bonn, June 9, 1903. *Ber. deut. chem. Ges.*, 36, 4616–4623 (1903). Translated by Eduard Farber.

RICHARD ANSCHÜTZ

·· *51* ··

Archibald Scott Couper

1831-1892

THE year 1931 was remarkable not only for its economic difficulties but also for a number of significant scientific anniversaries. A hundred years previously, the British Association for the Advancement of Science was founded, James Clerk Maxwell was born, and Michael Faraday discovered electromagnetic induction. Scientists from all over the world came to London and Cambridge to join in impressive celebrations of these events. On Oct. 9 of that same year a joint meeting of the Glasgow section of the Society of Chemical Industry and the Institute of Chemistry was held in Kirkintilloch, Scotland, a small town seven miles northeast of Glasgow. It was attended by a number of distinguished chemists from the east of Scotland. That afternoon a plaque was unveiled above the doorway of a home in the township with the inscription:

This plaque marks the birthplace of
BORN 1831   ARCHIBALD SCOTT COUPER   DIED 1892
whose brilliant pioneering contributions
to chemical theory have won for him international
renown, and whose genius, stifled by an early illness
was denied the opportunity of consummation

In the evening, Sir James C. Irvine, Principal of St. Andrews University, Scotland, and a distinguished chemist in the carbohydrate field, spoke to the assembled company of chemists and townspeople about A. S. Couper and his work.

Archibald Scott Couper was a brilliant thinker as well as a brilliant experimentalist. He prepared new chemicals and reported their synthesis accurately but neither Kekulé nor Kolbe could repeat his work. He proposed, independently of Kekulé and almost exactly at the same time, the doctrine of chain formation of carbon atoms in a paper entitled, "On a New Chemical Theory":

. . . I propose at present to consider the single element carbon. This body is found to have two highly distinguished characteristics:

705

1. It combines with equal numbers of [equivalents of] hydrogen, chlorine, oxygen, sulfur, etc.
2. It enters into chemical union with itself.

These two properties, in my opinion, explain all that is characteristic of organic chemistry. This will be rendered apparent as I advance.

This second property is, so far as I am aware, here signalized for the first time.[1]

Couper, furthermore, created the symbol of the valence line to illustrate the linking of atoms with each other. If he had not used an atomic weight of eight for oxygen his formulas would be almost identical with those in use today.

For butyl alcohol, $CH_3CH_2CH_2CH_2OH$, he wrote:

$$C\cdots O\cdots OH$$
$$\vdots\cdots H^2$$
$$C\cdots H^2$$
$$\vdots$$
$$C\cdots H^2$$
$$\vdots$$
$$C\cdots H^3$$

or in the French version:

$$C\left\{\begin{array}{l} O{-}OH \\ \\ H^2 \end{array}\right.$$
$$| $$
$$C{-}H^2$$
$$| $$
$$C{-}H^2$$
$$| $$
$$C{-}H^3$$

For acetic acid, $CH_3C{-}OH$, he wrote:
$$\overset{\|}{O}$$

$$\begin{array}{c} C\cdots O\cdots OH \\ \vdots\cdots O^2 \\ C\cdots H^3 \end{array} \quad \text{and} \quad C\left\{\begin{array}{l} O{-}OH \\ \\ O^2 \end{array}\right.$$
$$| $$
$$C{-}H^3$$

This mode of writing formulas has won universal adoption and, with further refinements, has served organic chemistry for the past

706

hundred years. The theoretical paper was published in 1858, when Couper was twenty-seven. He had begun the serious study of chemistry only two or three years previously, and after 1858 nothing further was published by him. He disappeared so completely from the chemical world that his work was well-nigh forgotten. To Kekulé went the honor for the theory of self-linking of carbon, while the synthetic papers on derivatives of salicylic acid were considered worthless because they could not be repeated. Valence lines were adopted universally but none sought their origin. There was one exception, however. Richard Anschütz, Kekulé's successor as professor of chemistry at Bonn encountered the name of A. S. Couper twice in his career, and both times in so startling a manner that he set himself the task of discovering the story of Couper's life and fate.

In 1885 Anschütz had studied the effect of phosphorus pentachloride on salicylic acid,[2] and reading Couper's paper of 1858[3] was able to confirm it completely. Couper had obtained as a distillation product from the reaction mixture a liquid which he analyzed to be "terchlorophosphate of salicyl" of formula $C_{14}H_4Cl_3PO_6$ ($C = 6$, $O = 8$). This substance was in fact obtained if Couper's directions were followed exactly and distillation carried out as soon as the reaction was finished. Higher yields were obtained by Anschütz and Moore by distilling at reduced pressure. Kekulé, who had run the reaction more than twenty times with minor variations in procedure, always kept the reaction too long at a temperature of 180 to 200°, thus decomposing Couper's compound and obtaining only o-chlorobenzoyl chloride.

Kekulé died in 1896, and Anschütz, who took over Kekulé's chair in Bonn, began the task of writing a detailed biography, a work that was not finished until 1929. He discovered that Couper, almost simultaneously with Kekulé, had proposed the self-linking of carbon atoms, and pursuing Couper's writings further, found the English version of his salicylic acid paper.[4] This paper was more extended than the article that had appeared in the *Comptes rendues* and contained the first "structural formulas" in the modern sense of the word. From that time on Anschütz made an intensive effort to secure information about Couper, a quest that finally proved completely successful through the assistance

707

of Alexander Crum Brown of Edinburgh University. Although Couper, because of his last name and French publications, was first thought to be a Frenchman, the discovery of his publications in English led to inquiries in Great Britain and to contact with Crum Brown. The details of the "quest" have now been published by Leonard Dobbin.[5]

Archibald Scott Couper was born on the thirty-first of March, 1831, at the Townhead of Kirkintilloch, Dumbartonshire. He was the only surviving son of Archibald Couper, who owned a large cotton-weaving establishment that had been in the family for several generations. The young Couper was of a somewhat delicate constitution and received most of his education at home. He seems to have been permitted to follow at will any subject that interested him, a pattern he followed even in his university years. His university studies began in Glasgow where he was mainly occupied with the humanities and classical languages. In the summer of 1851 Couper and Alexander Hamilton, a university friend who later became a Presbyterian minister, spent some time in Germany, living with a German family in Halle, and learning the language with remarkable speed. In the summer of the following year they again visited the Continent and at the summer session of Berlin University met a student by the name of Berring, who later became a prominent German engineer. Couper did not study any particular subject that summer. Berring described him as follows[5]: "Couper was a very handsome man of tall slender build, and of distinguished aristocratic appearance. His fine face, with its glowing color, was animated in the most engaging manner by the well-nigh marvellous sparkle of his deep-black eyes. He was not, however, in robust health and always had to be concerned about guarding it."

On his return to Scotland in August, 1852, he enrolled at the University of Edinburgh. There he studied logic and metaphysics under Sir William Hamilton (1788–1856), and moral philosophy with MacDougal. It is most likely that the philosophical power demonstrated by Couper in his theoretical papers is due to the influence of Sir William Hamilton. The latter, although not a great originator, exercised a powerful influence over the thought of the younger generation in Scotland. At a time when German philosophy was almost entirely neglected at British universities, Hamilton spent three years studying in Germany, and when he finally was called to the chair of logic and metaphysics at Edinburgh, he emphasized the importance of German philosophy, especially that of Kant. He is credited with bringing English philosophy out of its insularity, and was noted for the spirit of criticism he inculcated into his students, a spirit markedly evident in Couper's work.

After a year in Edinburgh, Couper returned to Germany, visited Berring in Westphalia and toured southern Germany, northern Italy, and the Tyrol with his friend Alexander Hamilton. They returned to Scotland and about a year later Couper began his extended stay on the Continent. He roomed with Berring in Berlin until his departure for Wurtz's laboratories in Paris in August, 1856.

Sometime in the years 1854 to 1856 Couper decided to concentrate on the study of chemistry. Berring believes that Couper first studied with Rammelsberg, and it is known that he attended Sonnenschein's lectures on analytical chemistry and was permitted to do independent work in Sonnenschein's laboratory for two months in the summer of 1856. He then proceeded to Paris where almost immediately he began independent research. His first paper "Recherches sur la benzine"[6] reported the synthesis of two new compounds, bromobenzene and p-dibromobenzene, $C^{12}H^5Br$ and $C^{12}H^4Br^2$ ($C = 6$). His second paper, on salicylic acid, was presented to the French Academy of Sciences on June 7, 1858.[7] A few months earlier Couper had completed the manuscript "On a New Chemical Theory." He asked Wurtz to present it to the French Academy, but Wurtz, who was not at the time a member, procrastinated before asking someone else to present it. During that interlude, Kekulé's paper "On the Constitution and Metamorphoses of Chemical Compounds and on the Chemical Nature of Carbon"[8] appeared. Its central theme was the tetravalence and self-linking of carbon. How aptly did Kekulé later describe the situation: "Certain ideas at certain times are in the air. If one man does not enunciate them another will do so soon afterwards." Couper took Wurtz to task for the delay and Wurtz directed him out of his laboratory. Couper's manuscript was presented to the Academy on June 14, 1858, by Dumas[9] and very soon after pub-

709

lication was attacked by Kekulé,[10] who claimed both priority and greater significance for his own work.

Couper returned to Scotland in the late autumn of 1858 having accepted the position of second assistant to Lyon Playfair, professor of chemistry at Edinburgh University. He suffered a nervous breakdown soon afterward and underwent treatment at a mental hospital. After a few months he was released in good health only to suffer sunstroke on a fishing expedition. He never recovered, and lived for the next thirty-four years incapable of protracted intellectual work, cared for by his mother in his home in Kirkintilloch. He was able, in later years, to take daily walks and occasionally to chat with friends or write a letter. To the chemical world he was dead.

Three aspects of Archibald Couper's life and work deserve more detailed attention. The first is the nature of his attack on the theoretical problems confronting chemists. Coming late into the chemical field, he was not, as Kekulé had been, steeped in the evolving complexities of chemical formulas. He confronted the current formulas, as it were, "from the outside." We have his own statement to the effect that he analyzed them as if they were words of a strange language. His linguistic studies in Glasgow and the philosophical training under Sir William Hamilton combined to give him the power to discover the order underlying the type formulas of Gerhardt. "To reach the structure of words we must go back, seek out the undecomposable elements, viz., the letters, and study carefully their powers and bearing. Having ascertained these, the composition and structure of every possible word is revealed."[11]

His philosophical training permitted him to apply this linguistic technique to a seemingly very different discipline, that of chemistry[11]:

It would be well to call to recollection the parallelism of chemical research with that of every other search after truth; for it has been in overlooking this that in chemistry false and vacillating theories have been advocated and a wrong route so often pursued. In mathematics the starting point is not generalizations, but axioms, ultimate principles. In metaphysics, Descartes led the way of progress by analyzing till he thought he could reach some ultimate elements beyond which it was impossible for him to go, then studying their force and power, and proceeding synthetically. The recognition of this method wrought the regeneration of science and philosophy.

With this tool in hand, the twenty-seven-year-old Couper, going back "to the elements themselves" discovered those properties of the element carbon which were sufficient to account for most of the formulas then in use and made way for the structure building of organic chemists ever since. The formulas current till that time never attempted to discern the relation of the atoms in the "radicals" substituted in Gerhardt's types. Ethanol was ${\begin{array}{c} C_2H_5 \\ H \end{array}}\Big\}O,$ the ethyl group taking the place of hydrogen in the water type, and few bothered to trouble their heads about the structure of the ethyl group. The enunciation of the self-linking and tetravalence of carbon not only permitted the rational explanation of radicals but made the "types" superfluous. Chemicals with no resemblance to inorganic "type compounds" were now clearly conceivable. Couper shattered the banks of the canal that attempted to constrain organic compounds in the paths of inorganic chemistry.

It is generally assumed, and no doubt correctly, that it was Butlerov who first used the term "chemical structure" at the Science Congress in Speyer in 1861.[12] In his earlier paper "Comments on A. S. Couper's New Chemical Theory"[13] Butlerov had used the terms "structure" and "molecular structure" several times. The above quotation shows, however, that the word "structure" was introduced into discussions of formulas by Couper himself. He asserts that the way to understand formulas is identical with the approach used in elucidating the structure of words. No formulas before those of van't Hoff and le Bel (1874) were accepted as architectural representations of molecules. By the word "structure" was meant mode of connection, not spatial relation, thus permitting its identical use in linguistics and chemistry.[14]

Couper was sufficiently trained philosophically to question

711

whether even the elements were the ultimate building blocks of nature. He considered the possibility that elements are themselves composite bodies. It was a view that, according to him, "the chemist is perhaps not unwarranted to adopt."[15]

In another area also Couper showed his greater freedom from current chemical thought when compared with Kekulé. He proposed an "affinity of degree" for carbon, having the values 2 and 4 corresponding to carbon monoxide and carbon dioxide respectively. Kekulé vehemently denied the possibility of variable valences in spite of accumulating evidence to the contrary. Later, Kekulé similarly opposed Naquet's view[16] that sulfur could show several valences in its compounds. In this, as well as in his formulas, it was Couper who was followed by the chemical world, although here also he did not receive the credit due him. Wurtz in 1861 published his conclusion that elements satisfy their affinity in stages, without referring to Couper.[17] In fact, Kekulé and Wurtz felt free to laugh about the vanished Couper. In a letter to Wurtz accompanying a copy of his "Lehrbuch," Kekulé states his desire as far as possible to make no priority claims in theoretical matters, nor to "trumpet" his views "à la Couper" as a "nouvelle théorie chimique."

The second aspect that needs further attention is the blame or lack of blame due to Wurtz in Couper's subsequent illness. Anschütz was at first relieved to find that the illness did not commence in Paris but only after Couper's return to Edinburgh after he had entered on his new position. This led him to the conclusion that Wurtz was blameless. But in his later publications on Couper he was more willing to accept the verdict of Couper's associates. They believed that Couper's disappointment in being forestalled by Kekulé was a significant causative factor. Such a delicate constitution in geniuses is by no means rare. Van't Hoff's inaugural address when he became professor of chemistry at Amsterdam concerned itself with the role of the imagination in science.[18] A study of two hundred biographies of famous scientists indicated the remarkable prevalence of "pathological" or "morbid" expressions of imaginative power at times bordering insanity or even crossing that border. Some of the greatest, among them

712

Kepler, Descartes, Davy, and Newton, clearly showed such inclinations. Genius, as Wilhelm Ostwald so eloquently exhorted his audiences, requires careful and sympathetic nurturing if it is not to be broken in its early flowering.

Finally we may speculate whether Couper in good health would have anticipated Kekulé in the enunciation of the benzene ring formula. The ring as a possible structural form which came to Kekulé in 1865 in a vision of a snake biting its tail, was already incorporated in Couper's 1858 papers. For cyanuric acid he had proposed the formula:

$$HO—O—Az—C—AzO—OH$$

with two units of affinity joining each carbon and nitrogen. Transcribed into modern symbols and equivalent weights it becomes:

$$HO—N = C = N—OH$$
$$C = N(OH) = C$$

It was the first ring formula ever published and subsequent research corroborated the ring and the order of ring atoms, though not the bonding and the location of the OH groups.

Furthermore, Couper was the first to publish a structural formula for an aromatic compound, salicylic acid, that showed the linking of every atom:

or transcribed

713

This formula only required ring closure and the shift of a hydrogen and hydroxyl group to turn it into the present formula:

$$
\begin{array}{c}
\text{CH} \\
\text{CH} \quad\; \text{C--OH} \\
\text{CH} \quad\; \text{C--CO}_2\text{H} \\
\text{CH}
\end{array}
$$

On one person at least the story of Couper's life made an ineradicable impression. Immediately after the First World War, when the British were stationed in Bonn and some were attending Anschütz's lectures, the latter went out of his way to befriend them even though they belonged to the occupying powers. When admonished about it, Anschütz replied: "There may be another Couper among them."

GENERAL REFERENCES

R. Anschütz, "Life and Chemical Work of Archibald Scott Couper," *Proc. of Roy. Soc.*, Edinburgh, *29*, 193–273 (1909); "Archibald Scott Couper," *Archiv für die Geschichte der Naturwissenschaft und der Technik, 1*, 219–261 (1909).

R. Anschütz, editor, "Über eine neue Chemische Theorie," von Archibald Scott Couper (Ostwald Klassiker der exakten Wissenschaften Nr. 183), Leipzig, 1911, p. 40.

Archibald Scott Couper, "On a New Chemical Theory and Researches on Salicylic Acid" (Alembic Club Reprint No. 21), Edinburgh, 1953, p. 45.

L. Dobbin, "The Couper Quest," *J. Chem. Educ., 11*, 331 (1934).

Sir J. C. Irvine, "Scotland's Contribution to Chemistry," *J. Chem. Educ., 7*, 2808 (1930).

"Couper Centenary Meeting," *Chem. and Ind., 9*, 383–4, 931–5 (1931).

R. Anschütz, "August Kekulé," Verlag Chemie, Berlin, 1929.

James Kendall, "Young Chemists and Great Discoveries," Appleton-Century, New York, 1939.

H. S. Mason, "History of the Use of Graphic Formulas in Organic Chemistry," *Isis, 34*, 346–54 (1943).

NOTES AND REFERENCES

1 *Phil. Mag.* [4], *16*, 104–116 (1858); reprinted in Alembic Club Reprint No. 21, p. 14 ff.

2 *Ann., 228*, 308–321 (1885).

3 *Compt. rend., 46*, 1107 (1858).

4 *Edin. New Philosophical Journal* (N.S.), 8, 213 (1858).
5 *J. Chem. Educ.*, 11, 331 (1934).
6 *Compt. rend.*, 45, 230–232 (1857).
7 *Compt. rend.*, 46, 1107–1110 (1858).
8 *Ann.*, 106, 129–159 (1858).
9 *Compt. rend.*, 46, 1157–1160 (1858).
10 *Compt. rend.*, 47, 378–380 (1858).
11 *Phil. Mag.* [4], 16, 104–116 (1858); Alembic Club Reprint, No. 21, p. 18.
12 *Z. Chem.*, 4, 549 (1861).
13 *Ann.*, 110, 51–66 (1859).
14 The geometry implied by Couper's formulas has been called "rubber sheet" geometry because a formula depicted on a rubber sheet would represent the same chemical no matter how the sheet is bent or twisted. The branch of geometry studying this type of system is known as "topology" or *"analysis situ"*; cf. J. Senior, *J. Chem. Educ.*, 15, 464 (1938).
15 *Phil. Mag.* [4], 16, 104–116 (1858); Alembic Club Reprint, No. 21, p. 22.
16 *Compt. rend.*, 58, 381 (1864).
17 Repertoire de Chimie pure, 3, 418–421 (1861).
18 Quoted in E. Cohen "Jacobus Henricus van't Hoff," Leipzig, 1912, pp. 150–165.

My attention has been drawn to the fact that long before Couper, Wm. Higgins used lines to indicate links between atoms, but his approach was never followed up in organic chemistry; cf. E. R. Atkinson, *J. Chem. Educ.*, 17, 3 (1940); T. S. Wheeler, *Proc. Chem. Soc.*, 221 (1959).

O. THEODOR BENFEY

·· 52 ··

Dmitrii Ivanovich Mendeleev

1834-1907

DMITRIĬ IVANOVICH MENDELEEV was born in Tobolsk, Siberia, on January 27, 1834. According to his own recollection, he was the seventeenth child, though a sister believed he was the sixteenth.[1] At any rate, he was the youngest in the family. His father, Ivan Pavlovich Mendeleev, had been educated at the Pedagogical Institute in St. Petersburg, and had then taught philosophy, fine arts, and political economy in the gymnasium at Tobolsk. He was transferred to Tambov, then to Saratov, and in 1827 he returned to Tobolsk where he remained until his death.[2]

Shortly after the birth of Dmitriĭ, his father became blind from cataracts and was forced to give up teaching. His small pension could not support the family, and this task fell upon the mother, Marya Dmitrievna Mendeleev, an extremely able and remarkable woman. Her family, the Kornil'evs, had been leaders in the development of Siberia for many years, operating glass and paper factories and the first printing press in the region. The family still owned a virtually abandoned glass factory in a village near Tobolsk. Marya obtained permission from her brother Vasiliĭ, a wealthy merchant of Moscow, to reopen it. She ran it so successfully that she was able to support her family and complete the education of her younger children.[3]

Young Dmitriĭ was educated in the Tobolsk gymnasium. He disliked the classics, especially Latin, preferring mathematics and physics. His abilities were so evident that his mother determined that he should have the best education possible. When he was fourteen years old, his father died, and at almost the same time, fire destroyed the glass factory. By this time the older children had left home, and only Dmitriĭ and a sister were living with their mother. She decided to seek the help of her brother in Moscow, and with her two children she made the long journey from Siberia.[4] The brother at first welcomed them, but when he learned that his nephew wished for a higher education, he refused to help, on the grounds that he himself had not had one, and he saw no need for it. Marya angrily determined to go her own way, and took her children to St. Petersburg.[5]

She decided to place Dmitriĭ in the Chief Pedagogical Institute in which his father had been trained. At this time, the Institute accepted new entrants only every other year, and in this year it was not taking new students. By her continued and insistent efforts, and with the aid of friends of her husband, she at length overcame the difficulties, and Dmitriĭ was admitted in the middle of the first course. Three months later, worn out by her efforts, his mother died. His sister soon afterwards succumbed to tuberculosis, and Dmitriĭ was left alone in St. Petersburg.[6]

There was little time for mourning, however. Work at the Institute was hard and continuous. The student body was small and most of the professors, who also taught at the University of St. Petersburg, were excellent. Mendeleev took full advantage of the opportunities for intensive study. At the end of the year he was dissatisfied with his progress, although he had passing grades, and so he repeated the entire course from the beginning. He was soon recognized as one of the best students.[7]

His interest in chemistry was greatly stimulated by the professor of that subject, A. A. Voskressenskiĭ (1810–1880), who had studied with Liebig and who carried on some research in organic chemistry, but who was primarily a teacher.[8] He based his instruction on the ideas of Berzelius, but he also knew and taught the more modern theories of Dumas, Laurent, and Gerhardt. Thus, from the beginning of his studies, Mendeleev was aware of all the current developments in chemistry.[9]

The difficulties of Mendeleev's student years were increased by the fact that for a large part of the time he suffered from tuberculosis. In spite of this he carried on active work. Even before he graduated he published two papers describing the analysis of minerals from Finland. His dissertation at the completion of his course in 1855 was entitled "On Isomorphism and Other Relations of Form to Composition."[10] His interest in isomorphism remained in his later life, and the similarity in crystals of related elements was one of the factors which led him to the periodic law.[11]

Because of his ill health, Mendeleev was sent after graduation to the south of Russia where the climate would be more favorable to him. Before he left, Zdekauer, a famous St. Petersburg physician, told him that he did not have long to live. He went first to

Simferopol, and then, because of the Crimean War, he was transferred to the gymnasium in Odessa. There he met the most famous physician of Russia, N. I. Pirogov. The latter, after examining and treating him, gave him a letter, saying, "Keep this letter and some day return it to Zdekauer. You will outlive us both." This prediction was fulfilled.[12]

In 1856 Mendeleev's health had improved so greatly that he returned to St. Petersburg and successfully defended his thesis for the degree of Master of Chemistry. The subject was "On Specific Volumes." He was then appointed docent at the University of St. Petersburg, teaching theoretical and organic chemistry.

In 1859 he received a stipend for two years' study abroad. He went to Heidelberg, intending to study with Bunsen. There he was assigned a desk with Carius, who was working on sulfur compounds. The odor of these was too much for his still weak chest and so he set up a private laboratory to work on his own problems of capillarity and surface tension.[13] This work demonstrated Mendeleev's interest in atoms or molecules and the forces which act between them; most of his theoretical work throughout his life is a reflection of this interest. In the course of these studies at Heidelberg he noted that for every liquid there existed a temperature above which it could not be condensed from gas to liquid form. This he called the absolute boiling point.[14] His work was largely neglected, but the phenomenon was rediscovered in 1869 by the English scientist, Andrews, who gave it the name used today, the critical temperature.[15]

At Heidelberg Mendeleev was one of a group of young Russian students who often met for social relaxation. The friendships formed here lasted for the rest of his life. One of these students was A. P. Borodin (1834–1887), later professor of chemistry at the Medico-Surgical Academy in St. Petersburg, but more famous as a composer. Mendeleev was able to be of great personal service to Borodin.[16]

Borodin and Mendeleev both attended the famous Chemical Congress at Karlsruhe in 1860.[17] It was here that the distinction between atoms and molecules was clearly shown, and the significance of atomic weights was pointed out. The great generalization of the periodic table could not have been made until this was done. There is no doubt that both Mendeleev and the other discoverer of the table, Lothar Meyer, began to work it out, at first probably subconsciously, only after they had attended the Congress and seen the paper of Cannizzaro which made the distinction clear.

In 1861 Mendeleev returned to St. Petersburg and resumed his lectures on organic chemistry. At the same time he wrote his textbook of organic chemistry, published in 1861, with a second edition in 1863. The book was a great popular success and received the Demidov prize.

Mendeleev's interest in technological questions had been strong ever since the days when he played in the old Siberian glass factory.[18] In 1863 he found an opportunity to make a practical application of this interest when he was called to Baku by the industrialist Kokorev to act as adviser for a small oil refinery there. The development of the Baku petroleum industry was just beginning and the products were meeting strong competition from American kerosene which could be imported into Russia more cheaply than the Russia equivalent could be made. As a patriot, Mendeleev was anxious to aid the development of a Russian chemical industry in every way possible. The interest in petroleum which was aroused in him in 1863 remained throughout his whole life. He continued to act as consultant to the growing industry, to make technical suggestions for improvements in refining methods and for the production of valuable products from the higher boiling petroleum fractions, and to study problems of distribution of petroleum and the economic factors which affected the industry.[19]

In 1863 Mendeleev married Feozva Nikitichna Leshcheva, chiefly at the suggestion of an older sister who felt that he needed a wife. The couple had two children, Vladimir and Olga. The marriage was not happy, however, and quarrels over the children were continuous. Eventually a virtual separation was arranged, Mendeleev living in his quarters in St. Petersburg while his wife and children lived at his country estate of Boblovo. Whenever Mendeleev went to the estate of Boblovo, his wife moved back to St. Petersburg.[20]

In 1865 Mendeleev was appointed to the chair of technology at the University of St. Petersburg. At this time he received the degree of Doctor of Chemistry for his thesis "On the Compounds of Alcohol with Water." In this he first presented his hydrate theory of solutions: solutions are actually chemical compounds. He later developed this theory in a number of important physico-chemical studies. In 1867 he was appointed professor of general chemistry at the University, a chair which he held for twenty-three years.[21]

When he began to give the course in general, or inorganic, chemistry, he felt the need for a new textbook. He planned what was to become his "favorite child" which contained "my likeness, my experience as a teacher, and my most sincere scientific ideas,"[22] his great textbook, "General Chemistry," known in its English translation as "Principles of Chemistry." This book was first published in 1868 and went through eight Russian editions and numerous translations into English, German, and French. It is truly his monument. Like all his writings it is a blend of objective treatise and personal observations and reminiscences. The footnotes often take up more space than the text, and in them Mendeleev describes his own ideas and experiences in a highly personal way that is unique among scientific writings of recent times.[23]

In arranging his ideas for the book he felt the need to bring to inorganic chemistry the same degree of order that was being achieved in organic chemistry. He was struck by the apparent chaos which resulted from attempts to relate the properties of various inorganic compounds to each other and by the lack of any systematic ideas concerning them. For his own information he prepared individual cards for each element, noting on these the atomic weight and the properties of the element and its compounds. In arranging these cards he saw a repetition of chemical properties after each eight or eighteenth increase in atomic weight. In this way, mostly by a consideration of chemical properties, he was led to the discovery of the periodic table.

At about the same time, Lothar Meyer (1830–1895), in Germany, also set on the track by the discussions at the Karlsruhe Congress, was approaching the same generalization from the standpoint of physical properties. There is no doubt that the time was

723

ripe for this discovery and that the two men were working independently toward the same conclusion. To both belongs the honor of discovering the periodic law. Mendeleev, however, was the bolder of the two. He not only recognized the periodic nature of chemical and physical properties, but he saw the presence of vacant spaces in his table and realized that they would be filled by as yet undiscovered elements. Meyer later admitted that this was a step which he had not ventured to take.[24]

Mendeleev had been active in founding the Russian Chemical Society which held its first meeting on November 6, 1868.[25] He planned to present his paper on the periodic table at the meeting of March 6, 1869, but on that day he was ill. The paper was read for him by his friend, N. I. Menshutkin (1842–1907), a noted Russian analytical chemist who was a colleague at the University of St. Petersburg. The communication did not evoke any unusual interest at this meeting.[26] The paper was soon published, both in Russian[27] and in a brief note in German.[28] Mendeleev showed his genius even more clearly in his second paper on this subject, for in this he predicted in detail the physical and chemical properties of three elements which should fill empty spaces in the table.[29] He called these elements eka-aluminum, eka-boron, and eka-silicon, from the Sanskrit word for one and the name of the element above them in the table.

The lack of attention which his work attracted at first was probably due to the fact that chemists of that day were familiar with previous attempts to classify the elements made by Döbereiner, Odling, de Chancourtois, and Newlands, and thought that this was merely another attempt of a formal nature with little or no real physical basis. Even the predictions alone did not seem surprising, but when they were fulfilled almost exactly by the successive discoveries of gallium (1874), scandium (1879), and germanium (1885), chemists realized that in the periodic table they had a tool of the utmost value. Mendeleev had been watching for these discoveries and pointed them out as they were made. From this time on he was recognized both at home and abroad as one of the foremost scientists of the day. He was especially honored in England.[30]

It is a remarkable fact that Mendeleev actually spent only a few years in developing the periodic table, and then went on to other work. He always retained an interest in the table but after about 1874 he did little with it. This is probably because to him it represented merely one phase in his continuing interest in atoms and the forces between them, which he later approached from other points of view.

During the 1870's Mendeleev was expanding his technological interests. He worked on many of the natural resources of Russia, such as coal, salt, metals, and small chemical industries. He continued his efforts to expand the petroleum industry.[31] In 1876 he visited America to study the Pennsylvania oil fields. He brought back a number of technical and economic ideas for the improvement of the Russian industry, but he was not impressed with America itself. He found the country uninterested in science and carrying on the worst features of European civilization. His general conclusion was that "a new dawn is not visible on this side of the ocean."[32]

Out of his studies of the oil industry he developed another great generalization, his theory of the origin of petroleum. He believed this to have been formed from purely inorganic sources, by the action of water on heavy metal carbides deep in the earth. He gave many arguments based on cosmology and geology and even performed chemical experiments in support of his theory which he continued to defend to the end of his life. Although it has been generally abandoned today, this theory was the source of much important work in Mendeleev's time.

In the early 1870's he began work on the properties and behavior of gases at high and low pressures. He invented a very accurate differential barometer and was led to a study of a number of problems in meteorology. He was interested in balloons and foresaw that navigation of the air would become important. Very prophetic were his remarks:[33]

> In other countries there are many coasts along the ocean of water. In Russia such areas are comparatively small, but on the other hand, she possesses greater shores along the free ocean of air than

any other country. For Russia, therefore, it is more suitable to take possession of this ocean, the more so that this bloodless conquest will constitute an epoch with which the newest history of culture will begin.

In 1887 he actually made a balloon ascent at Klin to observe a total eclipse of the sun.

In 1876 Mendeleev went through a serious domestic crisis. At this time he was almost completely separated from his wife, Feozva Nikitichna. At the home of his sister, Ekaterina Kapustin, he met a seventeen-year-old art student, Anna Ivanovna Popov. He soon fell deeply in love with her. Her family did not like his attentions, nor the gossip which began to circulate in St. Petersburg. They made several attempts to separate the pair, and finally sent Anna to Rome to continue her art studies. Mendeleev soon followed her, leaving word behind that if he could not marry Anna, he would leap into the sea. She consented, however, and Mendeleev returned to Russia and secured a divorce. According to the laws of the Orthodox Church, he could not remarry for seven years. Eventually a priest was found who was willing to ignore this rule and marry them. Two days later the priest was removed from his position but, according to the story, he took with him 10,000 rubles.

Officially, Mendeleev was now a bigamist, but nothing was done to him. It was said that later a nobleman in a similar situation was refused permission to remarry and appealed to the Czar, saying that Mendeleev had two wives. The Czar replied, "Mendeleev has two wives, yes, but I have only one Mendeleev."[34]

The second marriage proved very happy. Anna Ivanovna introduced her husband to art and artists. He became an accomplished critic of painting and a considerable collector, eventually being elected to the Academy of Art. The couple had four children, Lyubova, Ivan, and twins, Marya and Vasilii.

As a scientist and professor at the University of St. Petersburg, Mendeleev was unavoidably involved in the political turmoil which affected all nineteenth century Russia. In the middle of the century science and scientists had been left comparatively free to conduct their classes and research as they saw fit. This was because the government was devoting most of its attention to stamping out the bands of anarchists and socialists that arose continually under the Czars. It is probable that this period of freedom for science accounts for the outburst of scientific discovery which is marked by the activity of such men as Butlerov, Menshutkin, and Mendeleev at that time. Gradually, however, the government began to suspect that scientific freedom encouraged political unrest. In 1871 measures were taken to curb this newly discovered danger. The Minister of Public Education, Count Tolstoĭ, an exceedingly reactionary official, introduced measures to reduce scientific teaching in the gymnasia and replace it by the old classical curriculum.[35] Mendeleev was a member of a commission appointed to advise Tolstoĭ. Both because of his scientific background and his early dislike for the classics, he was outspoken in his condemnation of the Count's ideas. A bitter enmity developed between the two men.

This came to a head in 1880 when a vacancy occurred in the chair of chemical technology at the Imperial Academy of Sciences. There was no doubt that Mendeleev was the most famous chemist in Russia and had an international reputation of the highest. It seemed obvious that he would be the choice to fill the vacancy, but internal politics now came into the open.[36] The Academy from its beginning in 1725, had been divided into a German party, composed largely of foreigners who had been brought in to supply the often existing lack of native scientists, and a Russian party, made up of those Russians who were so outstanding that they could hardly be denied admittance. In general the Russian party was liberal politically, and the German party tended to be extremely conservative. Naturally the latter had the support of the government as represented by such men as Tolstoĭ. The permanent secretary of the Academy in 1880 was K. S. Veselovskiĭ, an arch-conservative member of the German party. He was also jealous of the scientific development of the University of St. Petersburg, which was reducing the prestige of the Academy, formerly the sole center of scientific research in Russia.

Two names were proposed for the vacancy. Mendeleev was supported by Butlerov, the famous organic chemist whose call from Kazan to St. Petersburg in 1869 had been largely at the insistence of Mendeleev, and by the Russian party in general. The other candidate was Friedrich Konrad Beilstein (1838–1906), a member of an old Baltic German family and at that time professor in the Imperial Technical Institute at St. Petersburg.[37] Beilstein had received his early education in St. Petersburg and his chemical training in Germany. In 1866 he returned to Russia where he devoted himself to compiling his famous "Handbook of Organic Chemistry," in which he listed the methods of preparation and properties of all organic compounds known to him. He preferred to remain in Russia rather than to return to Germany, since in the latter country he would have had to undertake laboratory research, which he did not enjoy. He was a somewhat cold, sarcastic, and withdrawn man, not popular with the students, but very much in favor with the conservative German party. Tolstoĭ and Veselovskiĭ were determined to prevent the election of Mendeleev, and in this they succeeded. On November 11, 1880, Mendeleev's candidacy was rejected in the Physico-Mathematical Section of the Academy by a vote of ten to nine. In 1881 Beilstein was elected to the chair.

A tremendous burst of indignation throughout Russia followed. Nearly every scientist sent his personal protest and all scientific bodies expressed their adverse opinions frankly. None of these influenced Tolstoĭ, who in 1882 became President of the Academy of Sciences, and who shortly before his death told Veselovskiĭ, "Only remember, Mendeleev must not be recognized by the Academy in any way."

Tolstoĭ was followed as Minister of Education by the equally reactionary Count Delyanov, who also felt a personal animosity toward Mendeleev. After the assassination of Alexander II in 1881 the policy of the government became more and more repressive toward the Russian universities. The students reacted with unrest and riots. The universities were frequently closed for long periods and many students were exiled to Siberia. Mendeleev felt strong sympathy for the students and came to be regarded with greater and greater suspicion by the authorities.

In the spring of 1890 a student uprising led to the formulation of a petition to the Minister of Education asking relaxation of a number of academic rules to restore the university to its former condition. The students asked Mendeleev to present this petition to the Minister, who was Count Delyanov. Mendeleev did so, and soon received it back with the notation, "As to the disposal of the paper by the Minister of Education, it is returned to State Councillor Professor Mendeleev, since neither the Minister nor any one of those in the service of His Imperial Majesty has the right to accept such a paper."[38]

Upon receiving this rebuff, Mendeleev resigned. At his last lecture the students gave him an ovation. After this he did not enter the University again except at a jubilee meeting of the Chemical Society.[39]

In spite of the enmity of Delyanov and the conservatives, Mendeleev enjoyed the friendship of one of the powerful officials at court, Count Sergius Witte, who as Minister of Finance from 1892 did much to improve economic conditions in Russia. Under Witte's influence Mendeleev developed further the strong interest in economics which he had always felt. He began to write books and pamphlets on the natural resources of Russia and their exploitation, and to work for a protective tariff.

He performed a brilliant and useful investigation for the government at this time by working out the formula for smokeless powder. It is said that he determined the composition of the French smokeless powder by analyzing the statistics which showed the movement of the materials used in such powders on the French railways.[40]

In 1893, at the suggestion of Witte, Mendeleev was appointed Chief of the Chamber of Weights and Measures, the institution charged with overseeing the accuracy of the Russian system of measures. Here he found a new outlet for his genius. He worked out the composition of the alloys and the method of manufacture for the prototypes of both Russian and metric units. He converted the Chamber into an institution of pure research and founded a journal of metrology, while installing an inspection system which guaranteed more effectively the honesty of the weights used in commerce.[41] Thus in the last period of his life he carried on in-

729

vestigations in an entirely new field, and showed all his accustomed scientific brilliance.

Much has been said of the scientific genius of Mendeleev, but he was a distinct and unusual personality in his private life as well. Although he had a deep love for children and an abiding interest in and respect for the individualities of his students and colleagues, he was often impatient and irascible, especially with those who took up his time unnecessarily. His taste in literature ran to adventure and romance. He preferred Dumas, Jules Verne, and Cooper to Dostoevskiĭ. At one time when he was suffering from cataracts (as his father had before him), his secretary read him a passage from a Dumas novel which included the sentence, "At this instant the knight rose, swept out his sword, and six soldiers lay dead on the tavern floor." Mendeleev's comment to this was, "Very good. In our literature one person is killed and there are two volumes of suffering, but here on one page six men are killed and no one has any regrets."[42]

A characteristic always noted in the pictures of the older Mendeleev is his enormous head of hair. It is said that he had it cut once a year in the spring, and that he would not deviate from this custom even when he had an audience with the Czar.[43]

Unconventional, absent-minded, often firmly wedded to his theories even when the evidence began to show them incorrect, Mendeleev yet added to nearly every field that his versatile genius touched and gave to chemistry one of its greatest generalizations. The scientists of the world recognized their loss when he died of pneumonia in St. Petersburg on January 20, 1907.

NOTES AND REFERENCES

1 O. E. Ozarovskaya, "D. I. Mendeleev in the Recollections of O. E. Ozarovskaya," Moscow, 1929, p. 50.
2 L. A. Chugaev, "Dmitriĭ Ivanovich Mendeleev. Life and Activities," Leningrad, 1924, p. 6.
3 Chugaev, p. 6; Ozarovskaya, pp. 150–1.
4 B. N. Menshutkin, "Life and Activities of Nikolaĭ Alexandrovich Menshutkin," St. Petersburg, 1908, p. 168.
5 Ozarovskaya, p. 53.

6 Menshutkin, p. 169.
7 Chugaev, pp. 8, 9.
8 D. I. Mendeleev, "Alexander Abramovich Voskressenskiĭ," in Brokhaus Efron, "Encyclopedic Dictionary," St. Petersburg, 1892, vol. 13, pp. 243–44.
9 Chugaev, p. 20.
10 Chugaev, p. 9.
11 H. M. Leicester, *Chymia*, *1*, 69 (1948).
12 Chugaev, p. 10.
13 Chugaev, pp. 10–11.
14 D. I. Mendeleev, *Ann.*, *119*, 1–11 (1861).
15 D. I. Mendeleev, "The Principles of Chemistry," 1st English ed. from the 5th Russian edition, London, 1891, Vol. I, p. 135.
16 B. G. Kuznetsov, "Lomonosov, Lobachevskiĭ, Mendeleev," Moscow and Leningrad, 1945, p. 322; Ozarovskaya, pp. 133–4.
17 C. De Milt, *Chymia*, *1*, 153–69 (1948); *J. Chem. Educ.*, *28*, 421–5 (1951). The latter reference contains a letter from Mendeleev to Voskressenskiĭ describing the Congress.
18 Kuznetsov, p. 218.
19 D. I. Mendeleev, "Oil," in Brokhaus Efron, "Encyclopedic Dictionary," St. Petersburg, 1897, Vol. 20A, pp. 939–52.
20 Ozarovskaya, pp. 134–5.
21 Chugaev, p. 11.
22 Ozarovskaya, p. 158.
23 See also H. M. Leicester, *Chymia*, *1*, 67–74 (1948).
24 B. G. Kuznetsov, "Sketches in the History of Russian Science," Moscow and Leningrad, 1940, p. 92.
25 Menshutkin, pp. 223–4.
26 B. N. Menshutkin, "Chemistry and the Way of Its Development," Moscow and Leningrad, 1937, pp. 229–30.
27 D. I. Mendeleev, *J. Russ. Chem. Soc.*, *1*, 60–77 (1869).
28 D. I. Mendeleev, *Z. Chem.*, *12*, 405 (1869).
29 D. I. Mendeleev, *J. Russ. Chem. Soc.*, *3*, 25–56 (1871); *Ann. Supplementband*, *8*, 133–229 (1872).
30 W. Tilden, *J. Chem. Soc.*, *95*, 2077 (1909).
31 Kuznetsov, ref. 16, p. 221.
32 H. M. Leicester, *J. Chem. Educ.*, *34*, 331–3 (1957).
33 Kuznetsov, ref. 16, pp. 216–17.
34 Ozarovskaya, pp. 135–40.
35 H. M. Leicester, *J. Chem. Educ.*, *24*, 442–3 (1947).
36 H. M. Leicester, *J. Chem. Educ.*, *25*, 439–42 (1948).
37 E. Hjelt, *Ber.*, *40*, 5041–78 (1907).
38 Chugaev, p. 12.
39 Ozarovskaya, p. 74.

40 Kuznetsov, ref. 16, p. 230.
41 Ozarovskaya, pp. 74–77.
42 Ozarovskaya, pp. 129–30.
43 W. Tilden, *J. Chem. Soc.*, *95*, 2081 (1909).

HENRY M. LEICESTER

·· 53 ··

Adolf von Baeyer

1835-1918

ADOLF BAEYER came into this world during the reign of Friedrich Wilhelm III of Prussia; his death, at eighty-two came shortly before the downfall of the Hohenzollern monarchy. His life spanned a significant period in the sciences—from the overthrow of spontaneous generation and the discovery of the microorganisms to the demonstration of cell-free fermentation and detection of the bacteriophages, from the fundamental laws of electrolysis announced by Faraday to the discovery of the x-rays and their interference in crystals. This was the period of technology—from the first railroad to the conquest of the air by Zeppelins and airplanes, from the first electromagnetic telegraphs to the spanning of the oceans by wireless telegraphy and telephony. The late and hesitant development of the German chemical industry was decisively fertilized from Baeyer's laboratory through the artificial production of the most important plant pigments and the synthesis of the valuable triphenylmethane dyes.

The dawn of organic chemistry flushed the horizon in his early years. The investigation of the benzoyl compounds by Liebig and Wöhler had just laid the foundation of the radical theory of carbon compounds. Baeyer's last scientific studies were linked with the discovery of trivalent carbon in the triphenylmethyl radical by Gomberg and of quadrivalent oxygen in the pyrone salts by Collie. Hardly had Baeyer, in his first research (1857) under Bunsen's influence, believed that he had demonstrated the difference between methyl chloride (from methyl alcohol and hydrogen chloride) and chloromethane (from methane and chlorine), than Kekulé in his classic publication on "The constitution and metamorphoses of chemical compounds and the chemical nature of carbon" prepared the way for the recognition of the equality of the four hydrogens of methane. This was the basis for the development of the type theory of structural chemistry. In his doctoral examination, Baeyer was bewildered by Mitscherlich's question:

735

"Which is the most important hydrocarbon?" Several years later, Kekulé benzene formula unlocked the chemistry of the aromatic compounds. The periodic system of the elements was discovered while Baeyer was a docent in Berlin. He lived to see thirty of the vacant spaces filled by newly found elements. The real start of stereochemistry by van't Hoff and Le Bel came during Baeyer's term at Strasbourg. In the discovery of radium around the turn of the century, which gave the impulse to the elucidation of atomic structures, Baeyer saw with emotion the beginning of a new era in scientific research.

The period of organic chemistry, led by the classicists Adolf Baeyer and Emil Fischer, was the period of organic analysis and synthesis. It was the period of simple organic compounds, whose mighty stream was fed by the springs of vegetable and animal life and reinforced by the great tributary welling from coal tar. It was the period of materials which could be distilled and crystallized. The chief guiding principle was the theory of valence; forty years later its insufficiency led to the supplementary doctrine of partial valences. During Baeyer's time chemical studies became involved with substitutions and additions, especially in the benzene series, with condensations of simple aliphatic to polymembered ring compounds, with degradation of cyclic natural products to their simple parent substances. The topics were simple; they combined scientific, technical, and pedagogical significance. The working tools were not complicated; the most important technique was ultimate analysis, and frequently this was the only quantitative method. Great discoveries often came from qualitative observations alone.

Into this early period of structural chemistry entered, as the first student under Kekulé, Adolf Baeyer, an investigator of Scheele's type. He owed it to this great teacher that for sixty years he remained an up-to-date chemist who knew how to lead. Through years of cordial and intimate friendship, Kekulé, who made it a custom to express his views while they were still germinating and ripening, had brought his friend, who was six years his junior, to a vantage point where the prospects, although sometimes clouded over, were mostly clear and extensive. Kekulé had given him the new orientation with which Baeyer, on his

736

own, was able to master both the old and the new provinces of organic compounds, to find his way along the broad highways and explore many side paths. Kekulé's explanation of methane and his benzene formula were the guiding stars by which the organic research chemists successfully plotted their courses for many years.

Baeyer, a born empiricist, was essentially different from Kekulé the theoretician, who "wished to command Nature" through his deductive and critical procedures. "Kekulé had no interest in the compounds themselves, but merely whether they conformed to his ideas. If so, all was well, if not, they were dismissed. It seemed to me unnecessary to pursue his ideas still further. I found that it was my task to come closer to Nature again and to view things for myself . . ." Baeyer's method led him to a deep and respectful love for the uninvestigated materials. Quite justifiably, Baeyer attributed his great success to the fact that he had "entered science at just the right time." Doubtless he would have become great in any period. However, the mastery in organic chemistry could have come to him only, during the period from Kekulé to Emil Fischer, in the period of simple methods, of direct observation, in short, in the period of the test tube. Before his seventieth birthday, Baeyer told the author: "Chemistry has changed. I would not again study organic chemistry."

When Baeyer began to work in indigo, there were no dye factories in Germany. Chemistry belonged to the professors. In the years that followed, the chemical laboratories of the German universities exerted an influence on the industry such as probably will never again be possible, in view of the tremendous growths of the undertakings. But at that time, the university teacher Baeyer could become a founder and promoter of the German dye industry. Without devoting time and energy to the technical development and accomplishment of his syntheses, Baeyer nevertheless created industries and contributed much to the economic welfare of his country. He took no part of the profits. An industrialist once told him: "Professor, you have allowed much gold to run through your fingers." This was intended as criticism; unwittingly it was high praise.

Adolf Baeyer was born in Berlin on October 31, 1835. His father, Johann Jacob Baeyer, one of the creators of the European geodetic survey, was working at the time as a captain on the Prussian general staff in East Prussia, where he and the astronomer Bessel were engaged in triangulation studies. The mother was Jewish. Emil Fischer, in 1917, wrote of Baeyer: "He combined the good characteristics and talents of the Germanic and Semitic races." The grandfather, J. E. Hitzig, an eminent student of the history of literature as well as an authority on criminal law, had made his home the center of Berlin's literary life. However, Baeyer was entirely indifferent to the environment in which he grew up. Even as a young boy he showed a one-sided and deep interest in natural phenomena and was very fond of making chemical experiments, a taste that carried through to his extreme old age. In the valuable autobiography,[1] which formed the introduction of his collected works (2 volumes) issued in honor of his seventieth birthday by his friends and students, he tells of this hobby. Other details have been gleaned from letters preserved from his boyhood. Before starting on a trip, the eight-year-old assigned to his governess the care of eight date stones, which he had planted in pots. They were to be watered respectively with water, milk, wine, ink, etc., so that he could learn the effects of these various liquids. His first chemical discovery came at twelve: he observed a crystalline double carbonate of copper and sodium. It is known that the experiments which he made at thirteen with a piece of indigo subsequently had an influence in the choice of the topics, which in the course of almost twenty years of work culminated in some of the most brilliant syntheses that organic chemistry has witnessed.

After a thorough grounding in mathematics and science at the Friedrich Wilhelm Gymnasium, Baeyer began the study of physics and mathematics at the University of Berlin. However, after one year, he knew what he really wanted and transferred to Heidelberg to enter the Bunsen laboratory. In Berlin, even sixteen years after Liebig had issued his scathing *Über das Studium der Naturwissenschaften und über den Zustand der chemie in Preussen*, there was still no teaching laboratory, either under Mitscherlich or Heinrich Rose. In fact, Liebig himself had not transplanted his

738

Giessen method to Munich. Consequently, chemists from all countries streamed to Heidelberg. There, Baeyer came into stimulating contact with Kekulé, Roscoe, Lothar Meyer, Butlerov, Lieben, Beilstein, Pebal, and Schischkoff. From them, far more than from Bunsen, he received the impulse for his first researches, which dealt with organic radicals. Bunsen initiated the beginners into the methods of analysis. By the time he was forty, he had lost all interest in organic chemistry. The studies pursued in his laboratory naturally fitted into Bunsen's pattern, and this was true of the dissertation *De arsenici cum methylo conjunctionibus*, with which Baeyer qualified for the doctorate at Berlin in 1858. Baeyer ordinarily stated that he was not proud of his showing in the oral examination. However, in its congratulatory message fifty years later, the Berlin faculty could point out that the minutes showed that the examination had been graded favorably.

Kekulé was Baeyer's real teacher. The former had become a *Privatdozent* at Heidelberg in 1856, but for him, as for every other young chemist who came to Heidelberg in those years to work independently, there was no place in the Bunsen laboratory. Together with Kekulé, Baeyer occupied a small private laboratory which was most primitive. There were no fume outlets, and the discovery of the highly toxic arsenic monomethyl chloride during the study of cacodyl compounds actually endangered Baeyer's life. When Kekulé accepted a call to Ghent in 1858, Baeyer went with him. There was no longer a school of organic chemistry in Germany.

In 1860, Baeyer returned to Berlin and qualified at the University with a lecture on uric acid, which he had begun to investigate at the suggestion of Adolph Schlieper, a factory owner who had studied with Liebig. He tried to find working quarters but there were none available. Eventually, a friend of General Baeyer, the physicist Heinrich Dove (1803–1879), called his attention to the Gewerbeinstitut, where it was planned to install a chair of organic chemistry. However, Baeyer's application was without success at first. When the matter of influence was discussed with him on a certain occasion, Baeyer smilingly remarked: "I too got ahead only because of influence." The Crown Prince, who was a friend of Baeyer's brother, made efforts in his behalf, and the nomination of Stahlschmidt, which had already been approved, was voided. Baeyer received the modest teaching post with its salary of 600 thalers; he held it for twelve years.

The Berlin years were a time of slow scientific development and peaceful maturing. How much of the later researches was rooted in the early beginnings of this chapter of his life, how much did the fruitfulness of his first years there shape his entire career to beyond his sixtieth birthday? In the relatively spacious laboratory at the Gewerbeinstitut, which subsequently developed into the Charlottenburg Technical University, there gathered around Baeyer his earliest group, vying with the circle around A. W. Hofmann, who had returned from England in 1865 to set up a large laboratory at the University of Berlin. The first years were devoted to the study of uric acid; order was brought into the labyrinth of the purine derivatives. These studies paved the way for the determination of the structures of these compounds, a triumph that was not completed until many years later by Emil Fischer. Next came the opening studies on indigo (1865–85), through the reduction to indole derivatives and to indole itself, followed by the syntheses of indigo blue from indole and isatin. The reduction led readily to oxindole, but it seemed all but impossible to remove its oxygen and so to reach the parent material. Baeyer accomplished the deoxidation by a new method, namely, distillation over heated zinc dust. The formation of indole from indigo blue itself by the zinc dust distillation procedure was the topic of the first scientific lecture with which Baeyer inaugurated (1868) the meetings of the newly founded German Chemical Society.

The Baeyer laboratory experienced its most important success when the new method was applied to alizarin, the pigment obtained from madder. In this way, C. Graebe (1841–1927) and C. Liebermann (1842–1914) in 1868 obtained anthracene from alizarin; they were fortunate enough to reverse the process and almost immediately to obtain alizarin in technically feasible yields from anthracene, a coal tar constituent. Their work laid the foundations of the alizarin dyestuff industry in Germany, and in

740

a few years drove the French madder off the market. The economic significance of the competition is disclosed by several statements in Baeyer's academic address "The chemical synthesis" (1878). The Department of Vaucluse alone produced madder roots worth 20 million marks yearly; by 1875 the artificial madder from 12 German factories was valued at 15 million marks.

This alizarin work made Graebe and Liebermann famous; Baeyer always viewed the success of his students without envy. The success belonged to the school, the method was due to him. Baeyer had urged Graebe to try the zinc dust distillation method on alizarin in order to discover its parent compound and to elucidate its constitution. However, Graebe was not inclined to follow this advice. His response was that Baeyer should do it himself and it was up to him, the originator of the method, to apply it. Finally Baeyer put his suggestion into a more positive form: "Graebe, you are my assistant, and I now order you to distill alizarin over zinc dust." The oustanding success of the Baeyer school was due not only to its leader's method of research but especially to the wealth of ideas, suggestions, and guiding advice that Baeyer unselfishly passed on to his juniors.

His studies of uric acid directed Baeyer's attention to problems in physiological chemistry. The investigation of condensations began with several observations of the reactions of acetone. What a rich harvest came from these small seeds because of his experimental skill and creative mentality! In his paper on the intermolecular removal of water and its significance for plant life and fermentation (1870), he explained the course of photosynthesis in green plants by assuming that formaldehyde is the intermediate product, an idea that came from Alexander Butlerov's experiments on formaldehyde condensation. Unfortunately, Baeyer never again wrote a line about this theory.

Baeyer pursued the loss of water by acetone much further in another direction. This led him to the varied and remarkable condensations of hydrocarbons and phenols with aldehydes and with phthalic anhydride, which resembles the aldehydes in some of its reactions. The earliest of the phthaleïn and anthraquinone dyes, which were thus discovered in test tube experiments (1871), were gallein and cerulein, which dye like logwood and redwood on metallic mordants, and the renowned fluorescein, which in the form of eosin and many other derivatives found wide markets. In developing this field, the industry discovered in the related rhodamines the most brilliant dyes that synthesis had thus far produced. Accordingly, the most important research areas of the Strasbourg and early Munich periods were actually initiated in the Berlin period of Baeyer's career. The doctoral work which Emil Fischer submitted at Strasbourg dealt with fluorescein and orcinphthalein.

In the early part of 1872, when Baeyer was thirty-seven, he was delivered from the numerous trials and tribulations that had so often muddied the stream of his academic career. When the new university was founded in the recently recovered Alsace, he went to Strasbourg as head of the laboratory which was still to be equipped. The independent professorship was all the more welcome because he had married Lydia Bendemann in Berlin, and they were the proud parents of a daughter, Eugenie. Emil Fischer gave a fine account of the few years in Strasbourg in the above-mentioned collection of Baeyer's works. The ever-growing circle of collaborators included Emil and Otto Fischer, Guido Goldschmiedt (1850–1915), later professor in Prague and Vienna, Eduard Hepp (1851–1917), Edmund ter Mer (born 1852), Conrad Schraube (1849–1923), and Julius Weiler (1849–1909), all of whom made reputations in the dye industry.

Justus von Liebig had died in Munich on April 18, 1873. Called there from Giessen in 1852, Liebig had given up chemical laboratory instruction, and as time went on he withdrew more and more from organic-chemical experimentation. The last decades of his life were devoted primarily to advancing applications of chemistry to agriculture and medicine. His public lectures (attended by the royal family, the court, and a large public), his fame, and his popularity had aroused in Munich a general interest in chemistry and created a respect for its accomplishments, even though there were no local chemical industries. Consequently, the way had been smoothed for his successor. Of course, there were no teaching laboratory facilities at the University of Munich, nor were there any chemistry students. Baeyer who was called in 1875, after Kekulé and H. H. Hlasiwetz (1825–1875) had refused the chair, realized that the most urgent problem was the erection of a large university laboratory, and the Munich authorities were wise enough to meet his somewhat sweeping demands. The ground floor of a large laboratory was placed by the side of the Liebig auditorium. The first classes were held in this laboratory in the fall of 1877. In size and good planning of its facilities it represented a definite advance. For many years it was used as a model for the new laboratories built for teaching purposes in Germany and other countries. An almost palatial residence was erected for Baeyer on the grounds of the Chemisches Institut.

Baeyer was accustomed to say regarding the subsequent more than forty years of his life: "From then on I experienced nothing that was notable." To him, the only things worth relating were his youthful development and rise to his high position. This offhand treatment is a frequent characteristic of the autobiographical accounts of eminent men. They report in great detail about their early years, but say much too little about their impressions and realizations after they have been matured by work and experiences.

Baeyer's life in this period adhered to a strict pattern of alternating school terms and vacations. Devoted to teaching and research, he was almost impervious to outside influences. His family life was one of utmost peace and comfort. He avoided publicity and did not enjoy participation in congresses. Honors and distinctions came in great numbers but were accepted merely as the inevitable concomitants of his scientific accomplishments. He gave almost no public lectures and never wrote for the general public. He preferred to move within the bounds of his own private circle. His wife was heard to say: "Adolf, no matter what you do, you will never become as famous as Liebig."

The first half of the Munich period was occupied with the comprehensive continuation and brilliant completion of the researches that had been started in Berlin and Strasbourg: phthaleins, indigo, acetylenes, and hydrobenzenes are the key words in the main chapters. The principal field of study was indigo; its most important section was opened by going from isatin, the oxidation product of the dyestuff, to indigo blue, and the synthetic preparation of isatin. This was the introduction to the lucid and elegant direct syntheses of indigo for which a program, long unnoticed, had been laid down in a paper as early as 1869. "A two-membered carbon chain and a nitrogen atom must be introduced into benzene and the two then bound to each other. The necessary conditions actually exist in nitrocinnamic acid." The surprisingly beautiful synthesis from o-nitrocinnamic acid, o-nitrophenylpropiolic acid, or o-nitrobenzaldehyde lead via an intermediate product to indoxyl, the actual parent substance of indigo, discovered at that time in urines by Eugen Baumann (1846–1896) and Ferdinand Tiemann (1849–1899). Finally in 1883, Baeyer was in a position to announce after many efforts that "now the position of every atom in the molecule of this dyestuff has been established by experimental methods." The industry eagerly embarked on a study of the means for translating Baeyer's synthesis to the industrial scale, but the success was of short duration. The yields of the ortho-substituted benzene derivatives were much too low. A more suitable basis for the technical process was developed by Karl Heumann (1851–1894), professor in Zurich, based of course on Baeyer's studies: Two carbon atoms are joined with a nitrogen atom, introduced into the benzene ring, and the indole ring is then closed. It was now possible for the Badische Anilin- und Soda-Fabrik, and somewhat later the Höchst Pfleger werke, operating on the sodium amide process of Johann Pfleger (born 1867), to take up the lengthy battle against cultivated indigo. It was so cheap to produce this vegetable product in the Bengal plantations that it seemed most unlikely that the natural product could be driven off the market. About the turn of the twentieth century, the world consumption had a value of around 100 million marks and the Germans imported 2000 tons. After that, the synthetic product rapidly took over.

The theory of carbon compounds was greatly influenced by Baeyer's investigations of acetylenes, his strain theory, his comprehensive studies of the structure of benzene, and the related series of researches—carried out mostly with the collaboration of

744

Victor Villiger (1868–1934)—on the constitution of the terpenes. It is easy to discern the influence of the early studies in the researches conducted when he was sixty-five. Just as unusual as his vigor was the ability of Baeyer in his later years to shift his characteristic working methods to new topics. His late investigations of oxonium salts brought surprising revelations about oxygen compounds, namely, the role of quadrivalent and basic oxygen, while new relations between constitution and color resulted from his final studies of carbonium compounds. The last paper, finished on the day World War I broke out, dealt with pyrone compounds. It was almost his three-hundredth paper and constituted the worthy close of the career of the aged scientist, who had never grown weary of carrying out experiments.

Baeyer was never a theoretician in the sense that he worked for a theory; rather the theory served him as a particularly variable and plastic expression for the observation and as an aid to the new experimental approach. In the introduction to his thirteenth paper on *The determination of position in the terpene series,* Baeyer called attention to the results obtained by G. Wagner in Warsaw and in a few words conceded: "From the new theory it follows that almost all of the formulas I set up are incorrect." He truly could say: "I have never stubbornly held to a particular viewpoint when it no longer could be reconciled with the facts. I strolled in a pleasant region among the substances and enjoyed the sights. At one time this thing looked this way, and perhaps tomorrow it had another appearance. Consequently, why should one obstinately retain a certain opinion?" Baeyer never scrupulously avoided, as many scientists do, putting out an hypothesis which had insufficient experimental basis and seemed destined to have no more than a short life. He used the device of the hypothesis because of its plasticity. However, particularly important to him were the formulas of structural chemistry, which are largely independent of the theories of our time and are therefore destined to be carried forward in a new dress even though our theoretical views change radically.

Nobody has delineated Baeyer's personality as well as he did himself:

What characterizes a great scientist? He should not issue orders, but listen, and adapt and remake himself according to what he has heard. . . . This was the method of the ancient empiricists: they put their ears to nature. The modern scientist does the same thing, and I have tried to do likewise. It has a very peculiar effect on men when they get close to nature They then develop quite differently as compared with those who approach nature with a preconceived idea. Everyone who comes to nature with his mind made up will, to an extent, stand before nature like a general. He will have a desire to order her around. . . . I have never planned my experiments to find out if I were right, but to see how the compounds behave. This is the reason also why I am so indifferent to theories.

It is the fate of a scientist to play a secondary rôle to his work. Whoever is fortunate enough to raise the veil from the secrets of nature will be overshadowed by what he has unveiled rather than created. This was not Baeyer's fate. His personality rose above his accomplishments; it affected his friends and students more directly and powerfully than his scholarly output. His appearance was imposing and pleasing; his face expressed clarity, repose, and mental strength; the blue eyes were expressive, penetrating, brilliant. He was every inch a man.

In the fortieth year of his Munich professorship, the physical ailments of old age made it necessary for him to relinquish his beloved lecture course, which had for so many years been an integral part of his life, and which even into his eightieth year was never a burden to him. Four years later, he died peacefully on August 20, 1918, retaining his full mental powers to the end. His remains were laid to rest in the Waldfriedhof in Munich.

GENERAL REFERENCES

Heinrich Wieland, "Adolf von Baeyer, zu seinem 100," Geburtstag, in Naturwissenschaften, 23, 743 (1935).

Karl Schmorl, "A. von Baeyer." Wissenschaftliche Verlagsges, Stuttgart, 1952 (Grosse Naturforscher, No. 10).

746

NOTES AND REFERENCES

1 A. v. Baeyer, "Erinnerungen aus meinem Leben," Braunschweig, 1905. Unfortunately it covers only the first half of his life.

From Bugge, "Buch der Grossen Chemiker," vol. 2, pp. 321–335, abbreviated. Translated by Ralph E. Oesper.

RICHARD WILLSTÄTTER

·· *54* ··

Johannes Diderik van der Waals

1837-1923

WITH Johannes Diderik van der Waals, who died on March 8 at Amsterdam, at eighty-five years of age, one of the great figures in the history of modern physics and physical chemistry has passed away. His thesis on the continuity of the liquid and gaseous state was a revelation in the study of fluids, the remembrance of which was to glorify the golden jubilee of his doctorate next June, and after establishing it he continued for some forty years to apply his efforts to the same subject, marking the steps of his success by further brilliant discoveries. When the Nobel Institute honored this lifework, van der Waals was still occupied rounding off the comprehensive views science owed to him. For about half a century he was in the front of the workers in the domain he had opened. In the ten years which separate us now from then his forces began to give way, and later bodily and mental sufferings, borne with modest resignation, set in. At last, only short visits allowed us to show to the venerated and beloved friend, whose heart we felt remained unchanged, what he had done for us.

Van der Waals was born on November 23, 1837, at Leyden. He was a self-made man who took advantage of the opportunities offered by the University which he later honored by his curatorship. It was not until he was thirty-six years of age that he wrote his thesis. With it he himself opened the period of Dutch science, which his elder friend Bosscha and he hoped to be one of the results of secondary education.

In 1877, van der Waals became a professor at Amsterdam, and began to exert his great influence on the development of Dutch physics. One of the characteristics of his highly admired teaching was the introduction of Gibbs's great work to the chemists. I vividly remember as an example of it how Bakhuis Roozeboom, to whose first experiments the Leyden physical laboratory had been in the position to give some help, obtained results, which were inexplicable until van der Waals came to give him the key to it in Gibbs's doctrine of phases, his deep insight clearing the way for Roozeboom's brilliant work on the phase rule.

751

Very much was done by van der Waals for the Royal Academy of Sciences at Amsterdam. For twenty-four years he was the soul of the Board, and in 1896 he even accepted the secretaryship of the Academy, a post which he filled until 1912. Here as everywhere else he showed a never-failing unselfishness and high conception of duty. We owe to him the modern form of the Proceedings and their English translation, which he directed, both with an incomparable energy. The great efforts he bestowed on these periodicals have been well rewarded by the effect their stimulating influence had on Dutch science.

The scientific work of van der Waals forms a monumental whole of a special style. Characteristic of it is the intuition by which he introduced happy simplifications and approximations leading to a high degree of qualitative agreement of his theories with Nature, which in the case of the law of corresponding states rose even to a surprising quantitative approximation.

The first idea of the image of the fluid state which was gradually developed by van der Waals came to him when he combined the kinetic theory of gases with the determination of the cohesion in Laplace's theory of capillarity. With the aid of very happy approximations he built up the kinetic theory of the fluid state. Such a simplification gave in the first place the calculation of a molecular pressure which represents the cohesion, and the result of the calculation led him to the profound conception that the molecules of the gaseous and the liquid state are identical and exert identical forces. Secondly, he accepted as by inspiration an exceedingly appropriate form for what would be the outcome of the calculation of the kinetic pressure at higher densities. The simple equation of state which he obtained in this way reproduced the well-known diagram of Andrews-Thomson, as the representation of a series of stable and unstable states of mechanical equilibrium. It gave a deeper insight into the continuity of the liquid and gaseous state as well as a luminous explanation of the critical phenomena. It stood even the crucial test which van der Waals only with apprehension undertook to apply to it; that is, the calculation of the critical data of carbon dioxide of Andrews from the deviations from Boyle's law according to Regnault. Finding correct values for these meant a great discovery. The various thermal properties of fluids treated until then in different chapters of physics proved now to be at least approximatively contained in a single equation with only two specific constants, the volume and the attraction of the molecules, their molecular weights being given by their composition. Later researches have proved, more and more, the greatness of the genius which led van der Waals to his equation of state. Even now it is the most appropriate one to discuss qualitatively the properties of fluids.

Directly from this can be derived the second great discovery of van der Waals, namely, that it is only necessary to introduce the reduced values of volume, temperature, and pressure obtained by dividing the values of these variables by their critical values into the equation of state, to reduce this equation to the same equation for all substances. Simple as this substitution is, it took seven years before it was arrived at, and then only by van der Waals himself, who had been wrestling for a long time with the explanation of the deviations between his equation of state and reality. He had followed many false tracks in order to find some regularity in the deviations of the different substances, and had reached the conviction that to compare substances they have to be considered in corresponding states; that is, at the same values of the reduced variables. At that moment he found the law of corresponding states. Its scope is far wider than that of the equation of state. It involves the bold idea that the thermal properties of all substances can be derived from those of a single one simply by numbers of proportionality; and, what is marvellous, the law approximates more closely to Nature than the equation from which it is derived. How much I was under the influence of its great importance as much as forty years ago may be best judged by my taking it then as a guide for my own researches. It has had a great effect on the work of liquefying the permanent gases (in his thesis van der Waals predicted that air had to be cooled below $-158°$ C. to be liquefied, which has proved nearly correct) and of attaining the *nadir* of temperature.

This cannot be better illustrated than with the words of our deeply mourned Sir James Dewar in a letter to me, expressing

753

that van der Waals was "the master of us all, whom we cannot honour too much." All substances, except for small differences, appear in the light of the law of corresponding states, as van der Waals expresses it, as individuals of the same kind. He liked to direct attention to the fact that his friend Dewar had proved that, taking temperature as a measure, hydrogen was, according to his prophecy, a dwarf. To read to van der Waals a report of the experiments which proved that helium, though a very small dwarf, was yet well shaped, was a happy moment in my life, especially as the report showed the profit derived from van der Waals' law of corresponding states and at the end referred to his words that "matter would always show attraction."

As all normal substances are almost copies of the same model, van der Waals was anxious to bring his equation of state in closer approximation to this general model and to understand the differences between the various substances. To his pondering on the influence of association into double molecules on the deviations, we owe his theory of binary mixtures, which covers a yet vaster and more varied field than his previous discoveries. It is especially this theory to which, in connection with the beautiful work of our deeply mourned Kuenen, I owe the strong ties which united me to van der Waals. For many years I went to his study at Amsterdam for a "monthly private course," that is, a consultation on the Leyden work, and I found van der Waals always at his table filled with papers, with the portrait of his wife, who died at an early age, on the chair in front of him. In these hours it often occurred that from an unpublished calculation he could rightly predict some error to be found in the diagrams of the experiments; and it is from them that I have got an idea of the amount of work from which his genius came to his intuitions.

It would occupy too much space here to refer in detail to the work of van der Waals, which groups itself around these three great discoveries. I can only point out that he tried to combine the theory of specific heats with that of the equation of state, and that in the end he was occupied with the very interesting problem of the influence of the conglomeration of greater number of molecules: that of quasi-association. Rounding off in this way the chapter he wrote in the history of science, he gave us, at the same time, a glimpse of that chapter which the next generation has to write, containing a rational application of quantum considerations in van der Waals' theory of the fluid state.

Not less than the extraordinary intellectual gifts which made possible his great lifework, his friends admired his severe culture of the ideal and his noble character. We remember the pious heart, in whose friendship we rejoiced, and with a feeling of deep sorrow at the loss of his presence, we give him here the tribute of our profound gratitude.

From: *Nature, 111,* 6.09 (May 10, 1923).

HEIKE KAMERLINGH ONNES

·· 55 ··

Sir William Henry Perkin

1838-1907

SIR WILLIAM HENRY PERKIN was born in London on March 12, 1838. His father was George Fowler Perkin, a builder and contractor, who died in 1865 at the age of sixty-three. As a very young boy Perkin entered the City of London School with a very distinct bias for chemistry. The manner in which the young Perkin became interested in chemistry is revealed in his own words spoken some years later:[1]

As long as I can remember, the kind of pursuit I should follow during my life was a subject that occupied my thoughts very much. My father was a builder, the first idea was that I should follow in his footsteps, and I used to watch the carpenters at work, and also tried my hand at carpentering myself. Other things I noticed led me to take an interest in mechanics and engineering, and I used to pore over an old book called "The Artisan," which referred to these subjects and also described some of the steam engines then in use, and I tried to make an engine myself and got as far as making the patterns for castings, but I was unable to go any further for want of appliances. I had always been fond of drawing, and sometimes copied plans for my Father, whose ambition was that I might be an architect. This led me on to painting, and made me think I should like to be an artist, and I worked away at oil-painting for some time. All these subjects I pursued earnestly and not as amusements, and the information I obtained, though very elementary, was of much value to me afterwards. But when I was between twelve and thirteen years of age, a young friend showed me some chemical experiments and the wonderful power of substances to crystallise in definite forms, and the latter especially struck me very much, with the result that I saw there was in chemistry something far beyond the other pursuits with which I had previously been occupied. The possibility also of making new discoveries impressed me very much. My choice was fixed, and I determined if possible to become a chemist, and I immediately commenced to accumulate bottles of chemicals and make experiments.

At the time Perkin entered the London School, science was not a part of the curriculum, but fortunately a Mr. Hall, one of the class masters, was in the habit of giving two weekly lectures on chemistry and natural philosophy during the dinner hour. Perkin attended these lectures, often at the sacrifice of his mid-day meal, and was soon permitted to help Mr. Hall with the lecture demonstrations.

While Perkin's father was opposed to a career in chemistry, nevertheless, through the intercession of Mr. Hall, Perkin entered the Royal College of Science at the age of fifteen; listened to the chemical lectures of the great German chemist, Hofmann, and finally, in his seventeenth year, was appointed to an assistantship under Hofmann. This latter work allowed Perkin no time for his own research and therefore the boy fixed up a laboratory in his home where he could try his own chemical experiments in the evenings. One of the first pieces of private research that Perkin carried on in his own home was concerned surprisingly enough with a coloring matter even before his discovery of the mauve. In collaboration with Arthur H. Church, Perkin began the investigation of the products of reduction of dinitrobenzene and dinitronaphthalene. From the latter they obtained a colored substance which they named "nitrosonaphthyline." This coloring matter was the first representative of the group of azo dyes derived from naphthalene ever manufactured and subsequently was the subject of a patent and actually had a limited use as a dyestuff.[2]

Perkin's discovery of "mauve" took place during the Easter vacation of 1856 when he was just seventeen years old. Hofmann had previously made some remarks about the desirability of preparing quinine artificially. Perkin, basing his experiments on ideas which we know today to be unsound, first treated toluidine and then an aniline salt with bichromate of potash and obtained not quinine but a dirty dark precipitate from the latter.

It was the custom in those days for the organic chemist to be interested only in clear crystalline materials while dark tarry masses were always discarded as being worthless. Not so with Perkin. Some instinct caused him on this occasion to examine this dark mass. From this "useless" substance he isolated the first dyestuff to be produced commercially from coal tar—mauve or aniline purple. It has been stated that, had Perkin experimented with pure aniline instead of with a rather crude material then available, his experiments would have been a failure and no valuable dyestuff would have been discovered. This is not so; on the other hand it is true that magenta would not have been discovered, as it was several years later, had not the aniline used in the experiment been contaminated by toluidine.[3]

Almost immediately Perkin sent a sample of his dyestuff to a firm of dyers in Perth with the request that they try it on silk. Their report was: "If your discovery does not make the goods too expensive, it is decidedly one of the most valuable that has come out for a long time."

While the first trials on cotton were unsuccessful (because no one realized the need for mordanting cotton), Perkin was not completely discouraged and he decided to patent the process for manufacturing the dyestuff. It was not long before he had worked out methods for applying his mauve to cotton by means of mordants:[4]

The nature of my invention consists in producing a new colouring matter for dyeing with a lilac or purple colour stuffs of silk, cotton, wool, and other materials in the manner following: I take a cold solution of sulphate of aniline, or a cold solution of sulphate of xylidine, or a cold solution of sulphate of cumidine, or a mixture of any one of such solutions with any others or other of them, and as much of a cold solution of a soluble bichromate as contains base enough to convert the sulphuric acid in any of the above-mentioned solutions into a neutral sulphate. I then mix the solutions and allow them to stand for 10 to 12 hours, when the mixture will consist of a black powder and a solution of a neutral sulphate. I then throw this mixture upon a very fine filter, and wash it with water till free from the neutral sulphate. I then dry the substance thus obtained at a temperature of 100°C, or 212°F, and digest it repeatedly with coal-tar naphtha, until it is free from a brown substance which is extracted by the naphtha. Any other substance than coal-tar naphtha may be used in which the brown substance is soluble and the colouring matter is not soluble. I then free the residue from the naphtha by evaporation, and digest it with methylated spirit, or any other liquid in which the colouring matter is soluble, which dissolves out the new colouring matter. I then separate the methylated spirit from the colouring matter by distillation, at a temperature of 100°C or 212°F.

Surprisingly enough, the father agreed to back his son with financial and other types of support. When Perkin and his father discussed the possibilities of manufacturing the dyestuff with Hofmann, they met with discouragement but nevertheless father and son decided to go ahead with the venture. (Hofmann should not be condemned for his wrong advice, for anyone using ordinary sound business judgment would certainly have discouraged the two from what appeared to be almost impossible. Picture the team that was to found our modern organic chemical industry: a young man of seventeen with no factory or business experience and a limited chemical knowledge, together with a builder having no knowledge of chemistry or manufacturing whatsoever.)

A building was commenced at Greenford Green in June, 1857. Perkin wrote years later:[3] "At this time neither I nor my friends had seen the inside of a chemical works, and whatever knowledge I had was obtained from books. This, however, was not so serious a drawback as at first it might appear to be; as the kind of apparatus required and the character of the operation to be performed were so entirely different from any in use that there was little to copy from."

The many practical problems which Perkin and his associates had to overcome seem large in comparison with the actual discovery of the dyestuff itself. Raw materials that were needed to manufacture the dyestuff were almost as scarce as rare elements. One of the first problems was to devise a method for making aniline from benzene. Even obtaining a satisfactory supply of benzene was in itself a problem. Perkin and his brother searched the whole country before they were able to obtain a reasonable supply of benzene for which they paid $1.25 per gallon. When they finally got this material into their factory it was so poor that it had to be redistilled.

Nitric acid of sufficient strength to convert benzene to nitrobenzene was not available and the Perkins had to manufacture

762

their own, which in turn required the building of special apparatus.

Finally, the method of converting nitrobenzene to aniline had to be worked out by this eighteen-year-old boy and he had to devise the technique and the apparatus.

In spite of all the obstacles, within six months Perkin's dyestuff under the name of "aniline purple" or "tyrian purple" was being used in a London dyehouse and within a short time other concerns in France and England began its manufacture.

It is interesting to note that, in spite of Perkin's great pioneering work, the recognition of the value of his dyestuff took place quite slowly in Great Britain. It was not until the French had realized its great value that its use became general in Britain. In fact, the name "mauve," by which Perkin's dyestuff has been known to this day, was given to it in France. A few months before his death Perkin remarked on this: "The value of the mauve was first realized in France, in 1859. English and Scotch calico printers did not show any interest in it until it appeared in French patterns, although some of them had printed cloth for me with that colour."

It should also be noted that, along with the great difficulties involved in manufacturing a completely new chemical and starting a new industry, Perkin was troubled with the problem of introducing his new dyestuff to the trade. This latter was extremely difficult, for Perkin had had no contact with the dyeing industries up until his discovery of his new dyestuff. When the dyestuff was first tried on silk on a large scale, it took unevenly and Perkin had to spend many weeks working out a solution to this problem. The answer was the use of a soap bath for dyeing the dyestuff onto the silk. In the case of dyeing wool and cotton, even more difficult pioneering work had to be done. Perkin's application problems are summed up in his own words:

I distinctly remember the first time I induced a calico printer to make trials of this colour that the only report I obtained was that it was too dear, and it was not until nearly two years afterwards, when French printers put aniline purple into their patterns, that it began to interest English printers.

Before the aniline purple could be introduced for dyeing woolen and mixed fabrics, some weeks were also spent at Bradford in finding out suitable methods of applying it.

Thus it will be seen that in the case of this new colouring matter, not only had the difficulties instant to its manufacture to be grappled with, and the prejudices of the consumer overcome, but, owing to the fact that it belonged to a new class of dyestuffs, a large amount of time had to be devoted to the study of its applications to dyeing, calico printing, etc. It was, in fact, all pioneering work—clearing the road, as it were, for the introduction of all colouring matters which followed, all the processes worked out for dyeing silk, cotton, and wool, and also for calico printing, afterwards proving suitable for magenta, Hofmann violet, etc.

As usually happens when a new industry becomes successful, Perkin's position was soon assailed by imitators. Many patents appeared for making mauve which were only slight modifications of Perkin's original patent. Fortunately for Perkin, none of these modified processes yielded mauve as cheaply as Perkin's original "bichromate" method.

Perkin's introduction of mauve also led others to additional discoveries of dyestuffs derived from coal tar and gave the impetus to the establishment of other dyestuff factories. Particularly important was the discovery of magenta. Some five years after the start of Perkin's Greenford factory, Hofmann found that magenta, when ethylated or methylated, gave violet coloring matters, and Hofmann's violets, and a bit later certain rosanilines, began to compete with Perkin's mauve. Finally the discovery of methyl-violet and other related colors by Lauth enlarged the competitive picture. The newer dyestuffs were much less fast than mauve but they were much more brilliant. It was not long before the public became more concerned with brilliance than with fastness. These developments gradually caused a decline in the demand for mauve, which, within a few years, died out altogether. It has been said that, while mauve was a flourishing branch of the color industry, it did not complete ten years of existence.

Perkin was able to keep his factory going in spite of the adverse effect of the discovery of the new dyestuffs. In 1864 he introduced a new method for the alkylation of magenta, which enabled him to compete with the other violet coloring matters. These dyestuffs were introduced under the name of Britannia violets and were furnished in different shades of blueness, which were obtained by varying the degree of alkylation.

A revitalization of Perkin's manufacturing position happily occurred in the year of 1868 with the announcement of the synthesis of alizarin, the natural coloring matter of madder, by Graebe and Liebermann. Fortunately, for Perkin, their process was far too expensive to be of more than scientific interest. The starting material for their synthesis of alizarin was anthracene, a coal-tar chemical with which Perkin had become familiar while studying with Hofmann. The work of Graebe and Liebermann aroused Perkin's interest and in less than a year he had worked out a successful commercial process which soon made synthetic alizarin the prime red dye in place of madder.[5] The same problems which confronted Perkin in obtaining benzene were even greater in the case of anthracene. Nevertheless, by the end of 1869, Perkin's company had made a ton of alizarin and by 1871 they were making 220 tons per year.

By 1873, continental competition in the manufacture of alizarin had reached the point where Perkin and his associates realized that expensive changes in the plant at Greenford Green would have to be made. Perkin's ambition from the very beginning of his work on mauve had always been to devote himself to pure science. By 1873, however, Perkin found that his manufacturing establishment had provided him with the means for retirement on a rather modest basis. In 1874 his factory was sold and Perkin at the age of thirty-six retired from industry to devote his life to pure research.

Perkin's work in pure research did not only just begin after his retirement from the dyeing industry. It seems almost unbelievable that, simultaneously with the starting of the Greenford Works and while he was beset with the most complicated types of manufacturing and commercial problems, Perkin also carried on difficult and important researches in organic chemistry completely unrelated to coloring matters. Less than a year after the starting of the Greenford Works, he discovered that aminoacetic acid or "glycocoll" could be obtained by heating bromacetic acid with ammonia. By 1860, together with his fellow worker, Duppa, he had discovered the relationship between tartaric, fumaric, and maleic acids and had accomplished the synthesis of racemic acid from di-bromo-succinic acid.[6]

About 1867 he commenced his famous researches on the action of acetic anhydride upon aromatic aldehydes, and this culminated in the classical method of synthesizing unsaturated acids by what is now known as the "Perkin synthesis." Within a year, as a result of this work, Perkin had synthesized coumarin, the odor substance in tonka-bean and had thus made the first synthetic perfume or flavor. Furthermore, it is interesting to note that the continuation of work along these particular lines some years later led to his great discovery of the synthesis of cinnamic acid from benzaldehyde, which made possible the first synthesis of indigo by Baeyer and Caro.[7]

During Perkin's manufacturing period, his research work was carried on in a laboratory, in a house just outside the Greenford factory. With the aid of his co-worker, Church, he also carried on in this laboratory investigations on the structure of various dyestuffs and coloring matters. Thus, like a juggler, Perkin kept three lines of work going on at the same time: the study of technical processes for manufacturing dyestuffs, the study of the theoretical structure of dyestuffs, and organic synthesis.

After Perkin's retirement from business he had a new house built at Sudberry and converted the adjacent house in which he had previously been living into a laboratory. Here, almost up until the time of his death, he continued his researches. Here also in 1881 he first became interested in a certain physical property of some of the organic compounds which he had prepared, namely, their magnetic rotary power. He further developed his ideas so that the examination of this particular property of organic compounds became an important tool in answering various questions of chemical constitution, and the remainder of Perkin's life, for some twenty-five years, was devoted to this phase of physical organic chemistry. Many scientists have indicated that this was the great-

est of all of Perkin's work. Perkin's accomplishments in this difficult field are best summarized in a letter which Professor Bruehl,
himself one of the pioneers in the application of optical methods
for the determination of chemical constitutions, sent to Perkin in
1906:

> Availing yourself of the marvelous discovery of your great coun-
> tryman, Michael Faraday, you undertook to investigate the relations
> between the chemical composition of bodies and their magnetic cir-
> cular polarization that is to say one of the general properties of all
> matter. Before you began work there was little, almost nothing,
> known of this subject, certainly nothing of practical use to the
> chemist. You created a new branch of science, taught us how, from
> the magnetic rotation, conclusions can be drawn as to the chemical
> structure of bodies, and showed that the magnetic rotation allows us
> to draw comprehensive and certain conclusions as to the chemical
> constitution of substances, just as we may from another general
> physical property, viz., refraction and dispersion. And by showing
> that both these physical methods of investigation lead to completely
> harmonious results, you did essential service to both the branches of
> study, and also to chemistry, which they are destined to serve.

Perkin's personal life was essentially uneventful. His devotion
to science and to his family was so complete that beyond participating in the work of several scientific societies, he took no part
in outside affairs.

Perkin married Jemima Harriet Lisett in 1859. Unfortunately,
Jemima died in 1862, but she did give William Perkin two sons
who became distinguished professors of chemistry. Four years
after the death of his first wife, Perkin married a Polish girl,
Alexandrine Caroline Mollwo. From this marriage there was one
son, Frederick, and four daughters.

Apparently, Perkin's three sons inherited their father's scientific
curiosity and the work of two of them, William Henry and Arthur
George, was at times concerned with textiles.

The son, William Henry, after going through City of London
School and the Royal College of Chemistry, as did his father,

studied under the great von Baeyer and perfected a fine experimental skill in organic chemical research. At the University of Manchester he created a school of organic chemistry which received world-wide recognition. Interestingly enough, William Henry was the inventor of a durable flameproof finish for cotton called "non-flam," which was based on the precipitation of tin salts on the fabric. In 1912 he left Manchester for Oxford and founded there an even greater school of organic chemistry.

The second son, Arthur George, while not as famous as his elder brother, also became a skilled organic chemist, but most of his attention was devoted to dyestuff manufacturing and then to research on natural organic coloring matters at the University of Leeds. In 1916 Arthur George succeeded A. G. Green as professor of color chemistry and dyeing at the University of Leeds, and continued his textile researches until his health began to fail in 1937.

Perkin's retiring nature and lack of desire for publicity caused him to remain in comparative obscurity as far as the general public was concerned for most of his life. While some of his scientific colleagues saw that he received frequent recognition for his pure scientific work, his contemporary coworkers in the field of dyestuff manufacture and development did not always give him the recognition that was his due for founding the great dyestuff and organic chemical industry. In fact, an examination of the contemporary technical literature during the time of Perkin's active participation in dyestuff manufacture does raise some strong questions along these lines.

For example, the important book entitled "On Aniline and its Derivatives," by the German chemist, Reimann, published ten years after Perkin's discovery, certainly would not indicate to the casual reader Perkin's prime position in the development of the coal tar industry. The first dyestuff discussed in this book is magenta, and mauve is given a secondary position. Finally, in this authoritative source the only statement about Perkin's work which is given in a chapter on aniline blue and violet is as follows: "A violet, the first of all aniline colors was discovered by Messrs. Perkin and Church." The writer goes on to discuss in great detail the work of Hofmann and others without any additional word of appreciation for Perkin's great part.

Even Hofmann in his report on "Coloring Matters Derived From Coal Tars Shown at the French Exhibition, 1867," makes only brief mention of his own student's part in the founding of this industry; yet at that time, 11 years after Perkin's discovery, Hofmann points out how a great industry had already arisen based on the chemicals from coal tar, which not only has given us new colors but brought us also drugs, flavors and perfumes.

Finally, in William Crookes' mounmental work, "A practical Handbook of Dyeing and Calico Printing" (London, 1874), nothing is mentioned about Perkin's place in the founding of the synthetic dye industry, yet a number of chapters are devoted to the synthetic dyestuffs, their use, and even methods of application (developed by Perkin). Crookes was Hofmann's first assistant at the time Perkin came under Hofmann, and he must have known Perkin and the importance of his discovery. The question again is: Was there a deliberate attempt to play down Perkin's importance? Could there have been jealousy on the part of the older Crookes? Or, did Perkin's innate modesty tend to keep down any favorable publicity?

Another question which often arises is: Why did England pay so little attention to the important discovery of their own Perkin and allow the Germans to take the lead in the dyestuff and organic chemical industries? Perhaps no clear-cut answer can ever be found, but as one English writer puts his complaint: "Had the nation been far-seeing and wise, the industry would have flourished here (England) not merely for five or twenty years but permanently. Instead of this, Hofmann returned to Germany in 1865, Caro in 1867, Martius about the year 1870, Witt in the year 1879. Perkin retired in 1874 and the band of great discoverers had dwindled to two or three."

Perkin did receive some recognition from the scientific societies with which he was associated. He was elected into the Royal Society in 1866 and in 1893 he became one of the vice presidents. The Chemical Society, which published most of his researches, made him president in 1883. Perkin's real recognition, as far as the world was concerned, however, came about only a year before his death, and this was on the occasion of the international celebration of the fiftieth anniversary of his discovery of the dyestuff "mauve."

An international committee for the celebration was set up and the "giants" of the educational and scientific world of Europe and America were asked to serve. Among the American members were Leo Baekeland, Wilder Bancroft, Marston T. Bogert, Nicholas Murray Butler, Chittenden of Yale, Charles Herty, J. M. Matthews, Ira Remsen, J. Takamine, H. W. Wiley, Woodrow Wilson, as well as August Merz, Louis A. Olney, and Alan Claflin.

The main celebration was held in London at the Royal Institution on July 26, 1906, with a fine banquet during the evening at the Hotel Metropole. Present at the celebration were representatives of the important scientific societies of England, France, Germany, Austria, Switzerland, and the United States. Even representatives of the great German dyestuff companies were present to pay their respects to Perkin.

The spot chosen for the main celebration was of particular historical significance, for it was in 1825 at the Royal Institution that Michael Faraday had first discovered benzene, the basic coal tar chemical and the starting point for Perkin's mauve. On a table before the distinguished gathering sat the original specimen of benzene which Faraday had discovered. During the celebration the now-famous portrait of Perkin by Cope and the beautiful bust by Pomeroy were unveiled.

For a final evaluation of Perkin's life and the story of the last moments of the great man, we return to Perkin's friend and co-worker Meldola.

The influence which Perkin has exerted upon this generation is not to be measured solely by his achievements in pure and applied chemistry. His life was noble in its simplicity, and his single-minded devotion to his work, combined with a character known to be religious in the highest and best sense of the term, will bequeath to posterity an enduring example of humility in the face of success which would have marred many men of smaller moral calibre. The financial success of his early manufacturing experience was turned to account simply as a means of advancing science, and no distinction which he ever gained throughout a career which culminated in 1906, when the King conferred upon him the honor of knighthood, and when the nations of the world assembled to render him homage, had the slightest influence upon the modesty and gentleness of his disposition. It was his personality that caused him to be revered in his domestic circle, and to be beloved by all who enjoyed the privilege of his friendship.

. . . In his general mode of life Perkin was a man of extreme frugality, robust and active to the last. To one of his retiring habits, the strain accompanying the jubilee celebrations in 1906 and the subsequent ordeal of his American tour must have been considerable, but he bore all the excitement and fatigue without the least indication of discomfort. Literally, he died in harness; a few months previously he had read his last paper before the Chemical Society, and he was looking forward to being able to resume his research work quietly and uninterruptedly after the distractions of 1906. The illness which brought his noble and useful life to an end, which, in view of his activity, cannot but be regarded as premature, did not at first reveal any serious symptoms. The writer of this notice was with him a few hours before his death, and although he complained of suffering pain he spoke hopefully of his condition and anticipated being soon able to leave his room. The illness proved, however, to be more serious than he or his family were aware of; a sudden change for the worse occurred, and on July 14th, 1907, he passed away in perfect peace and in the full tide of his well won honor.

NOTES AND REFERENCES

1 R. Meldola, J. Chem. Soc., 93, 2214–2257 (1908), a detailed biography of Perkin.
2 W. H. Perkin and A. H. Church, Proc. Roy. Soc. (London), 8, 48–49 (1856).
3 W. H. Perkin, Hofmann Memorial Lecture, J. Chem. Soc., 69, 596–637 (1896).
4 W. H. Perkin, British Patent 1984 (August 26, 1856).
5 W. H. Perkin, British Patents 1948 (June 26, 1869) and 3318 (November 17, 1869).
6 W. H. Perkin and B. F. Duppa, J. Chem. Soc., 11, 22–30 (1859); 12, 1–7 (1860).

7 W. H. Perkin, J. *Chem. Soc.*, 20, 418–432 (1867); 32, 660–674 (1877).
(A complete bibliography is attached to the original publication by Sidney M. Edelstein.)

From: *American Dyestuff Reporter*, 45, 598–608 (1956).

SIDNEY M. EDELSTEIN

·· *56* ··

Ernest Solvay

1838-1922

I N THE little town of Rebecq, about thirty kilometers to the south of Brussels, Ernest Solvay was born the sixteenth of April, 1838. His father, Alexandre Solvay, was a distributor and a refiner of salt. In the back of the parental home there was a shop where salt was refined. Ernest Solvay grew up here, pláying between sacs of salt and observing, from morning to night, the refining operations of dissolving, concentrating, and crystallizing.

Ernest, who was not of robust health, received only a scanty school education and soon returned home to aid his father, while spending his leisure time reading and experimenting in electricity and chemistry.

One of his maternal uncles, Florimond Semet, directed a gas works at Saint-Josse, one of the suburbs of Brussels. The Semet family was of French origin, well-known in northern France where they had interests in several gas enterprises.

In 1859, Florimond Semet asked his nephew to help him in directing his gas work. At Saint-Josse Ernest Solvay started to work with enthusiasm, applying his inventiveness to all parts of gas manufacture. He developed several improvements in purifying the gas, separating the tar, and regulating the pressure. An ingenious provision for preventing the gas lines from fouling brought him congratulations from the stockholders and a bonus of 2000 francs.

He then attacked the problem of concentrating the ammonia-containing wash waters. He heated these waters to drive out ammonia and carbon dioxide which he wanted to absorb in the smallest possible volume of water.

DISCOVERY OF THE PROCESS

After he had used ordinary water for this purpose, he conceived an idea which, at first glance, might seem quite impractical. He replaced ordinary water by a solution of salt through which he passed the carbon dioxide together with the ammonia. To his great surprise he found that a white precipitate was formed which proved to be sodium bicarbonate. To explain this phenomenon, he

775

thought, at first, that ammonium bicarbonate was formed, and that this had caused a double decomposition with the sodium chloride. He verified his hypothesis by bringing ammonium bicarbonate together with a salt solution and stating that the precipitate of sodium bicarbonate was really formed.

Immediately, he grasped the importance of this reaction which permitted obtaining sodium bicarbonate from sodium chloride without heating. The Leblanc process, which was then in use, necessitated a sequence of reactions at high temperatures. He decided to pursue his study. Uncle Semet gave him a free hand, hoping that his nephew would perhaps find a way to get rid of the ammoniacal waste water.

On April 15, 1861, Ernest Solvay took out his first patent. He was just twenty-three years old. The patent had the title: "Industrial production of sodium carbonate by means of marine salt, ammonia and carbon dioxide." It was a simple statement of the principle, very brief, without any description of apparatus. In general outline it conforms with the process as used at present.

With funds provided by the family, Ernest and his brother Alfred, his junior by two years, organized a small experimental installation at Schaerbeck, on the market place which today carries his name. The first results were encouraging, and Ernest offered his process to several Belgian producers of chemicals.

These steps were not successful, but in their course Ernest Solvay had occasion to consult an attorney named Eudore Pirmez, a man of great experience in business matters who later played an important political role in Belgium. Monsieur Pirmez naturally asked Ernest Solvay about the value of his patent and suggested that he investigate its priority. In doing this, Ernest Solvay discovered to his consternation that the reaction he had found and believed to be new actually had been known for over fifty years, and that frequent attempts had been made to develop it into larger scale.

PREVIOUS ATTEMPTS

Let us briefly consider these attempts—their number, their importance, and the quality of those who made them will demonstrate Ernest Solvay's merits more clearly.

As we know now, the reaction was first pointed out by Augustin Fresnel, the famous author of the theory of light. In 1811, when he had just left the École Polytechnique and several years before he undertook his research in mathematical physics which made him famous, he had done chemical work. He had chanced upon the basic reaction and recognized its importance. Through one of his friends, he had sought the opinion of Vauquelin and Thenard. At that time, the industrial world began to make the Leblanc process workable, and in the enthusiasm of the first successes nobody was inclined to test the newcomer. Besides, Fresnel had not been concerned with the recovery of ammonia which was then a rare and costly product. Fresnel's discovery was certainly not ripe for an important industrial development.

Nevertheless, it was so alluring in its simplicity that it was taken up again a few years later. It is particularly noteworthy that in the year of Ernest Solvay's birth, 1838, two Englishmen, Dyar and Hemming, obtained a patent based on the same reaction. Soon it was followed, in 1840, by a French patent containing in broad outline the actual process, including the regeneration of ammonia by means of lime. Dyar and Hemming tried to develop their process industrially. After two years of fruitless effort they gave up. A little later, however, the attempts were renewed in the plant of the English industrialist Muspratt at Newton. One year of work, 200,000 francs of losses.

Again the reaction tempted new inventors, mainly in England and in France. Gossage, another great exponent of the Leblanc process and Deacon, the famous inventor of a process for manufacturing chlorine, had to give up after long struggles.

In 1854, two experienced French engineers, Schloesing and Rolland, experimented at Puteaux, in the outskirts of Paris, after obtaining several patents on equipment. They continued for four years. In spite of their careful and methodical approach they had to close the plant in 1858 after spending one and a half million francs.

THE STRUGGLE FOR SUCCESS

When they learned about all these predecessors and all the failures, Ernest Solvay and his brother hesitated. Besides, the famous Belgian chemist Stas, whom they consulted, thought the process was too delicate for an industrial application. Without Ernest's ardent conviction, the two brothers would perhaps have abandoned the enterprise. Pirmez encouraged them to continue. He expressed the opinion that since such outstanding engineers as Schloesing and Rolland had thought it worthwhile to spend such considerable sums of money in order to bring this new industry into being, the basic principle must be valuable. Later on, Ernest Solvay remarked: "You see that the financiers, who do not always judge things the way inventors do, sometimes find reasons for hope exactly where the others could find reason for despair."

And thus, the Société Solvay et Cie. was founded in 1863 with a capital of 136,000 francs in a legal form which was best suited to the family group exclusively interested in the business.

A factory was built at Couillet for an intended production of 12 tons per day. Operations started in January, 1865. The equipment used was that described in Ernest Solvay's second patent, of November, 1863, and represented an almost completely mechanized operation.

Many difficulties arose immediately. The carbon dioxide was not absorbed, the distillation of the ammonia did not function well, and so on. Nevertheless, the two brothers worked in relays day and night. Ernest was director, engineer, superintendent, designer, chemist, wheelwright, while Alfred had the functions of accountant, cashier, stock clerk, selling agent, etc.

In October, 1865, a new piece of equipment had to be discarded and the plant was shut down. New capital was needed, and the stockholders hesitated to provide it. This meant disaster. At that moment the mother of Ernest and Alfred, who had always encouraged and supported them in difficulties, came to their rescue. A new carbonator was installed, and in June, 1866, production rose to 1500 kilograms per day. A year later, this figure was doubled. The brothers had finally crossed the narrow borderline between success and failure. The continuation of the Société was henceforth assured.

WHY ERNEST SOLVAY SUCCEEDED

He had practical experience in the distillation of ammonia solutions. In the gas works of Saint-Josse he had become familiar with the handling of gases and liquids. In the course of a few years he succeeded in reducing ammonia losses to a tolerable level.

Besides, Ernest Solvay soon invented an apparatus for rapid absorption of carbon dioxide in the ammoniacal salt solution. Solvay's absorption tower quickly became famous; it constituted the most decisive progress. Reaction time was reduced from the 10 to 15 hours previously needed to about 5 hours. The furnace for burning limestone was greatly improved.

The filter press, which had been an important new development in chemical industry, was absolutely insufficient for the filtration of the sodium bicarbonate. In 1894, Ernest Solvay introduced the principle of the continuous rotary filter.

INDUSTRIAL EXPANSION

In 1872, a highly skilled German chemist, Ludwig Mond, residing in England, approached Ernest Solvay. He obtained a license for England and founded the Brunner, Mond and Company along the organizational plan of the Société Solvay et Cie. In 1873, the first English plant was built in Northwich.

The year before, construction of a large French plant had started at Dombasle, based on the important salt deposits about 15 kilometers east of Nancy. This became the world's greatest soda manufacturing plant. Thus in 1880, three plants were in operation: Couillet in Belgium, Dombasle in France, Northwich in England. During the next ten years, plants were founded in the United States, Germany, Austria, Russia.

Ernest Solvay realized the magnificent field of experience presented by these factories working under greatly varying conditions. Each one of them had to concentrate its efforts on overcoming its particular difficulties. A factory located where coal was expensive was to develop heat economy. A factory in a country of high wages placed particular attention on the reduction of labor costs.

Production and Prices. The highest output of Leblanc soda was reached in 1887 with 540,000 tons. Since 1888, the production of Solvay soda exceeded this figure and rose to 1,380,000 tons in

779

1900; 3,520,000 tons in 1920; and 5,100,000 tons in 1930. Of 7 million tons produced in 1937, 4.5 million came from Solvay plants.

The price of a ton of Leblanc soda was 700 francs in 1855. Around 1870, when Solvay soda began to appear on the market, the price had dropped to 350 francs. Because of the competition between the two processes, the price was soon reduced to one third of that figure.

Personnel and Social Improvements. One of the great advantages of the Solvay process is the great economy in labor. The process is highly mechanized. The task of the workers is thus reduced to supervision of apparatus and constant control of manufactured products.

The welfare of the personnel had always been foremost in Ernest's and Alfred's minds. As soon as the success of the process was established, numerous social improvements were introduced in the plants. The Société Solvay has always been far ahead of social legislation. Three of these measures may be cited: (1) a retirement plan of 1889, which provided 10 times the legal benefits; (2) Reduction of working hours since 1908; (3) Paid vacations, with double salary, since 1905.

THE MAN AND HIS IDEAS

Ernest Solvay had received only a simple education in primary school, no instruction in science or technology. He said of himself:

> I do not have the good fortune of being a scientist, and I have not received the classical education. However, I have not ceased to pursue a scientific goal, because I love science and I expect from it the progress of mankind.

Whenever he had an occasion, he gave to scientists, research workers, and students encouragement and facilities.

Thus he created around himself, in Brussels, that series of institutes which bear his name and which remain living testimonies to his enthusiasm and love for science: the institutes of physiology, of sociology, the international institute of physics and chemistry. One day in 1910 he presented his ideas on social improvements in the Belgian Senate. He was interrupted by a rather irreverent shout of "Utopia." Ernest Solvay replied in good humor:

My honorable colleague naturally ignores the pleasure that one provides for old men of action when one calls them frankly, squarely utopists. Actually, this is a good way to make them relive their youth and, by recalling identical situations, increase their confidence.

The Patriot. During the great war, Ernest Solvay remained in Belgium and incarnated the spirit of resistance. Since the end of August, 1914, he foresaw clearly the suffering which menaced the invaded country. With his usual sense for action, he created a national committee for help and food which soon extended its activities over the entire country. Thanks to this decisive act, Belgium was saved from famine and demoralization.

After the armistice, King Albert expressed Belgium's gratitude to the great patriot.

THE LAST YEARS

I should have liked to project on the screen the features of Ernest Solvay as I have known him in his last years. I should have liked to show you this expression of noblesse and frankness in his face, his shock of hair, his blue eyes which created a captivating impression of power and balance. You would then have better understood the kind of fascination, the kind of magnetism which he had for those surrounding him. In the years of struggle, in the hours of doubt and discouragement, his devoted brother Albert said of him: "Ernest cannot be wrong!"

All his family and his friends followed him, swept away by his ardent conviction, throwing into the venture their last resources in order to enable him to continue his work. Throughout his life, Ernest Solvay remained utterly simple. He did not love luxury nor honors. He passed away without suffering, in his sleep, on May 26, 1922.

NOTES AND REFERENCES

P. Heyer and C. Lefébure, "La Vie d' Ernest Solvay," Lamertin, Brussels, 1919.

Société Solvay et Cie.: Cérémonie de Commémoration du 50ième Anniversaire de la Fondation, Brussels, 1913.

H. Bolito, Alfred Mond. Secker and Warburg, London, 1933.

From an address before the Société Chimique de France, November 3, 1938, at the celebration of the centennary of Ernest Solvay's birth, *Bull. Soc. Chim. France, 5ᵉ serie, 6*, 405–421 (1939). Translated by Eduard Farber.

RENE ETIENNE

·· 57 ··

Josiah Willard Gibbs

1839-1903

O N THE one hundredth anniversary of his birth, we are here to do honor to the memory of Josiah Willard Gibbs, the greatest physical scientist that America has produced and one of the greatest original thinkers of all time.[1] The occurrence of genius is commonly believed to be a phenomenon of pure chance, and such it may well be so far as native talent is concerned; but talent has merely a potential value; it is fruitful only when it is properly cultivated; indeed, we may say when it is self-cultivated under favorable conditions. Genius may be assisted in this process of self-cultivation but, in all cases, genius flourishes best in an environment of complete intellectual freedom. The history of American science bears this out.

Let us review, briefly, the careers of the American men of genius who contributed to the development of physical science from Colonial times up to the last quarter of the nineteenth century. Up to 1880, America had produced five great physical scientists: Benjamin Franklin, Benjamin Thompson (Count Rumford), Joseph Henry, Henry A. Rowland, and Josiah Willard Gibbs.

Franklin and Rumford were products of prerevolutionary America; they were self-taught, having received only very meager common school education. The two men, although their lives were, in certain respects, very diverse, had much in common. Both were exceptionally versatile; both were keen observers and ready experimenters; both were of a practical and inventive turn of mind; both were keenly conscious of their social environment; and both did much to advance science and learning in other ways than through their scientific contributions. Franklin was active in promoting the establishment of libraries, colleges and learned societies —notably, the American Philosophical Society; Rumford founded the Royal Institution, whence came the epoch-making researches of Davy and Faraday.

Joseph Henry received his formal education, such as it was, at

Albany Academy. He began his scientific work while a teacher at the Albany Academy, where he remained until 1832 when he removed to Princeton. In 1846, he resigned his professorship at Princeton to become the first secretary of the newly founded Smithsonian Institution. Henry began his researches in electromagnetism while in Albany and continued them at Princeton. He was a genius of first rank, but his work has been rather overshadowed by that of Faraday.

Henry A. Rowland prepared for college, or attempted to do so, at Newark Academy. Although a brilliant student in other subjects, he had a keen distaste for Latin which he was unable to overcome. After a final unsuccessful effort to master Latin and Greek, at Andover, and lacking the necessary knowledge of these subjects for college entrance, Rowland entered the Rensselaer Polytechnic Institute, where he remained for three years. He then spent a year in the Sheffield Scientific School, at Yale, and returning to the Rensselaer Polytechnic Institute, he received his baccalaureate degree in civil engineering from that institution in 1870. Rowland was nine years younger than Gibbs, but his scientific work was contemporaneous with that of Gibbs's. Rowland's first great undertaking was an accurate redetermination of the mechanical equivalent of heat, the first determination of which had been made by Count Rumford three quarters of a century earlier. In the field of heat, American scientists have made greater contributions than in any other branch of physical science. It might be said that Rumford began the solution of the problem of heat, and Gibbs completed it.

Gibbs entered Yale College in 1854, after preparing at the Hopkins Grammar School of New Haven. He was evidently proficient in the classical languages, since, as an undergraduate at Yale, he took prizes in Latin and gave a Latin oration on graduating. He seems to have had an equal facility in mathematics, for he likewise took prizes in that subject. After graduating from Yale, in 1858, he entered the graduate school, where, after five years, he received his doctorate in 1863. After spending the following three years as a tutor in Yale College—two in Latin and one in natural philosophy—Gibbs went abroad, spending the winter of 1866–67 in Paris, the summer and winter of 1867–68 in Berlin, and the summer and winter of 1868–69 in Heidelberg. He returned to America in June, 1869, and for two years thereafter seems to have had no academic connections. In 1871 he was appointed professor of mathematical physics in Yale University, which position he held until the time of his death, on April 28, 1903.

It is an interesting fact, and it would seem a significant one, that of the five men, native of America, who achieved distinction in physical science, two were self-taught, one received his education in a small academy, and a fourth in a technical school; only one was the product of one of our better American colleges. Is it that men of potential genius did not enter the numerous American colleges during the Colonial and the postrevolutionary periods or is it that the course of training which these colleges thought fit to impose upon their students unfitted them for great achievement? Is the probability not that, while men of genius in America were able to overcome the handicap of lack of means, lack of education, and lack of technical training, they were not able to resist the blighting influence of eighteenth and nineteenth century scholasticism? Gibbs, alone, stands out as a notable exception. May it have been that there was something in the organization of Yale College that permitted Gibbs to cultivate his mind and to find free scope for his brilliant intellect? With his ready facility in the ancient languages and, doubtless, in other subjects as well, and with his excellent preparation, Gibbs probably found much time in which to inform himself on subjects that did not appear in the curriculum of Yale in his day. It is also a notable fact that he spent five years in the Yale graduate school, the first organization of this kind in America. Here, without doubt, Gibbs found further opportunity to follow his own bent. His experience as a tutor can hardly have been a profitable one; his mind, obviously, was not interested in the classics, and there is little doubt but that Gibbs was much more interested in the development of science than he was in teaching undergraduates. Later, when he was professor of mathematical physics, he never showed any inclination to simplify his presentation of a subject or to give introductory

787

courses for students who were not prepared for subjects as he presented them.

During his stay abroad, Gibbs must have informed himself very widely with respect to the physical sciences and trained himself in mathematics. The records show that, while in Berlin, he attended lectures in physics and technology, under Magnus; acoustics, under Kundt; electricity and electromagnetism, optics, acoustics, and capillarity, under Quincke; determinants and analysis, under Weierstrass; quadratic forms and probability calculations, under Kronecker; and least squares, under Foerster. It is not known what lectures he attended while in Heidelberg, but, judging by the lectures that he attended in Berlin, it is safe to say that he attended many lectures under the notable men who were at the University of Heidelberg at that time. These included: Professors Rummer, Cantor, Hesse, and Drs. Lüroth, Weber, du Bois Raymond, and Eisenlohr, in mathematics, and Professors Kirchhoff, Helmholtz, Bunsen, Kopp, and Dr. Horstmann, in physics and chemistry.[2]

Examining the record, we see that between 1858, when he graduated from Yale College, and 1871, when he entered upon his professorship of mathematical physics in Yale University, Gibbs spent ten years in preparation for his life work, not counting the three years which he spent as tutor in Yale College. The conclusion that one may draw from this is that the preparation which our American colleges afforded men of science in the nineteenth century was not necessarily fatal to the development of their genius, provided that they were able to devote sufficient time to their training afterwards. Gibbs, fortunately, was financially independent and was, therefore, able to follow his own bent. This was not true of the great mass of men in that day, as it is not true of the great mass of men in our colleges today. We may well ask ourselves the question: Are our colleges quenching the genius of our outstanding students through the formal curricula that they impose upon them and through the lack of opportunity for their self-development?

By training and tradition and by the force of the environment in which he was placed, Gibbs should have developed into a typical exponent of nineteenth century scholasticism. That he did not become such was in part due to his own intellectual and financial independence and in part, without doubt, to certain favorable conditions that existed at Yale in the 1850's and 60's.

Gibbs, like Franklin and Rumford, had a strong leaning toward science, with a turn toward invention; in 1866, while still a tutor in natural philosophy in Yale College, he invented a brake for railway cars and secured a patent for the same in April of that year.[3] At about that time, also, he invented a new type of governor of a higher order of approximation to astaticism than any of its predecessors. This governor was constructed in the shops of the Sheffield Scientific School and is in the collection of the Department of Physics of Yale University.[4] Until we have come to know that Gibbs was endowed with a mind which possessed a keen appreciation of and interest in things physical and practical, his life and works remain a profound mystery. Possessing intellectual powers of the highest order, as much at home in pure mathematics as in physics and chemistry, Gibbs constantly exercised his will to direct his thoughts along lines that lay within the framework of material phenomena.

It has often been stated that Gibbs never carried out an experiment. This statement is not borne out by the facts; it is known that Gibbs constructed some apparatus in his own home.[5] According to Professor Charles S. Hastings, in his Biographical Memoir on Gibbs in the National Academy of Sciences, Gibbs carried out an optical experiment. How many other experiments he may have carried out, no one can say, for Gibbs communicated to others only the results of major investigations. Speaking of this experiment, Professor Hastings, after reviewing its general purpose, says:

. . . the tentative explanation, however, involved the occurrence of certain phenomena in specular reflection which had never been seen or, at least, recorded. As it did not seem to him that such negative evidence was conclusive, he constructed an apparatus with his own hands so perfectly adapted to the end in view that his observations afforded the proof sought. A striking light is thrown upon the character of the great physicist by the fact that no reference to this theory, which must have cost much critical study, appears in his writings, nor is it known that anyone except the present writer ever saw the apparatus and made the experiment for which it was designed.

In the main, Gibbs depended upon experimental results available in the literature for data with which to test his theoretical investigations. That he was familiar with the literature and quick to make use of results there available is shown by examples that appear in his treatise of 1876–8, as well as in numerous subsequent papers. His chief interests were theoretical, and his physical sense was so keen that he could frame correct physical concepts with a minimum of experience with the phenomena themselves. In this Gibbs was highly exceptional; he introduced many new and exact concepts into science long before any observations relating to them had been made.

For fifty years, now, we have been hearing much and often about the manner in which American science, in general, and Yale University, in particular, failed to recognize Gibbs and his works. The explanation is simple: Gibbs was half a century in advance of his time and American scientists of his day were ill-prepared to comprehend the abstract philosophical results of Gibbs' theory. Much the same thing was true throughout the world; it seems that at the time of their publication, or soon thereafter, only two men comprehended the significance of Gibbs' work. One was Clerk Maxwell, who immediately called attention to the first two papers of Gibbs; in his "Theory of Heat," Maxwell incorporated a chapter dealing with the Gibbs' surface. As is well known, Maxwell constructed several models of this surface with his own hands, one of which he sent to Gibbs. Maxwell also called attention to Gibbs' later paper of 1876. Had Maxwell lived, Gibbs' theory would have become known to the scientific world much earlier than it was.[6] Another physicist who early recognized the significance of Gibbs's contributions was J. D. van der Waals, Sr. He called Roozeboom's attention to the paper on heterogeneous equilibria, and this led to the development of the phase rule in the hands of Roozeboom and his associates. Van der Waals, himself, throughout his life, was active in developing the consequences of Gibbs' theory, as is evident from his admirable text with Kohnstamm, entitled "Lehrbuch der Thermodynamik," published in two parts, the first in 1908 and the second in 1912.

That Gibbs's ability was recognized at Yale University is evident from the fact that he was appointed professor of mathematical physics in 1871 before he had published a single paper. Gibbs was early recognized by his contemporaries in America, being elected to the National Academy in 1879 and awarded the Rumford Medal in 1881. It is true, however, that while Gibbs's ability was generally recognized by his American contemporaries, his scientific contributions were not understood.

How Gibbs came to interest himself in the thermodynamics is not known; that he should have done so is not surprising. The two fields of physics that engaged the attention of physicists during the greater part of the nineteenth century were electromagnetic phenomena and phenomena relating to heat. Judging by the subjects upon which he lectured during 1871-2 and 1872-3, Gibbs at that time was interested in physical optics, particularly the elastic solid theory. According to Hastings, he arrived at the conclusion that the obstacles in the way of this theory were insuperable. Later, he was a proponent of the electromagnetic theory of Maxwell at a time when many other eminent physicists were reluctant to accept it.

Phenomena relating to heat were intensively cultivated by physicists from 1842 onward. The classical researches of Rumford had been forgotten for nearly half a century, when they were independently repeated and extended by Joule between the years 1837 and 1843. Mayer published his paper on the equivalence of heat and work in 1842. As early as 1824, Carnot had enunciated his celebrated principle,[7] now known as the second law of thermodynamics, but the significance of Carnot's principle was not recognized until the relation between heat and work had been clarified in the 1840's. The concept of absolute temperature was established in two papers by Sir William Thomson in 1848 and 1851. In 1851, Clausius combined the principle of Carnot with the principle of the conservation of energy, which, by then, had been well established through the experiments of Joule. Thereafter, many physicists were active in developing the elements of thermodynamics, applying the two principles—that of Carnot and that of the conservation of energy—almost exclusively to one-component systems. Clausius introduced the entropy concept in 1865. By 1870, the framework of thermodynamics had been erected and its application to one-component systems developed. The literature relating to thermodynamics was, however, in a state of confusion; concepts were not clear, physical quantities were not well defined, and the mathematical manipulations were cumbersome and unsuited for the purpose of describing the thermodynamic properties of physical systems generally.

It was natural that Gibbs, who doubtless was well acquainted with the literature of his day, should have become interested in a field where it was apparent that much remained to be done. In his first two papers of 1873, he developed the methods and forged the tools that he later used in treating physical systems from a very general point of view. He introduced the entropy concept and showed that a better description of phenomena is obtained by means of the energy-entropy-volume relation than by means of the pressure-temperature-volume relation. He showed how the state of a body may be represented by means of the energy-entropy-volume surface, every point of which corresponds to a definite state of the substance. He showed how, by means of this surface, the boundary between stable and metastable states may be readily traced, as also the boundary between metastable and unstable states, and showed, moreover, how states capable of existing in equilibrium with one another may readily be derived from the surface. By means of this surface, it is possible, at a glance, to obtain a picture of all the possible states of a physical system.

The first two papers were only preliminary to the third, which appeared in two parts in 1876 and 1878, respectively; in these, Gibbs treated systems comprising any number of substances—which might or might not interact with one another—existing in any number of homogeneous parts or states of aggregation.

Previous to Gibbs, the concept of reversibility, which means equilibrium at all points of a process, was clear, but the concept of equilibrium in a heterogeneous system was still vague. For very simple systems, such as water, the equilibrium conditions were recognized and James Thomson had shown that at the natural freezing point of water, three monovariant systems meet. The concept of equilibrium in a highly complex system, involving any number of component substances, had not been touched upon prior to Gibbs. Obviously, before being able to attack this general problem of equilibrium, it was necessary to have a criterion of equilibrium. Gibbs was well versed in mechanics, and it was, therefore, natural that he should seek for some general principle, similar to the principle of virtual displacements in mechanics, which might be applied to chemical systems. That he was influenced by the earlier work of Clausius seems certain, for at the head of his treatise "On the Equilibria of Heterogeneous Substances," he quotes a couplet from Clausius:

> Die Energie der Welt ist konstant.
> Die Entropie der Welt strebt einem Maximum zu.[8]

The statements of Clausius are physically meaningless. Gibbs formulated the underlying idea in a form such that it could be applied to real physical systems. He states the condition for equilibrium alternatively as follows:

> 1. For the equilibrium of any isolated system it is necessary and sufficient that in all possible variations of the state of the system which do not alter its energy, the variation of its entropy shall either vanish or be negative.
> 2. For the equilibrium of any isolated system it is necessary and sufficient that in all possible variations in the state of the system which do not alter its entropy, the variation of its energy shall either vanish or be positive.

We know nothing about the energy and the entropy of the universe; we have knowledge only of finite physical systems which we can place under observation and over which we have control; therefore, Gibbs limits his system to what he terms an "isolated system" and applies his criteria for equilibrium, which follow directly from the first and second laws of thermodynamics. Gibbs shows that the two criteria, as stated above, are strictly equivalent.

Having set up criteria of equilibrium, it was necessary to define the various thermodynamic quantities, particularly the energy and entropy in terms of the variables that fix the state of the system. The concept of an equation of state was not thoroughly familiar to the physicists in Gibbs's day, although it is clear that, since Andrews had already carried out his classical experiments with carbon dioxide and James Thomson had already arrived at the p-v-T surface as representing the possible states of a system, it was generally understood that the state of a simple substance is determined by these three variables. Gibbs, in his earlier paper, had shown that Thomson's representation is incomplete and that certain important thermodynamic quantities may not be derived from such a surface. It was for this reason that he introduced the energy-entropy-volume surface which gives a complete description of all thermodynamic properties of a substance.

In the case of a system containing any number of substances, it was not obvious what variables fix the state of the system. Gibbs assumed (implicitly) an equation of state involving pressure, temperature, and the relative amounts of the independently variable substances present. It was then necessary to derive an expression connecting the changes in energy with changes in entropy, volume and the amounts of the various substances in the different homogeneous aggregations of matter. To do this, he introduced a new concept, namely, the thermodynamic potential, which is the derivative of the energy with respect to the mass of a given component, other variables remaining constant, so that for a given homogeneous aggregation of matter, the energy is related to the variables which fix the state of the system by a differential equation of the form:

$$d\epsilon = Tds - pdv + \mu_1 dm_1 + \mu_2 dm_2 \ldots + \mu_n dm_n$$

where the μ's are the thermodynamic potentials of the various substances present and ϵ, s, and v are the energy, entropy, and volume, respectively, and the m's are the masses of the constituent substances. The thermodynamic potentials, μ, together with entropy and volume, are functions of the variables T, v, and the masses, m_1, m_2, . . . m_n, of the constituent substances in the different aggregations of matter which comprise the system. It is understood that the masses are independently variable and that substances may be present other than those which have been chosen as independent variables; but whatever variables may be chosen, they must be independent. Gibbs next assumed that, for a heterogeneous system, the total energy of the system is made up of the sum of the energies of all the different homogeneous parts which exist in equilibrium with one another or, as he says, *coexist*. The various homogeneous aggregations of matter, each of which has a definite equation of state, he calls *phases* and two aggregations of matter, having the same equation of state, belong to the same phase. The independently variable substance he calls *components*. What particular substances are chosen as components is arbitrary so long as they are always independent and serve to build up all the different phases of the system.

Having arrived at a means of defining the energy and entropy of the system, Gibbs proceeds to apply his criterion for equilibrium, namely, that the energy of the system shall be a minimum under the conditions that the total volume, the total entropy, and the total masses of the several components of the systems remain constant. This leads to the result that equilibrium obtains in the system when the temperature of any one phase is equal to the temperature of any other, the pressure of any one phase is equal to the pressure of any other, and the thermodynamic potential of any one component in any one phase is equal to the thermodynamic potential of the same component in every other phase.

The variables of the system are the temperature, the volume, and the relative amounts or concentrations of the several components in all the different phases; in order that equilibrium shall be established, these variables must adjust themselves in such a way that the condition for equality of the thermodynamic potentials of the several components throughout the system is fulfilled. This condition of equality of the thermodynamic potentials of each of the several components in the different phases thus represents a multiplicity of conditions which must be satisfied by the variables;

and when the number of independent conditions is equal to the number of variables, the system is completely fixed or, as we say, is *invariant*. Gibbs showed that a system will be invariant when the number of phases, r, is equal to the number of components, n, increased by two, or algebraically, when $r = n + 2$. When the number of phases is only one greater than the number of components ($r = n + 1$), one variable of the system may be fixed arbitrarily at any desired value within the physical limits of the system; such a system is said to be *monovariant*. When $r = n$, two variables may be arbitrarily fixed and the system is said to be *bivariant*.

We may illustrate the phase rule in the case of a system built up of only one substance, that is, a system of one component. Consider a system composed of pure water. Three phases (three different states of water) may coexist at a certain temperature which is an invariable property of water. We may, for example, have water vapor, liquid water and ice coexisting at the triple point, which is $0.0076°$ above $0°$ on the Centigrade scale, and at that temperature only. If the temperature is increased, ice melts and we have an equilibrium between liquid water and water vapor which may exist at a series of temperatures and pressures. If the temperature is lowered, liquid water freezes and we have a similar equilibrium between ice and water vapor; if the pressure is increased, vapor is condensed and we have an equilibrium between ice and water, the temperature diminishing with increasing pressure. At higher pressures, a new form of solid water (ice$_{II}$) appears and we have an invariant equilibrium between ice$_I$, ice$_{II}$, and liquid water.

Gibbs also considered equilibria in systems in which reactions occur among various of the molecules present. He derived a relation governing the equilibrium in such systems and showed how, in the case of dilute systems, this leads to a simple relation between the concentrations of the various substances concerned in the reaction. In brief, Gibbs, from thermodynamic considerations, derived the law of mass action which had earlier been arrived at by Guldberg and Waage on the basis of kinetic considerations. He showed, moreover, how this equilibrium depends upon temperature. In the earlier chapters of his treatise, Gibbs considered external forces to be excluded from his system; later he investigated what modifications are required when external forces act. He thus investigated the action of gravitational force, of electrical forces, and surface forces. Very important was his treatment of systems under the action of electrical forces; he showed, what was not then recognized, that in such systems the energy change is not equal to the work done against the external forces, but, rather, that it is equal to the sum of two terms: (1) the reversible work done against the external forces and (2) the reversible heat change which is equal to the product of the absolute temperature and the entropy. In these considerations, he anticipated Helmholtz, who arrived at much the same result in 1882. Even more important and original were Gibbs's contributions in the field of surface forces. Here Gibbs invented entirely new concepts which had never been thought of before and which have since been found indispensable in describing phenomena that occur at the boundary between two phases of multicomponent systems.

It is not possible to give an adequate picture of Gibbs's contributions in brief form. His papers on thermodynamics cover some 400 pages and are written in a highly condensed, although elegant, style. An adequate commentary on the thermodynamic theory of Gibbs would require several thousand pages.[9] Nor are Gibbs's contributions to thermodynamics his only important contributions; he was active in many other fields, particularly in vector analysis, multiple algebra, and the electromagnetic theory. The most important of his other contributions, however, is his treatise on statistical mechanics, which was published in 1902. Here, as in his treatise on thermodynamics, he reduces his assumptions to the very minimum and arrives at results of the greatest generality.

The generalizations of Gibbs concerning heterogeneous equilibria have exercised an influence upon chemistry which is second only to that of the law of the conservation of mass. Although some of the relations that follow from Gibbs' theory were subsequently discovered independently by other investigators, these were derived in a much less general manner than by Gibbs, and not infrequently they were applied when limiting assumptions (often implied) were not fulfilled and the results obtained were misleading. At the time of Gibbs, chemists concerned themselves very little with the physical properties of chemical systems; physical chemistry, as such, had not yet come into being and chemists were largely concerned with the development of organic chemistry. As physical chemistry developed during the 1880's, and later, Gibbs' work gradually came to the notice of physical chemists and the thermodynamics of Gibbs slowly replaced the earlier and less rigorous and elegant formulations. Except for certain new material and many examples, all of which fit into the framework of Gibbs' theory, modern texts on thermodynamics are essentially commentaries on Gibbs' thermodynamical theory.

Of all the relationships following from Gibbs' thermodynamical theory, the simplest and, at the same time, the most general, is the phase rule. With the aid of the phase rule, it is possible to arrive at a knowledge of the constitution of material systems and the relation of various parts of such systems to one another without destroying the systems themselves. In many respects, it is a more powerful tool than is chemical mass analysis, which is useful only if the systems in question may be resolved into their component parts without changing their nature and composition. In the case of metallic systems, for example, which are frequently very complex and the component parts of which cannot be separated from one another by analytical means, the phase rule enables us to determine the composition and number of substances present and the influence which these substances have on the properties of the material in question. Take such a simple case as that of carbon steel: here we have to do with iron in its several forms, together with several kinds of solutions of carbon in iron and with free carbon. Mass analysis enables us only to determine the gross composition of the steel; with the aid of the phase rule, we can determine the different kinds of substances present, how they may be transformed into one another by change of conditions, and how the properties of the steel depend upon the various substances present and the history of the sample of steel.[10] As an example, however, carbon steel is an oversimplified case of a metallic system; modern steels are extremely complex, containing, in addition to carbon, various amounts of such elements as tungsten, molybdenum, tantalum, uranium, chromium, nickel, silicon, titanium, and many others. The detailed structure of these steels has been determined with the aid of the phase rule.

What is true of the alloys of iron is true of the innumerable alloys of other metallic elements, such as magnesium, aluminum, zinc, copper, tin, nickel, chromium, antimony, bismuth, platinum, gold, and the like. These alloys have proved invaluable in modern industry. Except for the availability of such alloys designed to meet the needs of special conditions, modern machines, such as the automobile, the aeroplane, and the streamlined railway train, would not be practical.

The phase rule finds application, also, in the ceramics industry, in the cement industry and, particularly, in the chemical industry. In the oil industry, for example, it is necessary to separate very complex liquid mixtures into various components having desirable and necessary properties. The present art of the separation of hydrocarbon oils, by distillation, by solvent extraction and by other means, is based upon the phase rule.

I have discussed the phase rule somewhat in detail, as an example, but Gibbs' theory leads to many other important consequences. The laws governing the equilibrium in reacting systems follow directly from this theory. So, also, Gibbs' theory provides a foundation for the treatment of colloidal systems. Much remains to be done in this field, but Gibbs has provided the fundamental concepts by means of which the problems of colloid chemistry may ultimately be resolved. The unravelling of the nature of living systems, which are largely colloidal in nature, involves surface phenomena that are amenable to Gibbs' theory.

Because Gibbs was a man of retiring disposition and was very much preoccupied with his important researches, he had no large circle of friends and entered into no active correspondence with other investigators. We may, therefore, be misled into undervaluing Gibbs's versatility and his ability in directions other than those which he chose to follow.[11] A paragraph from the "Biographical Memoir of Josiah Willard Gibbs" by Professor Hastings throws much light on this situation. He writes:

799

It will surprise no reader of the numerous biographical notes concerning Professor Gibbs to learn that a man of so judicial a temperament was a very successful man of affairs. Happily for science, his position in the University was not such as to render that fact conspicuous, else he might have been called upon for work which, in view of his consciousness (conscientiousness) and inherent modesty, could easily have seriously interfered with his scientific pursuits. He did, however, give his services as a trustee to the affairs of the Hopkins Grammar School of New Haven, and he acted for many years (17) as treasurer of its funds, which had come down in part from colonial times.

Gibbs was extremely painstaking in everything that he did and pronounced judgment only after mature consideration. In faculty meetings, he spoke seldom, but when he spoke, it was to the point. It is said that on one occasion, after a lengthy discussion as to the relative merits of the languages and mathematics, Gibbs said: "Mathematics is a language too." Gibbs was kindly in disposition, considerate and ready to be of help to his students. He had a sense of humor and smiled easily. He never sought for honors or advancement except as they came through recognition of his work. Such honors came to him in great abundance. They need not be enumerated here; I mention only the Copley Medal awarded him by the Royal Society of London, in 1901. He was made an honorary member of nearly every scientific organization of note and received honorary degrees from many of the leading universities of the world.

Outstanding qualities of Gibb's character are his modesty and his devotion to science. He had not a few traits in common with Michael Faraday. At the beginning of the most productive period of his career, Faraday renounced all consulting work, from which he derived an income of from 500 to 1,000 pounds per annum—his salary at the Royal Institution was 100 pounds; for nine years following his appointment as professor of mathematical physics at Yale, Gibbs served without compensation. Gibbs, like Faraday, had great physical insight. Faraday, without mathematical training, invented the concept of the electromagnetic field, which later provided Maxwell with the foundation for the electromagnetic theory; Gibbs, with little experience with material systems, invented new

800

physical concepts, that have served as a basis for the development of chemistry during the past fifty years.

Of the inner workings of Gibbs' mind, we know little; he left behind few letters and no notes. We can best judge the quality of the man by what he said of his colleague, Hubert Anson Newton, in the "Biographical Memoir" which he wrote for the National Academy of Sciences. Here, in speaking of his friend, he unconsciously reveals himself. After discussing Professor Newton's scientific contributions, Gibbs writes:

> But these papers show more than the type of mind of the author; they give no uncertain testimony concerning the character of the man. In all these papers we see a love of honest work, an aversion to shams, a caution in the enunciation of conclusions, a distrust of rash generalizations and speculations based on uncertain premises. He was never anxious to add one more guess on doubtful matters in the hope of hitting the truth, or what might pass as such for a time, but was always ready to take infinite pains in the most careful testing of every theory. With these qualities was united a modesty which forbade the pushing of his own claims and desired no reputation except the unsought tribute of competent judges.

These words of Gibbs characterize Gibbs hmself much more truly than anything that I might hope to say.

GENERAL REFERENCES

Lynde Phelps Wheeler: J. W. Gibbs, the History of a Great Mind. Yale University Press, New Haven, Conn., 1951.

Muriel Ruckeyser: Willard Gibbs. Doubleday, Doran & Co., Garden City, New York, 1942.

NOTES AND REFERENCES

1 An address delivered in Yale University on the occasion of exercises held in commemoration of the one hundredth anniversary of the birth of Josiah Willard Gibbs.

2 There is no certain record of what lectures Gibbs attended in Paris, but Gibbs's own copies of lists of courses offered at the Sorbonne bear pencil marks against certain courses which were probably the ones Gibbs ex-

pected to attend, and perhaps did attend up to the time of his illness while in Paris. The marked subjects are: *Astronomy,* Puiseaux; *Calculus of Probability and Mathematical Physics,* Lamé or Briot; *Physics,* P. Dessains; *Rational Mechanics,* Liouville; *Differential and Integral Calculus,* Serrer; *Chemistry,* Balard. (For the information concerning Gibbs's studies while abroad, the writer is indebted to Professor R. G. Van Name, of Yale University.)

3 U. S. Patent No. 53,931, April 17, 1866.

4 Charles S. Hastings, "Biographical Memoirs," *Nat. Acad. of Sci.,* 6, 375 (1909). It is interesting to note that among Gibbs's papers was found a manuscript entitled "On the Form of the Teeth of Wheels in Spur Gearing." It has been suggested that this was a copy of Gibbs's thesis for the doctorate, but this is not certain; it does, however, bear witness to Gibbs's early interest in mechanical problems.

5 Professor Van Name reports an apparatus that Gibbs so constructed for an optical experiment, but it is not known what the nature of this experiment was.

6 It is of interest to note that Rowland's first paper on the magnetic circuit was not accepted for publication by American editors. Rowland sent the paper to Maxwell, who recognized its value and sent it to the *Philosophical Magazine,* where it was published immediately, Maxwell himself reading the proof in order to avoid delay. Only another genius can recognize genius.

7 Carnot's principle states that it is impossible to transfer heat from a lower temperature to a higher without the performance of work or, otherwise, leaving compensating changes in the system or its surroundings.

8 The energy of the universe is constant. The entropy of the universe approaches a maximum.

9 Compare, for example, "Commentaries on the Scientific Writings of J. Willard Gibbs," vol. I, *Thermodynamics,* Yale University Press, New Haven, 1936.

10 The phase rule is normally applied in conjunction with other physical observations such as crystalline structure, electrical, magnetic and mechanical properties.

11 A number of statements in the literature relating to Gibbs are without foundation. Such a one is the statement that he was a student of Clausius. Clausius was at Wurzburg when Gibbs was at Heidelberg and there is nothing to indicate that Clausius and Gibbs ever met. Another statement that gives quite an erroneous impression of Gibbs's character and of his home relations is to the effect that Gibbs was pressed into service by his sister to drive the family carriage because her husband, who was librarian at Yale, was too busy to do this. The truth of the matter is that Gibbs took very little exercise, walking only between his home and his office in the Sloane Laboratory. The members of his family, therefore, took advantage of every opportunity to induce Professor Gibbs to get out of doors. He

rather enjoyed driving the family carriage and occasionally rode horse-back as well.

From: *Science,* 89, 275–282 (1939).

CHARLES A. KRAUS

·· 58 ··

American Chemists
at the Century's Turn

*S. M. Babcock, Harvey Wiley, Ira Remsen,
T. W. Richards, and Edgar Fahs Smith*

REMSEN

SMITH

RICHARDS

BABCOCK

WILEY

AMERICAN chemistry was hardly a mature science as the twentieth century began, but here and there a center of activity was beginning to attract attention. During the previous century chemistry was a part of the usual college curriculum but seldom received significant emphasis before the last quarter of the century. Quite frequently it was taught by someone who worked in one of the other sciences or in medicine. Industrial chemistry, likewise, was of no great magnitude. This was an era when competition with the well-established German industry was usually foolhardy. Existing industrial operations of a chemical nature were empirical in character and rarely the kind to seek academically trained chemists on a large scale. Whatever chemical activity there existed in the United States was generally to be found in educational institutions, or to a lesser extent, in government. As a result we must turn to these institutions in order to examine the nature of American chemical activity as the twentieth century began.

While the five chemists examined here were not the only ones of significant stature during this period, they all represent men who were leaders in their field and in the development of American chemistry. Four were connected with universities which became important centers of chemical education; the other left teaching for public service, becoming Chief of the Bureau of Chemistry in the U. S. Department of Agriculture. All five were native-born but sought at least part of their education in Europe where Germany was the mecca of chemistry students. All of them returned to their homeland where their leadership helped to free America of its dependence upon Germany in the chemical realm.

Richards received the Nobel Prize for chemistry in 1915 for his atomic weight work. Four of these men became presidents of the American Chemical Society; Wiley in 1893 and 1894, Smith in 1895 and again in 1920 and 1921, Remsen in 1902, and Richards in 1914. Wiley played an important role, along with Frank W. Clarke, chief chemist of the U. S. Geological Survey, in converting the Society from an essentially local organization based in New York to a national society. Wiley was also prominent in the formation of the Association of Official Agricultural Chemists in 1884. He served as its second president in 1886, secretary from 1889 to 1912, and was made lifetime honorary president in 1912. Babcock was president of the A.O.A.C. in 1893. All five of these men were active in professional affairs and were frequently honored. Any further recounting of such recognition would be superfluous.

BABCOCK—PIONEER AGRICULTURAL CHEMIST, 1843–1931

Stephen Moulton Babcock was born near Bridgewater, New York, on October 22, 1843. He attended Tufts College where he received the A. B. degree in 1866, but engineering studies at Rensselaer Polytechnic Institute were cut short when he had to undertake operation of the Babcock farm because of a death in the family. Before long he was only a part time farmer and was serving as chemistry assistant to Dr. G. C. Caldwell at Cornell University, becoming an instructor in 1875. Two years later he went to Germany where he earned his doctorate under Hans Hübner at Göttingen. The aged Wöhler still frequented the laboratory but was no longer directing student work.

Upon returning to America Babcock resumed his instructorship at Cornell but in 1882 he moved to Geneva where he became chemist at the New York Agricultural Experiment Station. There he developed gravimetric methods for milk analysis which were later adopted as standard procedures. He also worked out a procedure for estimating the size and number of fat globules in milk. Another development was a viscosimeter for the detection of adulterants in oils and other fluids.

In 1888 Babcock moved to the University of Wisconsin where he became professor of agricultural chemistry and chief chemist of the Wisconsin Agricultural Experiment Station. At that time, when the commerical production of cheese was taking on considerable proportions, the sale of milk was surrounded with extensive fraud involving watering and skimming. Dean William A. Henry urged Babcock to devise a simple fat test which would make it possible to place milk sales on a butterfat basis. Babcock believed that it might be possible to modify the Soxhlet fat extraction procedure for rapid testing of milk. Before long his studies on fat solvents resulted in a test which gave satisfactory results on the milk of all but one cow in the University's herd. Dean Henry urged publication of the test but Babcock refused and continued his experiments. Others had used sulfuric acid to liberate the fat in milk but without real success. Babcock studied concentration and other factors until, in 1890, he had arrived at a simple test which gave accurate results for all milk samples tested, including that of the previously refractory Jersey, Sylvia.

The test, involving treatment of a measured sample of milk with sulfuric acid to liberate the fat, followed by centrifuging and dilution to bring the fat into the neck of the calibrated test bottle where direct reading of the volume gave the percentage of fat, was so simple and fast that it could be used on a routine basis under factory conditions. It came immediately into widespread use and had the effect of reforming milk marketing. William D. Hoard, agricultural journalist and onetime governor of Wisconsin, once remarked that the test had produced more honest farmers than reading of the Bible ever had.

The milk test gained Babcock international fame and many honors but was depreciated by him as a minor development. Seen in retrospect, and ignoring the economic implications, he was right. The test represented a practical development based upon principles which were generally known. Babcock deserves credit for his patience and insight in bringing the test to proper perfection but this was largely a matter of adjusting details until the test worked. The bulk of his other work reveals in greater degree the working of a keen scientific mind interested in fundamental problems.

In a study of the thinning of pasteurized cream he learned of the presence in milk of fibrin, a substance holding fat droplets together. This was destroyed by the high temperatures used in pasteurization. Babcock and another station chemist, Fritz Woll, learned that the consistency of pasteurized cream might be restored by calcium sucrate. Later they showed that the thinning might be prevented entirely by the use of pasteurization temperatures lower than the unnecessarily high ones which were common in the early days of the process.

Extensive studies were made on the curing of cheese in collaboration with Dr. Harry L. Russell, who came to the University following his studies with Koch and Pasteur. Russell concentrated on the bacteriological aspects of the problem, Babcock on the chemical. They learned that the curing was due to an enzyme present in the rennet of the milk itself, rather than being due to bacteria as was commonly supposed. An enzyme was isolated and identified which brought about the protein decomposition characteristic of the curing process even in cheese which had been made bacteria-free by chemicals rather than heat. This discovery led to the cold-curing of cheese, a practical application which led to significant improvements in cheese quality.

Other studies with university chemists and bacteriologists were made on milk sugar and its role in souring, the curing of silage, the nature of lactation in cattle, the centrifugal separation of milk fat, and the scientific nature of the hot-iron test on curd used in cheese-making. During his last decade of active service he was busy studying the problem of metabolic water.

It was characteristic of Babcock to ask unusual questions of his associates and of nature. He was puzzled over the source of water in organisms living on dry food or under arid conditions. In studies on germinating seeds, clothes moths, pea weevils, confused flour beetles, and other insects he sought the source of their moisture. The larvae of the clothes moth were found to be high in moisture content despite their diet of dry wool and hair. He found the source of moisture in the chemical reaction products formed during metabolism. By control of moisture losses such organisms succeeded in living under highly desiccated conditions on low-moisture foods.

Babcock's most significant influence on biochemistry resulted from his influence on others rather than from direct work of his own. From the time that he returned from his German studies he was puzzled about the standard diets so highly valued in feeding circles. The feeding doctrines of the German agricultural chemists headed by Dr. Emil von Wolff were highly popular. Wolff had collected extensive analyses for protein, fat, and carbohydrates in feeds and his followers generally held that successful diets could be formulated from such analyses provided proper attention was given to caloric and protein balances. Babcock's predecessor at Wisconsin, Henry P. Armsby, was an avid student of energy balances in large animals at the Pennsylvania Experiment Station where he had gone as director in 1887. Armsby's book, "Manual of Cattle Feeding" (1880) left a decided impression upon Dean Henry and F. W. Woll at Wisconsin, reflected in Woll's analytical studies and Henry's own book, "Feeds and Feeding," which became a sort of feed bible.

Babcock loved to chide Henry on his oversimplification of feeding problems. Back in his New York days, Babcock had shown his director two sets of analyses and asked which represented the better diet. Upon concluding that there appeared to be little difference, the director was told that one set of data represented feed, the other excrement. Through the years, Babcock frequently questioned the wisdom of designing feeding formulas from analytical tables and expressed a desire to carry out feeding experiments which would prove or disprove his contentions. At one time he succeeded in placing eight cows from the University herd on a salt-free diet to find out if salt was really essential. The cows all grew sick and one died within a few months whereupon the experiment was abruptly terminated by W. L. Carlyle, professor of dairy husbandry. Later, Babcock started an experiment in which two cows were fed chemically satisfactory rations derived from single plants. When one of the cows died Carlyle quickly rescued the other.

Babcock's cherished experiment was finally carried out by others in 1907 when he was busy with his metabolic water studies—but not so busy that he could not be the guiding hand in the work. Younger colleagues, when they learned his views, were eager to undertake the studies. In May, E. B. Hart, Elmer V. McCollum and Harry Steenbock of agricultural chemistry and George Humphrey of animal husbandry began the experiment with 16 Shorthorn heifers, aged five months. Four were fed a supposedly balanced ration prepared entirely from parts of the corn plant. Similar groups of four were fed similarly balanced rations from, respectively, wheat, oats, and a mixed ration made up from all

811

three plants. The experiments covered four years during which the heifers were bred twice.

The results were striking in their confirmation of Babcock's suspicions. The corn-fed animals throve, gave birth to healthy calves, and were clearly in good health. The wheat-fed animals developed poorly, aborted, or gave birth to calves which soon died, and were in such poor health that two of the cows were dead by the end of the third year. The animals fed oats and mixture were intermediate in their response but clearly not in good health. Some dietary switches were made during the fourth year. A healthy corn-fed cow declined rapidly on a wheat diet while a sickly wheat-fed cow gained in health. It was clear that protein and energy balances were not enough, that essential nutrients were missing in certain food materials. Experiments pointing in this direction were also being made by Hopkins at Cambridge and Osborne and Mendel at Yale, using rats as experimental animals. The appreciation of trace substances in nutrition was beginning. Babcock's younger colleagues were to play an important part in the vitamin and mineral studies which followed. Under Hart, Steenbock, and McCollum (who later moved to Johns Hopkins) the Wisconsin department became a foremost center for research in vitamin and mineral nutrition.

It was characteristic of Babcock that his name failed to appear on the bulletin reporting the single grain studies. A modest, unassuming man, he was content to ask important questions and cared little who received credit for the answer. His milk test was given freely to the dairy world. He published little during his lifetime, nevertheless his influence was profound. Those who were in steady contact with him gained much in guidance, encouragement, and stimulation. This was true not only of his colleagues in the College of Agriculture but of university colleagues generally. Louis Kahlenberg of the chemistry department and Edward Kremers of the pharmacy department esteemed him highly.

He retired as professor emeritus in 1913. He and Mrs. Babcock maintained their modest home in Madison and he continued to go to his laboratory regularly almost to the end of his long life. During these years he was interested in the fundamental constitution of matter and performed experiments directed toward the clarification of certain laws of physics, but was never satisfied with his results and published nothing on the subject. His death occurred in Madison on July 1, 1931.

WILEY—CRUSADER FOR PURE FOODS, 1844–1930

Harvey Washington Wiley was born on October 18, 1844, near Kent, Indiana. As a youth, he determined upon a career in medicine but encountered many difficulties before completing his education. His undergraduate days at Hanover College were interrupted by Civil War service and he did not receive his A.B. until 1867. As a student he economized by bringing food and fuel for his needs from his father's farm. While attending Indiana Medical College (M.D., 1871) he served as tutor in Latin and Greek at Northwestern Christian University (now Butler), and teacher of science at Indianapolis High School. Upon graduation he was offered the chair of chemistry at the Medical School but insisted on studying at Harvard to prepare himself properly. As a student at the Lawrence Scientific School (B.S., 1873) he came in contact with Josiah Parsons Cooke, Charles Edward Monroe, and Charles Loring Jackson in chemistry, and with Louis Agassiz in biology. He also heard a series of lectures by John Tyndall who appeared at the Lowell Institute during 1872.

On returning to Indianapolis, Wiley taught chemistry at Indiana Medical College and at Northwestern Christian University, but for only a year before moving to Purdue, where he became professor of chemistry and State chemist. In 1878 he made an extended trip to Europe, during the course of which he visited a number of university centers, enlightened himself on various health problems, and observed methods of science instruction. At the University of Berlin he heard lectures of Helmholtz on physics and Virchow on pathology. Virchow's remarks on adulteration of foods caused Wiley to seek an interview with Dr. Eugen Sell, chemist at the Imperial Health Office. Here Wiley observed his first polariscope and received experience in its use.

Upon returning to Indiana with such an instrument, he put it to use in studying the purity of commercial sugar products. He

813

found that commercial syrups were frequently adulterated with glucose and these results started Wiley on his lifetime crusade for pure foods. In order to obtain more information on glucose he obtained permission to study its manufacture at an Illinois factory. He concluded that glucose was a perfectly wholesome food and objected to it only when it was used to cheapen some other sugar product and sold under false pretenses. In 1883 Wiley was invited to become Chief of the Chemical Division in the U. S. Department of Agriculture. The extensive work which he had done on sugars while at Purdue together with his Republican sympathies led to the appointment. When Wiley came to Washington his laboratory consisted of five employees. In 1898 the Chemical Division became the Bureau of Chemistry; in 1912 when Wiley resigned from his position the Bureau had more than 600 employees on its payroll. In addition, a number of the investigations which were started within the Bureau became the foundation for new bureaus which originated out of the Bureau of Chemistry.

Wiley's earliest activities in the Chemical Division were a continuation of the sugar studies which had been started at Purdue. Various crops suitable for production of sugar were carefully studied. Wiley's determination of climatic boundaries for growing the sugar beet was so sound that profitable production of the beet is carried out even today only within the boundaries set up by him. His enthusiasm for production of sugar from the sorghum plant led to an intensive promotional campaign, which failed to result in widespread development primarily because the cane and beet were already flourishing sources of sugar. The studies on the diffusion process for extracting sugar from the cane plant did not supplant existing methods for sugar production simply because it stirred manufacturers to improve their equipment and thus led to the dawn of modern processing procedures.

The second area of important studies was connected with the improvements in agricultural analysis. Wiley was responsible for the introduction of several pieces of analytical apparatus and of a number of new methods of analysis, but his major contribution lay in his insistence upon standard methods. Up to this time agricultural analysis was on a very haphazard basis and results from different laboratories seldom agreed. The Association of Official Agricultural Chemists, founded in 1884 at Wiley's insistence, included chemists affiliated with various state and municipal food, drug, and fertilizer laboratories. The purpose of the organization was to serve as a clearing house for the study of methods with subsequent agreement upon standard procedures. The first methods of analysis were published in a small pamphlet of several pages. These methods were periodically expanded until now the "Official and Tentative Methods of Analysis" of the A.O.A.C. is a volume of more than 1000 pages.

Even during his days at Purdue Wiley was cognizant of the widespread problems of food adulteration. This evil became a passion with him while with the Bureau of Chemistry and one of his major projects in the Bureau was a survey of all types of food materials with a view toward learning the extent of adulteration. Bulletin 13, published in ten parts between 1887 and 1902, dealt with analysis of American foods, with a record of their adulterants. The picture was not a happy one and for a period of twenty years Wiley's major activities were concentrated toward reform. The extent of adulteration and misbranding of foods and drugs in the last quarter of the nineteenth century had reached an appalling rate and Wiley was convinced that national legislation was the only solution to the problem. However, Congress contained many representatives and senators who were motivated from the standpoint of their industrial connections rather than from the standpoint of public welfare and, although food legislation was introduced at every session of Congress from 1879 onward, there was a complete lack of success in passing any broad food legislation. For many years no bill was ever reported out to the floor of Congress.

In the face of these obstacles Wiley set out to educate the public to the need for reform. He began giving lectures to interested groups and writing popular articles. As a result of his activities such organizations as the American Medical Association, American Public Health Association, American Chemical Society, the Federation of Women's Clubs of America, and the National Consumers' League swung behind the campaign. In 1897 the National

Association of Food and Dairy Departments was organized to aid the cause. This organization consisted of chemists and others connected with state and local regulatory agencies.

At the turn of the century a certain amount of progress had been made in creating a public demand for food legislation, but Congress was not yet ready to take serious action. In 1902 Wiley was successful in obtaining an appropriation for a study on the effect of food preservatives and colors on human beings. A panel of volunteers from the Bureau of Chemistry submitted to feeding experiments which were designed to show the effect on the human system of such added chemical ingredients as borax, sulfites, salicylates, benzoates, formaldehyde, copper sulfate, potassium nitrate, and similar materials which were being introduced into foods as preservatives and coloring agents. The experimental feedings were attended with a great deal of publicity since Wiley had a flair for attracting attention to his activities. One news reporter designated the experimental group as the "Poison Squad" and this term was connected with the experiments thereafter. Reports of the experiments were published as Bulletin 84 from the Bureau of Chemistry. The first, dealing with borax and borates, appeared in 1904. In the years that followed, parts appeared which dealt with sulfur dioxide and sulfites, salicylic acid and the salicylates, benzoic acid and the benzoates, and formaldehyde. The conclusions in each case resulted in an unfavorable verdict for the preservatives and naturally aroused indignant protests from the food processors who were using these preservatives. Unsuccessful attempts were made to suppress the benzoate bulletin and the reports on copper sulfate and potassium nitrate were never published.

The studies were open to the justifiable criticism that adequate controls had not been used but, despite this, the evidence was clear that none of these agents could be considered beneficial toward human health; in certain cases the evidence of harmfulness was quite apparent. Wiley's bureau also succeeded in demonstrating during these years that foods such as catsup could be stored without preservatives if proper attention were given to the selection of sound fruit and to processing operations. As a result of these findings Wiley was on sound ground in fighting for legislation restricting the use of such chemical agents.

Help also came from other quarters as the growing need for regulatory legislation became apparent to more and more groups. At the St. Louis Exhibition of 1904 the National Association of Food and Dairy Officials placed an exhibit regarding food colors and preservatives near the food technology section with rather effective results in convincing the public of the need for some kind of official control. Several national magazines also assisted in educating the public by featuring a series of studies on the patent medicine industry.

A Federal Pure Food and Drug Act was finally passed in 1906, but only after overcoming rather effective delaying tactics on the part of congressmen sympathetic to industry. The furor created by the publication of Upton Sinclair's "Jungle," a novel depicting lack of sanitation in the packing industry, brought about passage of a Federal Meat Inspection Act. The momentum for reform in the food industry was responsible for sweeping the Food and Drug Act through Congress at the same time. The bill that placed enforcement of pure food and drug laws in the Bureau of Chemistry was signed by President Theodore Roosevelt on June 30, 1906.

Successful passage of the Act did not end Wiley's problems, however. During the next six years his efforts toward setting up efficient enforcement procedures were frequently hampered by various obstacles placed in his path by officials of the Department of Agriculture who were besieged for relief by members of the food and drug industry. Wiley's position advocating the prohibition of benzoates, saccharin, and alum in foods was appealed directly to President Roosevelt, who created a Referee Board of Consulting Scientific Experts to study the matter. Ira Remsen was chairman, the other members being Russell H. Chittenden of Yale, Christian A. Herter of Columbia, Alonzo E. Taylor of California, and John H. Long of Northwestern. Despite the competence and integrity of these men as chemists and pathologists, the work of the Referee Board was embroiled in politics from the beginning. They carried out studies on the safety of certain chemicals in foods and for the most part arrived at conclusions opposite to those of the Bureau of Chemistry. Wiley's earlier work was studiously ignored but his general procedures were utilized, and again with inadequate attention to controls. The findings of the Referee Board led to de-

817

cisions by Secretary of Agriculture, James Wilson, permitting use of benzoates, sulfites, saccharin, and alum in foods on a restricted basis.

In 1911 charges were brought against Wiley by the Attorney-General, holding that he had mismanaged appropriations in connection with the hiring of an expert on drugs. A Congressional investigation of the whole problem of enforcing the Food and Drug Act followed. Wiley was completely exonerated of any wrongdoing but severe criticism was leveled at certain officials in the Department of Agriculture who had clearly created the Referee Board without legislative authorization. Despite his victory, it was obvious to Wiley that internal obstacles operating within the Department of Agriculture had the effect of hampering his activities in enforcing the Food and Drug Act and his resignation from the Government service was tendered early in 1912.

He hoped to still bring about what he considered proper enforcement of food and drug legislation by appealing to the public. During the presidential campaign he worked actively for Woodrow Wilson's election even though he had always been a Republican. In the years which followed he lectured extensively on the Chautauqua circuit, wrote books dealing with the subject of food adulteration, and served as Director of the Bureau of Foods, Sanitation, and Health created by *Good Housekeeping*. In this latter capacity he scrutinized advertising for honesty and had an opportunity to reach the public through his monthly articles on health problems. The effectiveness of his work from this period forward, however, was not striking. The coming of World War I with its food shortage problems caused the public to lose its interest in the purity of foods and the social atmosphere of the 1920's was hardly conducive to further reform.

Wiley's early years were so busy with scientific and public affairs that his time was consumed almost entirely in his work. It was not until 1911 that he found time to consider the subject of marriage and at this time, at age sixty-seven, he began family life with Anna Kelton as his bride. Miss Kelton had herself been active in public affairs as a suffragette, and this activity continued to take up time during the years which followed. Two sons were born to the Wileys, the first being described in the public press as the "Pure Food Baby."

Harvey Wiley remained active in striving for the ideals which he cherished up to the end of his long life. During the twenties he was still writing articles on pure food problems and giving lectures. The annual meeting of the A.O.A.C. in Washington was always one of the high spots of his year. Only in 1929 did he finally have to miss their meeting on account of health. His death occurred on June 30, 1930, on the twenty-fourth anniversary of the signing of the first Pure Food and Drug Act.

REMSEN—BUILDER OF GRADUATE STUDY, 1846–1927

Ira Remsen was born February 10, 1846, in New York City. His father was a merchant whose lineage could be traced back to Dutch Colonial stock of New Amsterdam in 1642. Following the death of Ira's mother when he was eight he was brought up in the home of a Dutch Reformed minister, his great-grandparents. At fourteen he returned to hs father's home in New York City in order to attend the New York Free Academy (now College of the City of New York). His father wished him to become a physician so he was not permitted to finish college but was placed under the tutelage of a homeopathic physician. Because of dissatisfaction with his progress he left in order to enter College of Physicians and Surgeons, and graduated with an M.D. degree in 1867.

A term as a physician's apprentice convinced him that medical life was not to his liking and he decided to become a chemist. Since no American school offered what he considered satisfactory chemical education, he went to Munich to study with Liebig, only to learn on arrival that Liebig had stopped directing laboratory work on moving from Giessen. He remained at Munich for a year, taking analytical courses under Volhard and attending Liebig's lectures. He then moved to Wöhler laboratory at Göttingen where he attended lectures and carried out research work under Rudolph Fittig. His Ph.D. was granted in 1870 for a thesis on piperic acid.

At that time Fittig received a call to Tübingen as successor to

Strecker. Remsen went along as Fittig's assistant. During the next two years he not only helped Fittig with instruction but began research on para-sulfobenzoic acid and studied the contents of all 150 volumes of Liebig's *Annalen.* Here too, he began his life-long friendship with William Ramsay.

On returning to America he became professor of physics and chemistry at Williams College where, starting with nonexistent facilities, he built up laboratory instruction in science, carried on research, completed the translation of Wöhler's "Organische Chemie," started writing his own "Theoretical Chemistry," and courted and married Elizabeth Mallory, daughter of a prominent New York family.

The nine papers which resulted from his researches on the reactions of ozone on carbon monoxide, and the reactions of phosphorus trichloride on benzoic acid derivatives attracted the attention of President Daniel Coit Gilman of the newly founded Johns Hopkins University. Hopkins left seven million dollars for the founding of a hospital and university which were to place greater stress on science and advanced studies than was characteristic of existing American institutions. Remsen was chosen to become head of the chemistry department in 1876.

He entered enthusiastically into his new duties. A new laboratory was opened in 1877 and funds were available to attract research fellows. Harmon N. Morse (Ph.D., Göttingen, '75) accompanied Remsen as an associate and served Hopkins for many years. Research papers came from the laboratory in such a flood that James D. Dana, editor of the *American Journal of Science,* despaired. He could not publish them without making the journal a chemical journal. At his suggestion, Remsen founded the *American Chemical Journal.* He served as editor until the *Journal* was absorbed into the *Journal of the American Chemical Society* in 1913.

Johns Hopkins quickly became an important center of graduate instruction in the German tradition. During the years that Remsen and Morse were engaged in active instruction many American and Canadian students were attracted there. Graduates who figured prominently in chemical education during the next generation were William A. Noyes (Illinois), Harry N. Holmes (Oberlin), C. H. Herty (North Carolina, later editor, *Ind. Engr. Chem.*),

820

E. P. Kohler (Harvard), James F. Norris (M.I.T.), Lyman C. Newell (Boston Univ.), E. C. Franklin (Stanford), and E. Emmet Reid (Johns Hopkins). In the industrial area there were A. R. L. Dohme, pharmaceutical manufacturer, Charles T. Reese, chemical director of du Pont, and William M. Burton, president of Standard Oil (Indiana).

The research of Remsen and his students was primarily in the organic area although he published several papers dealing with inorganic double salts. His interest in aromatic compounds reflected his training under Fittig. His studies of the influence of aromatic substituent groups on the susceptibility of nearby groups toward oxidation led to Remsen's rule. The sulfonphthaleins also resulted from these researches.

Benzoic sulfimide was prepared in his laboratory by Constantin Fahlberg (Ph.D., Leipzig, '73), who came to Hopkins as a fellow in 1879. The great sweetness of the compound was noted at this time. Later, Fahlberg secured patents on the compound and methods for its preparation and, after assigning half of the patent rights to Adolph List of Leipzig, began manufacture of the compound as a sweetening agent. Although many felt that Remsen had been cheated he never attempted to contest the patents.

Remsen's teaching was characterized by organization and clarity. Even when heavily burdened with other obligations he never neglected his students and, indeed, continued to teach classes when he might easily have stepped aside. Early in his teaching career he recognized the lack of good American textbooks in chemistry and set out to remedy the deficiency. His texts clearly reflected an understanding of teaching problems and were well received. His "Organic Chemistry" went through five editions and was translated into German, French, Russian, and Japanese. His "Introduction to the Study of Chemistry" went through eight editions and was translated into seven foreign languages.

In 1901 Remsen became the second president of Johns Hopkins. By the time he resigned in 1912 the campus had been removed from the crowded downtown area to a spacious region on the outskirts of Baltimore, and the endowment of the university had been increased significantly. During these years he still gave some of the chemistry lectures and directed the research of several graduate students. He served three years on the Baltimore School Commission, and ten years on the Sewage Commission—at a time when the antiquated and unsanitary system was being modernized. His appointment by President Roosevelt to the chairmanship of the Referee Board has already been mentioned in connection with Wiley's work.

His retirement was not an inactive one. For several years he taught a course in history of chemistry, a subject in which he had a deep interest and broad personal understanding. In 1917 he became a consultant to the Standard Oil Company of Indiana. This work brought him back into the laboratory and necessitated a great deal of travel. He was frequently sought as a speaker and received many honors. His physical and mental powers showed little diminution as he approached eighty. Death occurred on March 4, 1927.

RICHARDS—CORRECTOR OF ATOMIC WEIGHTS, 1868–1928

Theodore William Richards was born on January 31, 1868, in Germantown, Pennsylvania, the son of a marine painter. He was tutored by his mother until he entered Haverford College at fourteen. By this time his scientific interests were already apparent and he concentrated in astronomy and chemistry. His ultimate choice of chemistry was dictated in part by poor eyesight, although the instruction of Lyman B. Hall, a former student of Wöhler and assistant to Remsen, may have been a further factor. On graduation, Richards became a student of Josiah Parsons Cooke at Harvard where he received the doctorate in 1888.

Cooke was one of the few American chemists who were developing the field of physical chemistry. He had worked with Regnault in Paris and, back at Harvard, had done a masterful study of the atomic weight of antimony. He had started to make a study of the ratio of oxygen to hydrogen to determine if it was not 16 to 1, in line with Prout's hypothesis, instead of 15.96 to 1 as determined by Dumas in 1842. Poor eyesight delayed the study and it was given to Richards as a problem. Careful weighing of hydrogen, and of water formed therefrom on passage over cupric

822

oxide, led to a ratio of 15.869 to 1, still farther from agreement with Prout's hypothesis.

The excellence of the work led to Richards' selection for the Parker Fellowship which gave him an opportunity for a year of European study. He spent a semester at Göttingen studying analytical chemistry with Jannasch and Victor Meyer. During the spring, visits of important laboratories were made.

On returning to Harvard he began the faculty association that lasted throughout the remainder of his life. His teaching was in the field of quantitative analysis until 1894, when Cooke's death created a need for a physical chemist. Richards received the chair following a year of study with Ostwald at Leipzig and Nernst at Göttingen. He brought back to Harvard the new ideas of solutions, which were being developed so enthusiastically in Germany, and soon began making contributions of his own. By 1901 his reputation was well enough established to attract the offer of a professorship at Göttingen, an offer which was declined when Harvard promoted him to a full professorship.

Richards most important research was in the field of atomic weights. In his doctoral research he had demonstrated that the accepted atomic weight of hydrogen was too high, that of copper too low. When Richards examined the earlier work on the atomic weight of copper he quickly detected fundamental analytical errors involving occlusion of solutes and gases in precipitates and lack of anhydrous conditions during weighing. During the many studies which followed Richards demonstrated an infinite capacity for elimination of inaccuracies. His deep interest in the secrets of the universe was coupled with a belief that only through precise knowledge of fundamental constants could the universe really be understood.

He recognized the advantages of the approach used by Marignac and Stas where silver chloride and bromide were precipitated from the metal halide under study. By applying this approach, the atomic weight of copper was corrected from 63.3 to 63.57, using five different methods. The work on copper sulfate made the atomic weight of barium open to question and this was next corrected from 137.0 to 137.37. With the assistance of graduate students, the atomic weights of strontium, zinc, magnesium, and calcium were studied. In the course of these studies, techniques were developed for fusing and handling salts under anhydrous conditions, and the nephelometer was invented as a means for measuring low concentrations of precipitates by light scattering.

In 1904 the silver-to-bromide ratios of Stas came under scrutiny. Richards always showed great respect for the work of his predecessors, particularly Stas, and failed to question the silver-to-bromide ratio until contemporary gas density measurements by Guye and others raised suspicions about Stas' values. When R. C. Wells prepared some very pure sodium bromide for temperature transition studies it was decided to check the atomic weight of sodium. The results were 0.2% lower than those of Stas, assuming his values for silver and bromine were correct. Analysis of Stas' work in the light of physicochemical principles revealed various errors and, together with further experimental studies, confirmed the new value for sodium. Subsequent work by G. S. Forbes and H. H. Willard revealed the need for a correction in the atomic weight of silver.

Through the years, Richards and his students improved upon the existing atomic weights. A total of 25 elements were studied in Richards' laboratory and two of his students, Gregory Baxter at Harvard and Otto Hönigschmidt at Munich, extended the work independently to include a total of 30 additional elements.

Richards was always interested in anomalies. The atomic weights of cobalt and nickel were carefully measured to learn if the reversal of order in the periodic table actually existed. When it was clear that cobalt had the higher atomic weight he was led to argue that atomic weight order was not the determining factor in periodic arrangement.

Baxter, at Richards' suggestion, determined the atomic weight of meteoric iron and nickel. Agreement with the values for the terrestrial elements gave Richards a contented feeling regarding uniformities in the universe.

When the isotope concept was beginning to dawn among students of radioactivity, Kasimir Fajans sent Max E. Lembert to Richards in order to find out if lead from radioactive sources had the same atomic weight as ordinary lead. The lack of agreement was an important factual discovery in the development of radio-activity theory. Richards subsequently carried out extensive research on lead from uranium sources, arriving at an atomic weight of 206.02 for such lead. He also showed that this lead was identical with ordinary lead in physical and chemical properties.

Besides his atomic weight work Richards had a broad interest in the new physicochemical theories developing in Europe and directed various researches on thermochemistry and electrochemistry. G. N. Lewis studied the chemistry of amalgam cells. The methods of calorimetry were improved through the introduction of the adiabatic calorimeter. Many studies were made on heats of dilution, heats of solution, heats of neutralization and heats of combustion. Faraday's laws were examined and the silver coulometer was perfected. All of this work was carried out with the same passion for accuracy as the atomic weight work. Richards was first of all an experimental chemist but he was always searching for the place of physical measurements in the understanding of nature. For more than a quarter century, for example, he was intrigued with the compressibilities of elements. He found in these studies evidence adverse to the concept of rigid atoms and detected the periodic character of compressibility. His search for a theory of matter based on these studies never came to full fruition but he returned to it from time to time and in his later years was particularly intrigued by the high pressure research of P. W. Bridgman.

Richards built Harvard to a foremost center of graduate instruction in chemistry. His own teaching from 1895 was in the field of physical chemistry where he offered both a graduate and undergraduate course. He placed great emphasis on the understanding of principles and liked to show students the historical unfolding of these principles. His undergraduate course carried the title, "Elementary Theoretical and Physical Chemistry, Including the Historical Development of Chemical Theory."

His ability as a teacher is reflected in the large number of his students who attained prominence during the next generation. Besides those already mentioned his students included A. B.

Lamb, L. J. Henderson, Grinnell Jones, and James B. Conant of Harvard, H. H. Willard of Michigan, J. H. Mathews, N. F. Hall, and Farrington Daniels of Wisconsin, Frederick Barry of Columbia, and his son, William T. Richards, of Princeton.

Richards was married in 1896 to Miriam Stuart Thayer, daughter of a professor in the Harvard Divinity School. One son, William, became a chemist, the other, Greenough, an architect. His daughter, Grace, became the wife of James B. Conant. Richards' health was never robust but by conservation of his resources he was able to accomplish much in chemistry while enjoying his family. His death occurred on April 2, 1928.

SMITH—COLLECTOR AND HISTORIAN, 1854–1928

Edgar Fahs Smith, the founder of another important school of chemistry, was born near York, Pennsylvania, on May 23, 1854, the son of a miller. He was educated at the York County Academy and Gettysburg College. By the time he received his B.S. degree in 1874 he had developed a deep interest in chemistry which he pursued by graduate work with Wöhler at Göttingen. He received the doctorate in 1876, presenting a thesis dealing with trisubstituted benzene derivatives.

Back in the States he held successive positions, teaching chemistry at the University of Pennsylvania, Muhlenberg College, and Wittenberg College before beginning his long tenure at the University of Pennsylvania in 1888. Here he retired in 1920 after serving as Vice-Provost for thirteen years and Provost for ten years. During these years he was responsible for the research of over 80 doctoral candidates, the instruction of hundreds of undergraduates, the counselling of Penn students to whom his door was always open, in addition to directing for many years the growth of a great university. As a teacher he was most effective in the laboratory where his persistent questions and admonitions to "Try it" had a stimulating influence. In contrast to Richards, he was little interested in theory and argued that "Facts remain, theories change overnight." Nevertheless he authored a text on "Theories in Chemistry" in 1913. His textbook efforts also included English translations of Richter's "Inorganic Chemistry,"

826

and his "Organic Chemistry," and Classen's "Quantitative Analysis."

His research interests, like those of his teacher, Wöhler, were varied. His initial interest in organic compounds was never completely lost but studies on inorganic and analytical problems predominated. Many papers on analytical problems came from his laboratory, particularly dealing with electrolytic methods. This technique was developed during his early period and Smith worked out methods for the analysis of nearly a dozen metals. The rotating anode was developed in his laboratory and important studies were made with the mercury cathode His book on electrochemical analysis went through six editions and was translated into German and French.

Atomic weights were subjected to study and values were reported for eight elements. The quality of this work was not in the same class of precision as that of Richards but was nevertheless important since it dealt with the less common elements (Cd, Pb, Mo, W, Sb, Ta, F, and B).

Studies on the complex acids of tungsten, molybdenum, and niobium (columbium) represented important contributions. In addition, investigations were made on the compounds of numerous other elements, i.e., platinum metals, rare earths, selenium, vanadium, zirconium, tantalum, rubidium, cesium, and thorium. Many of his students went on to become leaders in chemistry, among the more prominent being Mary E. Pennington (U. S. Bureau of Chemistry), Owen L. Shinn (Pennsylvania), Victor Lenher (Wisconsin), G. W. Sargent (Molybdenum Company of America), Allen Rogers (Pratt Institute), W. T. Taggart (Pennsylvania), Clarence W. Balke (Illinois and Fansteel Products Company), Joel H. Hildebrand (California), Harrison Hale (Arkansas), William H. Chapin (Oberlin), and Herbert S. Harned (Yale).

An absorbing interest of Smith's was the history of chemistry. Early in life he began the purchase of old books on chemistry and by the time of his death he possessed around 1000 such works, besides medallions, pictures, letters, and autographs of famous chemists. This collection filled his office in Harrison Hall. Following his death, his widow presented the collection to the University of Pennsylvania together with an endowment that would enable the university to make it available to scholars in the field.

Smith not only taught a course in the history of chemistry but frequently digressed on the subject in his other courses. He was especially interested in chemical activities in early America and frequent papers and brochures came from his pen. During his later years he found time for book-length biographies of Robert Hare, James Woodhouse, and James Cutbush. A small volume dealt with "Priestley in America." Other books were "Chemistry in America," "Chemistry in Old Philadelphia," and "Old Chemistries." He was also instrumental in the founding of the Division of the History of Chemistry in the American Chemical Society. In 1928 he was president of the History of Science Society although his death on May 3 made it impossible for him to fill out the term.

NOTES AND REFERENCES

BABCOCK

M. Curti and V. Carstenson, "The University of Wisconsin, A History, 1848–1925," University of Wisconsin Press, Madison, Wisc., 1949, vol. 2, pp. 386–395.

Paul de Kruif, "Finder of the Hidden Hunger: Babcock," chapter 9 in *Hunger Fighters,* Harcourt, Brace, New York, 1928.

Edward J. Dies, "Stephen Moulton Babcock, the Jolly Scientist," chapter 14 in *Titans of the Soil,* University of North Carolina Press, Chapel Hill, N. C., 1949.

W. H. Glover, "Farm and College," University of Wisconsin Press, Madison, Wisc., 1952, chapter 7 and *passim.*

Edwin B. Hart, sketch in "Dictionary of American Biography," 1st supplement, 1944.

A. W. Hopkins and A. Raisbeck, "Stephen Moulton Babcock," in *Dairy Farmer,* 27, No. 2, 7 (1929). Reprinted as chapter 1 in "The Ten Master Minds of Dairying," Meredith, Des Moines, Iowa, 1930.

L. S. Ivins and A. E. Winship, "Stephen Moulton Babcock," chapter 1 in *Fifty Famous Farmers,* Macmillan, New York, 1924

Louis Kahlenberg, "Stephen Moulton Babcock," *Ind. Engr. Chem.,* 16, 1087–8 (1924).

Harry L. Russel *et al.,* "Stephen Moulton Babcock . . . A Memorial to Him in Observance of the Centenary of His Birth," Wisconsin Alumni Research Foundation, Madison, Wisc., 1943.

WILEY

O. E. Anderson, "The Pure-Food Issue: A Republican Dilemma, 1906–1912," *Amer. Hist. Rev., 61,* 550–573 (1956).

W. D. Bigelow, "Harvey Washington Wiley," *Ind. Engr. Chem., 15,* 88 (1923).

E. J. Dies, "Harvey W. Wiley, Apostle of Pure Food," chapter 17 in *Titans of the Soil,* University of North Carolina Press, Chapel Hill, N. C., 1949.

W. W. Skinner, C. A. Browne, W. G. Campbell *et al.,* commemorative addresses at the 1930 meeting of the A.O.A.C., *J. Assoc. Official Agr. Chemists, 14,* iii–xxii (1931).

Mark Sullivan, "The Crusade for Pure Foods," chapter 27 in *Our Times,* vol. 2, Scribner's, New York, 1927.

H. W. Wiley, "The History of a Crime Against the Food Law," H. W. Wiley, Washington, 1929.

H. W. Wiley, "An Autobiography," Bobbs, Merrill, Indianapolis, Ind., 1930.

REMSEN

John C. French, "A History of the University Founded by Johns Hopkins," Johns Hopkins Press, Baltimore, Md., 1946.

Frederick H. Getman, "The Life of Ira Remsen," *J. Chem. Educ.,* 1940.

Benjamin Harrow, "Remsen and the Rise of Chemistry in America," chapter in *Eminent Chemists of Our Time,* Van Nostrand, New York, 1920.

Wm. A. Noyes, "Ira Remsen," *Science, 64,* 243–246 (1927).

W. A. Noyes and J. F. Norris, "Ira Remsen," *Biog. Memoirs, Natl. Acad. Sci., 14,* 207–257 (1931).

E. E. Reid, "Ira Remsen," *Ind. Engr. Chem., 14,* 1078 (1922).

RICHARDS

Gregory P. Baxter, "Theodore William Richards," *Science, 68,* 333–339 (1928).

George S. Forbes, "Investigations of Atomic Weights by Theodore William Richards," *J. Chem. Educ., 9,* 453–458 (1932).

Benjamin Harrow, "Richards and Atomic Weights," chapter 4 in *Eminent Chemists of Our Time,* Van Nostrand, New York, 1920.

Harold Hartley, "The Theodore William Richards Memorial Lecture," *Memorial Lectures Delivered Before The Chemical Society, 3,* 131–163 (Del. 4-25-29), London, 1933.

T. W. Richards, "The Ideals of Chemistry Investigation," *J. Chem. Educ., 6,* 2239–45 (1929).

EDGAR FAHS SMITH

Eva V. Armstrong, "Playground of a Scientist," *Sci. Monthly, 42,* 339–348 (1936).

Marston T. Bogert, "Edgar Fahs Smith—Chemist," *Science, 69,* 557–565 (1929).

C. A. Browne, "Edgar Fahs Smith, 1854–1928," *Isis, 11,* 375–384 (1928).

Charles A. Browne, "Edgar Fahs Smith, 1854–1928," *J. Chem. Educ., 5,* 656–663 (1928).

Wm. McPherson, "Some Experiences of Dr. Edgar F. Smith as a Student under Wöhler," *J. Chem. Educ., 5,* 1554–1557 (1928).

Walter T. Taggart, "Edgar Fahs Smith," *J. Chem. Educ., 9,* 613–619 (1932). This issue is a commemorative one and contains several papers about Smith, a bibliography of his scientific papers, books, and historical brochures, titles of doctoral theses carried out under his direction, besides several symposium papers dealing with the development of chemical education in America.

Francis P. Venable, "Edgar Fahs Smith," *J. Ind. Engr. Chem., 13,* 106–107 (1921).

AARON J. IHDE

·· *59* ··

Otto Wallach

1847-1931

THE honor, which is mine of speaking here on the life and work of Otto Wallach, who died on February 26, 1931, is also a task which holds a certain measure of difficulty. Upon only one occasion did I have the good fortune to meet Wallach. In the spring of 1928 a convention of chemists of northwest Germany was held in Göttingen. During one of the lectures a small white-haired man entered the room. "That is Wallach!" thought I at once. The few words I exchanged with him, and his appearance—the clear blue eyes beaming in his exceedingly fine and sage countenance—made an indelible impression on my memory. A brief meeting such as that cannot replace a long acquaintance. It afforded me, however, an experience of his remarkable personality which, I trust, may supply the mental plastic necessary to cement together the data I have collected from his writings and those of his school.

Wallach was born in Königsberg on March 27, 1847. His parents' home appears to have had but little direct influence upon his career. This, however, was largely affected by the circumstance that his father, a Prussian official, moved from Otto's birthplace to Stettin and finally to Potsdam, in the vicinity of the German metropolis. There the young Wallach received his elementary schooling, ending with the classical gymnasium.

In the higher classes of the school there existed a club for the encouragement of the study of literature and the history of art. Wallach's words make clear the influence which this activity had upon his inner life. "There I felt the first unforgettable urge towards art and its history. This pointed out to me, early in my life, the path leading from the drab plain of life's demands to the stimulating heights of art." Wallach remained true to this youthful inclination, and as one of the advantages of his later home in Bonn he mentions its proximity to the Belgian and Dutch schools of art. Many of his vacation trips were devoted to the study of art, and in his professional home in Göttingen he made a collection of water-color paintings.

Even during his early school years Wallach evinced a strong interest in chemistry, which, at that time, was not taught as a separate subject in gymnasiums, but was treated only in a rather stepmotherly fashion as an off-shoot of physics. Like many other rising chemists of that time, he made his first venture into the realm of chemistry under the guidance of Stöckhard's "Schule der Chemie" and with the help of primitive apparatus. "At home," he says, "these experimental tendencies, not always resulting in too fragrant products, found little sympathy, for I come of a great family of lawyers, little interested in the natural sciences." His relatives and friends, therefore, did not greatly sympathize with his choice of profession when he decided, in the spring of 1867, to study chemistry in Göttingen, where Friedrich Wöhler directed the chemical laboratory.

For personal reasons, Wallach passed his second semester in Berlin, whither A. W. Hofmann had just come from London as successor to Mitscherlich. Wallach then returned to Göttingen, where the conditions in the laboratory were definitely more agreeable than in Berlin. Concerning this period he wrote: "There followed a time of restless activity. In Wöhler's laboratory indolence was not tolerated: anyone who did not occupy his working place regularly must expect to receive from the 'Hofrat' a letter summoning him to vacate it." Work was carried out in the laboratory from seven o'clock in the morning until at least five o'clock in the afternoon; the gas used by the laboratory students was then turned off. "After that hour, in winter, many operations had to be finished by the scanty light of candles which the students had brought with them." So industrious was Wallach that, with the special permission of the "Honourable-Faculty," composed of the fifteen oldest professors, he was able to obtain his Doctor's degree after five semesters of study. His dissertation, carried out under the direction of Hübner, dealt with position isomerism in the toluene series.

The following winter semester brought Wallach to Berlin as assistant to Wichelhaus, who was later to become the well-known technologist. Here he gained valuable stimulus by visiting the German Chemical Society, founded in 1868, where he made the acquaintance of many of his German and foreign colleagues. In the spring of 1870 he accepted an assistantship in Bonn offered to him by Kekulé, who said in his letter: "It will not hurt you to come to Bonn. Here we lead a scientific artist-life."

In the memorial lecture which he delivered in 1897 before the Königl. Gesellschaft der Wissenschaften in Göttingen, Wallach strikingly portrayed Kekulé's individuality. Their different conceptions of art profoundly influenced the lives of the two men. Kekulé, the born artist, long wavered between chemistry and architecture as a profession, and then with the artist's intuition created structural organic chemistry. He continued to work intensively in the field of experimental science for only a few years after Wallach's arrival in his laboratory. "Kekulé was no busy bee," writes Wallach, "constantly endeavoring to enrich the hive of knowledge with the greatest possible number of new cells." Wallach, on the contrary, was the experimental artist: at the age of eighty he was still experimenting in his laboratory on problems that interested him.

Wallach's stay at Bonn lasted for nineteen years, with one brief interruption. For the third and last time he tried to establish himself in Berlin, entering, as its only chemist, a newly founded enterprise which later developed under the name "Aktien-Gesellschaft für Anilin-Fabrikation" (Agfa). The noxious gases of the factory, however, were so detrimental to his weak health that he had to resign his position. He soon found an opportunity of returning to Kekulé in Bonn, where, in the spring of 1872, he took over the position of assistant in the organic laboratory. A year later he became Privatdozent, and in 1876 Extraordinarius. Until then, Wallach had passed through "relatively easy years, free from responsibility," but now followed a period only too well filled with nonexperimental work. Kekulé, although remaining director of the Chemical Institute, withdrew more and more from active participation in the laboratory work, and in 1879 the instruction in pharmacy, a foreign field into which he had to initiate himself, devolved on Wallach.

Wallach's scientific work of this period is entirely different from his later famous fields of research: the discovery of the imino-chlorides by the action of phosphorus pentachloride on the acid amides may be mentioned as an example.

His new duty had a decisive influence on Wallach's future scientific career, for in teaching pharmacy he had to deal with the ethereal oils. The state of knowledge existing in the field at that time can be best illustrated by a quotation from the introduction of his first publication on the subject (August 10, 1884): "The numerous so-called ethereal oils are known to be mixtures, for the most part, of hydrocarbons of the terpene group with oxygen-containing compounds, often closely related to camphor, in which sometimes the oxygen-free constituents, in other cases the oxygenated constituents, preponderate. As a result of the examination of these constituents isolated from ethereal oils, in course of time a large series of compounds of the same composition has been described. These bear different names in accord with their origin, but they have not been examined experimentally to determine whether or not they are really different from one another. Hydrocarbons of the formula $C_{10}H_{16}$, namely, terpene, camphene, citrene, carvene, cinene, cajuputene, eucalyptene, hesperidine, etc., etc., are mentioned in such number that it seems highly improbable that they can all be different substances. It is the same with the corresponding oxygenated products, $C_{10}H_{18}O$, $C_{10}H_{16}O$, etc."

On August 4, 1909, on the occasion of the fortieth anniversary of his promotion, Wallach's former co-workers held a reunion in Göttingen to celebrate the appearance in Liebig's *Annalen der Chemie* of his hundredth paper concerning the ethereal oils. When returning thanks, Wallach took the opportunity to describe the immediate cause of his original interest in these substances. In a cupboard in Kekulé's private laboratory there had stood for fifteen years several unopened flasks containing ethereal oils, which Kekulé had procured for research purposes but had not used. Kekulé granted Wallach's request for permission to carry out a research on the mysterious contents of the flasks, with the words: "Yes, if you can make anything out of them!", accompanied by the ironical laugh that he gave only when he believed someone to be on the wrong track.

The opinion of leading organic chemists in 1884 concerning the

836

ethereal oils was similar to that which had been held very shortly before with regard to the synthesis of closed carbon chains. In May, 1929, in the first Pedler Lecture, William Henry Perkin mentioned that Adolf v. Baeyer, as well as Emil Fischer and Victor Meyer, rated as very slight the prospect of synthesizing small carbon rings.

The difficulties which Wallach had to overcome in his first struggles with terpene mixtures were by no means small. But only a year after his first publication he was able to state that "a great many terpenes, formerly designated differently and alleged to be of various constitutions, are undoubtedly identical."

Before we turn to a detailed consideration of Wallach's work, let us cast a glance over what had previously been accomplished by others. The first extensive researches in this field were carried out during the years 1852–1863 by Berthelot, who was particularly successful in working with turpentine oil and its products of re-arrangement. He was able to characterize d- and l- pinene, as well as d-, l-, and dl-camphene, the last of which he obtained by splitting out hydrogen chloride from pinene hydrochloride. He gave different names to the optical isomerides, however, and there-fore could not correlate them. To characterize the various pinenes, Berthelot used only the hydrochlorides.

The first insight into the constitution of the terpenes was af-forded by their transformation into aromatic compounds. In 1838, by the action of phosphorus pentoxide on camphor, Dumas and Péligot had obtained "camphene," which was, however, nothing other than p-cymene. In 1847, Caillot obtained terephthalic acid by the oxidation of turpentine oil with nitric acid. It was then known that terephthalic acid is an aromatic compound, and Caillot pointed out the relation between turpentine oil and the aromatic series, but he had no idea about further details of structure, such as the nature of the side chains.

Another step was taken when Barbier and Oppenheim, inde-pendently of one another, in 1872, obtained p-cymene by the action of bromine on terpin, which itself resulted from treatment of turpentine oil with sulphuric acid. p-Cymene was then supposed to be p-methyl-n-propylbenzene, and hence Oppenheim assigned the formula (I) to pinene. This formula and that (II) given by Kekulé to camphor illustrate the state of constitutional formulas at that time.

(I)   (II)

A further important observation was made in 1875 by Tilden, namely, the formation of a crystalline addition product from turpentine oil and nitrosyl chloride. Shortly afterwards, he and Shenstone found that the terpenes of the citrus oils also give a crystalline nitrosochloride. Both nitrosochlorides produced nitrosoderivatives by elimination of hydrogen chloride. Accordingly Tilden divided the natural terpenes into two groups: the turpentine and the orange group.

This classification was, however, insufficient, since it was based on too small an experimental foundation. On the other hand, Tilden was right in his prediction that the number of terpenes would prove far less than that which one had assumed from the statements then found in the literature. He had also already correctly suggested that the apparent differences between the terpenes occurring in various plants would, in large measure, be traced to their optical isomerism. These results of Tilden were known in 1877, but he had not developed their relations any further experimentally. As with so many important advances in the history of science, despite his breadth of vision and energy, a single man was unable to pursue a correct idea to the end and persevere with the correct method of work. Tilden's next step was a backward one in the determination of the constitution of the terpenes, for in 1878 he assumed all terpenes to be of aliphatic structure and to differ from one another only in the position of the double bond. For example, he ascribed to pinene the formula (III), which is given side by side with the formula (IV) proposed in the same year by

Armstrong. These formulæ serve to show still further the oscillating ideas of that time. The ideas underlying many of the formulæ proposed during this period were partly correct, e.g., Armstrong's formula for pinene.

$$
\begin{array}{cc}
\text{(III)} & \text{(IV)}
\end{array}
$$

(III)   (IV)

On the early history of terpene chemistry, Wallach commented in the following terms in a lecture which he delivered before the German Chemical Society in 1891:

> . . . if one casts a glance over the old literature of the terpenes, it does not appear a particularly enticing subject for investigation. There were isolated observations in almost incomprehensible abundance. The textbooks listed a large number of terpenes which were designated by special names according to their origin and were held to be really different from one another in virtue of their physical properties. As is to be seen from the literature, it may be that some of the investigators who had carried out extensive researches in this field of work had formed correct and definite ideas about the relations between the terpenes. Real clarity had been reached on no point. To introduce clearness into this widely branched and tangled subject, it was necessary to strive for the following:

> 1. All terpenes that are really different from one another must be sharply and definitely characterised by their properties so that recognition and distinction of the chemical individuals might be possible without difficulty.
> 2. The behaviour and the mutual relations of the individual hydrocarbons must be explicable on the basis of such an exact characterisation.

839

3. Only after the fulfilment of both of these preliminary con-
conditions would it be possible to investigate successfully the individual compounds with regard to their constitution.

The first step in the diagnosis of the terpenes had been taken by
Wallach before 1887. For this purpose he let several simple
reagents act on the separate fractions of natural terpene mixtures,
and investigated whether crystalline reaction products were thus
formed. Some of these reagents, such as hydrogen chloride, bromide, and iodide, nitrosyl chloride, and nitrogen trioxide, had
been successfully applied earlier in isolated cases; others, such
as bromine and nitrogen peroxide, Wallach used for the first time.

Time-saving devices for the preparation of terpene derivatives
were introduced by Wallach; Tilden's gaseous nitrosyl chloride
was replaced by acetic acid, ethyl nitrite, and concentrated hydrochloric acid; the addition of hydrogen halide was found to be an
almost instantaneous reaction in acetic acid solution; the addition
of bromide to an ordinary mixture of terpenes usually led to an
amorphous mixture of bromides, but by the use of certain solvents,
such as alcohol or acetic acid, the crystalline tetrabromides were
precipitated, the amorphous products remaining in solution. These
are only trifles, but taken together they were of essential importance for the success of the work undertaken by Wallach.

With respect to the mechanism of the formation of some addition
products various interesting observations were made. Before this
time it was very incompletely understood how far the addition of
hydrogen halide takes place with rearrangement. Wallach observed
that the so-called pinene hydrochloride (in reality, bornyl chloride)
is formed only in an anhydrous medium. Not until some thirty
years later did Aschan show that the veritable liquid pinene hydrochloride is formed below $-10°$, and that above this temperature it
undergoes spontaneous rearrangement into bornyl chloride. Like
pinene, in the absence of moisture limonene and dipentene also add
only one molecule of hydrogen halide, but on the other hand, in all
these cases, moist hydrogen halide leads to the formation of
dipentine dihydrohalide. With respect to the previously mentioned addition of nitrogen derivatives, it was determined that

usually a nitroso-group adds to one carbon atom of the double bond and the remainder of the addendum to the other carbon; thus, NO$\cdots$Cl, NO$\cdots$ONO$_2$, etc. It was observed that by the action of certain organic bases on the nitrosochlorides and the nitrosates, the anion radical, Cl or ONO$_2$, is readily replaced by a nitrogen-containing radical. The original bimolecular addition product is thus transformed into the unimolecular nitrolamine, containing added NO and NHR, which, in contrast to the initial products, usually showed a greater tendency to crystallize.

The important result of three years of work, during which Wallach proved to be a real "busy bee," made possible the listing of eight terpenes which obviously differed from one another, each of which was characterized without ambiguity, in such a fashion that anyone following Wallach's directions could again recognize it. These eight individuals were pinene, camphene, limonene, dipentene, sylvestrene, terpinolene, terpinene, and phellandrene. Terpinolene was discovered by Wallach and terpinene had not previously been distinguished from other terpenes.

Naturally, this classification was not final. It soon appeared that dipentene was nothing other than *dl*-limonene and should be omitted from the list. Pinene, terpinene, and phellandrene were recognized as mixtures of an α- and a β-compound. Forty years later it turned out that sylvestrene does not occur in nature, for Rao and Simonsen showed that the sylvestrene dihydrochloride used for its isolation is formed from carene present in the ethereal oil. Finally, it may be mentioned that the number of terpenes later recognized as well-characterized individuals, which occur less often in nature or which are artificially available, was increased by Wallach and others. Among the well-characterizable hydrocarbons we mention here only sabinene, the fenchenes, and the carenes.

Naturally, Wallach also included the oxygenated terpene derivatives in his investigations. Indeed, it is the oxide eineole which formed the subject of his first publication in this field. Moreover, during the first few years, terpin and α-terpineol were particularly zealously investigated. They afforded a great incentive to research because of their close genetic relationship to the most important of the terpenes, pinene.

Wallach also extended his researches to the sesquiterpenes, particularly the two most widely distributed members, cadinene and caryophyllene. He soon abandoned work in this field, however, since his technique, which was so valuable for the terpenes, was insufficent for a more profound penetration into the systematization and elucidation of the constitution of the sesquiterpenes. Wallach possessed the possibilities of only a single investigator and was opposed by the profuse multiplicity of nature. This he realized full well, and clothed the thought in the following expression, so typical of him: "The investigation of the ethereal oils, of both the new and the known constituents, by one single man can embrace only an exceedingly modest territory in proportion to the inexhaustible material which the plant world affords us."

Let us now turn to the second point of Wallach's program. His fine instinct for the best line of research to be pursued is shown by the fact that, after characterizing the individual terpenes, he considered the elucidation of their innumerable mutual relations of greater importance than the determination of their constitution. Long before Wallach, investigators who had dealt extensively with the subject had felt that many reactions in the terpene series are linked with rearrangement of the carbon skeleton. We need mention only Berthelot's conjecture that the transformation of pinene into camphene by passage through bornyl chloride is linked with a double change in the carbon skeleton. Before Wallach, however, chemists had not gone beyond surmises on this question. Wallach therefore proceeded to investigate the cause, conditions, and direction of isomerization by an examination of the greatest possible amount of material. His more exact researches dealing with reactions employed for the characterization of individual terpenes had already thrown light on these complex questions, as, for example, in the case already described of the action of hydrogen chloride on pinene, whereby a labile bond in a ring is broken. In most other cases the cause of isomerization lay in a simple displacement of a carbon double bond. Wallach early recognized that the formulas of the various possible dihydrocymenes should be considered for the individual monocyclic terpenes. In 1887 he attributed the following formula to pinene:

CH$_3$

C$_3$H$_7$

Far-reaching researches, then, soon showed that the isomerization of terpenes takes place under the influence of strong acids or high temperature (some 200° and more), while alkalies in general are without influence, save when a double bond can wander in the neighborhood of a carbonyl group.

The determination of the direction of isomerization was closely related to partial clarification of the constitutions of the products concerned. Today, the course of isomerization is still far from being elucidated in all the cases investigated. The reason for this is that an equilibrium is often established during isomerization, and we are unable to carry out an exact estimation of the individual components of the equilibrium mixture so formed. In the majority of cases, however, it has been possible to determine correctly the principal course of isomerization.

A double bond in the ring between two CH-groups wanders by preference into the position —CH=C(CH$_3$)—. Double bonds outside the ring wander into it, especially easily those directly attached to the ring itself, the so-called semicyclic double bonds. In the majority of cases, acid reagents proved to be distinctly more powerful instigators of wandering than elevated temperature.

In the collection of his work dealing with terpenes and camphor, published in 1909, Wallach assembled fourteen pages of tables of the most important transpositions which he had carried out with the most varied representatives of the terpene compounds. As an example, we shall quote here only the historically important table of those transpositions of pinene known at the time of its publication in 1891.

In 1884 Wallach had plunged into work in a neglected garden so overrun with weeds that the useful plants could not thrive. Many good gardeners had already attempted to improve its condition but each had soon damaged his hands and the weeds had begun to flourish again with renewed vigor. Ought we to reproach Wallach that, in his cleaning and ordering of the garden, he did not rely exclusively on the tools which he had brought with him, but also used those left lying there by his predecessors, if they still

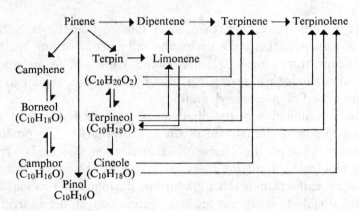

appeared serviceable for accomplishing his ends? To be sure, it was often necessary for him to make a fundamental repair in these corroded tools, or to use them in other ways than his predecessors had done. After about the beginning of 1890, the garden was well weeded and it soon enticed other gardeners to investigate the conditions of life and the properties of the plants, and to determine their species. Among them there were many old gardeners who knew from experience how bad the conditions in the uncultivated garden had been. There were also many new workers who, untroubled by the former times, delighted in the new order. They all owed gratitude to the chief gardener whose activity had opened to them a field in which they might work for many years.

First of all should be mentioned Tiemann and Semmler in Germany and Barbier and Bouveault in France, who took over a portion of terpene chemistry for the investigation of which Wallach had not found time, namely, the aliphatic series. Among those working with the cyclic compounds, v. Baeyer, Bredt, and Wagner should be especially mentioned. It is impossible to consider all of this work thoroughly in a short lecture. All that can be done is to point out cursorily its principal foundations. We shall there-

844

fore sketch very rapidly its further development, considering only a few selected examples of the last steps leading to the final results.

In the formulas for the terpenes presented up to the year 1891 we find the side chain containing three atoms of carbon written as C_3H_7. The question whether this might be a n- or an isopropyl group depended strictly on the constitution of p-cymene, since the chemist was not sufficiently advanced with the analysis of any single terpene to be able to decide the nature of the side chain on the basis of the results of degradation reactions. Owing to a series of errors and false assumptions one was inclined to the view that p-cymene contained a n-propyl group, until in 1891 Widmann cleared up the errors and conclusively established the presence of an isopropyl group in this compound. Hence the first possibility was afforded of attacking the complete clarification of the constitution of the terpenes. In 1887 Wallach had already considered the possibility that the terpenes might be built up from isoprene nuclei. He was not entirely convinced, however, of the general correctness of this hypothesis, for in the same paper he discussed the possibility of the existence of terpenes with a n-propylene group. Before 1887 the composition of no single compound of the terpene series from isoprene residues had been determined. It is true that Bouchardat had observed in 1875 that dipentene is formed by the polymerization of isoprene. Apart from this case, in which it was not possible to be certain of the purity of the isoprene used, Wallach first succeeded in proving the identity of dipentene with dl-limonene in 1888.

Thus the carbon skeleton of those terpenes and their derivatives which could be transformed into p-cymene was determined. Thereafter determinations of the exact formulas followed in rapid succession. First came the pulegone and menthol groups. Beckett and Wright had carried out the transformation of menthol into p-cymene in 1876, and in 1891 Beckmann and Pleissner succeeded in reducing pulegone to menthol by sodium and alcohol. When, in 1892, Semmler obtained β-methyladipic acid and acetone by oxidation of pulegone, he was able to propose the following formulas for menthol (VI) and pulegone (V) with a very great degree of

845

probability. Their accuracy has been proved by all subsequent researches.

(V) (VI) (VII)

In 1893 followed the establishment by Bredt of the correct formula for camphor (VII), it having been preceded by more than thirty incorrect formulæ proposed by earlier workers.

The clarification of the structures of pulegone, menthol, and camphor was only a single case. The real harvest from the persistent work of Wallach was reaped in 1895, when, with a single stroke, the structure of an entire series of terpene compounds was elucidated. It followed as a result of Wallach's principle, already mentioned, of establishing clearly the relations existing between the greatest possible number of compounds of the terpene series by clarifying their reciprocal rearrangements into one another. Each success with one member of such a group had, automatically, to affect the others. The center of this series was α-terpineol, for which the following formula (VIII) was demonstrated simultaneously by Wallach, and Tiemann and Semmler.

846

This formula had already been proposed by Wagner in the preceding year. Oxidation of α-terpineol with potassium permanganate yields a ketolactone which, by further oxidation, is transformed into acetic acid and terpenylic acid. The latter was reduced by Schryver to β-isopropylglutaric acid by means of hydrogen iodide. Since dehydration of α-terpineol by potassium hydrogen sulfate gives dipentene, the Wagner formula for limonene (IX) received further support. The transformation of limonene and α-terpineol into carvone by various methods led to the clarification of the structure of this ketone. Of these transformations we may mention here the preparation by Tilden and Shenstone of nitrosolimonene, whose identity with carvoxime (X) was proved in 1885 by Goldschmidt and Züner.

The determination of the structure of α-terpineol led to the clarification of the constitution of other genetically related compounds. Of these, only pinene need be mentioned. By treatment of α-terpineol bromide (XI) with silver hydroxide, pinol was formed, besides other products. Wallach also found pinol as a by-product in the preparation of pinene nitrosochloride:

The observations of Wallach led Wagner in 1894 to propose the formula for α-pinene (XII) which imitated the Bredt camphor formula. This proposed formula was verified by later research. The characteristic development during the years 1893–95 was the realization that the isopropyl group, formerly assumed unsubstituted in all terpenes, usually bore either a double bond of a hydroxyl group, or in some cases, as pinene and camphor, was joined to the ring by a second linkage. In 1894 this formula for pinene was still by no means definitely determined, and Wagner himself modified it again in the following year. In 1896 evidence was again contributed by Baeyer to the accuracy of Wagner's formula

847

of 1894 by the degradation of pinene to pinonic acid, and further, to pinic acid. This formula was accepted by Wallach as the best expression for the reactions of pinene, although he remarked: "This formula is not yet entirely satisfactory . . . namely, the formation of pinol hydrate by oxidation of pinene with oxygen is not at all clear."

Pinene is one of those compounds whose properties are not completely expressed by our customary method of formulation. With this terpene it is necessary to conclude, in the words of Wallach, that "The habit not only of speaking of the bonds between atoms in a molecule, but also of expressing these ideas by constructing rigid models, will certainly some day be considered a stage in the development of chemical theory which has been overcome. On the other hand, exact and reliable experimental determinations will always retain their value."

Arguing on the grounds of historical truth, on this occasion Wallach refuted the "lapidific statements, frequently found in newer work, that the constitution of this or that compound of the terpene series has been determined by this or that chemist. I believe one may say that, for none of the substances under consideration, what to-day is assumed to be correct with regard to its structure has been ascertained at a single blow. The proposition of a formula has significance, above all, as a hypothesis helpful to experimental research. Whether a man publicly proposes his working hypothesis or not is entirely a matter of temperament. Naturally it may happen that among the formulæ proposed—easy, indeed, to design on paper—the 'correct' one exists. If a formula, however, suggests no new idea, its mere proposal must be less valuable than work leading to the recognition that it is really tenable."

Wallach was in fact not the quickest in the race for the proposal of correct constitutional formulas, nor indeed could he be, because of his character. Those which he proposed at first were particularly for the purpose of orientation. After having suggested them, he sometimes neglected to propose modifications which might be more nearly in accord with the results of later experimental investigation, and the formulas were often developed by others. The majority of these correct formulas he may himself have considered, but as critical sovereign connoisseur of the subject and all its difficulties he perceived possible objections which made him hesitate to advance their publication first. Often, however, it was he himself who offered the final experimental proof of such formulas proposed by others, and he hesitated to accept a formula before it had been really proved.

About the year 1895 the heroic times in terpene chemistry ended and Wallach ceased to play the rôle of the pioneer. We can, in large part, pass over his later work and merely point out briefly a few of its more striking features. These should include the two investigations dealing with various dicyclic representatives of the terpene series and with simple alicyclic compounds. It is obvious that Wallach's extensive occupation with the terpenes must soon have led him to turn his attention to their simple analogs.

Wallach used experiments with the simple alicyclic five- and six-membered rings as models for his researches on their complicated analogs of the terpene series; in particular, for the study of isomerization reactions involving shifting of the double bond or rearrangement of the ring.

Among Wallach's newly begun later researches in the terpene series, those with thujone and fenchone may be mentioned. His work on thujone ran parallel with that of Semmler on tanacetone, which two compounds, in the course of the researches, were recognized as optical isomerides. In both cases, Wallach again proved to be the cautious experimenter who left the proposal of the correct formulas for thujone and fenchone to the younger and more enterprising Semmler.

In the conviction that enough material for the justification of the old formulas had not been advanced, Wallach remained constantly occupied with his old researches until his final years. He had begun as a busy bee; as such he ended.

Wallach's work found recognition everywhere. In 1889 he was called to Göttingen as successor to Victor Meyer. There he retained the direction of the Chemical Institute until 1915. During the entire time, he lived near the laboratory in the old home of Friedrich Wöhler. As a rare exception among the great German chemists, Wallach remained a bachelor.

GREAT CHEMISTS

In foreign countries Wallach received more special recognition by his English colleagues. In 1908 he was elected Honorary Fellow of the Chemical Society, and in 1909, Honorary Doctor of the University of Manchester. His native country did not lag behind in paying him honor: he became Honorary Doctor of the University of Leipzig and of the Technological Institute of Braunschweig and in 1912 the Verein Deutscher Chemiker also nominated him to honorary membership, and the Deutsche Chemische Gesellschaft to its presidency. As pioneer, *par excellence,* in organic chemistry, Wallach was awarded the Nobel Prize in 1910.

Was Wallach a genius? With regard to this query, recently raised, I believe that we can comprehend Wallach's personality better by studying his place in the history, not only of the terpenes, but of organic chemistry in general, than by trying to find a label which may be glued to him. Picture organic chemistry with Wallach's work removed—what a gap is left! When I say this, I think not only of his results in the field of the terpenes but also of his method of attack. He approached his problems, not with brilliant theoretical speculation, but only with an extremely sensitive recognition of the correct lines of work and of their technique, and followed with severe perseverance those paths which alone could lead to the goal. Wallach's highest ideal was not theory, not the formula, but carefully and reliably performed experiment. In this respect, he resembled his two compatriots, Emil Fischer and Adolf von Baeyer. He differed, however, in one essential point from them. While they accomplished much by the synthesis of natural compounds as well as by their analysis, Wallach was primarily the analyst. If, to use his own words, the methods of analysis in organic chemistry have reached so high a degree of perfection that it "has become possible to follow an analytical procedure therein with the same degree of certainty as the search for the elements in an inorganic substance," it is to a great extent a service rendered by Wallach.

We can conclude our review of the life work of Wallach in no more fitting way than by recalling the man who was in many respects the complement of Wallach in the history of the chemistry of the terpenes, as well as of organic chemistry in general, namely,

850

the great synthesist William Henry Perkin, founder and unrivaled master of alicyclic synthesis, to whom, by the artificial preparation of α-terpineol and dipentene, it was particularly assigned to give the final crowning glory to the work of Wallach.

From: *J. Chem. Soc.*, *1932* (1582–1597).

LEOPOLD RUZICKA

·· 60 ··

Victor Meyer

1848-1897

VICTOR was born September 8, 1848, in Berlin. Our father, Jacques Meyer, had come to Berlin from Hohensalza as a very young man. He gradually developed a cotton business which grew into a calico printing and dyeing plant. Although our father had no chemical or technical training he was an avid reader of Dingler's Polytechnical Journal. He was married in 1845. Of the four children Victor was the second, I the eldest.

Victor and I received our first instruction from our mother. In 1858 we entered the gymnasium. He was convinced that he would become an actor. Even after graduating in 1865 he was little inclined to follow our father's wish and study chemistry. Then he visited me when I was studying chemistry in Heidelberg, and suddenly arrived at a decision. Bunsen became his ideal— and remained so to the end of his life.

Victor spent his first semester in Berlin and attended A. W. Hoffmann's lectures, returning to Heidelberg to live with me. When I left there in the spring of 1866 he remained to continue his studies. On May 13, 1867, he obtained the degree of Doctor of Philosophy, *summa cum laude,* not quite nineteen years old and just beginning his fifth semester. From the government Bunsen had received a continuing order to analyze the mineral waters of Baden, and a special assistant had been granted to him for this work. He offered the assistantship to the young doctor; Victor accepted it and, therefore, remained in Heidelberg for another year.

IN BAEYER'S LABORATORY, 1868–1871

At the end of the summer term of 1868, my brother left Heidelberg and returned to Berlin to study in Adolf Baeyer's laboratory. The three years he spent in this atmosphere were decisive for his future. The series of his publications began with a notice about trimethyl-glyceryl-ammonium, an analog to "neurine." The discovery of a way to synthesize aromatic acids with sodium formiate

855

brought him into close contact with the most pressing questions of benzene chemistry.

STUTTGART, 1871–72

In 1871 he went from Berlin to Stuttgart as associate professor, a position which he described in a letter as "outright paradisiacal." One day he noticed in his audience an elderly stout gentleman who followed the lecture with greatest attention. It was Carl Kappeler, president of the Swiss Board of Education, who alone was responsible for filling the professorships at the Zurich Polytechnicum. After the lecture he had a long conversation with Victor; Kappeler told him that he would like to offer him a professorship but hesitated because he was too young for it. When Victor replied that this fault would be diminished from day to day, the old gentleman smilingly agreed, and it was not long before Victor became full professor of general chemistry in Zurich, after scarcely one year in Stuttgart.

ZURICH, 1872–1885

In the beginning Victor's activities in Zurich were anything but successful; he was bitterly disappointed by his initial reception. In a letter of March 2, 1873, he was very caustic about it. "I have brought down another assistant from Stuttgart so that I now have two unconditionally devoted assistants who should be able to oppose the intrigues of the Swiss. I can say, without superciliousness, that I have almost been deified by my Stuttgart students, they loved me far beyond my merits, whereas here I find only enmity and suspicion. . . ." Later on, after his marriage in March, 1873, the situation changed completely.

The year 1872 brought the discovery of the aliphatic nitro compounds. In the great field opened by this discovery Victor and a number of his students determined the constitution and the course of their many reactions. His interest was particularly aroused by the unexpected acidity of the primary and secondary nitroparaffins and by the reactions with nitrous acid. He explained the acidic function as an influence of the negative nitro group on the hydrogen atoms connected with the same carbon atom. Later

856

on this explanation was replaced by a different one, based on a desmotropic rearrangement taking place when the nitroparaffins form salts:

$$CH_3CH_2NO_2 \rightarrow CH_3CH=NO—OH$$

so that they are to be considered pseudo-acids in the nomenclature of Hantzsch.

Victor compared the reaction of nitrous acid upon primary and secondary nitro compounds with the reaction of this acid on primary and secondary aromatic amines, giving diazo compounds from the first and nitrosamines from the second. This leads to the formulas of nitrolic acids and pseudo-nitrols which Victor expressed in the following way:

Primary Aromatic Amine.

$$C_6H_5N\overline{|H_2} + O|NOH \rightarrow H_2O + C_6H_5N=NOH$$

Primary Aliphatic Nitro Compound (Nitrolic Acid).

$$\underset{\overset{|}{NO_2}}{CH_3CH_2} + ONOH \rightarrow H_2O + \underset{\overset{|}{NO_2}}{CH_3C}=NOH$$

Secondary Aromatic Amine.

$$\underset{\overset{|}{C_6H_5}}{C_6H_5NH} + HONO \rightarrow H_2O + \underset{\overset{|}{C_6H_5}}{C_6H_5—N}—NO$$

Secondary Aliphatic Nitro Compound.(Pseudo-Nitrol).

$$\underset{CH_3}{\overset{CH_3}{>}}C\underset{NO_2}{\overset{H}{<}} + HONO \rightarrow H_2O + \underset{CH_3}{\overset{CH_3}{>}}C\underset{NO_2}{\overset{NO}{<}}$$

The nitrolic acids thus appear to be derivatives of hydroxylamine $H_2N.OH$. If this were correct, then the reaction of nitrous acid

$$(CO_2H)_2CH_2 + NO_2$$

with malonic acid should yield an oximido body, the same as obtainable from hydroxylamine and mesoxalic acid:

$$(CO_2H)_2CO + H_2NOH \rightarrow H_2O + (CO_2H)_2C=NOH$$

This was actually found to be true (1883).

857

The year 1882 saw the start of a great new series of studies as a result of the discovery of thiophen. In the introduction to his book on thiophen (Braunschweig, Vieweg & Sohn, 1888) Victor wrote:

The first stimulus to the experiments on the isolation of thiophen I owe to an accident. In an experiment during a lecture I wanted to demonstrate to my audience the reaction by which benzene can be identified. The basis of this identification is that benzene, or rather, as we have to say now, thiophen-containing coal tar benzene, produces the deep-blue indophenine when treated with isatin and concentrated sulfuric acid. Immediately before the lecture I made sure that the reaction takes place, and I was greatly surprised to obtain a complete blank when I tried to use this phenomenon in the lecture itself for the purpose of characterizing as benzene the oil produced by distilling benzoic acid with lime. My assistant at that time was T. Sandmeyer, the discoverer of many reactions of which only a few are named after him; he immediately brought it to my attention that the test before the lecture had been made with a different sample of benzene, and with this sample the experiment proceeded readily as desired. The riddle was, however, not solved by this demonstration; I stated this surprising phenomenon to my audience right there and added the remark that a problem existed here which should yield important information through experimental work.

Experiments were begun the same day, and they indicated how the matter was to be pursued. It was found that the purest samples of benzene from coal tar invariably gave the blue color reaction, and that this could be eliminated by extracting or warming the benzene with sulfuric acid. When the sulfo acid obtained by the treatment with sulfuric acid was distilled, an "active" benzene was formed which again showed a positive indophenin reaction.

Three hypotheses were tried in an effort to explain these reactions: (1) Benzene itself is indifferent towards isatin and sulfuric acid; the product from coal tar, however, contains a small impurity which catalyzes benzene so that it reacts. (2) On the other hand, benzene produced from benzoic acid could contain an impurity which cancels the reaction. (3) Benzene from coal tar could be a mixture of two substances, very similar physically and chemically, although one is more reactive than the other; the more reactive one would combine with isatin and be the first to form a sulfo acid in the treatment with sulfuric acid.

The third of these hypotheses proved correct. The isolation of the "more reactive substance" was achieved through its quicker sulfonation reaction. Victor's thiophen book listed more than one hundred papers published by him with a large number of students during the years 1882 to 1887.

On July 13, 1884, Hans Hübner (born 1837) in Göttingen died suddenly of a heart attack, and Victor was proposed as his successor. At that time, his health was poor. In the spring he had had an attack of kidney stones, followed by a neuralgia which became almost unbearable during the summer. The pain markedly depressed his spirits. On October 23, 1884, he wrote about "the hundreds of people who reproach me for intending to leave Zurich . . ." and on October 26: ". . . I assure you that I am the least enviable man in the world, and that with all my outwardly successes and apparent glamor I have time and again wished with all my heart I were a poor artisan but had my health back."

GÖTTINGEN, 1885–1889

Victor arrived in Göttingen on April 23, 1885. He was surrounded by a staff of very able assistants, and work started immediately. Thiophen was still in the foreground. Experiments on vapor densities, which he had started in 1876, were suspended temporarily; a pyrochemical room still had to be built. In the summer of 1886 the number of students in the laboratory was 105 as "against 59 last summer. Even in the best time under Wöhler such a large number had never been reached."

During the lecture on February 4, 1888, there was a violent explosion. "I wish to inform you, in case it should be reported in the newspapers (which I don't hope) that nobody was hurt. The destruction in the lecture room, however, was tremendous. A mixture of air and carbon disulfide had ignited. I am now reading experimental chemistry for the eighteenth time, and yet every year

859

something new happens that one did not know. By the way, how do you like my lecture-experiment on nitrogen chloride? . . . Very often, it has exploded under our hands without harming us, since we were protected. This is one of the most interesting and exciting studies I have ever undertaken."

This way of working was characteristic of Victor. Danger attracted him, whether in the high mountains or at the laboratory bench, but he did not expose himself to it blindly, he met it with the tools of informed prudence. Experimenting was his element, and the lecture on experimental chemistry always was his greatest joy. At that, he was not even especially skillful with his hands, but he had an inventive head, untiring in planning new methods.

The new laboratory building was completed and the dedication ceremony was set for November 15, 1888. At that time something extraordinary happened; its dramatic course is best described in Victor's own words from his letters:

November 11: Strictly confidential! Yesterday I received a highly complimentary official invitation from the Baden Ministery to the chair of Bunsen in Heidelberg. Form and content of the letter are outright fabulous; I have to blush when I read it. . . . Yet this Thursday the new Institute is to be solemnly dedicated. . . . What shall I do in my unhappy state ("ich Unglücksmensch").

November 28: This is a bitter day: I have just declined Heidelberg—in the same hour I receive a telegram that the ground adjacent to Bunsen's laboratory has almost been bought, where I was to build an organic laboratory. Naturally, my resolution is firm and unchangeable, and I don't want to repent it.

December 1: We are taking this matter terribly seriously, and it will be a long time before the wound ceases to bleed.

March 24, 1889: After spending all winter in a feverish excitement about Heidelberg, a second call really arrived . . . it is and remains ungrateful to the Prussian ministery that has done so much for me, and I did not sign but declined for the second time.

Whereupon Emil Fischer received the call to Heidelberg and declined. In the meantime Bunsen had written to the Prussian Ministry, requesting that Victor be released to become his successor, and now Victor finally accepted.

HEIDELBERG, 1889–1897

In a letter dated October 2, 1889, Victor announced his arrival in Heidelberg. "Everything is beautiful and magnificent, but still much disorder and much to be done."

On January 28, 1890, he gave a lecture in Berlin on "Results and aims of stereochemical research." He had introduced the name "stereochemistry" two years before.

About his work Victor wrote on December 11, 1891:

> In the laboratory I am feeling quite well, thank God, I have a large number of very interesting projects. . . . Thus I am assiduously working on the action of CO_2 on H_2, and I am obtaining quite different results from those of previous observers, the same in the combustion of fulminating gas (O_2+H_2). . . . I have such convenient methods now that it is a pleasure to use them. Furthermore I have obtained astounding results in the reaction of chlorine and bromine on the very simplest organic compounds. . . . My nerves are behaving quite a lot better since the start of the semester. It is now one week that we have here the first female student.

On April 29, 1894, he wrote to Baeyer about his first observations which led him to the finding of steric hindrances in chemical reactions: "It is strange that substituted benzoic acids which have substituents to the right and left of COOH are scarcely or not at all esterified by alcohol and hydrochloric acid. The causes are steric and permit a kind of comparative measurement of the size of atoms and radicals.

yields about 95 per cent ester,

yields no ester at all. Methyl acts less repellent than bromine."

861

Among the groups which prevent esterification when present on both sides of a carboxyl is carboxyl itself. Now the question arose whether the twice ortho-substituted carboxylic acids cannot be esterified at all, or whether this occurs only in the reaction with alcohol and hydrochloric acid. The answer resulted from the action of methyl iodide on the silver salts of the acids; the methyl esters were obtained in almost quantitative yields.

The influential size of the substituents in the stereochemical sense is not the same as Kopp's "relative volumes." Stereochemically, methyl and ethyl act exactly like cetyl, $C_{16}H_{33}$. All the steric action of the long atom chain CH—CH . . . CH_3 is exerted only by the first carbon atom in direct bond with the benzene ring.

On July 23, 1895, he wrote to Baeyer: "I have very strongly taken up pyrochemistry again. The other day I built a small oven for vapor-density determinations in which platinum and a 30 per cent iridium-platinum can easily be melted. I should like to measure the density of mercury, iodine, zinc, cadmium and other so-called 'atoms' at 2000 to 3000° C."

At that time he was feeling quite well. However, the summer of 1896 was "one of the worst I ever had," and the beginning of 1897 found him in rather unsatisfactory health. In spite of his illness he was busy with many things, among others the plans for a new large addition to his laboratory building. Thus the summer semester was a very active one for Victor, and he was making plans for a vacation in his beloved Swiss alps.

Then, on August 8, like lightning out of a blue sky, came the news of his death. He had ended his life by taking prussic acid. On a small leaflet, we found these few words, written in a fleeting hand: "Beloved wife! Beloved children! Good bye! my nerves are giving out; I cannot go on."

His friend and neighbor Willy Kühne, director of the Physiological Institute, wrote a few days afterwards: "Already 13 years ago Victor was prevented from taking his own life, unfortunately, he could not be hindered in always being prepared to do it. Since that time he had stood up heroically under the neuralgic pains and sleeplessness, and he overcame them by his gigantic work until the fear of mental collapse . . . seized him in a sudden frenzy."

Selections from the biography by his older brother, Richard Meyer, in *Berichte der Deutschen Chemischen Gesellschaft, 41,* 4505–4718 (1908). Translated by Eduard Farber.

RICHARD MEYER

·· *61* ··

Johan Peter Klason

1848-1937

IN A *Festschrift* which his former students dedicated to their teacher on his sixtieth birthday, Peter Klason published his autobiography. As motif, he used the words from Goethe's Faust: *"Es irrt der Mensch so lang er strebt."* It might be an expression of Peter Klason's conception of himself. During his life as a scientist he often had a feeling of being a Faustian personality—searching and pondering, sometimes doubting himself and the correctness of his theories, his inquiring mind reaching for the goal of his aspiration.

Johan Peter Klason was born on April 4, 1848, the only son of Kristoffer Adam Claesson (1821–1906), manager of the Sannarps estate, later superintendent, and his wife Elsa Helena Claesson, née Billing (1823–1913). His father as well as grandfather and great-grandfather were agricultural superintendents for the property of a landowner of the nobility. They were descendants of a glass blower who had immigrated from Bohemia to Sweden. Klason's father was elected principal of the first agricultural school in Sweden, at Wrangelsro.

His mother was descended from an old family of clergymen in the diocese of Gothenburg. Her maternal grandfather, like her father, had been vestry keepers and "lived," quoting Klason's own words in his autobiography, "a happy existence with music, song, and carousing; besides, he was busy with blood-letting." Peter Klason wrote very little about his parents, but much more about his maternal grandmother and her competence. He was born in the modest cottage of his maternal grandparents near the manor house. Among the many rules his grandmother impressed on him was one which he never forgot: "Beware above all of pride. The deeds of humility are the ones which are everlasting."

At the age of five, Peter went to the mobile grade school which was then situated in his parish, Arstad, but at six he went to the more permanent school at Getinge. When he was nine years old, he started the first class in a school in Halmstad. In his autobiography he tells about the modest conditions in this school, which he attended until 1863, when he was transferred to a private school in Lund. He passed his maturity examination at the public school in Malmo in 1867.

Klason had not made up his mind about his future career. Therefore, he remained at home for a year. Evidently his intention was to be a farmer, but his desire to study was too strong, and in 1868 he entered Lund university and received a diploma in modern education. He was thinking of taking a course in metallurgy, but was discouraged by his friends' descriptions of the long and hard studies, and the difficulties in obtaining a diploma. After the necessary examinations in Latin, his way was open for studies in the humanistic fields, but he changed to a scientific course. The educational staff in the scientific field at the Lund University was remarkable: for botany, Agardh; for zoology, Sven Nilsson; for geology, Torell; and as teacher in chemistry, Blomstrand, to mention only a few names in the faculty of science.

Blomstrand's teaching chiefly comprised organic chemistry and the analysis of minerals. Klason probably spent most of his time on such subjects in the laboratory, at least during his first year. He also followed Blomstrand on his mineral excursions.

Research of the organic sulfur compounds had become a tradition in Lund. It had its origin with the work of William Christopher Zeise (1789–1847), a Dane, who had begun the experiments and produced ethyl mercaptane in 1833. Even Blomstrand was interested in this research. Following Blomstrand's suggestions, Klason wrote his doctor's thesis "On phenyl- and ethyl-sulfacetic acids and sulfonic acids derived from them" and defended it in 1874. He remained faithful to this topic for many years of his research work at Lund. During his years of study he also spent some time at the laboratories of A. W. Hofmann in Berlin, Kolbe in Leipzig, and others in Germany.

Not until 1887 did he become laboratory professor at the chemical institution with a very small salary. One can understand, therefore, that it was necessary for him to seek additional occupations for some extra income. In 1880 he held a teaching job at the Lund Cathedral School. He was thinking of industrial work and tried to qualify for a position in the recently finished gas works in Lund. For this purpose he spent a few months at the gas works in Malmo. Although he was not appointed to the position he wanted, he became president of the board of directors for the Lund Gas and Water Works. In this capacity he was in charge of the first effort to create a modern sewer system in Lund. In earlier times this city was completely without sewers; among the inconveniences ought to be mentioned the fact that the evil-smelling refuse from Klason's sulfur research at the laboratory was simply emptied into the gutter; consequently, the smell was detected throughout the whole town.

His position as controller at the Klippans Brewery also helped to better Klason's economic status. This was his first acquaintance with the brewery trade and was of great importance for his future prospects in the brewery association.

Klason at this time had thoughts of getting married; and naturally he wanted a better economical foundation than the academic career had to offer. The object of his tender passion was Marie Louise Hill, daughter of the well-known professor of mathematics, K. J. Hill.

When the professorship in chemical technology at "KTH" (the Chemical Institute of the Technical University in Stockholm) was open after the death of F. L. Ekman, a substitute teacher was appointed, but Professors Otto Pettersson and L. F. Hilsson found Klason a more suitable permanent representative for the post. For his inaugural lecture Klason chose the topic: "About manufacturing illuminating gas." It was then one of the few branches of chemical technology that Klason knew from personal contact. His chemical qualifications were superior to those of his competitors. As a remarkable sign of the times ought to be mentioned that one of his competitors had chosen the subject "The significance of electricity for the chemical technology." The Swede, Oscar Carlson, in 1890 had applied for a patent on a method to make hypochlorites and chlorates by electrochemical means; this later became the foundation for the electrochemical industry.

Klason was appointed professor on August 19, 1890, and also was named principal of the chemical technical school. He was confronted with many obstacles in his new position; the board of administrators needed his assistance. The chemical laboratory was overcrowded, and it was necessary to build a new one. The number of students had to be increased. The necessity for three or four years of instruction for the chemical technical school was disputed among the teaching staff and the administrators.

Klason once proposed that our universities should create technology departments, including technical botany. Perhaps Klason made this decision because he himself had much interest in botany during his student years. A more cogent reason, however, was that this subject was closely associated with fermentation technology and with wood research, subjects which now interested him to a high degree.

The old laboratories in the south wing of the Technical University had been inadequate, and it was difficult to find room for the study of new subjects. This went so far that the new professor of chemical technology had to give up his apartment in the building, and that the former kitchen of janitor Carlsson had to be used for fermentation studies.

The new building of the technical school was the most important issue during the first ten years of Klason's professorship. I shall not tire the reader by detailing the various difficulties, schemes, and all the different committees with which he had to be in touch before the new building was ready in the fall of 1898.

In Germany Klason had gained many experiences which he used in the laboratory. One could say without exaggeration that it was the most modern and practical laboratory in our country at that time.

The new laboratory building even contained premises for the electrochemical instruction which in Klason's opinion ought to be improved. This subject had been included in the school's curriculum since 1894. At first, the subject was voluntary, but after the faculty had the good fortune to acquire K. W. Palmaer as a teacher, it became compulsory for the students of chemistry in their third-year course. At this time physical chemistry, through Svante Arrhenius' contributions, had broken through the older concepts of chemistry, and it was therefore natural that much of the instruction was in the theoretical part of electrochemistry.

When Klason joined the university, only 80 students were admitted each year. This number increased later to 100, and in 1901 a heated discussion started whether 180 new students ought

870

to be admitted each year. This question was again discussed in 1908 and a number of 240 new students was proposed by the experts.

During his appointment at the Technical University, Klason had to answer a great many questions of chemical import, and in many other ways he came in contact with numerous chemical industries. I shall only mention here the inquiry into arsenic which was in the daily news at that time, caused by the assumption that the paint used in the offices for certain civil service departments in the old *Riksdags* buildings contained poisons. Another inquiry came from a lawsuit between a Swedish sulfite factory and the mining company that had delivered a sulfide ore which contained selenium.

Klason's greatest passion was research in lignin. He was determined to find the chemical composition of lignin of which all wood contains about 30 per cent. He spent almost forty years, particularly the last twenty-five years of his life, on this problem. His visit at the Delary paper mill during his student years aroused his interest in the research of cellulose. The pine trees interested him above everything else.

In his autobiography, Klason pays his homage to the pine trees of the north and he compares them with the palms of the south. He ends with these words: "The forest is our happiness, our comfort and our wealth."

His first results on this subject were announced in a lecture at the chemical association in 1891. His articles in Technical Tidskrift No. 58, (1893), "Contribution to the knowledge of the composition of wood from the pine trees, also the chemical process of manufacturing of cellulose" form the first real advance in Klason's wood chemical research, which comprises more than a hundred articles.

Klason attempted experimental research in conjunction with theoretical speculations in an effort to ascertain the nature of lignin and its chemical composition. He first thought that lignin was close to alizarin. Later on he supported its relationship with coniferin, and he considered it to be built up of coniferyl aldehyde.

During the first years of this century the interest in wood chemistry and wood pulp was very great and Klason found among his assistants and pupils in his technical school of chemistry at KTH many competent fellow workers. It was also at this time that Klason received an appropriation for pure scientific research in this field. He published many of his papers in different periodicals in collected form under the title "Chemical-technical research about Sweden's most important wood." It comprised five volumes, the last one published as late as 1930. This collection contained other subjects from his pen as, for example, articles on arsenic, manufacturing of copper, etc.

Klason did not arrive at a definitive lignin formula, but he made a decisive contribution to the research in this field. Some workers have voiced various objections against his theories, but it is beyond doubt that without his research the chemistry of lignin of today would lack the foundations on which it was created.

Long after his retirement from his professorship at the Technical University Klason continued his research on lignin, partly as a teacher at Skogshogskolan for almost ten years, and partly at the laboratory through the generosity of his successor, Professor Carl Kullgrens. Up to the time of his death he had access to the chemical building of the new Technical University.

I have mentioned Klason's interest in Sweden's brewing industry which began when he served as controller at Klippans brewery; this interest served to identify Klason with zymurgy, a subject which he introduced at the technical university. His fearless action against the extreme temperance movement during the 1890's and, at the same time his support of a sound education which was essential in our land as a safeguard against the misuse of alcohol, pleased the brewing industry very much. Through this action he came in closer contact with the Swedish Brewery Association. He was their chairman for more than thirty years. The association presented to him a gold medal and elected him honorary chairman.

The Swedish Paper and Cellulose Engineers Society demonstrated the same honor in electing him honorary chairman and also bestowed upon him its first Ekman medal in gold.

Klason was also a member of many Swedish and foreign scientific associations. The Academy of Engineers nominated him as their first honorary member in 1920, and in 1943 a medal was stamped in commemoration of him.

In many ways his students at the Technical University demonstrated their high esteem for Klason. He was an excellent teacher and a rare educator who understood the problems of youth. He was not only a teacher of organic chemistry and chemical technology, but in his lectures and in the intimate talks with the students in the laboratory he expressed much of his philosophy of life, his interest in history, art, and political economy.

During a certain period of his life Klason was in rather delicate health. Among other things he was afflicted with phobias and was unable to fulfill his duties as lecturer which therefore were taken over by his assistants. In addition he was somewhat fretful, particularly during the examinations. There is no doubt that his wife's bright and happy outlook on life and endless patience to a great extent overcame the causes of his neuroses which ceased when he was sixty years old.

His two most characteristic attributes were an unyielding integrity and a diligence which was quite inconceivable. He imposed great demands upon himself and others. He gave very little of his time to social life and pleasure, but he put great store on spending his leisure time with persons of similar intellectual interests. He found these companions largely in the academy to which he belonged until 1889 when he was an assistant at the University of Lund.

Further evidence of his quest for intellectual stimulation was his membership in the society called "The Seventeen." There he met such prominent personalities as Oskar Montelius, C. Wahlgren, Yngve Sahlin, and many others. They met monthly in the homes of members in a friendly, informal atmosphere.

Klason was not a friend of modern literature. He read the great classics and such authors as Tegnér and Runeberg in the evenings after he had gone to bed. He quoted with pleasure in his lectures and speeches stanzas from the classics and one might conclude that his whole world of thought dealt with the philosophers of antiquity. But this was not so, as is evidenced by his lifework of practical realities.

A rather moving expression of his admiration for the great Greek thinker Socrates were his words to his son just before his death—indeed his last intelligible words. In the fall of 1936

873

Doctor Torsten Klason and his wife had made an automobile trip and among other places they had visited Athens. Knowing well his father's great interest in the culture of Greece, Torsten Klason tried in his letters to give a detailed description of everything he had seen and experienced. On his deathbed his father asked Torsten: "Did you see the place where Socrates stood before his judges?"

Thus might his last words form a conclusion to the description of Peter Klason's mission in life. With the assurance that he had made use of his talents he could with confidence and trust stand before the Almighty on Judgment Day. His industrious and productive life ended on January 1, 1937.

NOTES AND REFERENCES

Three appendices to the above article give details of Klason's work:
1 Erik Söderbäck, "Peter Klason's research on organic sulfur compounds," pp. 582–604.
2 Bror Holmberg, "Peter Klason's work on lignin chemistry," pp. 605–616.
3 Bibliography by Carl Björkbom, pp. 617–634.
(The last two items are the two articles of 1936 mentioned in the biography.)

From: *Levnadsteckningar över K. Svenska Vetenskapsakademiens ledamöter, 142, 567–581,* Stockholm, Almqvist & Wiksells, 1954.
Translated by Julia Christine Molander.

SIGURD NAUCKHOFF

·· *62* ··

Henry Edward Armstrong

1848-1937

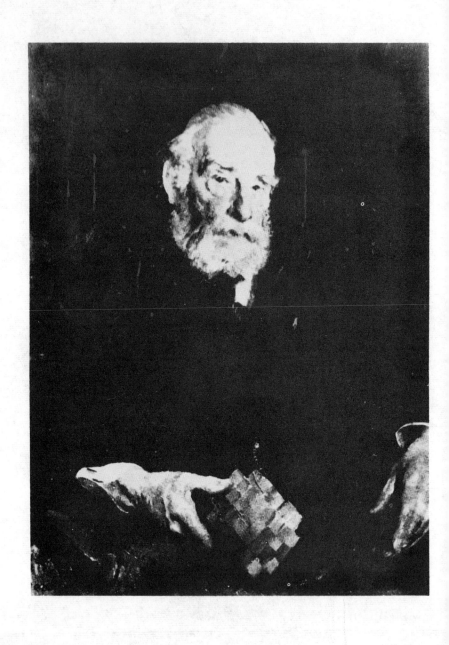

HOW ARMSTRONG would have hated an orthodox memorial lecture about himself. And his memory is so fresh in the minds of his friends that it is difficult not to think of him as present with us tonight. How much we miss his active, fertile brain. In his Frankland Memorial Oration, the lessons of Frankland's career set him thinking, and in the last half of the lecture all Armstrong's pet hobbies appear—the failure of science in education, coal conservation, the problem of nutrition, the value of pure milk, the need for a survey of the world's natural resources—particularly phosphates—ending with a doubt as to the quality of the essay that members of the House of Commons would write on "No Life without Phosphorus." Unfortunately he singled out Mr. Churchill, whose essay we have good reason to know would not be lacking either in appreciation of science or clarity of expression.

There is no need to chronicle the events of Armstrong's life, as that has been done already in the understanding study of his life by his collaborator and friend, his eldest son.

I cannot speak with the advantage of having been one of his pupils, although I was in a sense a step-pupil. I was fortunate to learn chemistry at Dulwich from H. B. Baker, to whom I can never be sufficiently grateful for having taught me both by precept and example that life without research loses much of its zest and excitement. Baker was one of the few schoolmasters who, like Frankland, managed to do research with very slender opportunities. We soon realized that Armstrong was one of his heroes, whose encouragement meant much to him. Baker often went to Lewisham on Sundays to talk over his problems with Armstrong, and on Monday mornings we heard all about it. This made us feel that we were in touch with what was going on in the great scientific world outside.

When the time came for me to be fattened, as Armstrong put it, for the University Shows, Baker told me to buy Armstrong's article on Inorganic Chemistry in the ninth edition of the Encyclopædia Britannica—and here it is. I have always kept it as a talisman, as Kolbe kept his first letter from Berzelius. Written in 1876, when Mendeléeff's generalization was coming into prominence, it was almost the first consistent attempt to arrange the subject matter of chemistry in natural periods. I found it a most welcome relief from the formal textbooks, with its crisp, suggestive summary of each family of the elements, each illustrated with their more important heats of reaction.

I owe my first meeting with Armstrong, as I owe much else at Oxford, to Henry Miers' hospitality. It was rather a nervous moment for an undergraduate to meet Armstrong in his more leonine days. We knew he could be disconcerting. There was the story of the meeting at which there was a slight difference of opinion between the chairman and Armstrong as to the length and relevance of his remarks. When the next speaker began "Mr. Chairman and Gentlemen," Armstrong was heard to murmur. "A very proper distinction on this occasion." But Armstrong forgot that I was one of the "spoon-fed, over-taught, over-provided, over-examined, over-read and under-practiced products" when he heard I was a pupil of Miers and Baker, had been in Munich with Groth and had made geological excursions with Zittel and Rothpletz. I had many a stimulating talk with him, and a happy friendship of more than forty years was unmarred by any clash, although sometimes Armstrong must have been suspicious of my fancy for ions. Once when I spoke to the Science Masters' Association on the Theory of Ionic Dissociation, with Armstrong, an ex-President, sitting in the front row, everyone was expecting a thunderstorm at my expense; I think I escaped because Armstrong knew I was not dabbling in "fair hydrone" but in alcohol even drier than those vintages of which he was such a good judge.

We had many interests in common—crystallography, geology, scenery and John Ruskin. I think Armstrong forgave Ruskin for his hostility to modern science because of his love of crystals, his long study of the geological structure of scenery and his beautiful drawings. I remember what pleasure Armstrong got from Pope's gift of Cook and Wedderburn's Library Edition of Ruskin, with its reproductions of so many of Ruskin's own drawings. He was a great admirer of Ruskin's style and of his fearless advocacy of the causes for which he cared. He thoroughly enjoyed the exuberance of Ruskin's purple passages, the eloquence of his defense of his heroes like Turner, and the invective with which he flayed the pretentious, the complacent, or the insincere. Armstrong, like Ruskin, would take infinite pains to find the right, the inevitable, word, and Ruskin had a genius for coining a word to emphasize his point. Of Sir John Lubbock's list of Best Hundred Books he wrote: "Putting my pen lightly through the needless . . . and blottesquely," as he did, "through the rubbish and poison of Sir John's list—I leave enough for a life's liberal reading." Armstrong probably felt a little envious, for he too was a great fighter.

The longest and most intimate talk I had with him was on a voyage to Morocco in 1936. It began by my asking him about the great chemists he had known in his younger days, and ended in a discussion of the history of organic chemistry when it was taking its modern form, which lasted until we reached Tangier. For me the talk was most revealing, as most of my impressions had come from Odling, Gerhardt's "l'ami Odling," an enthusiast for the French school. Gerhardt and Laurent had always been my heroes. Armstrong, a pupil of Frankland and Kolbe, belonged to the other camp. Kolbe had always been a puzzle to me. I didn't know the story of his partnership with Frankland, and that talk with Armstrong revived an old interest and gave me a much clearer picture of the contributions of the two schools. When I was asked to give this lecture it seemed to me that it would not be inappropriate that the first of this series of lectures paying tribute to his memory should give a sketch of chemistry as Armstrong saw it in his student days and of the men under whose influence he grew up. I only hope I can recapture some of the life and color of the picture that Armstrong gave me.

For Armstrong the history of chemistry was not just a succession of theories, as it is so often painted. He was interested in the personalities of the chemists who made them, their characters, and their practical contributions to the corpus of chemical knowledge. In the period we discussed, the efforts of almost all the outstanding chemists were directed to organic chemistry. It was a period of rapid growth, when there were great discoveries to be made by individuals. Each had his own theory of which he was tenacious, as it meant much to him; it was in a sense the scaffolding which enabled him to make his individual contribution to the structure of chemistry. And Armstrong judged not by the theory but by the results. "By their fruits ye shall know them." And was it not Armstrong who said that "Hypotheses like Professors, when they are seen not to work any longer in the laboratory, should disappear"?

The best landmarks of progress in these years are the great textbooks, not those written by compilers such as Gmelin, useful as they were, but those written by the men who were reshaping organic chemistry in the laboratory, and felt the urge and had the energy and imagination to give their picture of the whole range of the subject. Those milestones were the third edition of the great Lehrbuch of Berzelius translated by Wöhler in the years 1833 to 1841, in which organic substances are classified under their various plant or vegetable origins; Liebig's textbook of 1839 which opens with a brave phrase, echoing Lavoisier, "Organic chemistry is the chemistry of compound radicals," but after starting with compound radicals as a basis of classification he soon relapses into the Berzelian system; Gerhardt's Précis of 1844, using his own classification based on homologous series, his "Introduction to Chemistry by the Unitary Method" of 1848, and the four volumes of his Traité of 1853–56; Kolbe's textbook of 1854–60, written with his shrewd insight into the structure of organic acids; and finally Kekulé's unfinished Lehrbuch of 1859–67 in which organic chemistry began to take its modern form. Here they are as a visual record of Armstrong's conversation during those three unforgettable days.

He began with Laurent and Gerhardt, the two young rebels who saw the weakness of the Berzelian system, and gave their lives to remodelling organic chemistry and giving it a scientific classification based once again on the clear logic of a French mind. Here I was able to contribute something from my many talks with Odling. Armstrong admired the courage and tenacity with which Gerhardt and Laurent fought tradition and authority, fearless of the effects on their personal fortunes, but he deplored the completeness of their ultimate victory which he felt had obscured progress by preventing a full appreciation of the work of Frankland and Kolbe. For me their's is one of the epic partnerships, to be ranked with Lavoisier and Laplace, Liebig and Wöhler, and I would now add Kolbe and Frankland. They suffered almost persecution for their views, and Laurent died as a result of great privation. Their laboratory researches were carried out under incredible difficulties and lack of support, but they had the unquenchable fire of devotion to chemistry.

Laurent, the elder by eight years, was the son of a peasant, Trained as a mining engineer, in 1831, at the age of twenty-four, he was Dumas' lecture assistant, and was working with him on naphthalene and its derivatives. Armstrong was interested in him as one of the earliest chemical crystallographers, for besides preparing a large number of new substitution derivatives of naphthalene he measured their crystalline form and showed that they formed an isomorphous series. This gave added support to the view of the French chemists that in these substitution products chlorine occupied the same position as the hydrogen it replaced. It was probably also the basis of Laurent's theory of nuclei in which he pictured a parent structure with carbon atoms at the angles of a regular polyhedron and hydrogen atoms at the middle of each side replaceable by other groups, with the possibility of additive compounds corresponding to pyramids on the faces. Laurent's nuclei were comparable with Dumas' types, with the added hypothesis of the geometrical structure of the molecules.

Laurent is remembered for his association with Gerhardt and the important influence he had on Gerhardt's views, but he was a most skillful organic chemist, and he added greatly to our knowledge of many groups of organic compounds.

Gerhardt, born in 1816, was the son of an Alsatian chemical manufacturer. He published his first paper, on the classification of silicates, when he was eighteen, and finding the routine of his father's business intolerable, with the help of friends he spent two years with Liebig at Giessen. Returning home he quarrelled once again with his father and set out, at the age of twenty-three, to seek his chemical fortune in Paris, armed with a letter to Dumas from Liebig and 200 francs in his pocket. He kept himself by doing literary work, including the translation of Liebig's textbook, which gave him a wide view of the whole range of organic chemistry as it then was.

Right from the outset Gerhardt seemed to realize the need for some entirely new approach to the problems that were presented by the rapidly growing number of organic compounds. In most of his papers there is an attempt at a generalization, often based, so his opponents said, on insufficient evidence, but Gerhardt had the same sort of vision of a new system as Lavoisier, and each of his main papers marked a step toward the reorganization of organic chemistry at which he aimed.

By 1840 the battle over substitution had been won and the authority of Berzelius had begun to be seriously challenged. For Berzelius as for Lavoisier oxygen was the central element. His massive contribution to chemistry had been built up on Lavoisier's dualistic conception of chemistry, reinforced by the electrochemical theory of chemical affinity. The elements of organic chemistry, for Berzelius as for Lavoisier, were the compound radicals, into whose composition oxygen could not enter, as by definition a radical is an oxide less oxygen. Thus Berzelius wrote the formula of acetic acid $C_4H_6O_3.H_2O$, a combination of the oxide of the radical C_4H_6 with water, which in the acetates was replaced by metallic oxides. That electronegative and electropositive elements like chlorine and hydrogen could occupy the same place in chemical compounds was unthinkable for Berzelius.

But now dualism, the electrochemical theory and Berzelius' conception of radicals had received a severe blow. Even Berzelius' atomic weights were being replaced by those of Gmelin in which the values for carbon and oxygen were halved to make them 6 and 8, respectively. Dumas, Laurent, and others had shown that electronegative elements like chlorine could replace hydrogen atom for atom in organic compounds with little change in properties and, as Laurent showed, without change of crystalline form. Berzelius fought hard against the idea that such a replacement could take place, and assumed that the substitution was accompanied by a change of structure. He gave acetic acid the formula $C_4H_6O_3.H_2O$

and trichloracetic acid $C_2Cl_6.C_2O_3.H_2O$. But the facts were against him, and in 1840 he seized on Gerhardt's conception of bodies like nitrobenzene as conjugate compounds formed by the union of two residues with the elimination of water, the organic radical being called by Gerhardt a "copula." Berzelius' formulas now became conjugate, and substitution was admitted in the copula. Acetic acid was written as $C_2H_6.C_2O_3.H_2O$ and trichloracetic acid $C_2Cl_6.C_2O_3.H_2O$. And so conjugate compounds and copulas, Berzelius' practical admission of defeat, took their place in chemical literature for twenty years. In the hands of Kolbe they were made the basis of an important contribution to structural chemistry.

Gerhardt's paper on nitro compounds which started the idea of conjugate compounds and copulas was followed by work on cymene derivatives which gave him the notion of homologous series of organic compounds. This was the basis of a revolutionary paper in 1842 on the classification of organic substances. Gerhardt now saw the need to ensure that formulas should represent comparable magnitudes. These had been based previously to a large extent on the theory of dualism which he rejected. Following Ampère he insisted that the weights of equal volumes of vapor must represent comparable magnitudes and he first adopted four-volume formulas referred to one volume of hydrogen as unit. But later, realizing that inorganic formulas were on a two-volume basis, he made this the basis of his organic formulas, and he doubled the Gmelin equivalents for carbon and oxygen, thus arriving at practically the same values of molecular and atomic weights as we use today.

In 1844 he published the first volume of his "Précis de Chimie Organique" using the homologous series as the basis of classification together with the chemical families of compounds which contain the same number of carbon atoms and can be derived from one another. Gerhardt having lost faith in dualism, the electrochemical theory, and the Berzelian radicals, turned to a purely empirical outlook, thus avoiding the hypothetical formulas of other chemists, which he regarded as figments of the imagination. He used empirical formulas based on a two-volume basis and he used the word "equivalent" indiscriminately for atomic, molecular, and equivalent weights.

883

The new views roused a storm of opposition from the older chemists, and Berzelius did his best to discredit them in the *Jahresbericht* in which he had reviewed the current chemical literature since 1822. Gerhardt, undaunted by this formidable opposition, determined to get a hearing for his own point of view. In 1845 he founded a new journal, "Comptes Rendus mensuels de Travaux Chimiques," which contained both original papers and a summary by himself of current literature which gave him the opportunity of replying to Berzelius. It was a courageous venture in view of Gerhardt's slender resources, but with his indomitable energy he produced the new journal, completed the second volume of the Précis, and carried on his laboratory researches singlehanded.

In 1844 Gerhardt and Laurent had decided to collaborate. It was a fortunate and stimulating partnership, for Laurent like Gerhardt was seeking a logical basis of classification along rather different lines, and Gerhardt's impetuosity gained much from Laurent's better balanced judgment. Gerhardt had gone too far in his reaction against the older theories, in his use of purely empirical formulas and his neglect of any distinction between atoms and molecules. Laurent pointed this out to him, and Laurent's own constructive contribution to the new system came in 1846 in a paper on the organic compounds of nitrogen. In this he supports Gerhardt's two-volume formulas, and points out that in these formulas the sum of the atoms of hydrogen, nitrogen, and the halogens is always an even number. The examination of apparent exceptions to this rule showed that they were based on incorrect analyses, and numerous revisions of formulas were suggested.

Laurent then applied the two-volume formulas to elementary gases, and showed that their molecules must contain two atoms, which led him to the modern definitions of atom, molecule, and equivalent, and to the explanation of nascent action, which until then had been a mystery.

In 1848 came Gerhardt's final blow at dualism in his "Introduction à l'étude de la Chimie par le système unitaire," in which he classes substances both according to their chemical functions and in homologous series. He uses unitary formulas, and is still skeptical about Laurent's definition of atoms and molecules. He uses the term "proportional number" for both.

Gerhardt's violent reaction against the welter of formulas was natural. For most of them had no practical justification, and in his eyes they merely darkened knowledge. But Laurent now convinced him that he had gone too far in using only empirical formulas, as there certainly were groups of atoms which were transferred from one compound to another in chemical reactions and Gerhardt had already admitted this in his conception of residues and copulæ. It was along these lines that their so-called synoptic formulas were developed.

Their collaboration at this time was difficult, as Gerhardt was in Montpellier and Laurent in Bordeaux, and they met only once. They were eager to be working together in Paris, but the opposition to their views was intense and they were regarded almost as dangerous criminals by the older chemists who controlled all chemical appointments. When Laurent applied for posts, on two occasions they were given to Balard—"Balard who was discovered by bromine" was Laurent's bitter comment.

They criticized Liebig's work on the derivatives of melanine, and particularly his analysis and formula of mellone. Liebig was furious and published a tract "M. Gerhardt et la Chimie Organique," in which he called Gerhardt a highway robber and accused him of stealing other people's belongings and using them himself. Liebig also tried to break up the partnership by telling Laurent that Gerhardt was "un homme sans moralité" and others warned Laurent that his association with Gerhardt would ruin his prospects.

But Laurent's loyalty to Gerhardt was superb. He was now in Paris without an appointment, living by giving lectures and often in great want, but he never hesitated to take Gerhardt's quarrel on his own shoulders. There is a pathetic letter to Gerhardt saying that he has no alcohol or ether and must stop work unless Gerhardt can authorize him to buy 20 francs' worth of chemicals on his account. In another he says, "Poverty has just made me commit a crime—I have sold Masson a bad book on crystallography and the blowpipe for 500 francs."

In 1848 Gerhardt got a year's leave from Montpellier without

885

salary in order to be with Laurent in Paris. In the following year, as no appointment was forthcoming and Laurent had lost a small post he had at the Mint, owing to ill-health, Gerhardt borrowed some money and with Laurent opened a small laboratory where they could work together and make a living by taking pupils. Meanwhile their views were steadily gaining adherents, particularly in England, where Williamson was a stout friend and supporter.

Then came a series of discoveries in other laboratories which had a decisive effect on the development of Gerhardt's views. In 1849 Wurtz prepared the primary amines by the hydrolysis of isocyanates. In the following year Hofmann isolated the primary, secondary, and tertiary amines by the action of ammonia on alkyl iodides, and in the same year came Williamson's historic paper on etherification and his synthesis of ethers by the action of alkyl iodides on the alcoholates of potassium.

The formulas of alcohol and ether and their chemical relationship had been in hot debate for a quarter of a century, and Williamson now established the correctness of Gerhardt's view of their relative molecular magnitudes. He wrote their formulas as derivatives of water by the successive replacement of hydrogen by ethyl thus:

$$\left.\begin{array}{l} H \\ H \end{array}\right\}O \qquad \left.\begin{array}{l} C_2H_5 \\ H \end{array}\right\}O \qquad \left.\begin{array}{l} C_2H_5 \\ C_2H_5 \end{array}\right\}O$$

$$\text{Water} \qquad\qquad \text{Ethyl alcohol} \qquad\qquad \text{Ether}$$

Odling often told me that his contemporaries were never convinced about physical methods for determining molecular weights, but they accepted Williamson's chemical proof of the relative magnitudes of alcohol and ether as decisive. His notes for a lecture I persuaded him to give at Oxford in 1899 on "Chemical Theories under Discussion about the year 1850" contain the following passage: "Dependency then of determination of atomic weights on possibility of determining unit weights—means for determination of unit weights. Conclusions from gas or vapour densities and other physical considerations. Deduction of molecular or unit weight scarcely accepted by physicists and not at all by chemists. Necessity for determination of unit-weights on chemical grounds for

886

establishment of concordance of results with those based on physical grounds."

Gerhardt was no mere theorist as his enemies liked to make out. During these years in Paris, in spite of their difficulties, he and Laurent had a big output of research and the decisive moment came for Gerhardt with his synthesis of the anhydrides of monobasic acids in 1852. Hitherto, apart from Deville's preparation of nitric anhydride, the only anhydrides which had been isolated were those of dibasic acids such as sulfuric and succinic in agreement with Gerhadt's formulas, although dualistic formulas made the existence of monobasic anhydrides equally probable. Gerhardt by the reaction of acid chlorides with the alkali salts of monobasic acids succeeded in preparing a whole series of anhydrides. It was a parallel to Williamson's work on the ethers, when the method of preparation was conclusive evidence of their formulas.

Not only was Gerhardt's work a final proof of the untenability of the dualistic formulas for monobasic acids, but the similarity with the ethers set him thinking, and the paper contains the first statement of his theory of types in which he referred the formulas of organic compounds to four types: water, hydrogen, hydrochloric acid, and ammonia. By the substitution of various organic groupings for hydrogen the different classes of organic compounds could all be represented as derived from these simple inorganic molecules, thus giving a new method of classifying them and showing the relationships of their chemical composition. Gerhardt's type formulas were an unconscious recognition of the different combining powers of the atoms and groups, and led inevitably, I had always thought, to Kekulé's theory of atom linkage.

At this point, when we were discussing the influence of Williamson on Gerhardt, I fortunately asked Armstrong a question that he evidently regarded as very ill-informed. Forgetting for a moment the baptismal names of his first-born and his own early master, I asked whether he thought that Williamson or Frankland had made the greater contribution to chemistry. I was quickly left in no doubt as to his opinion, and only hunger ended his recital of the Kolbe-Frankland saga. No doubt the story was told in full in his Frankland Memorial Lecture, but the manuscript of this was unfortunately lost so I must try and reconstruct it from what Armstrong told me.

Till then Kolbe had always been an enigma to me, as I daresay he is to others. It seems so difficult to reconcile his queer formulas, his apparent conservatism, and his violent attacks on Kekulé and van't Hoff, with his success as a teacher and his great contribution to structural chemistry. Born in 1818, the son of a clergyman, Kolbe's training was under Wöhler at Göttingen, where he met Berzelius and was no doubt brought up by Wöhler in the true Berzelius tradition. His early work with Wöhler was on the chlorination of carbon disulfide to give thiophosgene and carbon tetrachloride. From the former he prepared a series of chlorinated methylsulfonic acids which, following Berzelius, he formulated as conjugate compounds with the radical methyl acting as a copula. Berzelius was delighted at the discovery of a series of analogs to the chloracetic acids. He devoted six pages of the *Jahresbericht* to Kolbe's paper, and won his heart by writing him an encouraging letter which Kolbe kept as a talisman all his life. There is little doubt that the success of this investigation colored the whole of Kolbe's life's work and outlook.

For Gerhardt, rational formulas were only a convenient means of representing the reactions in which a substance might take part, and the same substance could have more than one rational formula. Even Kekulé as late as 1861 still kept this Gerhardtian view. But for Kolbe the conjugate formulas of Berzelius, adapted as we have seen from Gerhardt, meant something real and he set out to try and prove their truth both by analysis and synthesis. Encouraged by the early success of his experiments he never ·wavered from this view, and this explains both his conservatism and the motive power behind his researches. Kolbe had also obtained trichloracetic acid by passing carbon tetrachloride through a heated tube, and hydrolyzing the resulting tetrachlorethylene in presence of chlorine. This was one of the earliest examples of the synthesis of an organic compound from its elements. Most of this work was done in Marburg, where Kolbe had gone in 1842 as Bunsen's assistant, and had learned his methods of gas analysis. In 1845 he came to London as assistant to Lyon Playfair, to carry out the

888

analysis of mine gases for the Commission that was sitting on explosions in coal mines. There he met Frankland, who had just been appointed by Playfair as junior assistant to undertake the analysis of minerals at the School of Geology in Jermyn Street.

Frankland, who was then twenty years old, had begun his chemical career, like Dumas, as a druggist's apprentice. This had taught him little, but a Lancaster surgeon named Johnson, realizing the lack of training of apprentices like Frankland, had made a small laboratory and lecture room to encourage them, and took an active interest in their studies. Struck by Frankland's keenness and ability he got an introduction for him to Lyon Playfair, and then, as Armstrong said, Frankland began "to learn chemistry on the Squeer's principle by making it." Within two years, with the help of Kolbe, he was making chemical history.

Kolbe's heart was in organic chemistry, not gas analysis, He wanted to discover the groupings in an organic compound, to prove the existence of the radicals which Berzelius called copulas. His first success came when he isolated the butyl radical (actually octane) by the electrolysis of a strong solution of valeric acid. He quickly interested the young Frankland in organic chemistry, and together they began a research to try and establish the molecular structure of the fatty acids by synthesis. They prepared ethyl cyanide and on hydrolysis it gave, as they hoped, propionic acid (they called it metacetonic acid), thus proving the existence of the ethyl radical in the acid. Once again the success of a first research was the turning point in a career. When Kolbe returned to Marburg he took Frankland with him to continue their joint research and to learn gas analysis from Bunsen. They first extended their work to methyl and amyl cyanides which gave, as they expected, acetic and caproic acids on hydrolysis. They then tried to isolate the radical ethyl by the action of potassium on ethyl cyanide; they failed to do this but discovered an interesting polymer of ethyl cyanide and investigated its derivatives. After three months in Marburg, Frankland had to return to England to teach chemistry at Queenwood College, a school in Hampshire, where Tyndall was his colleague. There he continued his attempts to isolate hydrocarbon radicals by heating ethyl iodide in sealed tubes with potassium, when he got a mixture of ethylene and ethyl hydride. The experiment was repeated using zinc in place of potassium, but a violent explosion during the analysis of the resulting gas shattered Frankland's eudiometer, and his experiments were held up until he went again to Marburg with Tyndall in the autumn of 1848. Analysis then showed that he had isolated what he called ethyl, which was in fact butane. He continued the work with ethyl and methyl iodides, studying the reactions of the halogens with the hydrocarbon radicals until, on July 12, 1849, in Marburg, came the dramatic discovery of zinc methyl, the first of the organo-metallic compounds. Frankland had added water to the solid residue left after heating methyl iodide with zinc, when a greenish-blue flame several feet long shot out of the tube causing great excitement in the laboratory. Bunsen was at first alarmed lest it should be cacodyl, due to an impurity of arsenic in the zinc, but it was quickly found that the metallic constituent was zinc, and the formula of the new substance proved to be $Zn(CH_3)_2$.

Shortly afterward Frankland was invited by Liebig to spend a semester at Giessen, and there he isolated the radical amyl and began to work on zinc amyl. At the end of the year he returned to England to take Playfair's place as professor at the Civil Engineering College at Putney until 1851, when he went as the first professor of chemistry to the newly founded Owens College in Manchester, where he remained until 1857.

Frankland was quick to see that his discovery of zinc methyl opened up a wide field of research, and he first prepared a number of the alkyl compounds with zinc and tin and later with mercury and boron and made a most careful and systematic study of their properties. He soon realized their importance as synthetic reagents —zinc methyl, he said, "will be capable of replacing electronegative elements in organic or inorganic compounds by ethyl—a kind of replacement which has never yet been attempted, but which the author anticipates will enable him to build up organic compounds from inorganic ones and ascend the homologous series of organic bodies." Frankland was the pioneer in using the organo-metallic compounds in organic synthesis for the next twenty years.

Armstrong often spoke of Frankland's extraordinary practical ability. "I have never met with a more skillful worker, and those early papers of Frankland's in a new and most difficult field bear witness to his great experimental skill and originality. He was a great thinker too, and within three years of his discovery of zinc methyl his study of its analog led him to the first general statement about the combining powers of the elements, afterward known as the theory of valency."

Zinc methyl was similar in constitution to Bunsen's cacodyl which Kolbe regarded as a conjugate compound of arsenic with methyl as a copula. Now according to Berzelius the presence of a copula should not alter the combining power of an element or group: acetic acid for instance had the same basicity as formic acid in spite of the presence of the methyl copula. Cacodyl like arsenic combined with oxygen and the halogens and formed an acid. Hence Frankland expected zinc methyl to behave similarly and was surprised to find that it had no combining power, merely exchanging its hydrocarbon groups for others. A study of the properties of stannous and stannic ethides, and a comparison of the formulas of cacodyl and organic antimony compounds convinced him that elements had a definite combining power and that the attachment of each methyl group reduced by one their power to combine with other elements. "No matter what the character of the uniting atoms may be, the combining power of the attracting element, if I may be allowed to use the term, is always satisfied by the same number of these atoms."

The paper containing this generalization which was to transform chemical theory was communicated to the Royal Society in May, 1852, but was not published for twelve months as it was mislaid by the Secretary (Professor, afterwards Sir, Gabriel Stokes), and Frankland thought it had not been thought worthy of publication. A delay at this critical moment was most unfortunate as, to quote Armstrong, "the problem first solved by Frankland was in the air—chemists everywhere had it in mind, especially in France." Gerhardt's types were a partial recognition of the same principle, extended by Williamson to multiple types with polyvalent radicals, the valency or atomicity of which was first indicated by Odling by the familiar dashes. But Frankland was the

first to see that there is a general law of atomicity or valency underlying chemical combination.

Meanwhile Kolbe had left Marburg in 1851 to spend three years
in editing Liebig's and Wöhler's "Dictionary of Chemistry" for
Vieweg, and in 1854 the first part of his "Textbook of Organic
Chemistry" was published. In the introduction he makes his own
position quite clear. He still regards the radical theory as the safest
basis for teaching chemistry and says that he belongs to the conservative party of chemists. He attacks Gerhardt and Laurent for
their unsound generalizations, and for the type theory. "Chemistry
is something more than a mere arithmetical exercise into which
Laurent and Gerhardt think they can convert it." He attacks Williamson's and Gerhardt's formulas for alcohol and ether on the
ground of the products of electrolysis of alcoholates. He refuses
even to accept Frankland's ideas on atomicity, as he would not
admit that electronegative elements could be replaced by electropositive radicals such as methyl and ethyl. His formulas are based
on dualism using Berzelius' copulas and Gmelin's equivalents. Not,
it would seem, a promising beginning! But Kolbe's strength was in
the laboratory and he collects for the first time in one chapter all
the methods of preparing derivatives of organic compounds by
means of chemical reagents, which have since become standard: —
oxygen and oxidizing agents, reducing agents, halogens, phosphorus
pentachloride and oxychloride, nitric and nitrous acids, and sulfuric acid. His classification of compounds is partly by radicals and
partly by acids and their derivatives, to our knowledge of which
he was to contribute so much.

The difference of opinion between Kolbe and Frankland was
soon settled by correspondence between them. Kolbe accepted
Frankland's theory and in 1857 they published a paper "On the
Constitution of the Fatty and Aromatic Acids, Aldehydes, Ketones, etc., and their Relation to Carbonic Anhydride," giving their
joint view that the oxygen atoms in oxides of metals and nonmetals
can be replaced by the same number of atoms of a positive atom
or radical, the replacement being accompanied by an increase in the
base properties of the compound. (Frankland's name was accidentally omitted as a joint author with Kolbe, but the paper

throughout uses the pronoun "we.") Thus Frankland had an important influence in changing Kolbe's outlook and even before their joint paper Kolbe was teaching that organic compounds can be regarded as derived from carbonic acid by the replacement of oxygen atoms by radicals. In this he was following a suggestion made by Liebig in 1847 in a paper on the chemical processes underlying respiration. Kolbe elaborated the theory in 1860 in his classical paper on "The Natural Relation between Organic and Inorganic Compounds," and it was the basis of his pioneer work which revealed the structure of so many organic compounds.

Using atomic weights of 6, 8, 16 and 35.5 for carbon, oxygen, sulfur, and chlorine, respectively, he first wrote formulas as follows:

Dibasic carbonic acid	$2HO.C_2O_4$
Monobasic methyl carbonic or acetic acid	$HO.C_2(C_2H_3)O_3$
Acetic aldehyde	$C_2(C_2H_3)H\ O_2$
Acetone	$C_2(C_2H_5)\ O_2$

Then realizing that the basicity of the acid was related to only two of oxygen atoms in C_2O_4 since it vanished when these two were replaced by other atoms or radicals, he distinguished between the oxygen inside and outside the radical $[C_2O_2]$ to which he gave the name carbonyl:

Carbonic acid	2HO.	$[C_2O_2], O_2$
Formic acid	HO. H	$[C_2O_2], O$
Acetic acid	HO. (C_2H)	$[C_2O_2], O$
Acetaldehyde	$\left.\begin{array}{c} H_2C_3 \\ H \end{array}\right\}$	$[C_2O_2]$
Ethyl alcohol	HO. $\left\{\begin{array}{c} C_2H_3 \\ H_2 \end{array}\right.$	C_2, O
Unknown alcohols	HO. $\left\{\begin{array}{c} C_2H_3 \\ C_2H_3 \\ H \end{array}\right.$	C_2, O
	HO. $\left\{\begin{array}{c} C_2H_3 \\ C_2H_3 \\ C_2H_3 \end{array}\right.$	C_2, O
Propionic acid	HO. (C_4H)	$[C_2O_2], O$
Lactic acid	HO. $\left(C_4\begin{array}{c} H_4 \\ HO_2 \end{array}\right)$	$[C_2O_2], O$
Glyceric acid	HO. $\left(C_4\begin{array}{c} H_3 \\ HO_2 \\ HO_2 \end{array}\right)$	$[C_2O_2], O$

893

These formulas, clumsy as they may seem to us, were based on Kolbe's own study of organic compounds and their synthesis. They had a very real significance for him and by comparison he considered Gerhardt's type formulas superficial and lacking in any fundamental basis. Having always two atoms of carbon in place of one must have made it difficult for him to appreciate the theory of atomic linkage, but he used his formulas with an uncanny instinct to predict the existence of unknown compounds, such as the secondary alcohols discovered by Friedel in 1862 and the tertiary alcohols by Butlerow in 1864, using Frankland's zinc methyl as a synthetic reagent. But more important still was the use he made of them in directing the research in his own laboratory to the elucidation of the structure of more complex organic substances. Outstanding examples of this are: the reduction of malic and tartaric acids to succinic by Schmitt in 1860, Kolbe's own researches on the constitution of lactic acid and alanin, and his synthesis of taurine in 1862, Volhard's synthesis of sarcosine in the same year, von Oefele's discovery of the sulfine and sulfone compounds in 1864, Kolbe's synthesis of malonic acid from cyanacetic acid in the same year, and finally his synthesis of salicylic acid and his discovery of nitromethane almost simultaneously with Victor Meyer.

While Kolbe was making these outstanding contributions to the synthesis of organic acids and to our knowledge of their constitution, Frankland was also active in the same field. In 1857 he left Manchester to get more time for research at St. Bartholomew's Hospital and in 1863 he succeeded Faraday at the Royal Institution.

With the help of the zinc alkyls Frankland, working with Duppa, synthesized a number of new members of the lactic acid series from which they prepared the corresponding acrylic acids and their derivatives. Finding that when ethyl acetate is heated with sodium a large volume of hydrogen is evolved they determined to utilize this reaction for the synthesis of higher members of the fatty acid series. In the course of this work they isolated acetoacetic ester independently of Geuther and used it to synthesize a large number of fatty acids, ketones, and ketonic esters.

894

Thus both Kolbe and Frankland, working outward from their early joint researches on independent lines, made a great contribution to synthetic chemistry just at the time when the theory of atomic linkage enabled such knowledge to be applied to the structure of organic chemistry. When Duppa died in 1873 Frankland's interest in organic chemistry seemed to lapse, but Kolbe was active until his death in 1884.

When the Kolbe-Frankland saga was ended Armstrong and I went back to where we had left Gerhardt and Williamson and the type theory in 1853, when Kekulé, the maker of modern organic chemistry, was just coming on the scene.

Gerhardt's types had an immediate success with the younger chemists. Williamson at once extended them to include multiple types to cover the case of polyatomic radicals and polybasic acids:

$$\left.\begin{matrix} SO_2'' \\ H_2 \end{matrix}\right\}O_2 \qquad\qquad \left.\begin{matrix} PO''' \\ H_3 \end{matrix}\right\}O_3$$

Odling introduced mixed types and indicated the atomicity of the radicals by the well-known dashes.

It was tragic that Laurent should have died in 1853 just when the long fight was practically over and Gerhardt's system to which he had contributed so much was winning general acceptance. Laurent had sacrificed everything for science and had achieved so much in the face of great difficulties. He died exhausted by the long struggle against poverty and against almost fanatical opposition.

In 1854 Gerhardt tasted success. He was appointed to a professorship at Strasbourg, where he was to build a new laboratory, and by the irony of fate he was asked to write the new edition of Berzelius' "Organic Chemistry." He accepted on condition that he could use his own classification in homologous series and chemical families, but at long last he had learnt the value of compromise. Only in the final chapters on Generalities does he use his type formulas and his own atomic weights; in the body of the work he uses Gmelin numbers and even gives the dualistic formulas. When Pebal asked him why he had not used his own clearer presentation

895

throughout, he laughed and answered, "Then nobody would have bought my book!"

In the final chapters he expounds his type theory, and shows how the formulas of organic substances can be derived from four types by the substitution of hydrogen by radicals or residues. Radicals he defined as groups of atoms which can be exchanged in double decompositions but cannot be isolated. "Chemical formulæ are not intended to represent the arrangement of the atoms in a molecule, but their object is to show in the simplest and most exact way the relation between substances." Gerhardt regarded his formulas as contracted ch emical equations, and while therefore substances might have more than one formula, most could in fact be represented by only one.

These chapters were his last legacy to science, as he died suddenly in 1856, when he was correcting the proofs, at the age of forty.

Gerhardt's interest was in classification, in finding a system within which the rapidly growing multiplicity of organic compounds would find their logical place, thus making possible the scientific study of their properties and relationships. He was skeptical as to the possibility of ever knowing the actual atomic structures of molecules. His formulas were formulas of convenience, but the progress he had made and the order he and Laurent had introduced were destined very quickly in the hands of Kekulé to give organic chemistry its modern form.

Kekulé after studying chemistry under Liebig from 1849 to 1851 spent a year in Paris, where he met Gerhardt who gave him the manuscript of his treatise to read. This left a lasting impression on him, and as Armstrong said "he was enthralled by Gerhardt." In 1853 he came to London as assistant to Stenhouse who was then Chemist to the Mint. In London he saw a great deal of Williamson and Odling, both enthusiasts of the Gerhardt school, and he always said that his structural theory was born in his dream about atoms on the top of an omnibus between Islington and Clapham Road, where he lodged. In 1856 he went to Heidelberg as *Privatdozent,* and his investigations of the constitution of mercury fulminate led him in 1857 to recognize the tetravalency of carbon and to add to Gerhardt's types the marsh gas type. In 1858 he developed the idea at length in a paper on "The Constitution and Metamorphosis of Chemical Compounds and the Chemical Nature of Carbon," and the first parts of his Lehrbuch were published in 1859.

Kekulé recognizes at the outset that the hydrogen, water, and ammonia types, to which he had added the marsh gas type, are only the recognition or expression of the combining powers of the elements or radicals, and he uses Odling's dashes to indicate their atomicity or basicity or what we call valency—but he made no reference to Frankland. His rational formulas are based on Gerhardt's types, and he explains in almost the same words as Gerhardt that these rational formulas are only reaction formulas, not constitutional formulas, and that they do not express the relative positions of the atoms in the compound. He emphasizes this "as some chemists seem to think that they can determine the constitution of compounds from their reactions." In any case, says Kekulé, this would need a perspective drawing and cannot be shown by the arrangement of atoms in one plane. Chemistry, he said, will never reveal the structure of the molecule, but possibly physics may.

When Kekulé comes to consider the carbon compounds in detail his great advance was the recognition of the formation of carbon chains with either single or multiple links between the carbon atoms, but he did not seem to realize the power of the instrument he had constructed. He wrote a few graphic formulas for two carbon bodies, such as acetic acid, which show accurately their constitution for the first time on a valency basis. He realizes that the properties of the atoms are dependent on their relative position in the molecule, and yet he does not apply these formulas to substances containing three carbon atoms when they would have explained the isomerism of the lactic acids, as he says that they cannot give a true picture of the positions of the atoms. The isomerism of ethylene dichloride and ethylidene dichloride is left unsolved when the solution is ready at hand if he had used his graphic formulas consistently. He criticizes the use of the formulas used by Kolbe in which the difference between alcoholic

897

and acidic hydrogen is explained. "Such formulæ have no advantage," he says, "over the type formulæ, they conceal a number of analogies and in other cases suggest analogies where none exist."

All this shows Kekulé was suffering from what Armstrong called "Gerhardtism," and that at this time he did not realize the full value of the new instrument he had put into chemists' hands. Gradually its value dawned on him, and he used it with greater confidence. The first volume of the Lehrbuch was completed in 1861, the second volume on aromatic compounds based on Kekulé's benzene ring appeared in 1866, and the third volume was never finished. Kekulé gave organic chemistry its modern form and fifty years later physical analysis, as he had predicted, established the reality of the formulas as to which he was at first so skeptical.

Kolbe never forgave Kekulé for his advocacy of Gerhardt's type theory, for his failure in the Lehrbuch to make any recognition of Frankland's contribution to the theory of valency or atomicity, and for his rather scornful reference to Kolbe's own work. For twenty years he lost no opportunity of attacking Kekulé's views and giving Frankland the credit that was his due. It is a curious example of how far personal ties can warp the judgment of one who had himself made such great contributions in the same field. Armstrong said that when he left Kolbe early in 1870 "he was already peculiar; he afterwards, in his last years, so fixed his mind upon certain grievances as to be little short of a monomaniac." Victor Meyer, and there can be no better judge, sums up the Kolbe paradox in a sentence: "Zwar wurde Kolbe in seinen späteren Jahren ein unermüdliche Bekämpfer der Valenztheorie, doch hat grade er in erster Linie zur Klarlegung des Valenzbegriffs beigetragen."

Armstrong's final word on the Kolbe-Kekulé controversy was in his review in *Nature* of Anschütz's "Life of Kekulé": "Nothing is more certain than that most of us only take in new ideas through experience—the want must be felt before it can be satisfied. Once assimilated, an idea is expelled or modified with great difficulty. It is that that makes scientific thought, the scientific habit of mind, so difficult of attainment. Kekulé at once fell victim to Gerhardt's magic influence, when he met him in Paris. His belief in Ger-

hardt's system became strengthened, in London, through association with Williamson and Odling. He does not seem to have been
intimate with Frankland. He appears to have been so satisfied
with the superiority of Gerhardt's system, that he took little, if
any, notice of Kolbe's work: I do not believe that he ever mastered
the inner meaning of Kolbe's formulæ. Kolbe had little use for the
Gerhardt formulæ, knowing that he had penetrated deeper than
they carried him. I feel sure he resented the way in which he and
Frankland were waved aside by Kekulé: and probably, this was the
subconscious, if not conscious, primary cause of the bitterness he
displayed towards him, in later life. In addition he was a linguistic
purist and idealist, and was greatly annoyed by Kekulé's at times
flamboyant masterful style. As I have said elsewhere, Kolbe's doctrine was ever the Pauline 'Alles prüfen'—Prove all things! He
took exception, therefore, to what he thought to be Kekulé's dogmatic, if not arrogant, declarations. Intellectually, Kekulé probably
was Kolbe's superior, but not as a constructive worker. Frankland
and Kolbe's synthesis of acetic acid (1846) is one of the most clear-
cut achievements in the early history of the development of the
doctrine of chemical structure: Kekulé seems never to have grasped
its significance and the extent to which it put their work in advance of his."

My last talk with Armstrong before we reached Tangier was
about the final episode in the battle of atomic weights, the Karlsruhe Conference.

In spite of the success of Gerhardt's classification among the
younger chemists, the gradual realization of the combining powers
of elements, and Kekulé's application of this idea in the theory of
atom linking, chemistry in 1859 was still in chaos. There was no
general agreement as to the basis of atomic weights or molecular
magnitudes, and the various formulas proposed for acetic acid
covered a page in Kekulé's Lehrbuch.

Kekulé saw that the acceptance of his theory of atomic linking
depended on agreement about atomic weights, and in the autumn
of 1859 he suggested to Weltzien, professor of chemistry at Karlsruhe, the idea of a chemical conference to discuss some of the
fundamental issues that were in dispute. Weltzien met Kekulé and

Wurtz in Paris, and they sent a joint letter to their colleagues abroad asking their views as to the usefulness of such an international gathering. As a result an invitation went out from the organizers inviting them to a three-day conference at Karlsruhe on September 3, 1860. Over a hundred chemists came from almost every European country; Liebig, Wöhler, and Mitscherlich were absentees, but most of the active workers were present, so that the organizers must have hoped for great results. But there is a sentence in Gerhardt's treatise which proved only too true a forecast.

"What I do not understand is that when chemists meet for discussions, each speaking his own language, such discussions are always fruitless, even when the chemists are in complete agreement as to the facts—either because, without realizing it, each expresses the same facts in a language which his opponent does not understand or because they all give to formulæ a significance they cannot have, that of representing molecular structure."

Weltzien presided at the first session, and at Kekulé's suggestion a small committee with Hermann Kopp as chairman was nominated to draw up questions for discussion by the conference. This committee, like others, grew until it contained more than half the members of the conference, and its meetings took up much of the time. Cannizzaro at its first meeting proposed that Avogadro's hypothesis should be adopted as the basis for determining molecular size. This was not agreed, and at the second session the questions for discussion were:

1. Is it convenient to make a distinction between the terms "molecule" and "atom"?
2. Should the term "compound atom" be replaced by "radical" or "residue"?
3. The idea of equivalents is empirical and independent of the idea of atoms and molecules.

This session was presided over by Boussingault, a chemist of the older school, who did not give it a clear-cut lead by his opening remark that it was chemists and not chemistry that got out of

900

date. The discussion was abortive, and the questions were remitted back to the committee, which produced three new subjects for decision at the last session presided over by Dumas:

1. Is it desirable to make chemical notation conform to the progress of the science?
2. Is it convenient to adopt anew the notation of Berzelius with some necessary modifications?
3. Is it desirable to distinguish by special signs the new chemical symbols from those in use fifteen years ago?

Cannizzaro immediately rose to attack the second proposal. It was illogical, he said, to go back to Berzelius in view of the advance made by Gerhardt's classification and his formulas based on Avogadro. After a eulogy of Gerhardt he pointed out certain inconsistencies in his atomic weights which could be remedied with the help of specific heats and the law of isomorphism. Realizing, perhaps, that he was not carrying his audience with him, he ended with a compromise: "If we cannot agree to accept the new system, do not at any rate decide against it, as it is gaining supporters daily . . . and let us adopt the barred atoms to express the doubled atomic weights."

Cannizzaro's speech gained no supporters. Strecker pointed out that the name of Gerhardt had been replaced by that of Berzelius by a majority vote of the committee. Erdmann argued that the issue was not clear enough to take a vote on it. Odling with his usual clarity of mind insisted that at any rate they could agree that an element can have only one atomic weight. Speeches by Kopp, Erlenmeyer, Lothar Meyer, Boussingault, and Will were indecisive, and Kekulé said that decisions as to theory and nomenclature could not be made compulsory by a vote, but that the discussion had been useful. Dumas summed up in similar words, and the sole conclusion reached by the conference was that barred atoms should be used to indicate those atoms whose atomic weights had recently been doubled.

So the first international chemical conference broke up in a somewhat chilly mood without fulfilling the hopes of the organizers, just as Gerhardt would have predicted. But it was not without results, for on the last day Pavesi had distributed a small pamphlet in a yellow cover, a reprint of a letter Cannizzaro had written to Luca in 1858 outlining a course of lectures in which he explained to his students the causes of the present uncertainties as to atomic and molecular weights. His exposition of the historical difficulties and their avoidance by the consistent use of the laws of Avogadro and Dulong and Petit was so clear and convincing that, as Lothar Meyer said, when he read it "the scales fell from my eyes, doubts disappeared and were replaced by a feeling of certainty." All the difficulties that had stood in the way of a general acceptance of Avogadro's law were resolved and the need of such relics of past controversies as the use of barred atoms disappeared. This made it possible for the theory of atomic linking to develop on a firm basis. However, it took some little time before all chemists accepted Cannizzaro's reformed atomic weights. Armstrong said that when he began to learn chemistry, two formulas for water, HO and H_2O, were still in use.

And this brings us to Armstrong's own training, which began in 1865, the year that saw the birth of the benzene ring, which was to absorb so much of Armstrong's thought and work. He "just slid into chemistry" under Frankland at the Royal College of Chemistry, and the story is best told in his own words. After four terms, "Frankland saw, I think, that to keep me at lessons was waste of time: at all events, he wanted someone to help him and paid me the compliment of asking me to work for him. . . . We were mainly concerned in devising methods for the determination of organic impurity in sewage and of sewage-matter in drinking waters. Frankland gave me only the barest instructions and left me to do the experimental work—the experience was invaluable: through it, at the age when I was only due conventionally to attend either Oxford or Cambridge, I became a confident, independent worker.

"I have always taken it as a high compliment and proof of his unselfishness that he advised me, in the summer of 1868, to go abroad and study under his old friend and companion at arms, Kolbe, then Professor at Leipzig."

902

Kolbe was "one of the most thorough and typical Germans of the old school it has been my good fortune to meet, a chemist who received but scant justice even from his own countrymen—few realise the extent to which he was the founder of our modern system of constitutional formulæ—because he dared to criticize and expressed himself in the biting terms of a clear and concise diction, in a pure German which no one else in those days had at his command: in fact, he took his countrymen greatly to task for their slovenly language. Of course, I was received with utmost cordiality. I well recollect how, on the afternoon of my arrival, Kolbe took me into his private laboratory and carried out with me the nitration of a quantity of phenolparasulphonate by means of sodium nitrate and sulphuric acid. He then suggested that I should take up the study of the mixture formed on sulphonating phenol. In those days we had not yet learnt even to distinguish three isomeric monoderivatives of benzene and phenol*ortho*sulphonic acid was unrecognized. It was at this time that Kolbe began 'to slang' Kekulé over his benzene formula—I had not even heard of this before going to Germany. Such was my introduction to the "aromatics' and the beginning of my affection for sulphonic acids. . . .

"Kolbe's laboratory, in those days, afforded wonderful opportunities. About a dozen of us were doing advanced work, in preparation for the Degree—seeking independence. Each had his *Arbeit*—his definite problem—in view, as his chief aim in life: we were all proud of being called on to show that we could do something. This was the distinctive feature of the German system. At most two or three had themes from the Professor—the rest were carrying out ideas of their own; the work was, therefore, varied. Whatever suggestion we made to Kolbe, he never discouraged us; his habit was to grasp the lapels of his coat, then to reply: 'Try it, try it.' We disputed with him constantly before the blackboard, often for hours together, nearly always taking exception to his theoretical views—but without his being offended. And we constantly compared notes together. Each of us, therefore, was interested in the solution of a whole series of problems."

Armstrong stayed at Leipzig till 1870, and these years with Kolbe left their mark on him. From Frankland he had learnt experimental technique, confidence in his power to attack a problem and the call of research. But Frankland was an individualist; he never founded a school, and as Armstrong said of him: "Frankland was so thrown upon himself, he so developed the art of self-help that he never learnt to order and use others sufficiently, which is the teacher's art; he kept counsel with himself." Frankland was a fine lecturer, but he disliked the routine of laboratory teaching.

Kolbe, on the other hand, was an outstanding teacher, and a great inspirer of research. In spite of his theoretical eccentricities, students flocked to his laboratory as they had previously gone to Liebig at Giessen. Armstrong owed to Kolbe his introduction to aromatic chemistry which came to be his most continuous and active scientific interest, and from him he learnt the value of that daily intercourse with students in the laboratory. Probably, too, his own provocative attitude toward easily accepted theories was influenced by Kolbe's hard hitting polemics.

Wherever Armstrong taught—at the London Institution, at the Finsbury Technical College, or at the City and Guilds Central College—his students were trained in method, they learnt to think for themselves. The result is seen in the unceasing flow of papers that came from his laboratory for half a century, inspired by him and representing the work of men who had the privilege of working side by side with him in the laboratory.

Although those papers contain no outstanding discovery, they covered many fields, and were a great contribution to our knowledge of the orientation of aromatic derivatives, the structure of the terpenes, the nature of enzyme action, and the morphological relations of the crystals of organic compounds. Armstrong always chose problems of real significance, but perhaps his greatest contribution was the stimulus he gave to his colleagues, his students, and his friends.

His mind was constantly ranging over a much wider field than chemistry, and while that may have diminished the intensity of his work on specialized subjects, it was the secret of his personality. I rather think that nature had meant him to be a biologist, as he had the eye and instincts of a naturalist, and a great love and understanding of living things; and he had too an intuitive perception of the things that matter to human life.

Armstrong was both a prophet and a pioneer. In so many directions he saw things ahead of his time, and having seen them, like his favourite writers, Ruskin and Carlyle, he lost no opportunity of preaching the gospel in trenchant phrases—the place of science in education, methods of teaching, the effect of diet on health, the value of fresh food, especially milk, the place of science in agriculture, the need for surveys of natural resources, fuel efficiency, and conservation. His utterances on all of them had the prescience that sets men's minds stirring long before the current of thought and knowledge has made things obvious. Christ's Hospital and Rothamsted were the larger laboratories where many of his ideas bore fruit.

In 1916, Armstrong was one of those who saw most clearly that when the war was over we had to face "a more enduring and difficult struggle in the fields of industry and commerce. The race will be neither to the swift nor the strong, so much as it will be to the intelligent and the persevering." He saw that coal was a key factor in our national economy. "At present our nation is without a coal conscience; get one it must without delay. In some way the public must be made to realise how absolutely coal touches our civilization at every point." Armstrong was a persistent and forceful advocate of the need for scientific method in the use of our national coal resources, and his was one of the voices that led to the formation of the Fuel Research Board in 1917. But it took yet another war to drive home the need for fuel efficiency that Armstrong saw so clearly thirty years ago.

Armstrong had both a very active brain and a pen that could keep pace with the rapidity of his thoughts, aided by wide reading and a responsive memory. All his occasional papers and addresses had such vigour and freshness and a character of their own. Today they are scattered and inaccessible, and a little volume of them would be a most fitting memorial to Armstrong's memory.

NOTES AND REFERENCES

J. Vargas Eyre, "Henry Edward Armstrong," London, Butterworths Scientific Publications, 1958.

Richard Willstätter, "Henry Edward Armstrong," *Nature,* vol. *120,* 1 (1927).

From the First H. E. Armstrong Memorial Lecture, delivered before the Society of Chemical Industry at the Royal Institution on November 21, 1945, published in *Chem. & Ind., 50,* 398–402, 406–410 (1945). This lecture, reprinted here with omission of a few paragraphs, includes biographical sketches of Auguste Laurent, 1807–1853; Carl Charles Friedrich Gerhardt, 1816–1856; Edward Frankland, 1825–1899; Hermann Kolbe, 1818–1884; and Friedrich August Kekulé, 1829–1896.

SIR HAROLD HARTLEY, F.R.S.

·· 63 ··

Henry Le Chatelier

1850-1936

Dabrowska. 1926

IN MAY of 1934, it was the writer's privilege to present a certificate of honorary membership in the American Ceramic Society to Henry Le Chatelier at his residence, 75, rue Notre-Dame-des-Champs, Paris. Professor Le Chatelier had just returned from the Eleventh International Congress of Pure and Applied Chemistry in Madrid, where the honorary degree of Doctor of Science had been conferred upon him by the University of Madrid. Although he was in his eighty-fourth year, this tall, slender, white-haired scholar of France evidenced a clarity of mind which might have been the envy of a young man. While folding the diploma of the American Ceramic Society in the quaint old parlor, he reminisced about his earlier work. He was fully informed on the latest developments in the fields of chemistry, metallurgy, and glass technology. He had retired from active service, but held the title of Emeritus Minister of Mines of France, and still served as consultant to the ministry. Later, in the old garden with its giant trees, Professor and Madame Le Chatelier graciously posed for motion pictures. There was an ever-present look of mutual solicitude on the faces of this interesting old couple.

Henry Le Chatelier was born in Paris, on October 8, 1850. He was the son of Louis Le Chatelier (1815–1873) who was Inspector General of Mines for France. His father was one of the engineers who created the French National Railways, in whose interests he worked from 1855 to 1868. He was consulting engineer to bankers who financed the railway systems, not only of France, but also of Spain, Austria, and Russia. He was an associate of H. de Sainte-Claire Deville in the establishment of the first aluminum industry of France, and of Sir William Siemens with whom he constructed the first open hearth steel furnace.

His mother, Elisabeth Durand, came from a family of artists and scientists which included sculptors, engravers, and geographers. She was an ardent Catholic and through her own early environment and her love of poetry fostered in her son that appreciation of art and letters which was evident throughout his life.

His mother was a rigid disciplinarian and so directed the lives of her children that they would not only prove concientious as students, but appreciate physical well-being and rest, as well. Henry arose early each morning and prepared his lessons. Later, on entering the École Polytechnique (1869), he would go to his father's study each morning at 7:30 and review his lessons for the day. He learned to respect law and order, and he enjoyed the almost military attitude in the École Polytechnique. Even his grandfather was a factor in determining Henry's career. He operated lime kilns, and during his vacations Henry would visit his grandfather's plants where he acquired his first interest in mortars and cements.

While Henry was at the École Polytechnique he assisted his father and, as the latter received visitors who were interested in the fields of agriculture, medicine, chemistry, and metallurgy, the son gained valuable experience. To observe the analytical mind of his father and the manner in which he solved problems was helpful. Not only would the father teach him mathematics, but he would provide him with essays on chemistry which had been written by Sainte-Claire Deville, Debray, Dumas, Chevreul, and others of his associates. The boy read the reports of the French Academy of Sciences. He was permitted to assist his father when the latter helped create the aluminum industry, and thus gained much first-hand information about this new metal. Sainte-Claire Deville permitted the lad to work in his laboratory and cooperated with the father in guiding the son's efforts. Henry Le Chatelier stated many years later that the influence of his father and the contacts with his father's associates were important influences in "shaping his career and establishing that reputation which he held as a chemist."

While we are considering his father, mother, grandfather, and others who influenced Henry's career, it might be interesting to note that his own brothers and sister were also interested in science. His brother Louis was a bridge and railway engineer, and constructed steel plants. Alfred was an army officer and had much to do with the development of the French colonial empire. This brother worked on high temperature enamels. His brother George was an architect. A fourth brother, André, the oldest of the children, worked with Henry in creating the autogenous welding industry and devised methods for the safe storing of liquid acetylene. He studied the resistance of metals to high temperatures, and devised metal lath, which is still in use. This substitute for wood possessed a much greater strength and was fireproof. The sister, Marie, married a Dr. Leroux who was a pediatrician.

Henry's early education was obtained in Paris where he attended a military academy for a short time and then entered the Collège Rollin, receiving the Bachelor of Letters in 1867 and Bachelor of Science in 1868. He entered the École Polytechnique in 1869 but his work was interrupted by the War of 1870. His studies were completed in 1872, and he registered as a mining engineer. In 1874 he was licensed to practice physical science. In 1877 he became professor in the École des Mines. In 1882 he was lecturer in the École Polytechnique. In 1883 he became professor in the Collège de France and later professor at the Sorbonne. The degree of Doctor of Physical and Chemical Science was conferred upon him in 1887, when he became professor of industrial chemistry and metallurgy in the École des Mines. Until 1897 he devoted himself to the mechanics of chemical reactions, establishing the laws of chemical equilibrium and the displacement of equilibrium. He studied solutions. By applying thermodynamic values he was able to anticipate possibilities, instead of depending on trial-and-error methods and performing costly experiments with possible negative results. In 1889 he won the title of chief engineer and that year returned to the Collège de France as professor of inorganic chemistry, remaining until 1908. In 1907 he had been appointed professor of general chemistry of the Faculty of Science of Paris—a title he retained until he became honorary professor in 1925. During the period 1908 to 1922 he directed the researches of more than one hundred graduate students, of whom twenty-four obtained the doctorate as his majors.

Le Chatelier was a reformer. He was not content with providing the descriptive material and facts which his colleagues presented, but constantly introduced theory and the newer ideas, presenting his own interpretation of fundamental principles and laws.

In the research field Henry Le Chatelier possessed great versatility. He is recognized chiefly for his contributions to thermodynamics and chemical theory. We are familiar with his principle on stress and strain, which is coupled with that on heat advanced by van't Hoff. It is not strange that he should have accomplished the synthesis of ammonia from the elements in 1901, anticipating Fritz Haber, who is usually the only one mentioned in connection with the process. Henry Le Chatelier was interested in allotropy, especially in carbon, silica, and certain metals. He made extensive solubility studies, including dissociation. He studied the dissociation of gases at high temperatures and the combustion of gas mixtures, and applied the results to the utilization of fuels and the economics of furnace operation. Later he entered the field of explosives and indicated their use in mining operations. While generally interested in metallurgy, he devoted himself more particularly to the production and properties of iron and steel. He applied the phase rule of Willard Gibbs for which he devised simple proofs, and it is said that without Le Chatelier's principle of mobile equilibrium the phase rule and phase law diagrams might have waited long for their practical applications. While working in the field of metallurgy he devised a metallurographic microscope with which he could study and photograph crystals in alloys. This device divulged the formation of compounds between iron and carbon, and proved the value of heat treatment in steel. His dilatometer enabled him to measure the expansion rate of metals. Le Chatelier experienced difficulty in the measuring of the higher temperatures in his studies. Instruments were in existence which would measure up to 500° C., but beyond that results were inaccurate. He adopted the platinum platinum-rhodium thermocouple, for gas thermometers were unreliable.

In the field of ceramics Le Chatelier was interested in mortars and cements, clay, silica, glass, and the silicates. He determined the coefficient of expansion and electrical conductivity of some of these materials.

Henry Le Chatelier published over five hundred journal articles and books. They included chemistry, ceramics, numerous biographies, and, toward the end of his life, articles on social welfare.

Le Chatelier's books included a volume on the measurement of high temperatures which appeared in 1900 under the joint authorship of O. Boudouard. This volume underwent numerous revisions

912

and translations, and is known in the United States under the title, "The Measurement of High Temperatures," by Burgess and Le Chatelier. In 1903 a volume appeared on "Hydraulic Materials." This dealt with lime, mortars, and cement. Again, the volume was revised and translated. In 1908 he published his "Lessons on Carbon." This volume had its beginning in his early lectures on the subject. The year 1912 brought his "Introduction to the Study of Metallurgy" which included industrial heating. In 1914 his volume on "Silica and the Silicates" appeared, and in 1925 his book on "Science and Industry." In the last-named volume he particularly stressed the Taylor system of organized management and production which originated in England and which he greatly admired.

In his books and journal articles Le Chatelier's exact scientific trend of mind is in constant evidence. He provides illustrations, but sparingly, and never superfluously. His translators were more generous in this regard than the author himself.

Le Chatelier was a great national figure. His linking of science with industry (especially with national defense) was important to France, for not only the nation but the Academy of Sciences had neglected this. His frequent appeals to the French Academy of Sciences, in which he referred to the utilization of science in industry and national affairs in Germany, Great Britain, and the United States finally won national support for research, and his favorable reference to our own nation undoubtedly prompted Woodrow Wilson to consult him in an advisory capacity when our National Research Council was established in 1916.

The reward of Le Chatelier's appeal to the National Academy of Sciences and the French nation came through his numerous appointments. He was on the French Commission on Explosives in 1902, the National Science Bureau in 1913, the Commission on Weights and Measures from 1913 to 1917, and the Commission for the Standardization of Metallic Products. Upon him was placed the responsibility for specifying standards for materials of construction other than wood, and his committee finally determined the standards for all products. In 1919 France made him a member of the Commission on Inventions, and in 1922 he was placed on the Committee for the Control of the French Monetary Circulation. Le Chatelier represented France at numerous international meetings.

Henry Le Chatelier was the recipient of many honors. These included the Jerome Ponti Prize of the French Academy of Sciences (1892), and the Lacaze Prize (1895). In 1907 he was made a member of the French Academy of Sciences. It may seem strange that the Academy should have waited so long, but one has only to think of the case of Louis Pasteur to realize that election to this body requires time. He had been a Chevalier of the Legion of Honor of France since 1886. In 1908 he became an officer, in 1919 a Commander, and in 1927 Grand Officer. In 1906 he was made a knight of the Order of St. Anne of Russia, and in 1928 a Chevalier of the Order of the New Republic of Poland.

His applications of science to industry brought him recognition which scientists rarely receive. Thus, in 1900 he received the Grand Prize of the Paris Exposition; in 1908 the Medal of Honor of the Society of Mineral Industry of France; in 1928, the Gold Medal of the Commission on Bridges and Highways of France. In 1904 he received the Grand Prize of the St. Louis Exposition (U. S. A.); in 1905 the Diploma of Honor of the International Exposition in Liége, Belgium; in 1906 the Grand Prize of the International Exposition in Milan, Italy. During 1910 he received the Grand Prize of the International Exposition in Brussels, Belgium; the Grand Prize of the Franco-British Exposition; and the Bessemer Gold Medal of the Iron and Steel Institute of London. In 1911 the International Exposition of Industries and Manufacturers of Turin, Italy, awarded him the Grand Prize. In 1916 he received the Davy Medal of the Royal Society of London. In 1932 he was awarded the medal of the Association of Engineers of Liège, Belgium. Henry Le Chatelier was not only a member and officer in many national and foreign societies, but was made an honorary members of innumerable organizations.

Le Chatelier's honorary degrees included that of Doctor of Engineering from Aix la Chapelle, Germany (1910); Doctor of Science from the University of Manchester, England (1920); Doctor of Technical Science from the Polytechnique Institute of Copenhagen, Denmark (1921); Doctor of Science, University of Louvain, Bel-

914

gium (1927); Doctor of Science, University of Madrid, Spain (1934).

It would hardly seem right to present this chapter without saying something of Le Chatelier's family life. On May 29, 1876, he married Genevieve Nicolas, the daughter of a former chum of his father at the École Polytechnique. There were seven children by this marriage, three sons and four daughters. The influence which Henry Le Chatelier enjoyed through his grandfather, his father, and mother, and their families is repeated through his influence and that of Mme. Le Chatelier on their children and grandchildren. The oldest son, Charles, became a mining engineer. The oldest daughter married an engineer. The next daughter also married an engineer and after her marriage cooperated with her father in establishing the *Revue de métallurgie*. The third daughter married an agricultural engineer. The son, Louis, is an engineer. The fourth daughter married an engineer, and the youngest child, a son, François, is a mining engineer. It is to this son that the writer is particularly obligated for much of the valuable information contained in the present article.

In June, 1936, Professor and Mme. Le Chatelier celebrated their sixtieth wedding anniversary surrounded by their children, thirty-four grandchildren, and six-great-grandchildren. Le Chatelier devoted all of his spare time to his family. The tall, slender, serious, but pleasant, father played with the children and would take them on numerous excursions. He interested himself in their studies and in the studies of his grandchildren. It is said that in the spring of 1936 he went to Miribel-les-échelles with his grandchildren to give them a review in chemistry and physics, and that on the eve of his death, disregarding his fatigue, he dictated to one of his children advice concerning the study of descriptive geometry to help a grandchild who was experiencing difficulty with the subject.

We must pay tribute to Mme. Le Chatelier. Her self-abnegation as the wife of a professor with a limited income, and her devotion to the education of her children to lighten the burdens of her husband as much as possible proved an important factor in helping to establish his brilliant career.

Le Chatelier traveled extensively in the interests of his studies and through invitation of foreign societies; also during his vacation, when Mme. Le Chatelier invariably accompanied him.

Finally, like most scientists who reach a ripe old age, he indulged in philosophy. On January 22, 1922, the French Academy of Sciences celebrated the fiftieth anniversary of Le Chatelier's graduation from the École Polytechnique and presented him with a bronze medal. Copies of this medal by an eminent sculptor had been distributed in return for subscriptions resulting in a fund of 100,000 francs. This fund was presented to the Academy of Sciences in Le Chatelier's honor and utilized for researches under his direction. There were many addresses in which he was given high praise and commendation. When his friends and associates had finished Le Chatelier thanked them and closed by stressing some of his own ideals. He emphasized the necessity for clear thinking verified by exact experimentation, and illustrated the importance of this procedure by citing the failures of a number of eminent men whose carelessness resulted in embarrassment following their published accounts of faulty researches. He told how his pleasure in life had come through studying the laws of the universe, observing their application and discovering new consequences. He warned against the tendency to invalidate or question natural laws and said that one should aim to confirm those laws which predecessors had disclosed. He felt that this attitude was an advantage which led to his own supplementary contributions and which accounted for that measure of his success which the Academy was celebrating. He could not destroy the edifices of the past, for he considered science "a collection of contributions made by many workers, which might be supplemented or modified by duly authenticated new discoveries." He stressed the importance of discipline which his parents had imposed upon him and which was practiced at the École Polytechnique while he was a student. He deplored the decreasing seriousness of study and increasing tendency toward pleasure and even license in modern colleges and universities. He likened the irresponsible student to a bold individual who dodges vehicles in crossing a street and risks being crushed, to say nothing of the fact that he seriously ties up traffic. To the young chemist he recommended modesty coupled with a reluctance to overthrow the findings of the past until he has positive proof. "One makes discoveries if he can and not merely through the wish to make them. The sensational is detestable." Of himself Le Chatelier said, ". . . throughout my scientific career I strove without any desire for the sensational, contenting myself each day with the conscientious pursuit of the task of the day. In the end I was amply rewarded."

Le Chatelier was a lover of liberty and cherished the privileges which men enjoyed in the French Republic. He differentiated between discipline and liberty. To him discipline meant the voluntary respect of the law, whether natural or social. He characterized civilized man through recognition and respect of the law. To him liberty consisted not in the breaking of laws, but, on the contrary, in the prevention of law violation. Liberty refuses to tolerate injustice and should modify laws instead of revolting against them.

Le Chatelier placed integrity above everything. At one time after he had received an honor, a statesman approached him for a favor to a particular political faction. Le Chatelier replied, "I have never sought an honor, and I, therefore, assume that when it was conferred it was mine without obligation." He might have enjoyed favors and promotions had it not been for this ideal. In fact, he lost his chair in the École Polytechnique through his conscientious adherence to his principles.

After his retirement and during the last years of his life, he became interested in numerous problems of a general nature. He campaigned for the return of the classical studies to college and university curricula, stressing the importance of literature and Latin as a part of a general education. As already intimated, he advocated scientific management according to the Taylor System, and others, for increasing the efficiency of workmen in French factories. He advocated political economy, recommending a more liberal status for the workman and a greater restraint on political expenditures. Shortly before his death, as president of the inaugural International Congress of Mines and Metallurgy and of Applied Geology, at which delegates from forty nations were present, Le Chatelier took occasion to indicate that much attention was being given to the development of industrial technique which was based on the collaboration of science and industry. He admitted that at one time he had supported this policy and that it was still desirable, but lamented the fact that not enough attention was being paid to social progress. Wishing to leave this thought as an indelible impression, he prepared an article entitled "Morals and Human Affairs." So anxious was he that the manuscript should be exactly right, that he corrected it on his deathbed, and insisted repeatedly that it be sent to a journal where the ideals expressed would make a sympathetic appeal, namely, the *Bulletin of the Social Union of Catholic Engineers of France*. It appeared in this *Bulletin* as a posthumous article in December, 1936.

After 1935 Le Chatelier suffered occasionally from angina pectoris. Several days before his death a particularly violent attack affected his heart, and he succumbed. His death was a peaceful one, on September 17, 1936, at his country estate, *Miribel-les-échelles* (Isère), France, in his eighty-sixth year. The writer pays tribute to Henry Le Chatelier, one of the world's greatest scientists, in a poem which was previously prepared for a memorial article.

> Father studied of Earth's minerals,
> Father's father burnt its lime,
> Mother's forebears mapped world nations,
> She herself was soul sublime.
>
> Thus, the son, one born of Genius,
> Nurtured by the mother's care,
> Guided by the father's wisdom,
> Must find interest everywhere.
>
> And he did, in Natural Science,
> Striving morning, noon and night,
> Wrest from Earth some of her secrets,
> Set them forth, as well he might.
>
> First the gross, the coarser findings,
> Then with microscope, the small,
> Next the laws, their explanation
> Gave this Savant, slim and tall,
>
> Always striving, earnest, modest,
> More to learn and more to give.
> Discipline, his life, his motto,
> Showing others how to live.

Not for pleasure, not for glamour
But to serve both Man and State,
In this service helped a woman,
That self-sacrificing mate,

Who with patience him encouraged,
Bore him sons and daughters rare.
These love art and science also,
Further lay Earth's secrets bare.

Nations far and wide our Scholar
Honored in their Guilds, and then
Made him of their Groups a member;
Always happy, where and when

He would visit, in his travels,
Their great scholars, more to learn;
Learn, but giving more than taking,
Adding to Minerva's urn.

Flames he measured, as to hotness,
Even solar heat, so high,
Glasses made he in the furnace,
Products pleasing to the eye.

But his sunset saw the smoulder
In his fellow worker's breast,
Which portraying surface under
Showed a feeling of unrest.

Showed that some had blessings many,
Others few. These torn with strife
Often suffered untold tortures,
Trudging through the walk of Life.

Thus, on death-bed, leaving Science,
He espoused the Public Weal,
Pleading strong the Cause of Justice,
Signing with his last Earth-Seal.

May his message bear fruition,
Lift from Life its shaded hood,
Make men see that Life's worth living,
Holding hope, and boding good.

Gone our Savant. Yes, in body;
Not in mind or soul, for they

919

Will abide with us forever.
They'll live Aeons, no mere days.

NOTES AND REFERENCES

This chapter was compiled from a number of articles on Henry Le Chatelier, written by the author and published in 1937:

"Henry Le Chatelier: I, His Life and Work," *Bul. Am. Ceram. Soc., 16,* 155–163 (1937).

"Henry Le Chatelier: II, His Publications," *J. Am. Ceram. Soc., 20,* 316–322 (1937).

"Henry Le Chatelier: 1850 to 1936," *J. Chem. Educ., 14,* 555–560 (1937).

ALEXANDER SILVERMAN

·· 64 ··

Herman Frasch

1851-1914

HERMAN FRASCH performed his great experiment in a 10 inch test tube 625 feet long. His laboratory was an island in the middle of a Louisiana swamp, a 75 acre oasis of dry ground, studded with giant cypress, all festooned with Spanish moss, and inhabited by muskrats, a colony of snowy egrets, and mosquitoes, billions of mosquitoes. Scarcely ideal experimental conditions, these, but in no other way could he find out whether his idea would work or not. A number of experts had told him bluntly that it would not; that he was crazy to think he could melt sulfur underground and pump it to the surface in molten form.

Yet his revolutionary idea was fundamentally quite simple. He had hit upon it because of his long experience with petroleum drilling and with pumping brine out of driven wells. All the equipment he proposed to use was as simple and standardized as a foot rule. Furthermore, Frasch was not only an able chemist, he was also a meticulous, forehanded engineer. At his desk he had carefully calculated all the factors involved; temperatures, pressures, thermal efficiencies, and specific gravities. But he could not check these figures by laboratory experiments. He could not even test them in a pilot plant. He was compelled to leap from paper calculations to field operation. The whole thing had to be a gigantic gamble.

It required courage to take such a long chance. Frasch never lacked self-confidence: at times he displayed an unblushing, almost brassy assurance. Even his warmest admirers had to admit that he was "opinionated," but his opinions were always well buttressed with facts and figures. He knew what he was talking about. He never went off half-cocked. Accordingly, his great sufur gamble was really a carefully calculated risk, and he was confident of success. He could not have foreseen all the problems and disappointments ahead nor suspected the persistence and resourcefulness that would be demanded of him. If Frasch had not been a remarkable man with a surprising assortment of gifts and skills, he would never have perfected his hot-water sulfur mining process. But it would never have been a commercial success, if he had not also been very lucky.

Some 500 feet beneath his island-laboratory lay a 100 foot stratum of limestone richly impregnated with sulfur. The structure seemed to be quite like the famous deposits in Sicily which, since Roman times, had been the world's chief source of brimstone. Following the close of the Civil War, forty years before, a dozen attempts to reach this buried treasure had failed. The insuperable difficulty was a layer of quicksand from which, when dug into, flowed a fountain of salt water charged with poisonous hydrogen sulfide gas.

The sulfur mine that could not be mined became notorious. It was thoroughly explored by core-drilling. Geologists wrote reports about it that were published in learned professional journals. At least three consulting mining engineers risked their reputations by suggesting novel, but impractical, methods of penetrating the tricky, dangerous quicksands. A lot of money was lost, some of it by gullible investors in companies that were little better than get-rich-quick schemes.

The final effort to mine this baffling deposit was made in 1890 by Abram Hewitt and his brother-in-law, Edward Cooper, a partnership that combined ample venture capital with successful mining experience. Their American Sulphur Company bought the sulfur island outright, and they planned to tunnel through the quicksand within a series of iron rings, 10 feet in diameter, lowered to the bottom of an old shaft and welded on top of each other till the last ring stood above the surface of the ground. As the men dug out the clay and gravel at the bottom of the shaft, the weight of the rings forced the improvised caisson lower and lower. All went well till they struck the quicksand. In surged a mixture of sand and water that carried the pump platform and workmen 40 feet up the shaft. With a clamshell bucket they scooped out the sand till the shield had been lowered the depth of four more iron rings, about 20 feet. Not an inch further would it budge.

Tragedy capped this failure. In one of their test wells the pipe had broken 25 feet below the surface and in attempting to salvage it five men were asphyxiated by a sudden gush of deadly hydrogen sulfide gas. This fatal accident persuaded Hewitt and Cooper to abandon their ill-starred venture.

How Herman Frasch first became interested in this thwarting sulfur mine is not known but, being Frasch, he investigated it scrupulously. He admitted having read all the literature, including the highly imaginative circulars of the stock promoters. Nobody else interested in this frustrating project had thought to do so, but he studied the world market for sulfur and the business of the powerful Sicilian monopoly. He reached a crucial conclusion: even if it were possible to reach this rich deposit, it could not be mined profitably by pick and shovel. Labor costs would be prohibitive. Sicilian miners were then being paid 30 cents a day; Americans, $1 to $1.25—and the Sicilian workday was two hours longer. Accordingly, he decided to devise an entirely new method.

Frasch had a gift for attacking familiar problems from a fresh point of view. Thus he excelled in improving old chemical processes by what appeared to be sensationally original, unorthodox means, and his hot-water mining process, while highly original, was a synthesis of ideas developed naturally by his training and experience.

He had his first schooling in chemistry in Germany, for he was born on Christmas Day, 1851, at Gaildorf, Württemberg, and did not come to the United States until he was seventeen years old. After finishing in the local school, his father, Johannes Frasch, prosperous apothecary and mayor of the town, sent him to the gymnasium at Halle. He was anxious that his son proceed to the University, but young Herman itched to get to America. He landed at Philadelphia and immediately got a position at the Philadelphia College of Pharmacy as assistant to the distinguished Professor John M. Maisch.

Arriving in 1868, amid the first burst of industrial expansion that followed the Civil War, Frasch seems to have sensed the growing importance of chemicals and the opportunities opening up to chemists. At all events, he continued his chemical studies enthusiastically. Pennsylvania petroleum was booming and astutely

925

he began to investigate this complex mixture of hydrocarbons, becoming one of the first and foremost specialists in this new field.

He continued teaching and built up a little consulting practice till 1877 when a patent was issued to him for an improved process for refining paraffin wax. This he sold to the Merian & Morgan Paraffin Company, in which John D. Rockefeller's Standard Oil Company held a substantial interest. Assured by an annual retainer fee from J. B. Merian and William Morgan, he moved to Cleveland, opened an office and small laboratory, and became known as "The Flying Dutchman" with the reputation of being the outstanding chemical consultant in the city, then a hotbed of petroleum activities.

The oil recently found in Ontario attracted his attention. Its high sulfur content gave it an evil odor—it was nicknamed "skunk oil"—and the kerosene refined from it, then the principal petroleum product, burned badly, coating the lamp chimney with soot and gumming up the wick. In 1882 he sold "exclusive use of three patents" for improvements in refining Canadian crude to the Imperial Oil Company, Ltd., for cash and stock, and in 1884 he moved to London, Ontario. The following year he bought the Empire Oil Company which had wells and a small refinery at Petrolia, Ontario. Despite a protective tariff of 9 cents a gallon,

HERMAN FRASCH.

—∴—

FABRICANTEN VON:

Brauermaterialien,

Bierschöne, und allen in das Brauerfach einschlagenden Chemicalien.

Saure Biere wieder hergestellt, und Auskunft ertheilt in allen Fällen in denen chemische Hülfe von Nutzen sein kann.

—∴—

OFFICE:

No. 716 RACE STREET.

JOHN RUEGENBERG.

—∴—

FABRICANTEN VON:

Künstlichen Fruchtessencen,

Brandy, Whiskey, Gin, Rum, und Wine flavors.

Beste Weinschöne, ohne Geruch oder Geschmach, ist unfehlbar.

Bittersmischungen feinster Art nach Verlangen. Kranke Weine restaurirt.

—∴—

LABORATORY: LANCASTER AVE.

Above Forty-fifth Street.

this struggling firm was almost bankrupt, but Frasch believed he could rescue it by making its products profitably salable. He had not completely solved these problems when, in August, 1886, he was called back to Cleveland by John D. Rockefeller.

A similar sour petroleum had been discovered in northwest Ohio and northeast Indiana, the famous Lima field. Although it was only salable as an industrial fuel, the Standard Oil Company and various subsidiaries, to maintain their dominating position in the industry, had not only bought many wells in this new area, but were taking in oil at 5 cents a barrel from independent producers. Their problem was becoming acute: they were storing skunk oil much faster than they could market it. As the best authority on this unmanageable crude, Rockefeller turned to Frasch; he gave him Standard Oil stock for his Empire property, bought his patents relating to the refining of sour oil, engaged him as a full-time consultant, and sent him to the brand-new Solar Refinery at Lima in charge of the first experimental research program ever undertaken in the American petroleum industry.

Frasch adopted a simple concept for the removal of the offending sulfur, based upon the reaction between a metallic oxide and the sulfur compounds in the oil, forming a sulfide which could be precipitated and from which the metallic oxide could be subsequently recovered for reuse. His basic patent, issued February 21, 1887 (U. S. Patent 378,240), covered the use of the oxides of copper, lead, iron, bismuth, cadmium, mercury, and/or silver in all possible combinations. From the start his process was an improvement over the old litharge treatment, but it took him the better part of two years to find the answers to such questions as (a) Which oxide or combination of oxides and in what proportions would do the best job cheapest? (b) Should the sulfur be precipitated in the first distillation or in the redistillation to separate the kerosene? (c) What type of agitation would insure the optimum formation of sulfides? (d) How best to recover and revivify the oxides?

The successful outcome of "Herman's Experiment," as the oilmen christened the Lima refinery, had far-reaching results. When the "last word" in petroleum refineries was built at Whiting, In-

927

diana, elaborate research facilities were provided and one of his assistants, Dr. William M. Burton, fresh from Johns Hopkins and later to perfect the cracking process, was installed as director. When the even greater refinery was built at Bayonne, New Jersey, larger laboratories were installed and the same policy of continuous research was adopted. Between 1899 and 1905, Frasch was assigned to Bayonne as special consultant on a part-time basis with a salary of $8000 a year, and here he studied the Beaumont and Coalinga crudes and developed the recovery of by-products from the "slops" from the Atlantic Refinery at Franklin, Pennsylvania. Here, too, he urged the adoption of metal baffles in the fractionating towers in place of the stone packing used in the Van Dyke towers. Had his idea been approved, it might well have brought the bubble tower into refinery technique fifteen years sooner. It is recognized that Frasch was the father of research in the petroleum industry.

A more immediate, direct result of his own researches was that Lima crude, when properly desulfurized, advanced in price from 14 cents to $1 a barrel. For his Empire Company and his stock in Imperial, Frasch had received Standard Oil stock paying 7 per cent dividends and selling for $168 a share. The enhanced value of the sour mid-continent oils, in which the company had a commanding position, raised the dividend to 40 per cent and Frasch sold half of his stock for $820 a share. He was now independently wealthy. He refused a regular executive post, but accepted a lifetime contract as part-time consultant with Standard Oil. He insisted that always, every year, he should have at least two sabbatical months of his own choosing.

Frasch had just perfected a new method of recovering the sulfuric acid used in refining the heavy fractions of crude oil, when he received his first patents (U. S. Patents 461,429 and 461,430) on his sulfur-mining process. Two Standard Oil officials, Frank Rockefeller and F. B. Squires, who had been closely associated with him in the Solar refinery experiments, became interested in this rather fantastic project and Frasch assigned to each a three-tenths interest in these and all future sulfur-mining patents. The three agreed to share, in proportion to their respective patent ownership, the expenses of development work. This was to

928

be conducted as a majority of the partners directed and to continue as long as a majority believed it promised success. If the project materialized, a corporation would be formed to take over and exploit the patents and to secure any property that had been acquired by the group.

It was under this agreement that Frasch went wildcatting for sulfur in the vicinity of the now-abandoned mine of the American Sulphur Company. He had been misled by his preliminary studies into thinking that the Louisiana deposit, like those in Sicily, extended underground over a large area. Four exploratory wells, each drilled 1000 feet through nothing but the typical sedimentary deposits of the Gulf Coast region, convinced him that all the sulfur in this neighborhood was beneath that island in the swamp, concentrated in the cap rock of a salt dome. These curious structures, described as "a billiard cue of salt, tipped with a limestone cap rock" are found in many parts of the world. But only along the Gulf Coast, between the delta of the Mississippi and the peninsula of Yucatan, is the cap rock loaded with sulfur. And only from the cap rock of a salt dome can sulfur be mined by the hot-water process.

With his partners' consent, Frasch went to Hewitt, and after some brisk negotiating, they came to an agreement. If he, at his expense, could produce sulfur, then a company would be organized in which each party would own half the stock—a fifty-fifty deal; the Cleveland group's patents and American Sulphur's property.

Frasch moved his drilling rig and expert crew over to the island and started a 10 inch bore. The infamous quicksand gripped the drilling bit as in a vise and it took three months to reach the limestone stratum, a job modern drilling tools could do in a day. Into the cap rock they firmly set the bottom of a 10-inch pipe, reduced the size of the bit, and continued an 8-inch bore through the sulfur bed. While drilling through this stratum a fountain of sulfurous water flowed continuously from the top of the drive pipe and they had to raise the rig eight feet high on a platform to be clear of the choking, smarting, dangerous gases. The men called it "the headache post."

The bore through the sulfur deposit was fitted with a 6-inch pipe at the bottom of which was a perforated section to act as a strainer. Above the strainer, in the 6-inch pipe, was an iron ring with a hole 2½ inches in diameter, and above the ring were larger holes in the pipe to provide for the hot water outlet. A 3 inch pipe was now lowered through the 6 inch casing and set upon the iron ring above the strainer. At 175 feet below the surface, an ordinary oil well sucker-rod pump was placed in the 3 inch pipe. At the top of this pipe was a tee which carried a pipe, fitted with a safety valve, beyond the wellhead. The gigantic test tube was now all set, ready for the experiment.

Frasch came down from Cleveland after Christmas, 1894, and he checked the steam and water lines himself. Superheated water was poured down the 6 inch pipe for twenty-four hours. Frasch opened the safety valve. A jet of steam burst forth which soon subsided and then ceased. Evidently the bottom of the well had sealed over with melted sulfur, so the sucker rod was set and the pump started. For four hours a molasses-colored stream of molten sulfur poured forth. Then the pump faltered and stopped. The steel sucker rod, corroded down to a matchstick, had snapped.

The Frasch process had brought to the surface liquid sulfur that solidified in minutes to sparkling yellow brimstone, better than 99.5 per cent pure elemental sulfur. But it was still far from a practical operation.

Twice the sucker rod broke, and Frasch, typically, cured this fault by eliminating the pump altogether and substituting compressed air. The sulfur froze in the pipe, which had to be pulled, disjointed, and over 400 feet chipped clean with cold chisels. In some wells the hot water drained away ineffectively through fissures. In others, where the limestone structure was exceptionally tight, it backed up and bleed wells had to be drilled to carry it away. When the sulfur melted out, the limestone collapsed, creating a new set of problems.

Working blindfolded, 600 feet down, it took Frasch six years to achieve commercial production. Luckily, the Louisiana dome was shallow, extraordinarily regular in formation, and comparatively easy to work. Otherwise the Frasch process might never have been perfected.

Having learned to mine sulfur efficiently, Frasch could not sell it profitably. The prime requisite of his process is millions of gallons of clean water: the prime cost is fuel. It took 4000 gallons of water, heated to 230°F. to raise a ton of sulfur. Water was plentiful; but the cheapest fuel was soft coal costing $4.05 a ton delivered. Again it was very lucky that, just as he had ironed the kinks out of his operation, the greatest gusher in all petroleum history was brought in only thirty miles away. Fuel oil at 60 cents a barrel, piped over from Spindletop, made the Union Sulphur Company (the 50-50 corporation that had been formed by Frasch and Hewitt) a financial success.

As a businessman, Herman Frasch displayed the same boldness, skill, and resourcefulness that characterized him as a chemist. He had to fight his way into the market and he audaciously invaded Europe, breaking the grip of the Sicilian monopoly in their oldest strongholds. So long as his basic patents were in force, the Union Sulphur Company had virtually a monopoly in this country, but he lowered the domestic price drastically. He realized that the cheaper sulfur was sold, the wider and greater would be its consumption, and he preferred to build for the future than to make an immediate killing. Recognizing that his biggest customers were acid makers buying an essential raw material and, as such, most interested in a known, staple price, he adopted the policy of selling sulfur only in carloads, f.o.b. mine, at a price openly quoted to all. He initiated and paid for research to remove the fire and explosion hazards from grinding brimstone. He himself worked on improvements in the design of sulfur burners for the manufacturers of sulfuric acid. Union Sulphur was one of the first American companies to enter into cooperative research with state agricultural experimental stations and it supported liberally studies on sulfur as a fungicide and insecticide. At the turn of the century, all this was managerial thinking far in advance of the times.

For the future of the Union Sulphur Company Frasch died at a critical period. After a long illness he passed away in Paris, May 1, 1914; three months before the Kaiser's armies invaded Belgium; five months before a second American company, using his hot-water method, pumped sulfur from a dome in Texas. He could not have foreseen World War I, but in anticipation of the new competition he was building up a huge stockpile of brimstone. This proved to be of inestimable value in meeting the war demands but, on the other hand, these demands enabled the new company to establish itself firmly.

By the time hostilities ended the sulfur situation had changed completely. Union Sulphur had lost its patent infringement suit and the hot-water process was thus thrown open to anyone. A third strong company had just come into production. Union Sulphur's own dome in Louisiana was beginning to show unmistakable signs of exhaustion. The company Frasch founded gradually faded away, but the American industry based upon his ingenious process had already become the chief supplier of "the most important chemical raw material."

Herman Frasch was awarded the Perkin Medal and received many other honors, but he has one unique distinction; he is the only chemist whose name is indelibly associated with two great processes in two distinct fields. In the petroleum industry the Frasch process means billions of gallons of "skunk oil" sweetened and rendered usable. In the chemical field the Frasch process has produced over 100 million tons of sulfur that, except for it, would have lain buried deep underground, useless.

NOTES AND REFERENCES

There is much first-hand biographical material in the presentation and acceptance addresses at the time of the Perkin Medal award; *Ind. Eng. Chem.*, 4, 138 (1912); *Chem. Met. Eng.*, 10, 78 (1912).

Also, material can be found in the testimony of witnesses and exhibits in the patent infringement suits, Union Sulphur Co. *vs.* Freeport Sulphur Co., U.S. Dist. Court, Delaware, In Equity No. 336, 1915; U.S. Court of Appeals, 3rd Circuit, Nos. 2391 & 2392, Oct. Term, 1918.

For Frasch's work in petroleum: Allan Nevins, "Study in Power," 2 vols., Scribners, New York, 1953.

Ralph H. and Muriel E. Hidy, "Pioneering in Big Business; 1882–1911," Harper, New York, 1955.

For his work in sulfur, see: W. W. Duecker, *Ind. Eng. Chem.*, 42, 2186 (1950); A. E. Marshall, *Chem. Eng.*, 57, 293 (1950); Williams Haynes, "Brimstone—The Stone That Burns," Van Nostrand, New York, 1959, chapters 4, 5, 6, 7.

See also M. Mansbach, *J. Am. Pharm. Assoc.*, 7, 163 (1918); *Dict. Am. Biog.*, VI, 602.

Obituaries: *J. Soc. Chem. Ind.*, May 30, 1914; *Chemiker Zeitung*, June 6, 1914; *World's Work*, July 1914; *N.Y. Times*, May 2, 1914.

WILLIAMS HAYNES

·· *65* ··

Scientists and Industrialists

The first 4 pages of the Latin index, a real table of contents, alphabetically
arranged, from Johann Joachim Becher's *Chymischer glücks-hafen oder
Grosse Chymische Concordanz und Collection*, Franckfurt, Johann Georg
Schiele, 1682.

CHEMISTS can be grouped together in several different ways according to which traits are considered important. A particularly appealing method for doing this consists in forming pairs of opposites characterized by being more or less completely exclusive. However, just as in setting up types of personalities, many transitions will be found, and their importance will grow with continued study.

This will certainly also apply to the attempted grouping in this chapter of chemists into scientists and industrialists. The two groups do not really exclude each other, because they tend either to make science more industrially minded or industry more scientific.

The discussion of chemists in their relationship to science and industry will provide the occasion to mention some of those many great men to whom separate biographies have not been devoted in this book.

In early times chemistry was not a full-time occupation. The anonymous ancient brewers, tanners, metal workers, and makers of glass and pottery knew everything about what they were to do; tradition told them so. Philosophers, physicians, and pharmacists discovered questions of chemical nature, thought and wrote about them. They became chemists for part of their working time. A few experiments were sufficient to give decisive answers to new questions, because well-established authority was available to explain them. Robert Boyle's skepticism (p. 136) sounded a warning without immediate resonance. His strength as a chemical scientist was still based on philosophy.

A rare combination of philosophy with interest in business enterprises and chemical experimentation dominated the variegated life of Johann Joachim Becher (1635–1682), the "Med. Doct. and Röm. Kays. Maj. Cammer- und Commercien- Rath" from Speyer, as he identified himself on the title page of his 810-page book: "Chymischer glückshafen oder grosse Chymische Concordanz und

937

Collection." Frankfurt, 1682. Equally famous was his "Chymisches Laboratorium, oder Unter-irdische naturkündigung," Frankfurt, 1690, based on his "Actorum laboratorii chimici monacensis, sed Physicae substerraneae libri duo" of 1669. His biographer, Urban Gottfried Buchern (Nürnberg and Althoff, 1722), saw in him "das Muster eines Nützlich-Gelehrten" (the paragon of a useful scholar). He won lasting fame through Georg Ernst Stahl (1660–1734), professor of medicine in Halle from 1694, who developed Becher's *terra pinguis* into phlogiston, the mysterious substance forming a principle of all combustion.

Rudolph Glauber (p. 116) was among the first to combine science with industry. In the eighteenth century several scientists manifested interest in the developing chemical industry. Jean Hellot (1685–1766) worked and wrote on the dyeing of wool and woolen fabrics (1750) and collaborated with Duhamel du Monceau (p. 178) toward the improvement of mining operations. Jean Antoine Claude Chaptal (1756–1832), a physician, became professor of chemistry at Montpellier where he had established the first commercial production of sulfuric acid in France. Louis XVI created him Comte de Chanteloup, and Napoleon bestowed many honors on him. From 1819 to his death Chaptal was active in the Chamber of Peers and in many public commissions. All the political upheavals did not change the fact that he was needed as a chemist, economist, and administrator. His two volumes on the use of chemistry in agriculture appeared in 1823, ten years after Davy's effort in this direction, and seventeen years before Liebig's exciting book.

Many of the great chemists in France were appointed by the government to administrative positions in industry, like Claude Louis Berthollet (p. 316). Gay-Lussac (p. 360) did much for chemical engineering, particularly in improving the manufacture of sulfuric acid. Leopold Gmelin (p. 454), so widely associated with the new rise of inorganic chemical science, ventured into industrial pursuits. James Muspratt (1793–1886) who had learned his chemistry mainly from books, like Nicholson's Dictionary (1808), started the manufacture of soda by the Leblanc process in 1822 near Liverpool and saw his son Sheridan publish a book in 1860 on "Chemistry, Theoretical, Practical, and Analytical, as applied and relating to the Arts and Manufactures" which gave to many young chemists the guidance that James had obtained from Nicholson's old book.

Friedlieb Ferdinand Runge (1794–1867) began his chemical career as an apothecary's apprentice in Lübeck in 1810. He received his M.D. in Jena in 1819, and his Ph.D. in Berlin in 1822. In 1816 he discovered that an extract from belladonna enlarged the pupil of the eye. Three years later he obtained, as a present, some coffee beans from Goethe and extracted caffeine from them. He could have devoted all his further work to the study of the alkaloids, but his affiliation with a textile plant in 1826 and a chemical manufacturing plant from 1831 to the end of his life developed other interests. Investigating the products from coal tar distillation, he discovered aniline, pyrrole, phenol, and rosolic acid. He tried his hand in making soaps, candles, sugar, and ink.

A textbook on the chemistry of dyes and dyeing appeared in three volumes which he published separately in 1834, 1842, and 1850. In the third of these volumes, he described the capillary action of blotting paper and demonstrated its use for determining the end point in precipitating dyes from their solutions. This can be considered the beginning of paper chromatography. He continued such studies on dyestuffs and published two collections of patterns, the second in 1855 under the philosophical title: "Der Bildungstrieb der Stoffe" (the formative tendency of the substances).

Runge resembles Scheele in some respects; both discovered many new substances and sought the general theory linking some of their special experimental results. They differ in Runge's greater preoccupation with industrial chemistry.

When a science grows, it creates its own impetus to further development. Creative men learn from their predecessors how to surpass them in extending the field of knowledge. Toward the end of the eighteenth century, chemistry had grown considerably in size. Peter Joseph Macquer's dictionary of chemistry comprised seven stout volumes (almost 6000 pages) in its second edition by Johann Gottfried Leonhardi, 1788–1791. Yet, even the great Lavoisier (p. 264) spent only a small part of his time in chemical research; for the rest of the time he was an economist, agriculturist, and businessman.

Berzelius (p. 386) was probably the first full-time chemist. Although for the most part he worked alone in his laboratory, he kept in personal contact with the young chemists of Europe and exerted great influence through his writings more than by his teaching. This influence had not penetrated to the popular level when young Liebig (p. 536) declared he wanted to study chemistry and encountered derisive laughter. He showed that chemistry is a worthwhile science to follow and that it had profitable applications. He demonstrated this when he explained to a manufacturer of Prussian blue that it was not the noise of his mixing equipment that assured a good product, but the addition of some iron to the mixture, an addition better made separately than by abrading the walls of his vessels. He ended it by demonstrating and pleading the use of chemistry in agriculture and nutrition. Although he did not become an industrialist, he went from pure chemistry to its applications.

At an early age, Charles-Frédéric Kuhlmann (1803–1881) began to combine science with industry. Later on, he also took an active part in community affairs, not in his native town of Colmar, Alsace, but in Lille in northern France, near the Belgian border. He began his chemical training with Louis Nicholas Vauquelin (1763–1829), a great experimenter who had started in very modest circumstances under Antoine François de Fourcroy (1755–1809), like Faraday under Humphry Davy, and who discovered the elements chromium and beryllium.

In 1823, Kuhlmann founded and financed a chair of chemistry applied to the arts and industry in Lille. Two years later, he started to manufacture sulfuric acid with two lead chambers. Soon he added a plant to make soda by the process of the unfortunate physician and inventor Nicolas Leblanc (1742–1806). This process started with the conversion of salt into "saltcake," sodium sulfate, which was then calcined with charcoal and ground limestone. The hydrochloric acid liberated in this first step was usually sent through the smokestack to contaminate the air. Kuhlmann,

940

however, utilized it to digest bones and thus improve their fertilizing value, particularly for sugar beets. In another connection with the new beet sugar industry, Kuhlmann regenerated the bone black, used for decolorizing the sugar solutions, by treating it with his soda by-product, hydrochloric acid.

In December, 1838, he reported before the Scientific Society of Lille on his experiments on nitric acid from ammonia. His method made use of "the little known force that had been called catalysis by Berzelius" (just a few years before). He passed a mixture of air and ammonia gas through a glass tube partially filled with the finely divided platinum called platinum sponge. Nothing happened at room temperature, but when the tube was heated to 300°, the platinum started to glow red, and the outgoing gas contained vapors of nitric and nitrous acids. He recommended this reaction, and the use of platinum sponge in general, to the attention of chemical manufacturers, because, as he said in 1847, here was a possibility of making France independent from importing the nitrates and nitric acid that are so important in wartime!

Upon the creation of a Faculté des Sciences at Lille in 1854, he retired from his teaching to devote more time to his expanding industrial activities. He bought up two smaller plants, and he added the manufacture of ammonium sulfate from gasworks liquor in 1860. The total of heavy chemicals from his plants reached 60,000 tons a year in 1873. In addition, he was finance director of his adopted town, and he became a member of the legislative body of northern France.

Although a professor, Robert Bunsen (p. 574) was an "applied" chemist almost all the time. In 1838, when he was only twenty-seven years old, he showed how blast furnace operation could be greatly improved by utilizing the wasted gases.

William Henry Perkin (p. 758) represents the rare, and the first, example of a scientist becoming an industrialist and returning to pure science. Otto N. Witt followed this example to a certain extent. Both of these scientists achieved industrial and financial success in the field of synthetic dyestuffs with their inventions. Peter Griess (1829–1888) made fundamental contributions to this field, but others reaped the rewards. As an assistant to A. W. Hofmann (p. 626) in London, Griess discovered, in 1858, that highly reactive diazo compounds are formed by treating aniline and other aromatic amines with nitrous acid. After he became a chemist at the large brewery of Alsopp and Sons, he continued his solitary work on diazo compounds and discovered that dyestuffs made from diazotized benzidine can be used for the direct dyeing of cotton. This discovery was of tremendous industrial importance, but his patent application of January 9, 1884, came too late. Paul Böttiger's German patent on these dyestuffs, called Congo red, was issued on February 2, 1884. Heinrich Caro (1834–1910), himself a highly successful industrial dyestuff chemist, said of Peter Griess: "Others have reaped where he had ploughed. Griess was not a lucky inventor."

Baeyer (p. 734), Emil Fischer (p. 982), Tiffeneau (p. 1390) and Richard Willstätter (p. 1366) remained scientists while furnishing chemical industry with new products. In the early part of this century, chemistry was still the exclusive domain of the university professors. Yet what they did often led to new industrial developments. The time it took for theory to become practice was very short in some instances, very long in others. Paul Ehrlich's theoretical work on new therapeutic chemicals was rapidly translated into commercial productions. What Moissan discovered about fluorine, or Alfred Stock and Arthur I. Schlesinger about boron hydrides had to wait for many decades before industry needed and developed them.

Among these great chemists, there were those who pursued science because they needed it as industrialists, like Ernest Solvay (p. 774), and those who applied their scientific knowledge in industry as consultants, like Teeple (p. 1410) and Arthur D. Little (p. 1192). There were also some whose excursions from science into industry were not always successful, like Wilhelm Ostwald (p. 1020). Few scientists were as fortunate as Carl Auer von Welsbach (1858–1929) who translated his own scientific study of the rare earths and platinum metals into their industrial use, particularly of thorium for incandescent gas mantles, osmium for electric lamps, and cerium in alloys with iron. The example of Bunsen, his teacher, inspired him: the Bunsen burner and spectroscopic analysis were among his tools.

942

Willard H. Dow (p. 1220) became an industrialists by building up an organization of his own. Usually, it was—and remains—rare to find a chemist in top administrative industrial position in this country. It was different in England, France, and Germany. Ludwig Mond (1839–1909) came from Germany and developed a large chemical enterprise in England, the Brunner, Mond et Co. In Germany, Carl Leverkus (1845–1925), Heinrich von Brunck (1847–1911), and Carl Duisberg (1861–1935) acquired prominence as industrialists comparable to that of Carl Bosch (p. 1398).

The scientific schools prepared chemists not only for science, but also for industry. The fact that schools in Germany, after the model set by Liebig, did so more than those in France and England was, in great part, the cause for the exceptional position that German chemical industry acquired in the second half of the nineteenth century and held for decades.

The picture of the chemist as a laboratory worker is quite incomplete. The experiments have to be planned, their results must be calculated and interpreted. G eorg Lunge (1839–1923) and Vincent Sidgwick (p. 1376) spent more time at the desk than in the laboratory or the lecture room; the former compiling analytical procedures and describing industrial operations, the latter coordinating and interpreting results of inorganic theoretical chemistry.

Many of the great chemists were great administrators, too, and some of them went far beyond the range of their particular university institutions. Marcelin Berthelot (p. 676) held high offices in the French government. Emanuele Paternò, born December 12, 1847, in Palermo, a student of Cannizzaro's, was very active in political affairs besides being a professor of chemistry at the Universities of Palermo (from 1872) and Rome (1892–1923). He became a senator in 1890, and in 1911 the title Marchese di Sessa was conferred upon him. He died on January 18, 1935.

Nicola Parravano, born July 12, 1883, began his chemical studies under Cannizzaro and obtained his doctor's degree in 1904 under Paternò in Rome. After directing applied chemistry at Padua (from 1913) and physical chemistry at Florence (1915–19) he came to Rome and directed the Institute of Chemistry from 1923 on as Paternò's successor. While doing outstanding work in metallurgy, catalysis, fuels, agricultural chemistry, and radioactivity, he showed great talent in the administration of science and its applications on a national scale. From 1929, he was head of the Accademia, a prominent and respected figure at all international conferences on chemistry and chemical economics.

Avicenna and Paracelsus, van Helmont and Boerhaave figure as prominently in histories of philosophy and of medicine as in the present volume on chemists. Hermann von Helmholtz (1821–1894), Einstein, and Heisenberg are among the few great scientists of more recent times to whom philosophers pay almost as much attention as do physicists. Modern chemists are absent from this honor roll.

The far-reaching thoughts they developed laid the foundations of chemical industry. Will the time come when chemists are not only scientists and industrialists but also philosophers? It could be only in a reversal of the situation that Robert Boyle so valiantly overcame!

NOTES AND REFERENCES

1 About Hellot, see "Mémoires de Paris," 1766, 167 (Paris 1769).
2 E. W. D. Tennant, "The Early History of the St. Rollox Chemical Works," *Chem. & Ind.* (*London*), *66*, 666 (1947).
3 J. Pigeire, "La Vie et l'Oeuvre de Chaptal," Spes, Paris, 1932.
4 K. R. Webb, J. A. C. Chaptal, *Chem. & Ind.* (*London*), 1443 (1956). See also: E. Armstrong and H. S. Lukens, *J. Chem. Educ., 13*, 257 (1936).
5 L. J. M. Coleby, "The Chemical Studies of Macquer," Allen & Umvin, London, 1938.
6 M. James, "Alfred du Pont," Bobbs Merrill, New York, 1941.
7 H. S. van Kloosters, "Bunsen, Berthelot and Perkin," in *J. Chem. Educ., 28,* 359 (1951).
8 A. W. von Hofmann, Emil Fischer, Heinrich Caro, "Peter Griess," in *Ber. Deut. Chem. Ges., 24, R,* 1007 and I–XXXVII (1891).
9 J. M. Cohen, "The Life of Ludwig Mond," Methuen & Co., London, 1956.
10 H. E. Armstrong, "The Mond's and Chemical Industry—a Study in Heredity," *Nature, 127,* 238 (1931).
11 H. E. Armstrong, "The Chemical Industry and C. Duisberg," *Nature, 135,* 1021 (1933).
12 C. Glaser, Obituary of H. von Brunck, in *Ber. Deut. Chem. Ges., 46 I,* 353 (1913).

13 J. D'Ans, "Carl Auer von Welsbach," in *Ber. Deut. Chem. Ges., 64 A,*
    49 (1931).
14 E. Berl, "Georg Lunge," in *J. Chem. Educ. 16,* 453 (1939).
15 W. H. Cliffe, "Peter Griess," *Chem. & Ind.,* 1958, 616.

EDUARD FARBER

·· *66* ··

Jacobus Henricus van't Hoff

1852-1911

JACOBUS HENRICUS VAN'T HOFF was born on August 8, 1852. His father, a physician, was a devoted student of Shakespeare's works. Both the mother and the children were deeply influenced by the father's predilection; often they all sat around the table, each with a copy in hand, following the father as he read aloud from his favorite author.

Young Henry had an appreciative eye for the beauties of nature and was able to describe eloquently what he had seen on his wanderings. At fifteen, he left the elementary school and entered the fourth class of the five-year *Hoogere Burgerschool* in Rotterdam. He became a leader of his class. The chemical instruction inspired him to experiment at home. Having passed the final examinations in 1869, he told his parents that he wished to continue in chemistry. The reaction was similar to that which Liebig experienced at the gymnasium in Darmstadt when his declaration, that he wished to become a chemist, produced scornful laughter. At that time, chemistry was not considered a possible career for normal people. Although conditions in Holland at the time differed from those during Liebig's boyhood, nevertheless van't Hoff's parents could hardly be blamed for objecting to his wish. The outlook for a chemist who planned to devote himself to pure science was far from favorable. Finally, it was agreed that he would study technology at Delft and then go on to the university. He applied himself so earnestly that after two years, instead of the usual three, he received the eagerly desired diploma and was top man in the examination.

The years in Delft were the beginning of a storm-and-stress period in the life of the nineteen-year-old, a period of unrest whose influence can be traced even into the last years of his life. Whereas his friends joyfully indulged in the pleasurable sides of student life, he immersed himself in August Comte's "Cours de philosophie positive." That the young student whole-heartedly accepted Comte as his guide is apparent to all who are acquainted with the elegant, stylized expositions of the French mathematician and philosopher.

949

Almost every page of his "Cours" contains guiding principles in which it is easy to discover a portion of van't Hoff's work program. Read, for example, the pages in which the French thinker describes the relations between chemistry and physics, or those in which he sketches the road to a more rational investigation in chemistry. "If the immediate relations of chemistry with the science of mathematics, and even with astronomy, are necessarily not extensive from the point of view of doctrine, it is not nearly so with respect to method. In this new sense, it is easy to see, on the contrary, that a sufficient preliminary use, among chemists, of the mathematical spirit and of the astronomical philosophy would inevitably exercise the greatest and most salutary influence on the manner of conceiving and cultivating chemistry, and hence would greatly hasten its later perfection." There is no doubt that these prophetic words contributed in considerable measure to van't Hoff's zeal for self-study of mathematics. With an iron determination, he began at Delft to study calculus; that he set high standards for himself in this regard is clear from his later statement: "My mathematical needs took me to the University of Leiden."

Whewell's "History of the inductive sciences from the earliest to the present time" was also diligently studied, so that the young technical student was now in a position to form an opinion of what the exact sciences had already accomplished and also, perhaps far more important to him, to appreciate the multiplicity of problems that were still unsolved. To obtain an insight into the ways and means by which a knowledge of natural phenomena is acquired and to learn something of the anaylsis of observational methods, he studied Taine's "De l'intelligence" which could be regarded as a positive psychology. The study of Comte and Whewell soon gave rise to the desire to become acquainted with the stories of the lives of the eminent ancients and moderns with whose mental products he had just become familiar; accordingly he read a number of biographies, acquiring information that stood him in good stead in later years.

However, all this was put definitely in the shade when he began to read Lord Byron's poetic works. In a very short time, he was utterly captivated by the English bard. From then on, the latter was his constant companion, in fact his model, almost his idol—

a fascination that was mirrored throughout van't Hoff's lifetime.

His qualifying examination was passed with flying colors in June, 1872. His decision to devote himself to chemistry remained firm, but he did not wish to continue at Leiden because no facilities or inducements in this direction were available at that university. Moreover, he did not find the atmosphere of the city itself to his liking. In the diary, which he kept in his last years, he noted: "In Leiden all was prose, the surroundings, the city, the people. In Bonn all poetry." Meanwhile the work in the laboratory went on zealously. "I have an excellent place in the laboratory; twelve of us are working in organic chemistry, and I am one of those looking for something new. So every day could be my happiest. Consequently I work very hard, sometimes without pause from 9 in the morning to 6 in the evening." This was written in Bonn, where he had gone, possibly attracted by the beautiful surroundings of the city, possibly by the desire to be under the direct influence of Kekulé. Whether the latter had any effect on him has been doubted by some in view of van't Hoff's statement in later years that Kekulé paid little attention to him. However, it is now generally conceded that Kekulé's work had a far-reaching influence on van't Hoff's development. Kekulé advised him to continue his studies at a large university. His next move was to Paris, where he wished to work for a time under the direction of Wurtz. In the meantime he passed (December 22, 1873) the *Doctoraal Examen* at Utrecht, which qualified him to obtain the doctorate later.

He arrived in Paris early in 1874, but he did not embark on a major piece of work during his stay in the French university. Instead, he enjoyed all the more the discussions which Wurtz held in the laboratory with the older students. Among them, van't Hoff was attracted especially by one whose name was destined to be linked with hs own, namely, Joseph Achille Le Bel (1847–1930), an Alsatian. At this time, the same thoughts were going through the minds of both, but neither mentioned his ideas to the other.

Van't Hoff did not stay long in Paris. His parents were impatiently awaiting the day when he would complete his university studies by acquiring the doctorate. So he returned to Holland bearing excellent testimonials from Kekulé and Wurtz. But before starting on his doctoral work, the candidate, now only twenty-two,

951

astounded the Dutch scientific world in September, 1874, with an 11-page paper in his native language bearing the lengthy title: "Proposal for the extension of the formulas now in use in chemistry into space, together with a related remark on the relation between the optical rotating power and the chemical constitution of organic compounds." There is no mention of the name of the author on the title page; it is found only at the close of the paper. Several months later, at the suggestion of Buys Ballot, professor of physics at Utrech, a French translation appeared with the title: "Sur les formules de structure dans l'Espace" van't Hoff was disappointed in his hope, expressed in the paper, that his views would stimulate a discussion in chemical circles. The time was simply not ripe for this step forward. On December 22, 1874, van't Hoff was awarded the degree *Matheseos Magister et philosophiae naturalis Doctor* at Utrecht, after he had defended his unimportant dissertation "Contribution to the knowledge of cyanoacetic acid and malonic acid" along with 32 theses. Even though one of the distinguished examiners told the young doctor: "Holland has a great shortage of men like you," this was rather a tribute to his general talent than to the merit of the dissertation. Returning home, he busied himself with the preparation of a French version of his Dutch article on the arrangement of atoms in space, which was published in 1875 with the title "La chimie dans l'Espace." He also began to seek a position, but without success. Finally, he was appointed assistant teacher in the Veterinary School at Utrecht, where he taught physics.

An incident occurred in November, 1875, which was important with respect to the rapid dissemination of the theory of the asymmetric carbon atom in that it brought this theory to the attention to the chemical world. Johannes Wislicenus,[1] who was then professor at Würzburg, inquired of van't Hoff whether he would give permission for a translation of his "Chimie dans l'Espace" by Dr. Herrmann, an assistant at Würzberg. In the letter Wislicenus said: "May I inform you that your theoretical development has given me much pleasure and great enjoyment, and in it I see not only an unusually ingenious attempt to explain facts that hitherto have not been cleared up, but I also believe that it will provide a goodly number of suggestions for our science and hence will be of epoch-making significance." The translation by Herrmann was published in 1876 under the title "Die Lagerung der Atome in Raume" with a foreword by Wislicenus. Like Byron after the appearance of his "Childe Harold," van't Hoff could now say, "I awoke one morning and found myself famous."

The brilliant development of the van't Hoff-Le Bel theory, i.e., stereochemistry, has certainly proved the error of the bitter criticism it originally engendered, especially from the pen of Kolbe.[2]

Even though some chemists feel that the theory of the asymmetric carbon has merely an historical and didactic significance, that as a theory it has had its day, nevertheless a look at the development of organic chemistry since 1874 reveals what an extraordinary, fruitful effect it has had on chemistry and its applications.

Only a few months after Kolbe's scathing criticism appeared, van't Hoff was appointed lecturer at the University of Amsterdam, where he later served as head of the department of chemistry from 1878 to 1896. His appointment was doubtless due to J. W. Gunning (1827–1900), professor of chemistry and pharmacy at Amsterdam from 1865. He became a lifelong friend to van't Hoff.

In reviewing the development of van't Hoff, it is not difficult to discern the roots of his "Views on organic chemistry" (1878, 1883) in the doctrines of Auguste Comte. The latter, in his "Philosophie positive," expresses the hope, in the pages devoted to chemistry, that he will succeed "in making some of the eminent minds which cultivate this fine science today realize the necessity of submitting all of the fundamental conceptions which compose it to a new and more rational elaboration." This path was followed by van't Hoff in his text, concerning which he himself stated in 1894, on the occasion of his lecture "How the theory of solutions arose": "Young as I was, I wished at that time to learn the relations between constitution and *chemical* properties. After all, the constitutional formula should eventually be the expression of the whole chemical behavior. . . . Thus there came into being my 'Views on organic chemistry,' which you surely do not know. Moreover, it is hardly worth while. However, to me it had the value that it sharply revealed to me an existing gap." The closing of this gap, and much that was of more importance, was accomplished by his "Études de dynamique chimique" (1884). This

953

book dealt not only with reaction rates, as indicated by the title, but in addition he discussed there the theory of equilibrium and the theory of affinity in such detail and extent that it seems justifiable to speak of a new *revolution chimique* taking place at that time, a turn in the course of chemical thinking whose consequences can be seen even up to the present in purely scientific fields as well as in the technical applications of science. The principal topics, such as principle of mobile equilibrium, condensed systems, transition temperature, measurement of electro-affinity, etc., attest to the service which this important book wrought. Admittedly, it met the same indifference initially that greeted his first book on the arrangement of atoms in space, but a review by Arrhenius in the *Nordisk Revy* (Uppsala) changed this situation. The review closes: "It has been the intention of the reviewer to call attention to the vast perspectives which the work of the author has opened for future research."

Since in none of his other books did van't Hoff appear so notably as an experimenter as in the "Études," it is well to point out this feature since there is a widespread opinion that his importance as a laboratory worker was of little weight. During his student career, he was anything but a deft manipulator, but thanks to his innate persistence and diligence, he knew how to acquire what was necessary in a short time. Convinced of the correctness of the dictum: "It is not sufficient to know the principles, it is necessary to know how to manipulate," it must have weighed on his mind that he could not afford to be lacking in a talent which he considered of prime importance for attaining success in his chosen science. Consequently, in Utrecht and later in Amsterdam he made every effort to develop new though simple equipment in order to acquire the requisite experimental skill. The difficult experiments in fields first cultivated by him such as the ones included in the "Études" give ample opportunity to see how far he approached this goal by self-training. Whoever saw him at work could testify that he arrived at an elegance in manipulation that could be the envy of many an experimenter. His chief aim was always to reach the desired goal with the simplest equipment in order to avoid as much as possible the less accurate corrections to which he had a pronounced antipathy. A typical instance is afforded by the great mass of important facts which he and his students gathered by means of the rather simple "dilatometer."

The ideas which van't Hoff developed in his papers submitted to the Swedish Academy of Sciences (1885), namely, "The laws of chemical equilibrium in the dilute, gaseous or dissolved state," "A general property of dilute matter," and "Electrical conditions of chemical equilibrium" have now become common property. However, at the time, the seed fell on fertile soil only in a single instance, and even this became apparent only after some time. It was Svante Arrhenius who appreciated the great significance of the van't Hoff theory of dilute solutions along with their relation to his own studies of electrolytic dissociation in dilute solutions. Accordingly, Arrhenius soon arrived in Amsterdam to remove the existing difficulties through intensive investigations. It is now generally known how this collaboration led to a theory of dilute solutions in the broader sense, and most chemists are aware of the great opposition that had to be overcome before this theory was accepted, an advance due in large measure to the efforts of Wilhelm Ostwald, the propagator of the new school of thought. No less important in the rapid development and dissemination of the new ideas was the *Zeitschrift für physikalische Chemie, Stoichiometrie und Verwandtschaftslehre,* founded in 1887 by Oswald and van't Hoff. These ideas were fruitful in other sciences, particularly physiology. However, it must be recognized that the much too sanguine hopes of many physiologists were not fulfilled, and Pekelhäring was correct when, in 1904, he presented van't Hoff with an honorary doctorate of medicine at Utrecht on the occasion of the dedication there of the van't Hoff Laboratory and said: "Whoever attempts with insufficient knowledge to apply physical chemistry to the processes occurring in the living organism, runs the risk—as has already been amply shown by experience—of coming to false conclusions."

Numerous young men soon came to Amsterdam from many countries to pursue their studies under van't Hoff's guidance. He was soon the recipient of many distinctions, including the Davy Medal of the Royal Society in London and the first Nobel Prize in chemistry (1901). In 1887 he received a call from the University of Leipzig. This catalyzed the Amsterdam authorities into providing the funds for a new laboratory, which was put into service in 1892. In the meanwhile the work had piled up so much that he sought means for obtaining relief from those duties which could be satisfactorily turned over to younger men, such as the lectures to medical students.

His intensive mental labors, the uninterrupted bodily strain required by the experimental researches, the wearing administrative tasks of the laboratory had a deep-seated effect on van't Hoff, an effect which was revealed plainly in later years when conditions had altered. There is little doubt that in Amsterdam he was a very different person than in Berlin, where he moved in 1896. Although a new laboratory had been built for him at Amsterdam, there was no lightening of his work load. His excellent health, his creative ability, which never sagged even when most taxing studies were under way, made it possible for him to meet the high demands he imposed on himself. A difficult task once completed, his mental abilities were readily restored by a period of rest and recreation. But eventually, the excessive demands which the Amsterdam post constantly made of him wore down his resistance; after long and careful consideration he accepted the distinguished invitation of the Prussian Academy of Sciences to make his home in Berlin. His time would now be his own, he could devote himself completely to his scientific work, and if he chose he could continue his pedagogic role by a weekly lecture at the University.

This move resulted in his "Vorlesungen über theoretische und physikalische Chemie" (1898), which was translated into many languages, and also his "Chemische Grundlehren nach Menge, Mass und Zeit" (1912). Furthermore, he now had the time to lecture to wider circles in Europe and America on the results of his work, satisfying a desire that he had nourished in vain for many years. But this was all incidental in comparison to the research projects which he conducted in his new surroundings with the assistance of collaborators from many countries and which he brought to a considerable degree of conclusion. The topic with which he and his co-workers were engaged was an intensive study of the conditions of the formation of oceanic salt deposits, particularly those being worked at Stassfurt. The question he wished to solve was divided into a number of parts: (1) What materials result if the individual salts, from which the Stassfurt minerals are constructed, are placed in water in any chosen quantities and the mixture is evaporated at constant temperature? (2) In what form, in what order, and in what amounts do these materials make their appearance? (3) What roles are played in this process by time, temperature, and pressure? Heinrich Precht (1853–1924), an acknowledged authority on the German potash industry, stated: "The studies conducted in Germany by van't Hoff benefited the potash industry especially. Many may regard them as theoretical investigations, but whoever has studied them in detail will appreciate the advantage they brought to the industry. Through his lectures in many countries, van't Hoff awakened interest in the potash industry to such an extent that it is impossible to evaluate the material value of these researches." van't Hoff brilliantly attained the goal he had initially set for himself when he moved to his new home, namely, to undertake a study of distinct German national flavor. If perhaps there are some who believe that a man of lesser stature could have carried such a task of self-denial to completion, it is enough to remind such carping critics that: "We should be thankful for a man such as he, who for the public good does something which is not glamorous."

A perusal of the diary which van't Hoff started in 1903 and continued almost to his death, will yield not only short statements about his commissions and omissions, but an insight into his particular state of mind and innermost thoughts. Thus he reports in these pages on the many cultural activities to which he devoted his hours of leisure, particularly the books he was reading. Many troubled thoughts are set down, because even this great man was not spared great sorrow. There gradually developed the pulmonary tubercular condition to which he finally succumbed. He, like his model Lord Byron, had always had a horror of having to endure pain. He was spared this ordeal, and several times he declared that there was nothing of which he could complain.

He died on March 1, 1911. The body was cremated and the ashes repose in the cemetery at Berlin-Dahlem. A lifelike marble relief portrait may be seen in the van't Hoff laboratory at Utrecht, and a bronze replica has been placed in the laboratory which he built and directed at Amsterdam.

GENERAL REFERENCES

Ernst Cohen, "Jacobus Henricus van't Hoff, sein Leben und Wirken," Akademische Verlagsgesellschaft, Leipzig, 1912.

A. F. Holleman, "My Reminiscences of van't Hoff," *J. Chem. Educ.*, 29, 379 (1952).

H. S. van Klooster, "van't Hoff in Retrospect," ibid., p. 367.

NOTES AND REFERENCES

1 Johannes Wislicenus (1835–1902) taught at Zürich and Würzburg and succeeded Kolbe at Leipsic in 1885. He made valuable contributions on stereoisomerism, acetoacetic ester, etc.

2 Hermann Kolbe, *J. prakt. Chemie* [2], 15, 474 (1877).

From: Bugge, "Das Buch der Grossen Chemiker," 2, 391–407.
Translated by Ralph E. Oesper.

ERNST COHEN

·· 67 ··

Henri Moissan

1852-1907

FERDINAND FRÉDÉRIC HENRI MOISSAN was born in Paris on September 28, 1852. His father was a minor official in the Compagnie des Chemins de Fer de l'Est; the mother aided the family income by sewing. The family came from Toulouse, a fact reflected in the looks and behavior of Henri Moissan. Throughout his life, his dark twinkling eyes, the unusual mobility of his gestures and his mode of thought betrayed his southern origin. In 1864 the family moved to the little city of Meaux (Seine-et-Marne) where his father, who later was praised for his perspicacity, allowed his son to enter the Collège municipal. There an excellent teacher of mathematics and sciences, James, sensed the outstanding endowment of the boy and encouraged him by free private instruction. Moissan in later years always remembered with sincere appreciation these services by his former teacher who, as he said: "fit naître en lui le goût travaille." Under his guidance, an interest in chemistry was awakened in the young Henri, which held him fast; this preoccupation obviously displeased the other instructors, since when Moissan left the Collège in 1870 he had not attained any kind of university rank.

In order to become self-supporting as soon as possible, but without forsaking completely his beloved chemistry, he became an apprentice in a druggist's shop in Paris. Here his chemical knowledge brought him his first practical success when he saved the life of a person who had been poisoned with arsenic. Despite this feat, he was not satisfied with his position. Conversations with his school friend, Jules Plicque, who was working in a laboratory headed by Dehérain at the Musée d'Histoire naturelle, led Moissan to resolve to devote himself entirely to chemistry. In December, 1872, he began to study chemistry in the laboratory conducted by Fremy in the Musée d'Histoire naturelle. He earned his living expenses by giving private lessons. He planned to enter industry as soon as possible, and set as his goal an annual income of 3600 francs. In 1874, he joined his friend Plicque in Dehérain's laboratory. The latter soon took note of his new student and was

961

attracted by him. Without trying to dissuade Moissan from his plan to go into industry, Dehérain pointed out that it might be of value to him sometime to secure an academic degree. The advice fell on fertile ground. Although it was difficult for him to cut down on his chemical work, Moissan started to make up his lower school deficiencies and studied first ancient languages and then physics. After several fruitless attempts, he passed the examination for the bachelor's degree in 1874, and in 1877 he became Licencié ès Sciences (B.Sc.).

Moissan's first scientific activity naturally was directed to the field pursued by Dehérain, namely, plant physiological chemistry. As early as 1874, they published in the *Comptes rendus* of the Académie a joint paper; "De l'absorption d'oxygène et de l'émission d'acide carbonique par les feuilles maintenues a l'obscurité." Later Moissan extended this investigation and used the results in a thesis for his apothecary examination. The essential finding was the definite proof that there is no direct connection between the oxygen uptake and the carbonic acid output by plants. Independent of the former, the carbonic acid is released because of the reactions occurring in the plant, even after days of complete exclusion of oxygen.

However, while he was still engaged in this plant physiological research, Moissan took the step which was to prove of primary importance to him and chemistry: he decided to devote himself to inorganic chemistry. The fact that he did this against the advice of Dehérain, who did not wish to lose his gifted student, testifies to the originality and determination of Moissan's spirit. It should be remembered that, at that time, almost all of the eminent French chemists, as well as their colleagues in other countries, had succumbed to the attractions of the vigorously flourishing organic chemistry. Only a few were dealing with inorganic problems since it was generally assumed that this branch of chemistry had already yielded its finest fruits and the later harvest could only be meager. The best of the isolated French inorganic chemists, such as Henri Sainte-Claire Deville, had turned to problems that were more or less physicochemical in nature, a branch which had long been underestimated and which was just beginning to be appreciated. In a speech delivered by the aged J. B. Dumas in 1876 on the occasion of the death of Charles Sainte-Claire Deville, the brother of the more famous Henri, he complained: "Our country occupies its place largely in organic chemistry, it neglects far too much the chemistry of inorganic compounds. Let us hope that there will soon arise, in the generation which follows us, a young scientist who will take up once more mineral chemistry and will know how to fertilize and revive it."

Moissan's publications numbered around three hundred; with few exceptions they dealt with inorganic-experimental topics.

His first inorganic research was on pyrophoric iron whose preparation had been described about fifty years earlier by Gustav Magnus (1802–1870), also in a first paper. Soon thereafter, Stromeyer had maintained that this pyrophoric material was not metallic iron at all but rather ferrous oxide. Magnus contradicted this statement vigorously. The re-examination of the question led to the finding, as is so often the case, that both were correct. The reduction of ferric oxide or the heating of ferrous oxalate yielded initially highly pyrophoric ferrous oxide, which on careful further reduction in a stream of hydrogen was converted into pyrophoric iron. Moissan was able to show that when hydrogen acts on Fe_2O_3 at various temperatures, there result in succession the oxides Fe_3O_4, FeO, and finally elementary iron. As with the latter, the oxides could be made to yield extremely active modifications by avoiding excessive heating, modifications which differed sharply in their behavior toward oxygen and nitric acid as contrasted with the forms that had been known for a long time.

At the suggestion of Sainte-Claire Deville, Moissan submitted his results to Debray, the discoverer of the ordinary ferrous oxide. His appraisal of the work was most favorable, and from then on he showed the greatest interest in the young chemist.

As already stated, Moissan passed his examination as *pharmacien de Iere classe* in 1879, and in this same year he was appointed Maître de Conférences (lecturer) and Chef de Travaux pratiques de Chimie (laboratory instructor) at the École supérieure de Pharmacie, a connection that was to continue during the most part of his scientific career. Besides he was Répétiteur de Physique (assistant teacher) at the Institut agronomique. In 1880, the degree of Docteur ès Sciences physiques was conferred on him by the University; the dissertation dealt with the iron oxides. The joys of independent research had completely conquered his former intention to go into industry, especially since he now had a regular though modest income. The fees from private lessons had been his principal means of support until then. His financial situation was also improved when his friend Landrin resigned the direction of the laboratory of the Union des Chambres syndicales. The chief function of this laboratory was to make analyses for private customers. These of course had less interest for Moissan, but gave him the opportunity to carry on his own work, which the other posts he held did not afford. Some earlier work on oxides of chromium was now supplemented by papers on chromium derivatives. He did not succeed in isolating the blue perchromic acid, discovered in 1847 by Barreswil, but he was able (1883) to prove that its formula is H_2CrO_5; he regarded it as a combination of CrO_3 with H_2O_2. A year later he described the crystalline H_2CrO_4, which corresponds to sulfuric acid.

Although these carefully executed studies were greeted enthusiastically by scientists, they did not meet the favor of the customers of the laboratory, whose analyses received a dilatory treatment. The orders fell off perceptibly; in fact the laboratory had to close its doors after a few years. This did not break Moissan's heart, since in the meantime he had become active in other fields.

In 1882 he married Leonie Lugan, the very young daughter of an apothecary in Meaux, in whose house he had been a welcome guest on his many visits to that city during his student days. The ancestors of M. Lugan had also been apothecaries; one of them had been a friend of the famous Vauquelin, the discoverer of chromium who had likewise started his career with pharmaceutical studies. The marriage was a most happy one and was terminated only by Moissan's death. His wife was his best comrade; she helped him as far as she could in his scientific labors and watched over his health, which he often abused by overwork. Their son, Louis (born 1885) was indoctrinated in chemistry at an early age by his father. M. Lugan proved an ideal father-in-law. He provided the new household with an excellent financial foundation

964

and advised Moissan to devote himself to scientific work without thought of financial return.

As soon as he found himself on an assured basis, Moissan began an exceptionally diligent and successful research activity which ceased only at his death. From among his many investigations, two chapters proved of special importance. These can be designated as "Fluorine" and "Electric Furnace," respectively. The following discussion will treat these main lines of research in continuous fashion without regard to the order of the publications. Only the outstanding features can be considered here.

The preparation of free fluorine was one of the great problems which the first brilliant period of inorganic chemistry could not solve. Many had worked on this problem before Moissan. The similarity of hydrofluoric acid to hydrochloric acid had been pointed out as early as 1810 by Ampère and Davy, and there was no longer any doubt that the former contained an unknown element which was named fluorine. Davy's extensive efforts to isolate this element were totally negative. The hoped-for decomposition of fluorides by treatment, in gold or platinum vessels, with chlorine or electricity failed completely. Even so there existed a widespread opinion that fluorine must be an extremely reactive material that tenaciously combined with other elements. The years merely brought confirmation of this idea. The Knox brothers and later Louyet, whose careless handling of hydrogen fluoride cost him his life, unsuccessfully tried to bring about a reaction between chlorine and mercury fluoride. Fremy made some progress. His efforts to secure a reaction between chlorine and oxygen on calcium fluoride were unfruitful but, on the other hand, he, like Gore, who in 1870 was the last before Moissan to attempt to isolate fluorine, made it highly likely that free fluorine resulted transiently from the electrolysis of molten calcium, potassium, and silver fluoride; but at the unavoidably high temperature the fluorine disappeared immediately because it at once attacked the containing vessel and the electrode. No progress followed from the attempt to electrolyze anhydrous hydrogen fluoride, which Fremy was the first to prepare by heating KHF_2, because the anhydrous acid did not permit passage of the current. When moisture was present, the products were only hydrogen and oxygen containing ozone.

The memory of Fremy's attempts were still alive in his laboratory and Moissan had learned about these experiments during his term of service there. He told himself that the preparation of free fluorine would have to be done at low temperatures and accordingly would most probably be accomplished with volatile nonmetallic compounds. However, very little was then known about such materials. Boron and silicon fluoride, which Moissan studied again in 1904, proved to be such stable combinations that he immediately became convinced that the reaction between fluorine and boron or silicon must be extremely violent. From that time on he used powdered silicon whenever he wished to test any gas for a possible content of free fluorine. Among fluorides of phosphorus, there was known the gaseous pentafluoride discovered in 1875 by Thorpe, and the phosphorus trifluoride described by Dumas as a liquid boiling at 60°. Struck by the lower volatility of trifluoride, Moissan started his research with an investigation of this compound. He soon announced (1884) several methods of preparing pure PF_3, which was gaseous, as expected. The most convenient procedure was to heat a mixture of lead fluoride and copper phosphide. The description of these experiments demonstrated the features of all of his later publications, namely, completeness and clarity. The methods of preparation, carefully worked out, were described so precisely that they could be repeated without difficulty; the chemical and most important physical properties of newly prepared substances were determined and reported in detail.

Moissan immediately used the new trifluoride in an experiment which had originally been proposed by Davy. The latter was of the opinion that free fluorine would most probably result from the reaction between oxygen and phosphorus fluoride, conducted in fluorspar vessels, because of the great affinity of phosphorus for oxygen. Davy could not carry out the experiment because the method for preparing phosphorus fluoride compounds was not known at that time. Moissan passed electric sparks through a mixture of phosphorus trifluoride and oxygen. The explosive reaction, however, did not proceed as expected; instead the product was the new gaseous phosphorus oxyfluoride, POF_3.

Moissan now changed his plan and attempted to bind the phosphorus of the phosphorus fluorides by means of glowing platinum. Since Fremy had already demonstrated the instability of platinum fluoride when heated, there was no danger that the fluorine would also be bound to the platinum. When Moissan passed the trifluoride over red-hot platinum sponge in a platinum tube, platinum phosphide and phosphorus pentafluoride resulted. Under these conditions, the latter probably immediately yielded a slight quantity of free fluorine; the issuing gas reacted with potassium iodide, silicon, mercury, and phosphorus, which was not the case beforehand. However, no free fluorine could be obtained. The experiments were rather costly since the platinum tube became unusable in a few minutes; consequently, Moissan gave up this line of attack. He, too, had now come to the conclusion that the preparation of fluorine at high temperatures was not feasible because of technical difficulties. Nevertheless, the characteristic fluorine reactions he had already obtained had whipped up his eagerness in much the same way as a detective is stirred when at long last he sees his quarry disappearing around a corner. Moissan, like his predecessors, now enlisted the aid of electrolysis and passed a current through arsenic trifluoride, which is a liquid at room temperatures. He rendered it conductive by adding hydrogen fluoride or potassium fluoride. But in a short time the current would no longer pass because arsenic had been deposited on the cathode; at least this was true of the weak electrical forces then available in the laboratory where he was working. Friedel provided better sources of power but Moissan decided that arsenic trifluoride would have to be abandoned chiefly because he had come to realize that this highly toxic compound was affecting his health.

Fremy and Gore had previously tried the electrolysis of hydrofluoric acid itself. Moissan prepared the anhydrous acid by Fremy's method, i.e., by heating potassium hydrogen fluoride in a platinum retort. He subjected this compound to electrolysis in a platinum U-tube cooled to $-50°$ by methyl chloride. New difficulties arose. Much hydrogen was evolved at the cathode, but the expected fluorine did not appear at the anode. It was found that the stoppers, which served for the insulated introduction of the anode, had been attacked and carbonized. They were replaced by pieces of fluorspar. The goal was now finally reached. On June 26, 1886, there streamed from the anode compartment a gas which immediately set fire to silicon and also exhibited the marvelous reactivity that had been expected of fluorine. With water it produced ozone; it liberated chlorine from potassium chloride.

On June 28 Debray read to the Académie a short communication by Moissan regarding his discovery, a statement which demonstrates that the critical judgment of its author was not dulled by his brilliant success. Moissan gave a brief account of his experiments and then stated: "It is possible in fact to advance various hypotheses as to the nature of the gas released; the most simple would be that it is fluorine, but it might be possible, for instance, that it is a perfluoride of hydrogen or even a mixture of hydrofluoric acid and ozone sufficiently active to account for the very energetic action which this gas exerts on crystalline silicon."

The validity of these findings had to be demonstrated to a committee appointed by the Académie; the members were Berthelot, Debray, and Fremy. Moissan, of course, made the most careful preparations, but when the committee appeared he obtained no fluorine. In fact, he could not secure any passage of the current through the hydrogen fluoride. After Berthelot sought to comfort the dismayed young scientist by citing the perverseness of inanimate material, the three eminent visitors left. The difficulty was cleared up in a few days. The fault lay in the doubly distilled hydrogen fluoride. In his original trials, Moissan had collected the product driven from the potassium acid fluoride directly in the platinum U-tube used for the electrolysis; the entrained potassium fluoride was caught here and provided the mixture with the conductance which the hydrogen fluoride did not have per se. Moissan now added some of the salt to the hydrogen fluoride before starting the electrolysis and from then on the generation of fluorine proceeded regularly. Of course, exceptions arose later on occasions. It almost seemed as though the fluorine wished to avenge itself on the master for having conquered it. This writer remembers that the fluorine apparatus failed for some reason when it was to be demonstrated to a student audience and could be shown in action only at the next lecture. The same thing happened during a lecture Moissan delivered in London before the Royal Society.

That fluorine really results from the electrolysis of a solution of potassium fluoride in hydrogen fluoride—electrolysis of hydrofluoric acid is actually as much of a misnomer as electrolysis of water—was demonstrated by Moissan by allowing the gas to be absorbed by heated iron, whereby no hydrogen was liberated. He likewise proved that a mixture of hydrogen fluoride and ozone had no special oxidizing powers.

The energetic action of fluorine on chemical substances was paralleled by the effect of its isolation on the scientific world, which at that time had not yet reached the *nil admirari* state of our time. The la Caze prize of 10,000 francs was awarded by the Académie to Moissan, who used the money to reimburse himself for what he had spent out of his own pocket for these experiments. Four months after the isolation of fluorine, Bouis, professor of toxicology at the École de Pharmacie, died and Moissan applied for the post. The Conseil of the École unanimously recommended his appointment, which was approved on December 30, 1886. He thus finally came into possession of a laboratory of his own, and though it was rather primitive and not very large he made it do until 1899. In 1888, he was elected to the Académie de Médecine in the pharmacy section, and in 1891 he succeeded Cahours in the Académie des Sciences. He had been on the list of candidates in 1888 and 1889, as successor to Debray and Chevreul, but had lost out to the older Schützenberger and Gautier. Until 1891, Moissan worked almost exclusively with studies of fluorine and fluorides. His book "Le Fluor et ses Composés" gives a good picture of his comprehensive researches.

As time went on, he considerably improved the method of preparing fluorine. He removed any hydrogen fluoride by passing the gas over sodium fluoride, and later by condensation with liquid air followed by fractional evaporation. The main advance came with the discovery (1899) that copper apparatus could be substituted for the costly platinum equipment. It was now possible to obtain up to 5 liters of fluorine in one hour. The handling of the gas was greatly facilitated when it was found (1899) that if moisture was carefully excluded glass is no longer attacked by fluorine; in fact the gas can then be stored for some time in glass vessels over mercury, provided it is protected from vibrations and hence from rupturing of the protective layer of mercury fluoride.

Mostly with the aid of free fluorine, Moissan prepared many new fluorine compounds, some of which he investigated thoroughly and described in excellent individual publications. He enriched organic chemistry (1888 and 1890, in part with Meslans) by describing the gaseous methyl fluoride, ethyl fluoride (b.p. $-33°$) and isobutyl fluoride, which are best prepared from the corresponding chlorine or iodine derivatives and silver or arsenic fluoride. The reaction between carbon and fluorine led to several carbon fluorides (1890) of which the most interesting was tetrafluormethane (b.p. $-15°$). It was prepared in pure form from fluorine and methane, chloroform, and carbon tetrachloride, or from the latter and silver fluoride.

Great interest was aroused by the gaseous sulfur fluoride SF_6 (prepared in 1900 in collaboration with Lebeau) because of its composition and its chemical properties. It resembled nitrogen in its chemical indifference and was not affected by heating to redness or by molten alkali. Sulfuryl fluoride prepared (with Lebeau, 1901) from sulfur dioxide and fluorine was fairly stable, whereas thionyl fluoride (1900) obtained from thionyl chloride and arsenic fluoride was quite unstable.

Among the metal fluorides he studied the fluorine derivatives of platinum (1889), of the alkaline earths (1890), of silver (1890, 1895), and of di- and trivalent manganese (1900). Noteworthy fluorine nonmetallic compounds of fluorine included the liquid iodine pentafluoride, IF_5 (1902), and nitryl fluoride, NO_2F (with Lebeau, 1905), a very reactive gas, liquefied at $-63°$, which like fluorine itself combines with silicon even at room temperature.

A pause in the study of fluorine chemistry came in 1891, and this line of study was vigorously resumed only after the preparation of the gas was made easier through the use of copper apparatus. The years 1891 and 1892 were occupied with successful studies of boron. It, too, was among the elements which were not known in the pure state prior to Moissan. Davy had observed the formation of the brown element when he subjected fused boron trioxide to a powerful electric current. Later, he and also Gay-Lussac and Thenard prepared it from potassium and boron trioxide. Deville and Wöhler improved this method by substituting sodium for potassium. In his first trials Moissan prepared boron by this procedure and from it he obtained, by heating with hydrogen iodide, the hitherto unknown boron triiodide, BI_3 (1891), which he immediately employed for several interesting reactions.

Since his experiments had shown that the boron which he was using was far from pure, Moissan retested the older procedures for preparing the element and came to the astounding discovery that even the most favorable case yielded a product containing only 70 per cent boron. The remainder consisted of boron trioxide, boron nitride, alkali, and iron. However, he succeeded in improving the reaction between boron trioxide and magnesium, which others had used previously, so that the product contained 94–95 per cent of boron; if the reduction was conducted in an atmosphere of hydrogen the purity rose to 99 per cent. No better method has since been found; all of the other suitable reducing metals form borides which cannot be removed from the reaction product.

A paper on the alkaloid, aricin (with Landrin 1890), and a second one on opium smoke (1892) are reminders that Moissan was professor of toxicology even though his chief interests lay in the inorganic field. He found that the poorer the quality of the opium the greater the content of the more harmful materials in its smoke.

While he was still studying boron, Moissan took up another problem of quite *general* interest: the artificial reproduction of the diamond. "The art of producing diamonds was pursued with the same ardor as was alchemy," wrote Berzelius in 1830. This effort, which earlier had taken very remarkable paths, was put on a firmer foundation after Lavoisier in 1773 had demonstrated, by burning diamonds with oxygen, that the gem consisted of pure carbon. But the artificial production of the diamond remained an unsolved problem one hundred years after Lavoisier's experiment. Although many had thought that they had found a satisfactory method, they invariably were proved wrong. In 1880, Hannay claimed to have obtained diamond chips by heating oils to redness with metallic lithium, but his claims were never confirmed. Not long after, Marsden said that he could prepare small diamond crystals by fusing silver with sugar charcoal. His paper received no attention, but since Moissan subsequently substantiated this claim by actual trials, Marsden deserves the credit for being the first to have prepared regular crystallized carbon. On the other hand, Moissan was the first to approach the subject in a comprehensive and systematic manner.

In the beginning he hoped—and here is the bridge from his fluorine researches to those dealing with the diamond—to arrive at diamonds by decomposing fluorhydrocarbons, since fluorine had been found to be a distinct "mineralizing" element in numerous instances. However, he obtained nothing but amorphous carbon. In his later trials he followed the paths of Nature herself. Whereas the earlier chemists, even Liebig and Wöhler, had supposed that natural diamonds were formed at relatively low temperatures, Daubrée, on the basis of studies of diamond-bearing meteorites and earths, stated in 1890 that diamonds must be formed under conditions of high heat and much pressure. The uniform development of the diamond crystal in all directions indicated that they are formed in a liquid or at least pliable environment. The fact that many diamonds are optically anisotropic and also that some specimens shatter for no apparent external reason indicates that they have been subjected to high pressure. Moissan himself investigated diamond-bearing earths from Brazil and South Africa. In them he found not only many microscopic diamonds but also graphite, a finding which made the high formation temperature still more likely. Without exception, the diamonds left some ash that contained iron. From this Moissan concluded that they had been formed in an iron-bearing environment and that perhaps, since iron is known to dissolve carbon, that they had simply crystallized out of iron. However, when he tried to prepare diamonds in this manner, he obtained graphite and amorphous carbon exclusively. At first he used an oxygen blast to melt the iron. Since he required higher temperatures than this afforded, he switched to the use of the electric furnace. This apparatus will be discussed later.

Moissan's attempts to prepare diamonds artificially had reached

972

an impasse when by chance they received a new impulse. On December 12, 1892, Charles Friedel reported to the Académie that he had found many tiny diamonds in a meteorite from Arizona. Moissan himself investigated a piece of this meteoretic iron and in addition to diamonds found that it also contained graphite and amorphous carbon. Previously, he, like many others, had doubted the occurrence of diamonds in meteorites, but now he was convinced that diamonds could arise from carboniferous iron and that he had not employed the proper experimental conditions in his early attempts. He had the happy thought of suddenly cooling molten iron that had been saturated with carbon in the electric furnace. The graphite crucible containing the iron was plunged into water. Carboniferous iron, like water, expands when it solidifies. When rapidly cooled, the outer layer of the metal solidifies first; therefore high pressures were exerted on the interior while the remaining iron became solid. Under these conditions, a portion of the carbon actually crystallized in the form of black and transparent diamonds. Treatment of the regulus with various acids dissolved away all the other materials so that the diamonds and the silicon carbide, formed at the same time, were left behind. These were separated by virtue of their divergent densities, only the diamonds sinking in methylene iodide.

The first communication of these findings was made to the Académie on February 6, 1893. The report soon reached the daily press and made the name Moissan extremely popular. The news that the precious stone could be prepared by a relatively simple process aroused fear or pleasure, depending on whether the reader actually owned diamonds or hoped to. However, the day of cheap diamonds of gem quality has not arrived even yet. Repetition of the experiment by Moissan himself (1894, 1896, 1905) and by others (Crookes, 1894; Majorana, 1896; Ludwig, 1901) invariably gave extremely low yields. They sufficed merely to prove that the diamonds yielded carbon dioxide when burned. Furthermore, the artificial diamonds, which were mostly black, and hence comparable to the naturally occurring carbonado, were minute. The largest obtained by Moissan was a colorless specimen 0.7 mm. long. In his laboratory it was called "Le Régent" after the famed brilliant in the Louvre.

973

In connection with his studies of diamonds, Moissan published also a whole series of observations on amorphous carbon (1895, 1902) and graphite (1894, 1895, 1897). He resumed his work on diamonds shortly before his death, employing improved apparatus.

Moissan's other researches with the electric furnace were of more importance to chemistry than his manufacture of diamonds. The first model of the *four électrique* which he used was quite small. It consisted of two pieces of lime, the upper serving as the cover. The lower piece was hollowed out so as to accommodate a 2-cm. carbon crucible containing the material to be heated, and two channels for the introduction of the approximately 1-cm. carbon electrodes, between which the arc was produced directly above the crucible. According to his collaborators, Moissan had contrived this furnace (1892) himself, without knowing anything of the various electric furnaces which had already been described in the literature and which were already in technical use. Davy (1810) and Pepys (1815) had used electricity as a source of heat; but practical importance had to await the means of producing stronger currents. Many forms of electrical furnaces were known before 1892. The so-called Moissan furnace was not really new; Pichon, Siemens, and Rogerson had previously described furnaces employing indirect heating by means of an arc. However, it would not be proper to deny him credit on such historical grounds. He had selected a furnace design which suited his experiments, one that was easy to construct and manipulate, one that eliminated all electrolytic action by the current and thus provided the best possible insight into the thermal reactions taking place in the furnace. He used this furnace with such skill that Moissan is generally regarded as the founder of high temperature chemistry, even though some of the reactions were discovered before him or independently of him. There is no doubt that his researches also contributed indirectly but definitely to the future technological advances in this field.

This little furnace was operated for the first time in June, 1892, in the École de Pharmacie. A small dynamo delivered the current of 40 volts and 45 amperes. Although interesting results were obtained, this apparatus was soon found inadequate. His slogan be-

974

came "More heat." To have more powerful currents available, he successively carried out his experiments in two other schools and at two electric power stations. Finally in 1900 an electric furnace was set up in his own laboratory. Its dimensions were much greater than his first model. Since large blocks of lime could not be obtained, he now constructed the furnace of limestone. The diameter of the carbon electrodes was 5 cm.; the graphite crucible had a capacity 100 times that of the original. If substances were to be heated in a particular atmosphere, the reaction was carried out in a carbon tube which passed through the furnace close to the arc. In some experiments, such as the preparation of titanium or the volatilization of carbon, the current consumption reached 2200 amperes at 80 volts. According to measurements by Violle, 3500° could be attained. Of course the temperature was much less than this in most of the experiments. It was shown that some of the reactions conducted in the electric furnace occur at 2000° or less.

In the application of the electric furnace Moissan had found an area which suited his tastes exactly. High temperature chemistry was a virgin field which yielded new facts and new compounds at every step, without requiring the previous preparation of the soil by modern theories or physiochemical methods. The concept of "the nonvolatile materials" was dispelled, just as fifteen years before the idea of "nonliquefiable gases" had been shown to be untenable. It was easy to prepare metals that had not been isolated previously; materials such as carbon, silicon, and boron, which were inactive at ordinary temperatures, reacted with almost all elements and formed carbides, silicides, and borides, of whose very existence practically nothing had hitherto been known. The results he had obtained thus far were compiled in his "Le Four électrique," a book of 400 pages published in 1897.

Moissan's studies of the metal hydrides were fruitful. These compounds had previously been rather rare and were considered to be alloys of "metallic hydrogen." Strangely enough, the crystalline lithium hydride, LiH, observed by Guntz in 1893, had received hardly any attention. Moissan prepared CaH_2, NaH, KH, RbH, and CsH from hydrogen and the respective metals (1898–1903). These compounds looked like salts rather than alloys; they did not conduct an electric current. They proved to be very reactive;

most of them ignited spontaneously when exposed to the air. If warmed with ethyl or methyl iodide, they yielded ethane and methane, and at room temperature they reacted with sulfur dioxide to give hydrosulfites, e.g., $K_2S_2O_4$. Acetylene reacted with them to yield acetylene metal carbides, and carbon dioxide with hydrides produced formates. The reaction between hydride and carbon dioxide, which at higher temperature yielded oxalate as well as formate, was found to be greatly influenced by water vapor. If moisture was excluded, potassium hydride and carbon dioxide did not react below $+54°$, whereas the reaction occurred even at $-80°$ provided the carbon dioxide had been passed over ice at $-85°$.

Moissan remained professor of toxicology at the École de Pharmacie for thirteen years. In 1899 he was appointed successor to Riche as professor of inorganic chemistry, which actually he had been all along. At the close of 1900, he was made a professor in the Faculté des Sciences at the University of Paris and took over the laboratory previously headed by Troost. He took a leading part in preparing the plans for the new chemistry section at the Sorbonne, but he died before they were realized.

In 1899 when the present writer came to Paris to work for a time with Moissan, he had just recently taken over the Riche laboratory. The École de Pharmacie, on the beautiful Avenue de l'Observatoire, was very attractive when viewed from the outside; the vestibule was adorned with mural paintings. The picture altered when the laboratories came into view. There was little light or space. Moissan's laboratory was on two floors. In one he himself worked along with one or two assistants; the rest of his collaborators were housed below on the ground floor. An international flavor permeated the atmosphere. In addition to several Frenchmen, there were at that time two Germans, an American, an Austrian, an Englishman, and two Norwegians who had come to learn his methods, particularly how to manipulate the electric furnace. The common language was German, which all understood very well with the exception of the Frenchman. In later years, Moissan continued to attract foreign students.

The most striking thing on entering the Moissan laboratory was its scrupulous cleanliness, which gave the lie to the old witticism that chemistry is the dirty part of physics. The wood floors were waxed every Saturday. Several days after the writer's arrival, Moissan was making his rounds through the room in which we were working. He suddenly took a look at the floor and asked: "Who did that?" Only then did I discover that this inquiry had been occasioned by a few drops of water from my wash bottle. We ordinarily spoke to Moissan rather seldom, but he kept himself well-informed about the progress of our work. The intermediary was usually Lebeau, who had been his assistant since 1890. Amiability was one of Moissan's fundamental characteristics, and with it he charmed everyone who came in contact with him. He had practically no personal enemies.

Although he spent much time in the laboratory, Moissan never lost his interest for nonchemical matters. He read almost every important piece of the current French literature and was an ardent collector of paintings and engravings. His special pride was several Corot landscapes which hung in his home on the Rue Vauquelin. He had an extensive collection of autographs from the period of the French Revolution. He was keenly interested also in technical questions and matters concerning the national economy. On his many trips he sought to gain a basis for forming his own opinion on such matters.

Moissan was considered one of the best scientific lecturers in Paris. To hear him was a real aesthetic pleasure, and his discourses were a welcome opportunity for foreigners to strengthen their knowledge of the French language. Without using much external effort—his slender, rather large, figure produced a more tranquil impression while lecturing than in face-to-face conversations—he held his audience through his clear exposition and the elegant, often humorous, form in which he presented his subject matter, an impression that was heightened by the pleasing tone of his voice.

The course of lectures on inorganic chemistry opened with an introduction to the entire field of chemical operations and theories, presented in a manner that made high demands on the acquisitive talents of the listeners. Many demonstrations were a feature of these lectures. The subsequent discussion of the individual elements was accompanied by not too many experiments, but these

977

had been carefully planned and required considerable apparatus, and they were carried out by his assistants. Moissan himself confined his attention almost entirely to the lecture. He was popular with the students, but nevertheless at times they behaved in a rather unseemly manner. The only seats in the auditorium were crude, low benches without numbers—no writing surfaces were provided. There was always a race to get the front places. At precisely 5 o'clock, the two doors at the top of the steep stairs were opened simultaneously by the janitors, and like a horde of savages, the students, who had been waiting a long time, rushed down the stairs; the women, with flying skirts, usually in the vanguard. The 15-minute interval before the lecture began was ordinarily filled by singing songs, mostly political in nature, and punctuated by stamping on the floor.

The general recognition which Moissan's personality and scientific achievements enjoyed were reflected in the many honors he received. In 1900 he was made Commandeur de la Légion d'Honneur. He was a member of almost all of the eminent academies and chemical societies. He was awarded numerous prizes including the Nobel Prize for Chemistry (1906). He was particularly pleased with the medal that was commissioned by his students and friends and handed to him in December, 1906, on the twentieth anniversary of the isolation of fluorine.

He could hardly look forward to more honors. The finest reward for which he hoped was the privilege of continuing his chemical career. He had no intention of resting on his laurels. In a speech he once declared: "We, all of us, should set our ideal so high that we can never attain it."

However, his plans for the future were made in vain. When he reached home from the laboratory on February 6, 1907, he suffered a severe attack of appendicitis. It yielded to treatment, but a recurrence on February 16 made an operation imperative. The operation was successful but the heart condition from which he had been suffering for some years was greatly intensified. He had come to realize in his later years that he had not taken enough care of his health. He once confessed: "Fluorine has taken ten years of my life." Death came to him on February 20, 1907. Thus closed this sunny life which shed so much light on science and gave so much warmth to his friends.

NOTES AND REFERENCES

Paul Lebeau, "Henri Moissan et Son Oeuvre," Institut de France, *Acad. sci., Paris,* Palais de l'Institut (1955).

F. P. Bundy, H. T. Hall, H. M. Strong, and R. H. Wentorf, "Man-made Diamonds," *Nature, 176,* 51 (1955).

From: *Ber. deut. chem. Ges., 40,* 5099–5130 (1907), abbreviated.
Translated by Ralph E. Oesper.

ALFRED STOCK

·· 68 ··

Emil Fischer

1852-1919

EMIL FISCHER was born on October 9, 1852, at Euskirchen, a small town not far from Cologne. The family was Protestant and had been in the Rhineland since the end of the seventeenth century. His father, with little formal education, nevertheless had become a successful business man. He made a name for himself in the community and was in comfortable circumstances at a fairly early age. The mother, nee Poensgen, came from a family that is still well known in Rhenish industrial circles.

The boy had a pleasant youth; his playmates were mostly his numerous cousins. After three years with a private tutor, he spent four years in the local public school. Then followed two years at the gymnasium at Wetzlar and two years more at the gymnasium in Bonn. Emil was an excellent student; he had a fine memory and a quick grasp of all kinds of subject matter. His final examination was graded "with great distinction" when he, as *primus ominum*, graduated from school in the spring of 1869.

There was some difficulty about choosing a career. In line with the family tradition, his father wished to train him for the business world so that Emil, the only surviving son (he had five sisters), could eventually become his successor. The youth preferred natural science, mathematics, and the exact sciences, especially physics. A compromise was reached and a trial period in business was begun. However, his dislike grew upon closer acquaintance with commercial matters, and his business tutor, his uncle and partner in the family lumber business, soon prophesized: "The boy will never amount to anything." Emil's father, conceding defeat, then consented to a university education. It is said that he clothed his decision in the declaration: "The boy is too stupid to be a business-man, so he had better become a student." However, he saw to it that chemistry was chosen as the field of study since it seemed likely that at least it would provide a living. The start of his higher education had to be delayed, since the eighteen-year-old youth had contracted a persistent gastric catarrh, and this had to be definitely cured before he could leave home.

He enrolled at the University of Bonn in the spring of 1871. He had no financial worries either during his student years or later in his career. Thanks to his father, he was a well-to-do student. It is true that the start of his studies did not bring him much pleasure. He listened to the brilliant lectures delivered by August von Kekulé with great satisfaction. In contrast, the laboratory instruction, in which Kekulé had practically no interest, was rather old-fashioned and unattractive. Emil's predilection for physics was still dominant and it required the full persuasion of his cousin and fellow student, Otto Fischer (1852–1932), to keep him from leaving chemistry. Together they transferred to Strasbourg in the fall of 1872, where the university in the newly regained Alsace had been provided by the German authorities with distinguished teachers and ample resources. Analytical chemistry was taught in modern dress by F. Rose in both the theoretical and practical aspects. It was especially the young Adolf Baeyer—the future discoverer of the synthesis of indigo—who attracted the young student and finally aroused his enthusiasm for chemistry.

In accord with the prevailing custom, as soon as he had finished his training in analytical chemistry, the young man began his doctoral work. The thesis topic was suggested by Baeyer. Here once more there were difficulties; his first experiment had an unfortunate ending. A precious preparation, which had required weeks to make, was lost together with several kilograms of mercury in the cracks and joints of the worn floor when Emil stumbled while carrying a large flask. However, neither Fischer nor Baeyer was discouraged by this accident. Research was successfully completed in the field of phthaleins, a class of dyes discovered by Baeyer, and the doctorate was conferred in 1874. According to his own account, the oral examination was not too brilliant, which is not surprising since, following the former French custom, every member of the Strasbourg faculty was privileged to put questions to the candidate. The geologist, in particular, was not impressed with the answers he received from Fischer, who had not prepared himself in this field at all. However, Baeyer who had a talent for recognizing latent powers, sensed the special and great endowments for chemistry possessed by the fledgling Doctor Fischer and immediately offered him a post as his assistant.

Fischer made his first great discovery while still at Strasbourg, that of phenylhydrazine. In his hands this compound later became an important reagent for his own researches, and it was an integral link in the synthesis of antipyrine, a successful febrifuge, carried out by his own student and friend Ludwig Knorr (1859–1921). The discovery of phenylhydrazine was in itself an accident, and it offers a prime example of how unexpected findings, that seem unfortunate at the time, can often lead to significant successes. The logical follow-up of what initially appeared to be an unsuccessful student experiment eventually led to this achievement.

In 1875, Baeyer accepted a call to Munich as successor to Justus von Liebig. He persuaded his young assistant, who had already earned his spurs, to accompany him to the Bavarian capital. In the fall of 1875, Fischer took over the assistantship in the organic division of the chemistry department.

He had spent seven semesters in Strasbourg. In addition to his training in chemistry, which occupied most of his time and attention, he had diligently studied physics under August Kundt and his assistant, Wilhelm Röntgen, and mineralogy under Paul Groth. However, the initial urge to change to physics had vanished. Baeyer's influence had swept the board. Fischer later declared that next to his father he owed to this teacher most of what he had accomplished in his life.

In Munich, Fischer and a number of his collaborators worked on the newly discovered hydrazines. At this university it was still the custom to recognize the doctorate from another school only after a local oral re-examination, the so-called *nostrification;* Baeyer lowered this hurdle for his assistant by quizzing him only about hydrazines, a field that of course was far better known to its discoverer, Fischer himself, than to any of his examiners.

At the insistence of Baeyer, Fischer qualified as *Privatdozent* in 1878. The assigned theme of the qualifying lecture was: "The present problems of chemistry." The candidate was given three days for preparation. Fischer was no born orator. Carefully writing down the text of the lecture was a necessity for him on all occasions. But by virtue of his excellent memory he was then able to deliver the speech freely and literally, without ever once referring to the manuscript. His speeches and lectures thus gave the impression of being freshly conceived and full of life. Moreover, until his last years, his very keen and impressive eyes were always directed to his audience so that every listener had the feeling that he was being spoken to individually.

His cousin Otto Fischer had followed him to Munich, and shortly before Emil's qualification they collaborated in a new field. Synthetic organic dyes had become of great interest to the chemical industry as well as to the consumers. The first of such coloring matters prepared from coal tar had been discovered through purely empirical methods. Their structure and constitution were still unknown. A. W. Hofmann, the brilliant head of chemistry at the University of Berlin, evolved a theory of the constitution of these dyes. Through their convincing experiments, Emil and Otto Fischer proved that a second theory was correct as regards another class of dyes, namely, the derivatives of triphenylmethane. This success contributed fundamentally to the further technical development of these artificial dyes, and their discoverers became widely known.

On the basis of this success, and because of a half-year's training under F. Rose at Strasbourg, Emil Fischer received the associate professorship in analytical chemistry at Munich in 1879. He retained his interest in organic chemistry, of course, but also took intense interest in the young chemists working in his division and their analytical researches. He spent the entire day from 8 to 6 in the laboratory and postponed the usual big meal from noon to the evening. His lectures were popular among the students, even though at first his rather unfamiliar Rhenish dialect created considerable difficulties among the Munich students.

In the meantime, his father had become reconciled to his son's choice of profession and, proud of his successes, bequeathed to him a sum that made him financially independent. Consequently, having no need to worry about money, Emil Fischer was able to devote himself entirely to his scientific activities and academic career, which in those days was still less lucrative for young professors than now. Actually, at twenty-seven, Fischer was in a position to refuse his first call to a full professorship (at the Technical University of Aachen) because he did not wish to leave the inspiring circle then active in the Munich laboratory.

However, two years later he accepted an appointment to the chair in chemistry at Erlangen. His new facilities consisted of a somewhat smaller chemistry building which required only a few necessary improvements, particularly the installation of an adequate ventilation system for the laboratories. To the former fields of his research he now added a new line, entering for the first time the border region between chemistry and physiology, namely, the chemistry of the purine compounds. These included the active materials contained in coffee, tea, and cocoa, i.e., caffeine (or theine) and theobromine, which in the course of time were found to be physiologically very important components in the cell nuclei and in the nucleic acids. Together with a number of capable younger associates, Fischer explored a whole series of compounds in this field with respect to their constitution, established their structure, and eventually accomplished their synthesis. The brilliant discovery of antipyrine, by Knorr, who had followed Fischer from Munich, occurred at Erlangen.

Fischer's successes had brought him to the attention not only of the scientific world but also that of the chemical industry. A number of his students were doing excellent work in industry. In 1883, the Badische Anilin- und Soda-Fabrik asked Fischer to take over the direction of its scientific laboratory, a post formerly held by Heinrich Caro (1834–1910). The offer was tremendously attractive from the salary standpoint and because of the much greater facilities available for research. None the less, Fischer refused to sacrifice the freedom provided by his academic surroundings, advantages which still form the most important basis of university teaching and research. His independent financial status doubtless made the decision much easier.

The last part of his Erlangen period was darkened by a serious illness. An obstinate chronic catarrh, which also attacked the intestinal tract, forced him to take a year's leave of absence. For the second time in his life, this serious ailment warned the young man not to overexert himself. From that time on he lived more carefully and worried excessively about simple colds that others passed over without much thought. It was his state of health that also caused him to refuse the flattering offer from the Federal Technical University of Zurich, where he would have succeeded Viktor Meyer.

Soon after he had resumed his duties he received a call from the University of Würzburg. The Würzburg authorities, who were aware of his illness, had made certain of his recovery before sending him this offer. One of the Würzburg faculty, the aged zoologist Semper, called on Fischer in Heidelberg where he was visiting and enticed him to ascend the Heidelberg hills and drink champagne together. Fischer came out of this examination in much better shape than the examiner, who reported back to his colleagues that "the candidate is completely healthy and probably will outlive all of you."

In comparison to Erlangen, Würzburg was tempting. It offered a wider professional scene of action, the faculty contained a number of especially inspiring colleagues in various fields, who awaited with open arms the now eminent young chemist. The city and its surroundings were much more attractive than Erlangen. Fischer accepted the call, but with open eyes. The rather old chemistry building had to be renovated, particularly by installing effective ventilation, and in addition a new building was promised in the not too distant future. Actually this was constructed by his successor, Otto Fischer, according to the plans drawn up by Emil Fischer. Nevertheless, Fischer counted his seven years at Würzburg among the happiest of his career. He enjoyed the city and its surroundings, the magnificent location on the Main in the midst of a fruitful hilly landscape, and the civic and ecclesiastical structures, in which German baroque had reached it peak. Since the city was not too large, a more intimate relationship was possible between the professors and students, and its development was favorably reflected in their scientific activities. Although a Protestant, Fischer was on very friendly terms with a number of the representatives of the Catholic theology, a fine feature of the tolerance that distinguished life in Würzburg at that time, which appealed greatly to Fischer, who abhorred all intolerance of religious and political faiths. By express order of the Bishop of Speyer, twenty-five Catholic theologians regularly attended Fischer's lectures so that they might be able to bring to the members of their congregations some understanding of the activities in the great chemical works of the Palatinate, particularly the Badische Anilin-und Soda-Fabrik, where many of the parishioners were employed.

A group of capable young chemists soon gathered around Emil Fischer. Ludwig von Medicus was already in Würzburg as professor of applied chemistry. Knorr and Hermann Reisenegger soon followed from Erlangen. Others included Wilhelm Wislicenus, Julius Tafel, and Oskar Piloty.

A definite change of Fischer's personal life occurred during this time. Years before he had accidentally become acquainted on the train between Munich and Erlangen with the Erlangen anatomist Gerlach and his daughter Agnes. Obviously a personable full professor, only thirty-two years old, would constantly be subject to attacks on his bachelorhood, but hitherto all such campaigns, especially by the faculty wives, had been fruitless. He himself once had written that "he had definitely decided to travel his life's path alone." However, this resolve seems to have become weaker at the start of his Würzburg period. In 1885 he closed a letter to Baeyer: "My best regards to your wife and tell her in all secrecy that I wish I too had one." His marriage to Agnes Gerlach ushered in an all too brief period of happiness for Fischer. She seems to have been a very attractive and lovable woman. His father was delighted with her when the young couple visited Euskirchen, and there are many other evidences of her beauty, her kindness, and her understanding care for her husband. They had three sons. Unfortunately, only seven years after their marriage, she died of a middle-ear inflammation.

Thanks to the happy domestic atmosphere, and especially because at this time of his life he derived particular joy from his achievements, the years in Würzburg represented a peak in his career. First the studies of the purine derivatives were continued and extended to related compounds. They led—later in Berlin— to a well-rounded picture of this important field. Especially important and successful were the investigations carried out in Würzburg on the simple sugars. Their structures, on broad lines, were already known, but the numerous cases of isomerism were still to be elucidated. Tenacious and painstaking steps finally enabled him to reach the complete application of the theory of the asymmetric carbon atom to this field and to untangle this complicated subject. At almost the same time he began the synthesis of the simple sugars, which reached an imposing apex in the synthesis of mannose, fructose, and glucose. On June 23, 1890, at a special meeting of the German Chemical Society he gave a comprehensive report on the status of carbohydrate research. It must have been an unusually fascinating lecture. Even so keen a critic as Carl Harries wrote: "I have never heard a better lecture with respect to form and content, filled with enthusiasm and genuine moderation; in it the truly great investigator came clearly into view. Emil Fischer became for us the yardstick by which to measure all other personalities."

When A. W. Hofmann died in the spring of 1892, the Berlin faculty suggested as possible successors Kekulé, Baeyer, and Emil Fischer. Negotiations were successfully concluded within two months after Baeyer stated that he would not leave Munich. It probably was not easy for Fischer to decide to leave Würzburg and take over at Berlin. He was only forty when he assumed the most important chair of chemistry in Germany. One of the principal promises made to him by the ministry was for a new chemistry building. The structure on Georgenstrasse, built by Hofmann when he went to Berlin from London in 1865, was no longer adequate for the ever-increasing teaching and research demands. However, it was almost eight years before the new building on the Hessische Strasse could be occupied. The negotiations conducted by Fischer in his customary insistent and tenacious manner with regard to planning this large project earned him the respect, recognition, and eventually the friendship of Privy Councillor, Friedrich Althoff, the influential Prussian Minister of Education. The great chemical industries had also taken a hand in these tedious negotiations, especially with the Prussian Ministry of Finance. For many years this laboratory structure was a model in the efficient arrangement of its rooms.

In Berlin, the researches were continued on the two main topics that had occupied his attention during the last years. The chemistry of the purines was brought to a certain degree of completion. The field of carbohydrates was widened and extended

990

primarily to the glycosides, the oligosaccharides, and the glycoside-splitting ferments (enzymes).

His work on the purines and carbohydrates won world-wide recognition and brought him the Nobel prize in 1902. It was the second such award in chemistry. When closing his remarks on this occasion the president of the Swedish Academy of Sciences said: "The special method of investigation which characterized organic chemistry during the past decades has found its highest development and finest form in Fischer's sugar and purine researches. They can be classed as being without superiors from the experimental standpoint."

Later, Emil Fischer brought these two fields together. The N-glycosides of the purines and pyrimidines occur in the nucleic acids, which are the building units of the nucleins. The first model experiments leading to the synthesis of definite nucleosides from sugar and purine—or pyrimidine—derivatives were carried out and nucleoside-like compounds were obtained by condensation with phosphoric acid.

His success in these two fields gave Fischer such confidence in the methods of organic chemistry that, after the first years in Berlin, he turned to a new topic, namely, the proteins. He began with the simple and feasible. In his synthesis of the sugars he had found several methods of resolving racemates into their optically active components. The simplest of the then known building units of protein, the amino acids are—with the exception of glycocoll—asymmetrically constructed. The material obtained by synthesis separates in the racemic form and, to be comparable to the natural product, must be resolved into its optically active components. The first amino acid studies, i.e., the first of Fischer's protein researches, dealt with the resolution of the synthetic optically inactive amino acids into their optical antipodes. As a supplement to these studies, Fischer sometime later investigated the application of the Walden inversion in the synthesis and transformation of the amino acids. He showed that this kind of substitution is much more prevalent than had been suspected.

In 1901, Fischer for the first time prepared the esters of the amino acids and stressed the fact that they can be distilled. This was an extension of work that had been initiated some ten years earlier by Theodor Curtius. Glycyl-glycine, the first simple dipeptide synthesized by Fischer, was described in 1901 in collaboration with Ernest Forneau. This same year also saw the publication of the first hydrolysis of casein with subsequent ester formation and fractional distillation.

These protein investigations were continued on a large scale for years. Amino acids that occurred in nature were prepared in the laboratory and new examples were discovered. The synthesis of the oligopeptides was extended and reached its peak in octo-deka-peptide, which had many of the characteristics of a natural protein. The analysis of protein hydrolysates was accomplished, with the collaboration of Emil Abderhalden, through the fractional distillation of the esters and led to a more precise understanding of the composition of the proteins.

Other areas of investigation were added in time. Following a visit by The Svedberg, the noted Swedish authority on colloids, Fischer attempted to prepare what for that time was regarded as a "high-molecular" but well-defined product. This iodophenylosazone of an aryldisaccharide had a molecular weight of more than 4000.

The ferments (enzymes) also engaged his attention in connection with his studies of carbohydrates and proteins. He was one of the first to emphasize the specificity of ferments and expressed this fact in the oft-quoted declaration: "A ferment fits its substrate as a complicated key its lock."

His frequent vacations in the Black Forest led him to an additional field of study. The large old evergreens there are often heavily festooned with lichens, and he became interested in the chemical substances contained in the latter. This study brought him, via the polyesters of phenolcarboxylic acids, to the "depsides." In close connection with these studies was an investigation of the tanning substances. Eventually they were found to be sugar derivatives of gallic acid and similar phenolcarboxylic acids.

Finally, in his last years he turned his attention to the fats. Although these researches were not completed, his study of the simple esters of glycerol produced an important finding: the acyl wandering in esters of aliphatic polyhydroxyl compounds, which had already played a part with respect to the polyphenols in the study of depsides.

His position in Berlin brought him many responsibilities and duties. He served several times as president and vice-president of the German Chemical Society. He was a member of the Prussian Academy of Sciences, and as such looked after the interests of chemistry, but also cooperated along other lines. For instance, despite vigorous opposition, he successfully campaigned for the granting of a large sum to defray the costs of a solar eclipse expedition whose main object was to test the theory of relativity.

He seldom took part in the work of the faculty of the university, but on the rare occasions when he was interested he knew his goals and usually gained his objective especially when the matter at hand involved the summoning of eminent scientists to become professors.

However, it became increasingly difficult for him to find the time for these outside activities without slighting his teaching and research duties. Thus he constantly sought to find some relief from the routine teaching by turning over to younger men first the main demonstration courses in organic chemistry and then those in inorganic chemistry. But even then he found that the academic teacher expends far too much time and energy on these extracurricular matters to the detriment of his most important duty, i.e., his research activities. These thoughts were largely responsible for his active and fruitful participation in the founding of the pure research laboratories under the auspices of the Kaiser Wilhelm Gesellschaft. One of the first of these was the Kaiser Wilhelm Institut für Chemie, built at Dahlem in the outskirts of Berlin in 1911. He took an active part also in the founding of the Kaiser Wilhelm Institut für Kohlenforschung at Mühlheim, which was completed in 1914 just prior to the outbreak of World War I. The scientific accomplishments of these research institutions, which were joined eventually by others devoted to various fields, proved the wisdom of the basic idea which he had so ardently advocated.

Although Fischer limited his own scientific endeavors to certain fields of chemistry, he never lost sight of the importance of other topics. A number of nonorganic eminent chemists were trained in his Berlin institute and the researches carried on there were not restricted to organic subjects. Franz Fischer, the discoverer of the

Fischer-Tropsch synthesis of hydrocarbons and Alfred Stock, the well-known inorganic chemist, are typical examples. Emil Fischer early sensed the significance of radioactivity. He provided working space in his Berlin laboratory to Otto Hahn and Lise Meitner until they, through his influence, moved into the newly erected Kaiser Wilhelm Institut für Chemie.

World War I was a heavy blow to Emil Fischer. His research activities were curtailed and conducted only with great difficulty. He not only endured the general results of the war and the German defeat but lost two of his three sons.

After the close of the war, the research activity was resumed at an increased pace. But cancer, that dread malignant disease which he himself had once tried to vanquish by chemotherapeutic means, attacked him. When the diagnosis was confirmed he put his house in order. But his will to live was gone. He died on July 15, 1919; his grave is in Wannsee near Berlin.

Scientific accomplishments, planned and carried out with far-seeing objectives, but firmly rooted in carefully executed small studies, an unswervable love of truth, which invariably submitted to the experimental findings no matter how seductive the theory, a keen understanding and an artistic intuition in minor as well as major occasions, reveal the great chemist in Emil Fischer. His comprehension of other problems in chemistry and the natural sciences and his entire personality make him one of the truly great German scientists. As stated by Richard Willstätter and echoed by all who knew Emil Fischer and his work:

> He was the unmatched classicist, master of organic-chemical investigation with regard to analysis and synthesis, as a personality a princely man.

NOTES AND REFERENCES

Emil Fischer, "Aus meinem Leben," Verlag Julius Springer, Berlin, 1921.

Kurt Hoesch, "Emil Fischer. Sein Leben und sein Werk," Verlag Chemie, Berlin (now Heidelberg), 1921.

Burckhardt Helferich, "Emil Fischer," Deutsches Biographisches Jahrbuch, 2, Überleitungs band, Verband der Deutschen Akademien, Berlin, 1917–21.

Burckhardt Helferich, "Emil Fischer, sein Leben und seine wissenschaft-
lichen Leistungen," Festschrift der Stadt Euskirchen, 1952.
Burckhardt Helferich, "Emil Fischer zum hundertsten Geburstag," Z. angew.
Chem., 65, 45–52 (1952).

Translated by Ralph E. Oesper.

BURCKHARDT HELFERICH

·· 69 ··

Sir William Ramsay

1852-1916

THE name of Sir William Ramsay calls to mind at once, with all their meaning, two capital discoveries, to some extent paradoxical: On the one hand, the existence in the atmospheric air of a series of gaseous elements, which their chemical inertness relegates to the very borderland of chemistry; on the other hand, the production of one of these gases, helium, by the spontaneous disintegration of the radium atom, two classes of facts essentially new and of fundamental importance, whose discovery was possible only to an investigator of the highest rank, capable through exceptional ability, natural or acquired, of bringing light into the darkness of the unknown.

Of Scotch origin—he was born in Glasgow in 1852—Ramsay's hereditary influences were most favorable. In his family were chemists and doctors of note, and one of his uncles, Sir Andrew Ramsay, was a well-known geologist. Thus, as he himself liked to recall, Ramsay was descended from ancestors well above the average intellectually and in scientific pursuits, and he was well aware that he owed to them his calling and his ability as a chemist.

Having begun his studies in his native city, Ramsay went to complete them in Germany, at first at Heidelberg, with Bunsen, and afterwards in Tübingen in the Fittig laboratory, where after some researches on the ammonia compounds of platinum, he studied the toluic acids. Organic chemistry attracted him by the flexibility of its combinations and the ingeniousness of its structural theories. On his return to Glasgow, where he secured a post as assistant, he studied specially the pyridic group, doubtless attracted by the problem of the synthesis of the cinchona alkaloids.

In 1880, at the age of twenty-eight, given the title of professor of chemistry at the University of Bristol, Ramsay began, in collaboration with his assistant, S. Young, a series of works on physicochemistry which were not slow in being noticed. They had for an object the revision of the physicochemical properties of a certain number of liquids, water, alcohols, ethers, hydrocarbons, etc., with a view especially of determining exactly the relation of these properties to the atomic or molecular weights.

For the execution of so many delicate researches, all kinds of new apparatus had to be designed and constructed, with the result, extremely fortunate for his following career, that Ramsay became a very adroit blower of glass. Many of these contrivances are in everyday use in laboratories.

It was in 1887 that Ramsay was called to the University College at London, to succeed Williamson in that chair of chemistry already renowned, which he was by his efforts to make shine with a great light. For thirty years in fact, Ramsay was to display in this post of honor the most fertile and brilliant activity. His peculiar qualities as an experimenter and his originality stood out in striking relief in a work which he published in 1893 in collaboration with Shields. Following a remarkable series of researches on surface tensions and densities at different temperatures, Ramsay gave to science the first experimental method of determining the molecular weights of substances in a liquid state.

We shall leave here various other works, of a special nature, in order to come without more delay to those researches which were to immortalize the name of Ramsay.

In 1894 Ramsay was forty-two years of age. His work was already considerable in amount and his reputation solidly established, but he could not yet be called a celebrity. In possession of scientific knowledge as profound as it was extensive and varied, a penetrating mind with broad vision, a philosopher mindful of the general movement of the sciences, and eager to solve the mysteries of nature, free from all dogmatism and with mind open to even the most daring conceptions, an experimenter of finished technique, an enthusiastic spirit, Ramsay was ready for epoch-making discoveries. Given a favorable occasion, his genius would be fully equal to the task. Here is the occasion.

As often happens in scientific research, a chance observation may lead to the most unexpected results. Lord Rayleigh, who for several years had pursued with meticulous care the determination of the density of the principal simple gases (hydrogen, oxygen, nitrogen), noticed that the density of the nitrogen extracted from the air through absorption of other known gases was always greater than that of chemical nitrogen, coming from different sources—oxides of nitrogen, ammonia, urea, etc. The difference affected the third decimal and did not exceed one-half per cent, but it was certainly more than experimental error.

Three hypotheses could explain this irregularity. The atmospheric nitrogen might be constituted in part of complex molecules of nitrogen comparable to the oxygen compound called ozone. Conversely, in the chemical nitrogen a certain proportion of the molecules might be dissociated into free atoms. But the density of neither of the gases, after being kept for eight months, underwent any change, and the permanent existence of condensed nitrogen or of dissociated nitrogen (atomic nitrogen) would scarcely be likely. Lord Rayleigh, who had at first accepted these explanations, rejected them to adopt the third hypothesis, according to which the atmospheric nitrogen is constituted of a chemical nitrogen mixed with an unknown gas of greater density. Being consulted by Lord Rayleigh, Ramsay was of the same opinion, and the two scholars at once united their efforts to isolate the mysterious gas whose existence was thus revealed.

It is interesting to recall here that in the fundamental experiments in which Cavendish, a century before, had established the formation of nitric acid by the prolonged action of electric sparks on a mixture of oxygen and nitrogen in the presence of moisture, the celebrated English chemist had noted that even after a very long time there always remained, after absorption of the oxygen in excess, a small gaseous residue representing about one one-hundred-and-twentieth of the volume of nitrogen. But the observation has passed unnoticed, and until the researches of Lord Rayleigh, the nitrogen in the air had been considered as a simple gas, identical with "chemical nitrogen."

While Lord Rayleigh, taking up again the experiments of Cavendish, verified the fact that atmospheric nitrogen does indeed leave, after the action of the oxygen and the spark, a residue which could not be overlooked, Ramsay attacked the problem by a purely chemical method, that of absorbing the nitrogen by magnesium at red heat. The repeated action of this metal increased the density of the gas. From 14, its weight in relation to hydrogen, the density increased little by little to become fixed in the neighborhood of 20.

What remained was a new gas, absolutely distinct from nitrogen, characterized, aside from its density, by a peculiar spectrum very rich in lines in all regions and, a fact without precedent, by absolutely no ability to combine with any other substance whatsoever.

At the British Association meeting at Oxford in 1894, at the memorable session of August 13, Lord Rayleigh and Ramsay announced in turn that the nitrogen of the air is not pure nitrogen, and that it contains a small proportion of a gas more dense and much more inert, to which they gave, on account of its chemical inertness, the name of argon (α priv.; $\epsilon\rho\gamma o\sigma$, energy). This communication caused a great sensation among the audience, and the daily press took up the matter at length.

But chemists are generally conservative, and although the discovery was affirmed by two scholars so well-qualified, many remained incredulous. It was not certain that argon was a simple substance. The molecular weight, according to the density, being 40, it might be a form of nitrogen cyanide CN_2; it was noticed also that a triatomic molecule of nitrogen N_3 would have a weight of 42, a figure not far from the one given above.

A few months sufficed for Ramsay to clear up the question and dissipate all doubts. The comparison of the specific heats at a constant volume and at constant pressure shows an equally unexpected fact—that the molecule is monatomic, and consequently the new gas can only be an element.

To find in the air a new gas, and, in addition, one of absolute chemical inertness, is indeed a truly great discovery. It brought at once to the authors a deservedly great renown. Ramsay was not slow in adding to it through other researches not less surprising. And it was here again that a fortunate opportunity presented itself to him; he exploited it with admirable and masterful decision.

Early in 1895 Ramsay learned, through a letter from Sir Henry Miers, that Hillebrand, chemist in the United States Geological Survey, had observed, while treating a uraniferous mineral, cleveite, with boiling sulfuric acid, the giving-off of a gas which appeared to him to be nitrogen. The effect produced on Ramsay by this news was entirely characteristic of his scientific temperament. Many chemists, while finding the observation interesting, would have put off the study of the subject until later, when they might have more leisure. Ramsay, on receipt of the letter from Sir Henry Miers, called the laboratory aid and dispatched him immediately to the shops of the mineral merchants of London to buy all the cleveite that he could find. The cleveite arrived toward noon; before night it had been treated and the gas collected. During the two following days the known gases, except argon, which it had been expected would be found, were eliminated and the residue introduced into a spectrum tube. The spectrum of argon was not observed. There were few lines; one of these—yellow—was very brilliant. It was thought at first to be the line of sodium, present, perhaps, in the corroded electrodes. But Ramsay laughed at the idea; he was not in the habit of using dirty spectrum tubes, and, besides, he had made the tube himself. A comparison spectrum of sodium was observed simultaneously. The two lines were distinct and in no way superposed. It was then beyond doubt that it was a new gas, and the hypothesis was advanced that it might be helium.

Helium was that element, still unknown on the earth, whose existence in the sun was known through a spectroscopic observation carried out by the French astronomer Janssen at the time of the solar eclipse of the year 1868, and the subsequent suggestions of the English physicists Frankland and Lockyer. Was this new gas of Ramsay's helium, or was it not? The answer was not long in coming. The spectrum tube was sent to Sir William Crookes, who measured with great care the wavelength of the yellow line and found it identical with that of the solar line of helium. Scarcely a week had passed since Ramsay had received the letter from Sir Henry Miers.

At the general reunion of the Chemical Society in March, 1895, the discovery of terrestrial helium in the gases from cleveite was announced. Its molecular weight was 4, and a study of the specific heat indicated that the molecule was monatomic, like that of argon, which it also resembled through its complete chemical inertness.

During the two following years Ramsay hunted carefully for other sources of argon and helium. Argon and helium were found in certain mineral waters, those of Cauterets among others; today we know that they exist in all subterranean waters and gases.[1] Furthermore, helium can be derived from a series of rare minerals; this observation was of great interest in what followed, after it was discovered that the same gas was given off in the disintegration of radium, as we shall see later on.

Their resistance to any combination assigned to argon and helium a place apart among the elements, and they did not fit in any of the groups of Mendeleeff's table. Ramsay boldly suggested that they constituted the first two known terms of a new group, characterized by a valence of zero. Secure in observed analogies in the other groups of the periodic system, Ramsay, in a communication to the meeting of the British Association in Toronto in 1897 with the suggestive title, "An Undiscovered Gas," predicted the existence of at least one other inert element, situated between helium and argon, near fluorine, and having an atomic weight not far from 20.

Before another year had passed, not only had Ramsay's prediction been realized, but more, in collaboration with Morris Travers, two other elementary inert gases had been discovered, whose places he also fixed in the periodic system, near bromine and iodine, with the neighboring atomic weights of 82 and 130.

Ramsay submitted to a close examination different thermal waters, such as those of minerals and of meteorites, without being able to discover any of the gases which he sought. Their presence in all the subterranean gases was to be demonstrated later,[2] thanks to the use of a method of fractionating by means of cooled charcoal inaugurated by Sir James Dewar.[3]

But if the three gases to be discovered really existed, ought they not to be found in considerable proportion in the atmospheric nitrogen along with argon? One hundred cubic centimeters of liquid air having been reduced through spontaneous evaporation to several cubic centimeters, Ramsay vaporized them in a gasometer, then eliminated from it the oxygen and nitrogen by appropriate means. The gaseous residue thus prepared furnished the spectrum of argon with, in addition, a yellow line and a very brilliant green line. Besides, the density was a little greater than that of pure argon; the residue examined was then argon mixed with a certain proportion of a heavier gas.

In order to isolate this gas, Ramsay aided by Travers, prepared 15 liters of argon, a task requiring several months, and liquefied it by cooling with liquid air. The clear liquid obtained was submitted

1004

to a fractional evaporation very skillfully conducted, with the purpose of separating the gases more, or less, volatile than argon. The success was complete.

The first fractionation furnished a light gas, about ten times more dense than hydrogen, and characterized by a magnificent spectrum with brilliant lines in the red and the yellow. Ramsay called it neon. It is moreover accompanied by a certain proportion of helium, present also in the air, and from which it can be separated by the use of liquid hydrogen ($-253°$), which solidifies the neon and leaves the helium in a gaseous state.

The end products of the distillation of liquefied argon retained the two other new gases, which could, however, be separated by liquefaction and fractionating. Ramsay called them krypton and xenon; their densities in relation to hydrogen were 41 and 65.

For the three new gases, neon, krypton, and xenon, the study of the specific heats led, as for helium and argon, to a monatomic molecule. They are likewise chemically inert. Their atomic weights 20, 82, and 130 were found to occupy exactly the places indicated by the periodic table.

Thus, in the atmospheric air, which during more than a century had been believed to be perfectly known, Ramsay had succeeded, in the four years from 1894 to 1898, in isolating a complete natural group of simple gases. Indeed a splendid achievement. Striking proof of the fundamental truth comprehended in the periodic law. Witness, just as noteworthy, of the scientific faith and the ability in experimentation of this master. Nearly all the apparatus had to be invented, and Ramsay also had to construct most of it himself. Only those who have handled small quantities of gas and have prepared absolutely pure gases, giving spectra entirely free from foreign lines, are able to understand all the technical difficulties of such a work.

A little before the discovery of krypton, Ramsay thought he had isolated another element in the atmospheric argon; it had the same density as argon, but its spectrum was entirely different; he called it metargon and described several principal lines. Metargon was not, however, a new element; it was recognized that the lines indicated were due to traces of carbonic oxide, which occurs as an impurity in argon. Other chemists were working on the same problem, and Ramsay, too much hurried, had insufficiently purified his argon. I shall cite Ramsay himself in this connection:

> Should we under such circumstances regret the publication of an error? It seems to me that an occasional error should be excusable. No one can be infallible; and besides, in these conjectures one has always a large number of good friends who promptly correct the inaccuracy.

It is certain that anyone may be deceived; but it is not anyone indeed who would have been capable of discovering krypton and xenon in the air, which contains, by volume, 1 in 20,000,000 of the first and 1 in 170,000,000 of the second.

This research on the rare gases of the atmosphere will remain a perfect model of original research. And if there was anything to be admired more than the ability in experimentation and the scientific penetration displayed, it was the energy and persevering ardor, qualities doubtless less brilliant, but which in this kind of work were absolutely indispensable.

Another question, in this connection, could not fail to present itself to Ramsay's mind. Are there not in the same group of inert gases, noble gases, as he liked to call them, other elements, heavier than xenon as predicted by the periodic system, or lighter than helium, such as nebulium, whose presence is probable in the nebulæ and coronium, which appears to exist in the solar corona?

We shall recall in passing that, beside the inert gases, Armand Gautier recognized in the atmospheric air an appreciable proportion of a gas lighter than helium and which was not other than hydrogen, whose production proposed a most suggestive geochemical problem.

Ramsay busied himself then in the search for new rare gases. With Watson he examined the lightest gases in the atmosphere in the hope of obtaining a gas less dense than helium, but without success. He was not more fortunate in the systematic study, undertaken with Richard Moore, of the distillation products of an enormous mass of liquid air (120 tons), put at his disposal by George Claude. Ramsay arrived at the conclusion that if the air

1006

contains gases heavier than xenon, the proportion of them is extremely small and does not exceed one twenty-fifth of one-billionth.

The discovery of the rare gases had excited universal enthusiasm. Physicists and chemists far and near wished to study these new elements; and it is interesting, for the glory of Ramsay, to indicate briefly the principal results that have issued from this study.

Some, interested especially in the problem of affinity, sought, but in vain, to arouse chemical activity which they supposed to be dormant in the rare gases.[4] Others, on the other hand, sought for them in natural media. Following a systematic study of a great number of subterranean gases (gas from thermomineral sources, volcanic gas, fire damp), some simple conclusions have been formulated:[5]

(1) All the natural gaseous compounds contain the five rare gases, and certain of them contain appreciable quantities of helium, some as much as 6 per cent (thermal gas of Maizières, Côte-d'Or), and even 10 per cent (thermal gas of Santenay, Côte-d'Or). (2) The quantitative relation krypton-argon has practically the same value in all natural mixtures, the atmospheric air included; the relation krypton-xenon, different from the preceding, is likewise constant, as is also the relation xenon-argon, and the relations of these three gases with neon; it is possible to explain the constancy of the relations by the chemical inertness and the analogous properties of these gases, which have thus been able, since the time of the original nebulæ, to come through free and mixed together and without their quantitative relations being sensibly changed, all the cataclysms of astronomy and geology. (3) Helium, it is true, accompanies the other members of the group on all their voyages, but it escapes all proportionality; and it could not be otherwise, inasmuch as only helium is produced continually from radioactive substances, and these are unequally divided in the different strata.

You see, gentlemen, what unexpected and weighty problems have been brought up by Ramsay's discovery. What an exceptional destiny is that of these five gases, whose chemical inertness has assured to them, since the beginning of time, an eternal inviolability, and has thus made of them, like the demigods, immortal witnesses of all the physical phenomena of the earth and of the evolution of the spheres!

For what practical applications are the new elements destined? Lighting tests in neon have proved very encouraging. Argon is used in incandescent lamps. And above all—Ramsay himself made the proposition—balloons have been inflated with helium, and by this means made noninflammable.

We now come to the year 1902. Pierre Curie and Mme. Curie had just obtained radium, the magnificent completion of an admirable work begun by Mme. Curie in 1897, a little after the discovery of radioactivity by Henri Becquerel in 1896. It was a logical outcome that Ramsay was attracted toward these most interesting researches. The new domain thus opened to science had as yet been explored only by physicists; it seemed to him immediately that chemistry also could and ought to enter on the scene. He entered boldly on the subject; he was to make conquests in it of vast importance.

Frederick Soddy had come from Montreal, where he had been assisting Sir Ernest Rutherford in his beautiful work on thorium. The curious fact had been discovered that a material substance was continually given off from thorium; it was given the name of emanation. Actinium and radium also gave off an emanation. These new substances were evidently of a gaseous nature; and, with all the skill already acquired in the manipulation of small quantities of a gas, Ramsay found himself very well fitted to make a study of them. In collaboration with Soddy he tried to obtain the spectrum of the emanation of radium. As the amount of emanation which comes from even a relatively large quantity of radium is extremely small it was necessary to devise a special spectrum tube. It consisted of a thermometric capillary tube with an electrode made of a platinum wire soldered at the end, the second electrode being mercury, which was put in in advance with the very small quantity of emanation with the aid of a pump. Traces of impurities prevented seeing the spectrum of the emanation until later; but what was the surprise of Ramsay and Soddy when, after the passage of sparks through the gas for some time, they saw appear, little by little, the lines of helium!

The discovery of Ramsay and Soddy was not slow in being

1008

taken up; the formation of helium was demonstrated as coming from actinium by Debierne, from thorium and uranium by Soddy, from polonium by Mme. Curie and Debierne, and from ionium by Boltwood.

It is fitting to recall, before leaving this subject, that Rutherford had previously expressed the idea that the particles "given off by the radioactive elements ought to be made up of atoms of helium."

Another problem, in some degree the reciprocal of the preceding, naturally presented itself: If the disintegration of heavy elements can lead to light elements, would it not be possible, by an inverse method, to condense light atoms into heavy atoms and thus realize in all its fullness the dream of the alchemists? Ramsay was not afraid to take up the subject. Collie and Patterson, having submitted the glass of an ordinary empty tube to cathodic bombardment, had announced the production of helium, which had been formed by the condensation of four atoms of hydrogen. Ramsay confirmed this result, and, going further, found that if the hydrogen is moist—that is, if it is accompanied by oxygen—there will be, moreover, formation of neon, created by the addition of the atom of helium (4) to the atom of oxygen (16). It seemed to him, therefore, that under analogous conditions sulfur would lead to argon and selenium to krypton.

Here, as well, the question should be taken up again. Its breadth, perhaps, surpasses that of all the others. Ramsay will have the honor of having opened up the new field, thanks to his incomparable talent in experimentation, as well as to his boldness and the independence of his scientific conceptions.

These are, in fact, Ramsay's most pronounced characteristics. They are shown again, and in a most brilliant manner, in another work on the radium emanation which he carried out in 1910 with the assistance of Whitlaw Gray. According to the theory of disintegration, the atom of emanation results from the loss of a helium atom by an atom of radium. If the atomic weight of radium is 226 and that of helium 4, the weight of an atom of emanation ought theoretically to be 222. Emanation, whose resistance to all combination had, moreover, been shown, came thus to occupy in the column of rare gases in the periodic system the place predicted for a homolog of xenon. Ramsay wished to prove this by experiment.

And what an experiment! The volume of emanation at his disposal at any one time never exceeded five one-thousandths of a cubic millimeter (much less than the smallest head of a pin), and to determine the atomic weight it was necessary to weigh this infinitesimal volume of gas. A modification of the microbalance of Steel and Grant was constructed, whose sensitiveness attained several millionths of a milligram. The skill shown in preparing, purifying, and weighing the minute quantities of emanation was truly wonderful; and it was this work more than all the others which showed Ramsay's marvelous experimental talent. The result justified the effort. The mean of five determinations gave the number 223 for the atomic weight of radium emanation, a full and complete verification of the theoretical predictions, which Debierne also confirmed by an entirely different method (diffusion).

The brilliance of his work had brought to Ramsay the highest distinctions not only in his own country but all over the world. Academies and learned societies hastened to open their ranks to him. Our Academy of Sciences, which had elected him a correspondent in 1895, named him an associate in 1910. He was also an associate member of our Academy of Medicine. In the year 1904, the Academy of Stockholm awarded him the Nobel prize in chemistry.

One of the characteristic traits of Ramsay's personality was his enthusiasm, which he communicated to all those who worked under his direction, and the impression which he produced on his students, even during a very brief contact, remained ineffaceable. Friendly and patient with all, to "do well," according to his own expression, was all that was necessary to become his friend.

Ramsay was a remarkable teacher with an elegant and picturesque manner of expressing himself, impulsive, clear, concise, and with the great charm of simplicity. In his lessons he did not hesitate at times to use the most advanced teachings; he was the first in England to introduce the works of Raoult, Arrhenius, and van't Hoff.

Everything which lives is in a process of evolution. The real life of an experimental science like chemistry is in progress and discovery. On this subject, Ramsay was of the opinion that he wanted original research to occupy early as great a place as possible in the work of a student. He distrusted examinations such as are usually held to judge candidates, which were too often dependent on chance. He feared especially that they might result in unjust and unfortunate eliminations capable of discouraging a student in his choice of a vocation. The professor who has followed the student during several years in the course and especially in the laboratory seemed to him to be better fitted than anyone to appreciate his true value. Ramsay always forcefully maintained these ideas and their logical consequences.

In our time of general reorganization, when all institutions and all methods are undergoing revision, it is to be regretted that the great voice of Ramsay is not more listened to in this important matter of teaching.

Ramsay wrote but few didactic works. His little treatise on "Modern Chemistry," which has been translated into French, is a brief but substantial account of the principles of chemical philosophy. The same qualities are found in the highest degree in all Ramsay's writings. They are noted especially in several dissertations in which he developed his own ideas, and whose titles alone are enough to indicate their originality: "The Electron Considered as an Element," "Element and Energy," "Helium in Nature," "Problems Presented by Inorganic Chemistry," etc.

Ramsay was a polyglot and spoke fluently French and German. At the International Congress of Applied Chemistry held in Rome in 1906 he gave in French a lecture on "The Purification of Drain Water," a subject far enough away from the matters of pure science with which he was supposed to be entirely occupied.

From the beginning of hostilities, Ramsay, with his ardent patriotism, threw himself into the conflict. He fought with all the means in his power, through research in the laboratory and through his original suggestions, by pen and word, which he made the auxiliaries of his most indisputable authority. Of him also could be employed the famous phrase, "Je fais la guerre." It was through his persevering efforts chiefly that cotton was, too late perhaps, declared contraband of war. He died in full activity, sixty-three years old, while his genius was still so rich in promise for science and for humanity, brought down by an incurable disease that carried him off in a few months.

NOTES AND REFERENCES

1 Charles Moureu, "Recherches sur les gaz rares des sources thermales; leurs enseignements concernant la radioactivité et la physique du globe," *J. chim. phys.*, *11*, no. 1, 63–152 (1913). Charles Moureu and Adolphe Lepape, "Les gaz rares des Grisous," *Ann. chim.*, 9e s., *4*, *5* (1915–1916).

2 Charles Moureu and Adolphe Lepape, *loc. cit.*

3 "Séparation directe, sans liquéfaction, des gaz les plus volatils de l'air," *Ann. chim. phys.*, 8e s., *3*, 12 (1904).

4 Troost and Ouvrard, *Compt. rend.*, *121*, 394 (1895); Berthelot, *Compt. rend.*, *120*, 581–660, 316 (1895); *124*, 113 (1897).

5 Charles Moureu and Adolphe Lepape, *loc. cit.*

From: *Rev. sci.*, October 1919, in the translation published in Annual Report of the Board of Regents of The Smithsonian Institution, 1919, pp. 531–546, with corrections of translator's errors and some omissions.

CHARLES MOUREU

·· 70 ··

Otto Nikolaus Witt

1853-1932

OTTO NIKOLAUS WITT was born March 31, 1853, in St. Petersburg. At that time, his father, Johannes Niklas Witt, was professor of theoretical and technical chemistry at the Technical State Institution of St. Petersburg (Leningrad). By descent, Otto Witt was three-quarters German, one-quarter Russian. When his family settled in Munich (1864), he went to the gymnasium there. Then he studied at the Zurich Polytechnikum (1871).

A splendid period started in 1870 for the department of chemical technology at the Polytechnikum. Johannes Wislicenus, who had taught at Zurich University, took over the theoretical part and Emile Kopp the technological part of the instruction. Wislicenus left for Würzburg in 1872, but his successor, twenty-six-year-old Viktor Meyer, was his equal.

Emile Kopp had a thorough scientific background and great practical experience in many industries. He had followed the development of synthetic dyestuffs with great interest. To Kopp we owe an elegant method for separating purpurine and alizarine from madder. Dyestuff chemistry was very prominent in lecture and laboratory work. All of us had either prepared, or seen our colleagues prepare, every synthetic dyestuff known at the time, and we were familiar with all the pertinent literature. Thus, when Witt joined the dyestuff plant of Williams, Thomas & Dower in Brentford, near London, in the fall of 1875, he brought with him a thorough knowledge of the field in which he was to work. Only a few months later he produced his two pioneering achievements, the theory concerning the relationship between color and chemical constitution, and the discovery of chrysoidine.

At the dyestuff plant, Witt was charged with scientific work and new developments. Soon he developed the idea that between the practically useless aniline yellow, monoamidoazobenzene, and the technical dyestuff, Manchester brown or Bismarck brown, which is a triamidoazobenzene, there should be a diamidoazobenzene with an intermediate color, that is, an orange. In January

1876 he prepared it by reacting diazobenzene chloride with meta-phenylenediamine.

Since chrysoidine proved to be of technical value it was put on the market in the spring of 1876, and it was well received by dyers and printers. Up to then only one commercial basic yellow dyestuff, phosphine, had been available, and it was very expensive. Chrysoidine had been obtained a little before Witt by Caro at the Badische Anilin und Soda Fabrik; but the German plant apparently had not recognized its value and began marketing it only after it had become available from England. The method of manufacture was kept a secret. However, early in 1877 A. W. Hofmann published the analysis, the chemical composition, and the method of producing it. It was a good dyestuff for silk and cotton, but less suited to wool which is dyed in an acid bath. Therefore, Witt prepared acidic azo dyes, the tropaeolins.

In January, 1876, Witt published his pioneering paper "Concerning the structure and formation of coloring carbon compounds," which is the foundation of the still dominant theory of chromophores and auxochromes. The only publication on the theory of dyestuffs before 1876 was the famous paper by Graebe and Liebermann "On the connection between molecular constitution and color in organic compounds." This paper is based on Graebe's studies of the quinones and those of Graebe and Liebermann of the anthraquinone dyes and contains the nucleus of the quinone theory of dyestuffs.

Witt formulated three theses: (1) Aromatic compounds become dyestuffs through the simultaneous presence of a color-producing and a salt-forming group in their molecules. The first is given the name *chromophore;* a compound containing a chromophore is not yet colored, in fact in most cases it is colorless and becomes a dystuff only through the addition of a salt-forming group. (Later on, Witt gave the name auxochromes to the salt-forming groups.) (2) The chromophore exerts its color-producing influence more in the saltlike compounds of the dyestuffs than in their free forms. (3) Of two similar dyestuffs, the one which forms the more stable salts is the better one.

The salt-forming groups, amide and hydroxyl, form parallel

1016

series of dyestuffs with the same chromogen (i.e., the chromophore-carrying substance). Thus, the amide derivatives of azobenzenes correspond to the hydroxyl derivatives, like rosaniline to rosolic acid, etc. He predicted that fluorescein should have a corresponding amide compound; such a compound, rhodamine, was actually found in 1887 by Ceresole.

Witt left England in 1879 and joined the firm of Leopold Cassella & Co. in Frankfurt am Main, working at the Chemieschule in Mülhausen. In 1882 the Verein Chemischer Fabriken in Mannheim decided to add a dyestuff plant to its other works and offered Witt the scientific and, in part, also the technical direction. Witt accepted and moved to Mannheim. After three years, however, he found out that his field was not industry, but teaching and basic science. In the fall of 1885 he went to Berlin and worked in Liebermann's laboratory. In 1886 he became *Privatdozent* at the Technische Hochschule and in 1891 full professor of technical chemistry.

From 1886 on he investigated the peculiar situations arising from the application of patent laws to chemical inventions. The result of this work was a book on "Chemical homology and isomery and their influence on invention in organic chemistry" (1889). This highly interesting book caused the president of the German Patent Office, von Bojanowsky, to invite Witt to give a series of lectures for the members of the Patent Office. These lectures, held in 1891–92, were published under the title "The German chemical industry in its relationship to patent matters."

In 1887 Witt began the publication of a comprehensive technology of fibers, comprising the entire field of fiber production, bleaching, dyeing, and printing.

In 1889, he founded *Prometheus,* the German equivalent to the English magazine *Nature* and the French *La Nature.* He succeeded in obtaining excellent collaborators for his journal, but its main reason of success was the great number of Witt's own literary contributions. The style in which he explained scientific facts and problems to the layman reader of *Prometheus* was a model for every effort in this field.

On March 22, 1915, although suffering from an attack of the

1017

grippe, he went to the session of the Deutsche Chemische Gesellschaft to present his lecture on naphthaline sulfonic acids. That same night, a heart attack ended a life full of work and success.

From: *Ber. deut. chem. Ges.*, *49*, 1751–1832 (1916). Translated and abbreviated by Eduard Farber.

EMIL NOELTING

Wilhelm Ostwald

1853-1932

MOST chemists are so deeply concerned with the objective part of their work that they do not reveal much about the life that produced this work. In their autobiographies they will usually tell us more about their teachers and colleagues than about themselves. They are not poets interested in describing emotions and problems of the individual, nor philosophers or psychologists concerned with the general sources of science and thinking.

When Wilhelm Ostwald reached the age of seventy-two, almost twenty years after he had retired from the professorship at the University of Leipzig, he started to write his autobiography.[1] During three years of work, it grew into a 1200-page book and a highly individual story. He was a dexterous and thoughtful chemist, "made from the C-H-N-O-S-P combination from which a Bunsen, Helmholtz, Kirchhoff came . . . an able and very skillful experimenter, mechanic, glass blower . . . an indefatigable worker, clear, concise, strictly logical in oral and literary presentation." Karl Schmidt, his chemistry professor at Dorpat, thus characterized him in a letter of November 8, 1881, written to the director of the Polytechnikum at Riga as recommendation to the post of full professor there. Ostwald also was a philosopher who founded a new journal for the philosophy of science (*Annalen der Naturphilosophie*, 1902) and published several books about it. In addition, he was a psychologist trying to find the general rules of creativity and applying them in a series of books on great men ("Grosse Männer," started 1909). He was also a poet, listening to sudden inspirations, observing and consciously following them. While he freely admitted the existence of the philosopher and psychologist in himself, he would have protested violently against being called a poet. He almost detested poetry although he loved the other arts; he was actively interested in music and painting.

Against being called a poet he would have objected that he observed himself only as he observed any experimental event, and that whenever he generalized from his self-experience he did it as a scientist, not as a poet. Even his activities as an artist, particu-

1021

larly in painting, were mainly introductory, leading to a science of color measurement and color harmonies.

Wilhelm Ostwald was born September 2, 1853, in Riga, the second of three sons. His father had given up the ambition to study art and had followed his father's profession of a cooper. Wilhelm grew up in the joy of making things by hand with the perfection of art as a goal. Whether he made firecrackers or decalcomania picture (by a method he invented for himself), he had no aversion to repeating monotonously the same operation hundreds of times. He remembered, at the time of writing his autobiography, how excited he was when he discovered that there are two places between object and lense where a sharp image is produced, although he soon learned that this had been known long before. He was about fourteen at that time. He was an avid reader, consuming a novel of three volumes in one afternoon.

There are three features of his early youth which remained characteristic and can be recognized in the grown man: persistence in serial experiments, conscious openness to sudden revealing inspirations, and intensity of literary interests. This combination may appear strange; persistence and openness to inspiration, sudden creativity and passive absorption in the work of others seem to contradict each other. However, contradiction is closely related to complementarity and to dynamic balance which, for Wilhelm Ostwald at least, was responsible for much of his work. On the other hand, these three features, or character traits, developed into an inclination to quick generalizations and a certain impatience with people who could or would not follow him. In one of his letters he made a characteristic remark about the inapt quality of people (*die ungeeignete Beschaffenheit der Menschen*) for carrying out his plans. (Letter to Arrhenius, December 12, 1913: see Grete Ostwald: "Mein Vater", p. 164)

As a part of his examinations for the degree of candidate (about equal to a B.A.) he selected to report about the thermochemical work of Julius Thomsen (1826–1909, Copenhagen). "Lightning-like," the thought struck him that instead of measuring heat in chemical reactions, any other property could serve to characterize and follow chemical events in solutions. He was equipped to measure densities; why not use this easily and accurately measurable property?

With this broad proposition he started on the numerous and repetitive experiments. They led to tables of affinities for 12 acids from 600 measurements of densities and refractive indices. This was his doctor's thesis at the University of Dorpat (1878). He was conscious of having provided not only a considerable number of data, but of having opened a field of investigation that should rank with thermochemistry. The equality had to be expressed in a corresponding name; he selected the term, volume-chemistry.

Since a position at the university was not immediately available, he started teaching at the high school. He did so with such intensity and pleasure that he conceived the need for a textbook. In 1880, the year of his marriage, he found the publisher for it in Leipzig, but the completion took another five years.

In the meantime he became full professor at the University of Riga (1882). For his "studies in chemical dynamics" he constructed an improved thermostat. He measured the rates at which substances like acetamid or methyl acetate were hydrolyzed in dilute solutions containing acids. The "activities" of these acids were the same as those he found in his previous work. The studies by Svante Arrhenius, published in June, 1884, showed him that affinities and electrical conductivity in solution parallel one another. He recognized the originality of his young fellow-chemist and efficiently helped him to find due appreciation. It was as if Wilhelm Ostwald wanted to return in a productive way his thanks for the recognition with which M. M. Pattison Muir (1848–1931, Cambridge, England) had furthered him in 1879. He was happy to exercise this function again a few years later, when he "discovered" the work of Willard Gibbs (1874–78) on thermodynamics and made it available in a German translation (Leipzig, 1892).

Helping others in this way has its rewards. Through Arrhenius' work Ostwald intensified his interest in electrochemistry. For this work he improvised the tools and invented appropriate glass vessels that became standard equipment. In 1884, one result was a "dilution law" for the electrical conductivity of acids in aqueous solutions, stating that when acid S at dilution v_A has the same conductivity as acid B at dilution v_B, the conductivity will also be the same at the respective dilutions $m \cdot v_A$ and $m \cdot v_B$. This law is actually an approximation; it has to be modified through accounting for interactions between the ions, as was later found.[2]

The work at the University of Riga was very fruitful, although it also brought some annoying frictions with administrative personnel. Even without such frictions, however, he would have accepted the call to the University of Leipzig. Here, in 1887, he started with two students and a broad program of developing a physical branch in chemistry. The founding of a new journal, the *Zeitschrift für physikalische Chemie* with van't Hoff as coeditor, was only one form for the new program. The title of his textbook expressed it in a different way; it was called "Lehrbuch der allgemeinen Chemie" (1885). Physical chemistry is general chemistry! The great aim was a "chemistry without substances" which he had "always" pursued, that is, "the system of those general concepts and relationships (laws of nature) which can be applied to all substances, without dependence on their nature" (Autobiography, II, p. 387). The last chemical textbook he wrote was called "Principles of Chemistry" and carried the subtitle, "A Chemistry without Substances" (1907).

The year 1887 brought other triumphs of general chemistry in the theory of dissociation by Arrhenius and "the rôle of osmotic pressure in the analogy of solutions with gases" by van't Hoff. Ostwald gave a systematic presentation of this new chemistry in the "Grundriss der allgemeinen Chemie" in 1888 and its importance for analytical chemistry in a textbook in 1893. To understand the new advances better, they should be seen against their historical background. Therefore, he started publishing "The Classics of Science" in 1888. On the other hand, the new technical methods had to be made easily accessible. For this he wrote a physicochemical methods book (1893). All this occurred while he was engaged in teaching and experimenting and writing papers and book reviews. In one afternoon, he translated a 30 page French publication for the collection of classics in science.

The immersion in all these specific activities still left him time for general thoughts. The most general of these thoughts was concerned with the concept of energy. His early work on chemical reactions aimed at numerical definitions of chemical energy, called "affinity." After a discussion with his students in Leipzig about the problem of matter and energy he perceived the solution in a "lightninglike illumination." It was accompanied by "an almost physical sensation in my brain." Formerly he had been content with a parallelism of matter and energy; now energy became the guiding standard. The mental process culminated in "pentecostal inspiration." It happened while he was visiting a colleague in Berlin, in the spring of 1890. He "recognized that everything we sensually experience can be reduced to energy relationships between our sense organs and the world around us" (Autobiography, II, 158 ff.). On that morning he saw the world—the trees, the birds, the skies—as if for the first time.

Thus he found the key to unlock great treasures of theoretical insight and practical applications. He presented them in a large number of publications in journal articles and books. Their subject surpassed the physical sciences. The biological nature of genius appeared in a new light ("Grosse Männer," Vol. 1: Studien zur Biologie des Genies, 1909). The entire field of culture could now be understood (Die energetischen Grundlagen der Kultursissenschaft, 1910).

A speech he gave at Lübeck in 1895 was greatly misunderstood and violently assailed. The title was: The Defeat of Scientific Materialism ("Die Überwindung des wissenschaftlichen Materialismus"). Before its content became known, he was almost made an honorary doctor in theology as a fighter against materialism; but what he actually said seemed to be worse than even this enemy! Energy as the "final reality" above matter, force, and mind! One special conclusion he derived from his new approach was the abolition of atomism.

After the excitement connected with that meeting in Lübeck he felt completely exhausted. Sleepless nights and inability to work made a long vacation necessary. When he returned to the laboratory in the fall of 1896, he felt his enthusiasm for experimenting gone. He found some consolation in the fact that Liebig had experienced a similar tiredness at about the same age. It is so good to know that when we are weak, we are only normal, subject to an impersonal rule. And yet, at that time a new institute was being built for him. At the opening ceremonies in 1897, he gave a talk illustrated with experiments on the new liquid air and with a theoretical part on his studies concerning the importance of time in chemical reactions.

Its background was his occupation with the phenomena of catalysis. In 1894, on the occasion of a review in his *Zeitschrift,* he had almost casually formulated a new definition of a catalyst as a substance which influences the velocity of a reaction without taking part in it as a component. He expressed it more succinctly at a conference in Hamburg, 1901: "A catalyst is any substance which changes the velocity of a reaction without appearing in its end product." With all his laboratory weariness he carried out a large amount of experimentation on catalysis.

After unsuccessful attempts to combine nitrogen with hydrogen over in an iron catalyst, he achieved the combustion of ammonia to nitric acid on platinum in 1901. The process was gradually developed to an industrial scale, particularly through the efforts of Eberhard Brauer and the great need for nitric acid during the first World War. In 1917, production of nitric acid by this process reached 26,000 tons (nitrogen equivalent).[3]

The Nobel Prize in chemistry was given to him for his work on catalysis in 1909. In accepting it, he congratulated the award committee for having selected for the prize that part of his work which he himself valued most highly!

In some respects, however, catalysis was just an incident in his activities. The philosophy of nature occupied a great part of his interests. To the dismay of some philosophy professors, he lectured about it, brought out a book (1901), and founded a journal devoted to this subject. In 1903 and 1904 he was invited to visit and lecture in the United States. In 1905 he was appointed, by the German government, the first exchange professor to this country.

This came just at a time when he was in serious conflict with the University. The particular reason was concerned with religious questions at the official obsequies for Johannes Wislicenus (1835–1902), a freethinker. They came to the breaking point when Ostwald asked to be relieved of lecturing duties. In view of his appointment as exchange professor, Ostwald accepted the request of the ministry to defer his resignation from the professorship at the University till his return in 1906. Then he was free to devote all his time to his interests outside of university chemistry. He moved to the Landhaus Energie which he built for himself in a suburb of Leipzig.

One of the many things that needed attention was the process of ammonia oxidation. Two patent applications in Germany were rejected because they lacked inventive novelty over previous patents in this field. He became so discouraged that he firmly resolved, after examining his abilities with scientific objectivity, to abandon his efforts in the commercialization of patents and to concentrate on writing books. This occurred in 1907, but he started other business ventures several times in later years, and always with bad results. He wrote a book on the theory of values, but he did not know how to handle the exchange of values in business. This paradox was not the only one in his life. When he described how the universality of energy impressed itself upon him, he deplored that language is apt to mislead; yet he let himself be misled by language when he developed a "mathematical" formula for happiness, and when he uttered other broad generalizations. He relegated historical and artistic work to a level far below science, yet he achieved his best work when he based it on history and art. He dedicated his "Lectures on natural philosophy" (1901) to Ernst Mach, because, among other things, he had declared we must be satisfied with an incomplete picture of the world (*Weltanschauung*) and avoid hypothetical or metaphysical answers to the great questions of life. Neither Mach nor Ostwald had the fortitude—if it could be called fortitude—to live without attempting to answer these questions; perhaps nobody can, except those who are carelessly cynical or emotionally invalid.

Of all his own books, his favorite was one on the history of electrochemistry ("Electrochemie, ihre Geschichte und Lehre, XVI + 1151 pp., Leipzig, 1896); yet this book was his only one to see not more than one edition.

From the standpoint of his concept of energy he wrote and acted for the organization of science, for a new look on education, and for a rational foundation of our whole life. He joined in the efforts to create a United States of Europe. Through Ernst Haeckel (1833–1919) he became active in the Monisten Bund. At the end of its congress in Hamburg, 1911, he declared: "Thus I close the First International Monistic Congress and open the Monistic Century!"

Ostwald's sixtieth birthday was celebrated by a great number of his friends, colleagues, and former students in many parts of the world. The Akademische Verlagsgesellschaft in Leipzig (Dr. L. Jolowicz) brought out a privately printed study by Edwin E. Slosson: "Wilhelm Ostwald," as Volume IV of the collection "Grosse Männer," 1913. Slosson added up the literary production of his hero; he counted 22 books (with new editions) containing 15,850 pages, 120 papers with 1,630 pages, reviews of articles on 3,880 pages, book reviews occupying 920 pages, and 300 pages of printed speeches. To this had to be added the volumes of the *Zeitschrift für physikalische Chemie,* the *Annalen der Naturphilosophie,* and 18 of the *Klassiker der Exakten Wissenschaften* which he had edited.

His greatest project for the following years was the theory of colors. It arose out of his artistic interest in painting. Its physicochemical side had been the subject of his letters to painters (*Malerbriefe*) in 1904. A more academic treatment of the subject followed in 1916. He introduced it with a personal note: "In my psychological complex, there is a strongly emphasized visual element connected with a corresponding memory. As a consequence, color in nature has always excited my liveliest attention and has led to an extended collection of chromatic apperceptions and recollections. The active form of this interest was first carried out in artistic experiments in painting. . . . Another strong element of the same complex, the inclination to form general connecting concepts, had, sooner or later, to result in raising my activity with colors from the primitive artistic level to the higher one of scientific study."[4]

Two historical reminiscences helped him in building a system of colors. One was the psychophysical law which Gustav Theodor Fechner (1801–1887) formulated in 1859: The increase in magnitude of sensation S is proportional (factor c) to the relative increase in stimulus R:

$$\delta S = c\,(\delta R/R)$$

The other was the development of photometry in 1760 by Johann Heinrich Lambert (1728–1777). He knew the first from his earlier omnivorous reading, the second because he had included it in a volume of his *Klassiker*. Ostwald rendered previous attempts at developing color scales more definite and precise by adding the scale of "grays" and arranging the colors in a three-dimensional system. In books and charts he published the results of his thoughts and experiments. With the "color organ" he provided a scientific basis for selecting harmonizing values. In this country, his work found active supporters; the Container Corporation of America published a "Color Harmony Manual" in 1942 (with later editions).

In some way, he reverted, on a higher plane, to the kind of activity he had performed in his youth. Just as the boy had patiently filled hundreds of firecrackers, so the septagenarian mixed pigments and printed thousands of strips of paper.

In February of 1929 he presented his new system before the Academy in Berlin. He was proud to find enthusiastic approval from Albert Einstein, but no public agency in Germany could be moved to support his work. His last literary work was a collection on "Goethe, the Prophet" in the year of the one hundredth anniversary of his death.

Wilhelm Ostwald died of uremia on April 4, 1932, survived by the gentle companion of his life, his children, and grandchildren. His daughter Grete converted Landhaus Energie into an Ostwald Museum which persisted through war and Russian occupation.

GENERAL REFERENCES

J. R. Partington, "Wilhelm Ostwald," *Nature, 172,* 380 (1953).

Edmund P. Hillpern, "Some personal qualities of Wilhelm Ostwald recalled by a former assistant," *Chymia, 2,* 57–64 (1949).

Eduard Farber, "A Study in Scientific Genius—Wilhelm Ostwald's Hundredth Anniversary," *J. Chem. Educ., 30,* 600–604 (1953).

NOTES AND REFERENCES

1 This autobiography, "Lebenslinien," and his daughter Grete's book "Wilhelm Ostwald mein Vater," Stuttgart, 1953, are extensively used in the present biography.

2 H. S. Harned and B. B. Owen, "The Physical Chemistry of Electrolytic Solutions," Reinhold, New York, 1943, p. 186 ff.

3 Alwin Mittasch, "Salpetersaüre aus Ammoniak, geschichtliche Entwicklung der Ammoniakoxydation bis 1920," Verlag Chemie, Weinheim, 1953, p. 57.

4 Wilhelm Ostwald, "Abhandlungen der Sächsischen Gesellschaft der Wissenschaften," 34, III, Leipzig, 1917; cit. from Grete Ostwald's book, p. 179.

EDUARD FARBER

Albrecht Kossel

1853-1927

O N SEPTEMBER 16, 1953, Albrecht Kossel would have been one hundred years old. Much of what he found and thought for the first time is today such a self-evident part of knowledge that its origin is almost forgotten and scarcely mentioned. Building blocks of proteins, primary and secondary parts of the cell substance, prosthetic groups, and nucleoproteides are concepts that he originated.

Albrecht Kossel was born in Rostock. Although he was at the head of all classes at the Rostock Gymnasium, his inclination was toward physical sciences, not languages. He was especially interested in plants, and he knew their location in the surroundings of Rostock so well that he was entrusted with leading excursions during a meeting of the German Society of Scientists and Physicians. He would have liked best to study botany. However, his father objected for economic reasons. Thus, Albrecht studied medicine, starting in 1872. The newly formed Imperial University at Strasbourg attracted him, and he remained there for almost his entire student time. He spent only a few semesters at Rostock and passed his state examinations there.

At Strasbourg, Felix Hoppe-Seyler (1825–1895) aroused his interest in the new physiological chemistry. Hoppe-Seyler mastered physiology as well as pure chemistry. Albrecht Kossel became his assistant in 1877, and, in 1881, *Privatdozent* for physiological chemistry and hygiene. Two years later, Emil Dubois-Reymond appointed him director of the chemical division at the Physiological Institute at Berlin. This position was not very attractive financially and, because of a heavy teaching schedule, left him very little time for his own research. Nevertheless, he remained there for more than ten years, until he received a call to the Institute of Hygiene at Marburg in 1895. At the same time, the directorship of the Physiological Institute became available to him. Now he was able to unfold his plans freely, and collaborators from the United States, Belgium, England, Finland, France, Italy, Japan, and Russia came to him.

1033

In 1901, he succeeded Willy Kühne (1837–1900) at the Physiological Institute at Heidelberg which he directed until he retired. Heidelberg was the home of his wife, a daughter of the former Germanist Adolf Holtzmann. The International Congress of Physiologists was held at Heidelberg in honor of Kossel. In 1910, he received the Nobel Prize in medicine for "the contributions to the chemistry of the cell through his work on proteins, including the nucleic substances." After his retirement, he worked at the Institute for Protein Chemistry, financed by Fritz Behringer of the firm Oetker's Baking Powder, and with laboratories at the new medical clinic under Ludwig Krehl. There, Kossel worked until he succumbed to a heart attack on July 5, 1927.

Kossel's first publications, in the *Zeitschrift für Physiologische Chemie* founded by Hoppe-Seyler, dealt with a physicochemical theme, the dissociation of salts in aqueous solution by means of diffusion (1878–79). His next subject of research belonged to the field of protein chemistry, the composition of the peptone from fibrin. With his following publication (1879) he entered a field which he was never to leave. He isolated "nuclein" from yeast. At that time, nuclein was the name of an amorphic substance that occurs in all tissues; it contains nitrogen and a high proportion of phosphorus, is soluble in alkalies, and insoluble in water or acids. The first nuclein had been isolated by Friedrich Miescher, in 1869, from the nuclei of pure cells. To Hoppe-Seyler, who knew only lecithin as containing nitrogen together with phosphorus, this discovery seemed so surprising that he delayed publication of Miescher's work for two years. In the meantime, he had checked and completely confirmed Miescher's finding.

The preparation of yeast-nuclein was very simple. Pressed yeast was washed with water, dissolved in alkali, and this solution was added, dropwise, to a hydrochloric acid solution. The precipitate thus formed was nuclein. By boiling with water, Kossel separated this nuclein into 3 fractions: (1) insoluble, free of phosphorus and similar to protein; (2) soluble, containing phosphoric acid as such and in chemical combination; and (3) volatile. The proteinaceous nature of the insoluble fraction (1) was first concluded only from its elementary composition. Later on, the protein was split into tyrosine and several other amino acids. Among the substances in the soluble fraction (2) were hypoxanthine and xanthine.

This detailed investigation showed that, during hunger, the nuclein-phosphoric acids are much less easily removed from tissues than the other combined phosphoric acids. He concluded that the physiological function of nuclein must be different from that of a reserve substance. It should have a role in the growth of tissues. Thus, the muscle of embryos contains more nuclein than that of the adult animal.

When he analyzed a large quantity of pancreas glands, he discovered adenine which he also obtained from yeast and cell nuclei, from plants, and from the urine of people suffering from leukemia. As a component of nuclein, adenine should occur in all cells that are capable of developing. He found adenine in the alcoholic extract from tea leaves and discovered theophylline on this occasion. In the nucleic acid of yeast he also found an additional component that behaved like a carbohydrate; he thought it was a mixture of a hexose and a pentose.

At this time (1893), Leon Lilienfeld prepared a nucleic acid from the thymus gland. Kossel found that it differs from yeast-nucleic acid and resembles that from sperm. In addition to the previously known cases, he now isolated thymine and cytosine (with A. Neumann).

Thus, Kossel had at hand all the components of nucleic acid, today called deoxyribonucleic acids. Only the carbohydrate had not been identified; Levene succeeded in doing that about thirty years later. Of the components in ribonucleic acid, A. Ascoli, working under his direction, found uracil in 1900; its chemical constitution was established by H. Steudel in 1901.

Kossel described his work on protamines and histones in a monograph which appeared posthumously in 1929. All protamines contain arginine; some have, in addition, histidine or lysine, others again contain all three of the basic substances with a six-membered ring (hexone bases). Of the monoamino acids, alanine and serine are present in all protamines, proline and valine in many of them. In all of them, tryptophan, phenylalanine, and the sulfur-containing amino acids are absent; tyrosine was found only in the protamines of tuna fish and lumpfish (*Cyclopterus lumpus*).

1035

The next step for Kossel was to determine the arrangement of the amino acids in the large molecule of protamines. In connection with these studies, he traced the formation of urea by the action of alkalies on protamines and gelatin.

Kossel once remarked that when he had found a new substance he wanted to continue the work himself on purification, analysis, and chemical constitution. After he had thus identified a specific substance, he started to think about its physiological function. For him, each one of the substances in the living protoplasm was part of a development beginning before this substance's occurrence and continuing afterward. Methods for investigating the intermediary steps in metabolism were not well developed at his time, so that he had to use the chemical structure of a substance as the basis for estimating its origin and future.

In the organs of plants and animals, he always encountered the same group of substances: purine and pyrimidine structures, amino acids, sterols, and others. Obviously, they are fundamental for many processes of life. He called them *Zell-bausteine* (building blocks of the cell) and saw a parallel between them and the basic similarity in histological organization of all cells. From the primary building blocks, he derived secondary ones which differ from one organismic species to the other, sometimes even from one kind of tissue to the other, and are specific for them. Adenine and guanine are among the primary building blocks; theobromine, theophylline, and caffeine belong to the secondary ones.

One of the most important life processes in animals seemed to him the remodeling of the proteins, either by different arrangements of the same building blocks, or by changes within these structural parts. Kossel assumed that during the development of the fertilized egg, the simple protamines and histones are remodeled by a gradual incorporation of monoamino acids. He arrived at this assumption from the fact that arginine (also frequently the other basic amino acids) occurs in all proteins. Often he spoke of the complex proteins as containing a protamine nucleus which could, however, change during the course of growth. Finally, he hoped that a logical systemization of the complex proteins would be achieved if it were possible to find a nucleus of amino acids surrounded by other amino acids in specific arrangements, in

1036

analogy to the benzene ring as a nucleus in many organic compounds. Even if at his time (nor at ours!) a scientifically complete system of the proteins had not been accomplished and a picture of typical proteins could not be formulated, the first steps in this direction had, in his opinion, succeeded in reforming the physiology of nutrition and metabolism.

In his separate papers on his discoveries and observations, Kossel mentioned their general bearing only briefly, if at all. The connections between the special details, and the concepts concerning the chemistry and physiology of protein and the chemical structure of the cell are found only in his general lectures, e.g., in his Nobel Prize lecture (Stockholm, 1910). In an academic speech he delivered as vice-rector of Heidelberg University in November, 1908, he concluded: "The physical and chemical studies of the last few decades have brought us knowledge of phenomena that have completely changed our essential concepts of matter. Newly discovered radiations, the properties of radioactive substances, transformations of the elements—these are processes which provide us with a new theoretical basis for our concepts of the atom. These discoveries have again taught us that we are only beginning to lay the foundation upon which we must build an explanation of the processes of life. We know only fractions of the phenomena to be explained, and we are but starting to develop the means for arriving at explanations. Nevertheless, the hypothesis of vitalism assumes already now that it will never in the future be possible to reduce all the phenomena of life to physical and chemical processes. Regardless of whether this opinion is fully or partially accepted, science will continue to act as if a limit to insight did not exist."

There is scarcely anything fundamentally new that we can add to this standpoint of Kossel's.

Selections from *Naturwissenschaften, 42,* 473 (1955). Translated by Eduard Farber.

KURT FELIX

Paul Ehrlich

1854-1915

BORN at Strehlen near Breslau on March 14, 1854, Paul Ehrlich came from one of those Silesian Jewish families whose members bear a remarkable physical resemblance to each other. They had been scattered all over Germany, preferring academic professions and tending to move in liberal civic circles. Many of them were eminent teachers and some had made reputations in the various sciences. In particular, his cousin Karl Weigert (1845–1904) was a prominent histologist. He was director of the pathological laboratory of the Senckenberg Foundation at Frankfurt-am-Main from 1884 on.

Ehrlich's father was meditative and his mother, in contrast to the mothers of many prominent scientists, was of a decided practical bent.

After the lower school at Strehlen, the boy completed his secondary education at the gymnasium in Breslau. He did especially well in mathematics and Latin. One of the few individual characteristics which can be reported of the reserved youth was exhibited in his treatment of the topic that had been assigned for the compulsory school-leaving essay: "Life, a Dream." The usually cautious Ehrlich boldly wrote that, since life is an oxidation process, dreaming also must be a chemical process occurring in the brain, a kind of cerebral phosphorescence. Quite properly the essay was graded "insufficient," and this mark deprived him of the privilege of being relieved of the oral examination. This penalty was no slight matter to him, and he protested strongly. Obviously, the scientific idea was dominant in him as opposed to the humanistic emphasis which alone was given any nourishment in the Breslau Gymnasium. Like many of the young men of the time he was probably imbued with a Haeckelian philosophy.

Accordingly, he enrolled at the University of Breslau as a passionate realist and had high hopes that the study of science would bring him all that he looked forward to. He followed no special plan in his science courses. He attended the lectures of the great

1041

anatomist Wilhelm Waldeyer who, in grandiose manner, proclaimed the superiority of anatomical concepts in therapeutics. These lectures made a great impression on the young Erhlich, and it was probably then that he decided to study medicine. He had also regularly heard the lectures on histology by his cousin Karl Weigert. In addition, it is reported that he had avidly read Heubel's book on lead poisoning. Already, Ehrlich had become a peculiar type of medical student, endowed with an excellent ability to learn but interesting himself only in the major and general medical relationships. He attended the lectures of Julius Cohnheim and Rudolf Heidenhain, men who along with Ludwig Traube supported in Germany the other leading ideas of the time, namely, the physiological ideas in medicine and promoted them so effectively that eventually Ehrlich broke away from the predominance of anatomical concepts. At that time already he was envisaging an art of staining microscopic preparations of both healthy and diseased tissues, so well-developed that they could provide direct insight into the life processes. He also was contemplating the world of structural organic chemistry, a branch which was growing to tremendous proportions and, despite its complexity, remained as lucidly and harmoniously beautiful as the many-colored world of microscopic preparations. Moreover, since the dyes, particularly after the preparation of the first aniline dye (mauve) and the synthesis of indigo, had been shown to be carbon compounds with known structures in which the addition and removal of radicals and atoms led to ever-different color effects, pure science and pure medicine were now contiguous in the fields of organic chemistry and histology. In this common area, thought the young student, there would be found the exact scientific medicine that had been the goal of physicians for thousands of years.

It is likely that Paul Ehrlich closed all other books and stopped attending all other lectures. His ability to learn, so definitely exhibited earlier in Strehlen, and shown in his later years over an ever-widening area, was now devoted ardently and exclusively to the study of histology and organic chemistry. After one semester at Breslau he was at the University of Strasbourg for three semesters and then studied at Freiburg and Leipzig. According to the *vita* submitted with his doctoral dissertation, he took the state medical examination after his tenth and twelfth semesters, a statement that implies that he was obliged to repeat one or more sections of the examination. This autobiographical sketch includes a list of all of his university teachers, and he states that he worked for several years in the laboratory of Cohnheim and Heidenhain. It was there that his first analytical investigations by staining were carried out. During the period up to 1878, i.e., in the course of an unusually prolonged university student career, he evidently had stained countless microscopic preparations and had tested far more than the customary number of dyes before finally submitting his dissertation to the Leipzig faculty. Its title reads: "Contributions to the theory and practice of histological staining". (An English translation, along with the German text, is now readily available in *The Collected Papers of Paul Ehrlich,* compiled and edited by F. Himmelweit, 4 volumes, including a complete bibliography. Pergamon Press, New York, 1957–58.)

This slim composition was lost for many years and was eventually disinterred by Leonor Michaelis, professor of chemical medicine at Berlin. It is assuredly one of the classics in the epochmaking literature of medical science. Even now, its contents have not been exhausted; it affords an incomparable glimpse into the scientific soul of Paul Ehrlich; moreover, it is an excellent key to the subject: "Paul Ehrlich as a Chemist." If no more than his later researches were available, it would be difficult to determine now what his own share had been and how much had been contributed by his co-workers. The dissertation, composed by him alone, tells us what no one can take from Ehrlich; it reveals his unique mentality and proves that, when he left the university and before he was a clinical assistant, he had already embarked on the road that was to make him the founder of chemotherapy. Consequently, this dissertation will be analyzed here in some detail. He himself had discussed this matter in the *Archiv für mikroscopische Anatomie,* 13:263 (1887).

The dissertation is in two parts. The first is headed: "The chemical conception of staining." He proceeds from the fact that despite the tremendous amount of scientific labor expended on the *technique* of histological staining, the *theory* of this process had received almost no attention. Hence he begins his scientific investigation by posing an elementary and original question. It is of little import that here too he had had forerunners. It is of significance only that to him the staining in itself appeared to be a fundamental scientific component, superior to all technical details. Even in his early stages he did not limit himself to the specialized literature; he read books on the practice of dyeing and hoped thus to glean basic information extending far beyond the bounds of his particular field. However, he was aware of the limits that would need to be drawn here. For the most part, dyeing is textile dyeing, and at that time this technique was limited to a few materials, principally silk, cotton, and wool. The published information, therefore, derived entirely from the relation of the dyes to these few materials. Moreover, to him it seemed likely than any expected advances would have to come from the territory that is common to the dyers and the histologists. He proved that all selective histological staining, i.e., all staining which is to differentiate between tissues, falls into two large groups. In the first, namely, addition or direct staining, the pigment enters unchanged into one tissue but not into another. In the second category, the so-called adjective staining (dyeing), the coloring matter combines initially with another compound (mordant) such as alum, and then as a color lake adheres to the tissue (fiber). Ehrlich chose carmine to represent the first group of dyes and hematoxylin the second. The simple dye is soluble, the lake is insoluble. He then dealt exclusively with the first group because the majority of histological staining belongs to this category, and especially because the aniline dyes, from fuchsin to eosin, which are so clearly known from the chemical standpoint, belong here. The staining of nerve tissue with gold solutions belongs here also. The question then naturally arises whether the binding of the soluble pigment on a tissue involves physical relations, such as adhesion, or whether there is true chemical union between coloring matter and tissue. It was already known that the animal fibers, silk and wool, are colored by simple bathing in the dye solutions without the intervention of a third material, a mordant. This simple process can be translated directly to selective histological stainings. According to Wagner[1] and others, chemical changes do not occur; the animal fibers and the dyestuff remain unchanged. As a proponent of the chemical theory of dyeing Ehrlich first of all selected Schützenberger,[2] who thought that the animal fibers itself played the part of mordant and through chemical binding deprived the dye of one of its fundamental properties, namely, its solubility; a color lake is thus produced, an organic base takes the place of the usual metal oxide. Ehrlich did not accept the arguments of the mechanists and did not hesitate to combat the seemingly decisive nonequivalence of dyestuff and tissue by citing examples (such as the behavior of mercuric chloride toward silver chloride) to show that pure chemistry also contains instances of compounds which do not conform to the laws of equivalence. When he attempted to carry over into organic chemistry the relationships from inorganic chemistry, he encountered certain difficulties. Inorganic chemistry abounds in double compounds. However, he got around this hurdle by citing little known cases from organic chemistry which can be accounted for by assuming double compound formation, and he thus tried to weaken the arguments opposing chemical binding as the basis of staining.

These speculations by a twenty-three-year-old medical student are rather bold. They might be described as fanciful except for the fact that they constituted the starting point of a road that was to lead straight to those results which converted this medical student into the epoch-making master of the healing art. Perhaps it is not valid to read into those youthful speculations something that properly can only be derived from the eventual successes. However, a remark which occurs at this point in the dissertation shows that, from the start, Ehrlich knew precisely the goal he hoped to reach by means of these "imaginings" to which his predilection for the broader relationships had brought him. In this incidental remark he states:

> I have spent somewhat more time on these relationships—which
> so far as I know, have not yet been expounded—because I believe
> they have a general medical interest. Thus, those who assume, along
> with Rossbach, Ranke, Binz, etc.,[3] that the alkaloids combine selec-

tively with the protein of the body will feel free to regard elective staining as a parallel to the action of poisons. The difference between them would then reside in the fact that the dyes combine with the dead protein compounds, the alkaloids with the living.

Here is the most fundamental sentence in the dissertation. This far-reaching thought, whose effects were to have a great influence on medicine, was relegated to a mere remark probably because it was included in a doctoral dissertation. At the time of the composition of this essay, any physician who hoped to be taken seriously in science was not permitted to develop any ideas, rather he had to present facts. Therefore, a paper which really should have demonstrated the chemical affinity of specific protoplasmic parts for specific poisons and remedies became instead the doctoral dissertation: "Contributions to the theory and practice of histological staining."

During the rest of his life Ehrlich now had only to develop the idea which he had conceived. He had embarked on a course toward a specific remedy, he had begun with a fruitful method, a method which during his lifetime he found no reason to change. The strength of his work lay in the fact that he had started with selective histological staining and the constitution of the staining agents. Its weakness was the inadequacy of the biology of his youthful years, which while still deeply immersed in an insufficient mechanistic philosophy had no desire to see its own basic problems.

In his dissertation, Ehrlich moreover adopted the views of O. N. Witt, the eminent theorist in the field of dye chemistry, who believed that every aromatic dyestuff must possess a salt-forming group and also a chromophoric group, such as the azo group. In his further exposition, Ehrlich demonstrated that he had a thorough grasp of organic chemistry. He pointed out that all synthetic dyes have either a distinct acidic character, as in the case of eosin, or a marked basic character, such as shown by fuchsin. Instances were cited to prove that it is possible to arrive at desired elective staining on the basis of chemical relationships, and that it is not necessary to rely solely on mere trial and error experiments.

1046

The second and more extensive part of the dissertation gives a description of the chemical, technological, and histological aspects of the aniline dyes. Here once more Ehrlich proves himself to be thoroughly at home in his chosen field; he had become both a genuine medical man and chemist.

Already, at that time, the name Ehrlich was known in German chemical circles and a bright future was foreseen for him. Friedrich von Frerichs (1819–85), director of the medical clinic at the Charité Hospital in Berlin, gave him a position there which he held even after von Frerichs died. In due course he was made senior house physician, titular professor (1884), and in 1887 he qualified as a *Privatdozent*. However, after von Frerichs' death in 1885, Ehrlich's position was not agreeable. The former had looked on him as an exception, had relieved him of routine duties, and had seen to it that he could pursue his researches without interference or annoyance. Things changed when Karl Gerhardt (1833–1902) took over. He did not appreciate the usefulness of a head physician of this type. Gerhardt was strictly a clinician, and it was his aim to train clinical men. Actually, Ehrlich went on as before for a time. In accord with the rules, he was made associate professor in 1890, but his independence of thought and deed carried him more and more out of step with his superior. He had no desire to become a clinician, he wished to remain what he was: a medical research man.

Perhaps it was a fortunate turn of fate that as early as 1887, the sickly young man became definitely tubercular. He applied for leave and, accompanied by his wife,[4] went to Egypt to recover. He was thus spared the daily wear and tear of the friction with Gerhardt and did not use himself up as has been the case with many of his type. During the years at the Charité he had been extremely active; no less than 44 papers, his book, "Das Sauerstoffbedürfniss des Organismus" (Berlin, 1885), and several doctoral researches conducted under his guidance are the permanent fruits of this period. In contrast to his later practice, Ehrlich had worked almost without collaborators. What help he needed came mostly in the form of expert advice from the chemical industry, with which he had developed close contacts. Because he included

in his researches as many as possible of the aniline dyes that were
then being discovered, he required information about their structures and methods of preparation. In turn, he offered useful suggestions to his industrial friends. In particular, von Weinberg[5] appreciated his talents and gladly provided him with chemicals and
useful counsel. Information concerning these friendly contacts
is important to the history of chemotherapy. For instance, in his
fundamental paper "Chemotherapeutische Trypanosomen Studien" (*Berliner Klinische Wochenschrift,* 1907) Ehrlich wrote:

> When I was beginning my experiments, I lacked every outside op-
> portunity to be active in this field of chemistry and, therefore, I am
> permanently indebted to Arthur von Weinberg for having gener-
> ously placed at my disposal for many years the rich treasury of his
> chemical knowledge and talents.

The earliest studies by Ehrlich at the Charité dealt with the
staining of white and red blood corpuscles. With the exception
of several clinical-anatomical investigations, which may be regarded as *études d'occasion,* these studies of blood cells were his
first major pieces of research. After the discovery of leukemia by
Rudolf Virchow (1821–1902) and a type of pernicious anemia
in 1868 by Anton Biermer (1827–92), a clinical science of blood
diseases had been established, and blood preparations had been
stained. But Ehrlich was the first to use dyes as reagents to characterize particularly the white corpuscles, and he thus brought
order into the confusing multiplicity of forms of these cells under
normal and pathological conditions. If he had accomplished nothing
beside this, his name would still belong among the foremost clini-
cians of his time. Entirely apart from the diagnosis of true blood
diseases, a methodically stained blood smear is one of the most
valuable means of obtaining a picture of the patient's condition
not only when he is not suffering from a blood disease in the narrow sense of the term, but when he is ailing in any respect. Thus,
Ehrlich's great general principle, at its first application, resulted
in an important advance in the field of diagnosis. He might have
spent the rest of his life with this lovely method, simple as it was,
but he was through with it as soon as he had demonstrated its

great and very important possibilities. He did not become a specialist in blood diseases. Other things were more alluring.

The introduction by Ehrlich (1881) of methylene blue for staining bacteria is most important. All of the dyes previously used for this purpose suffered from the disadvantage that they stained not only bacteria but also, to a greater or lesser degree, tissue constituents, blood corpuscles, serum, fibrin, mucus, etc. Consequently, the bacteria did not stand out distinctly enough. In methylene blue, Ehrlich recognized a dye capable of staining microorganisms and cell nuclei quite distinctly, while coloring the other constituents of a microscopic preparation much less. Among his numerous discoveries, this one marked a decisive advance. At this time, he must have conceived the idea of consciously and planfully constructing a molecule in such manner that it would provide optimum protection to the tissues of the organism and also inflict maximum damage to the microparasite which had invaded the organism. The concepts "organotrope" and "parasitotrope" must have been present in his mind in some form or other at this time. Furthermore, the link with bacteriology had now been found.

The discovery of the diazo reaction in urine (1882) also came during this period. This is still one of the most important reactions for diagnosing infectious diseases. The connection with Ehrlich's stain-analytical studies is obvious. Despite its significance, the discovery of this reaction was not much more than a by-product of Ehrlich's principal researches.

On March 3, 1882, Robert Koch (1843–1910) announced the discovery of the tubercle bacillus to the Berlin Physiological Society. His staining method was cumbersome and yielded poor delineation. The day after this memorable meeting, Ehrlich was able to show Koch the method of staining tubercle bacilli that in essence is still being used. The modern theory of tuberculosis was built up to a large extent by the aid of this method.

In 1885, after Ehrlich had completed the new approach to the blood diseases, he published a fundamental text, "The Oxygen Need of the Organism" a staining-analytical study in which he applied his research principle to the living organism for the first time. What he was now attempting went far beyond the staining of a microscopic slide preparation; he was dealing with the chemistry of the living cell. He used alizarin blue, a dye that is reduced with difficulty, and indophenol blue, which is readily reduced. He found that certain tissues reduce only indophenol blue, whereas others also reduce alizarin blue. All tissues that reduce the latter also reduce indophenol blue. These processes in the living organism actually involve reductions similar to purely chemical reductions. Nevertheless, Ehrlich recognized a difference. In the living organism, his experiments succeeded, to his amazement, with water-insoluble dyes, whereas, *in vitro,* soluble materials undergo chemical reactions more readily. Living cells cannot be stained by most water-soluble dyes because the coloring matters do not infiltrate these systems. However, the cell is capable of taking up fine particles of certain undissolved dyes and of then converting them into a reactive state. The dyes used must be such that they lose their color when the oxygen is taken from them and regain the color when oxygen is again supplied. Finally, if the dyes are to break down into particles of sufficiently small dimensions, they must form colloidal solutions. In these experiments, Ehrlich also took account of the fact that the dyes are initially taken up on the basis of physical rather than chemical conditions. He prepared coarse-grained, heavy metal lakes and determined what metals are taken up by the various organs. He had reached a point where he could methodically cause a particular metal to be deposited at a designated region in the animal body.

Through these staining experiments it had now become possible to introduce a quantitative aspect into the study of the reactivity of a tissue. It had also become apparent that the affinity of protoplasm for the dyestuff molecules is dependent on whether the protoplasm is dead or alive. At this time he did not yet have available the terminology of colloid chemistry, but it appears he thought that perhaps the physical and the chemical reaction were not so completely separated as the scientists then supposed.

Important fundamental questions remained: What parts of the body or what portions of the tissue are stained when a dyestuff of a particular structure is introduced and then manifests the degree of its avidity for oxygen? How great is this avidity and

1050

how can it be measured? Why are certain portions stained in a particular manner and others in a different manner? Thus the study of the oxygen need of the organism resembled an expedition into rugged virgin country from which the explorer returns and reports merely what he saw, but tells nothing about why he undertook the journey, leaving his audience to guess the reason for the entire venture.

Still another difficulty stemmed from the lack of a general biology resting on proper foundations. When Ehrlich speaks of affinities and avidities, it is not clear whether he is employing these terms in their ordinary chemical sense, or whether he is using them to denote a broader conception of the desire for oxygen in which morphological structure and vitality are factors.

At this stage he had to seek collaborators. Hematology had now come into being with the assistance of A. Lazarus. Ehrlich had associates of marked independent standing. On the other hand, the men who worked with him were placed in his debt because their successes often were in no slight measure due to his brilliance, knowledge, and practical sense. On the whole, it is frequently difficult to assign to his associates all of the credit that may properly belong to them. Ehrlich's researches flowed over into the chemical industry. Institutions as well as individual scientists used his ideas and, in some instances, entered into active association with him.

In the same period that saw the beginning and growth of the staining of living tissues, Ehrlich also discovered the methylene blue staining of the peripheral sensory nerves *in vivo*. About fifteen years later, this finding led to the treatment of neuralgias with this dyestuff, a method which is in line with the methodical administration of remedies of known constitution to act on prescribed tissues. However, the results of vital staining with methylene blue have as yet been far more important as an adjunct to the microscopic anatomical study of the nervous system.

The results of his investigation of thallin, a now-outmoded febrifuge, were published in 1886. This investigation is of importance here, because it demonstrates clearly how far his staining-analytical work of 1878 had already carried him into rational therapy.

1051

These, in brief, were his accomplishments while an assistant at the Charité. On his return, from Egypt, fully recovered, he found the doors of various government research laboratories closed to him for reasons that are now difficult to comprehend. He furnished a small private laboratory in Berlin, disregarding the drain on his limited financial resources, and set to work. He began with the immunization of laboratory animals against abrin and ricin, two virulent poisons obtained from plants. His goal was to show that immunity is a chemical process, and the complete independence of his method of operation is shown in that he did not feel bound by his previous successes. He was now dealing with materials of unknown structure. He was searching for—and found—the only thing that perhaps could be found, the quantitative relation between poison and animal, the basis of the testing methods that had by now become necessary for curative sera. He also worked to discover the hereditary relationships in immunity, and he was also to show that the immune bodies are transmitted to the child by the nursing mother. When Robert Koch brought out tuberculin in 1890, he turned over a clinical observation station in the Moabit Hospital to Ehrlich, and when the Institute for Infectious Diseases was opened, he placed a small laboratory at Ehrlich's disposal. So the years passed, rich in well-anchored work which proved that fundamentally Ehrlich was turning more and more to the immunity sciences.

In the meantime, Friedrich Althoff (1839–1909), the Prussian Minister for Ecclesiastical, Educational, and Medical Affairs, a blunt, odd, but above all intelligent and bold person, had noted that the nation had something exceptional in Ehrlich. But even his influence was not sufficient to induce the Prussian faculties to disregard their ingrained denominational scruples and provide Ehrlich with a position commensurate with his demonstrated abilities. If, in addition to his other handicaps, Ehrlich had now also been entirely deprived of funds, an entire segment of science might have been delayed or even never developed. But Althoff was precisely the man to deal with impossible situations of this kind. If the faculties would not yield, the matter would have to be handled without them. As a result, a Royal Institute for Serum Research and Testing was set up in 1896 at Steglitz, a suburb of Berlin. Two years later, the Institute for Experimental Therapy was founded at Frankfurt-am-Main. This well-furnished laboratory fitted in well with Ehrlich's plans and the mayor's designs for the University of Frankfurt. In 1906 it became still more effective as a research center by attaching to it the Georg-Speyer-Haus für Chemotherapie, built by Franziska Speyer as a memorial to her husband.

Ehrlich proved himself equal to these extraordinary strokes of good fortune. In the years around the turn of the century he evolved the side-chain theory, one of the most controversial scientific postulates of the era. Lauded to the skies by some, declared unworthy of discussion by others, it was also of the highest philosophical interest within the framework of its time. Admittedly it was not entirely what it should have been, but equally it certainly was a fruitful premise for the greatest successes of rational medicine.

The theory proceeds from the simple fact that substances can act on each other only when they are in contact, or to use Ehrlich's own phrase: *Corpora non agunt nisi fixata.* He assumed that every material to which the body reacts fixes itself to the protoplasm molecule of certain cells. This applies to any substance, such as the toxin of an infecting agent, an enzyme, a fat, a carbohydrate, or a protein. He compares the process of infection, which therefore becomes only a special case, with nutrition. In the latter, the ingested foods are assimilated in the protoplasm of the body; in other words, they are fixed in the protoplasm and act then in a sense as the protoplasm of the organism being nourished. Accordingly, the protoplasm molecules must possess many sites for attachment and the material, which attaches itself, must have a binary structure. At its one end, the "haptophoric" group, it must fit into the site of attachment, the "receptor," but it must be able to exhibit its specific action with its free end. In the side chain theory it is assumed that the foreign molecule irritates the cell protoplasm, this irritation consisting in the saturation of the receptors of the cell protoplasm by the haptophoric groups of the foreign material or, in case suitable receptors are not available,

1053

they are produced by the cells initially of their own accord. He called antigens all substances that affect the body in this way, render it immune, for instance. Accordingly, the protoplasm molecule possesses definite places in its receptors for these binary or dipolar antigens, regions or sites that show a degree of similarity to unoccupied chemical valences. These are not true free valences, because the unsaturated protoplasm does not have the character of a nonsaturated chemical compound. In his book on the oxygen need of the organism, and originally also in his theory of the immunizing process, Ehrlich gave the name "side chains" to these sites of attachment. This term quickly acquired a different meaning. According to a rule stated by Weigert, the organism reacts to an injury to any of its parts by overcompensation. Ehrlich assumed that the protoplasm molecule correspondingly reacts to saturation of its receptors by producing an excess of receptors, and that it repels any superfluous receptors and permits them to enter the blood stream. Thus, as a sequel to many infections there are large supplies of free receptor side chains in the blood plasma, where they capture invading infectious antigens; in other words, they attach themselves to the haptophoric groups of the antigen. In the case of diseases which confer lasting immunity, so many free side chains are in the blood that no significant fixations on the cell occur. Consequently, the body can never again fall prey to these diseases and its blood plasma, now a carrier or storehouse of receptors, can serve as a curative serum and also as a protective agent. In this sense the side-chain theory proved of much value; it provided explanations, it revealed relationships, it led to remedies. On the other hand, it has remained a pure hypothesis; a receptor or haptophore group has never been seen.

Ehrlich moved to Frankfurt in 1898 while in the middle of his studies of immunity, while he was engaged in an endless program of researches, and while he had in his hands an apparently inexhaustible method and an extensive supply of modern equipment. Because of his convictions and desires, the new Frankfurt Institut was given the name, *für experimentelle Therapie* rather than *für Serumtherapie*. Evidently he was planning to go beyond serum therapy. Actually, he was destined to take up in Frankfurt the dyestuff therapy of the protozoal diseases, to advance the treat ment of diseases due to spirilli by means of aromatic arsenic compounds, and to arrive at a successful attack on syphilis with salvarsan. Following this triumph, which brought him world-wide acclaim, he was to proceed methodically to the curative action of metalloids and metals, thus laying the foundation for a future approach to the cancer problem.

From 1906, the Georg-Speyer-Haus was also under his direction. The chemical industry in the Frankfurt region provided him generously with compounds, often tailored to fit his demands and suggestions, and these manufacturing establishments also opened their other facilities to him. Associated with him were men who were authorities in their respective fields. Among them were the bacteriologists Max Neisser and Julius Morgenroth; the chemists Robert Kahn and Albert Bertheim, who made notable contributions to the study of aromatic arsenic compounds, Paul Karrer, and Hugo Bauer; Kiyoshi Shiga and Sahaschiro Hata from Japan, H. Apolant, the student of cancer, and others. These men, some as employees, others as members of the staffs of the two institutes, had under them sections of the various fields of the investigations on which Ehrlich was working concurrently, or in the course of time they had charge of sections in which they continued to work independently after Ehrlich had turned to other topics.

Ehrlich was at the peak of his career in these Frankfurt years. From his little room, where he was almost buried under heaps of journals and other papers, lines of communication ran to the scientific centers of the whole world and to the expeditions investigating places of epidemics. Almost all of the honors and recognitions than can come to a scientist were conferred on him. In 1907 he was made Geheimer Obermedizinalrat, and in 1911 he became Wirklicher Geheimrat with the title Excellency. The Nobel Prize in Medicine and Physiology was divided between him and Elie Metchnikoff (1845–1916). His life from 1902 to 1915 and his special working habits are charmingly pictured in "Paul Ehrlich," written by his secretary, Martha Marquardt.[6]

Ehrlich designated as "amboceptor" every side chain, hence every receptor, which is so constructed that one of its ends can

One of the program notes, written by Paul Ehrlich to Dr. Hugo Bauer, dated May 17, 1914. It starts out: "1. Would it be interesting to see how (2,2′ diamino-4,4′ dimethyl-diamino-diphenyl-methane) reacts with selenium? Tetramethyldiamido-selenopyrene? I shall see whether one can get starting material." The other paragraphs refer to the corresponding compounds with tellurium and with sulfur ("thio-").

1056

anchor the antigen, for instance, a bacterium, a toxin, etc., while its other end carries groups of atoms which can combine with atom groups taken up from the blood plasma, so that they bear on this other end the so-called complement, the supplementary portion. This, again, is initially no more than a symbolic picture to illustrate the fact that the immune bodies, etc., are active only when they are bound to fresh blood serum, no matter (to a certain degree) whether the serum comes from the same animal as the antibody or from another animal. While the amboceptors themselves are strictly specific, the complements are nonspecific. The theory of complements was then further developed and led to ideas which proved to be very important. Jules Bordet, bacteriologist and pathologist, director of the Pasteur Institute at Brussels, who received the Nobel Prize in 1919, and Gengout had prepared their hemolytic system from red corpuscles and sera which dissolved red blood corpuscles. With the aid of these combinations they had worked out a serodiagnostic method for many pathogens. August von Wassermann (1866–1925) director of the department of experimental therapy at the Koch Institut for Infectious Diseases, from 1906 director of the section of experimental therapy and biochemistry at the Kaiser Wilhelm Institut in Berlin-Dahlmen, following in part the imaginative scheme evolved by Ehrlich, made the capital discovery (1908) that syphilis in man can be detected by the complement-fixation method. Further investigation disclosed the astounding fact that the Wassermann reaction actually does not disclose the presence of antitoxins combating the spirochetes but, instead, shows the presence of an entirely different body, probably a lipoid-like degradation product of the body cells that have been damaged by the spirochetes. In this case, a false lead resulted in a very important discovery. It becomes quite evident here that what Ehrlich had pursued from his staining-analytical experiments on was not real chemistry; instead he had developed a symbolic description of a natural process, i.e., a fictional approach quite in the sense of the Hans Vahinger's "As If" philosophy. (Compare, in this connection, Robert Koch's "Das Als-Ob im ärtzlichen Denken," Munich, 1924.)

Ehrlich had the ability to close his interest in a field of study that had not been exhausted. The studies within the frame of the side-chain theory were continued until 1904. He then began his work on the experimental treatment of cancer, which occupied him until 1906. These researches, conducted in close association with H. Apolant, produced only a number of observations and insights into spontaneous and induced cancer in laboratory mice.

Ehrlich now embarked on his final and most excellent field of study. This was no less than an attack on protozoal diseases and spirilloses by chemical agents, whose structures were known and could be systematically modified. The first trials were made with dyestuffs, then came the aromatic arsenicals. He had accordingly returned to the methods of his earlier years; he had reverted, at least with respect to the curative agent, to purely chemical methods. Now, under the most favorable external circumstances, his great talent and wealth of knowledge and ability could once again be applied to this important field. With the aid of the side-chain theory he had already arrived at a procedure which, as Weigert early appreciated, had its weaknesses. Even though it had yielded many facts, this line of attack had not been able to demonstrate that blood contained immune bodies as a secretion which could be isolated and chemically explored. Particularly in his letters to Weigert, Ehrlich revealed how he was occasionally disturbed by the inadequacy of the basic biological ideas on which the symbolically designated concepts were supposed to rest. However, something entirely different came to be involved. Ehrlich had realized that the potentialities of the purely biological experimental therapy were exhausted for the time being. It must have been gratifying that he could revive the idea of internal disinfection, thus becoming the father of chemotherapy, with which he was destined to surpass the treatments based on experimental therapy, that is, the therapy with curative sera and vaccines.

His goal had now become to find materials that would inflict as much damage as possible on the pathogenic agent without appreciable damage to the afflicted organism. To use his terminology, this meant the use of curative agents that combine the highest parasitotropism with the lowest organotropism. He wished, so he stated in one of his favored comparisons, to shoot magic bullets

1058

which would strike only the invader, not the victim. He coined the expression, embodying the desire of which he may have already dreamed in his early years, *"therapia magna sterilans,"* the specific healing by means of a remedy which, once administered, destroys the causative agent root and branch. This magniloquent expression, which did not entirely live up to its promise, reveals the romanticism that tinged Ehrlich's precise studies throughout his career.

It is not surprising that Ehrlich began with trypan red, since the use of dyestuffs had been the subjects of his earliest researches. Trypan red with one stroke actually did cure mice that had been infected with trypanosomes. It surely was a great moment when, for the first time, he saw mice survive a deadly dose of these organisms, and when peering into his microscope he found that the blood no longer contained trypanosomes. Trypan red is an azo dyestuff and Ehrlich believed the curative action resided in the azo group $N=N$. It was an obvious step to go from nitrogen to related elements, and it was not long before he was making analogous trials with arsenic compounds. It was found that all strains of trypanosomal organisms are destroyed by arsenic compounds, but that certain strains become resistant to arsenic after several transfers from host to host and repeated exposure to arsenic. This finding of course gave rise to explanatory theories.

His studies with arsenic compounds led Ehrlich to investigate atoxyl, which Paul Uhlenhuth, professor of hygiene and bacteriology at Freiburg, had used (1905) to combat fowl spirilloses and which even then had been pointed out by the latter as being effective against syphilis. Although not the first, Uhlenhuth had discovered the curative action of arsenic compounds against protozoal diseases. Charles Laveran and Mesnil had found already in 1902 that arsenious acid is active against such diseases in laboratory mice. Actually, a rather old remedy was being applied here, because prior to the introduction of cinchona bark (1638) arsenic was used, though with trepidation, against malaria, which is a protozoal disease. In 1905, Koch also used atoxyl in the treatment of African sleeping sickness, but with unsatisfactory results.

In the short span of a human lifetime, Ehrlich had acquired a masterful ability to manipulate molecules almost at will and by planned alterations of the molecules to arrive at compounds possessing carefully calculated curative effects. His letters, notations, and other memoranda show clearly the chartered course of his researches. Those who think that he merely used a cut-and-try method when testing the host of compounds that came to him from many sources are in error. Of course the valuable aid given to him by the chemical industry and by his own chemical associates must not be forgotten—assistance which he gratefully welcomed. Soon after atoxyl had come on the market (1902) Ehrlich and Shiga tried its action on trypanosomes, but the particular strain, the only one available to them, did not respond. In 1905 he again turned his attention to this compound and together with Bertheim found that atoxyl is the monosodium salt of paraaminophenylarsinic acid, a crystallizable compound.

This finding opened the way to chemotherapy employing aromatic compounds of arsenic. The next hurdle to be surmounted was an adequate method for preparing sufficient quantities of this "arsanilic acid" or its sodium salt. Ludwig Benda, a chemist at the Cassella Company, accepted this assignment and worked out the procedure in the plant laboratory. Ehrlich's demands on the chemists often reached incredible heights, and it was only because of the efficient collaboration of experienced and inventive chemists like Benda that his desires were met to some extent.

However, atoxyl could not be regarded as a final solution to the problem of treating human patients suffering from diseases due to protozoa or spirilli. It was too toxic and left undesirable aftereffects, particularly disturbances of vision. The monosodium salt of an acetyl derivative or arsanilic acid, acetarsanilic acid, was widely used under the name "arsacetin." It was much less toxic than atoxyl, but it also left disturbances of vision as soon as the amount administered reached the point at which a cure could be expected with a single dose.

Atoxyl and also arsacetin killed the parasites *in vivo* but not *in vitro*. Recalling his experiences on the oxygen need of the organism, he now tried previously reduced aromatic arsenic compounds. About this time, Benda on his own initiative prepared

1060

parahydroxymetanitrophenylarsinic acid and sent it to the staff at the Speyer-Haus for reduction and testing. Through an error the compound was not used. Knowing nothing of this older specimen, Ehrlich and Bertheim prepared this compound some time later and reduced it. The reduced product (p,p'-dihydroxy-m,m'-diaminoarsenobenzene) later was named Salvarsan. In the meantime Albert Neisser had carried out his transmittal of spirochetes to anthropoid apes and to rabbit testes and had successfully treated this inoculated syphilis with arsenic preparations. Moreover, Hata, who was familiar with the technique of transmitting syphilis to rabbits, came to the Georg-Speyer-Haus early in 1909. Now the chief objects of attack in the chemotherapeutic researches were the spirilli of relapsing fever and the spirochetes of syphilis in place of the trypanosomes. A preparation bearing the laboratory number 606 was superior to all others with respect to rabbit syphilis. It was the hydrochloride of the reduced product just discussed, namely, salvarsan.

A patent covering the "Ehrlich-Hata 606" was applied for in 1909. Ehrlich put the preparation into the hands of several trusted physicians. The first favorable results were announced in 1910 at the Internists' Congress held at Wiesbaden. Slowly and cautiously Ehrlich widened the circle of physicians entrusted to use "606." They numbered around 500 by the time salvarsan was placed on sale in the apothecary shops. The method of administration was quickly improved. In neosalvarsan (arsphenamine) whose effective constituent is the sodium salt of dihydroxydiaminoarsenobenzene monomethane sulfinic acid, the physician had available an agent that could be injected intravenously, and in this form it largely superseded salvarsan. Eventually, other salvarsan compounds made their appearance, including myosalvarsan, which can be injected subcutaneously, and spirocid which is easily taken by mouth. The complex silver salts of salvarsan and neosalvarsan were found to be very effective.

No medicinal preparation had ever been so thoroughly studied as salvarsan. Because of it, syphilis became better understood and the medical treatment of this scourge became more fundamental than before. The success of salvarsan was one of the great events in medical history, and following in Ehrlich's footsteps, other valuable chemotherapeutic agents appeared. Pertinent instances are Optochine which is a specific against pneumococci, and Germanine which is useful against sleeping sickness. The fact that salvarsan and its derivatives have now been displaced by antibiotics and sulfa drugs takes nothing away from their usefulness and merit at the time they were in use.

World-wide acclaim came to Ehrlich, especially at the International Medical Congress at London in 1913. A *Festschrift* was issued on his sixtieth birthday on March 14, 1913.

The outbreak of World War I proved fatal to Ehrlich. To him it signaled the collapse of his ideal: the peaceful competition of all peoples in humanitarian endeavors. Seriously afflicted with arteriosclerosis, his health deteriorated rapidly. He died on August 20, 1915, and was buried in Frankfurt-am-Main.

GENERAL REFERENCES

Paul Ehrlich Centennial, New York Academy of Science, Annals, vol. 59, Art. 2, pp. 141–276, 1954.
Paul Karrer: Paul Ehrlich, J. Chem. Education, vol. 35, pp. 392 / 6, 1958.

NOTES AND REFERENCES

1 J. Rudolf v. Wagner (1822–1880), professor of chemical technology at Würzburg. For many years he was the editor of the *Jahresbericht über die Fortschritte* (later *Leistungen*) *der chemischen Technologie*.
2 Paul Schützenberger (1829–99), professor at the Gewerbeschule in Mühlheim, then in Strasbourg and from 1870 in Paris.
3 Michael J. Rossbach (1842–1894), medical doctor and pharmacologist at Jena. Heinrich Ranke (1830–1909), pediatrician and professor at Munich. Arthur H. Binz, professor and director of the Chemical Institute of the Landwirtschaftlichen Hochschule (Agricultural College) in Berlin was head of the chemical section of the Speyer Haus in Frankfurt from 1918–21. He also served as chief editor of the *Zeitschrift für angewandte Chemie*.
4 He married Hedwig Pinkus in 1883, when she was only nineteen.
5 Arthur von Weinberg (1860–1943), chemist and, from 1883, director of Leopold Cassella & Co., and then a member of the board of the I.G. Farbenindustrie.

6 Martha Marquardt, "Paul Ehrlich als Mensch und Arbeiter," Deutsche Verlagsgesellschaft, Stuttgart, 1924. An extended English edition of this book, with the title, "Paul Ehrlich," with an introduction by Sir Henry Dale, was published by Henry Schuman, New York, 1951.

Selected from Bugge, *Das Buch der Grossen Chemiker, 2,* 421–442.
Translated by Ralph E. Oesper.

RICHARD KOCH

·· 74 ··

Arthur Rudolf Hantzsch

1857-1935

ARTHUR RUDOLF HANTZSCH[1] was born in Dresden on March 7, 1857, a year notable to chemists by Kekulé's publication on the constitution of mercuric fulminate in which he enunciated the tetravalency of carbon. The town of Dresden, situated where the Elbe River leaves the mountains, is beautiful not only because of its location but also because of its buildings and art collections. Augustus the Strong had built a palace in elegant baroque; here was the seat of a brilliant opera and of one of the great collections of paintings. These surroundings may well have influenced Hantzsch, who even as an old man possessed and admired elegance of bearing, of language, and of taste. Hantzsch's father was a wholesale dealer in wine, carrying on a business which had been founded by his grandfather, originally a cooper. His mother was the daughter of an artist, Prof. J. U. Bähr, of Riga. According to his own account, Hantzsch was an emotional child with little self-reliance. He had many interests and developed early a love for nature and the sciences dealing with it.

Animals and particularly the records of their prehistoric forms fascinated him. It is not likely that these subjects were treated to any considerable extent in the curriculum of the famous Kreuz Gymnasium which he attended, but the adolescent was also gifted for languages and enjoyed the sound of spoken Greek so much that he studied this language privately. A flair for language, for communication by the written and the spoken word, confidence that words can transmit complicated thoughts and intuitions, and annoyance when communication failed were characteristic of Hantzsch in later years.

Chemistry was not taught at the Gymnasium, but Hantzsch must have had some contact with it from quite an early age. He has recorded that chemistry, which had seemed mysterious, gradually replaced zoology as his main interest, and that he carried out some chemical experiments while he was attending the Gymnasium. Subjects in which he was not interested were neglected, and Hantzsch left the Gymnasium in 1875 with only a moderate cer-

1067

tificate. Such records are not infrequent in the lives of great scientists and make one wonder about talent lost by too rigorous elimination at the college threshold.

As soon as Hantzsch had obtained his matriculation certificate in 1875, he began to study chemistry under Professor R. Schmitt and Dr. W. Hempel at the Polytechnikum (now the Technische Hochschule) in Dresden. Schmitt, a pupil and later an assistant of Kolbe, was a man of great ability, known for working out a large-scale process for the production of salicyclic acid by Kolbe's reaction, and for his discovery that phenolsodium carbonate is an intermediate in this synthesis. He was one of those who, led by Hofmann, had in 1867 founded the German Chemical Society. Hantzsch received the greater part of his formal scientific training under Schmitt and his colleagues. It culminated in a thesis "On Paraoxyphenetol and Some Aldehydes and Alcohols Derived from Hydroquinone" which Hantzsch submitted to the faculty of the University at Würzburg in 1880. He had worked in Würzburg for one semester, completing the thesis because the Polytechnikum in Dresden was not entitled to grant a doctor's degree. The professor of chemistry at Würzburg was Johannes Wislicenus. Thirteen years later Hantzsch became his indirect successor in Würzburg, and he succeeded Wislicenus at Leipzig in 1903. Wislicenus must have examined Hantzsch in chemistry. The other subjects of the doctor examination, passed *summa cum laude,* were physics and mineralogy. One of Hantzsch's contemporaries in Würzburg remembers him as an extremely hard worker, mixing little with fellow students, and, apart from his research work, much preoccupied with his engagement—dating from 1879—to the eldest daughter of the sculptor Johannes Schilling, whom she had served as model for the figure of Germania in the Niederwald monument on the banks of the Rhine. This monument and the reports of contemporaries testify to her great beauty. While in Dresden, Hantzsch had served a year in the Army.

The young doctor spent the summer of 1880 in Hofmann's laboratory in Berlin working on a few, not very exciting organic problems. For the beginning of the winter semester, Hantzsch accepted a position as instructor in the Institute for Physical Chemistry of the University at Leipzig under Gustav Wiedemann.

1068

Hantzsch, however, devoted his experiments to a synthetic problem in organic chemistry, whose brilliant solution established the fame of the 25 year old as the originator of a new synthesis of the pyridine nucleus. Baeyer had obtained collidine (sym-trimethylpyridine) by heating acetaldehyde ammonia. Stimulated by this work, Hantzsch examined first the behavior of ketones with acetaldehyde ammonia and obtained at high temperatures a mixture of pyridine bases which could not be resolved even by repeated fractional distillations. Then Hantzsch tried the reaction of acetaldehyde ammonia with ethyl acetoacetate. One mole of the aldehyde ammonia with two moles of the keto ester lost three moles of water in a smooth reaction, and the diethyl ester of dihydrocollidine dicarboxylic acid was obtained. Oxidation, saponification, and decarboxylation led to the free sym-collidine formulated in Hantzsch's "Habilitationschrift" as the symmetrical trimethylpyridine in analogy to benzene. On the cover of this thesis, Hantzsch issued an invitation to his "Probevorlesung" (trial lecture) on "The Relation between Chemical Constitution and Physical Properties of Organic Compounds." This lecture represented the last of the obligations which Hantzsch had to fulfill in order to obtain the *venia legendi,* i.e., the right to lecture at the University as a "Privatdozent." This coveted right is bestowed by a German faculty only after close scrutiny of the candidate, after he has shown by his Habilitationsschrift the ability to carry out independent research, after a colloquium at which any member of the faculty may question the candidate and after the Probevorlesung.

The contents of the Habilitationsschrift were published in a paper in Liebig's *Annalen* in 1882. Work on the syntheses with α-keto esters and aldehyde ammonia compounds and on the chemistry of the reaction products occupied Hantzsch for the next three to four years. He stayed in Leipzig until 1885. He had married in 1883, and we can assume that the young, successful Privatdozent with his beautiful wife was happy in the town famous not only for its University, but for its Gewandhaus orchestra, for its Conservatory of Music, as the seat of the Supreme Court, as the center of German book printing and publishing, and as an important commercial center. Kolbe ruled over chemistry at the Chemical Insti-

1069

tute of the University. As editor he used the *Journal für Praktische Chemie* to review and criticize, often scathingly, the happenings on the chemical scene. He had suggested that Hantzsch publish the collidine synthesis in his Journal. When Hantzsch refused, the temperamental Kolbe told Hantzsch, "Then we are divorced people." Nevertheless Kolbe prophesied that he would one day be his successor in the Leipzig chair.

Kolbe was also one of those who recommended Hantzsch as his second choice when the head of the Swiss school authorities, the able Kappeler, consulted him about a successor for Victor Meyer who had left the Swiss Federal Institute of Technology to accept a call to Göttingen. Kolbe's first choice was Ernst von Meyer, his son-in-law. There were others who had recommended Hantzsch as their second choice, but like Kolbe's, their first choice had been influenced by personal reasons. Sitting unannounced in the audience among the students, Kappeler listened to Hantzsch and decided to offer the twenty-eight year old Privatdozent the full professorship in Zürich. This was in the Zürich tradition; Victor Meyer had been twenty-four years of age when he was called to this chair. There was free exchange of academic personnel between Germany and Switzerland, not even a change in nationality was required. Hantzsch had entered the exalted group about which—as the story goes—the archangels had once complained to the Lord; these men enjoyed greatest independence, highest social position and income, and longest vacations, and all that for following their heart's desire. The Lord had replied that there was justice, though hidden, because He had created their colleagues.

Hantzsch spent eight fortunate and happy years in Zürich. His two daughters and one son were born there. In the Swiss mountains he found both aesthetic and physical satisfaction, and the freedom of religious and political opinion in Switzerland was in accord with his own liberal outlook. Throughout his life, and not least at the end, the Swiss Federation was for him the pattern of a fine national and social organization. He called Switzerland his second Fatherland, and few of his vacations in later life were spent elsewhere. He worked, and worked his collaborators hard in the laboratory, but on weekends and during vacations he and his assistants joined in strenuous and courageous hikes and mountain climbs. Roland Scholl told of these excursions when he came to Leipzig to celebrate Hantzsch's seventieth birthday.

Although Hantzsch never abandoned synthetic work, his chief interest was not the preparation of compounds, but the relationship between physical and chemical properties and constitution, the subject of his Probevorlesung in 1882. Synthesis to him was a tool rather than an end. The proper interpretation of experiments in which Tscherniac had obtained the first synthetic derivatives of thiazole led to a thorough investigation of these compounds, stimulated by Hantzsch's interest in chemical "mimicry." This term, adopted from zoology, was used for compounds which "simulate" the behavior of other chemical individuals. Thus, thiophene had been found by Victor Meyer to resemble benzene, although it contains one sulfur atom instead of an ethylene group. Similarly, thiazole resembles pyridine from which it differs by replacement of ethylene by sulfur.

There are four major topics which dominated Hantzsch's interest, oximes and the stereoisomerism on $C=N$ bonds, diazo and azo compounds and the stereoisomerism on $N=N$ bonds, the relationship between physical properties (particularly light absorption), and structure, including the intricacies of the sterical arrangement of atoms in molecules and the nature of acids and bases. The interest in stereochemistry was marked by the publication, with his pupil Alfred Werner, of a paper on stereochemically isomeric compounds of nitrogen. Johannes Wislicenus had shown that compounds with carbon to carbon double bonds can form cis- and trans-isomers depending on the orientation of the substituents on the doubly linked carbon atoms. In the paper which opens the 1890 volume of *Berichte der Deutschen Chemischen Gesellschaft,* Hantzsch and Werner extended this interpretation to compounds with carbon–nitrogen double bonds and explained the supernumerary isomers which had been observed with oximes and other compounds containing carbon–nitrogen double bonds. At the end of this paper, Hantzsch gave Werner credit for having independently "formulated the central idea with its most important consequences, when I first expressed the vague idea that nitrogen, just as well as carbon, might give rise to geometrical isomerism." While Werner's share in the formulation of the new theory is

1071

great, the experimental proof was due wholly to Hantzsch's energy and experimental skill. In one year, working with substances which were frequently extremely labile, he accumulated with his collaborators evidence for the stereoisomerism, and for the tautomerism, of the oximes.

With methods similar in principle to those used by Wislicenus he sought to decide for the aldoximes which of the respective compounds were the cis- and which were the trans-isomers. Likewise, the Beckmann arrangement was used not only to obtain a new line of evidence for the structural identity of isomeric ketoximes, but to establish their "geometrical" configurations. The basis of these correlations was the assumption that intramolecular reactions of groups prove their proximity not only in ring closures but also in elimination reactions. This principle was widely accepted until Meisenheimer proved in 1921 that the Beckmann rearrangement proceeds as a trans-reaction. Wislicenus, and after him Hantzsch, formulated their correlations on the basis of mechanical analogies. At that time the quantum theory had not yet made investigators cautious in the use of mechanical analogies for phenomena at molecular dimensions.

Many of the leading chemists of Hantzsch's generation, particularly the organic chemists, devoted a considerable part of their labors to compounds of biological, medicinal, or technical importance. Their contributions, therefore, can be appreciated not only by the progress which they made in isolation, analysis and synthesis, and in the understanding of the reactions of compounds, but also for the significance of these compounds in biology, medicine, and industry. Hantzsch's interest was elicited by the chemical problem as such. The relation of chemical and physical behavior to structure as represented by formulas and models dominated his work. While he rejected concern with practical applications of chemistry, he was tireless in his quest for knowledge, determined, skillful, and inventive, and interested in inorganic as well as organic chemistry. He was guided in the choice of his research by observations which indicated problems the elucidation of which would lead to a better understanding of chemical systems and their transformations. He had an extraordinary ability to see analogies and correlations between seemingly unrelated properties.

1072

His interests were wide, but he was always occupied and pre-occupied with chemistry. In talking to his collaborators he referred to little notes, often jotted down at night, and they might receive postcards and letters written on vacations with questions, suggestions and ideas.

In 1893, Hantzsch publlshed in Zürich a small volume, "Grundriss der Stereochemie."[2] In the same year, having declined invitations to chairs in Kiel, Worcester, Mass., and Rostock, Hantzsch left Zürich to succeed Emil Fischer at Würzburg. Fischer had admired the synthetic work of the young Hantzsch, particularly his collidine synthesis, and had recommended him as his successor. In Würzburg Hantzsch spent what he remembered as the happiest and most carefree period of his life. He liked the small town, the easy and stimulating social intercourse of all ranks in the University from professors to students, and the beautiful surroundings which invited excursions. His first task in Würzburg as it had also been in Zürich, was to supervise the erection of the new laboratory. It had been planned by his predecessor, but some minor changes were made to increase the accommodation for physicochemical work. Among the men with whom Hantzsch associated in Würzburg was Wilhelm Röntgen; the two families were close neighbors.

During the early years at Würzburg, Hantzsch completed the work on geometrical isomers on carbon–nitrogen bonds. In 1894 he published his first paper on the diazo compounds in which a similar isomerism was proposed for nitrogen to nitrogen double bonds. This led into the chemistry of diazo and azo compounds. With consummate experimental skill in preparative work and by the application of physicochemical measurements, particularly cryoscopic determinations and conductivity measurements, he elucidated the maze of inter-relations between the diazonium compounds containing quaternary nitrogen, the geometrical isomers of diazo compounds with trivalent nitrogen, and the reactions of these, often unstable, substances.

The geometrical isomerism on $C=N$ and on $N=N$ double bonds was not universally accepted. Victor Meyer and Karl Auwers did not trust the formulation of cis- and trans-oximes, and even the discovery of isomeric hydrazones did not convince them in the beginning. A controversy arose which was noteworthy for the courtesy displayed by both sides. The work on diazo and azo compounds became the subject of more acrimonious debate with Ludwig Bamberger, Hantzsch's successor in Zürich. After many years of argument, this controversy ended with the acceptance of Hantzsch's point of view by Bamberger in 1912. In later years, Hantzsch referred with regret to the sharpness of this debate; he was greatly affected by Bamberger's long illness and spoke of him with great warmth of feeling and sympathy. Such feelings might also come to the surface impulsively and unexpectedly in his relations with the members of his laboratory, particularly his collaborators and the staff. Hantzsch, though reserved, was not wont to disguise his judgments of criticism or of appreciation and his frank statements could, on occasion, greatly enliven discussions after lectures and at faculty meetings.

While Hantzsch used chemical symbols and formulas, not only as a means for recording results and as an aid in constructive thinking, he was aware of their limitations. He realized early that the more reactive form of tautomeric compounds—compounds in which two or more forms are in rapid exchange—might channel a reaction so that only derivatives of this species are isolated, even though the parent form be present in the starting material as trace amounts only. Hantzsch writes:

> It must become more generally recognized that we cannot explain chemical reactions by structural formulae, for by them one can represent only the initial and the final state of a system. And even the possibility of this will become the smaller, the further we depart from the chemistry of carbon, in which the theory of valency founded wholly on structure has proved so valuable, and go over into the chemistry of other elements.

Moore states about Hantzsch's work on diazo compounds that he "widened the experimental basis of his research in every possible direction, seeking in each class of substances for its most stable member, and since he was convinced on general grounds that tautomerism played a great part in the reactions, allowed for this in the choice of experimental conditions and in the interpretation of his results. Gradually he built up a technique which, on the organic side alone, is a marvel of insight an dingenuity. Even more important historically is the decisive part played for the first time in this research by physical methods of investigating organic problems." While Hantzsch had great imagination and insight in applying physical data to chemical problems, he preferred to leave the tedium of measurements and mathematical details to his collaborators.

The work on the diazo compounds became the backbone of a book, "Die Diazoverbindungen" published in 1902, and republished with many additions by Hantzsch and Reddelien in 1921.

The changes in constitution of acids or bases in the formation of salts had been important in the work on diazo compounds. Such changes became the object of special investigations in which Hantzsch showed that aliphatic nitro compounds form salts not in the nitro form but in a tautomeric aci-form. As a result of this work Hantzsch published in 1899 a paper dealing with the characteristics of salt formation involving constitutional change. It was postulated that such a change can reveal itself in several ways; by abnormal and time dependent neutralization and hydrolysis phenomena and by changes of color in salt formation and in the liberation of acids and bases from salts. In some cases constitutional changes may suppress certain reactions, e.g., with phosphorous pentachloride, phenylisocyanate, and dry ammonia, while the compounds nevertheless give salts. The formulation of these postulates marked a milestone in the understanding of anomalous salt formation. Not all the postulates stood the scrutiny of later experiments and interpretations. In Hinshelwood's[3] description of the development of a theory, Hantzsch's paper may be classified as the first stage of "oversimplification, reflecting partly the need for practical working rules, and even more a too enthusiastic aspiration after elegance of form. In the second stage the symmetry of the hypothetical systems is distorted and the neatness marred as recalcitrant facts increasingly rebel against conformity. In the third stage, if and when this is attained, a new order emerges."

Hantzsch owed his call to Würzburg mainly to the brilliant synthesis which he had discovered; the call to Leipzig as the successor to Wislicenus which he received in 1903 must have been

1075

prompted by his accomplishments as a physical organic chemist. Thus, we find Hantzsch in Kolbe's chair 21 years after Kolbe's prediction. He occupied this chair for a quarter century until his retirement in 1927.

The chemical laboratory in Leipzig was located in a large rambling building on the Liebigstrasse, a few minutes' walk from the Laboratory for Applied Chemistry and less than a mile from the Laboratory for Physical Chemistry, where Wilhelm Ostwald taught. The residence of the director was connected to the building; it had ample rooms and a little garden, much used by Hantzsch and his family during the summer months. The big auditorium accommodated about 350 students. There was a laboratory bench for demonstrations, large blackboards stretched along the wall in the rear of the bench, and covering hoods which were also accessible from an anteroom containing all sorts of facilities for the preparation of demonstrations and a collection of chemicals. Hantzsch lectured five times a week from 9:15 to 10:00 in the morning, during the summer semester on inorganic chemistry, during the winter on organic chemistry. As head of the department, Hantzsch gave the "Grosse Vorlesung" (big lecture), as was customary in German Universities, which was attended by beginners not only in chemistry but also in medicine, physics, and general science, and a grand lecture it was. The assistant, an experienced mechanic, had spent much of the preceding day under Hantzsch's direction setting up series of experiments which were run off while Hantzsch lectured from a few notes jotted down on a little card which he carried in his vest pocket. The lecture was brilliant; the delivery reflected Hantzsch's keen interest in the subject; and formulas and equations were developed on the blackboards in his clear handwriting. The blackboards were flanked by two doors leading to the preparation room and crowned by marble busts of Kolbe and of Wislicenus. In celebration of Hantzsch's 70th birthday in 1927, his pupils had a large bronze relief of Hantzsch made which was installed in the center over the blackboards.

After the lecture, Hantzsch used to make the round of his graduate students, discussing with each of them the problems at hand and often doing small-scale experiments—watchglasses

1076

were his favorites when he observed color changes or tried to make recalcitrant substances crystallize. A similar visit took place in the afternoon. As an examiner Hantzsch was more interested in the students' ability to think in dealing with chemical problems than in their cramming knowledge. He was impatient with slow wit, apt to blame it on drinking, and he did not disguise that the habits of German fraternities, particularly their duelling, were not to his taste. The staff of the laboratory included a number of faculty members who taught in various fields of chemistry, and with their assistants and pupils were engaged in research; K. Schäfer and F. Hein in inorganic chemistry. H. Stobbe, G. Reddelien and C. Weygand in organic chemistry, and B. Rassow in chemical technology.

Shortly after his return to Leipzig, Hantzsch's wife died. He remained a widower for seven years and then married Hedwig Steiner of Zürich. The later years were clouded by the tragic death of his only son, who having served as a very young man in World War I, was killed in 1921 on the Grossglockner in the Alps in an attempt to rescue other climbers who were in danger. The tragedy for Hantzsch was accentuated by the death during the same year of one of his sons-in-laws, Professor Löhlein, who succumbed to an infection which he had incurred performing an autopsy. Outwardly he reacted to these blows by working even more intensively with his students and at his desk.

Hantzsch continued in Leipzig the research initiated at Zürich and at Würzburg, but more and more his interest centered around the relations between color and constitution. The guiding concept of this work was that profound changes in color indicate changes in structure which can be represented by structural or stereochemical formulas. Solvation without change in chemical structure of the solute could produce only minor shifts in absorption. Conversely, minor chemical changes like the replacement of a hydrogen atom by a methyl group would as such have little or no effect on light absorption, unless the location of the methyl group differed from that of the hydrogen.

In the investigations centering around the relation of light absorption to constitution, Hantzsch encountered the limitations of classical structural symbolism. He made use of the insight

1077

gained by Werner that metals which are bound in the classical way by replacing ionizable hydrogen can, in addition, form intramolecular complexes and cause the formation and variation of colored salts in systems like the violurates. The chemistry of organic metal complexes led Hantzsch to the conclusion that absorption phenomena can be explained by the assumption of intermediary states which we would now call resonance hybrids. Hantzsch realized that the stable state of certain molecules would have to be described as an intermediate of more than one structure. About the salts of dinitro-triphenyl methane

$$R-C \left\langle \begin{array}{l} \bigcirc =NO_2 \cdot \text{Metal} \\ \bigcirc -NO_2 \end{array} \right.$$

and of di-amino-triphenyl methane

$$R-C \left\langle \begin{array}{l} \bigcirc =NR_2Cl \\ \bigcirc -NR_2 \end{array} \right.$$

with bases or with acids, respectively, he wrote: "The difference between the quinonoid and the nonquinonoid part of the conjugated complex does not really exist, for in every other way there is identity. The formulas can be simplified to

$$R-C \left\langle \begin{array}{l} C_6H_4NO_2 \\ C_6H_4NO_2 \end{array} \right\} \text{Metal}$$

and

$$R-C \left\langle \begin{array}{l} C_6H_4NR_2 \\ C_6H_4NR_2 \end{array} \right\} X$$

He realized clearly that the difference between the quinonoid and the benzenoid part of these molecules has vanished and that the respective moieties are intermediate in character between benzenoid and quinonoid.

Similar considerations were applied to acids. In this work, the publication of which began in 1917 with a paper on the ultraviolet absorption of carboxylic acids and their salts and esters, Hantzsch tried to penetrate into the nature of the acidic function and its dependence on chemical structure. He showed that acids in aqueous solution are present more or less as hydronium salts, $X^-[H_3O]^+$, which he formulated like the oxonium salts of Baeyer and Villiger and Collie and Tickle in analogy to ammonium salts. He realized that the hydrogen ion of the Arrhenius–Ostwald theory is, in fact, the hydronium ion, and that in aqueous solutions the acidic functions attributed to the hydrogen ion are those of the hydronium ion.

Carboxylic acids form the hydronium salts $RC{\overset{\overset{-}{O}}{\underset{O}{}}}\Big\}\overset{+}{H_3O}$ in which the two oxygen atoms of the carboxylic group are equivalent. The extent of hydronium salt formation of these acids depends on the concentration of H_2O and on the nature of R, i.e., on the content of real, ϵ-acid, form— $RC{\overset{O}{\underset{O}{}}}\Big\}H$ —and of ester, ψ-acid, form— $RC{\overset{OH}{\underset{H}{}}}$ —in the undiluted acid. Similar ϵ and ψ forms contribute to the structures of other acids, including the mineral acids. Inasmuch as the ψ form does not exhibit acidic functions, these functions are developed when weak acids are diluted with water. The acidic function of strong acids, however, in which the ϵ form predominates, is diminished by aqueous dilution because *the tendency to form salts, the essence and the real measure of acidity,* is partly used up in the hydronium salt formation.

In discussing acids at the Centenary of the *Gesellschaft Deutscher Naturforscher und Aerzte* at Leipzig in 1922, Hantzsch talked of certain carboxylic acids, as 70% in the ϵ and 30% in the ψ form. There was consternation and Kurt Hans Meyer came to Hantzsch's assistance by interpreting the data as a kinetic equilibrium between both forms, but Hantzsch agitatedly insisted that each individual molecule was to be represented by 30% of the one and 70% of the other form—years before the theory of resonance was formulated. With oxygen-containing solvents like alcohols, ketones or ethers the acids may similarly form onium salts, or such solvents may stabilize the non-acidic ψ-forms of the acids. A principal means for detecting acidic functions and strengths of acids were basic indicators which, competing with the solvents for the acids, form more or less of the indicator salts and by their color indicate the position of the equilibrium involving acid, solvent and indicator. Another means for measuring the strength of acids was the rate of decomposition of ethyl diazo acetate which depends on the degree to which the diazonium salt is formed. When these ideas were applied to strong acids and measurements of the rate of inversion of sucrose were included, the now well accepted sequence of strength of the mineral acids, perchloric, hydrobromic, hydrochloric, nitric was established.

It is noteworthy that Brönsted, in his classical paper on *Acid and Basic Catalysis* states, "we may find after all—in spite of much divergency—that the ideas of Hantzsch are, in many ways, not incompatible with those of the present review."

Hantzsch used physical properties not only to characterize stable forms but also to gain evidence concerning entities which could not be isolated but are present, for example, in solutions in absolute sulfuric acid. The insight thus gained led to some of the most brilliant experiments in Hantzsch's career, the formation of salts by mixing nitric acid and perchloric acid or acetic acid and perchloric acid and their characterization by conductivity and incompatible with those of the present view."[11]

It was Hantzsch's genius to use widely different methods to gain information about a system. Optical data of absorption and refraction, conductivity, catalytic and direct chemical action, and other methods served in unison to elucidate the problem at hand. The physicochemical data, however, were often not obtained with the most perfect quantitative methods. It was the concerted interpretation of these data together with information about behavior in reactions, with other chemical data, and with analogies which yielded results of often amazing perspicacity. This method was attacked by specialists who had obtained measurements of higher accuracy and who objected to the far-flung conclusions Hantzsch drew from "semi-quantitative" data. Hantzsch felt hurt by the insinuation of carelessness and frustrated by misunderstanding. When, however, a colleague offered a more profound, a more mathematical or a more general approach, Hantzsch was delighted and generous in his acknowledgement.

When Hammett, in 1926, published his first paper on the theory of acidity Hantzsch wrote him expressing his interest and pleasure:[4] "That you unconditionally acknowledge my theory of acids and were even able to give its mathematical foundation pleases me particularly because most of the German chemists and particularly the physicochemists ignore or even refuse it."

Many honors came to Hantzsch; he received titles and honorary degrees, became a member of several academies and an honorary member of the Chemical Society, but few scientists of his stature have been criticized with the aggression to which he was exposed. Part of this is due to the fact that he reinterpreted the results of others, which naturally caused irritation. Part of it was caused by Hantzsch's method of roaming all over chemistry and chemical physics in collecting data and drawing analogies. In addition, his use of symbols could cause misunderstanding. The operation of any symbol reaches cases where the symbol no longer adequately represents the observations. The mathematical symbol is then modified by further approximations. Structural symbols may be redefined by additional qualities, e.g., statements about size may supplement elements of location. Hantzsch's stereochemical concepts and ideas on the specificity of affinities, for instance that sodium is preferentially linked to oxygen but that silver may be bonded to nitrogen are cases in point. The difference between homopolar (covalent) bonds and heteropolar (ionic) bonds which Hantzsch suggested was not readily accepted. Hantzsch's understanding sometimes transcended the correlations which could be logically deduced from the data, and his assistants were sometimes amazed by the conclusions at which he arrived intuitively from seemingly unrelated observations. Hantzsch's eagerness to understand old and to discover new facts was that of the great scientist. He would have agreed with William Herschel's statement, "If we add observation to observation, without attempting to draw not only certain conclusions, but also conjectural views from them, we offend against the very end for which observations ought to be made."[6] With his ability to recognize analogies and to suggest interpretations, Hantzsch combined a keen ability for observation. He told the writer that it was not important which chemical problem he tackled as long as he followed up courageously those of his observations which he could not understand and did not pause to rejoice in verifications of his predictions. "What one can predict is not new anyhow." Verification of prediction interested him only where the experiment confirmed or contradicted a theory. Since Hantzsch wrote to Hammett, the approach to chemical problems has greatly changed and Hantzsch is now widely recognized as a pioneer in the application of physical methods to chemical, and particularly organic chemical, problems. What many of his contemporaries called speculation has become the fountainhead of important developments in physical organic chemistry.

Hantzsch's 70th birthday, in 1927, was marked by a celebration attended by representatives of universities and scientific societies, by colleagues and former students. Many had come to Leipzig, others had written or wired; F. Bergius, K. H. Meyer, T. S. Moore, R. Scholl, F. Hein, K. H. Bauer, G. Reddelien, H. Hibbert, C. Weygand, F. Timm, A. Weissberger, H. Carlsohn, and A. Burawoy were among his pupils the nor later in academic positions; a great number attained distinguished careers in industry. Hantzsch, who was a reserved man and in general rather adverse to display of emotion, was deeply touched—particularly by the respect and affection demonstrated by his former students.

Shortly after his 70th birthday Hantzsch retired from his official duties. He continued work on his publications and he maintained several assistants, selected from his most gifted recent pupils, to continue experimental work on various problems. As his retirement approached, Hantzsch, maybe for the first time in his life, had also accepted the offer of an industrial firm to supervise some of their research. A special small laboratory was installed in the basement of the laboratory building, and there, in great seclusion, he proceeded with work probably on vulcanization catalysts for rubber; the smell of thio compounds and Hantzsch's interest in thiazole and other sulfur chemistry led to this interpretation for the mysterious happenings "in the cellar."

1082

When, about a year after Hantzsch's 70th birthday, his second wife died, he moved to Dresden, to a house in the neighborhood of the Gymnasium he had attended as a boy. No longer responsible for a large laboratory and deprived of the companionship of his wife, he became even more occupied with his research. He paid frequent visits to Leipzig to supervise the work of his assistants. Work and the happy association with his daughters, grandchildren, and a few intimate friends occupied his remaining years. His reaction to the Nazi government was shame and deep disgust, and he went out of his way to express these sentiments in calling on Jewish colleagues. His mind and body remained vigorous up to the time of his death in 1935 at the age of 78.

GENERAL REFERENCES

A. Burawoy, "Arthur Hantzsch," *Ber. deut. chem. Ges., 68,* 65 (1935).
B. Helferich, "Nachruf auf Arthur Hantzsch," *Ber. Math.-phys. Kl. sächs. Akad. Wiss. Leipzig,* 87, 213 (1935).
T. S. Moore, "The Hantzsch Memorial Lecture," *J. Chem. Soc., 1936,* 1051.
Fr. Hein, "Arthur Hantzsch," *Ber. deut chem. Ges.,* 74, 147 (1941).

NOTES AND REFERENCES

1 This biographical sketch leans heavily on T. S. Moore's Hantzsch Memorial Lecture, *J. Chem. Soc., 1936,* 1051, from which passages are quoted verbatim. In this lecture Professor Moore, a pupil of Hantzsch during the Würzburg time, discusses Hantzsch's work with full use of chemical symbols. The indebtedness of the present writer to Professor Moore and to the authorities of the Chemical Society as copyright owners is gratefully acknowledged.
2 Second edition, Leipzig, 1904.
3 C. N. Hinshelwood, *Chem. & Ind., 1957,* 1642.
4 I am grateful to Professor Louis P. Hammett for permission to quote from this letter.
5 Quoted from Milton K. Munitz, "Theories of the Universe," Glencoe, Ill., p. 264.
6 *Chem. Rev., 5,* 337 (1928).

ARNOLD WEISSBERGER

·· 75 ··

Giacomo Ciamician

1857-1922

GIACOMO LUIGI CIAMICIAN was born in Trieste to a family of Armenian origin on August 25, 1857. He first studied in his native town where Auguste Vierthaler was his chemistry professor. Later, at the University of Vienna, he studied with Barth and Weidel. After having applied himself to natural science, he decided definitely for chemistry, but he certainly would not have been successful in his experiments in plant chemistry if it had not been for his profound knowledge of botany which he had acquired as a young student.

In 1880, he passed his examinations for his Ph.D. at the University of Giessen and then went to Rome, attracted by the reputation of Stanislao Cannizzaro, who made him his assistant at the Institute of General Chemistry of the University of Rome. He stayed seven years at the laboratory of this illustrious master. During this time he continued his beautiful researches on pyrrole and its compounds, which he had started in Vienna; he obtained brilliant results that assured his reputation in all scientific circles.

In 1887, he became professor of general chemistry at the University of Padua; in 1889, he applied for, and obtained, the correspondent chair at the University of Bologna. There he lectured until the last days of his life, teaching with equal success general and inorganic chemistry as well as organic and biological chemistry.

Ciamician was not only a very competent laboratory man and an indefatigable worker, but he also was a teacher of the first order, who was able to communicate to his students his love for physics and chemistry. In 1908, before the Société Chimique de France, he gave a well-received account of his work on photochemistry, which made his audience appreciative of his talents as a speaker as well as of the originality and the interesting subject matter of his researches.

Giacomo Ciamician left us important scientific contributions; although most of his publications appeared in the Italian periodicals, he often honored our *Bulletin* with memoranda of remarkable

1087

clearness. The work of Ciamician is chiefly connected with physics, organic chemistry, photochemistry, and plant chemistry; it was pursued without relaxation from 1877 to 1922, and was only interrupted by the premature death of the illustrious chemist.

At the beginning of his scientific career Ciamician was interested in spectroscopy; he made a comparative study of the spectrum of homologous elements belonging to the same group in the periodic system. His researches in this field were those of a forerunner, because at the present time we recognize the value which it is possible to attribute to the spectographic techniques in theoretical chemistry as well as in many analytical applications.

The research which Ciamician dedicated to organic chemistry was mostly connected with the chemistry of pyrrole and its derivatives. Its close affinity with chlorophyll and hematine are well known, and one finds it again in the nucleus of numerous alkaloids. His investigations in this field were undertaken from 1880 to 1888 and have been described in nearly 80 memoranda. The monograph which he published in 1888 on "pyrrol and its derivatives" won a prize from the Academia dei Lincei. In 1904, he published the general results which he had obtained in the *Berichte* of the German Chemical Society. In the course of these researches Ciamician prepared the tetraiodopyrrol or iodol, which constitutes an interesting successor of iodoform.

During ten years, from 1889 to 1899, Ciamician studied the essential oils of numerous plants: parsley, celery, anise, sassafras, clove, etc. Particularly known is his work on the transformations of saffron and eugenol into their isomers, very important reactions in the heliotropine and vanillin industries.

His research on photochemical reactions was the subject of more than 50 notes published from 1900 to 1915. They form a very important and very original part of the work of this scholar. We all are aware of the considerable upswing in photochemistry since this epoch, and particularly the work of Daniel Berthelot, our eminent late colleague, is present in our memories.

In 1886, in Rome, Ciamician had described the effect of light on nitrobenzene in an alcoholic solution; he returned to this question and studied it systematically in 1900. On June 6, 1908, he explained his work on photochemistry at a conference of the Société Chimique de France. He had been led to this study by the idea that, in biology, using only the means Nature has at its disposal, it is indispensable to reproduce all the substances composing organized beings—above all, the plants—without the help of agents foreign to the living world. The examination of the means which serve the organisms in chemical reactions naturally presents great difficulties, and even if the way traced by Ciamician is followed by numerous biologists, the actual progress is still slow.

Besides the enzymes, which are the principal catalysts of the organic world, it is necessary to define and study the visible or invisible luminous radiations whose influence on the life process is of main importance. Ciamician had especially in mind the phenomena going on in green plants for which light constitutes the source of energy; he wanted to carry out the transformation of radiating energy into chemical energy as it occurs in plants.

The work which he pursued in this field was accomplished with the help of Paolo Silver who was, during the largest part of Ciamician's scientific career, a valuable collaborator in his devotion and experimental skill.

The phenomena of oxidoreduction, so important in biology, can be reproduced under the influence of luminous radiations by making them act on pairs of conveniently chosen substances, of which one oxidizes at the cost of the other, which then undergoes a transformation in the opposite sense. This is produced in certain cases by simply transposing hydrogen, for instance, making the alcohols react on substances with a carbonyl group: quinones, ketones, aldehydes. Quinone is thus transformed into quinhydrone and hydroquinone under the influence of the alcohol which oxidizes to aldehyde, operating with light under specific experimental conditions. The polyatomic alcohols act the same way, being transformed into sugary substances which are identical with natural sugars; this is, for instance the case with mannitol, which leads to d-mannose. The aromatic nitro derivatives are reduced by an identical process in the presence of alcohols and aldehydes, and Ciamician studied particularly the effect of benzaldehyde on nitrobenzene.

The phenomena of autoxidation, polymerization, and condensation can be observed under the influence of light. Also one can find hydrolyses with the opening of closed chains; this is the case

1089

with o-methylcyclohexanone, which is transformed at a ratio of 25 per cent into normal heptylic acid and heptylene aldehyde. Menthone and dihydrocarvone undergo similar photochemical changes, and the experiments on the effect of light on odoriferous substances are of evident importance in the theory of the perfume of flowers. Ciamician also studied the condensations of hydrocyanic acid with aldehydes and ketones, hoping to accomplish the synthesis of the amino acids of plants, a problem that greatly interests the biologists.

In collaboration with Ciro Ravenna, professor of agricultural chemistry in Pisa, Ciamician attacked the question of the origin and the transformation of the chemical compounds in plants. Considering the plant organism as a real laboratory, he tried to accomplish syntheses by injecting several products. Among the most demonstrative experiments should be mentioned the synthesis of salicin, which was produced by injecting saligenin into corn plants, a species which does not contain traces of this glucoside in its normal state.

Naturally this question had to lead this scholar to the determination of the rôle of alkaloids in plants. To Ciamician, these compounds do not seem to be residual products of the vegetable metabolism. Instead of eliminating them, the plants modify them and make them more resistant. It would seem that the alkaloids are destined for very specialized functions and constitute genuine vegetable hormones.

The fact that the alkaloids flow toward the injured parts of plants that have been subjected to pinching, for instance, can probably be interpreted as a means by which they try to re-establish, with the help of the alkaloids, the functional equilibrium disturbed by the lesion.

On the other hand, in the kidney bean, the function of the chlorophyll is heightened by an injection of caffeine or theobromine. One observes an overproduction of starch, which does not justify the consideration of the alkaloids simply as waste substances.

Even if certain of Ciamician's conclusions are not in complete harmony with those of physiologists such as Clautriau or Pictet, who have studied this problem, the fact still remains that his researches make a very important contribution toward the knowledge of the fate of the alkaloids in plants, a particularly captivating question of vegetable biology.

In a last article, published in 1923, in the *Bulletin de la Société de Chimie Biologique,* Ciamician concluded from his work that "the plants practice a chemistry corresponding to what we do in our laboratories; they do it with infinitely simpler means, but with similar intentions. Since their organism is not as differentiated as that of animals, they make up for it with a more perfect chemism."

Ciamician, who taught chemistry of minerals among other subjects at Bologna, was never without interest in the recent problems that arose in this branch of science.

He studied electrolytic dissociation, solid solutions and, in a memorandum published in 1918, relating to "The nature of chemical affinity and the valence of atoms," he developed his views on the fine structure of the atom in perfect accord with the present theories.

This short account shows the great importance and the extension of Giacomo Ciamician's work. He liked to explain his work or the most interesting chemical problems of the present day in brilliant conferences in Italy as well as in France, Germany, Austria, and the United States; in all these countries, he had gained the respect of the scientific world. A profound friendship existed between him and Albin Haller, Emil Fischer, and Henry E. Armstrong. He was a member of all scientific societies in Italy, and of numerous societies outside his own country, and honorary member of the Société Chimique de France.

Among the numerous honorary distinctions which had been granted him in the course of his career, he attached a special value to the Légion d'Honneur, which was bestowed on him by the French government. He was considered, in fact, to be one of the most faithful friends of France in Italy.

In the Italian Senate, where he had a seat from 1910, he was not interested in purely political questions. He gave advice that was always well considered in the discussion of problems of public education or chemical industry. He rendered the greatest services to his country and the Allies during World War I, and he had the good fortune to see his native town, Trieste, become Italian again.

Death brutally put an end to the great activities of Giacomo Ciamician, at the moment when he had a right to look forward to brilliant results of his work; but his work will not be forgotten, and his image will always remain that of a great scholar, who knew how to honor science to which he had dedicated his whole life.

From: *Bull. soc. chim. France,* 4e s., *41,* 1562–66 (1927). Translated by Eduard Farber.

RENÉ FABRE

·· 76 ··

Svante Arrhenius

1859-1927

THERE are two Arrhenius families in Sweden; one was said to have originated in Bavaria. The eminent chemist, Svante Arrhenius, came from the other, from the northern part of the district of Kalmar. The family name is said to be derived from that of the village Ārena in the parish Mālilla. The branch from which Svante came lived on the Klövdala farm in the parish Jåreda. His uncle, Johan Arrhenius, was a famous botanist and agricultural writer who had contributed markedly to the development of Swedish agriculture by his literary activity and who, for years, was secretary of the Swedish Agricultural Academy in Stockholm. Johan and his brother, Svante Gustaf Arrhenius, were students at Upsala in the 1820's and stayed on there for a time. Svante Gustaf became a land surveyor and later a supervisor of the University of Upsala. Since in the beginning this post brought but little income, he also was employed as overseer in the ancient castle Wik on Lake Mālar in the province of Uppland. His wife was Carolina Thunberg of Klövdala; their son, Svante August, was born at Wik on February 19, 1859. Several years later, the father's position improved enough so that the family could move to Upsala where he could devote himself entirely to his university position.

Svante Arrhenius' outstanding abilities manifested themselves early. Of his own accord, and against his parents' wishes, he learned to read at three. At a very young age, he acquired an incredible skill in arithmetic by watching his father add the columns in the account books. This early knowledge of numbers is particularly interesting if it is recalled that, in his future work, he especially liked to discover relationships and laws in masses of observational data. When he was eight, he entered the fifth grade of the Cathedral School. Although the youngest in his class, he was superior to most of the others with respect to information and ability. He did particularly well in physics and mathematics. M. M. Floderus, the principal of the school, and the author of the physics text then most widely used in the schools, taught this subject. He had a high opinion of the young Arrhenius, who finished school in 1876, at the age of seventeen.

Svante Arrhenius, therefore, was not one of the great number of famous scientists who were more or less irked by school and made poor scholastic records, like Liebig and Berzelius. The latter, for instance, came to Upsala from the gymnasium in Linkoping, with a certificate in which the principal had noted that he "was a young man with good natural abilities, bad manners and questionable expectancy," a certificate which weighed heavily on the boy's spirit. If an explanation of this rather common occurrence is sought, it may be that it involves young men of quite specialized interests, whereas Arrhenius, as was gradually revealed, had very extensive interests. In this connection, it may also be pointed out that Arrhenius—in contrast to many Swedish scientists—had practically no financial difficulties during his student days, a condition furthered by his pronounced thrift.

After graduation from secondary school, he embarked on his university studies for the first state examination, studying mathematics and chemistry, followed by physics. He became a candidate for the bachelor's degree at Upsala in 1878. Then followed, again at Upsala, the examination for the intermediate degree, the licentiate in philosophy, as well as the doctoral disputation.

Arrhenius was not as satisfied with his chief instructor in physics at Upsala as he had been in secondary school. Tobias R. Thalén (1827–1905) was known as an eminent and competent experimental physicist and an excellent lecturer. Consequently, the dissatisfaction could not have been due to any incompetence of this teacher. Arrhenius, in his autobiographical notes published in connection with the presentation of the Nobel Prize for Chemistry (1903), stated that the practical instruction in physics at the time (1881) was deficient. Otto Petterson, who was professor of chemistry at the University of Stockholm from 1881 to 1908, stated in an interesting article regarding this Nobel Prize: "The 80's were not a favorable time for those who wished to do experimental work in physics at Upsala." Thalén's notable achievements did not prevent him from giving scant encouragement to young researchers in his laboratory, and he showed but little inclination to secure the necessary equipment for them. Moreover, the apparatus for the usual physics exercises was scanty. A more serious reason why Thalén and Arrhenius did not get along with one another was because of their entirely opposing points of view; Thalén placed the main emphasis on exact experimental studies, whereas Arrhenius was always expounding new hypotheses. He was ready to test them by approximate experiments, but he had no desire to make tedious accurate measurements, since it was his goal to obtain a general view of hitherto unknown relationships quickly from approximate experiments.

Arrhenius left Upsala as early as 1881 in order to continue his training in physics at Stockholm under E. Edlund, the physicist of the Swedish Academy of Sciences. In him, Arrhenius found a teacher to his tastes, and it is reported that "Edlund was soon prepossessed by Arrhenius' method of working and later greatly furthered his interests." He gladly placed at the young man's disposal the wealth of apparatus belonging to the academy so that the experimental studies relating to the doctoral research could proceed.

In his doctoral thesis of 1884, and also in a rather short paper published in 1887, Arrhenius already was discussing the electrolytic theory of dissociation, which soon was to prove so fruitful and to become his greatest accomplishment. Here is another instance demonstrating that the best ideas of leading men are often found in their early studies. Arrhenius was only twenty-five when he published his famous doctoral work.

This dissertation was written in French and has the title: "Recherches sur la conductibilité galvanique des électrolytes." It makes up Papers 13 and 14 in Volume 8 of the Supplement of the Acts of the Royal Academy of Sciences, printed in 1884. These papers had already been announced at the meeting of the Academy on June 6, 1883, and accepted for publication; later they were combined to form the doctoral dissertation. The first part (No. 13) has 63 pages and No. 14, the second part, occupies 89 pages in Volume 8, cited above.

The first part begins with an account of the experimental studies conducted in Edlund's laboratory; they provide the basis for the theoretical presentation. These investigations dealt with the determination of the electrical conductivity of electrolytes at high dilutions, to 0.0005 normal or less. Heinrich Lenz (1804–65) professor of physics in St. Petersburg, and Friedrich Kohlrausch

(1840–1910) had made similar measurements in the 1870's, but these did not extend to such great dilutions as Arrhenius thought necessary for his purposes.

The third and last chapter of the first part bears the title "Theory." The new theoretical views were formulated in 56 theses, which, with consecutive numbering, go through the entire work, each thesis being preceded by a statement of its basis. The reader of these theses is struck by the admirable acumen and the well-considered judgment with which most of them are formulated, particularly if it is remembered that the data available for their derivation were very scant in comparison to what was subsequently brought to light because of these theses. With discerning clear-sightedness, the originator combines separate phenomena and provides them with a concentrated explanation. Only a few of the theses have not stood the test of time or have had to be greatly modified.

The first thesis states that, for very dilute solutions, the electrical conductivity of a solution of a salt is proportional to the concentration, other conditions being the same. The second states that the conductivity of a dilute solution of two or more salts is continuously equal to the sum of the conductivities which a solution of each of the salts would have at the same concentration. According to theses 7, 8, and 9, respectively, the electrical resistance of an electrolyte solution rises with increases in: (1) the internal friction; (2) complexity of the ions; and (3) the molecular weight of the solvent. This last thesis is an example of those propositions that have not been completely confirmed. Besides the internal friction of the solvent, Arrhenius also considered another factor related to the nature of the solvent; it is, however, as is known now, not the molecular weight of the solvent but its dielectric constant that is of significance in this connection. His statement can be explained— he worked only with a limited number of solvents: water, several alcohols, ether—for which it is approximately true that the dielectric constant decreases as the molecular weight rises.

Whereas the thirteen theses advanced in the first of the papers were set up mainly on the basis of actual experiments, with no accompanying hypotheses for their explanation, the second part

(No. 14 in Volume 8 of the Supplement) bears a more pretentious title "Théorie chimique des électrolytes." Here can be found the explanation of the results given in Part I and the bold structure of ideas which came to be known as the theory of electrolytic dissociation.

In thesis 15, it is stated first of all, but only for a solution of a hydrate, that the latter consists "in addition to water, of two constituents, namely an active (electrolytic) part and an inactive (nonelectrolytic) part," and, further, that on dilution of the solution the active part increases and the inactive part decreases. This is then extended to other dissolved electrolytes (salts): "The activity coefficient is a figure which gives the ratio between the number of ions actually present in the electrolyte to the number of ions which must be present there if the electrolyte should be completely transformed into simple electrolytic molecules." Here, as was his custom, Arrhenius employs the term *electrolyte* to denote the solution as a whole, while he otherwise and also, as can be seen, immediately thereafter uses this term to denote the dissolved materials (salt, acid, base) from which the conductivity stems. Consequently, the activity coefficient is the same as the degree of electrolytic dissociation, and the active (electrolytic) part is the same as the ions. His expressions, *active* and *activity coefficient,* naturally are reminiscent of Guldberg and Waage's *active mass.* It is likely that Arrhenius obtained the idea for his terms from the writings of these Norwegians; he frequently cited their publications, which, at that time, were still unappreciated. Arrhenius later stated that he, too, did not know of this work until quite late in his own investigation. The meanings which he and they ascribe to *activity* are not identical but are closely related.

Arrhenius himself pointed out that his theory was not without predecessors. In this connection, he cited such eminent authorities as Alexander Williamson (1824–1904) of the University of London, and the physicist, Rudolf Clausius (1822–88) at Bonn. The former had touched on this field in 1851, and, in 1857, the latter had advanced the hypothesis that a dissolved salt is dissociated to a certain extent into its two mobile ions even though no current is passing through the solution.[1]

Thus, the pre-existence of ions in the solution had been presented previously, at least by Clausius and in fact later (1921) Arrhenius stressed that Gay-Lussac had advanced similar ideas as early as 1839. In his well-known theory of the formation of ethyl ether on heating alcohol and sulfuric acid, Williamson does not speak of ions, but only of radicals (fragments of molecules) and does not attribute any electrical charge to them.

The question has been raised as to whether Arrhenius should really be credited with the fundamental development of the theory of electrolytic dissociation. The answer is definitely "Yes," and for the following reasons: Clausius, as was indicated above, limited himself to stating that a small part of the salt must be split beforehand into ions, but he did not state or calculate how much of the salt is thus affected.

The essential advances that we owe to Arrhenius reside in the appreciation that the salt, in many instances, is largely split into ions before any electric potential is applied to the solution. He stated how the extent of the splitting of the salt into ions can be computed quantitatively. This procedure is not to be found in the doctoral dissertation which is being discussed here, but in the paper of 1887 which will be taken up later.

The chemical applications begin after thesis 15. Thus we find the pregnant statement: . . . "The strength of an acid is the higher, the greater its activity coefficient (its molecular conductivity). The same holds true for bases." In thesis 31, it is asserted that the dissociation becomes complete at infinite dilution of the solution and, in 34, that in solutions of the salts of weak acids, strong acids displace the weak acids.

Although the Clausius pronouncement did not necessarily have a revolutionary effect on the chemical ideas of the time, this was by no means true of the views put forth by Arrhenius. Three objections in particular were raised. The first was the difficulty of comprehending how sodium chloride, for example, which was customarily regarded as a particularly stable material, could be split into its components (more precisely, into its ions) by merely dissolving it in water. The obvious answer to this was that this spontaneous process is no more remarkable than the accepted fact that solid sodium chloride, which is not significantly volatile at room temperature, dissolves readily in water and thus spreads throughout the liquid as a gas does in an empty space. The second one was: How is it possible for free sodium to be present in an aqueous solution when metallic sodium violently reacts with water, or how can free chlorine be present in the colorless, odorless solution, since a water solution of chlorine is yellow and has a penetrating odor? The response to this question was that sodium ions and chlorine ions are not the same as metallic sodium or chlorine gas. Both of these ionic species are electrically charged in contrast to the free elements; furthermore, the chlorine ion consists of only one chlorine atom, whereas molecules in chlorine gas contain two atoms. The third objection was that the sodium and chlorine ions should be capable of being separated by diffusion; this actually is possible to an extent, although the electrical forces oppose the separation so potently that the diffusion can be detected only by virtue of the resulting electrical charges of the solution or water, not by chemical means.

However, some Swedish chemists approved of the research. These included Otto Petterson, then professor at the Technical University in Stockholm, and A. G. Ekstrand, then docent in chemistry at Upsala and later editor of the *Svensk Kemisk Tideskrift*. On the other hand, Thalén had a low opinion of the work, and even Per T. Cleve (1840–1905), professor of chemistry at Upsala, was said to have been quite hesitant in his appraisal. As a result, the paper itself was given the mark *non sine laude* and the defense was graded *cum laude*. According to the then prevailing custom, this was not sufficient to qualify the candidate for a docentship; *cum laude* would be required for both the dissertation and the defense. It is reported that a later inquiry regarding the granting of a docentship was definitely rejected.

This appraisal of the doctoral work was long a topic for discussion. Considering the difficulties in judging revolutionary views, together with the fact that the available experimental data were not especially satisfactory, and also that the presentation is not always easy to follow, the verdict was not too surprising. Fortunately, this failure had no serious consequences.

Wilhelm Ostwald, who was then professor at the Polytechnikum in Riga, came to Upsala in the summer of 1884. He had already worked in the field of physical chemistry; among other things, he tested the Arrhenius theory of the relationship between conductivity and reaction velocity on 34 acids and found that it held true. He was anxious to meet the author of this theory. In his introduction to the volume of the *Zeitschrift für physikalische Chemie,* issued in 1909 to commemorate the twenty-fifth anniversary of Arrhenius' doctorate and the electrolytic dissociation theory, Ostwald wrote: "Along with several contestable views it [the dissertation] contained so many and such profound new thoughts that I was soon convinced of their fundamental importance." On his visit in 1884, he spoke to the authorities in Upsala in very favorable terms concerning the dissertation and later reported:

> I can still plainly recall the scene in the chemical laboratory in Upsala, where the head [Cleve], himself an eminent chemist, heatedly asked me, pointing to a beaker containing an aqueous solution—"And you too believe that sodium atoms are swimming around there in this fashion?" When I agreed, he quickly looked at me in such a manner as if he had considerable doubt about my chemical rationality. However, this did not prevent the esteemed older colleague from receiving us both with true Swedish hospitality, and later he did what he could to remove the difficulties surrounding the granting of the docentship.[2]

Ostwald himself offered Arrhenius a place at Riga, with the result that an application for docentship in physical chemistry at Upsala was acted on favorably. The appointment was to start at the end of 1884. In September, 1884, Arrhenius accompanied Ostwald to a scientific congress at Magdeburg, and they planned to go from there to Riga in order to lay out a program of studies in physical chemistry. However, Arrhenius had to return home because his father was seriously ill. The latter died in 1885.

Arrhenius soon left Upsala again. Through the influence of Edlund, he received a travel grant from the Swedish Academy. This sum (4500 Swedish crowns) plus his own means enabled him to enjoy a number of years of travel and study. He worked with Ostwald in Riga; with Kohlrausch in Würzburg (1886), where he became acquainted with Walther Nernst; with Ludwig Boltzmann (1844–1906) in Graz (1887); with van't Hoff in Amsterdam (1888); and again with Ostwald, who had been called to Leipzig in the meantime. These years were filled with intensive and most fruitful work, and, to use an expression probably coined by Arrhenius himself, "the dissociation theory matured." These were also joyful years—not only because he was happy in his work, but also because of the pleasure that came to him from his natural jovial nature and humor, which made him a favorite among so many of his friends and associates. He had the opportunity to become acquainted with the leading men in his field in Central Europe, and the fact that he was almost generally called "Svante" indicates how well he was liked.

The summer and fall of 1888 were spent in Sweden. Part of the time, he worked with Edlund until the latter died in August, and in the fall semester, he lectured on physical chemistry at Upsala. Here, for the first time, the new theories were set forth in connected form before an extremely interested audience. The years 1889 and 1890 found him abroad again. Most of this time was spent at Leipzig, where he served as assistant during the summer semester of 1889. He also was at Graz for a while.

During this period, an event occurred which was of vital interest to chemistry in general and to the completion of the dissociation theory in particular. This event was the publication of the famous paper by van't Hoff on "Lois de l'équilibre chimique," first in the *Archives Néerlandaises* and then in more extended form in the *Transactions of the Swedish Academy* of 1886. In this research, van't Hoff encountered a great difficulty which he could not explain. Solutions of salts, acids, and bases possess a greater osmotic pressure, higher vapor tension, and larger depression of the freezing point than the calculated values. It should be noted that, of course, no splitting of the salt into ions had been assumed in these calculations. Accordingly, van't Hoff had to limit his statement and declare that the laws of osmotic pressure and the related phenomena applied to a "majority of compounds." The great class of electrolytes (salts, acids, bases) had to be classed "exceptions."

1103

This great difficulty was resolved, and the theory of electrolytic dissociation was given its quantitative formulation, in the paper which first appeared in the *Ofversigt* (Review) of the *Transactions of the Swedish Academy* for the year 1887 under the title "Attempt to compute the dissociation (activity coefficient) of compounds dissolved in water" (10 pages).[3] The term "activity coefficient" appears in parentheses; in other words, Arrhenius now takes off the mask and plainly states that the fission products of the dissolved salts are its electrically charged ions.

Arrhenius here proceeds on the assumption that an osmotic pressure must be ascribed to the dissolved ions. "In the paper [his doctorate dissertation] referred to above, I have termed those molecules whose ions move independently of each other, active, and the other molecules, whose ions are closely bound to each other, inactive. Likewise, I have raised the possibility that, at infinite dilution, all inactive molecules are converted into active ones. I will make this assumption the basis of the following computations. I have denoted as activity coefficient the ratio between the number of active molecules and the sum of active and inactive molecules. Accordingly, at extreme dilution, the activity coefficient of an electrolyte will be unity. At low dilutions, it will be less than one and, in accord with the principles stated in the cited work, for not too concentrated solutions [solutions where disturbing influence due to internal friction, etc., can be neglected] it can be placed equal to the ratio between the actual molecular conductivity of the solution and the upper limiting value, which the molecular conductivity of this solution approaches at extreme dilution."

The degree of electrolytic dissociation was then quantitatively calculated by the formula:

$$\alpha = \Lambda/\Lambda_\infty$$

in which: Λ = the molecular (or equivalent) conductivity at the given concentration and Λ_∞ denotes the limiting value, to which: Λ approaches asymptotically with rising dilution. Furthermore, the formula for the so-called isotonic coefficient, i, is derived, i.e., the ratio between (1) the actual osmotic pressure or the depression of the vapor pressure, elevation of the boiling point or lowering of the freezing point of the solution and (2) the value which is calculated in case there is no splitting into ions:

$$i = 1 + (n - 1) \alpha$$

in which n denotes the number of ions into which a molecule splits. Thus, the "exceptions" to van't Hoff's law were explained at once, and the two values of the degree of dissociation, which thus could be derived from such diverse groups of phenomena as the electrical conductivity, on the one hand, and the osmotic pressure and the dependent values, on the other, exhibited a brilliant agreement, through which once more the theory of electrolytic dissociation received substantial confirmation. These papers of 1884 and 1887 represent the core of Arrhenius' most distinguished work in chemistry.

Two other theories influenced the revolution that was initiated by the work of Arrhenius and van't Hoff. The first was the Guldberg and Waage law of mass action, which had been formulated in 1867; it had not previously received deserved attention, but now its significance became apparent. The second was Nernst's theory of electromotive force (1888) which rests on the theory of electrolytic dissociation and the theory of osmotic pressure. Arrhenius' discoveries were made possible by the work of mainly two men, Friedrich Kohlrausch (1840–1910) and Wilhelm Hittorf (1824–1914). Kohlrausch had developed a method which was generally applicable for measuring the conductivity (resistance) of electrolytes and, in addition, had made extensive and accurate measurements. The fundamental work of Wilhelm Hittorf, whose studies of the migration of ions (1853–59) had been mostly disregarded at the time, had been cited by Arrhenius. Of course, Hittorf did not assume that free ions pre-exist in the solution; he believed that they are formed only when an imposed electric tension separates the molecules into their ions. He obviously could then speak of the mobility of these fragments.

The discoveries of van't Hoff were based on the experimental material gathered by Pfeffer and Raoult. In this connection, it should also be remembered that as early as 1870 Guldberg had deduced the connection between the lowering of vapor pressure and depression of the freezing point in the case of solutions, so that van't Hoff's discovery can be linked more accurately with the discovery of the laws of osmotic pressure and its relation to vapor pressure, boiling, and freezing points of solutions. Mention has already been made of the principle assumptions which served as the basis for Nernst's theory of electromotive force.

In a certain sense, the theory of electrolytic dissociation is a pattern for the modern theory of the transport of electricity through gases and opened the way for the latter, thereby, in great measure, contributing also to the development of the atomic theories of the present time. Another significant result of general nature is the erection of a bridge between physics and chemistry, i.e., the search for causes that are common to physical and chemical events.

The introduction of the theory not only required much work but also brought on heated conflicts between the champions of the earlier chemistry and the "wild horde of the Ionians" as the adherents of the newer views were sometimes called. It cannot be stated exactly how long the strife lasted, but the fact that the Nobel Prize in chemistry was given to van't Hoff in 1901—the first time it was awarded—and then to Arrhenius in 1903 "for the extraordinary service which he rendered to the development of chemistry through his theory of electrolytic dissociation" may be taken as the official close of the battle. At the banquet following the presentation of the prize, the first conferred on a Swede, Cleve delivered a fine tribute in which he recalled the countercurrents which were directed against the new views at the beginning.

In 1891, Arrhenius received a call to the University at Giessen but chose instead a post in physics at the Technical University of Stockholm offered to him in September, 1891. This post was converted into a professorship of physics in 1895, a promotion that was not without difficulties. He occupied this chair until 1905, when he became head of the physical chemistry division of the Nobel Institute of the Academy of Sciences.

During the period at the Stockholm University, a stream of students from home and abroad came to Arrhenius, the greatest such stream since the time of Karl Linnaeus (1707–1778) and J. J. Berzelius (1779–1848). Among the foreigners to learn from Ar-

1106

rhenius were: Richard Abegg, Georg Bredig, Viktor Rothmund, Ernst Cohen, Harry Jones, Thomas Madsen, Hans Euler, and many others.

Besides membership in numerous Swedish scientific societies, including election to the Academy of Sciences in 1901, honorary memberships were also conferred by many foreign academies and societies. In 1902 he was given the Davy Medal of the Royal Society of London.

From 1902 on, Arrhenius applied the laws of theoretical chemistry to Physiological problems, especially those of serum therapy (immune chemistry). Comprehensive surveys were published in his "Immunochemie" (1907) and his "Quantitative laws in biological chemistry" (1915). His studies in these fields were met with resistance at first by Paul Erhlich and his school, but their fundamental importance became more and more evident as time went on.

Among his numerous studies of cosmic physics are the joint publications with N. Ekholm concerning the northern lights and the hypothesis that the ability of radiation pressure to transport cosmic material can be used to explain comets, the corona, polar aurora, and the zodiacal light. Here also can be found his idea that spores of living matter are transported in this manner from planet to planet with the resultant spread of life throughout interstellar space. He also developed a theory designed to explain the ice ages and other great climatic changes experienced by the earth's surface. This theory is based on the ability of carbon dioxide to absorb the infrared heat radiation sent out from the surface of the earth. In periods of intense volcanic activity, the carbon dioxide content of the atmosphere is increased so that the heat radiated from the earth's surface is held back more and the temperature of the atmosphere rises; the reverse holds for periods of weak volcanic action. The content of water vapor in the atmosphere, which rises and falls with the temperature, acts in the same direction and consequently reinforces the result. The vegetation, which is dependent on the temperature, acts as a regulator. However, it was not possible to bring this hypothesis into complete agreement with geological chronology. His "Lehrbuch der kosmischen Physik" (2 volumes) first appeared in 1903; in this he set forth his bold speculations.

During later years Arrhenius wrote several textbooks and works of a popular nature which, like his scientific writings and researches, tend to testify to his extraordinary productivity and capacity. In 1898 he published his "Lehrbuch der theoretischen Elektrochemie" which was translated into many languages. The text is not easy to read; in general his style is very concise and somewhat heavy. He made it a custom to indicate what was still to be done in the fields about which he was writing. His "Theorien der Chemie" (1906) is likewise characterized by this admirable conciseness. Among his many books written for the general public was "Die Chemie und das moderne Leben " (1919). In the introduction he states that the chief motive for writing this book was that the war had demonstrated the special importance of chemistry and that this science more than any other was serving the material culture of the time.

Other books revealed to the general public the main features of cosmic physics and cosmogony; of course, he stressed his own ideas and views. Among these volumes were "Das Werden der Welten" (1906: 8th edition, 1924); "Der Mensch vor dem Welträtsel" (1908); "Die Schicksale der Sterne" (1915). Most of these comprehensive and poular works appeared during the time he was head of the Physical-Chemical Section of the Nobel Institut in the outskirts of Stockholm. New researches were also being conducted in this laboratory. Many men who later became prominent scientists worked there under his guidance.

His first marriage was to Sofia Rudbeck. Their son, Olev Wilhelm (b. 1895) became a botanist and made important contributions, especially on the importance of soil acidity with respect to the culture of sugar beets. Three children were born of his second marriage to Maria Johansson.

Arrhenius had a natural, healthy constitution but he never spared himself. In his later years he was head and member of several large organizations and was so in demand that he found it difficult to find time for scientific work. Consequently, beginning in 1925, he made it a practice to arise at 4 A.M. in order to steal a few peaceful hours with which to work on the new edition of his

1108

"Entwicklung der Welten." This extra effort may have contributed to the first attack of weakness that struck him near the end of 1925. His full powers never returned. In the spring of 1927 he therefore resigned his post as director of the Nobel Institut. The Academy of Sciences granted him an honorary pension. During the summer of 1927, he wrote his memoirs. After a brief illness (acute intestinal catarrh), which laid him low in September of that year, he died in October 1927. He was buried in Upsala, the city in which he grew up and where he had fought the opening battles of his crusade in behalf of his theory of electrolytic dissociation.

GENERAL REFERENCES

"Nobel, the Man and his Prizes," edited by the Nobel Foundation, Sohlman's Förlag, Stockholm, 1950.

Svante Arrhenius, "Worlds in the Making," Harper, New York, 1908.

H. C. Urey, "The Planets: Their Origins and Development," Yale University Press, New Haven, 1952.

H. S. Harned and B. B. Owen, "The Physical Chemistry of Electrolytic Solutions," 3rd ed., Reinhold, New York, 1957.

Hans von Euler, "Arrhenius," in *Chem. & Ind.* (*London*), *1959*, 245.

E. Riesenfeld, "Arrhenius," in *Ber. deut. Chem. Ges., 63A, 1,* (1930)

NOTES AND REFERENCES

1 A. W. Williamson, *Ann., 77,* 37 (1851); *81,* 73 (1852); R. Clausius, *Pogg. Ann., 101,* 338 (1857).

2 W. Ostwald, *Z. physik. Chem., 69,* IV (1909).

3 Also published in German in *Z. physik. Chem., 1,* 631 (1887).

From: Bugge, "Buch der Grossen Chemiker," 2, 443–462. Translated and abbreviated by Ralph E. Oesper.

WILHELM PALMAER

·· 77 ··

Ossian Aschan

1860-1939

ADOLF OSSIAN ASCHAN was born May 16, 1860, at Helsinki (Helsingfors). His parents were Karl Achates Aschan, a teacher of zoology and botany and vice-rector at a lyceum, and Mathilde Helena Waenerberg, the daughter of a ship's captain. Through them he inherited characteristics of the two nationalities in Finland, the Finns and the Swedes. From his father's side he received a heritage of scientific ability, documented by the professions of his paternal ancestors. From his mother he inherited diligence, tough persistence, and the ability to organize his work skillfully, as he said himself in an autobiographical sketch.

When Ossian had to choose his life's profession he did not select science. His brother Allan became an apothecary, like others by the name of Aschan before him. Ossian became a student of bridge, road, and water engineering at the Polytechnical School in Helsinki. In the Finland of that time the study of science offered no prospects except to teach, as his father did; chemistry as a field of study was still less promising in a country that had practically no chemical industry. However, in order to have the necessary scientific foundation for his engineering studies, he attended lectures on mathematics, physics, and chemistry at the University.

Chemistry as a science was not well represented in Finland at that time. Gadolin's successor in the chair of chemistry was Chydenius, who was seriously ill for many years so that he could not teach. Besides him there was only one lecturer in chemistry, Wahlforss, who pursued inorganic chemistry and remained out of step with the new organic chemistry. However, Wahlforss was an outstanding teacher, and it was mainly through his influence that Aschan found his way to chemistry.

In 1881 Aschan left the Polytechnic Institute as a chemical engineer and, at the same time, obtained the degree of *magister philosophiae* at the university. Then followed practical work in chemical industry, first in a saltpeter plant in Turku, and next in a dye works in Petersburg. The director of the latter advised him to take a course in dyeing given in Berlin. Aschan used this opportunity to study with August Wilhelm von Hofmann at the university. The investigation started there was completed in Stockholm and led to the doctor's degree in 1884. After returning to Helsinki he was engaged as a geologist and as the director of a municipal laboratory for food analysis.

In 1887 Aschan started work in the field of alicyclic compounds, which was to occupy him all his life. It was not a special scientific inclination that led him to these compounds; up to that time he had tried his hand on topics of aromatic chemistry. The stimulation came from the outside; it was the same that had influenced Wladimir Wassiljewitsch Markovnikov ten years before and now induced Nicolai Dimitrijewitsch Zelinsky, who was of about the same age as Aschan, to study this field. The problem was to exploit the vast naphtha reserves of Russia as advantageously and completely as possible. Russian industry had approached Markovnikov with the request to find out what substances were present in Caucasian mineral oil and how they could be separated. For Aschan the problem was the more specialized one of finding uses for the naphthenic acids remaining as residues from naphtha distillation. This is an example for the frequently encountered fact that progress in chemical research is by no means always aimed in the direction toward logical developments but is influenced by technical problems more strongly than other branches of science. It became soon evident that a technical solution of Aschan's task could not be reached immediately. Aschan recognized that, first, a very thorough scientific investigation was required before anything technical could be developed.

In order to be better equipped with the experimental techniques needed for this task, Aschan journeyed again to Germany in 1890. He worked with Johannes Wislicenus in Leipzig and with Adolf von Baeyer in Munich. In 1894 we see him again in Germany, with Victor Meyer in Heidelberg, where he also met J. W. Brühl. Together with Brühl, Aschan worked on Roscoe-Schorlemmer's textbook of organic chemistry, and from him he obtained firsthand knowledge of the importance of the physical properties of organic compounds for elucidating their chemical constitution.

In the meantime, Aschan's first fundamental study of cam-

phoric acid was completed in 1893, and work on a Swedish textbook of organic chemistry was completed with Edvard Hjelt. An
extensive dissertation on structural and stereochemical studies in
the camphor group appeared in 1895. It contained new experiments and a critical survey of all previous work on the structure
of camphor. He weighed the theoretical conclusions from the experiments with great caution. He could not accept Bredt's formula
for the constitution of camphor because a few reactions were not
in accord, although none definitely contradicted it. A few years
later he reviewed the problem again and in 1903, he decided in
favor of Bredt's formula.

In 1898 Aschan became a teacher at the Polytechnic Institute,
and in the following year he substituted at the University for
Edvard Hjelt, who had been elected rector. Aschan was well prepared for extensive tasks in teaching, because in addition to the
Swedish book on chemistry (with Hjelt) he published the "Aus-
führliche Lehrbuch der Chemie von Roscoe-Schorlemmer" with
Brühl and Hjelt in the years 1896 to 1901. His book of over
1000 pages on alicyclic compounds appeared in 1905; for it he was
awarded the Vahlbruch Prize, amounting to 10,000 marks, from
the University of Göttingen. How great this honor was can be
judged from the fact that its first recipient, in 1898, had been
Wilhelm Conrad Röntgen.

In 1908 Edvard Hjelt resigned as professor to become a senator
and devote himself to political activities for Finland. Thus, the
professorship in which Aschan had acted as a substitute became
vacant. At that time Aschan was in Berlin as director of the scientific laboratory of the Chemische Fabrik auf Actien, vorm. E.
Schering. Now his country recalled him, and he followed gladly.

The main part of his experimental work was concerned with
camphene and the group related to fenchone. At the same time he
started on a problem of as much scientific as technical importance,
the polymerization of isoprene to rubber.

This research paralleled efforts to maintain the national Finnish
spirit at the University against the encroachments by the Russians.
Aschan's interest in political events was so great that he accepted
the election to the Finnish parliament as representative of the

Swedish Popular Party. He was a member in the central organization of this party from 1910 to 1916. In addition, he also was a representative in the city council

The events of World War I gave a new direction to his experimental work. In 1916 it became urgently necessary to reduce the amounts of rosin and alum in sizing paper. The research on this problem led to extensive work about the pine rosin acids, $C_{20}H_{30}O_2$. Although their existence had been known for almost a hundred years, none of the rosin acids described in the literature could be said to be chemically pure. The first success was achieved in work with Finnish talloil, the by-product obtained from the cooking liquor used in the manufacture of sulfate cellulose from pine wood. From talloil, a pure acid, pine abietinic acid, was isolated. Upon Aschan's suggestion, Artturi I. Virtanen tried to determine its chemical nature. By converting the chloride of this acid into the hydrocarbon, retene, Virtanen was able to develop a preliminary structural formula.

In 1916 Aschan also laid the groundwork for a central laboratory for the chemical industry in Finland, and he furthered its development as a director and consulting chemist. He endeavored to make his inventions useful to his country; among other things, he proposed that his experiences in producing and polymerizing isoprene be offered to Germany in exchange for bread flour. The proposal was, however, not carried out.

After the end of the war, Aschan had the good fortune to remain active as a professor for about ten more years. He retired in 1927, but even then he continued his scientific research. None of his predecessors had represented the science of chemistry at the State University as long as he had, except for Johann Gadolin (1760–1852), the first Finnish chemist at the University which at that time was located at Turku. The number of Aschan's pupils and, through them, his influence on chemistry in Finland, was very great.

Scientific and industrial organizations showed their great appreciation for his achievements. Many honors came to him. His collaboration with the German firm of Schering has already been mentioned. After the world war, the Hercules Powder Company of Wilmington, Delaware, and its subsidiary in Rotterdam, Holland, invited his collaboration.

In view of his great scientific and technical accomplishments, it might appear as if there could not have been much time for other pursuits. However, as has already been mentioned, he was politically active in parliament and in the city council. He did more for the public. Especially noteworthy were his efforts against prohibition. An organization, over which he temporarily presided, fought against such a law because its circumvention could be more harmful than the dangers involved in a moderate use of alcoholic beverages. He recommended educating the people without legal prohibition.

Finally, Aschan even found time for his private hobbies. He liked music. He was a member, for a time even president, of a choir and of the Swedish Oratory Society. His musicality was inherited particularly by his daughter Inger, the youngest of three daughters. His wife, Elin, whom he married in 1885, was the devoted companion of his life until he died February 25, 1939.

From: *Ber. deut. chem. Ges.*, *74A*, 189 (1941). Translated by Eduard Farber.

WALTER HÜCKEL

·· 78 ··

Philippe-Auguste Guye

1862-1922

IN THE afternoon of March 27, 1922, the brilliant intelligence and great heart that was Philippe-Auguste Guye was extinguished. The news of his death caused painful surprise; most of us did not expect it. We knew that Guye had neglected his health. He carried on so many tasks that it would have overburdened the strongest men: the preparation of his lecture courses and the direction of his laboratory, with all that this implied in research, discussions, and editorial work; the direction of the *Journal de chimie physique* and that of so many commissions and councils; the maintenance of a flood of correspondence, because it was never in vain when one addressed this discreet and warm-hearted man. Everybody wrote to him on scientific questions as well as for advice or support. He never left a letter unanswered, and he did not neglect the innumerable duties he had accepted. Rising early, retiring late, he experienced fatigue at a relatively early age. About twelve years before his death he had a breakdown which he mastered after a rest cure. Some time later again he felt tired but did not cease to devote himself to others. Last December he took a vacation and went south, but his stay there did not produce the desired result. Guye returned to Geneva still weaker and passed away, spent by constant work, before he reached sixty.

Philippe-Auguste Guye, a citizen of Geneva, was born at Saint-Christophe (Vaud) the twelfth of June, 1862. He studied in Geneva and obtained his doctor's degree there in 1884. As an assistant to Carl Graebe (1841–1927) and privatdocent (1885) he published several papers on organic chemistry with Graebe. Then Guye went to Paris where he dwelt until 1892. He always remembered vividly and gratefully these years in Paris during which he found himself through contact with eminent scholars. He particularly recalled being influenced by Charles Friedel (1832–1898, successor of Adolphe Wurtz).

The reputation of the young scientist preceded him to Geneva, where he returned in 1892 to take charge of the associate professorship in theoretical and technical chemistry, which had been

1121

established especially for him and was transformed into a full professorship in 1895. He remained in this post until he died.

Guye's scientific work comprised almost 200 papers in his own name and more than 600 publications from his laboratory which were directly inspired by him. It is, therefore, impossible to do more than just indicate the essential traits of such a vast productivity.

His first problem was that of the rotatory power of optically active substances. The principles which Pasteur had formulated concerning the asymmetric carbon atom had been spectacularly confirmed by Le Bel and van't Hoff. While the mere study of the constitutional formula of a chemical compound permitted one to predict its optical activity and to calculate the number of its isomers, nevertheless it provided no means to foresee the amount, or at least the direction, in which it would turn the plane of the polarized light. Guye's hypothesis of the "asymmetric product" was to fill this gap. His hypothesis attributed the principal rôle in optical activity to the mass of the groups connected with the assymmetric carbon atom. The development of the hypothesis becomes very simple if, in a first approximation, the centers of gravity of the four groups connected with the carbon atom are placed at the corners of a regular tetrahedron. When the masses that are combined with the carbon are not all different, the center of gravity of the molecule is located at least in one of the six planes of symmetry of the regular tetrahedron. If, however, the carbon atom is asymmetric, the center of gravity will be outside of these planes. Designating the distances of the center of gravity from each of the six planes of symmetry in the molecular model by d_1, d_2, d_3, d_4, d_5, d_6, then further arbitrarily counting the distances as positive on one side of the plane, negative on the other, Guye defined the product of asymmetry as

$$P = d_1 \cdot d_2 \cdot d_3 \cdot d_4 \cdot d_5 \cdot d_6.$$

This product should measure the dissymmetry of the tetrahedron and, at the same time, the degree of optical activity.

At first, the hypothesis seemed to be confirmed qualitatively. The sign (positive or negative) of optical rotation changed when a substitution in an optically active molecule displaced the center of

1122

gravity in relation to one of the planes, and the sign remained the same when the center of gravity stayed on the same side of the plane. In his first work on this subject Guye examined over a hundred optically active derivatives in seven different series; they all verified, with a few exceptions, his bold and fruitful hypothesis. These findings caused a great stir and provoked a considerable number of parallel studies.

However, the exceptions to the rule increased in numbers. Guye tried to explain them by assuming that the tetrahedron was deformed through the chemical affinities of the substituent groups, since the masses, instead of being strictly concentrated in the corners of the tetrahedron, are located at distances depending on their molecular volumes.

The other problem which Guye studied at the same time was molecular constitution. In 1890 he found a relationship between the volume b in the equation of van der Waals:

$$\left(p + \frac{a}{v^2}\right)\left(v - b\right) = RT$$

the critical coefficient and molecular refraction. This enabled him to determine molecular weights at the critical point (of temperature and pressure, where the difference between gas and liquid disappears) and to state that at that point water and alcohols are polymeric. A series of experiments started from here: measurements of temperatures, pressures, and critical volumes or surface tensions, of theories like the calculation of the constants a and b in the van der Waals equation, and of modified forms of that equation. Guye can rightfully be said to have contributed very essentially to the study of polymerizations in liquids.

In 1900, and for several years thereafter, he undertook experimental studies of the industrial electrolysis of alkali chlorides. This resulted in a publication on the theory of electrolysis using diaphragms. By a simplified calculation he established a whole set of relationships from which the yields of electrolytic operations with diaphragms could be calculated in advance for different schedules. The final confirmations of this elegant theory showed that it can be applied whenever one of the products of an electrolytic process becomes an electrolyte itself and thus contributes to the flow of the current.

From 1903 on the investigations on atomic weights, the most important part of Guye's work, described in almost 100 reports and articles, began to be published. He approached this particularly difficult subject in the full bloom of his talent. It is the work of his maturity, and it is hard to decide which to admire most: the magnificent order of the over-all plan he followed during twenty years, the perfection of the technique, or the importance of the results achieved.

The starting point was a divergence in the value for the atomic weight of nitrogen obtained by purely chemical methods and from physicochemcial measurements of the density of this gas. By six chemical methods, Jean Servais Stas (1813–1891) had obtained a remarkable agreement for an average figure, namely, 14.044, whereas the physicochemical measurements particularly favored by Guye at that time gave 14.005. Such a difference was not admissible, especially for the fundamentally important atomic weight of nitrogen. Therefore, Guye began to organize research in Geneva to find the necessary corrections. He thought that these corrections should involve simultaneously the chemical methods for establishing the relationship between nitrogen and oxygen more directly than Stas had done and the physicochemical methods. For the latter, precise measurements of densities and compressibilities had first to be carried out with several gases containing nitrogen, then these had to be calculated by means of the new statistics which Guye had applied to deviations from the law of Avogadro. Among these methods of calculation, that called reduction of the critical constants deserves to be especially mentioned; Guye described it in one of the most beautiful of his papers.

It was no easy matter to carry out such a plan, because after all it required improving upon Stas, that great experimenter, and in addition surmounting new difficulties in physicochemical procedures. The successful accomplishment of this program perhaps best characterizes the special gifts of his school.

Guye had often expressed the thought that one can never be absolutely certain that a gas is pure. It could be ascertained only

1124

by preparing the gas under varying conditions from different chemicals and with several methods for purification. Besides, chemical means of purification permit only the removal of known impurities. Therefore the chemically purified gas must always be subjected to a physical purification, either liquefaction and fractional distillation, or fractional freezing. According to the Geneva school, the best criterion of purity for a gas consists in measuring a characteristic property, such as density—needed anyway for the calculation of the atomic weight—which must be found the same for samples of different origins after careful physical purification. This technique was not created in one day; gradually, with necessary improvements, it reached such high perfection that Guye's laboratory became justly famous for it. The measurement of gas densities by the classic method profited from the research at Geneva; through a series of improvements it reached an absolute guaranty of precision of about 1 in 10,000.

Four years of organized teamwork were necessary to demonstrate that the 14.044 value of Stas was inaccurate. In a lecture presented on June 10, 1905, before the Société Chimique de France, which was reproduced in English in 1906 and in German in 1907, Guye formulated the following conclusions: Physicochemical and direct chemical methods are in as perfect an agreement as possible, the average being 14.008 for the former, 14.009 for the latter. The value which Stas obtained by six indirect methods should, therefore, be abandoned.

However, it was not sufficient to make these statements; it was also necessary to explain how the illustrious Belgian chemist could have been so mistaken. By a painstaking analysis of the experimental procedures Guye showed that, contrary to all expectations, none of the indirect methods of Stas was accurate to the second decimal for the atomic weight of nitrogen, and that the error was ascribable to the atomic weight of silver. According to Guye, this atomic weight should be reduced to 107.89.

These conclusions of the Geneva school were naturally received with attention, but it took no less than nine years before the results of Professor Guye acquired full status. The International Committee for Atomic Weights decided to adopt the new value of

14.01 for nitrogen in 1907 and, two years later, 107.88 for silver. This latter modification was arrived at, following work at Harvard and Geneva.

Side by side with purely scientific studies Guye was creatively active in a quite different direction. He was not actually a technologist, but none of the great industrial questions was alien to him. His name was an introduction to the leaders of industry; his charm made them his friends; his resolute integrity opened factory doors for him that were jealously closed to anyone else.

His name is inseparably connected with the electrochemical synthesis of nitric acid. He had begun the study of this problem in 1893 with Aloys Naville and Charles-Edmond Guye (his brother), then continued it with other collaborators, and in spite of all kinds of difficulties had finally succeeded. The principles embodied in his patents of 1895 also guided subsequent inventors: the cooling of gas, after it has passed the electric arc, by an excess of air, and the contraction of the gas stream between the electrodes.

Guye quickly realized that the problem of nitric acid is not limited to its synthesis. The great use for combined nitrogen is in fertilizers, and the costly product is the concentrated nitric acid. The nitrous gases from the electric ovens permit only the initial recovery of 30 per cent acid. The nitrate of calcium is inconvenient because it is hygroscopic. Guye and his group studied how to convert the chlorides of potassium and sodium into nitrates by means of dilute nitric acid, and they established the practical conditions which avoid forming nitrosyl chloride, the great stumbling block in this reaction. They also contemplated the use of nitric acid to solubilize the phosphates alone or in mixture with potassium salts.

Because of his polite manner and his scientific reputation, Guye exerted great influence on scientific societies, Swiss as well as foreign. Aware of what a journal can accomplish for the development of a science he created the *Journal de chimie physique,* which soon became the medium for physicochemists in all countries who wanted to publish their papers in French. Guye also was instrumental in creating the *Helvetica Chimica Acta.* The success of this journal and its high scientific level justified the ideas of its promoters.

His fruitful and disinterested activity naturally brought him

1126

many distinctions. They were numerous and of the highest order. However, Guye placed the affection of his students above these marks of appreciation and these honors; those who write these lines bear moving testimony for this fact. (This article resulted from the collaboration of several former students and friends of professor Philippe-Auguste Guye, and it was edited by one of them.)

From: *J. chim. phys.*, 20, 1 (1923), abbreviated. Translated by Eduard Farber.

E. BRINER

·· 79 ··

John Ulric Nef

1862-1915

JOHN ULRIC NEF, together with Arthur Michael[1] and Ira Remsen,[2] was prominent in the establishment of graduate study in the universities of the United States and in the transfer thereto of the science and techniques of organic chemistry from the university laboratories of Europe. Nef was a great experimentalist, an inspiring teacher, and a pioneer in theoretical organic chemistry. His Ph.D. trainees went into many of the American universities, especially in the Midwest, and helped to establish research in organic chemistry at the graduate level in these institutions. Nef was very inspirational and imbued his students with an intense love and devotion for their science.

John Ulrich Nef was born on June 14, 1862, at Herisau, Kanton Ausser Appenzell, Switzerland, as the eldest of two sons of Johann Ulrich Nef (1834–1884) and Anna Katherina Mock Nef (1842–1910). His father was employed as a foreman in one of the textile mills for which that Swiss canton was famous. Being of an adventurous turn of mind, he came to the United States in 1864 to investigate the possibilities of the textile industry here; finding a suitable position as foreman in a textile mill at Housatonic, in southwestern Massachusetts, he brought his family there in 1866 and settled them in a small farmhouse four miles from the town. At this time his son Ulrich, as his mother addressed him, was only four years of age. The son later attended school at Great Barrington and every school day, rain or shine, he would walk the four miles to that town and return again in the afternoon. In addition, he had his regular chores to perform at home. His father was an excellent preceptor and instilled in his son a love of books, music, sports, and work. It was to this early training that the son ascribed his lifelong belief in a balance between strenuous intellectual work and equally strenuous physical exercise, as a foundation for a well-rounded life. He became a strong swimmer and once saved his younger brother from drowning. It was while swimming underwater as a youth that he burst an eardrum and became nearly deaf

1131

in one ear. He loved to walk at a vigorous hiker's pace and in later years he played an excellent game of tennis.

When sixteen years of age, it was settled that he should enter college and after spending two years in a New York City college preparatory school, he entered Harvard University at the age of eighteen with the class of 1884. He had planned to enter medicine but from the time he took his first course in chemistry he was fascinated by the tremendous opportunities for research and discovery presented by this discipline. He must have had a good teacher of chemistry. His start in college was not unusually brilliant and he even encountered some difficulties with German—the Appenzeller Deutsch of his home life being insufficient. His facility in scholarship increased, however, and in his senior year he far outdistanced his fellow students in chemistry and received as a reward the Kirkland Traveling Fellowship which enabled him to study further in Europe. His expenses at Harvard had been largely met by summer employment in the textile mills. While in Boston he attended concerts regularly and developed an interest in music and the fine arts which he maintained throughout his life.

John Ulric Nef left for Europe in the summer of 1884, accompanied by his father, who had unfortunately contracted tuberculosis. They spent a summer together in the beautiful region of the Vierwaldstätter See and then his father returned to America where a few months later he died at the age of fifty. Arriving in Munich, where he had elected to study with Professor Adolf von Baeyer[3] at the University of Munich, young Nef threw himself into his work and into the cultural life of that German city at its greatest period. After only two years of study he received the Ph.D. *summa cum laude,* in 1886, at the age of twenty-four, with a thesis entitled "Über Benzochinoncarbonsäuren," and concerned with some aspects of tautomerism, a phenomenon which had been discovered earlier by Baeyer in the isatin series. Geheimrat Baeyer was very fond of this intense young man and stated, as reported by Richard Willstätter, that Nef was the most brilliant of all the students he had during his long tenure of the chair of chemistry at Munich. After receiving his degree, Nef continued working in the Baeyer laboratory for an additional year.

1132

In 1887 Nef accepted an appointment at Purdue University, Lafayette, Indiana, at a salary of $1200, payable quarterly. In making this offer, President Smart wrote as follows: "We have a laboratory at Purdue University in which are 48 individual desks with closets, drawers and individual reagents each. We have room for 16 desks more. The amount of time a man will have for private research will depend on his power of organization. He will be occupied in class and laboratory work about 4 hours a day."

John Ulric Nef demonstrated the "power of organization" required and plunged into an intense period of research activity. The lights of his laboratory burned far into the night. He had no assistance; all the work was done with his own hands. He continued the work begun with Baeyer and published several papers in the *American Chemical Journal* of Ira Remsen, one of which was republished in German in Liebig's *Annalen.*

Nef spent the summer of 1889 in Switzerland. He became much interested in mountain climbing and made many difficult ascents. He loved the mountains and spent numerous summer vacations (every one from 1891 to 1897) in the Alps.

A new American university was opening in Worcester, Massachusetts, under the presidency of G. Stanley Hall and with Jonas Gilman Clark as the benefactor. It was to be operated as a graduate school and opened its doors on September 1, 1889, with John Ulric Nef as assistant professor of chemistry at a salary of $2,000 a year. A new laboratory was to be built. Following the resignation of Professor Arthur Michael, Nef was named, in April, 1892, director of the Chemical Laboratory. He brought his mother to Worcester but her mind began to fail badly and in 1891 he took her to Switzerland where she was placed in a Protestant sanitorium near Herisau and where she died in 1910. Her son visited her there frequently in the academic summer vacations.

At Clark, Nef worked on the structure of the salts of β-keto acids and of nitroparaffins, and he initiated his researches on bivalent carbon compounds, especially the isocyanides and the fulminates. All was not well with the new university, however. Promised funds did not materialize and in 1892 eight important faculty members resigned. These included J. U. Nef, associate professor of chemistry, A. A. Michelson,[4] professor of physics, and Franz Boas,[5] docent in anthropology. But for Nef, a new position was forthcoming. In the rapidly developing United States of America, another university was beginning and this one had an assured financial backing.

On October 1, 1892, the University of Chicago opened with funds donated by John D. Rockefeller, who gave to it $37,708,000 during the period 1890 to 1910. William Rainey Harper was its president. Born in a log cabin in Muskingum, Ohio, Harper was that variety of the human species, always rare on the American scene and now essentially extinct, that could be termed a great university president. With the Rockefeller donations, he gathered together a great faculty and even included in it nine former presidents of colleges and universities. The professorship in chemistry was given to John Ulric Nef and he began October 1, 1892, under a contract designating a salary of $3000, payable monthly, and including a private research assistant. He had insisted upon the latter. Here he remained for the rest of his life. He was named to the head professorship of the department in 1896. Later on, Nef turned over the administrative detail of the department to Dr. Julius Stieglitz while retaining a firm rein on all matters of policy. Stieglitz had been "hired" by Nef in 1892 as a docent. The German university rank of docent, carrying little honor and no pay, never became popular in the States.

Nef was temperamental and impulsive. In 1894 President Harper felt constrained to write him as follows: "Your letter of April 6th has been received. I am not willing that you should carry out the plan which you indicate in it, and I hope that you will not do anything rash."

In establishing graduate work in chemistry at Chicago, Nef had written in 1892 to his friend Professor C. Loring Jackson at Harvard and had been advised that an applicant for the Ph.D. at Harvard must have had either Latin or Greek, preferably both. Indeed, Ira Remsen has stated that he wrote his Ph.D. dissertation in 1870 at Göttingen in Latin. This emphasis upon the classics was not maintained in the science departments at the new University of Chicago.

1134

The task of instructing large classes of undergraduates in a science in which most of them showed little interest was always irksome to Nef but in Alexander Smith[6] he selected a great teacher of freshman students. The department was housed first in a city flat, but in 1896 it was moved to the fine Kent Chemical Laboratory.

John Ulric had stated that "a scientist should be married to his science." Nevertheless, he married in 1898, at the age of thirty-six, and found in Louise Bates Comstock, of Rochester, N. Y., an understanding helpmate. She was a highly cultivated young woman who had spent five or six years of study and travel in Europe and, as one of Nef's graduate students, she understood and appreciated the rigorous demands of his profession. The summer of 1898 was spent by the young couple in European travel. Their marriage was a happy one but was not destined to endure, for in 1909 Louise Nef contracted pneumonia and died after a very short illness. This was a great blow to Dr. Nef. One son, John Ulric Nef, Jr., survived this union. This member of the third generation bearing this name is a distinguished historian and is likewise a professor at the University of Chicago, where he was the principal founder of the Committee on Social Thought, of which he is the chairman.

In 1903, Dr. Nef suffered a severe nervous breakdown caused by intense overwork and in 1911 he experienced another. He had planned to spend the summer of 1915 in a leisurely trip through the Canadian Rockies, accompanied by his young son, then a lad of sixteen years. Nef's mountaineering was not restricted to the Alps. The greater part of the summer of 1908 had been spent in Estes Park, Colorado, where he had astonished the natives by hiking alone from Elkhorn Lodge to the summit of Long's Peak and back in a single day. His Swiss friends had commented: "Er könnte nicht laufen, er müsste immer springen" (he could not walk, he must always spring). On his 1915 walking trip in the Canadian Northwest, begun in June, he found himself in poor health and hurried to San Francisco at the end of July. There a medical examination showed him to be suffering from acute dilatation of the heart; although his health was not considered to be at all critical, he died suddenly, at the early age of fifty-three, while visiting one of his former students, Dr. Herman A. Spoehr, at the

Coastal Laboratory of the Carnegie Institution located at beautiful Carmel-by-the-Sea in California.

The late Professor William Lloyd Evans, a Nef student, has described Professor Nef as follows:

Nef was rather small of stature with a massive brow, and bright, penetrating eyes. He had an all-consuming and contagious love for his science. One became fascinated with the rapidity of his thought which so out-distanced even the marvelous speed of his words that his students could only take sketchy notes which they would later piece out and amplify in order to get the full value of his lecture. His eager restless enthusiasm for the problems in which he was engrossed, developed in him an appearance of brusqueness which amounted almost to impatience when the research did not progress smoothly. Back of this intellectual eagerness, however, dwelt kindly human qualities. He was by temperament intense and found his relaxation in long walks which he pursued at an unaccompaniable speed. He loved music and was a weekly attendant during the season of the Chicago Symphony Orchestra.

Nef was a member of the American Chemical Society, Deutsche chemische Gesellschaft (1885), American Association for the Advancement of Science (secretary, Section C, 1893), Chicago Academy of Sciences (1893), National Institute of Social Sciences, New York (1914), American Academy of Arts and Sciences (1891), Royal Society of Sciences in Upsala (1903), and the National Academy of Sciences (1904). He was awarded the honorary LL.D degree by the University of Pittsburgh in 1915.

Nef was a highly individualistic worker. Save for three early articles (1884–87) and his last (1917) posthumous one, Nef never published with a co-worker. Even his Ph.D. dissertation with Baeyer appeared with his name as sole author. He straddled, as it were, both sides of the Atlantic and published in the German chemical literature, largely Liebig's *Annalen*. The work of his Ph.D. students appeared independently, mainly in the American chemical literature. His own personal work, carried out with one postdoctoral research assistant, was published under his own name in 34 articles running to some over 1500 printed pages. Although he was fluent in German, it was his custom to send his articles in

1136

that language to his friend Johannes Thiele[7] for full conversion to the idiom. In 1899, the *Annalen's* editor, Volhard, wrote to Nef: "Ihre schönen Arbeiten erachte ich für eine Zierde der Annalen" (I consider your fine manuscript [concerning phenylacetylene] an adornment for the *Annalen*).

Nef prepared a large number of compounds which he described with extraordinary care and precision. He reflected his training with Baeyer in laying great stress on careful manipulation, was most particular regarding cleanliness and orderly assembly of apparatus, and worked as quantitatively as possible. He believed in simple apparatus and in not doing too much at once. He kept a file of research samples. The personality of Nef was so overwhelming that he imparted these traits to his students in no uncertain fashion. Wherever they were, Nef students maintained a clear desk and kept their laboratories scrupulously neat. The story is told of the wrath visited upon a luckless graduate student when Dr. Nef entered the laboratory and spied a burnt match on the floor, and of the time when the doctor, while watching a reaction which at last went out-of-hand, backed away from the apparatus and fell over a stool which should not have been at that spot in the laboratory. Drs. Oscar Hedenburg and J. W. E. Glattfeld were his last personal (postdoctoral) assistants at Chicago and although Nef was in poor health at the time and was doing little or no personal laboratory work, he told them exactly what to do and kept all notebook records himself.

Nef's first independent work, published from Purdue, was concerned with an extension of his work with Baeyer on derivatives of *p*-benzoquinone. At the time he initiated this work, which was mainly concerned with the tetrahalogen derivatives, there were three formulas in vogue for the parent substance. Of the three, the currently accepted one, originally proposed, but not established, by Fittig, was put on a sound experimental basis by Nef. On moving to Clark, he turned his attention to the sodium salts of β-ketonic esters for which he favored the enolic formula. In common with many organic chemists of the time, he did not like shifting tautomeric structures, stating that: "To explain the behavior of an organic compound one formula is sufficient." From the sodium salts of β-ketonic esters he proceeded logically to a study of similar salts of primary and secondary nitroalkanes. He showed that acids did not regenerate the nitroalkane but gave a carbonyl compound. In modern terms,

$$2R_2C{=}\overset{\oplus}{N}\begin{smallmatrix} \nearrow O\ominus \\ \\ \searrow O\ominus \end{smallmatrix} + 2H_3\overset{\oplus}{O} \rightarrow 2R_2C{=}O + N_2O + 3H_2O.$$

This is known as the Nef reaction—one, however, of several "Nef reactions."

In order to study the various salts of nitromethane, it became desirable to prepare the mercuric salt which had been reported to be an explosive, yellow solid. In preparing this dangerous substance, Nef noted that the warm liquid filtered from it gradually deposited crystals which he recognized as the fulminate of mercury. This chance observation was utilized by Nef to establish the true formulas of the fulminates, which had hitherto been considered, following Liebig and Gay-Lussac, to be salts of a dibasic acid. Nef formulated the reaction as follows:

$$(H_2C{=}\underset{\underset{O}{\|}}{N}O)_2Hg \rightarrow 2H_2O + Hg\begin{smallmatrix} \nearrow O{-}N{=}C \\ \\ \searrow O{-}N{=}C \end{smallmatrix}$$

He recognized the bivalency of the carbon atom in fulminic acid, isolable only as its salts. In conclusive proof of this, he isolated the carbon hydrohalide addition compound, HON=CHCl. This compound, extremely poisonous, crystallized from ether at 0° in long, transparent needles which turned green on warming to room temperature and exploded with violence. In a search for other bivalent carbon compounds, he studied prussic acid, its salts, and the alkyl isocyanides. He favored the formula H—N=C for prussic acid. He was greatly interested in the peculiar compounds (2RNC)· 3HCl and in those obtained from metallic cyanides by the action of alkyl hypochlorites.

In later work he was intrigued with that most unsaturated of carbon compounds, acetylene. He prepared and studied its halogen substitution products, all poisonous and spontaneously combustible

1138

compounds. Diiodacetylene possesses an odor deceptively like the isocyanides and dissociates explosively at $100°$ into its elements. Nef formulated it, probably incorrectly as $I_2C=C$. In connection with his studies on acetylene, Nef established the ethynylation of a ketone, a reaction which has been exploited in recent times and which constitutes a key step in the modern, commerical synthesis of vitamin A,

$$R_2CO + NaC\equiv CH \xrightarrow{\quad} \xrightarrow{\text{HOH}} R_2C(OH)-C\equiv CH + NaOH$$

The above is the "Nef reaction" of the acetylene chemist and is not to be confused with the "Nef reaction" of the nitroparaffin chemist.

All this difficult and dangerous experimentation set Nef to speculating on the nature of the valency of carbon. Recognizing explicitly that the nature of valence was at the time unknown, he began by attacking the Kekulé concept of the constancy of the tetravalency of carbon. He considered that carbon, like other reactive elements, should have several valence states, in this case two and four. This was an entirely logical assumption. He then exploited the ascribed tendency of carbon to react in these two valence states as a general phenomenon in the reactivity of carbon compounds. His theory of methylene dissociation postulated that a carbon compound, like an alkyl halide, first dissociated into a reactive bivalent carbon radical which then could react in various ways. He explained the Wurtz reaction as follows, the product yields being those established by him:

$$2CH_3-CH_2I \rightarrow 2CH_3CH < + 2HI$$
$$2HI + 2Na \rightarrow 2NaI + 2H$$
$$2H \rightarrow H_2$$
$$CH_3-CH < \rightarrow CH_2 - CH_2 \rightarrow CH_2{=}CH_2 (21.7\%)$$
$$\qquad\qquad\qquad | \qquad |$$
$$CH_3-CH{<}+H_2 \rightarrow CH_3-CH_3 (25.8\%)$$
$$2CH_3-CH{<}+H_2 \rightarrow 2CH_3-CH_2-$$
$$2CH_3-CH_2- \rightarrow CH_3-CH_2-CH_2-CH_3 (50.0\%)$$

Nef hoped that his methylene dissociation theory would serve organic chemistry as the Arrhenius ionic dissociation theory served inorganic chemistry. The theory was a logical one for the time and contained germs of truth which served to stimulate further work.

Our modern theory of the transition state is foreshadowed in the words of Nef (italics mine): "Excluding all reactions called ionic, a chemical reaction between two substances always takes place by their union to form an addition product. The one molecule being unsaturated and partially in an *active molecular condition,* absorbs the second molecule. The resulting addition product often dissociates spontaneously giving two molecules."

With the later establishment of the covalent electronic bond, the modern radical theory evolved from the concept of its homolytic splitting followed by recombination and further reactions of the dissociated products:

$$C:C \rightarrow C\cdot + \cdot C$$

These radicals are not of necessity bivalent although such are known, as in diazomethane decomposition (Nef's long-sought methylene) and in the alkaline haloform reactions:

$$CH_2{=}N{=}\overline{N} \longleftrightarrow \overline{C}H_2{-}N{\equiv}N$$
$$\overset{\oplus}{} \overset{\ominus}{} \qquad \overset{\ominus}{} \overset{\oplus}{}$$
$$CH_2{:} + \overline{N}{-}\overline{N}$$
$$nCH_2{:} \rightarrow (CH_2)_n$$
$$CHCl_3 + K\overset{\oplus}{} \ OH\overset{\ominus}{} \rightarrow Cl_2C{:} + K\overset{\oplus}{} + Cl\overset{\ominus}{} + H_2O$$

These speculations, with much experimental data offered in their support, were published in four long articles in Liebig's *Annalen.* The fourth appeared (1897) in an article of 172 pages length. These pages were for many years the most thoroughly thumbed of any of the journals in the Kent library and were considered to be "required reading" by all the Nef students at Chicago. An important point to be derived from them is the emphasis placed by Nef upon *all* the products of a reaction and not just the one desired end-product. To Nef by-products were as important as the main product in delineating the true nature of the reaction under study. In this respect he did not overlook polymerization. In 1904 he wrote: "Experience has shown that many unsaturated compounds can not be isolated; but polymerize spontaneously. It is clear that when the per cent of active particles present in an unsaturated compound becomes relatively great the possibility of their uniting with each other to form condensed molecules increases." Here, indeed, is a true conception of our present theory of polymerization which had to be laboriously rediscovered by others many years later.

During the last period (1904–1915) of his relatively short life, Nef and his students at Chicago devoted their entire attention to a comprehensive study of the dissociation of the sugars in alkali and when under oxidation in neutral, acid, and alkaline media. The results were published in three long articles of 98, 118, and 179 pages, respectively, in the *Annalen,* appearing at intervals of three years.[8] The experimentation was designed in the hope that some light might be thrown on the fermentation of sugars. In this extensive and difficult work, Nef and his students separated the saccharinic acids (alkali rearrangement products of the sugars) and established the structures of their various types. He established the concept of the intermediate enediol and its movement along the carbon chain:

$$
\begin{array}{ccccccccc}
\text{HC=O} & & \text{HCOH} & & \text{CH}_2\text{OH} & & \text{CH}_2\text{OH} & & \text{CH}_2\text{OH} \\
| & \rightleftharpoons & \| & \rightleftharpoons & | & \rightleftharpoons & | & \rightleftharpoons & | \\
\text{HCOH} & & \text{COH} & & \text{C=O} & & \text{COH} & & \text{CHOH} \\
| & & | & & | & & \| & & \| \\
\text{HOCH} & & \text{HOCH} & & \text{HOCH} & & \text{COH} & & \text{C=O} \\
| & & | & & | & & | & & |
\end{array}
$$

He studied chain degradation and especially lactic acid formation by alkali. With Oscar Hedenburg, he discovered the second and highly unstable form (1,5) of the aldonolactones. He obtained the next lower aldose by rapid air oxidation of an alkaline solution of an aldonic acid, which constitutes the "Nef reaction" of the sugar chemist and represents the third "name reaction" ascribed to him.

Nef's untimely death in 1915, at the age of fifty-three, brought his personal researches to an abrupt end, but they were continued by his students. During his last period at Chicago he trained most of his major students who, imbued with the intense research spirit imparted by Nef, continued thereafter in carbohydrate research, with their own students, in universities and research institutes located mainly in the Midwest. There can be cited the names of

Ernest Anderson (Arizona), William Lloyd Evans (Ohio State), J. W. E. Glattfeld (Chicago), Oscar Hedenburg (Mellon Institute), W. Lee Lewis (Northwestern), Herman A. Spoehr (Carnegie Institution), and Fred W. Upson (Nebraska). Among earlier students at Chicago were S. F. Acree (National Bureau of Standards), Lauder W. Jones (Princeton), and William McPherson (Ohio State). Considering that Nef only had 25 Ph.D students at Chicago, this is a very high percentage (40 per cent) of students who later made their mark in fundamental research activities. The great personality of Nef was impressed upon these students, and all of them respected and revered their master.

Nef and his school were interested in the chemical reactivity of carbon compounds and were never interested in synthesis alone, although organic synthesis was the main theme of their American contemporaries. None of his immediate students would have known what were meant by the "Nef reactions" now so well-established in that vast collection of "name" reactions of the modern organic chemist. His work foreshadowed the modern theory of the transition state, and of organic radicals and their polymerization. The contributions of Nef and his school to theoretical and synthetic chemistry were profound and timely, and his influence on the development of organic chemical research, especially in the United States, has been immeasurable.

GENERAL REFERENCES

F. Henrich, T. B. Johnson and Dorothy A. Hahn, "The Theoretical Speculations of John Ulric Nef" in *Theories of Organic Chemistry,* John Wiley, New York, 1922, pp. 334–60.

L. W. Jones, "John Ulric Nef," *Proc. Am. Chem. Soc.,* 44–72 (1917).

J. U. Nef, "On the Fundamental Conceptions Underlying the Chemistry of the Element Carbon," *J. Am. Chem. Soc.,* 26, 1549–77 (1904).

M. L. Wolfrom, "John Ulric Nef," *Biographical Memoirs,* National Academy of Sciences, U.S.A., XXXIV (1960), pp. 204–227.

NOTES AND REFERENCES

1 Arthur Michael (1853–1942). Born in Buffalo, New York; studied in Germany and France from 1872 to 1879; professor of chemistry at Tufts College, 1881–1890 and 1894–1907; professor of organic chemistry at Harvard, 1912–1936.

1142

2 Ira Remsen (1846–1927). Born in New York City, he was educated at the College of the City of New York, Columbia (M.D.), and Göttingen (Ph.D.). He was professor of chemistry at Johns Hopkins University from 1876 and president there from 1901 to 1912.

3 *Das Buch der Grossen Chemiker,* Band II, G. Bugge, editor, Verlag Chemie, Berlin, 1930, p. 321 ff.

4 Albert A. Michelson (1852–1931), physicist and first American Nobel laureate, renowned for his accurate measurement of the velocity of light, went with Nef to the University of Chicago.

5 Franz Boas (1858–1942). Renowned anthropologist. Born and educated in Germany. Professor at Columbia University and associated with the American Museum of Natural History in New York City.

6 Alexander Smith (1865–1925). Born in Edinburgh; Ph.D. from Munich in 1889. Professor of chemistry at Wabash College, Indiana (1890–1894), Chicago (1894–1911), and Columbia (chairman, 1911).

7 Johannes Thiele (1865–1918). Pupil of Volhard and his successor (1910) as editor of the *Annalen.* Professor of chemistry at Strasbourg.

8 In the Sharp Chemistry Library of The Ohio State University, these articles have been so thoroughly thumbed that all three volumes of these *Annalen* have had to be rebound.

MELVILLE L. WOLFROM

·· *80* ··

Charles Moureu

1863-1929

LIFE

ON JUNE 13, 1929, François-Charles-Léon Moureu passed away at Biarritz. He was a member of the Institut and of the Académie de Médicine, professor at the Collège de France, and Grand Officier of the Légion d'Honneur. This event plunged French science into widespread mourning, affecting particularly the Société Chimique de France, because in its former president it lost the person who had promoted its prosperity and its luster.

Charles Moureu was born on April 19, 1863, at Moureux, a small village in the Bearn country. He was the last of seven children in a rather poor farmer's family. Nothing in his humble origin, in the rustic house of his parents, or in the misfortune of losing his father very shortly after his birth indicated the brilliant future lying in store for him.

His education started in the grade school of the village. This beginning of his intellectual formation left an indelible impression, and he always felt deeply grateful to his old teacher. With remarkable intuition his mother believed that this flowering intelligence had great promise, and without regard to the heavy burden of educating her six other children she did not draw back from the additional sacrifices which the further education of her son Charles would necessarily involve.

In the period beginning with his college career his biography cannot be separated from that of his brother Félix. After obtaining the diploma of a pharmacist, Félix had opened an apothecary shop at Biarritz which soon prospered. This circumstance became a decisive influence in the career of Charles. The brother, replacing the lost father, became banker, guide, and friend at the same time. It was he who oriented the student toward pharmaceutical studies and, thereby, toward a scientific life.

In November, 1884, Moureu entered the École Supérieure de Pharmacie at Paris. He soon distinguished himself by earning the principal awards in the competitions held for the most gifted of the students.

After that, it was an uninterrupted series of successes. As an intern in the hospitals of Paris he gained successively the silver medal (1887) and the gold medal (1889). In 1891 he won the title of chief pharmacist of the Asiles de la Seine. At the same time, he conquered several academic grades: Licencié ès sciences physiques in 1888, pharmacist of first class in 1891, doctor of toxicology in the École Supérieure de Pharmacie de Paris in 1899. From this listing one may judge how much hard work occupied the life of this student. In his eyes, however, this was only an accessory. The main thing that took hold of his spirit and his time was an irresistible inclination, an ardent passion for science and, especially, for chemistry.

At that time, he had the good fortune of meeting, in the family of Bertrand Louber, the wonderful companion of his life who understood and helped him and joyfully shared with him the austere existence of a scholar. From now on, nothing stood in his way; he was able to satisfy his aspirations and to give free rein to his creative abilities.

He did not have to wait long for results. His doctor's thesis, dealing with the difficult subject of acrylic acid and its derivatives, had demonstrated a real experimental skill and an inventive mind. Shortly afterward his publications started to multiply while the fields of his investigations and the importance of his discoveries expanded. The originality of the researcher and his activity quickly attracted attention. Encouragements, rewards, official recognitions, and finally the highest titles followed upon one another with incredible speed.

Success, instead of blunting his zeal, exalted it; if he had worked without truce before, he now worked with redoubled effort. However, this intensive productivity was not of long duration; World War I interfered.

It was a critical moment; it was necessary to win or else be subjugated. In the unity of general patriotism, the French chemists went to work. This scientific mobilization, its protagonists, its secret labor, its results, all this has been magnificently described by Moureu in his book: "La Chimie et la Guerre. Science et Avenir" (*Chemistry and the War. Science and the Future,* Paris, 1921).

The end of the great drama did not open up an era of calm immediately. Less than anyone else Moureu was inclined to let

1148

things slide; a new phase of his life began. The material and moral ruin to which he was a wounded witness released his energy. He saw in science the source of abundance which would permit recovery. He devoted himself to chemistry with increased and improved facilities as successor to Berthelot's chair at the Collège de-France to which he was elected in 1917. However, since the events of the war had elevated him to the summit of the general interest, he no longer remained encircled by the limited horizon of his own research. All of science became his concern, because its many branches form a unity. He campaigned energetically to save our several scientific organizations by attracting devoted persons and resources.

He became a master in negotiations to achieve the annual reunion of the world's great chemical organizations. The resultant International Union of Pure and Applied Chemistry asked him unanimously to become its first president. He contributed to the dignified union between the scientists of the two parties formerly at war, a work in the interest of peace which he steered between the dangers of ill advised dissoluteness and too opinionated rancor.

This is, in bold outline, the life of Moureu after the afflictions of the war until the day when his strength, spent in the service of so many generous causes, finally abandoned him.

The death of his brother Félix in 1928 gave him a shock from which he could not recover. Nevertheless he made an effort to attend the Congress at Cambridge in September, 1928. The following winter his health was bad and his strength continued to decline. His doctors, alarmed with good reason, advised a sojourn in the south, at Cambo. This sojourn at Cambo soon became unbearable to him. He went on to Biarritz where, a few days later, death overcame him at the age of sixty-six.

Moureu had a strong personality which emanated a captivating charm. In his manners as in his thought or language, he was an enemy of vulgarity and always gave a high impression of the refinement of the scientist. He gave himself entirely to his teaching, either by lecture or in writing. His nature did not permit him to do anything incompletely, and his biography could almost be condensed into one word: enthusiasm.

BOOKS

Charles Moureu's considerable work, in its variety, is evidence of his indefatigable activity.

The most important of his books was the "Notions fondamentales de Chimie organique" (1st ed., 1902, English translation of the 6th ed. with the title: "Fundamental Principles of Organic Chemistry," by W. T. K. Braunholz, 1921).

Another book that had a resounding success was "La Chimie et la Guerre." The first purely technical part is a kind of inventory of the applications which chemistry found among the belligerents. In the second part the author takes a broad view and issues severe warnings with calm impartiality. Certain pages of magnificent flight of the imagination are veritable hymns to the beauty of science.

Moureu was first of all an organic chemist. Nevertheless his scientific curiosity incited him to start other studies in which he soon became master; it was he in particular who introduced the systematic study of the rare gases in France. Moureu thought that the gases contained in thermal springs should reveal by their composition useful information about the mysterious origin of these waters and their therapeutic action. The previous analyses had given all that could be expected about the known gases; now it was desirable to investigate the new rare gases. This was the start for work on hydrology and the physics of the Earth.

ACROLEIN AND ACRYLIC ACID

Acrylic acid, $CH_2=CH—COOH$, the first of the acids with an ethylene group, was very incompletely known in 1890, when Moureu began its study for his doctor's thesis. His process for obtaining this acid, later elaborated still further with his student Chaux, consisted in oxidizing the corresponding aldehyde, acrolein $CH_2=CH—CHO$ in an indirect way. It was first converted, by addition of hydrochloric acid, into $CH_2Cl—CH_2—CHO$, or rather its trimeric compound, which was then oxidized. The β-chloropropionic acid, $CH_2Cl—CH_2—COOH$, thus obtained was transformed into the unsaturated acid through elimination of HCl.

This method made acrylic acid accessible and permitted the

1150

preparation of a new series of derivatives, such as the anhydride, the chloride, the amines, the nitrile, and several esters. All these substances are remarkable for their tendency to polymerize; most of them resinify more or less rapidly.

Moureu returned to these studies because of the war. His first contacts with acrolein had left with him the impression that this was a dangerous material. He proposed its use as a war gas and had it accepted as such when he succeeded, together with Lepape, in obtaining it in stabilized form. The process consisted in conducting the classical preparation (reaction of acid potassium sulfate with glycerin) with certain precautions which were found effective in leaving stabilizing impurities in the product. The nature of these favorable impurities is unknown, but a systematic study, in which Dufraisse, Pougnet, and P. Robin participated, led to the finding of phenol and from there to the discovery of the stabilizing action of phenols. Later, as will be described further on, this stabilizing action was demonstrated as due to an antioxygen effect.

ACETYLENIC COMPOUNDS

Moureu successfully developed practical methods for obtaining substances which contained the triple carbon bond together with others of the chemically active groups. This resulted in a long series of new substances, some of which aroused great interest, as for example the *heptinocarbonate de methyl,*

$$CH_3—(CH_2)_4.\,.\,C{\equiv}C—CO_2.CH_3,$$

a perfume better known under the name *vert de violette,* and the acetylene dinitrile, $N{\equiv}C—C{\equiv}C—C{\equiv}N$, or carbon subnitride.

On the other hand, the knowledge of the acetylenic bond was enriched by his studies which showed the extraordinary reactivity of this carbon linkage.

CHEMICAL CONSTITUTION OF SPARTEINE

In collaboration with A. Valeur, Moureu undertook a study of long duration to find the constitution of a natural product, sparteine, an alkaloid of the furze plant. This important work is a model in precision of the experiments and logic in their interpretation. The result was the following constitutional formula in 1912:[1]

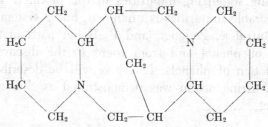

Sparteine (Moureu's formula, 1912)

Sparteine (present formula)

SYNTHETIC RESINS AND THEIR ELECTRICAL INSULATING PROPERTIES

Moureu and Dufraisse tried to utilize the well-known tendency of acrolein to form more or less transparent resins. They found, first of all, that there are two, and only two, reactions of resinification, and that all the various appearances of the resins were only caused by the variation in proportions in which the two kinds of resin were produced. The first reaction is the transformation into the insoluble diacryl of Redtenbacher, the second the transformation into a soluble resin or viscous condensate. The first is produced by the catalytic action exerted by autoxidation products of acrolein, or by light even in the absence of oxygen. The second reaction is catalyzed by basic substances; a great number of salts, particularly those of the heavy metals, also produce this resin.

The condensation of acrolein with phenols gives a useful material called "orca" (an anagram of acro). Although formed like the resins of the bakelite type by condensing an aldehyde with phenols, "orca" does not resemble the bakelite resins either in the conditions of its formation or in its properties. It is characterized by two main properties which distinguish it from similar resins; it is transparent and a very good electric insulator. It is so transparent that even in a thickness of one meter it looks "optically clear." Together with its optical dispersion, this property might be useful in optics. As an electrical insulator it surpasses all known materials except amber.[2]

CATALYSIS OF AUTOXIDATION
ANTIOXIDANTS AND OXIDANTS

From all the observations on acrolein, Moureu and Dufraisse theorized that the phenols hindered the absorption of free oxygen by acrolein. Thus started the idea of an experiment which seemed strange, if not absurd, at that time. The idea was that an oxygen-absorbing substance (acrolein) should be combined with another substance which itself avidly attracts oxygen (a polyphenol), because such a combination of two appetites would arrest the consumption of oxygen instead of increasing it. This was actually found to be true, as stated October 21, 1917, and later confirmed for a large number of substances; this was the "action antioxygène," antioxidant action.

New as they were, these experiments were not the first to show an antioxygen effect; other very interesting observations had been made before.[3] The best known of these was the extinction of phosphorus in air by diverse vapors.

For a systematic exploration, Moureu organized a large program at the organic laboratory of the Collège de France. A great number of catalysts were prepared, all of them painstakingly purified to avoid errors due to impurities. A multitude of measurements of the rate of oxygen absorption was needed, since each catalyst was tried with several autoxidizable substances, often at various concentrations. Each experiment was rigorously controlled, and so were the calculations and the graphs, and arrangements were made to permit later checks on all the data. The collaborators in this long and difficult work were Badoche, Berchet, Chaux, Johnson, Laplague, Lotte, and Panier des Touches.

The following survey of March, 1929, gives an impression of the size of the experiments. At that time, 529 catalysts, inorganic or organic substances, had been tried with more than 30 synthetic or natural materials. The 88,500 measurements of oxygen absorption had served to construct 5100 graphs. To this was added a bibliography comprising over 10,000 documents.

Thus the true nature of the antioxygenic phenomenon could be established with certainty. This phenomenon consists in a kind of paralysis of the oxygen which seems to have lost its reactivity. The gas rests, as if inert, in contact wtih the autoxidizable substance which is provided with a protective substance, and at the end of the experiment both substances are recovered in their original state of purity without alteration; this really is an antioxygenic effect. The results can be condensed into the following twin propositions: (1) Every autoxidation must be preventable by an appropriate antioxidant, and (2) every chemically reactive substance must be able to function as an antioxidant under the proper conditions.

In view of the importance of autoxidations on the surface of the Earth, the antioxygenic action in its generality must be regarded as one of the great phenomenons in nature. In order to emphasize its significance while honoring our departed master, the famous English chemist, H. E. Armstrong, designated this phenomenon as "the Moureu effect."

Another great result was the recognition of the inverse catalyses. This means the property of one and the same catalyst to be able either to promote or to prevent autoxidations, in other words, to function at times as a pro-oxidant, at others as an antioxidant.

This relatedness of the inverse catalyses must not be forgotten in the practice of the antioxidants, otherwise there may be great trouble. An apparently insignificant change in the composition of the catalyst, or in the conditions of its use, may actually reverse the direction of the catalysis. The result is then the opposite of what was hoped for, because the action of oxygen is speeded up instead of being slowed down.

Although relatively young, antioxidants have already begun to find numerous useful applications. Several biological conclusions, published in 1922,[4] have been experimentally tested and may lead to applications, particularly in medicine.

Ahead of biology, industry widely uses the data on antioxidants and pro-oxidants. The example of fuels for internal combustion in motors is typical. But of all the industries, that of rubber is the most advanced in putting antioxidants to work.

RUBRENE

Rubrene is a hydrocarbon, $C_{42}H_{28}$ which Moureu and Dufraisse discovered.

This was the last study that Moureu undertook, starting in 1926. Its constitutional formula is

It is an orange-red crystallized substance which gives solutions of rose color and yellow-green fluorescence. These solutions are stable in the dark or, with exclusion of air, under light, but they are rapidly discolored by irradiation in the presence of air. The product of oxidation, called oxyrubrene, is formed by the addition of one molecule of oxygen to one of rubrene; its formula, with R representing rubrene, is RO_2 (with solvent inclusion when the substance is crystallized). Under the action of heat or light, it dissociates into rubrene and free oxygen, $R + O_2$.

This property of rubrene to form an addition product with oxygen which dissociates and regenerates the absorbed oxygen has been called reversible oxidability. This would be unique among organic compounds if there were not another example, and a really capital one, the example of the respiratory pigments of the animals, of which hemoglobin is the representative. Up to now most of the authors placed the reversible oxidability of hemoglobin on the atom of iron it contains. After the example of rubrene, the essential function of hemoglobin can no longer be considered as necessarily located in the atom of iron; it may, certainly, be connected with this atom, but it can also belong to an atomic group around the iron, or to a group without iron.

Oxyrubrene, $R(O_2)$, corresponds quite well with the intermediary peroxide, symbolized as $A(O_2)$, which is postulated in the theory of the antioxidants. On the other hand, the rubrene problem, which touches on the mechanism of autoxidation in living organisms, has been highly illuminated by the research on catalysis in autoxidation. The fundamental phenomenon of oxidation through free oxygen is thus approached in its widest generality, and the studies of Moureu's laboratory have brought apparently divergent experiences together toward the solution of a great scientific problem.

NOTES AND REFERENCES

James F. Norris, "Charles Moureu," *J. Am. Chem. Soc., 52*, 31 (1930).
1 Robert Robinson, "The Structural Relations of Natural Products," Oxford University Press, London, 1955, p. 74.
2 *J. Phys., 5*, 161 (1924).
3 *Chem. Rev., 3*, 113 (1926).
4 *Compt. rend. 174*, 258 (1922).

Selections from the biography by Charles Dufraisse, *Bull. Soc. chim. France, 49,* 741 (1931). Translated by Eduard Farber.

CHARLES DUFRAISSE

·· *81* ··

Frederic Stanley Kipping

1863-1949

FREDERIC STANLEY KIPPING was born on August 16, 1863, at Higher Broughton in Manchester. He was the eldest son of James Stanley and Julia Kipping and had two brothers and four sisters. His father held a post in the Manchester branch of the Bank of England of which his paternal grandfather was head. His grandfather on his mother's side was C. A. Duval, a Manchester artist of considerable reputation. James Stanley Kipping played chess against many of the champions of his time, including Paul Murphy, whom he defeated on one occasion when this world champion was playing a number of opponents simultaneously. F. S. Kipping regarded himself as only a moderate player, but his eldest son, C. S. Kipping, headmaster of Wednesbury High School, inherited his grandfather's skill and is a composer of chess problems of worldwide repute and has edited various chess journals.

Kipping early acquired that interest in open-air life which was never to leave him. His father owned a small farm near Higher Broughton, which was at that time practically in the open country. Here he made himself generally useful and gained a fair knowledge of animals and practical agriculture. In the early days the Kipping children had a governess, but at the age of eleven Frederic Stanley entered Manchester Grammar School on the same day as Herbert Brereton Baker. (It is remarkable that both these boys became Longstaff Medallists of the Chemical Society.) He had already become interested in chemistry through his father's friend and neighbor, J. Carter Bell, the public analyst for Cheshire, who showed him various simple precipitation reactions in inorganic chemistry, and advised his father to make him an analytical chemist. No doubt at this time that honorable profession was still generally regarded from the Dickensian point of view, so clearly indicated in "Our mutual friend."

These early influences were strengthened by the teaching of Francis Jones, of whom H. Brereton Baker (*Trans. Chem. Soc.* 1926, p. 1021) wrote: "Besides Jones's personality, what affected

1159

us boys most was seeing him always at work on research. Many of those who have since given their lives to original investigation owe most of the impetus which has driven them on, to the work on boron hydride which they watched in progress. No schoolmaster had an influence like his on the making of a chemist." Kipping remarks that the practical chemistry at Manchester Grammar School consisted almost entirely of qualitative analysis but unaccompanied by any clear explanation of its principles. During the holidays he assisted Carter Bell with the ordinary routine analysis of water, milk, and other foodstuffs. He also spent a year at the Lycée de Caen where food and sanitary arrangements were poor but the teaching of Latin was especially good. Kipping matriculated at the University of London in 1879 in the first division and thereupon entered Owens College, Manchester, his family having meanwhile removed to Platt Abbey, a house familiar to this day to all those who travel on a 42 'bus along the Palatine Road to the Burlington Street laboratories. After three years, in which he studied mathematics, physics, botany, chemistry, and zoology, he graduated B.Sc. (London) with second-class honors in zoology. He found Miles Marshall, the professor of zoology, an excellent and inspiring teacher, and Roscoe extremely kind and interested in his students. Schorlemmer, who was the first professor of organic chemistry in this country, did not attract him, however—his lectures were read without emphasis or pause from notes held close to the nose. After a short experience of this mode of presentation of organic chemistry, Kipping devoted Schorlemmer's lecture hours to the practice of billiards in an adjacent hotel, thus acquiring a facility which he never lost. On the whole, with the exception of zoology, he found college work dull and unsatisfactory, but he used the fives courts a good deal and played cricket and lacrosse.

After graduation as an external student of the University of London in 1882, he obtained a post as chemist to the Manchester Gas Department in Rochdale Road and later at Gaythorne Street. The duties of the post, except for occasional work throughout the night, were not heavy but afforded him very useful and varied analytical experience which, at the age of nineteen, may have laid the foundation of the scrupulous care and accuracy of his research work. He had plenty of time for reading and was frequently able to leave the laboratory at 4:30 to 5:00 p.m. to catch a train on the former M.S.J. and A. Railway to Old Trafford in order to play tennis at the Northern Lawn Tennis Club. Here, and on many other grounds, he played in matches against the leading clubs of Lancashire and adjoining counties. He remained in the service of the corporation for about three years, to the age of twenty-three. Until then he seems to have shown no particular signs of devotion to chemistry although he was doubtless maturing. About this time, however, a friend of his family, Dr. Adolf Liebman, a chemist at Levinstein's, strongly advised a period of study in Germany and pointed out the lack of opportunity for advancement in Kipping's post at the gasworks.

Following this advice he entered the University of Munich in the spring of 1886 and was there given a working bench in one of the organic laboratories which was supervised by W. H. Perkin, Jr., who had entered von Baeyer's institute in 1882. There he carried out various organic preparations, and after some months commenced research under Perkin's guidance on the synthesis of closed carbon chains. Thus began a scientific association which was to last until the death of Perkin in 1926 and was destined to influence the lives of both men, not only on the scientific but also on the personal side. Late in 1886 Perkin returned to England and thenceforward Kipping continued his research unaided except for the written advice which Perkin sent him from time to time. At that time Claisen, Bamberger, and von Pechmann were *Privatdocenten* and Nef was a student. Work in the laboratory began at eight and continued till six or after, with a rather long interval for *Mittagessen*—and chess. There was much skating in the winter. Kipping saw very little of von Baeyer. He refers to one occasion, however, on which he showed him with some pride a product he had isolated. The Geheimrat looked at it under a lens, snapped out "Ach, Harz" and stalked away. This may have been the origin of Kipping's critical, and, to say the least, realistic attitude to his students' laboratory efforts. However, he took his Ph.D. degree *summa cum laude,* after which he returned to England, and for a short time assisted his father, who had turned his attention to chemical manufacturing on the small scale. The preparation of sulfur chloride and of carbolic disinfecting powder in the stables of Platt Abbey were not very congenial or successful ventures and did not last very long.

In the autumn of 1887, T. E. Thorpe and Emerson Reynolds, as examiners for the University of London, awarded Kipping the degree of D.Sc. He was the first candidate on whom this degree was conferred on the grounds of research. It would appear, however, that his Munich work sufficed for both his doctorates, a happy state of affairs which would not now commend itself to faculties of science. Immediately afterwards he was offered the post of demonstrator under W. H. Perkin, Jr., who had by now been appointed professor of chemistry at the Heriot-Watt College in Edinburgh. The remuneration was £20 a year "with prospects". Most of the teaching was done in the evening, but Kipping was usually on duty for most of the day, spending much time in research, again under Perkin's direction. In March, 1888, he married his cousin, Lily Holland, the daughter of W. T. Holland, J.P., of Bridgwater, and granddaughter of C. A. Duval. During their engagement Perkin met his future wife, Miss Holland's elder sister, at the house of Kipping's parents.

During the Edinburgh period the writing of the famous "Organic Chemistry" (Perkin and Kipping) was begun. This work was one of the earliest textbooks on the subject, and was first published in 1894. It has enjoyed an enormous reputation and has passed through many editions, the latest of which (1949) presents an excellent picture of the present-day position of the science. After about a year at the Edinburgh College, Kipping was made assistant professor of chemistry and lecturer in agricultural chemistry at a total remuneration of £150 a year.

In late 1890 an event occurred which greatly influenced his future work and afforded him many stimulating contacts and the opportunity of directing the research of beginners. H. E. Armstrong, to Kipping's "astonishment and satisfaction," offered him the post of chief demonstrator in the chemistry department at the Central Technical College of the City and Guilds of London Institute at £240 a year. (The college is now incorporated in the Imperial College of Science and Technology and the chemistry department closed. Many will remember the heated discussion which took place about 1910 regarding the wisdom of this step, Armstrong having built up a most flourishing school of research.) Kipping accepted this offer "with alacrity" and he and his wife removed from Graham Street, Edinburgh, to a small house at 7 Milborne Grove, South Kensington, Kipping then worked with Armstrong for a time, first on certain problems connected with colour and constitution and then on the products of the action of sulfuric acid on camphor, one of which was shown to be 3:4-dimethylactetophenone (*p*-acetyl-*o*-xylene). This led to a study of a crude sulfonation product of bromocamphor prepared by W. J. Pope, who was at that time lecture assistant to Armstrong. Thus began the fruitful association of Kipping and Pope which lasted for six years, during which many joint papers were published.

Shortly afterward (1893) Arthur Lapworth arrived in Pope's laboratory from Birmingham, where his father was the distinguished professor of geology, and was placed under Kipping's supervision. Here again a very successful collaboration resulted, the work being mainly on derivatives of camphor. Kipping contributed, many years later, a warm tribute to Lapworth which was quoted by Sir R. Robinson in his obituary notice. "Although he was considerably my junior in age, we soon became fast friends; perhaps it would be truer to say that our relationship, even in those early days, was rather that of congenial brothers. He became a frequent visitor at our house in South Kensington where he often met Pope, Forster and other workers in Armstrong's laboratories. During one vacation when he had made no holiday plans, we asked him to stay with us at Bridgwater: here it was that he met his future wife, Kathleen Holland."

The work of Perkin, Kipping, and Lapworth has left a lasting impression on experimental and theoretical organic chemistry which may perhaps best be realized if we attempt for a moment to consider what the record of the years 1895–1930 would be if the work of these three men were left out of consideration. That they married three sisters is surely not unworthy of being placed on record.

Kipping has referred to his constant attendance at the meetings of the Chemical Society and to the considerable amount of work which he performed for the Society's *Abstracts*. He mentions that the leading figures at the meetings after Armstrong (Secretary "and chief manager even when not himself the President") were Dewar, Ramsay, Dunstan, M. Lamb, Groves (Editor), Greenaway (Sub-Editor), Sir William Crookes ("who was very kind to young chemists"), Perkin, Sr., R. Messel, Pickering, J. M. Thompson, Gladstone, Collie, Sir Frederick Abel, Chattaway, Pope, Lapworth, and Forster.

He found little time for recreation but whenever possible he and his wife went for long rowing excursions on the Thames, returning only when the light faded. During six years they heard, from the gallery of Covent Garden Opera House, nearly all the great operas and most of the famous singers of the day.

In 1897 Kipping was elected to the Royal Society at the age of thirty-four, and soon afterwards was appointed to the chair of chemistry at University College, Nottingham, in succession to Professor Frank Clowes. He found the laboratories and classrooms in Shakespeare Street compact and well-arranged, but there were only four full-time students who were working for the Associateship of the Institute of Chemistry, the remainder consisted of a few ill-prepared part-time students of engineering. Most of the evening students were working for the qualifying examination of the Pharmaceutical Society. He refers to certain short courses given in those early days to students of mining, dyeing, plumbing, and brewing, and adds: "I came to the conclusion that such so-called technical education was valueless . . . the more intelligent students of these subjects were encouraged to attend the evening classes in pure chemistry during two or three years, and their practical work was so arranged that it had a direct bearing on their daily occupations." The number of students of chemistry steadily increased, and Kipping, first unaided, and then in collaboration with members of his staff, initiated various lines of research which will be considered later. He also acted as external examiner to the federal Victoria University and to the Royal University of Ireland, and much appreciated the kindness and hospitality of Professor Dixon of Cork and Professor Senier of Galway, but greatly regretted the necessity of failing so large a proportion of the Irish candidates. Both before and after the First World War he was external examiner to the University of Birmingham and wrote in 1942: "There the standard was high, and the unfailing kindness of

1164

Professor and Mrs. Frankland with whom I stayed remains a most pleasant memory even now."

During the First World War, Kipping and his staff collaborated in the scheme for the preparation of synthetic drugs which were at that time unobtainable in Britain; he also lectured on musketry and map-reading to the Officers' Training Corps and superintended practice on a miniature rifle range in an old clay pit.

Like all other chemistry departments of university rank, Kipping's laboratories were crowded after the armistice of 1918, and it became necessary to find immediate temporary accommodation for the forty or fifty full-time students who wished to work for the Pass and Honours degrees of the University of London. The Shakespeare Street buildings of the College were situated between the City Library on the one side and the City Museum on the other, forming one large block which was and is a familiar—and I think pleasing—aspect of Nottingham. To meet the demand, one of the large rooms of the museum was cleared of its stuffed animals and converted to a laboratory, capable of providing about seventy working benches for the more elementary and part-time students. This met the immediate needs, but after 1922 it became obvious that the student population of the College as a whole would remain permanently at a much higher figure than that obtaining before the war.

The College Council thereupon decided to build a new University College. Fortunately this was made possible through the great generosity of Sir Jesse Boot, later Baron Trent, who not only purchased the splendid site now known as University Park, but also defrayed the cost of the building and equipment and endowed the chair of chemistry, Kipping thus becoming the first Sir Jesse Boot Professor of Chemistry. The college was opened by H. M. King George V in 1928.

In 1936, after the College Council had, on several occasions, refused to accept his offers to resign, he retired from the chair and was appointed emeritus professor of chemistry. The Council made arrangements for him to work in his old laboratory at Shakespeare Street, and there he continued research on silicon compounds till the outbreak of war in 1939 when he and Mrs. and Miss Kipping removed to Criccieth. Shortly after his retirement the University of

Leeds conferred upon him the degree of D.Sc. *honoris causa,* in recognition of his long services to university teaching and research.

In the same year, soon after Kipping published Part L of *Organic derivatives of silicon,* his staff and former students entertained him to dinner. Robison, the discoverer of the mechanism of the calcification of cartilage, was in the chair, and over seventy were present. It was a most happy and inspiring occasion; the respect and affection in which Kipping was held were manifest in every word which was spoken. The dry, humorous remarks, the caustic comments, the rather gruff encouragements stored for many years in the memories of his pupils were then released in the speeches. Happy is the man who can inspire such regard.

For a year or two after his retirement he continued to supervise the work of a few research students and published one more paper, Part LI, which was unique in one respect. At the end it contained these words. *"Envoi.* As this is my last paper may I express here my sincere thanks to the Chemical Society for having published so much of my work over so long a period—F. S. K." I do not recall a similar acknowledgment by any other Fellow of the Society.

On the outbreak of war in 1939 Kipping, with his wife and younger daughter, took a house on the sea front at Criccieth and there it was my privilege to see him in 1946 and 1947. He was surrounded by the proofs of the revised, almost rewritten, edition of "Perkin and Kipping," in the production of which he had been joined by his younger son, Frederic Barry, university lecturer in chemistry in the University of Cambridge. He was, it need hardly be mentioned, as interested as ever in the progress of chemical research and in the forthcoming promotion to university status of the old college at Nottingham. It must have been a source of considerable satisfaction to Kipping that his son not only entered academic life, but, like his father, collaborated with Pope on various stereochemical themes. F. B. Kipping has also published much independent work in general organic chemistry and in stereochemistry.

In the spring of 1949 the health of Mrs. Kipping caused him much anxiety, and after only a week's illness he died on May 1 in his eighty-sixth year.

Kipping's interest in derivatives of camphor was due to his

association with Armstrong at the Central Technical College. Kipping states: "Armstrong then asked me to examine a crude sulphonation product of bromochamphor prepared by W. J. Pope; thus began the joint research work which extended over six years during which period many joint papers were published."

The first paper described the sulfonation of camphor and bromocamphor with anhydrosulfuric acid or chlorosulfonic acid. "The camphor-sulphonic chloride prepared from the acid obtained by either of these methods is a mixture of optical isomerides, but as the dextro-rotatory modification is present in rather the larger proportion we have been able to isolate and examine it. The optically inactive, or feebly active, mixture of sulphonic chlorides shows a very remarkable behaviour; it is deposited from solution in well-defined crystals which, although apparently homogeneous, are simply mixtures of the two active compounds in variable proportions and are partially resolved into enantiomorphous forms on recrystallization.

"The sulphonic derivatives of bromo- and chlorocamphor are optically active and remarkable for the extraordinary facility with which they crystallize; the sulphonic chlorides, the amides, the acids and a number of salts are described, the optical and crystallographical characters of many of the compounds being given." Such details appeared in many subsequent papers published by Kipping throughout his life, both in collaboration with Pope and with other workers. The importance attached to crystallography by other pupils of Armstrong, e.g., Lowry, is well known.

The authors add: "Speaking generally the sulphonic derivatives of camphor are compounds of exceptional beauty [here, surely, we detect the Perkin touch] and judging from the results thus far obtained will probably lead to conclusions of considerable importance." When we consider the part played by bromocamphorsulfonic acid in almost every study of optically active bases during the last fifty years, this prophecy may be regarded as entirely justified.

In two further communications Kipping and Pope extended their detailed study of camphorsulfonic acids and their derivatives, and showed that the preliminary effervescence observed during the combustion of sulfonic halides of camphor and its halogen derivatives is due to the evolution of sulfur dioxide and formation of the

1167

so-called π-halogen derivatives (so named owing to their pyrogenic formation), in which the atom so introduced replaces the -SO₂Hal group in the $CH_3—C—CH_2SO_2Hal$ residue of camphor. Thus bromocamphorsulfonic chloride yields α-bromo-π-chlorocamphor

$$CH_2—C—CHBr$$
with CH₃ above, CH₃.C.CH₂Cl inside, CH₃—CH—CO below

Many derivatives of this type were obtained, and in several papers published in collaboration with Lapworth (whose first research at the Central Technical College was carried out under Kipping's supervision) their properties and those of other derivatives of camphor, especially nitrocamphor and camphoric acid, were carefully examined. The titles listed in the bibliography indicate the scope of this work. Lowry's work on bromocamphor, mutarotation, and similar themes was also an outcome of the assiduous cultivation of the camphor field in South Kensington at the turn of the century. Two of the compounds investigated by Kipping alone or in collaboration with Lapworth may be mentioned in passing:

Sulfocamphoric acid

α-π-Dibromo-α-nitrocamphor

Reference may here be made to two stereochemical investigations in one of which Kipping and Salway approached the vexed question of the "Arrangement in space of the groups combined with the tervalent nitrogen atom" and the other, where, with his student, Peters, he investigated "Iodonium compounds of the type IR′R″R‴" and the configuration of the iodine atom" (T. 1902, **81**, 1350).

1168

The work of Kipping and Peters on iodonium compounds consisted in the fractional crystallization of phenyl-*p*-tolyliodonium *d*-bromo camphorsulfonate. Not the slightest evidence of resolution could be obtained.

Between 1900 and 1905 Kipping published a series of eleven papers entitled "Isomeric partially racemic salts containing quinquevalent nitrogen." All of these except the last were published under his name only. The work arose out of experiments on the resolution of *dl*-hydrindamine which were later extended to *dl*-methylhydrindamine and *dl*-benzylhydrindamine. The resolution of the first two bases was successfully achieved and the active components proved of the greatest service in later work; the *d*- and *l*-methylhydrindamines were, in fact, essential to Kipping's most outstanding success. Before the *d*- and *l*-bases could be separated, however, much exploratory work had to be carried out, and many of the observations which were made during the course of the almost endless fractional crystallizations were most unexpected and confusing. The research, in fact, offered numerous opportunities for the exercise of the skill, care, and patience which characterized all Kipping's work. The somewhat tentative explanation which he put forward to account for the unexpected results was, at the end of five years, replaced by the correct one, and he was able to say, "Nevertheless all the old facts remain as recorded, and as regards the experimental part of the work there is, as far as the author knows, nothing to correct and nothing to withdraw." (*T*. 1905, **87**, 636.)

The main results of this work will now be described as briefly as possible. (*T*. 1900, **77**, 861.)

"When *dl*-hydrindamine is combined with various optically active acids it shows an altogether unusual behaviour, giving in some cases what appears to be a homogeneous partially racemic salt, in others a mixture of unequal quantities of two isomeric salts; the latter are not the ordinary isomerides which are obtained from most externally compensated bases under such conditions. They do not represent salts of the separate enantiomorphously related components of the base, but are both comparable to partially racemic substances."

dl-Hydrindamine and α-bromocamphorsulfonic acid unite to form

1169

unequal quantities of two salts containing different quantities of water of crystallization . . . absolutely different in appearance and with different specific rotations. Hydrindamine and chlorocamphorsulfonic acid give unequal quantities of two isomeric salts which are respectively analogous to those of the bromo-acid. These two series of salts were designated α- and β- by Kipping. The conversion of either of these α-salts (bromo- or chloro-) into the corresponding β-salt or vice versa by crystallization only, has never been observed.

Kipping came to the tentative conclusion that the isomerism was due to stereoisomerism among the groups attached to the quinquevalent nitrogen atom but the arguments do not lend themselves to summarization, especially after the lapse of fifty years. Five years later, however, the conditions under which the β-salt could be converted to the α-modification were accidentally established during an attempt to convert β-l-hydrindamine bromocamphorsulfonate into the β-l-chlorocamphorsulfonate. He finally showed that the production of the so-called α- and β-salts was due to the existence of *cis* and *trans* forms of the bromo- and chlorocamphorsulfonic acids which are convertible through the unstable enolic form. In support of this stereochemical explanation, Kipping quotes the rapid racemization of *d*-methylhydrindone in presence of alcoholic sodium ethoxide

$$C_6H_4 \underset{CO}{\overset{CH_2}{<}} \hspace{-4pt} > \hspace{-4pt} C \underset{CH_2}{\overset{H}{<}} \quad \longleftarrow \longrightarrow \quad C_6H_4 \underset{CO}{\overset{CH_2}{<}} \hspace{-4pt} > \hspace{-4pt} C \underset{H}{\overset{CH_2}{<}}$$

doubtless by passage through the unstable enolic form.

Kipping's work on organic derivatives of silicon was commenced with the object of obtaining compounds of which the optical activity was due to the presence of an asymmetric silicon atom, and clearly arose out of his work on the stereochemistry of nitrogen. This, in its turn, was probably a consequence of his still earlier interest in camphor. It might be imagined that the discovery of the Grignard reagent was a determining factor in Kipping's choice of this field of research; but although the progress of his work was greatly eased by the use of these reagents, the research was commenced one or two years before 1900 (the year in which Grignard made his initial observation), and in Part I Kipping and Lloyd make no reference to the French chemist's discovery.

Kipping's work in this field, which extended over a period of nearly forty years, may be regarded under three main headings: (1) experiments connected with the preparation and resolution of asymmetric compounds of silicon, (2) work on the structure of the simpler condensation products derived from compounds of the type $R_2Si(OH)_2$ and $RSi(OH)_3$, and (3) the study of the products obtained from arylchlorosilanes R_2SiCl_2 or R_3SiCl and sodium. Of these three main lines, the first attracted great attention at the time, the other two were disregarded.

Since 1940 the extension of the second line of work under the auspices of the Dow Corning Corporation has brought his name to the notice of hundreds who had never heard of him previously. Kipping certainly spoke truly when, in 1912, he remarked to a student who had used the term "polymerization" loosely and rather carelessly: "Polymerization, that's a blessed word, it's like Mesopotamia." The personal application of this comment was not apparent for nearly thirty years. His former students and colleagues welcome the utilization of his silicols and silicones, but deny with much warmth that this publicity adds anything to his scientific reputation, which was firmly established many years before the plastic age commenced. Their "welcome" is accorded rather to the demonstration, so frequently made but so readily forgotten, that no limit can be placed to the results which may spring from careful scientific investigation carried out for its own sake and for no other reason.

The reactions employed by Kipping for the synthesis and, in three cases, resolution of his asymmetric compounds were simple in the extreme, but the experimental difficulties were considerable.

In Part I, three chlorine atoms of silicon tetrachloride were successively replaced by the phenoxy, methoxy and ethoxy groups, but attempts at resolution, by replacing the fourth chlorine atom by the methoxy group or by the anion of an optically active acid, were unsuccessful.

Five other asymmetric compounds of silicon were prepared between 1905 and 1910 by the successive replacement of the chlorine atoms with alkyl and aryl radicals by means of the Grignard reagent. The sulfonic acids of *dl*-benzylmethylethylpropylsilicane and *dl*-benzylmethylpropylisobutylsilicane resisted all attempts at their resolution, although numerous optically active bases including cinchonidine, cinchonine, l-menthylamine, strychnine, brucine, and quinine were employed.

His first success was obtained by the sulfonation of *dl*-phenylbenzylethylpropylsilicane. When using sulfuric acid at ordinary temperatures or below 70° C. benzene is eliminated (but not toluene), probably with formation of Si.Et.Pr.CH$_2$Ph.OH which then yields the disulfonic acid of the oxide (Pr.Et.CH$_2$C$_6$H$_4$SO$_3$H. Si)$_2$O. This elimination of benzene appears to be characteristic of the Ph-Si link under such conditions. Later on he used chlorosulfonic acid instead of sulfuric acid, obtaining the same sulfonic acid.

Kipping finally isolated a crystalline, deliquescent di-ammonium salt of this acid, of which he remarks in a footnote, "This was the first crystalline silicon compound obtained during at least six months' work, so the author has been careful not to over-rate its beauty."

This acid was also obtained by the sulfonation of benzylethylpropylsilicol, obtained by the action of water on the corresponding chloride (Part II), and also (Part IV) by sulfonation of benzylethylpropylsilicyl oxide (R$_1$.R$_2$.R$_3$.Si)$_2$O. Kipping then conclusively showed by numerous analyses of the *l*-methylamine salt, that the sulfonic acid was a derivative of the oxide and not of the silicol. Attempts to resolve this acid by fractional crystallization of the *l*-menthylamine, *d*-bornylamine, cinchonidine, cinchonidine hydrogen, and strychnine salts were unsuccessful, but with *d*-methylhydrindamine resolution was accomplished, although much care was needed in interpreting the results owing to the low specific rotation of the *d*- and *l*-sulfonic acids. Thus on crystallizing the *l*-methylhydrindamine salt of the *dl* acid sparingly and readily soluble fractions, differing widely in m.p. but not in specific rotation, were obtained (Part II). Expulsion of the volatile base and conversion to the *l*-menthylamine salts gave products which did not differ appreciably in either m.p. or specific rotation. By suitable

1172

alternate use of the volatile *l*- and *d*-methylhydrindamines by methods which are obvious and need not be described in detail, it was conclusively proved that resolution had occurred, the *d*A*d*B, *l*A*l*B, *d*A*l*B, and *l*A*d*B (where A and B represent acid and base), salts being very carefully compared. Finally, by removal of the volatile bases two sodium salts of specific rotation +5·8° and −5·9° were obtained (Part VI).

It is interesting to speculate as to whether, had it not been for the unexpected elimination of the phenyl group during the sulfonation of phenylbenzylethylpropylsilicane, Kipping would ever have studied the sulfonation of an asymmetric silicol or oxide. Had he not done so the negative results obtained with two sulfonated silicanes suggest that success might never have been achieved. Still more remarkable is the coincidence that the only bases which were found capable of resolving the sulfonated silicyl oxides were the *d*- and *l*-methylhydrindamines which he had himself prepared for the first time in the course of earlier work and submitted to a most exhaustive examination.

A year or two later, in collaboration with B. D. W. Luff, he carried out a successful resolution of the disulfonic acid of *dl*-benzylethylisobutylsilicyloxide, also by the aid of the *d*- and *l*-methylhydrindamines, thus amplifying and confirming his earlier results. In this case the specific rotations of the sodium salts were larger, +10·4° and −10·5°.

Several years later Kipping prepared *dl*-dibenzyldiethyldipropyl-silicoethane and obtained brucine and *l*-menthylamine salts of the disulfonic acid. Separation of the racemic and meso forms of the acid or the resolution of the first-named was not effected, owing to lack of material (Part XXIV). With reference to this hydrocarbon and the corresponding diphenyl compound, Kipping writes: "Although their molecules contain linked silicon atoms both silico-hydrocarbons are attacked only very slowly if at all by boiling aqueous alkalis, and even when they are warmed with sodium methoxide in methyl alcohol or acetone no rapid evolution of hydrogen is observed. The grouping →Si-Si← is not necessarily unstable to alkalis, and whether the silicon atoms become separated or not is determined by the nature of the atoms or groups with which they are combined." The behavior of the →Si-Si← link to alkali is also mentioned.

During the purification of benzylethylsilicon dichloride which was so important an intermediate compound in much of his work, Kipping isolated dibenzylethylsilicylchloride (PhCH₂)₂SiEt.Cl. This was converted to dibenzylethylpropylsilicane and sulfonated, using chlorosulfonic acid in chloroform (Part XII). After separation of the mono- and disulfonic acids by means of their strychnine or *l*-menthylamine salts, the monosulfonic acid was successfully resolved by brucine but by no other base although several were employed.

Shortly afterwards Kipping and T. A. Smith prepared the tin analog of the silicane, dibenzylethylpropylstannane (PhCH₂)₂-Sn.Et.Pr, but the sulfonation of this and of dibenzyldiethylstannane was impossible owing to the elimination of both the benzyl groups by the acid.

About this time Kipping returned to the study of a similar problem on which Caven (*T*. 1902, **81**, 1362) had already carried out experiments in his laboratories—the stereochemistry of asymmetrical derivatives of phosphoric acid. Caven had been unable to resolve compounds of the type O=P⟨NHR, NHR′, OH⟩. Kipping and Luff prepared phenyl *p*-tolyl hydrogen phosphate OP(OPh)(OC₇H₇).-OH and crystallized its salts with eight optically active bases without effecting resolution. Evidence that the acid was, in fact, a *dl*-compound was obtained by the separation of the *dl*-hydrindamide into two inactive compounds, the *dAd*B, *lAl*B and the *dAl*B, *lAd*B isomers. By crystallization of the *d*-hydrindamide and *l*-menthylamide two fractions differing in m.p. and specific rotation were obtained in each case, indicating a resolution of the *dl*-acid. Similar results were obtained by Kipping and Challenger with the *l*-menthylamide of phenyl-β-naphthyl hydrogen phosphate. In none of the cases was it possible to remove the optically active -NHR group by hydrolysis so as to obtain the corresponding acids. This stability appears to be characteristic of amides and substituted amides of this type.

1174

Over thirty years later Davies and Mann (*J. Chem. Soc.* 1944, p. 276) pointed out that these and similar experiments aiming at the isolation of the optically active acids were foredoomed to failure owing to resonance.

When Meisenheimer and Lichtenstadt (*Ber. dtsch. Chem. Ges.* 1911, **44**, 356) announced the resolution of methylethylphenylphosphine oxide Kipping published a second and final paper on this subject.

Some consideration must now be given to the work on the condensation and dehydration products of the dibenzyl- and diphenylsilicanediols $R_2Si(OH)_2$. Much of this was carried out with Robison, who was first a student and later a junior colleague of Kipping.

These investigations do not lend themselves to detailed summary as they were mostly concerned with the careful examination and final separation of mixtures of condensation products, a study of their reactions, in some cases their interconversion and the determination of their molecular weight. The work was laborious and involved much detailed study of closely related substances and the manipulation of intractable oils, many of which were finally induced to crystallize. Kipping realized from the beginning (see Part X) that the various so-called silicones, e.g., Et_2SiO, Ph_2SiO and Ph.Et.SiO, were associated and not simple molecules; this was in fact stated by Dilthey in the case of the diphenyl derivative in 1905. In his first paper with Robison (Part V) Kipping studied the loss of water from dibenzylsilicanediol $(PhCH_2)_2Si(OH)_2$, and in Parts XVIII and XX established that under various conditions the diol yield trianhydrotrisdibenzylsilicane diol

$$O \underset{\diagdown SiR_2-O \diagup}{\overset{\diagup SiR_2-O \diagdown}{<}} SiR_2,$$ dianhydrotrisdibenzylsilicane diol $HOSiR_2-$

$O-SiR_2-O-SiR_2.OH$ and anhydrobisdibenzylsilicane diol $HOSiR_2-O-SiR_2OH$ where $R=CH_2C_6H_5$. Heat or alcoholic hydrogen chloride, acetyl chloride or alkali were employed as condensing agents.

During this period a similar and even more extensive study of the condensation products of diphenylsilicanediol was carried out, and in three papers, Parts XVI, XVII, and XXI, the existence of five crystalline condensation products was established, namely, HO.SiPh$_2$—O—SiPh$_2$.OH, HO.SiPh$_2$—O—SiPh$_2$—O—SiPh$_2$—OH, HO.SiPh$_2$—O—SiPh$_2$—O—SiPh$_2$—O—SiPh$_2$.OH

$$Ph_2Si\underset{\diagdown O—SiPh_2}{\overset{\diagup O—SiPh_2}{}}\hspace{-4pt}\diagdown\hspace{-4pt}\diagup O \text{ and } O\underset{\diagdown SiPh_2—O—SiPh_2}{\overset{\diagup SiPh_2—O—SiPh_2}{}}\hspace{-4pt}\diagdown\hspace{-4pt}\diagup O$$

In the case of four of these products crystallographic measurements were carried out.

When dichlorosilicanes of the type RR′SiCl$_2$ are decomposed with cold aqueous ammonia the corresponding diols, e.g., benzyl-ethylsilicanediol and phenylethylsilicanediol RR′Si(OH)$_2$, are obtained (Part XIX), and from the second of these the crystalline condensation product HO.SiPhEt.O.SiPhEt.OH can be isolated. Kipping refers to the ease with which these two diols yield oily condensation products, probably of the types already established in the case of diphenylsilicanediol, and adds "as the components of these mixtures have doubtless much lower melting-points than the corresponding derivatives of diphenylsilicanediol they cannot be isolated by the methods which were found to be of service in the case of the latter compounds." These substances containing alkyl groups foreshadowed the numerous polymers derived from Alkyl$_2$Si(OH)$_2$ which have since found such important technical applications. So far as can be seen from Kipping's papers he found no evidence for the existence of the simple silicones R$_2$SiO.

Only by a careful study of the original papers is it possible to realize the complicated relations existing between these various condensation products and the experimental skill and patience required for their separation from still more complex substances.

With his student Meads he also examined the condensation products obtained by the hydrolysis of phenyltrichlorosilicanes which are derived from four, five, six, or more molecules of PhSi(OH)$_3$. Here, and in many of his papers, he drew attention to the possible analogy between the structure of these compounds and that of the silicates, and between HO.Sn(C$_7$H$_7$)$_2$.O.Sn.-(C$_7$H$_7$)$_2$—O—Sn(C$_7$H$_7$)$_2$—OH and the polymeric stannic acids. He also found that (C$_7$H$_7$)$_3$SnOH is strongly associated in benzene solution (*J. Chem. Soc.* 1913, p. 2034).

1176

It is a pleasure to recall that the Dow Corning Corporation presented him in 1945 with a complete set of his fifty papers on "Organic derivatives of silicon" very clearly typed on strong paper and bound in boards made from a "silicone" polymer. These three volumes he presented to the Royal Society and they have been of great help to the writer in preparing this memoir.

No one who worked in the Nottingham laboratories between 1907 and 1910 will have forgotten the riddle of the constitution of the yellowish-white, amorphous, insoluble organic substances which are produced as by-products when any Grignard compound reacts with silicon tetrachloride. When all organosilicon halides are removed from the mass of magnesium salts with ether and these salts are dissolved in water, these compounds remain. Their most striking property is the rapid effervescence of hydrogen which takes place on addition of potassium hydroxide. Kipping never published a full account of these substances although he worked on them from time to time. It soon became clear that these compounds contained $\rightarrow$Si-Si$\leftarrow$ links. The evolution of hydrogen would seem to be analogous to that observed when silicoethane Si_2H_6, silicooxalic acid $H_2Si_2O_4$, silicomesoxalic acid and similar compounds are treated with alkali. In the case of the ethyl compound, Martin and Kipping suggested the possible structure $C_2H_5Si(OH)_2.SiO_2H$. The formation of such compounds was particularly marked in the case of the cyclohexyl derivatives, volatile chlorides containing $\rightarrow$Si-Si$\leftarrow$ links being detected (Part XLII) and light thrown on their method of formation.

Several years later it was found that wet piperidine was a more satisfactory reagent for the fission of the $\rightarrow$Si-Si$\leftarrow$ link, and the hydrogen evolved—the "hydrogen number"—was frequently employed as evidence of structure although the reaction was not of universal application, a few compounds such as $Si_2(C_6H_5)_2$ and $Si_2(C_6H_5)_2(C_2H_5)_2(C_3H_7)_2$ being found to resist fission.

On the conclusion of his work on optically active silicon compounds and the condensation products of the diphenyl- and dibenzylsilicanediols, Kipping gave much attention to the reaction between sodium and organosilicon halides of the type R_2SiCl_2 and R_3SiCl. The original object was to obtain a simple unsaturated compound $R_2Si = SiR_2$, but this was never achieved. Diphenylsilicon dichloride, e.g., gave two crystalline compounds of the formula Si_4Ph_8, one of which in later work was shown to be octa-phenylcyclosilicotetrane $Ph_2Si \underset{SiPh_2}{\overset{SiPh_2}{<>}} SiPh_2$ whereas the consti-

tution of the other "is best represented by . . . $SiPh_2.SiPh_2.SiPh_2.-SiPh_2. . . .$"

This is much more reactive than the cyclic compound. It slowly changes on exposure to light and air and undergoes atmospheric oxidation in toluene at 100° C., it combines with iodine at ordinary temperature giving a diiodide and is readily attacked by ethylene dichloride and tetrachloroethane, giving products which after hydrolysis contain oxides, Ph_8Si_4O and $Ph_8Si_4O_2$, one of which is $\underset{Ph_2Si—SiPh_2}{\overset{Ph_2Si—SiPh_2}{|}} >O$. The structure of the dioxide and an isomeric dioxide are discussed in Parts XXV and XXVI.

In 1932 Kipping and Blackburn (Part XLVI) showed that nitration of tetraphenylsilicane yielded a small amount of a pure nitro compound which, on decomposition with bromine, gave m-bromonitrobenzene. The main product of nitration, however, was extremely ill-defined and with bromine yielded a mixture of m- and p-bromonitrobenzene approximately in the proportion of $2:1$. The occurrence of o-nitration was not established. The pure tetranitro compound was reduced to the corresponding amine, which was thoroughly examined.

Part L of "Organic derivatives of silicon" is noteworthy as marking the author's Jubilee and also because it emphasized his definite, although late, entry into the field of aromatic substitution. Had he undertaken work of this kind earlier most interesting results would no doubt have been forthcoming. The paper describes the nitration of phenyltriethyl-, diphenyldiethyl-, and triphenyl-ethylsilicanes $PhSiEt_3$, Ph_2SiEt_2 and Ph_3SiEt. A comparison of the bromonitrobenzenes obtained from the resulting crude products of nitration with those obtained from crude nitrated tetraphenyl-silicane showed that m-nitration diminishes and p-nitration increases as the phenyl groups are replaced by ethyl groups. "-$SiPh_3$, in fact, is more strongly *m*-orientating than -CCl₃, although rather less so than NO₂."

When more than two phenyl groups were present in the silicanes the nitration product was found to be mainly of a very ill-defined nature. Kipping thought it probable that *m*- and *p*-nitration might occur in the same molecule.

Selections from: *Obituary Notices of Fellows of The Royal Society,*
7, No. 19, 183 (1950).

FREDERICK CHALLENGER

·· 82 ··

Leo Hendrik Baekeland

1863-1944

LEO HENDRIK BAEKELAND lived a life that to chemists must seem nearly ideal—it was filled with accomplishments and satisfactions, a busy life that earned him much wealth and many honors. He was most happily married and his friends were an international legion.

Baekeland was, as his close associate L. V. Redman described him, "truly a great creative chemist." Yet being Continental-born, he was not driven by that compulsion which kept so many American leaders of his generation on the treadmill of their own ambitions. He took time to enjoy good living, books, music, sports, and hobbies. His life was therefore exceptionally well-rounded.

He was born in Ghent, Belgium, November 14, 1863. His parents, Karel and Rosalia (Merchie) Baekeland, were not prominent or wealthy people. But they were responsible, respected citizens of the ancient Flemish city and they gave their son ideals and principles which were the foundation of his own character.

The boy attended the public schools where from the first grade he was a brilliant pupil. Always at the head of his class, he displayed phenomenal intellectual capacity. While at high school, he took on extra night courses in chemistry, physics, mechanics, and economics, and on graduation day—he was sixteen, the youngest boy in the class—he carried off four medals and a government scholarship at the University of Ghent. In 1884, at twenty-one, he received his doctorate in the natural sciences, *maxima cum laude.*

At the University Baekeland studied chemistry under Edward Swartz, formerly assistant to Kekulé, discoverer of the benzene ring. Professor Swartz, an inspiring teacher, made this precocious student his laboratory assistant, and on the side, Baekeland earned more money by private tutoring. He was, by this time, supporting himself without help from his father. Thus at an early age he exhibited some of his marked characteristics: a thrifty sense of money values, the ability to write and speak effectively, and his independent spirit.

In 1887 he was named by the government professor of chem-

1183

istry and physics at the Higher Normal School at Bruges. The following year he was back in his native city as assistant professor of chemistry at the University. In 1889 he was promoted to associate professor. While at Bruges he won a signal honor. In competition with the graduates of the four Belgian universities, he won the title of Laureate in Chemistry, a gold medal, and a three-year traveling fellowship.

Baekeland had not the least intention of spending three years in the laboratories of great-name chemists at various universities. He knew he was well grounded in chemistry. His ambition was to apply his knowledge practically and profitably. Besides, he was very much in love with Celine Swartz, the pretty daughter of his old professor.

Accordingly he postponed his fellowship until he could use it to finance a prolonged honeymoon trip combined with a chemical scouting expedition. He stayed at Ghent, teaching, and laid siege to the charming young lady. They were married August 8, 1889.

Leo and Celine Baekeland started their honeymoon by visiting French and British universities. We can guess the nature of his inspection of their faculties and laboratory facilities from the point of view he expressed in an address years later:

> My real chemical education began only after I left the university and was confronted with the big problems and grave responsibilities of practical life, and this education I received mainly in the United States. I hope to remain, until I die, a post-graduate student in that greater school of practical life which has no fixed curriculum and where no academic degrees are conferred, but where wrong, petty theories are quickly cured by hard knocks.

All this lay in the future. But even at that time his interest was focused on workaday chemical problems. We can imagine his astonished amusement when at Oxford he was told that "no gentleman works with his hands, but we have a fine collection of books on chemistry."

Nowhere did he find what he was seeking. At Edinburgh he was almost persuaded. There he met that amazing teacher, Crum Brown, surrounded by eager students working in fine laboratories.

1184

But there were no facilities for testing the results of applied research, and he learned that such mundane matters were considered quite undignified. Still seeking an academic niche in which to pursue his practical bent, he and his bride sailed for America.

In New York he found in Professor Charles L. Chandler, a chemist who cherished science for its services to mankind. Also at Columbia University there were both encouragement and opportunities for the kind of chemistry he dreamed of practicing. But a youthful hobby unexpectedly reshaped his entire career.

Since boyhood he had been a keen amateur photographer. Naturally he was interested in the chemistry of photography, and back in 1887 had been granted Belgian Patent No. 78,957, his first of many, for the invention of an automatic self-developing dry plate. A successful manufacturer, Dr. Van Monkhaven of Ghent, bought this patent—it did not prove commercially feasible—and he encouraged young Baekeland to continue working in the chemistry of photography. At a New York Camera Club meeting Baekeland met Richard A. Anthony of E. & H. T. Anthony & Co., later Ansco. Anthony promptly offered a job to this young chemist whose photographic background made him about as rare as a Chinese mandarin on Fifth Avenue. The stunning salary offered the prospective chief (and only) chemist of the Anthony firm clinched the matter. Baekeland accepted the first and only job he ever held.

Two years later, in 1891, ambition and independence spurred him to open his own consulting laboratory where he would be free to develop the chemical ideas that teemed in his virile brain. Clients beat a path to his door. As he learned while laid up several months by a serious illness, he was too successful as a consultant. Gravely appraising his situation, he resolved to simplify his consulting activities and concentrate his own researches upon the one most promising project.

The fruits of this resolution were Velox, the photographic paper that could be printed by artificial light, and the Nepera Chemical Company, organized with the financial aid of his friend, Leonard Jacobi of Yonkers, New York, to manufacture and market this revolutionary photographic specialty. Now it was that he felt those "hard knocks" which he was later to praise so warmly as the best teachers in the school of experience. This new venture was

1185

launched in the financial gale of the panic of 1897. He had the usual troubles in manufacturing his new product on an industrial scale. Most difficult were the least expected problems of sales. He first approached commercial photographers, the largest concentrated market, and here he met that stubborn resistance to innovations in established processes inborn in many businessmen. So he turned to the amateurs and found them more venturesome, in fact, quite keen to find a way of indulging their hobby in the evening hours. By 1899, after a hard struggle, Nepera's annual report showed black figures, and the sales of Velox mounted rapidly.

George Eastman's Kodak sales were also zooming, thanks to his introduction of the roll film. Velox fitted perfectly into Eastman's plans to make photography a great popular hobby, and he wrote that he was interested in buying. Baekeland did not reply for three days—it would not do to appear anxious—and then he answered that he might sell—for a price—and that he would be in Rochester a week from the following Tuesday.

But for what price? The question gnawed at his brain day and night. All the way up on the New York Central sleeper he lay awake, wondering what the aggressive and reputedly hard-boiled Eastman would pay. Not till the train reached Rochester did he come to a conclusion. He would ask $50,000; he would not accept less than $25,000.

During breakfast at the Hotel Seneca and driving out to the Kodak offices he rehearsed questions and answers for the coming interview. He was shown immediately into George Eastman's office and greeted cordially.

"Dr. Baekeland, I am delighted to meet you. You have a perfectly wonderful thing in that Velox paper of yours—wonderful, full of possibilities. I have the greatest admiration for your accomplishment. Won't you be seated?"

Baekeland sank weakly into a chair. None of his carefully planned speeches fitted this opening.

"Dr. Baekeland, will you take a million dollars for Velox?"

It was fortunate, as Baekeland told it to me, that he was seated, else he would have sunk through the floor.

His partner, Jacobi, went to California to live, and Leo Baekeland also retired, but to a little laboratory he fitted out on the grounds of his home in Yonkers. Electrochemistry was in the air, a new and industrially enticing field, so at thirty-six Baekeland went back to school, the Technische Hochschule at Charlottenburg, near Berlin.

He stayed there only one winter semester, and apparently he came to see the sights and enjoy the opera and theater of the German capital quite as much as to profit by the professional opportunities. At least, this was the first impression he made upon a hard-working American fellow student. But young Charles Herty soon learned that, for all his casual manner, this big grasshopper in that hill of busy ants had a profound knowledge of chemistry and amazing chemical abilities. Nothing escaped his quick intelligence in the lecture room; in the laboratory he managed, without seeming effort, to do vast amounts of first-class work.

Upon his return Baekeland was called upon by Elon H. Hooker to iron out a difficulty that prevented continuous operation of the Townsend electrolytic cells installed at the new-built plant of the Hooker Electrochemical Company to produce caustic soda and chlorine. The diaphragms, made of asbestos paper, were short-lived. Baekeland corrected this by using asbestos cloth impregnated with a mixture of iron oxide, asbestos fiber, and gummy iron hydroxide. At this time he was also much interested in air conditioning, food preservation, and various electrical control instruments.

Soon, however, he became absorbed in getting a superior synthetic shellac from the well-known, but exceedingly refractory, reactions between phenol and formaldehyde. Again his approach was entirely realistic. He knew that we were importing between 40 and 65 million pounds of shellac each year from India. He realized the advantages and drawbacks of this raw material of the best varnishes. He knew that since 1871, when the great Adolf von Baeyer first investigated the reactions between phenol and various aldehydes, many chemists had gummed up their apparatus with the hard, tarlike, infusible, insoluble substances produced by these reactions and had consigned them to the laboratory slop jar. In fact, his work began with a literature search during which he painstakingly repeated all the experiments of his forerunners. Then he tried all sorts of solvents upon each of the unpromising gunks resulting from these reactions. He learned what would not work; there was no hint as to what would. But he was not discouraged.

He began again and in place of formaldehyde he tried many other aldehydes. All reacted with phenol more or less violently and he got some suggestive variations. He began adding different quantities of various acids and alkalies. The former kept his messy products soft. The bases rendered them harder and reduced foaming during the reaction so that the product he obtained was less like a hard, dirty sponge. But he found nothing even close to the shellac he sought.

Suddenly, one day, he thought that if these condensation products of his were so damnably tough and unreactive, why not make a virtue of this vice? Surely there were uses for such a chemically stubborn substance. He quit trying to make a shellac substitute and started to hunt for a resin which could be molded permanently into definite shapes.

With this fresh objective he reversed his former methods. Instead of trying to hold down the reactions he stepped them up by every chemical and physical means. He tried various chemical accelerators. Instead of cooling, he applied heat. He combined heat with pressure; pumped air into an autoclave and raised the temperature to 200°C. Instead of the usual tarry mass he obtained a clear liquid that promptly solidified. He turned the autoclave over and out plopped a clear, hard hemisphere, its surface engraved with a perfect reproduction of the seams and boltheads that fastened the retort together. He examined the new material, eagerly, critically. It looked like amber, but was much harder. He could not dissolve it. He cut it with a knife, and so surmised it could be machined. It did not change its shape when heated or pressed. It did not absorb water, nor did it conduct electricity.

For two years longer the inventor of Bakelite worked with this new resinlike material. He perfected a two-stage production process and produced three distinct types for different purposes, one of them as a shellac substitute. He learned how to use this unusual substance; molding it, casting it, machining it, testing it to uncover its limitations and find its possibilities. He took out over 400 patents, covering every stage and variation of its production and many of its broader applications. It was five years after he began these researches before he announced Bakelite to the world at a memorable meeting in the Chemists' Club, New York, on February 15, 1909.

As in the case of Velox, he exploited Bakelite himself. "At the beginning," he confessed, "I had the erroneous idea that almost anyone would be able to make the new material . . . that it would simplify matters if I issued licenses on a royalty plan for the use of my patents without going myself into the trouble of any manufacturing work." It took him some time to prove that the safe and proper way was to manufacture a semifinished product, ready for use in its final applications.

Thus Dr. Baekeland not only opened up an entirely new field in synthetic plastics, but his General Bakelite Company created the pattern upon which the new industry was to function. As in the case of most successful patents, there were infringement suits, which Baekeland always won, and in 1922 he combined with two of his litigation rivals, the Condensite Company and Redmanol Chemical Products Company, into the Bakelite Corporation, which five years before his death, became a unit of the Union Carbide & Carbon Corporation.

After the earlier merger, which brought him several former competitors who became valued associates, he devoted less and less time to the details of what had become Big Business. He spent more and more time on his estate in Florida, which ironically had been owned by that archenemy of modern science, William Jennings Bryan. There he grew exotic tropical plants and with his neighbor, Dr. David Fairchild, the botanical explorer, introduced several new fruits and flowers. His first hobby was automobiling. He owned one of the first cars, and in 1907 took his family motoring through Europe, a trip that furnished him material for a humorous travel book. In later years, he became an ardent yachtsman, sailing from the Hudson River to Miami and back, and exploring the little known islands of the Caribbean in his auxilliary yacht, the *Ion*.

In the midst of so many activities Baekeland was a prolific contributor to scientific and technical journals—52 papers published between 1903 and 1940—and he was constantly called upon as a public speaker. Though he never quite lost his Flemish accent, his use of English was correct and dexterous, and some of his addresses are masterpieces of scientific exposition. He also found time to take an active part in professional societies, and he was chosen for important posts: president of the American Chemical Society, the American Institute of Chemical Engineers, the American Electrochemical Society, and the Chemists' Club. He was honorary professor of chemical engineering at Columbia University for many years, and this was no empty title.

He carried his many honors lightly, which was fortunate, for they would have overwhelmed a less sturdily modest man: honorary degrees from Brussels, Edinburgh, Pittsburgh, and Columbia, and the following medals: Nichols, 1909; John Scott, 1910; Willard Gibbs, 1913; Chandlar, 1914; Perkin, 1916; Messel, 1938; Franklin, 1940. His native country bestowed upon him two orders, the Crown of Belgium and Leopold of Belgium, and from France, the Legion of Honor.

NOTES AND REFERENCES

Much of Baekeland's life work is ably recorded in his own papers and addresses, particularly his Perkin Medal acceptance (*Chem. Met. Eng.*, Feb. 1, 1916, p. 148) and there are a number of excellent biographical sketches, the most complete being H. V. Potter, *Chem. & Ind.*, Aug. 4 and 18, 1945, pp. 242, 251; but also Jas. Kendall, *Ibid.*, Jan. 29, 1949, p. 69; *Chem. Met. Eng.*, 40, 140 (1924); *Ind. Eng. Chem.*, 20, 1274 (1928); A. D. McFadyen, *Chem. Ind.*, 46, 614 (1940).

For a lively account of the man and his work, see Maurice Holland, "Industrial Explorers," New York, Harper & Bros., 1928, pp. 92–112; see also *J. Frank. Inst.*, 230, 159 (1940); "Who Was Who," II, 36. Obits: *Chem. & Ind.*, Apr. 1, 1944, p. 134; *Nature*, Mar. 25, 1944, p. 369; and *N.Y. Times*, Feb. 24, 1944.

WILLIAMS HAYNES

·· 83 ··

Arthur Dehon Little

1863-1935

ARTHUR D. LITTLE was an outstanding leader among American consulting chemists during the first third of the present century. Because of arresting articles he wrote for the *Atlantic Monthly* and other magazines and several of his addresses which were reprinted and widely read, he was by far the best known to the general public of any of his contemporaries. He therefore occupied a position of great influence during an exciting, crucial period in the history of chemistry and chemical industry in the United States.

These were times of revolutionary change. No one recognized this more clearly than he; no one has so vividly pictured the great transformations of his day.

"When I opened a laboratory in Boston," he wrote in one of his best essays, *The Handwriting on the Wall*, "the street cars were drawn by horses, and I remember the clang of the first electric cars on Boylston Street and the consternation they caused among their equine competitors. From my window on Beacon Street 2000 bicycles an hour could be counted, where now automobiles pass. I have seen the fishtail burner supplanted by the Welsbach mantle, and the incandescent electric lamp develop from carbon to tungsten filaments and so to the white light of argon-filled bulbs. I remember the thrill when I first saw an airplane sweep at dusk across the disc of the rising full moon and soar to invisibility above."

In this delightful style he itemized the marvels he had witnessed—the phonograph; wireless telegraphy and the radio; x-rays; the rare gases found in the atmosphere and nitrogen snatched from the air; electrochemistry; catalysts and colloids—"all these great developments, so far-reaching in their influence upon industry, our mental outlook, and our entire social structure, have taken place within the easy recollection of a man still on the job."

Dr. Little was not content to paint pretty word pictures of the changing world in which he lived and worked. It is seldom given to a man to comprehend the causes and implications of stirring

1193

contemporary events, and the more thrilling these events are, the greater are the chances that he will misinterpret them. The years during which Arthur D. Little was a chemical consultant were packed with many startling chemical developments. He was sensitive and imaginative and he responded acutely to these stimulants.

His insight and his foresight were both extraordinary. Living in the very eye of this tornado of chemical progress, he correctly identified new trends that were to have profound effects upon chemical science and technology, upon research and education, upon chemical production and consumption. He also greatly strengthened, and in a great measure directed, fresh influences to which we owe much chemical advance in both the scientific and commerical areas. He was at once prophet and promoter of chemical progress.

This altogether remarkable chemist was a rock-ribbed New Englander; a Bostonian, a very proper Bostonian. He was born within the walls of Fort Independence, one of the Revolutionary defenses of Boston Harbor, on December 15, 1863, the oldest of four sons of Thomas Jones and Amelia (Hixson) Little. His father, an artillery captain in the Civil War, had been severely wounded and ordered to this sinecure command for his recovery. He was the direct descendant of George Little who settled in Newbury, Massachusetts, about 1640.

When Arthur Little was quite young the family moved to Portland, Maine, and he received his earliest education in the public schools of that city. Later he attended the Berkley School in New York City. Young Arthur never dreamed of being a railway conductor or a fireman or even the ringmaster of a circus; when twelve years old he determined to be a chemist. Beguiled by a schoolmate's promise to show him some great experiments, he invested all his wealth, ten cents, in a piece of glass tubing, a bit of zinc, and five cents' worth of sulfuric acid. That afternoon the boys rigged up a hydrogen generator. It promptly blew up, luckily without damaging results, but he had witnessed the marvel of metal bubbling in acid and was completely converted to chemistry. No doubt, the noisy climax of this first experiment was a baptism never to be forgotten. A year later he had his own laboratory.

His absorption in chemistry did not prevent him from being a regular contributor to the school paper. It was apparently his chief extracurricular activity. At the Massachusetts Institute of Technology he became freshman editor, and eventually editor-in-chief, of *The Tech,* the college newspaper, and later, under his inspiration and guidance, the *Technology Review* became one of the best of the collegiate alumni journals.

Thus was the twig bent. Throughout his life, chemistry and literature were to be the mainsprings of Arthur D. Little's career.

Between 1881 and 1884 he was an undergraduate majoring in chemistry at M.I.T. He left before graduation to take a summer course in papermaking at Amherst and then became a chemist, later superintendent, of the Richmond Paper Company whose little 10-ton plant at Rumford, Rhode Island, was the first sulfite mill in America.

From this first job in the first American sulfite papermill, Little's chemical career was studded with pioneering accomplishments. The sulfite wood pulp process was theoretically right enough, but as installed at the Richmond mill it was all wrong in its engineering. It fell to the youthful superintendent to revise the apparatus and correct the layout--the classic task of "ironing the kinks out of a new process." He did so, and incidentally devised the "Little Digester," the subject of his first patent. This assignment accomplished, he was sent to New Bern, North Carolina, to install the sulfite process in another mill, and his place at Rumford was filled by Roger B. Griffin. The following year, 1886, these two aspiring young chemists formed the consulting firm of Griffin & Little.

They opened an office, eight by twelve feet, with an adjoining laboratory about twice as large, on the top floor of an antique building on Milk Street in Boston. Years later the distinguished Dr. Little used to speculate sadly upon how many clients refused to climb six stories when the decrepit elevator's dingy door bore the sign "Out of Order." In those days the loss of a single client was a catastrophe. Although the consulting chemist was not highly esteemed and was very poorly paid, nevertheless this unpromising profession was definitely overcrowded in Boston. The new firm had six hungry competitors. Each was anxious to analyze a sugar sample for seventy-five cents and delighted to make a sanitary report on water for five dollars.

Somehow the firm of Griffin & Little managed to scrabble along, as an old New Englander would say, and each year their income grew a little and their reputation a great deal. They did every routine analysis they could corral, but it was a few papermill clients who kept them from bankruptcy. Naturally they specialized in this field, and together they wrote "The Chemistry of Paper Making," for years the authorative text on this subject. Gradually their practice turned more to engineering problems, to plant construction, to expert technical appraisals of processes and products. Twice they moved into bigger, better quarters. They built up a small staff of carefully chosen specialists. They even bought out a couple of their competitors. Then, in 1893, this successful partnership ended in a tragedy, a laboratory explosion in which Roger Griffin was killed.

Shocked as he was by his friend's death and crippled by the loss of an able partner to share the growing burdens of their expanding practice, Little decided to carry on alone. He did so for seven years till 1900. Then he formed a second partnership with Dr. William H. Walker, professor of chemical engineering at M.I.T. The firm of Little & Walker, Consulting Chemists and Engineers, continued for five years. Then the junior partner found the demands of business infringing so seriously upon his academic duties that he withdrew. In 1909, Arthur D. Little, Inc., Chemists, Engineers, and Managers, was organized, A precarious consulting practice had evolved into a great research institution.

Sometimes, in reviewing Arthur D. Little's many accomplishments, it is overlooked that he was the originator of this type of organization. The staff of experts he gathered together; the splendid building he built on Memorial Drive in Cambridge to house their activities; the multiplicity of services, ranging from pure science to market survey, which he and his associates offered to industry were bold innovations that have served as models for scores of similar institutions here and in foreign countries. All these were the natural evolution of his experience, a practical expression of ideals of research.

One graphic example will illustrate this. In the early days, when routine analyses were bread-and-butter jobs, one of the first regular clients was the old house of D. & L. Slade, spice millers who guarded their reputation for quality by having samples of their purchases tested microscopically and chemically for purity. It was a worthwhile precaution. Their raw materials came from Java and Ceylon, from Arabia and Tibet, from many out-of-the-way places; since the days of the Venetian and Florentine merchants, the trade in spices had been infamous for its sophistications. This close association continued many years, and the Little staff became adept in recognizing the cleverest adulterations; they devised better methods for their ready identification, they set up standards, and then logically they were called upon to do similar work for other foods.

Dr. Little's first and lasting chemical interest was cellulose. Papermaking by a new process was his initial chemical enterprise and this was the chief activity of his early years. He was granted patents on waxed and waterproofed papers and did much good work on the utilization of wood wastes. During this same period, he was introducing the chrome tanning process of Schultz and contributing advances to the electrolytic alkali process, to alcohol fermentation, casein products, the production of chlorates and hypo-chlorites; all of these were for the most part chemical pioneering.

In 1889 the Count de Chardonnet displayed his artificial silk, made from cellulose nitrate, at the Paris Exposition, three years after Griffin & Little opened their laboratory. They immediately reproduced his experiments. From the first, Little became a rayon enthusiast and while it was still a stiff, brittle, highly flammable fiber, he foretold that it would some day replace silk and even rival King Cotton. Cross & Bevan had hardly worked out their new viscose process before he obtained the American rights to their patents. Between 1893 and 1896 he offered these patents to J. P. Morgan, Frank Vanderlip, and Bernard Baruch, as well as to the leaders of our textile and paper industries. None of these astute gentlemen leaped to grasp this splendid opportunity. It was 1900 before the viscose process was firmly established in the United States. Then Courtaulds, the famous English textile firm, which had energetically taken up the viscose process and became the world's largest maker of viscose rayon, bought two struggling experimental plants and organized the American Viscose Company.

All this time Little and his associates were eagerly experimenting with these new man-made fibers. The dangerous flammability of cellulose nitrate, which had inspired the discovery of viscose rayon, spurred other chemists to combine cellulose with other acids in the hope of getting a safer spinnable compound. Cellulose acetate had been reported in 1869, but it involved tricky reactions and high-cost reagents. The acetate fiber, although it had intriguing properties, was unanimously voted "commercially impractical." Little refused to accept this verdict. He could hardly have foreseen that twenty years in the future synthetic acetic anhydride would cut the price of this most costly ingredient by two thirds. However, he did sense the possibilities in fibers of different, distinctive characteristics. Thus he anticipated the blending of various synthetic and natural yarns which have given us a wealth of specialized fabrics from cobweblike sheers to noncrushable velvets.

Believing in cellulose acetate's future, Little continued these experiments over several years; by using, not cotton or filter paper, but the regenerated cellulose of the viscose process, he and his associates produced a number of marketable products. A thickish, clear sheet, three-feet square, was sold in competition with highly flammable celluloid. In January, 1903, they made the first commercial textile fiber. Two small companies were organized to make these acetate products, but they were only fitfully successful. Soon, however, their facilities and the know-how of the Little group were to render great service in helping supply a nonflammable dope to tauten and coat the canvas wings of fighting airplanes.

World War I came unexpectedly as a climactic end of the old era and the bright prelude to the new Chemical Age. Only one who lived through those experiences could sense the chilling anxieties roused by the famine of coal-tar dyes and medicines, of nitrate and potash, or feel the desperate urgency bred by the quick, great need for TNT, for phosgene, for salvarsan, for many chemicals not then made in America, and also for undreamed-of tons of such old stand-bys as sulfuric acid, caustic soda, chlorine, and benzene. Dr. Little was in the middle of many wartime activities, and his brief article, "The Sinews of War," tells that dramatic story well. His own war work was chiefly with the new Chemical Warfare Service and the Signal Corps in the production of acetone, airplane dope, combat gases, gas-mask materials and smoke filters, flares, etc.

The war was a dramatic demonstration of two great lessons that Arthur D. Little had been teaching for years: (1) Chemicals are the key materials of our modern industrial civilization, and (2) research is the mainspring of our material progress and continued prosperity. The prophet of chemical progress was not now without honor in his own country. The promoter of chemical progress found before him a new world of opportunity.

In the postwar period Dr. Little continued to be a chemical pioneer. In his favorite field of cellulose chemistry he blazed a new path in the utilization of Southern pine in papermaking, thus opening the way to the great kraft paper and newsprint industries which have revolutionized the use of Southern timber resources and revitalized the economy of a half dozen states.

The vapor-phase cracking of petroleum evolved by Little and his organization was applied at Tiverton, Rhode Island. An experimental plant was built as a joint enterprise of the Barnsdall Corporation, the National Distillers Products Corporation, and the banking house of Blair & Company. Here were produced, on a commercial scale, high-test aviation gasoline, tertiary butyl-, isopropyl-, and other alcohols, and propylene and other unsaturated olefins. This operation was, in its technology and the products it produced, a forerunner of the petrochemical industry which has since loomed so large on the chemical horizon.

Arthur D. Little's many accomplishments won him merited honors: the Perkin Medal in 1931; honorary degrees from Pittsburgh, Manchester (England), Tufts, and Columbia. He was president of the American Chemical Society, 1912–14; the American Institute of Chemical Engineers, 1919; and the Society of Chemical Industry, 1928–29. This exceedingly rare "triple crown" was a fitting tribute alike to the man and the chemist.

Little was a handsome, clean-cut man with bushy eyebrows and ruddy complexion, slender and erect, of medium height, quick-moving with a brisk, heel-first step. His was a distinctive person-

1199

ality, a chemist who collected Chinese porcelains, a somewhat austere New Englander with a twinkling eye and winning smile, a gentleman to the core who never lost the common touch. He was a meticulous man—careful in his dress and in his choice of words, discriminating in his tastes for literature and music, food and drink, and highly selective in his few close friendships. The impression that he lastingly created was one of secure dignity and captivating charm.

In his perceptive sketch of this distinguished, delightful gentleman Maurice Holland wrote: "If Arthur D. Little did nothing except talk, or write an occasional paper, he would still be contributing his share to the cause of scientific research."

That is true. His writings and speeches were potent influences in creating our new chemical epoch. In education he promoted the first chemical engineering courses based on unit processes. By precept and practice he raised the professional status of both chemists and engineers. He preached the gospel of research in practical terms by showing businessmen and bankers that a laboratory is as vital as an accounting room to the profitable life of an industrial company. He opened the eyes of thousands of Americans to the fact that their health, wealth, and safety depend vitally upon chemicals and that their future will be shaped by the results of continuing chemical progress. To read his essays and addresses, collected under the title of "The Handwriting on the Wall," is an illuminating and pleasurable experience. Here, too, he was meticulous. Often he labored a full day rewriting and polishing a single page. His speeches, so deftly delivered, were carefully written out and then carefully rehearsed.

He lived his active life fully to the end, for he died suddenly of a heart attack at his summer home at Northeast Harbor, Maine, August 1, 1935, aged seventy-one. His widow survived him only two months. He and Henrietta Rogers Anthony were married January 22, 1901, and lived a life of peculiarly close and happy companionship. They had no children, but his nephew, Royal Little, grew up in their home. He recalls vividly the evenings they all spent together, reading aloud, listening to music, and above all, hearing Dr. Little review his working day in a manner as fascinating as the best of novels.

1200

The majority stock of Arthur D. Little, Inc., was left to be administered by trustees, the profits to go to M.I.T., thus avoiding the intrusion of outside interests or a struggle among his old associates for control of the corporation. Later the Little staff purchased the estate stock and pooled their own shares in a retirement trust, a harmonious and profitable method of carrying on the aims and ideals of the founder.

NOTES AND REFERENCES

Dr. Little's book, "The Handwriting on the Wall," Boston, 1928, is full of biographical facts and reveals much about the man himself. As often, the Perkin Medal presentation address, F. D. Keyes, *Ind. Eng. Chem.*, 23, 236 (1931), contains excellent material as do several biographical sketches: *Ibid.*, 20, 1395 (1928); Maurice Holland, *Industrial Explorers*, New York, 1928, pp. 149–69; Earl P. Stevenson, *Newcomen Soc. Address*, Boston, May 5, 1953; *Proc. Am. Acad. Arts & Sci.*, LXXI, 1937; "Who Was Who," I, 735; *Am. Bict. Biog.*, XXI, 500.

For Little's part in American rayon development, Williams Haynes, "Cellulose: The Chemical That Grows," New York, Doubleday, 1953, pp. 125–47; for Arthur D. Little, Inc., *Ibid., American Chemical Industry*, 6 vols., New York, Van Nostrand, 1945–54, VI, 249; for genealogy, C. T. Little, "Descendants of George Little," Boston, 1888.

Obits: *Industrial Bull. of Arthur D. Little, Inc.*, Aug.-Sept. 1935; *Science*, Oct. 18, 1935; *Technology Rev.*, October 1935; *Boston Transcript*, Aug. 2, 1935; and N.Y. Times, Aug. 3, 1935.

WILLIAMS HAYNES

·· 84 ··

Walther Nernst

1864-1941

I ACCEPT with pleasure the invitation of the editors of this magazine to dedicate a few lines to the scientific personality of Dr. Walther Nernst, who died recently. For he was one of the most characteristic and most interesting scholars with whom I have been closely connected during my life. He did not miss any of the conferences on physics in Berlin, and his brief remarks gave evidence of a truly amazing scientific instinct combined both with a sovereign knowledge of an enormous volume of factual materials, which was always at his command, and with a rare mastery of the experimental methods and tricks in which he excelled. Although sometimes good-naturedly smiling at his childlike vanity and self-complacency, we all had for him not only a sincere admiration, but also a personal affection. So long as his egocentric weakness did not enter the picture, he exhibited an objectivity very rarely found, an infallible sense for the essential, and a genuine passion for knowledge of the deep interrelations of nature. But for such a passion his singularly creative productivity and his important influence on the scientific life of the first third of this century would not have been possible.

He ascended from Arrhenius, Ostwald, and van't Hoff, the last of a dynasty that based its investigations on thermodynamics, osmotic pressure, and ionic theory. Up to 1905 his work was essentially restricted to that range of ideas. His theoretical equipment was somewhat elementary, but he mastered it with a rare ingenuity. I refer, for instance, to the theory of electromotive powers in solutions of locally variable concentration, the theory of diminution of the solubility by adding a dissolved substance. During this period he invented the witty Null method of determining the dielectric constant of electrically conducting bodies by means of Wheatstone's bridge (alternating current, telephone as indicator, compensating capacity in comparison bridge branches).

This first productive period is largely concerned with improving the methodology and completing the exploration of a field the principles of which had already been known before Nernst. This work led him gradually to a general problem which is characterized by the question: Is it possible to compute from the known energy of the conditions of a system, the useful work which is to be gained by its transition from one state into another? Nernst realized that a theoretical determination of the transition work A from the energy-difference U by means of equations of thermodynamics alone is not possible. There could be inferred from thermodynamics that, at absolute zero, the temperature of the quantities A and U must be equal. But one could not derive A from U for any arbitrary temperatures, even if the energy-values or differences in U were known for all conditions. This computation was not possible until there was introduced, with regard to the reaction of these quantities under low temperatures, an assumption which appeared obvious because of its simplicity. This assumption is simply that A becomes temperature-independent under low temperatures. The introduction of this assumption as a hypothesis (third main principle of the theory of heat) is Nernst's greatest contribution to theoretical science. Planck found later a solution which is theoretically more satisfactory; namely, the entropy disappears at absolute zero temperature.

From the standpoint of the older ideas on heat, this third main principle required very strange reactions of bodies under low temperatures. To pass upon the correctness of this principle, the methods of calorimetry under low temperatures had to be greatly improved. The calorimetry of high temperatures also owes to Nernst considerable progress. Through all these investigations, as well as through many stimulating suggestions with which his untiring inventive genius supplied experimenters in his field, he promoted the research work of his generation most effectively. The beginnings of the quantum theory were assisted by the important results of those caloric investigations, and this especially before Bohr's theory of the atom made spectroscopy the most important experimental field. Nernst's standard work, "Theoretical Chemistry," offers, not only to the student but also to the scholar, an abundance of stimulating ideas; it is theoretically elementary, but clever, vivid, and full of intimations of manifold interrelations. It truly reflects his intellectual characteristics.

Nernst was not a one-sided scholar. His sound common sense

engaged successfully in all fields of practical life, and every conversation with him brought something interesting to light. What distinguished him from almost all his fellow countrymen was his remarkable freedom from prejudices. He was neither a nationalist nor a militarist. He judged things and people almost exclusively by their direct success, not by a social or ethical ideal. This was a consequence of his freedom from prejudices. At the same time he was interested in literature and had such a sense of humor as is very seldom found with men who carry so heavy a load of work. He was an original personality; I have never met any one who resembled him in any essential way.

BIOGRAPHICAL NOTE

Walter Nernst was born on June 25, 1864, in Briesen (West Prussia). He graduated from the gymnasium as *primus omnium* (1883) and passed his examination for the doctor's degree *summa cum laude* (1887). In between he had studied physics at several universities, and he continued to change the place of his subsequent research work until Göttingen captured him for a long period, from 1890 to 1905. Then he became the successor of Hans Landolt in Berlin's Second Chemical Institute which Nernst soon converted into a physicochemical institute and which he directed until 1922. For two years he presided over the Physikalisch-Technische Reichsanstalt, and from 1924 to 1933 he directed the institute of experimental physics at the University.

In 1893, a year after he was married, he published a textbook with the translated title: "Theoretical Chemistry from the Standpoint of Avogadro's Rule and Thermodynamics." This title characterizes not only the content of the book but also the main line of Nernst's lifework. The thermodynamics of chemical reactions, considered from the viewpoint developed by Avogadro, led Nernst to several new theoretical concepts. To prove them by experiments he constructed several ingenious practical devices.

In his theory of electrochemical processes, he considers the metallic electrodes as a reservoir of ions. They have a tendency for electrolytical dissolution which has typically different values for different metals. When these ions enter into the solution, they encounter, or they create, a pressure in the reverse direction. The example of gas behavior served here as well as it did in van't Hoff's theories of osmotic pressure. Nernst amplified these theories by stating the analog of "ideal solids" to the ideal gases.

Much wider was the range of his thermodynamic theorem. Definitions of the first and the second law of thermodynamics state that no *perpetuum mobile* of the first or second kind is possible. In analogy, Nernst expressed his theorem in the words: "It is not possible to build a caloric machine which will reduce the temperature of a substance to absolute zero."

Old rules, like that found by Trouton for the connection between boiling points and heats of vaporization, now appeared as simple consequences from Nernst's third law of thermodynamics.

From his electrochemical work Nernst derived new views of hydrogen in metallic compounds. When lithium hydride is electolyzed in molten condition, hydrogen appears at the anode, like a halogen.

Two of his technical inventions attracted much attention but did not become widely accepted. One was the Nernst lamp, a ceramic rod which was preheated by an auxiliary current to a temperature of about 2200° C. at which it becomes a highly effective converter of electrical energy into light. The other was an electronic piano in which the player regulated the source of electrical energy which excited the strings to vibration. Nernst had no musical inclinations or abilities—somewhat astonishing in view of the frequent connection between musical and mathematical genius.

GENERAL REFERENCES

Max Bodenstein, "Walther Nernst," *Ber. deut. chem. Ges.,* 75 A, 79 (1942).

From: *Scientific Monthly,* February 1942, p. 195, with the biographical note by Eduard Farber.

ALBERT EINSTEIN

·· 85 ··

Moses Gomberg

1866-1947

THE death of Moses Gomberg on February 12, 1947, brought to a close the career of a brilliant scientist who had won recognition as one of the world's leading authorities in organic chemistry. He was born on February 8, 1866, in the small town of Elizabetgrad, Russia, the son of George and Marie Resnikoff Gomberg. From 1878 to 1884 he was a student in the Nicolau Gymnasium of his native town. In the latter year his father was accused of anti-Czarist activities and was forced to flee with his family, and his estate was confiscated. With help from friends they were able to go to Chicago where for a time hardship became their lot. Neither father nor son had a knowledge of English and they both worked in Chicago at whatever occupation they could find, and for a time at least in the stockyards. The son, however, with indomitable energy earned the means to complete his high school course and to enter the University of Michigan from which he was graduated in 1890 with the degree of Bachelor of Science. An assistantship enabled him to continue in graduate work, and two years later he received the degree of Master of Science. He took his doctorate in 1894 with a thesis on the reactions of caffeine, under Professor A. B. Prescott.

Even before his appointment as instructor in 1893, he was planning to study abroad and in order to earn the necessary funds, he spent his spare time in analyzing materials for his numerous clients. His versatility is shown by the fact that his work included the analysis of minerals, water, fats and oils, foods, patent medicines, and drugs. He was also employed frequently as an expert witness in toxicology cases, and he thoroughly enjoyed matching wits with the opposing lawyers. However, he was greatly disturbed by the necessity of doing this type of work because it interfered with the progress of his research, and he dropped it as soon as possible. Thereafter he refused steadfastly to accept consulting work of any kind.

A leave of absence from 1896 to 1897 permitted a year of study in Germany and he decided to spend two terms in Baeyer's laboratory in Munich. Thiele suggested a problem involving the preparation of isonitramino- and nitrosoisobutyric acid, and this work resulted in a 22 page paper in Liebig's *Annalen*.

The third term of the year was spent in Victor Meyer's laboratory in Heidelberg. In discussing the choice of a problem, Gomberg said that he wanted to prepare tetraphenylmethane. Meyer, as well as other chemists, had been interested in the synthesis of this compound and had tried various methods but without success. Consequently, Meyer suggested other more suitable problems but Gomberg was determined to go ahead, and his confidence was well deserved for he was successful in his attempt. His method consisted in oxidizing triphenylmethanehydrazobenzene to the corresponding azo compound and heating the latter to 110 to 120° C. However, the yield was very poor, only 2 to 5 per cent.

His next step, when he returned to the University of Michigan, was to investigate the preparation of the related hexaphenylethane in the hope of obtaining this completely phenylated hydrocarbon in greater yield. Accordingly, triphenylchloromethane in benzene was treated with sodium but without appreciable action. However, when molecular silver was used, a colorless compound precipitated, which was assumed to be hexaphenylethane. An elementary analysis gave low values for the percentage of both carbon and hydrogen. When further analyses gave the same result, it was concluded that the compound contained oxygen; and, after the silver had been shown to be free of oxide, it was suspected that oxygen of the air was oxidizing the initially formed hydrocarbon. By working in the absence of air, Gomberg obtained a hydrocarbon which was extremely unsaturated in its behavior. In benzene solution it absorbed chlorine, bromine, and iodine, and when exposed to air a stable peroxide was formed. In view of these remarkable properties, in his first paper (1900) on the hydrocarbon, Gomberg wrote, "The experimental evidence . . . forces me to the conclusion that we have to deal here with a free radical, triphenylmethyl, $(C_6H_5)_3C$. On this assumption alone do the results described above become intelligible and receive an adequate explanation." Following the publication of this paper, other chemists[1] immediately became interested in his hydrocarbon, and confirmed its striking properties. Moreover, it was shown that triphenylmethyl was but one of a large group of similar triarylmethyls.

1212

However, for almost ten years, the existence of free radicals was questioned. Although the chemical evidence in favor of the tri-valency of carbon was convincing, molecular weight determinations of the hydrocarbon indicated a value practically double that of the free radical. Consequently, a great deal of skepticism was shown, for there had been other somewhat similar cases involving radicals such as Gay-Lussac's cyanogen, Bunsen's cacodyl, and Frankland's and also Kolbe's alkyls. These had been described as free radicals but later were found to be dimolecular. It was assumed that Gom-berg's hydrocarbon was just another instance of history repeating itself, and the concept of free radicals was ignored.

The situation in the period of 1900 to 1905 was confused by the fact that the new hydrocarbon was not regarded as hexaphenyl-ethane because its properties were so different from what were expected. Furthermore, in 1902 Ullmann and Borsum had pre-pared a compound which was universally accepted as hexaphenyl-ethane until Chichibabin showed two years later that it was p-ben-zohydryltetraphenylmethane,

$$(C_6H_5)_3C-\langle\rangle-CH(C_6H_5)_2.$$

In the meantime, various quinonoid structures had been sug-gested, but none of them proved satisfactory in explaining the unique properties of the Gomberg hydrocarbon. As all attempts to prepare a different hydrocarbon with the structure of hexaphenyl-ethane failed, the majority of chemists began to look upon Gom-berg's compound as hexaphenylethane, and considered it to be un-stable, (i.e., reactive to iodine, oxygen, etc.) per se. Gomberg, how-ever, remained unshaken in his belief in the existence of triphenyl-methyl and time and again reiterated his faith in the concept of free radicals.

A study of other triarylmethyls hastened considerably the ac-ceptance of the idea of free radicals, and an early suggestion (Flürscheim, 1905) that colorless hexaphenylethane dissociates in solution into colored free radicals, $Ar_3C-CAr_3 \rightleftarrows 2Ar_3C$, was adopted. Under comparable conditions some radicals, like tri-phenylmethyl, remain only slightly unassociated, others are present in solution to a greater extent (20–80 per cent), while others like tri-p-biphenylmethyl (Schlenk) exist as free radicals even in the solid state.

1213

Later, Wieland showed that tetraphenylhydrazine dissociates to give a free radical with divalent nitrogen, and other cases of free radicals with abnormal valences were reported. It was evident that Gomberg had opened an entirely new field in chemistry which was of extreme importance. This was further emphasized when Paneth demonstrated the transitory existence of the radicals ethyl and methyl, and it was soon shown that such transitory radicals are intermediate products in certain chemical reactions.

Another phase of Gomberg's work was concerned with the development of the quinonoid theory. Solutions of triphenylmethyl have an orange-yellow color, and Schmidlin found that there is both a colorless and a colored form present. In order to account for the two forms, Gomberg assumed that one of them must be quinonoid. In 1901, Gomberg and other investigators obtained double salts of triphenylchloromethane which were intensely colored, and Kehrmann assigned a quinonoid structure to such compounds, e.g.,

$$(C_6H_5)_2C = \text{[quinonoid ring]} < \begin{matrix} H \\ Cl \end{matrix} \cdot FeCl_3.$$

Baeyer vigorously opposed this view and claimed that the color was due to salt formation and could be explained on the basis of his theory of halochromism. In considering this problem, Gomberg reasoned that if there was a quinonoid form of p,p',p''-tribromotriphenylchloromethane in solution in liquid sulfur dioxide, a bromine atom would become labile and a shift of chlorine and bromine might be expected. To test this idea, he dissolved p,p',p''-tribromotriphenylchloromethane in liquid sulfur dioxide, and, after a few days allowed the sulfur dioxide to evaporate slowly. The resulting product contained 85 per cent of p,p'-dibromo-p''-chlorotriphenylbromomethane,

$$(Br-\text{[ring]}-)_2C-\text{[ring]}-Br \longrightarrow$$

$$(Br-\text{[ring]}-)_2C=\text{[ring]}< \begin{matrix} Cl \\ Br \end{matrix} \rightleftharpoons$$

$$(Br-\text{[ring]}-)_2C-\text{[ring]}-Cl$$

1214

The shift of the chlorine atom and the bromine atom provided positive evidence in favor of the quinonoid theory. But in no case so far, had it been possible to isolate the two tautomeric forms of any triarylmethyl salt. However, Gomberg was able to isolate the benzenoid and the quinonoid form of p-hydroxytriphenylcarbinol in the crystalline state, thus helping to establish the quinonoid theory on a firm basis:

$$(C_6H_5)_2C\text{—}\langle\ \rangle\text{—OH} \longrightarrow (C_6H_5)_2C=\langle\ \rangle\underset{OH}{\overset{OH}{\big\langle}}$$

One of his last investigations was concerned with a study of the reducing action of the binary system $Mg + MgI_2$ on organic compounds in anhydrous ether and benzene. Gomberg postulated that the active reducing agent was magnesious iodide which was formed by interaction of the metal and its halide according to the following formulation: $Mg + MgI_2 \rightleftarrows 2MgI$. This hypothesis served to explain the reduction of C=O, C=N, N=N, and other unsaturated groups in compounds. By this new reducing agent aromatic ketones were reduced to pinacols in high yields through the intermediate formation of colored free radicals (analogs of sodium ketyls).

$$2Ar_2C=O \xrightarrow[MgI_2]{Mg} 2Ar_2C\text{—OMgI} \rightleftarrows \begin{array}{c} Ar_2C\text{—OMgI} \\ | \\ Ar_2C\text{—OMgI} \end{array}$$

Aromatic aldehydes, acids and their alkyl esters were found to be converted into benzoins. In the preparation of the Grignard reagent from triphenylmethyl bromide and magnesium Gomberg showed that the first step is the quantitative formation of triphenyl-methyl⇄hexaphenylethane. The Grignard reagent is produced in the second step by the reaction of the free radical with the mixture of magnesium and magnesium bromide,

$$2(C_6H_5)_3CBr \xrightarrow{Mg} 2(C_6H_5)_3C + MgBr_2 \xrightarrow{Mg} 2(C_{65})_3CMgBr$$
$$\big\updownarrow$$
$$(C_6H_5)_3C\text{—}C(C_6H_5)_3$$

The reaction is unique in that a Grignard reagent can be prepared from a hydrocarbon (hexaphenylethane).

1215

Other investigations included the first synthesis of unsymmetrical tetraphenylethane and one of the first syntheses of pentaphenylethane, the preparation of benzyl ethers of carbohydrates, the synthesis and study of certain dyes, a study of the $(ClO_4)x$ radical and the synthesis of biaryls by the diazo reaction (Gomberg reaction). However, an examination of his publications reveals that most of his life was devoted to the investigation of triarylmethyls and related compounds.

Professor Gomberg was a member of many learned societies: the American Philosophical Society; a fellow of the American Association for the Advancement of Science; the Franklin Institute; the National Academy of Sciences; the American Institute of Chemists; the Netherlands Chemical Society, of which he was an honorary member; and the American Chemical Society, of which he was president in 1931. His achievements were recognized by the award of various honors: he was the recipient of the Nichols Medal in 1914; of the Willard Gibbs Medal in 1925; and of the Chandler Medal in 1927. He received the degree of Doctor of Science from the University of Chicago in 1929, the same degree from the Brooklyn Polytechnic Institute in 1932, and the degree of Doctor of Laws from the University of Michigan in 1937. He would have been less than human had he not been pleased by these marks of distinction, but none of them ever changed the even tenor of his ways. All evidences of his attainments were received with modesty that was one of his characteristic traits. He never sought preferment, and all forms of academic advertising were alien to his soul.

During the First World War he joined the group of civilian chemists working on gas warfare under the direction of the Bureau of Mines, prior to the organization of the Chemical Warfare Service. His assignment was the preparation of mustard gas; and although this was abhorrent to his nature, he accepted it without hesitation. Ethylene chlorohydrin was the intermediate which was required, and the method which he developed was the first in this country for the commercial preparation of this important compound. This work was done in his laboratory in Ann Arbor. Later in 1918, he was commissioned as Major in the Ordnance Department, acting as an advisor in the manufacture of smokeless powder and high explosives. Except for the year of study in Germany, this

1216

was the only break in his teaching career which extended over a period of forty-three years.

He was chairman of the department of chemistry from 1927 to 1936 when he retired. He stressed the necessity of a thorough basic training in all branches of chemistry with a minimum of specialization. He believed that teaching on the university level was impossible without research, and in regard to Ph.D. candidates he felt that the emphasis should be placed on the training of the candidate and not on the issuance of a publication. He had strong convictions on such matters and was not adverse to expressing them, but he never spoke with harshness or with intent to hurt. In his contacts with students, he was sympathetic, gave generously of his time, and was always ready to offer friendly advice.

Gifted with a remarkable memory, he presented his lectures with the full use of a wealth of historical material and so vividly that they left an indelible imprint on his students. A great teacher and scholar, he inspired his students by his methods and ideals, and his colleagues by the vigor and clarity of his mind. To this greatness, he added an innate kindliness and unassuming modesty that endeared him to all.

He never married and lived quietly and happily with his younger sister.

He was a great scientist, a wise counselor, and a loyal friend whose memory will long remain a living force.

NOTES AND REFERENCES

[1] Among the chemists who participated in the discussion of the structure of the unusual hydrocarbon were Baeyer, Markownikov, Thiele, Flürscheim, Schmidlin, Werner, Hantzsch, and Wieland.

From: *J. Am. Chem. Soc., 69,* 2921 (1948).

C. S. SCHOEPFLE

W. E. BACHMANN

·· *86* ··

Herbert Henry Dow

1866-1930

HERBERT H. DOW'S associates in The Dow Chemical Company delighted to argue whether he was greatest as a chemist, a chemical engineer, or a businessman. At times their debates waxed hot. Such a separation of his capabilities was, of course, impossible and apt to become invidious, but this hearty partisanship among his colleagues was full of meaning.

Their endless arguments were pure hero worship, a sublimation of the affection and admiration Herbert Dow inspired in everyone who came in close contact with him. At the time of his death, one of the chemical trade papers truly called him "the idol of Midland, Michigan." The almost idolatrous esteem of this great man and his many-sided accomplishments was, and still is, his finest monument. It explains not only his continuing influence upon the company he founded, but also the niche he occupies in the annals of the American chemical industry.

Very specially Dr. Dow personified the epochal changes transpiring in the chemical field during the first quarter of the present century, the years of his active career as a chemical manufacturer. He was typical of the transformation of the individual proprietor into the corporation executive which happened quite generally throughout the chemical industry at this time. Simultaneously and in a fashion just as typical of the whole industry, The Dow Chemical Company grew from the modest producer of two simple chemicals, bleaching powder and bromine, into a gigantic, fully integrated mass producer of over 500 chemicals, ranging from chlorine and caustic soda to bromindigo and the polymers of dichlorodiethylformal and alkali polysulfides. Historically, he was a perfect personal exemplar of the exciting, revolutionary period that saw the birth of the Chemical Age of our American economy.

Herbert Henry Dow was born February 26, 1866, at Belleville, Ontario. His father, Joseph Dow, a real Yankee tinkerer of the old school, had been sent to Canada to establish a branch sewing machine factory for his employers, but he returned to Birmingham, Connecticut (now part of Derby), before his son was three months old. The Dows are an old New England family, established when Henry Dow came from England to the Massachusetts Bay Colony in 1637. Herbert's mother, Sarah Bunnell, was also a descendant of the first Massachusetts settlers.

Although the family moved to Cleveland, Ohio, when he was twelve. Herbert Dow bore throughout his life the strong impress of this ancestry and his strict upbringing. He had the Puritan virtues: he was honest, hard-working, thrifty, God-fearing. He was also blessed—or cursed—with a New England conscience. One of his oldest associates, Thomas Griswold, wrote of him that "He seemed unconsciously to practice all the rules of personal efficiency laid down by the teachers. He had no interest in avocations or recreations as such, but only if he could turn them into an asset of some sort." His methods and his thinking both reflected his New England background; he was saved from Puritan austerity and priggishness by his magnanimous spirit and a lively sense of humor.

It is remembered that as a boy he was an inveterate trader and also that he usually got the best of the bargain. He was also a great collector—birds' nests and eggs, butterflies, minerals, arrowheads, postage stamps—and when his interest changed, he sold or swapped his old collection to start his new hobby. At ten years of age he earned the money for his railway fare to the Philadelphia Centennial Exposition, which he visited with his father and where he was lastingly impressed by the huge Corliss steam engine.

Inspired by an article on ostrich farming in Australia in "The Youth's Companion," he became a true industrial pioneer by manufacturing one of the first incubators. His initial set of eggs failed to hatch because the kerosene lamp, which furnished the heat, did not maintain an even temperature. He solved this by inventing a practical heat-control apparatus, and the apex of his success was the sale of an incubator to a rancher in California for $100. This success attracted imitators and he met their cut-price competition by advertising a set of blueprints with full directions to "build it cheaper yourself." This juvenile business venture embodied the invention of one of the earliest automatic control instruments and a new philosophy of sales, both prophetic of his activities as a chemical industrialist.

In Cleveland, where Joseph Dow was master mechanic of the Chisholm Steel Shovel Works, the family lived in a big house with spacious grounds at the corner of Superior and Cass Avenues, and Herbert with a chum went into market-gardening, selling vegetables to the neighboring stores. His father taught in the Sunday school and he sang in the choir and organized a quartet which gave many concerts to raise church funds: more forecasts of the future.

Young Dow dreamed of becoming an architect, but he won a scholarship at the Cast School of Applied Science, which offered no course in architecture, so for some unknown reason he elected to specialize in chemistry. The Case faculty was a group of driving, inspiring enthusiasts; the curriculum was preeminently practical; in the laboratories students were expected to carry on original research in applied chemistry. In this atmosphere Herbert Dow blossomed. He speeded up his regular course assignments to find more time for chemical hobbies of his own. In his junior year he became interested in lithium, then a rare and costly metal which had become a medical fad, and in the laboratory he recovered several samples, along with bromine, from Ohio brines.

During the winter term of 1887 to '88 he went to work on his graduation thesis, "The Chemical Uses of Fuel in Boilers," by conscientiously collecting samples of petroleum and natural gas from wells near Cleveland. At one operation he visited, the boss driller called his attention to the brine from this well.

"Just taste it," he said, "it's the bitterest brine I ever struck."

"Why?" was the question that popped into the young chemist's head and he determined to find out. Analysis revealed an exceptionally high content of both lithium and bromine.

Dow finished his thesis on boiler fuels, but that very acrid brine haunted him. He knew oil was selling for a dollar a barrel, he had figured out there was three dollars' worth of lithium in a barrel of that brine. His commercial instinct, always keen and always stimulated by his chemical investigations, told him that this particular well was more valuable for its wasted by-product than for the oil that was being sold with difficulty in an over-supplied market. At the same time his very sound business sense told him that the bromine content of the brine was even more important industrially than the higher-priced, but less-demanded, rare metal.

1223

Here was the tiny acorn that was to grow into the mighty Dow Chemical oak, and young Dow must have sensed intuitively that he had hold of a good idea. He accepted a poorly paid position with the high-sounding title of professor of chemistry and toxicology at the Huron Street Hospital College of Medicine because it gave him a laboratory and an assistant so that he might continue his study of native brines. It was a task that was to engage his best attention the rest of his life.

Recovery of bromine, a heavy, very volatile, brownish-red liquid, is one of the older American chemical enterprises. David Alter started it during the early 1840's from brine found in Pennsylvania oil wells. The process was simple, but needed close attention if a pure product was wanted. First, the brine was evaporated till the salt (sodium chloride) crystallized out. Then, the concentrated liquor, called bittern, was treated with chlorine or either hydrochloric or sulfuric acid, which, reacting with the potassium and calcium bromides, freed the bromine that was driven off by heating and collected under water. The business settled in the Pomeroy district along the Ohio Valley and in the Kanawha Valley of West Virginia, where there was the favorable economic combination of a bromine-rich brine and abundant fuel. The demand was not big, but it was increased, especially during the Civil War, by the discovery of dry-plate photography and the medical vogue for bromides, the first tranquilizer drugs. Shortly afterward bromine recovered as a by-product from the famous German Stassfurt potash deposits appeared on the market and the price dropped from $10 to $4.50 a pound. The American industry shrank to a few plants operating only where waste wood from lumbering operations or local natural gas made fuel costs very low.

Dow combed this situation, he read and he experimented. He went scouting to find brine with the highest bromine content and found it at Canton, Ohio, and Midland, Michigan. Among the family archives are expense accounts of these trips. One four-day, triangular journey from Cleveland to Toledo to Findlay cost $7.80, with one hotel at $1 and another at $.70 a day, which included meals, and "shave and shine" for $.20.

He convinced himself that bromine could be freed from raw, cold brine and recovered by blowing it out of the liquid. By thus

1224

practically eliminating fuel costs he believed he could make the cheapest bromine in the world.

His idea was tried out in 1889 at Canton, Ohio, by the woefully underfinanced Canton Chemical Company. The processes worked: he did liberate bromine from cold brine by sulfuric acid; he did collect the bromine by dribbling the treated brine over a series of burlap sheets spread above a fan; he did make ferric bromide by passing the liquid bromine through iron scrap. The company failed because of "mechanical troubles" caused by lack of capital. A critical point was the pump, a museum piece that simply could not raise enough brine from a 1000-foot well to produce enough bromine to make the operation profitable. Within the year his backers withdrew and Dow returned to Cleveland.

He had learned valuable lessons. One might improvise buildings and certain apparatus, but mechanical and electrical equipment should not be bought from the junk dealer. It was many years before he again tried to pump from so deep a well, and this was one reason why he moved to Midland where the bromine-rich brine was closer to the surface.

During the autumn of 1890 Dow's second bromine venture was launched in the Midland Chemical Company, a partnership in which he supplied the knowledge and work and J. H. Osborn furnished the money. They rented a brine well near the end of Midland's Main Street and an unused barn from an adjacent flour mill. Here he developed his second revolutionary idea, the separation of bromine from raw brine, not by chemicals, but by an electric current. His notebook dates the first commercial operation of any electrochemical process in the United States:

Tues., Dec. 9: Tried the dynamo.

Jan. 2, 1891: Started pump at 7 a.m. On hand $2.26.

Jan. 4: Bromide of iron started running for the first time this morning. Ran power 24 hrs.

The first "kink" in the electrolytic process was exact control of the current; if too weak, all the bromine was not liberated; if too strong, chlorine also came over, a serious contamination for medinal uses. It took a couple of years to get good working practices and several more to achieve his goal of accurate automatic control. Because of a larger demand, he switched his end product from ferric to potassium bromide, using potashes (crude potassium carbonate) leached from wood ashes bought from nearby sawmills. This new raw material introduced a number of undesirable contaminants, and by cut-and-try experiments he learned that, being mostly organic substances, they could be driven off by calcining the bromide to red heat. Still the product, although as good as any on the market, was not quite up to U.S.P. standards.

Herbert Dow now turned salesman. After two futile calls in Cleveland, he went to Rosengarten & Sons in Philadelphia.

"We buy only from firms of the highest reputation," they told him rather brutally, "and do not, for our own reputation's sake, dare buy from a little one-horse concern in Michigan." However, in the end, he sold two barrels, "as a trial," at $.17 a pound, exactly half the market price.

Returning to Midland, he inspected two barrels and found them full of black specks. For two days he and his bride— Grace Ball, a Midland girl, also of New England ancestry—picked over those two barrels to remove every speck and imperfectly formed crystal. The shipment was made, C.O.D., but no check was forthcoming. An anxious week later, came a letter saying that examination showed the bromide did not meet U.S.P. standards and asking what price concession would he be willing to make.

"That letter," so he wrote years later, "sent my heart down into my boots. We needed the money very much. . . . Fortunately for the future success of the organization there happened to be a business man in our office who volunteered to answer the letter. In substance our reply was as follows: 'We are in receipt of your letter of recent date. If the goods are not satisfactory, please return them'."

Their reply was a check in full payment of the account. Meantime the Midland Chemical Company struggled for lack of cash. Before offering potassium bromide they had sold bromine as a disinfectant and antiseptic and a mixture of alkali bromides as "mining salt" for the extraction of gold ores. But again the output of a makeshift plant hamstrung profitable operations. To provide additional capital two more partners were taken in, and then, on

1226

August 17, 1892, the Midland Chemical Company was incorporated with an authorized capital of $100,000, only about $10,000 of which was paid in. Young Dow evidently lost financial control, for he was elected a director, but not an officer, of the corporation which hired him as manager. Another $10,000 was raised by a bank loan in Cleveland; land was bought at the other end of town; the barn was deserted for a new-built plant. Here the centers of interest were a big, new 50-kilowatt generator, a giant of its day, and the first Dow electrolytic cell, a long, troughlike apparatus with carbon electrodes piercing the wooden partitions which divided it into six smaller cells.

In 1894, the year after the historic sale to Rosengarten, the Midland Chemical Company made a profit of $11,781.78. The following year it began paying dividends at the rate of 2% monthly.

Herbert Dow had become interested in chlorine. It was much more plentiful than bromine in the brine and it had many more chemical possibilities. He hated to see it going to waste, for he knew it could be recovered electrolytically and he wanted to convert it into bleaching powder (calcium hypochlorite), then imported from England, for which the demand was growing rapidly.

Very humanly, his directors' response to this proposal was, "Let's make a little money before we squander it on more experiments." That was the correct business philosophy of the Gay Nineties. But they did give him permission to build a pilot plant on their property with the understanding that any patents he developed belonged to the corporation.

Dow went along with his plan, but two hours after the current was switched on his little new plant was demolished by an explosion of the hydrogen which was also released by the electrolytic dissociation of the sodium chloride. Fortunately nobody was hurt, but the bromine plant was damaged, and the special meeting of the directors turned into an indignation meeting. Dow did not resign as a director, but he moved 300 miles away from Midland to Navarre, Ohio.

Here, behind an 8-foot wooden fence he proved within a few months that he could liberate chlorine from a solution of salt in water by electrolysis without an explosion. All of his directors had not deserted him, and the faithful Osborn, with two of the Case

1227

faculty, Cady Staley, president, and Albert W. Smith, professor of chemistry, and James T. Pardee, a classmate, organized the Dow Process Company to exploit this chlorine project. Back in Midland Dow built across the street from the bromine plant and bought its debromized brine as his raw material.

Shortly afterward this new partnership was incorporated as The Dow Chemical Company and its financial resources were strengthened by the sale of stock to 57 individuals. Three years later, Dow Chemical took over the Midland Chemical plant and bromine process. In 1902 a subsidiary was formed, Midland Chemical II, to manufacture chloroform from carbon tetrachloride, a process evolved by Professor Smith.

The path ahead was steep and stony, but the goal, if far away, was now clearly visible. For the first ten years technical advances were greater than financial returns. That was Dr. Dow's way, a fixed policy expressing a typically chemical philosophy of industry:

> Here at Midland our job is to make chemicals out of our brine. I want to see us extract every chemical opportunity out of our raw material. . . . But I am not at all interested in making anything, except to salvage a by-product or a waste, that we cannot make cheaper and better than anyone else is making it.

At the time Dr. Dow was awarded the Perkin Medal, in 1930, Edwin O. Barstow, one of his oldest associates, summarized how these ideas were translated into action:

> Carbon bisulfide, with chlorine, gives carbon tetrachloride; sulfur chloride and impure sulfur as by-products.
> The by-product sulfur is used in the manufacture of limesulfur, a fungicide spray material, and also for the manufacture of epsom salt.
> Carbon tetrachloride, treated with iron borings and water, gives chloroform and by-products of ferrous chloride and ferrous hydrate.
> By-product ferrous chloride and ferrous hydrate, treated with chlorine and hydrochloric acid, give ferric chloride.
> Benzene, treated with chlorine, gives monochlorobenzene with by-product hydrochloric acid.
> Chlorobenzene with caustic soda solution at high temperatures

1228

and high pressures gives sodium phenate solution, and this with by-product hydrochloric acid gives phenol.

Phenol, combined with caustic soda and carbon dioxide, gives salicylic acid, and from this we manufacture a full line of salicylates, including methyl salicylate, salol, and aspirin.

And so on and on, juggling their basic elements, chlorine and bromine, sodium, calcium, and magnesium, the list of Dow products has grown and grown.

Herbert Dow's career after 1900 was meshed with the development of The Dow Chemical Company. Although this is no place for a company history, nevertheless a few high points are too illustrative of the man to be omitted from his biography.

In the very early days Dow had to fight and win two costly price wars with powerful foreign competitors in bleach and bromine. The bleach victory was won, as it were, by default, for the Leblanc process employed by the United Alkali Company, Ltd., was already obsolete. The war with the German bromine cartel was quite different.

Recovering bromine as by-product from the Stassfurt potash salts, the Bromkonvention dominated world trade and when Dow began exporting bromides to Europe they warned him to stop or else—. He kept right on and a year later the price of German bromides in New York was suddenly cut to $.15, half of the Dow price. Dow immediately withdrew from the American market and began shipping every pound of his bromides to Germany and England, just underselling the cartel, which naturally had not cut prices in these territories. In their eagerness to crush this upstart the Germans cut their American price to $.10. This was below Dow's cost, so he began buying their material, repackaging it, and shipping it abroad. The Konvention got into double trouble: their members quarreled as to who should supply this unprofitable market and their customers here began complaining about deliveries. It took nearly four years to convince the Germans they had best pocket their losses and withdraw with tarnished prestige.

About this time, 1909, Dow made a serious decision that illustrates what his colleagues called "his uncanny foresight in anticipating chemical trends." Bleach was the company's big bread-and-butter product. He tore down the bleach plant in 1915 and substituted for his chlorine cells new ones to recover caustic soda (sodium hydroxide) and chlorine with hydrogen as a by-product. With this drastic move he also forsook his pet idea of raw brine and in a series of triple-effect vacuum evaporators also recovered sodium chloride, magnesium chloride, and calcium chloride. The waste "mud," flushed periodically from the chlorine cells in the sewer, thus became three potential raw materials.

Carbon tetrachloride and chloroform introduced the company to organic synthesis, a field they cultivated with outstanding success. Both chemicals were first synthesized in the United States by Dow, and "carbon tet" was the first synthetic organic to reach big tonnage production.

Dow's great expansion during the World War I years was in several respects unique. Production of 30 million pounds of caustic, 23 million pounds of phenol, and over a million pounds of acetic anhydride were mighty contributions to the war effort, and the company filled big gaps in our chemical armory by supplying phenol and indigo, mustard gas (dichlorethyl sulfide) and metallic magnesium for flares, all new products of Dow research. Most of the wartime production was sold to the U. S. Government "at cost," and an audit of these thousands of accounts by the Cleveland Trust Company showed a net profit of 1-2/3 per cent. That also was Dr. Dow's way.

But conversion of this tremendous war effort to peaceful purposes was a typical Dow achievement. Taking phenol as an example—at the end of the war there was on hand a surplus of nearly 40 million pounds, seemingly a six-year peacetime supply. Dow had an unshipped stock of 4 million pounds and a new phenol plant almost ready to go into production. Unexpectedly the phenolic resin business boomed, and within three years three of the wartime producers were reactivating their plants. Not Dr. Dow—he wanted not the conventional sulfonation of benzol, but a new, more efficient process from chlorbenzene. Everyone said it could not be made to work, but Dr. William J. Hale perfected it, and in 1925 when Dow phenol came back on the market, the price dropped from $.36 to $.21.

Except for metallic magnesium during the closing years of his

1230

life, Dr. Dow's chemical hobby was always bromine, and back in 1909 he had highly amused one of his chemical stockholders by forecasting a demand for his favorite of over a million pounds a year. He did not quite live to see his company producing a million pounds a month, but he did see test runs that assured him a process had been worked out to extract bromine from the sea which made such a fantastic output perfectly possible.

This undreamed demand was for ethylene dibromide, needed for the production of tetraethyl lead, the gasoline antiknock.

Outside of the company Herbert Dow had three absorbing interests. First, the city of Midland, which he found a wretched, unpaved, half-abandoned lumber town and left a model community. Second, his orchards and gardens where he turned 160 acres of sandy, cut-over land into a veritable Eden, a true show place, famous for its charm and beauty, an exceptional horticultural museum of rare fruits and flowers.

His third great interest was his family. From the days when as a bride Grace Ball helped him pick the specks out of bromide crystals to the years when he was head of one of the country's chemical enterprises, a bank director, a man of many philanthropies, Grace Ball was his helpmate, comrade, and confidant. In Midland, her memory is as warmly cherished to this day as his is. They had seven children and, save a boy who died young, all grew up and married: Willard, who succeeded him as president of the Dow firm, to Martha Pratt; Alden, the famous architect, to Vada Bennett; Helen, to William J. Hale; Ruth to Leland I. Doan, who in turn succeeded his brother-in-law to the company's presidency; Margaret to Harry Towsley; and Dorothy to Anderson Arbury, a physician and dentist, of Ann Arbor and Mirland, Michigan.

On October 15, 1930, Herbert Dow died at the Mayo Clinic, having failed to rally from a serious operation. He left the company he founded three valuable legacies: a tradition of bold, ceaseless research for new products and better processes; the habit of painstaking engineering, aimed always at the continuous operation automatically controlled; an example of corporate management distinguished for its friendly, human relations with its own people, its cordial cooperation with its neighbors, and its straightforward dealing with the rest of the business world.

1231

NOTES AND REFERENCES

The official biography, Murray Campbell and Harrison Hatton, "Herbert H. Dow: Pioneer in Creative Chemistry," New York, 1951, is excellent in its step-by-step development of Dow's chemical ideas.

The chapter in Williams Haynes' "Chemical Pioneers," Van Nostrand, New York, 1939, pp. 259–78, is interesting for a personal interview setting forth Dow's chemical philosophy.

Dow's Perkin Medal address and those of J. T. Pardee and E. O. Barstow, were printed in full in *Oil, Paint & Drug Reptr.,* 21, Jan. 13, 1930; see also *Ind. & Eng. Chem.,* 22, 113 (1930); *Am. Dict. Biog.,* XXI, 261; "Who Was Who," I, 336.

Obits: *Midland (Mich.) Republican,* Oct. 15, 1930; *Detroit Free Press,* Oct. 16, 1930; *Am. Dyestuff Reptr.,* 671, Oct. 27, 1930.

For Dow Chemical Company; H. H. Dow, *Dow Diamond,* February 1938, p. 69; Mark E. Putnam, "Twenty-five Years of Chemical Engineering Progress," Am. Inst. Chem. Engrs., 1933; Williams Haynes, "American Chemical Industry," 6 vols., New York, Van Nostrand, 1945–54, VI, 113–24.

WILLIAMS HAYNES

·· 87 ··

Alfred Werner

1866-1919

Alfred Werner, son of a factory foreman, was born in Mülhausen, Alsace, on December 12, 1866. His predilection for chemistry became quite noticeable while he was still attending the lower schools, and when only about eighteen he submitted for criticism the results of his first independent chemical investigation to Emilio Noelting, who was then director of the school of chemistry at Mülhausen. In 1885, Werner entered the army and served a term as one-year volunteer at Karlsruhe and at the same time attended Engler's lectures on chemistry at the technical high school. The next year he moved to Zürich and in this city he made his home the rest of his life.

Three eminent chemists, Lunge, Hantzsch, and Treadwell were then teaching at the Eidgenossiches Polytecknikum (now called the Eidgenössiche Technische Hochschule) and they were responsible for Werner's excellent training. After receiving his diploma as technical chemist, 1889, he became assistant to Lunge; and at the same time, as co-worker with Hantzsch, began the study of purely scientific problems. His doctorate thesis, "On the Spatial Arrangement of the Atoms in Nitrogen Compounds," was accepted by the University of Zürich in 1890. Werner then spent one semester in Paris studying with Berthelot at the Collège de France. On his return to Zürich, he applied for a license to teach at the Polytecknikum, submitting with his application a dissertation, "Contributions to the Theory of Affinity and Valence." In this he disposed of many traditional notions and laid the foundations of a new valence theory. In the autumn of 1892, when only twenty-six, he published "A Contribution to the Constitution of Inorganic Compounds," a paper which later became quite famous, for it marks its author as the founder of the modern views in this field and insures to him a rank in the history of chemical thought equal to that of August Kekulé.

Only one year later, in the fall of 1893, he was appointed successor of Viktor Merz, becoming extraordinary professor of chemistry and director of chemical laboratory A at the University of Zürich. Two years later he was promoted to a full professorship. He soon became one of the best known and most highly respected teachers and investigators at the University. Flattering offers from Vienna (1899), Basle (1902), the Eidg. Technische Hochschule (1905), and Würzburg (1910) were declined. Honorary doctorates were conferred on him by the University of Geneva and the Technical High School in Zürich. He was elected honorary or corresponding member of numerous scientific societies. Among the latter were the Königliche Gesellschaft der Wissenschaften in Göttingen; the physikalisch-medizinsche Sozietät in Erlangen; the physikalischer Verein in Frankfurt; the Société de physique et d'histoire naturelle in Geneva; the Société impériale des amis d'histoire naturelle, d'anthropologie et d'ethonographie in Moscow; Chemical Society of London, etc. The Swiss Chemical Society honored him by establishing a Werner Fund and also issued a Werner plaquette.

The highest scientific honor, the Nobel Prize, was awarded to him in 1913, and this occasioned a most enthusiastic ovation to their master by his students at Zürich. Even at this time, a serious disorder, arteriosclerosis, was beginning to make its destructive action evident, and at the end of 1915 he no longer felt able to deliver the general lectures. He resumed these at intervals but never for long, and finally the progress of the disease compelled him to relinquish his professorship in 1919. On November 15, 1919, death released this brilliant investigator, not yet fifty-three, from his distressing illness. He died while mentally deranged.

Werner was a plain, sincere character, possessed of a simple, candid disposition and endowed with high intelligence and firm determination. With a prodigious capacity for work and an endurance that seemed almost inexhaustible, he persisted at his theoretical and experimental problems, overcoming all human and material obstacles until he had reached his goal. It is obvious then that Werner was not an easy taskmaster to those working under his direction; his demands on them seemed often to reach the limits of possibility. However, this strict training certainly was a great asset to many of his pupils throughout their entire lives.

Especially in his younger years, Werner made it a practice to

1236

discuss the newer work appearing in the literature or his own investigations for hours with his assistants and he demanded that sharp criticism be exercised during these sessions. His assistants did not always find it easy to follow the trend of his thoughts, for he had a fabulous memory which extended over the whole field of chemistry, both inorganic and organic, and he could pass from one subject to another with great facility. If the topic chanced to be, say, the isomerism of inorganic complex compounds, the discussion in a few moments would very likely be centered around analogous phenomena exhibited by terpenes, alkaloids, or dyestuffs. He insisted that his auditors have clear knowledge of the constitution and configuration of the individual compounds and be able to work freely with these concepts. He personally found no difficulty in these fields as he had a remarkable faculty for envisaging spatial relationships.

Under circumstances more favorable than those obtaining at Zürich, this eminent investigator would doubtless have established a large school of chemical thought. Nevertheless, his Zürich laboratory produced numerous men who occupy prominent places in the chemical industries and a goodly number of eminent teachers. Among these are Berl, Dilthey, Dubsky, Jantsch, Karrer, Pfeiffer, Schaarschmidt, and Stiasny.

He lectured only on organic chemistry until 1902 when he also took over the inorganic division. His lectures were well prepared, original in the arrangement of the material, and characterized by the clarity with which even the most complicated problems were treated. His delivery was convincing, and he exhibited such enthusiasm for his science that his hearers were carried with him.

His teaching abilities were also evidenced by his two principal books, of which the more important is "New Ideas in Inorganic Chemistry." In this he examined critically a vast mass of scattered data which were then, for the first time, classified systematically by means of his coordination theories. His "Stereochemistry" was also of fundamental importance, for it was the first comprehensive, critical treatment of this important field. Even present-day investigators of stereochemical problems find it necessary to refer repeatedly to Werner's text.

Werner developed a personal technique for his experimental

researches on organic complex compounds. On his laboratory table stood several microburners and microfilter supports, together with several hundreds of small glass dishes, whose contents were of all colors. Although none of these dishes was labeled, he was quite sure that confusion was almost an impossibility. The laboratory in which he did his first work consisted of very inadequate rooms, those in the basement well deserving their popular designation, "the catacombs." In 1909, he had the pleasure of moving into a spacious new laboratory built from his own plans. From this issued, in particular, his important researches on optically active inorganic compounds.

Werner's wife, née Emma Giesker, a native of Zürich, was a member of an immigrant German family. He also showed great affection for his children, one boy and one girl. He was a very sociable soul, finding recreation from mental toil among his friends in billiards, chess, or a Swiss card game, jass. A few weeks of the fall vacation were usually spent in the mountains; he did not enjoy longer pleasure trips. He was an ardent attendant of scientific conventions, and frequently lectured in foreign countries.

As a native of Alsace, Werner's cultural sympathies were both French and German, but he always emphasized that German science was responsible for his professional training. Of his teachers he especially revered Arthur Hantzsch. His published articles almost without exception appeared in German journals, and his books were also written in that language. However, his sympathies were with France during World War I.

Even the first of Werner's scientific papers, his doctorate thesis, written at the age of twenty-four, is of considerable importance since in it he laid the foundations of a new chapter of stereochemistry, namely, of nitrogen. Although published in the *Berichte* under the names of Hantzsch and Werner, the latter alone is responsible for the fundamental idea, viz., that in the numerous compounds of trivalent nitrogen (oximes, etc.), the three valence bonds of the nitrogen atom are directed toward three corners of a tetrahedron, whose fourth corner is occupied by the nitrogen atom itself. In this article, Werner successfully combated the views of V. Meyer and K. Auwers who sought to explain the isomerism of the benzil oximes by denying in this case the validity of the van't

Hoff principle of the free rotation of singly bound carbon atoms about the C—C axis. His excellent extension of the van't Hoff theory of the stereochemistry of carbon has been substantiated throughout. The experimental development of his new views is due especially to Hantzsch, as Werner's participation was not for long. Problems of an entirely different kind soon absorbed his interest.

Only a year after the appearance of his "Stereochemistry of Nitrogen," his habilitation essay, "Contribution to the Theory of Affinity and Valence," was published in 1891 in the *Vierteljahresschrift der Züricher Naturforschenden Gesellschaft,* and because of the limited circulation of this periodical the new ideas were only tardily recognized. This paper was a forerunner of Werner's masterly coordination theory. In this paper of 1891, he pursues a totally new path; he rejects the usual concept of valence as a directed single force; and assumes that affinity is an attractive force originating at the center of the atom and acting uniformly toward all parts of the surface. (For the sake of simplicity, the atom was imagined to be spherical.) Valency for him, then, became an empirical number concept. He succeeded in deriving the van't Hoff configuration formulas without assuming directed single forces; he worked out an acceptable interpretation of stereochemical rearrangements, and attacked the benzene problem from a new angle. These ideas were developed at greater length in 1906 in a paper, "The Variable Affinity of Simple Compounds," and in conjunction with Thiele's theory of partial valence have been extremely fruitful for organic chemistry.

Werner's greatest achievement was without doubt the establishment of the coordination theory, with whose aid the young investigator, only twenty-six, cleared the way for a new phase of development of inorganic chemistry. According to his own statement, the inspiration came to him like a flash. One morning at two o'clock he awoke with a start; the long-sought solution of this problem had lodged in his brain. He arose from his bed and by five o'clock in the afternoon the essential points of the coordination theory were achieved. (In this connection, see the article on Werner in the *Schweizerische Chemikerzeitung* for 1920.)

The significance of Werner's coordination theory may be better

1239

appreciated if it is pointed out that chemical compounds are conveniently classified as of the first order and as of higher orders (molecular compounds). As compounds of the first order are considered all those whose molecules are made up of two distinct atomic species (chlorides, oxides, sulfides, nitrides, hydrides, etc.). In this class are also placed those substances which are derived from these simplest compounds of the first order by replacement of single atoms by either atoms of another species or by groups of atoms (radicals). This includes the vast majority of the almost inconceivably large number of organic compounds. The Kekulé valence theory has proved absolutely essential in systematizing all these materials; its success is a veritable triumph.

Werner rejects the application of the Kekulé valence theory to molecular compounds, and to a certain extent he places them in a separate category, developing a new theoretical basis which permits of an orderly, comprehensive arrangement of even these compounds and, furthermore, his assumptions lead to a simple explanation of numerous cases of isomerism exhibited by these substances.

According to Werner's hypothesis, inorganic molecular compounds contain single atoms which function as central nuclei, around which are arranged in simple, spatial geometrical patterns a definite number of other atoms, radicals, or other molecules capable of independent existence. The figure expressing the number of atoms grouped around one central atom of a molecular compound was designated by Werner as the coordination number of this atom. The concept of coordination number, to which are also joined the concepts of "auxiliary valence number and force" and "indirect linking," forms the central point of the Wernerian system. Only a few coordination numbers come into consideration, the most important being 3, 4, 6, and 8. The number 6 occurs especially often. Thousands of molecular compounds of cobalt, chromium, platinum, etc., correspond to the 6 type. In all of these, as Werner pointed out in his first paper, the spatial configuration is octahedral in that around the central metal atom lie the six coordinated atoms in the corners of an octahedron.

This mode of representation was so novel and departed so

widely from all previous proposals that only a few of Werner's fellow chemists recognized the import of his ideas. The chief obstacle was the "organic" orientation of the majority of the chemists of that time, for that branch of the science was then experiencing great triumphs. Werner now entered upon a twenty-year period of experimental work, whose intensity has hardly ever been equaled. He and his co-workers constantly prepared new series of molecular compounds and studied their constitutions and configurations. More than 200 dissertations were produced under his direction; his own publications exceed 150. The structure of the chemistry of inorganic complexes revealed itself in more and more harmonious form and finally, after eighteen years, he made the important discovery of the optically active inorganic compounds, whose existence he had foreseen from his octahedral hypothesis. This constituted the experimental proof of one of the most important deductions of his theory, and in consequence the great significance of the coordination theory for the chemical systematics was generally recognized.

Now began the triumphant march of the coordination theory, but its author could no longer take an active part in its progress. Starting from a study of the metal-ammonia salts and of the double salts, two classes of materials which were then not considered of particular importance or interest, this theory, while still under Werner's guidance, embraced almost the whole of systematic, inorganic chemistry and its tentacles extended into the organic field, where today its importance is commonly acknowledged. Coordination concepts are playing an increasingly important role in crystallography, for it appears that, in general, crystals are built up in conformity with these teachings. If, in addition, it is assumed that these same considerations are valid in the theory of adsorption and of solution—although all this is still in the course of development—the comprehensive significance of Werner's life work follows as a matter of course.

Particular interest attaches to the question as to whether Werner's train of ideas was the culmination of a lengthy logical series of developments; i.e., whether it is possible to name certain individuals who had preceded him in more or less clearly recognized essential portions of his theories. In the writer's opinion, this is not the case. Of course, in formulating his coordination theory, Werner employed certain ideas arising from Kekulé's valence theories, from van't Hoff's stereochemistry, and from the electrolytic dissociation theory of Arrhenius. The structure of his teachings appears, however, to have been erected as an entirely independent creation. This becomes especially evident if Werner is compared with Jörgensen, to whom (preceding and contemporaneous with Werner) is due credit for fundamental studies of the metal-ammonia salts, Jörgensen did not wish to break away from the usual inflexible valence theories; his formulas could not give lasting satisfaction, for they aroused no incentive to a further development of chemistry. Furthermore, Jörgensen was not sufficiently informed regarding the inner, theoretical, and experimental relationship of all the various classes of molecular compounds.

Mendeleev was perfectly aware of this inherent connection. In his text "Foundations of Chemistry," which Werner knew in its German translation, he clearly emphasized the constitutional similarity of metal-ammonia salts, hydrates, and double salts; indeed he also included alloys and solutions in his discussion. However, his attempts to bring order out of this chaos were not successful, although he did demonstrate that the pure valence formulations then in vogue could not be maintained. He was also correct in his systematic placement of certain series of compounds, such as polymeric metal halides, Al_2X_6, etc. (which he considered as double halides). The privilege of reaching the goal toward which Mendeleev had turned his thoughts was reserved for Alfred Werner, whose creation of the general coordination theory was the work of a genius.

REFERENCES

Karrer, P., *Helv. Chim. Acta,* 3, 196 (1920). Männer der Technik, 1925, p. 290, Herausgeber C. Matschoss; *Schweizer. Chemiker-Zeit., 1920,* p. 73.

Pfeiffer, P., *Z. angew. Chem.,* 33, 37 (1920).

Lifschitz, J., *Z. Elektrochem.,* 26, 514 (1920).

Morgan, G. T., *J. Chem. Soc.* (London), 117, 1639 (1920).

A practically complete bibliography of Werner's publications may be found in *Helv. Chim. Acta,* 3, 225 (1920).

From: *J. Chem. Educ.*, *5*, No. 9, 1090 (1928). Translated by Ralph E. Oesper. Original German article appeared in "Deutsches Biographisches Jahrbuch, 1917–20," Stuttgart, 1928.

PAUL PFEIFFER

·· 88 ··

Wilder Dwight Bancroft

1867-1953

IN 1632, twelve years after the *Mayflower* sailed from South-hampton and during the period of the "Great Migration," John Bancroft, accompanied by his wife and two young sons, left his English home in Norfolk to take a farm near Lynn, in the colony of Massachusetts. Although he died soon after, his son Thomas became the progenitor of a long line of stalwart churchmen and farmers; and, during more than a hundred and thirty years, five generations of Bancrofts developed a tradition and pattern of life which, as it has been said, "combined civic duties, rock-ribbed Calvinism and farming in equal proportions."

This seemingly settled and unchanging pattern and way of life, however, was shattered when, in November 1775, a son, Aaron, was born to Samuel Bancroft, farmer and deacon of the church in Reading, Massachusetts, and his wife Lydia Parker. Looked upon, even as a boy, as the "family rebel," Aaron liked neither the occupation nor the Calvinistic creed of his father, and, breaking with long-established tradition, he became a prominent Unitarian minister, a leader of the schismatics, and a soldier of the Revolution. He also wrote a "Life of George Washington," which enjoyed considerable popularity; and it was his constant prayer that he might be granted a "teachable temper."

The character and cultural mutation introduced by Aaron into the Bancroft line was continued and confirmed in his son George: scholar, politician, and diplomat; Secretary of the Navy under President Polk and founder of the U. S. Naval Academy at Annapolis; U. S. Minister in London and in Berlin; author of "History of the American Revolution" and of "History of the Formation of the Constitution of the United States of America." By his first wife, Sarah H. Dwight, he had two sons and a daughter; and the elder son, John Chandler, named after his grandmother, Lucretia Chandler, wife of Aaron Bancroft, became the father of Wilder. It is, I believe, in the mental qualities, outlook on life, personality, and character of his grandfather and great-grandfather, that we can

1247

find the key to the personality and character of the subject of this notice.

Wilder Dwight Bancroft was born on October 1, 1867, at Middletown, Rhode Island, a small town and residential suburb of Newport, R. I. He was the elder of two children whom his father had by his first wife, Louisa Denny, daughter of a mill-owner, who died when Wilder was only four years old. Bancroft's father had studied law and was associated for a time with a firm of stock-brokers in Boston, but he later devoted himself to painting and studied art in France. His love of art, however, did not pass to his son. As a boy, Bancroft attended Roxbury Latin School and Milton Academy, where he showed outstanding ability, but little is known of his special interests or aptitudes during that period of his life. It was not, apparently, until he became an undergraduate at Harvard University in 1884 that any particular interest in science began to develop.

At that time, the senior professor of chemistry at Harvard was Josiah P. Cooke, whose books, "The New Chemistry" and "First Principles of Chemical Philosophy," may entitle him to be regarded as a pioneer of the older physical chemistry, and whose deductive method of approach to the study of chemistry cannot but have exercised an important influence on Bancroft's mind. There is little known about Bancroft's interests in science while at Harvard, but he showed prowess on the football field and was a member of the Harvard football team.

On graduating A.B. in 1888, Bancroft was appointed an assistant in the chemistry department. In the following year he proceeded to Europe where he worked more especially under Wilhelm Ostwald in Leipzig (1890–2), and under van't Hoff in Amsterdam (1892–3). He also spent some time at Strasbourg (1889–90) and in Berlin. In 1892 he presented a thesis entitled "Oxydationsketten" and after the usual oral examination was awarded the degree of Ph.D. by the University of Leipzig. In Amsterdam he continued his electrochemical studies and carried out experiments of an exploratory character on the chemical potential of metals.

On returning to America in 1893, Bancroft took up his former post as assistant at Harvard and in the following year was promoted to the rank of instructor. In 1895 Professor Cooke died and

Bancroft left Harvard to join the staff at Cornell University as assistant professor of physical chemistry. In 1903 he became professor and, in 1919, World War Memorial professor of physical chemistry. Thereafter the whole of his life was spent at Cornell. In 1937 he retired from his chair, and for a year was visiting Tallman Professor at Bowdoin College, Brunswick, Maine.

For more than forty years Bancroft was a member of the staff of Cornell. They were very strenuous years, but years which were full of work in which he could find satisfaction and happiness; and as time passed he became one of Cornell's best known and most outstanding professors. As a teacher he sought to impress on his students something of his own high character and enthusiasm for scientific truth. He lectured interestingly and clearly, using the original memoirs as the basis of discussion. His aim was not so much to impart a knowledge of a large number of facts as to impress on his students the importance of thinking things out for themselves; and he assessed the merits and standing of a student not by the range or number of facts which he was able to commit to memory, but by his willingness and ability to think and to draw his own conclusions from the facts discovered by himself or by others. To make people think may, perhaps, be regarded as a major aim of Bancroft's many writings, and the success with which he achieved this aim may be reckoned as among the most important of his contributions to the advancement of physical chemistry in America.

To younger chemists in whom he detected merit, Bancroft gave much help and encouragement, and there are not a few who have since attained to positions of eminence in chemistry, who look back with gratitude to the stimulus, encouragement, and help which they received from him.

Bancroft was interested in teaching, in making known to others what he had learned himself. He was obsessed with the importance of chemistry and he strove to make its importance more widely known and appreciated. "It should be the aim of all chemists," he wrote in the Jubilee volume of the *Journal of the American Chemical Society*, "to have chemistry take its place as the fundamental science," and he also urged physical chemists "to develop the borderlands between physical chemistry and the other sciences, such as, biology, geology, physics, medicine, engineering, psychology, etc." Nor was it on his students and fellow scientists alone that he wished to press the importance of chemistry. Its importance must be recognized by the community as a whole, and he suggested that universities should teach chemistry as a cultural study—as part of a general education. He urged, also, the institution of courses of public popular lectures on chemistry for those not to be chemists—"chemistry of or pertaining to all the people"—pandemic chemistry, he called it. Bancroft drew up a syllabus of such a course, a course not to teach a man chemistry but to teach him about chemistry, but he recognized, as all teachers have recognized, that the success of such a course depends more on the teacher than on the syllabus.

In 1895, physical chemistry—the newer physical chemistry of which Arrhenius, van't Hoff, and Ostwald were the pioneers—was only in its infancy in America, and Bancroft, with boundless energy and full of missionary zeal, sought, on joining the staff at Cornell, to develop this branch of science. In his view, physical chemistry was not merely a branch of chemistry but covered the whole of chemistry, and he aimed at presenting the science as a complete and systematic whole.

While in Amsterdam, Bancroft had no doubt become acquainted with the work of Bakhius Roozeboom and had become impressed with the importance of the phase rule as a basis of classification of heterogeneous systems and as a guide in their investigation. Although it owed its discovery to the great Yale mathematician, Willard Gibbs, there was, in America, almost no knowledge of the great generalization or recognition of its practical importance. There was, moreover, no exposition in English by means of which the student could become acquainted with it. Bancroft, therefore, set himself the task of making good this deficiency and published his first book, "The Phase Rule," in 1897. In this work, at the cost of what must have been much labor, he collected together in a systematic manner the existing items of knowledge scattered throughout the literature, and was, as Bakhius Roozeboom wrote, "exceedingly successful in making clear the coherence of the phenomena and in presenting an inspiring picture of the imposing science of heterogeneous equilibria." Unfortunately he was not

1250

quite successful, as he himself admitted, in producing a book which a student could read with profit and without difficulty. Nevertheless, it was a remarkable work to be written by one who was under thirty years of age and still on the very threshold of his teaching career. Along with the many papers written by Bancroft and the experimental work carried out by his pupils under his inspiration and guidance, "The Phase Rule" constituted a very important pioneering advance into a domain which, later, was vigorously and fruitfully cultivated in America. As Bancroft pointed out, the renowned Geophysical Laboratory at Washington is a wonderful example of what can be done with the phase rule as an instrument of research.

It is, perhaps, worthy of note that Bancroft, in this book, introduced into phase rule terminology the words nonvariant, monovariant, divariant, etc., suggested to him by his colleague, Joseph E. Trevor.

In his desire to further the study of physical chemistry in America, Bancroft no doubt recognized, as Ostwald in Germany had recognized, that if this new branch of science was to grow and develop, it must have a special organ through which it could express itself, and so, in 1896, he founded *The Journal of Physical Chemistry* as "an organ for the publication of research in all branches of experimental and theoretical physical chemistry." Until 1932, Bancroft was editor of the *Journal* (associated during the first thirteen years with J. E. Trevor), contributed many articles to its pages, and wrote also for it many book reviews and abstracts of scientific papers published elsewhere. Not only did Bancroft found the *Journal of Physical Chemistry* and thereby, it may be, rendered his greatest service to chemistry, but he also financed it out of his private resources. In 1924, when the financial burden became too great for him, he handed the Journal over to the American Chemical Society, the Chemical Society, and the Faraday Society, under whose auspices it was published until 1932. In 1947 its title was altered to *Journal of Physical and Colloid Chemistry*. It would be impossible with any accuracy to assess, as it would be difficult to exaggerate, the value and importance of this journal in promoting the development of physical chemistry in America by uniting the workers in this new domain of knowledge, by giving them their own organ of publication and thereby making effective advance possible.

From 1913 until his death, Bancroft was also associate editor of the *Journal of the Franklin Institute,* an institute founded, in 1826, in the State of Pennsylvania, to "diffuse information on every subject connected with the useful arts." To this journal Bancroft contributed, in 1925, an article on the development of colloid chemistry.

The numerous papers on emulsions, colloids, adsorption, etc., which from just before the First World War appeared in the *Journal of Physical Chemistry* under the name of Bancroft and of his pupils, were evidence that a new interest, one which became, perhaps, his strongest and most enduring interest, had developed in Bancroft's mind.

For some time interest in the colloid state had been growing in America, as in Europe, and although books on colloid chemistry existed, they had been written, in Bancroft's opinion, in too purely descriptive a manner and presented the subject empirically. By 1920, he considered that theory had developed sufficiently to allow the data to be presented deductively, and this he sought to do in his "Applied Colloid Chemistry," which first appeared in 1921 and of which two further editions were published, in 1926 and 1932.

This book, in its enthusiastic presentation of the subject, its critical sifting of reputed facts and explanations which the author regarded as doubtful or conflicting, its stimulating suggestiveness of how information gained in one field of investigation may be applied in many other fields, is entirely characteristic of Bancroft and deals clearly and comprehensively with a wide range of facts and observations. It is a book which is not only interesting and easy to read, but is sometimes almost entertaining, as when Bancroft writes: "There is one experiment which I always like to try, because it proves something whichever way it goes. A solution of iodine in water is shaken with bone-black, filtered, and tested with starch paste. If the colourless solution does not turn starch blue, the experiment shows how completely charcoal extracts iodine from aqueous solution. If the starch turns blue, the experiment shows that the solution, though apparently colourless, still contains iodine which can be detected by means of the sensitive starch test." One

1252

can almost see the engaging twinkle in his eyes as he carries out this experiment in front of his class.

Although Bancroft was the author of only two books, writing, with him, may almost be said to have been an inherited characteristic, and he wielded the pen with ease and dexterity. He was an omnivorous reader and a voluminous writer, living constantly under the urge not only to seek out truth but to proclaim to others the truth when found. He had a wonderfully retentive memory and was a great encyclopedist. In the many papers which he published in the *Journal of Physical Chemistry* and elsewhere, and in the numerous lectures and addresses which he delivered, Bancroft sought to bring together the facts already known, to sift them carefully and critically, to point out what he regarded as errors or defects in the interpretation of experimental data, to indicate what, in his opinion, were the fundamental problems to be investigated, and to put forward generalizations for testing by experiment. Ideas, suggestions of problems for investigation, sprang in almost bewildering profusion out of an extensive knowledge and exuberant imagination; and not a few of these problems were thereafter investigated by Bancroft's pupils in his laboratory at Cornell and under his stimulus and direction. It is, I believe, in his numerous writings and in the stimulus and encouragement which he gave to workers in widely different fields to take the data and conceptions from one branch of study and to consider their application to another, that we find Bancroft's chief contribution to the advance of scientific thought and knowledge.

Tall and strongly built, robust both physically and mentally, and with a fair and fresh complexion, Bancroft looked out on a world which was to him so full of interest, through blue eyes from which a smile was never far distant. Throughout most of his life he retained as a spectator an enthusiastic interest in athletics, especially baseball and football, in which, in his younger days, he had gained no little distinction. Independent, as always, of the opinions of others, Bancroft was also inclined to be unconventional in dress. Van't Hoff tells how, during a visit which he paid to Bancroft in 1901, he was surprised to see his host dressed in knickerbockers and shoes, and how he reminded him somewhat of an *impressario*. He recounts, also, a somewhat hair-raising ex-

1253

cursion to Taughannock Waterfall which he and his wife made in a horse carriage with Bancroft as driver. By some mistake they had got on to a road long disused and they had to descend and push or pull the carriage over the roughest parts, or even to lift it over a water conduit. However, they all arrived back again without serious mishap, and van't Hoff committed his feeling of relief to his diary in the words, "How fortunate we were to have such a safe driver as Wilder."

Bancroft found relaxation mainly in playing golf, and he was one of the organizers of the Country Club at Ithaca. He greatly enjoyed taking part in national and international congresses and conferences where he could discuss scientific problems with fellow workers. On such occasions, his genial and enthusiastic manner and his witty talk ensured for him a cordial welcome.

Bancroft was ambidextrous and, when lecturing, he liked sometimes to astonish and impress his audience by a demonstration of his ambidexterity. Standing at the middle of the blackboard he would begin to write a line with his left hand and then, transferring the chalk but without altering his position, would complete the line with his right hand.

On June 19, 1895, Bancroft married Kate Bott, of Albany, N. Y., whose father had emigrated from Germany to the United States about the middle of the nineteenth century, and whom he had first met during his period of study in Berlin in 1893. She died in February, 1942.

In 1937, when Bancroft retired from the active work of his chair, he was still in the enjoyment of good health and could look forward to spending the evening of a very busy life in the unhurried, happy, and peaceful pursuit of his scientific interests. But this was not to be. In 1938, after returning from Bowdoin College, he was run over by a motor car on the Cornell Campus and received very severe injuries. For several months he lay in the hospital and, although, thereafter, he was able to move about quietly with the help of a walking stick and to pay occasional visits to the chemistry department, he never fully recovered his health. A year or two before he died he fell out of bed during another period in the hospital and was then confined to his home.

During his many years of partial or complete invalidism Bancroft, undaunted by the cruel rub of fortune, remained cheerful and retained his interest in science and athletics; and smiling into the frowning face of Fate, he fulfilled his allotted span of life. Peacefully, on the morning of February 7, 1953, he died in his sleep.

Bancroft is survived by two sons and three daughters, of whom the eldest is married to M. L. Nichols, professor of chemistry, Cornell University.

With his alert and wide-ranging mind, with his independence of outlook and fearlessness in expressing his views, which were in no way inferior to those of his New England forebears, Bancroft was an outstanding personality and exercised a great influence on the development of physical chemistry in America. It may be that in his editorial chair Bancroft was apt to regard himself not only as the professor but also as the autocrat of physical chemistry; it may also be that with his unusually wide knowledge and confidence—not unjustified—in his own judgment, he was inclined to be intolerant of the views of others when they differed from his own and to express his criticisms not only freely but, occasionally, with an unnecessary acerbity of language, and so was apt to make personal enemies of those who, through association in work and community of interests, should have been his friends. If, in the interests of scientific truth, he provoked controversy; if sometimes he even seemed, almost wilfully, to revert to the character of his grandfather, "the aggressive partisan who appeared to court unpopularity," yet in the social relations of everyday life how considerate and lovable he could be, how gracious and charming his manner, how interesting and entertaining his conversation. He died leaving a wealth of achievement as his monument and a treasured memory that will not quickly fade.

Bancroft's scientific interests were very varied and evidence of his encyclopedic mind is given in the numerous papers and articles which he wrote on electrochemistry, oxidation–reduction cells, and overvoltage; phase rule; osmotic pressure and dilution law; contact catalysis; corrosion; colloids and emulsions; hydrogenation; charcoal; theory of photography and the photographic plate; photochemistry; structural colors; proteins; coloring of glass by metal oxides, etc. To discuss here his scientific contributions in detail

1255

would be impossible; and one must restrict oneself to indicating only some of the more important aspects of his scientific work.

In the Preface to his "Phase Rule," Bancroft classified the facts and phenomena of physical chemistry into the divisions: Qualitative Equilibrium, Quantitative Equilibrium, Electrochemistry, Mathematical Theory. "My idea," he wrote, "is that all qualitative experimental data should be presented as particular applications of the Phase Rule and the Theorem of Le Chatelier, while the guiding principles for the classification of quantitative phenomena should be the Mass Law and the Theorem of van't Hoff." The view thus expressed explains no doubt why, when Bancroft first began his studies of heterogeneous equilibria with the investigation of ternary mixtures, he approached the subject not from the standpoint of the phase rule but from that of the law of mass action.

At a time when the systematic study of heterogeneous equilibria was still in its early years, Bancroft and his pupils made many valuable contributions to the advancement of knowledge in this domain, a general discussion and exposition of the principles of the phase rule marching hand in hand with the experimental investigation of a wide variety of systems. It is possible to deal here only with some of the most important aspects of Bancroft's work in this field.

Organic chemists had made known the existence of isomeric substances which could exist in two different solid forms, each corresponding to a single definite constitution, but which, in the liquid state, could undergo transformation one into the other until a state of homogeneous equilibrium between the two molecular species was established. The behavior of such substances gave rise to much controversy, and Bancroft was the first to show that many of the observed facts became more intelligible when one studied the heterogeneous solid-liquid equilibria met with in the case of these "dynamic isomerides." To the value of his work in this domain Ernst Cohen paid tribute in the words: "Einen nicht unwesentlichen Dienst bei dieser Zeit- und Streitfrage auf dem Felde der 'geometrischen' Isomerie haben auch physikalisch-chemische Untersuchungen geleistet, so namentlich . . . das Studium der Gleichgewichtsverhältnisse von Bancroft."

The behavior met with in the case of dynamic isomerides depends on the rate of transformation of the one isomer into the other in the liquid state. If the transformation is relatively very rapid, so that equilibrium in the liquid state is rapidly attained, the system will behave like a one-component system; but if the isomeric change is comparatively slow, the behavior will be that of a two-component system; and, in the absence of compound formation between the isomers, a two-branched freezing-point curve will be obtained.

If isomeric transformation takes place with measurable velocity and if the temperature of the liquid equilibrium mixture is allowed to fall, a point on the freezing-point curve of one of the solid isomers will be reached, and that form will separate out, if supercooling is excluded. This is called the "natural" freezing point. The stable solid modification in the neighborhood of the melting point is that which is in equilibrium with the liquid phase at the natural freezing point.

The two solid modifications of dynamic isomerides may be monotropic or enantiotropic. It was found by Soch, working in Bancroft's laboratory, that in the neighborhood of the melting point, the yellow form of benzil-2-carboxylic acid, melting at 141.5°, is the stable form, whereas, at room temperature, the white modification, melting between 125 and 130°, is the stable form. Investigation showed that there is a transition point at about 65°. The two isomeric forms are therefore enantiotropic.

The behavior of a number of different dynamic isomerides was investigated by Bancroft's pupils.

The boiling-point curves of binary liquid mixtures were also investigated by Bancroft and his pupils. Among the mixtures which show a minimum in the boiling-point curve it was found that in many cases one or both of the components is associated. The reason why in such cases a minimum is obtained was first explained by Bancroft as due to the fact that the boiling-point curves of such components intersect.

In other directions, in the investigation of the freezing-point equilibria in three-component systems, in the indirect determination of the composition of the solid phase separating from two-component systems, etc., Bancroft and his pupils were pioneers. At a much later period, when Bancroft's interests had extended to biochemical phenomena, use was made of phase-rule principles in the investigation of the behavior of proteins toward hydrogen chloride and ammonia. It was shown that casein, zein, arachin, fibrin, and gliadin form no chemical compound with ammonia, and that casein, arachin, fibrin, gliadin, and edestin, but not zein, form definite compounds with hydrogen chloride.

To Bancroft's interest in colloids and the colloid state reference has already been made. In his mind, colloid chemistry, which he defined as "the chemistry of life and inheritance and of bubbles, drops, grains, filaments and films," extended over almost the whole field of chemistry and physical chemistry.

Of the subjects which at an early stage attracted Bancroft's interest, one may mention the preparation and properties of emulsions.

In order that a permanent emulsion may be produced on shaking together two immiscible liquids, e.g., water and oil, an emulsifying agent, such as soap, must be added. It is, of course, clear that two different emulsions are possible, an emulsion of oil in water and an emulsion of water in oil. According to the adsorption-film theory of emulsions put forward by Bancroft, an emulsifying agent is adsorbed into the surface separating the two liquids and forms there a coherent film. This film, if in contact with two phases, oil and water, will have two surface tensions, and will tend to curve toward the side having the higher surface tension. The dispersed liquid, therefore, is on the side of the film having the higher surface tension. Since soaps of univalent cations (Na^+, K^+) are readily dispersed in water but not in oil, they form a film which is wetted more readily by water than by oil. Consequently, the surface tension is lower on the water side than on the oil side, and the film tends to curve so that it encloses globules of oil in water. Thereby the area of the side of the film of higher surface tension is reduced compared with that of lower surface tension. Soaps of bivalent cations, however, are freely dispersed in oil, but not in water, and the film is wetted more easily by the oil than by the water. Thereby the formation of globules of water in oil is favored. According to this theory, the preferential wetting of the adsorbed film by water or by oil is an important factor.

The theory put forward by Bancroft was investigated more fully

1258

by his pupils, more especially by G. H. Clowes, and the antagonistic action of Na^+ and Ca^{++} on oil–water emulsions established. This antagonistic action of ions has been found to be of great importance not only in the interpretation of many biological phenomena but also in the oil industry.

In Bancroft's view, surface adsorption was a factor of the greatest importance in many diverse phenomena. In the development of the photographic plate, for example, Bancroft was the first to suggest that adsorption of the developer on the silver bromide grain is the important thing, a view which was later worked out more fully by Sheppard. "If the reducing agent is adsorbed much more strongly by exposed silver bromide than by unexposed silver bromide, the former will develop more rapidly than the latter, and we shall get a negative. If the reducing agent is adsorbed more strongly to unexposed than to exposed silver bromide, we shall get a positive. If there is not much difference in the adsorptions, we shall have exposed and unexposed silver bromide developing at so nearly the same rate that we get a more or less uniform fogging."

Sensitizers, also, of the photographic plate, Bancroft pointed out, must be such that the dye is adsorbed strongly by the silver bromide, does not bleed into the gelatin sufficiently to act as a color screen, and is a reducing agent powerful enough, when exposed to light, to produce a latent image on silver bromide.

In 1922 the First Report, and in the following year the Second Report, of the National Research Council's Committee on Contact Catalysis were published in America. Both reports were written by Bancroft, the chairman of the committee, and were a very stimulating and valuable contribution to the study of contact catalysis. In these reports, which appeared at a time when contact catalysis was largely an empirical art, Bancroft not only showed the position which had been reached but also pointed out what were the fundamental questions which had to be answered and indicated many problems, minor or major, which called for investigation.

For Bancroft, contact catalysis formed an aspect of colloid chemistry and embraced phenomena in which adsorption and surface action play an important part. Two things of fundamental importance, he suggested, had to be done: (1) to determine in what cases definite intermediate compounds are formed, and what they are; (2) to determine what bonds and contravalencies are opened when adsorption takes place and to show that the opening of these bonds and contravalencies accounts for the formation of the re-action products. Later, Bancroft pointed out that the attempt to determine in which group a particular reaction falls, whether there is formation of definite compounds or of indefinite complexes, had led to the brilliant work at Princeton on catalysis at an inter-face.

In the activation process, however, adsorption is only one factor. "In organic chemistry we get activation and reaction as a result of the formation of radicals . . . The conclusion to be drawn is that the organic chemistry of the future will deal with the reactions of radicals instead of the reactions of the molecules."

Even if it might be difficult to point to direct experimental con-tributions by Bancroft to the solution of the problems of contact catalysis, there can be no doubt that through his writings he did much to define and clarify the *science* of catalysis and to encourage others to carry out the necessary experimental investigations.

Towards the end of his academic career Bancroft took up the study of anesthesia, drug addiction, and insanity from the stand-point of colloid chemistry. It can be accepted that for the normal, healthy functioning of the animal organism, a certain balance must be maintained between the degree of dispersion or the hydra-tion and dehydration of the body colloids. Starting with Claude Bernard's theory that the reversible coagulation of the colloids of the sensory nerves produces or accompanies anesthesia, Bancroft and his co-workers concluded from their experimental investiga-tions that narcotics coagulate reversibly the cell colloids and, con-versely, that a reversible coagulation of the cell colloids, however produced, will cause narcosis. At low concentrations, narcotics may have a stimulating effect by decreasing the stability of the col-loids. Similarly, the action of drugs, such as morphine, is due to a coagulation, reversible or irreversible, of the nerve colloids. Ad-ministration of peptizing agents, such as sodium thiocyanate, will facilitate return to normality.

A relation between the state of flocculation or deflocculation of the brain colloids and mental disorders was also believed to have been established, different forms of mental disorder depending on whether the coagulation of the colloids was too great or too little.

The conclusions reached by Bancroft and his fellow workers led to much controversy and were not entirely confirmed by other research workers. It seems very clear that, although the state of aggregation or dispersion of brain colloids no doubt has a bearing on the physiology of narcosis and insanity, factors of importance other than those considered by Bancroft enter in and affect the colloid state.

On many other problems in colloid chemistry and other sections of physical chemistry, Bancroft shed a powerful light which was both exploratory and clarifying, and the inspiration of his enthusiasm and critical exposition still lives.

For particulars about Bancroft I am indebted more especially to his son-in-law, Professor M. L. Nichols, of Cornell University.

From: *J. Chem. Soc.* (*London*), *1953,* pp. 2506–14, abbreviated.

ALEXANDER FINDLAY

·· 89 ··

Marie Curie

1867-1934

A STROLLER in the Latin Quarter of Paris in the winter of 1897 who happened to look into a small building used for storage on the rue Lhomond—that part of old Paris where the French preserve by the street names the glory of their scientists—would have seen a tall handsome man with a brown beard and a woman with a beautiful intellectual face gazing intently at some glass receptacles which were aglow in the darkness with a curious greenish light; even a thin vapor arising from some of the fluid in the basins was faintly luminescent. This couple was Pierre and Marie Curie, who after a day of hard labor in their workshop returned after dinner, as they frequently did, to see that things were all right for the night and to wonder at this curious auroral glow that was produced by the hitherto unknown element, radium, which they were in the process of isolating from the ores of uranium. This faint luminescence was due to the alpha rays which the radium and its emanation gave off, bombarding the atoms of the air, changing their chemical nature and exciting their electrons, and the Curies were observing the birth of the world of the infinitely little and the dawn of the new alchemy. Though they did not know it, their discoveries were to revolutionize the opinions of 2000 years, completely transform modern physics, aid astronomers in their study of the stars, restore to life and health thousands of human beings, and inspire a host of investigators along innumerable lines of study in wholly new fields. It is of interest to discuss briefly what led to this remarkable discovery, for in science no one stands alone; if Röntgen had not discovered in 1895 the rays which bear his name, the name of the thirty-year-old Marie Curie might never have been known to fame.

About the year 1890 physics was supposed to be more or less finished, for it was felt that all the important laws had been discovered, and the only thing remaining was to measure the known phenomena more accurately. It is true that certain scientists in England and Germany were studying the luminous bands and other phenomena which occur when a fairly high-voltage electrical current is passed through a glass tube containing various gases at low concentration. Faraday and Crookes were two who had spent time on this subject without casting much light on its nature. About 1890 an English physicist, J. J. Thompson, studying the effects of the transmission of electricity through rarefied gases, began to make observations which pointed to the fact that the explanation of the luminous phenomenon must be that under the influence of electricity the gas in these laboratory aurora is broken down into electrified particles, for the colored streamers were deflected by a magnet or an electric current outside the gas-containing tube, as Plücker had described in 1858.

It was while working with such a tube in 1895 that Roentgen noticed that photographic plates lying on a table nearby were fogged, and in a few months the discovery of x-rays was made. He, as Plücker in 1858 had noted, saw that the glass of the tube assumed a bright greenish color while the current was passing, and it was thought at first that this greenish color was the source of the radiations.

Poincaré, the famous French mathematician, showed the first x-ray pictures taken by Roentgen at a meeting of the Paris Academy of Sciences in January, 1896, and in the discussion which followed made this same suggestion as a possible explanation in reply to a question by Henri Becquerel. The father of Becquerel had been a famous chemist, and the son possessed a considerable supply of uranium salts which had come into his possession after his father's death.

Uranium salts give off a greenish phosphorescence when exposed to light, so Becquerel covered some photographic plates with black paper, laid the uranium salts on them together with some metal objects and, to his astonishment, found that he had a Roentgen shadow picture. Being a scientist, he tried some uranium which had not been exposed to light and found that it photographed just as well. Then he took some fresh samples of very pure, recently prepared uranium and found that it did not photograph. Becquerel recognized that the photographic effect must lie either in the atoms of the uranium or in a contaminating substance present. Today we know that the uranium breaks down in the course of years into radioactive substances. For a long time these rays were called

Becquerel rays. Becquerel was unable to continue these investigations and suggested, late in 1897, to Pierre and Marie Curie, who shortly before had been married, that they follow up this discovery and find out what was the substance in uranium which possessed photographic capacities.

This selection had a touch of genius in it, for Pierre and Marie Curie combined that persistent and clear-sighted intellectual energy which is so necessary for scientific discovery. They were poor, struggling to do work under disadvantageous conditions, and gladly turned to this new field where Pierre Curie's knowledge of physics and Marie Curie's knowledge of chemistry were needed to solve the problem. In 1898 they announced the discovery of radium.

There has been much discussion as to the part which each played in this discovery. Marie Curie has always said that it was a combination of two closely related minds. It was her duty to do the arduous chemical analyses which were necessary to find the minute traces of radium in the ores with which they worked. They tested all the minerals in the college collection and found a few which had photographic power and also were capable of ionizing the air about them so that it would carry a minute electric current instead of acting as a very perfect insulator, as does ordinary air. These ores were chiefly those containing uranium. It was Pierre Curie's share, as a trained physicist, to take each substance —and there were over thirty known elements in the uranium ores—and determine, with an apparatus which he had invented some time before, the amount of ionization that each sample produced. Thus, as they eliminated metal after metal, they finally found that mixed with bismuth and barium were minute traces of intensely ionizing substances. The first was polonium, the second radium.

The quantity of current which flows when the ionization is produced is a measure of the radioactivity of the element. Radium salts are never sold by weight, but by the ionization which they produce as compared to a standard, and the x-ray used in the treatment of cancer is also measured by this means. In this phase of their work they fell back upon the discoveries which had been made in the past showing that not only x-rays made air a conducting medium, but that all gases became conducting when a current of electricity was passed through a glass tube containing a rarefied gas, thus returning to the early work of Faraday and others who had noted this phenomenon.

Now we know that the currents through these tubes or through what is called an ionization chamber are produced by the separation from a gas of the electrons, a swarm of negatively charged particles so minute that we shall never be able to see them, which themselves being charged with electricity or, according to the modern view, consisting of an electrical charge, are able to transfer a current by moving from one pole to another. Faraday many years before had brought forward a similar idea to explain the conduction of electricity through fluids and the basis of all electrical deposition of metals which had long before reached a practical development, as every piece of Sheffield plate testifies, for the silver in a solution of silver salt is carried from one pole and deposited upon the copper, which forms another pole. Today we know that x-rays are produced by the beating of these electrons upon the surface of a metal, which so perturbs the atoms of that metal that they radiate x-rays, just as an electric current in the ordinary lamp bulb heats the filament and makes it give off electrons, as Thomas Edison showed in 1883 without knowing the explanation.

Thus Marie Curie by her chemical discovery of the element radium inaugurated what may be called modern physics, and it must have been to her a marvelous satisfaction that her daughter, Irène Joliot-Curie, has followed in her foorsteps, making one discovery after another, which would render the name Curie imperishable had her mother never been famous. But it has been granted to no other woman so to revolutionize by a single discovery the whole subject of atomic physics.

When Pierre Curie in 1903 found that radium gave off heat, many of the theories of physics, especially that dealing with the conservation of energy, seemed to be shattered, but shortly afterward it was shown that this heat was produced by the breaking down of the atoms of radium, and the heat production could be accounted for by the slow, spontaneous destruction of this newly discovered element which in some 1700 years loses half of its substance. The final stage which this breakdown reaches is lead, a

1268

lead which cannot be distinguished from the ordinary plumber's lead except by the most refined methods of analysis.

In passing, it may be said that this fact has been used to measure the age of the earth, for the minerals which contain uranium also contain lead and the amount of this lead gives a measure of the number of years that the uranium has been in existence. Hence, like the rings of the great redwood trees in California which show that they are the oldest living creatures, so the amount of radium lead in minerals points to millions of years of life of an ore in which the original uranium has been slowly changed through a series of breakdowns into lead.

The first radium obtained was very impure, and after 1898 Pierre Curie interested himself in the physical properties of this new substance and discovered that it gave off particles which could pass through air for a distance of one to two inches and then suddenly stop. These are now known as the alpha particles from radium and are actually electrified atoms of helium gas. The gamma and beta rays, the latter being negatively charged particles, were found by others, chiefly Rutherford.

Marie Curie then devoted herself to the separation of large quantities of radium from the residue of many tons of uranium ore from Joachimstal in Bohemia, which were placed at her disposal by the Austrian government. After years of hard work requiring a most laborious series of chemical separations and crystallizations of the impure product, she finally succeeded in making a small quantity of absolutely pure radium, the chemical properties of which she studied. She also prepared sealed tubes containing carefully measured amounts of the pure salts which are deposited in the various bureaus throughout the world, including the Bureau of Standards in Washington, to serve as standards for the measurement of radium, just as the standard meter and standard yard are deposited and used for the checking of accurate measuring instruments.

In the meantime, a host of investigators, including the famous Lord Rutherford, who died only a few months ago, began to investigate this profitable field. The Curies had noticed in 1899 that all the apparatus and even the walls of the room in which they worked became radioactive. It was soon found that radium gave off a gas which is now known as emanation or as radon. This gas is really the active substance which characterizes radium, for, if the gas is pumped off, radium ceases to radiate, but in the course of a few days regenerates more radon, which can again be pumped off and used for practical purposes, for a great deal of the treatment of cancer is done with radon rather than with radium. This radon gas has a very short life, losing half of its value in a little over three days.

Further studies showed in the course of the breakdown of radium that a large number of products were obtained, some with an extremely short life measured in thousandths of a second, others which lasted for millions of years. In the uranium-radium family there are sixteen known members, the last being lead. It was soon found that thorium also possessed radioactivity, and the thorium family has thirteen known members, ending again with lead. Later a nactinium family was found, also of many members, and its termination is also in lead. But this was the work of other hands.

Others also invented elaborate theories for the constitution of matter based upon Marie Curie's discoveries. We believe for the moment that an atom of matter is composed of a central nucleus, which contains neutrons and fragments of hydrogen known as protons, and around this as a center rotate the electrons, one for hydrogen and up to 92 for uranium, the metal with the highest atomic weight. The Curies vaguely dreamed of this celestial system with a central sun and surrounding planets, and Irène Curie just missed the discovery of the neutron by a few months. The central mass of neutrons and protons determines the nature of the element and the electrons control its chemical reactions. The electrons can be pulled off by exposure to Roentgen or gamma rays and heat. This does not change the actual chemical nature of the substance, for the atom which has been stripped of some of its electrons collects these quickly from neighboring atoms and becomes normal again. In a gas this recovery takes only a few minutes. But Lord Rutherford showed, in 1919, that if alpha particles from radium are allowed to play upon nitrogen gas some of the nitrogen is destroyed and changed into oxygen and hydrogen. Apparently the helium particle is able to break into the center of the atom and change the atomic weight, for nitrogen has an atomic weight of 14 and the oxygen produced of 17. Helium with an atomic weight of 4 and nitrogen with 14 make an atomic weight of 18 against the oxygen with 17, leaving a missing weight supplied by hydrogen with an atomic number of 1. Both helium and hydrogen can be found in the sealed tube originally containing only nitrogen. This was the first artificial production of new elements and is the field in which Irène Curie has made herself famous.

Whether the radium which Marie Curie discovered will ever be produced artificially by some such process is as yet unknown. Probably it will be found that the amount of energy used up is so enormous that the transformation must remain a laboratory experiment, but Professor Ernest O. Lawrence, of California, has produced several pounds of radioactive sodium by bombarding ordinary salt with atomic bullets, which has certain interesting uses in that if a small quantity is placed on a person's tongue and an electrical machine attached to his foot, it will be found that this sodium is in a few moments in the general circulation, thus testing the speed of absorption. Radioactive iron is being used to study the way in which anemia is cured by iron, and a host of interesting problems have developed from this work. All these things are mentioned merely to show the marvelously fertilizing effect of a single important discovery.

In the light of all these astonishing events it seems as if the pioneer work of Marie Curie was very simple, but this is because the facts have become a part of everyday knowledge and it is the gift of the genius such as this woman possessed to interpret the results of simple chemical analyses, and to infuse into dull decimals a life of the spirit. Thousands of chemists could have done the analytical work which she did, as she employed merely textbook methods, but in her mind lay the power to conceive theories to explain not only what had already been discovered but to open paths for further investigation. In many instances she was unable to carry these on in person, but they were immediately seized upon by others who used the ideas which she had developed to make important discoveries.

Her mind was an extraordinary one. She had no interest in people in general or for the ordinary matters that fill the minds of so large a proportion of the world. She cared nothing for names and titles, as some amusing incidents related in a recently published biography by her daughter, Eve Curie, show. She cared only for a few friends and her scientific work. In this field she had the power of enormous and prolonged concentration on a problem. In her later years, despite serious ill health, she worked in a variety of fields and contributed to all of them. She studied the causes underlying the destruction of cells by radium, for example. During World War I, when her laboratory was closed, she applied herself to the practical use of x-rays and did valuable work in organizing and directing a field system of portable x-ray machines by which surgeons could be guided in the treatment of injured soldiers. It must have greatly pained her, who longed to benefit the human race by her labors and refused to patent or accept money for her method of refining radium, to know that the discovery of radium, which has meant so much for the saving of human life, was also used extensively to coat luminous tapes to guide soldiers through the barbed wire entanglements of the battlefields and to illuminate gunsights in order that men might shoot each other with greater facility.

Her direct contributions to the treatment of cancer were few. She was immensely interested in the work of the Curie Institute under Dr. Claude Regaud, for which she was responsible, and was of great help in teaching the staff the technique of preparing and measuring the radium they were using.

It was interesting to see her mind at work. As she passed through the great Physical Laboratories of Columbia University on her first voyage to America she must have thought of the abandoned storehouse in which she had worked. While nothing interested her but some of the subjects with which she was familiar, she would immediately stop and discuss any work in her own field with a member of the staff, wholly forgetful of time, appointments and the friends who wondered why she did not turn up for lunch, concentrated and interested in the new things that she was able to see in other people's investigative labors. There was not one atom of jealousy in her nature.

That she was a genius there can be no doubt. True, all genius is aided by circumstances and she might have remained a teacher of chemistry in a French school if it had not been that Becquerel made and tested an erroneous theory, and as a result an opportunity was given to her to investigate a new field of science. But it is true also that many others were working in the same direction, but had failed to accomplish anything.

The argument has been made that because simultaneous discoveries are not infrequent in science genius is merely a question of mass action and if only a sufficient number of persons work on a problem, the discovery will be achieved. But since the pioneer work of Plücker in 1858 innumerable persons had run an electric current through an evacuated glass tube and studied the phenomenon which ensued, although it was not until 1895 that Roentgen found that every such tube gave off x-rays. It is related that one English scientist of great ability noted that his photographic plates were fogged in the neighborhood of such a tube, but instead of searching for the reason, he complained to the maker of the plates that they were defective and obtained a new box. Roentgen had the flash, the intuition, if you will, which made him find out why his photographic plates were fogged. So Marie Curie had the intuition which led her to devise the hypothesis that it was the breaking-down of the atoms of uranium which caused it to give off radiation. Without this working hypothesis radium might not have been discovered for another hundred years.

After her husband's death in 1906 Marie Curie was appointed to his chair of radio-physics in the Sorbonne and continued his lectures. In 1910 she published an important work, a "Treatise on Radioactivity" which summarized their labors and those of others up to that time. Later she wrote a charming memoir of her husband, which is too little known, although an admirable translation has been printed in this country. She also published a book on "Radiology and the War" which was drawn from her experiences in organizing a field radiological service for the French army. She continued her scientific researches despite continued ill health and published many short papers on various topics. Her laboratory became a center for research students from all parts of the world.

Much has been made, and I think too much, of the difficult circumstances under which the Curies worked, their poverty and the lack of appreciation in France in the early period of their discoveries, but truly they lived an ideal life. They believed, in spite of her dreams for the emancipation of her native Poland and their desire to help humanity, that they were powerless to change the social order; that if they had had the power they would not have known what to do, and so in working without understanding they would never be sure that they were not doing more harm than good by retarding some inevitable natural evolution. In science, on the contrary, they felt they could accomplish more with their lives than in any other direction; that the field here was more solid and obvious, and however small a territory it might be it was truly their own possession. Marie Curie writes of her early days in Paris: "This life, painful from certain points of view, had for all that a real charm for me. It gave me a precious sense of liberty and independence. If sometimes I felt lonesome, lost in the great city of Paris, my usual state of mind was one of calm and great moral satisfaction. All that I saw and learned delighted me. It was like a new world opening to me, the world of science which I was at last permitted to know in all liberty." Of the abandoned shed which was the best laboratory the School of Physics could give them she writes:

> Despite the exhausting work it was in this miserable old shed that we passed the best and happiest years of our life, devoting our entire days to our work. I shall never be able to express the joy of the untroubled quietness of the atmosphere of research and the excitement of actual progress with the confident hope of still better results. The feeling of discouragement that I sometimes felt after some unsuccessful toil did not last long and gave way to renewed activity. We had happy moments devoted to a quiet discussion of our work while walking around our shed.

Another and far different person has described the same sensation:

> I do not know how far it is possible to convey to anyone who has not experienced it the peculiar interest, the peculiar satisfaction, that lies in a sustained research. It is a different thing from any other sort of human effort. You are free from the exasperating conflict with your fellow creatures that, for me, is its peculiar merit.

1274

Scientific truth is the remotest of mistresses. She hides in strange places; she is attained by tortuous and laborious routes. She is always there, winning you to her, and she will not fail you. She is yours and mankind's forever. She is reality. You cannot change her by advertisement or clamor nor stifle her in vulgarities. Things grow under your hands when you serve her, things that are permanent as nothing else is permanent in the whole life of man. That, I think, is the peculiar satisfaction of science and its enduring reward.

So I think that if Marie Curie had been asked in her last days, as she looked across to the sunlit mountains of Savoy from her room at the sanatorium at Sancellemoz, what her life had been, she would have replied that it had been full of human affection and companionship with one whom she loved, full of the joys of research, of hard work and of final achievement, crowned at last with the highest of human rewards, the admiration by the few great minds capable of understanding the superb nature of those discoveries which were hers and render her name imperishable as long as the human race exists.

From: *Sci. Monthly,* April 1938, p. 378, read at a memorial meeting held at Columbia University, New York, on Jan. 20, 1938.

FRANCIS CARTER WOOD

·· *90* ··

Vladimir N. Ipatieff

1867-1952

RUSSIA has produced many notable chemists, but three tower above all others. They are Lomonosov, Mendeleev, and Ipatieff. Of these it has been suggested that Ipatieff stands out as having "exerted greater influence on world chemistry than his two fellow countrymen."[1]

An examination of Ipatieff's life and achievements shows three significant periods. The first period embraces his childhood, education, and progress up to and including his administrative work during World War I. The second period covers his work during the Russian Revolution, when he was active until 1930 in developing the Russian chemical industry as well as his scientific investigations. The third period includes the time from 1931 until his death on November 29, 1952, in Chicago, at the age of eighty-five.

Special emphasis will be given here to the first period, since in it will be found the clues to the development of his outstanding work and personality. The successes which he accomplished in his later life may be traced directly to his chemical experiences in this first period.

FIRST PERIOD, FROM 1867 TO 1917

Vladimir Nikolaevich Ipatieff[2] was born in Moscow on November 21, 1867 (according to the Roman calendar). His early education in reading and writing was provided by his mother, who was well educated and whose family was well represented in the intellectual aristocracy of occupations, such as teachers, tutors, mathematicians, and physicians.

Since his studies with his mother progressed slowly, however, he was entered in a local school where he remained for a couple of terms after which, at the age of eight, he was admitted to a preparatory class of the Fifth Classical Moscow Gymnasium.

His mother's impaired health and her removal to the Crimea resulted in his eventual withdrawal from the Classical Gymnasium to study at his father's home in Moscow, in order to prepare for admission to the second class of the Third Moscow Military Gym-

1279

nasium. Following the usual custom among the Russian nobility, Ipatieff began to prepare for a military career. The loss of his mother's influence, at the age of ten, undoubtedly affected him in many ways. His mother died when he was twelve years old, and his governess, who later became his stepmother, was almost the antithesis of his mother: she was noted for her penuriousness, she generated neither love nor respect, and had no interest whatsoever in his or his brother's education. She also influenced the acquisition of certain religious prejudices, in spite of which he became a devout member of the Russian Orthodox Church.

An uncle who served as a private tutor to wealthy Moscow families provided him and his brother with additional education, and interested Vladimir in various extracurricular (scientific) subjects which were not part of the work of the gymnasium.

Upon promotion to the sixth class Ipatieff became interested in mathematics and studied it beyond class requirements. Although his teacher in mathematics considered that he had sufficient ability to study higher mathematics and that he should be admitted to an artillery or engineering school, his grades were too low and he was denied admission to the Mikhail Artillery Academy. Upon graduation he entered the Alexander Military School in Moscow on August 31, 1884.

Ipatieff's first serious interest in chemistry had started in the fifth or sixth class of the Third Military Gymnasium. When he entered the Alexander Military School his interest in science was renewed. In spite of unsuitable texts, ineffective teaching, and poor organization of laboratory work, chemistry interested him more and more, and as a result of his interest he finished at the top of his class with the highest grades in both mathematics and chemistry.

His real teachers were Mendeleev's "The Fundamentals of Chemistry" (third edition, 1884) and Menshutkin's "Analytical Chemistry." He read these books, carrying out the reactions and experimenting as he proceeded.

Ipatieff was made an officer on August 7, 1887. On becoming an officer each appointee received a sum of money from the government. Since this would not pay for everything, his father gave him some extra cash for clothing. Undecided for a time whether to buy a winter coat or a small chemistry laboratory, Ipatieff did not hesitate long and, as might be expected, the laboratory was his choice.

In August, 1889, Ipatieff took a competitive entrance examination and was accepted by the Mikhail Artillery Academy, where his dream of devoting himself to the subject of chemistry was about to be realized.

Soon after joining the Mikhail Academy, Ipatieff learned of the Russian Physical-Chemical Society which was sponsored by St. Petersburg University. In spite of the fact that only graduates of institutions of higher learning were eligible, Ipatieff was admitted to membership in 1890 and remained a member until 1937, when the Soviet Government cancelled his membership and forbade Russian chemists to mention his name in their scientific publications. It was in the Society that he reported many of his scientific discoveries and came in personal contact with such scientific stars as Dmitri Ivanovich Mendeleev, 1834–1907, Nikolai Aleksandrovich Menshutkin, 1842–1907, Fedor Fedorovich Beilstein, 1838–1906, and others who were a great inspiration to him.

In 1891, in spite of his heavy work load at the Academy, he finished some analytical work on crystallization in steel. His paper was suggested and approved as a report before the Imperial Technological Society. Although he was not a member of this technical society, his paper, "Chemical Investigations of the Structure of Steel," was published in the Society's *Annals* in 1892. To his delight, he was asked to read his paper before the Russian Physical-Chemical Society at a meeting in March, 1892. The report was well received, and even the outspoken and critical Mendeleev, who was chairman, said a few words of approval.

Ipatieff's two chemical manuals published for Academy students, his work on the structure of steel, and his success in the field of chemistry and chemical technology marked him for appointment at the Academy as an instructor.

Soon after he received the appointment as instructor at the Mikhail Artillery Academy he married Barbara Ermakova, whom he had known for ten years.

At the Academy he lectured on theoretical chemistry and published a set of notes entitled "Principal Laws of Chemistry," which went into a number of editions. Besides all this, Ipatieff was required by Academy regulation to present an approved dissertation to the Academy conference three years after his appointment as an instructor. Since Ipatieff was familiar with the literature of carbides (compounds of metals with carbon) he decided to present a dissertation on their preparation and chemical properties.

Toward the end of 1894 Ipatieff reported his discovery of dimethyltrimethylene glycol to the Chemical Society. As a reward for this discovery the Chemical Society gave him the Butlerov prize for the best work done by a young chemist.

Early in 1895, Ipatieff presented his dissertation. The final subject was "The Action of Bromine upon Tertiary Alcohols and of Hydrogen Bromide upon Acetylene and Allene Hydrocarbons in Acetic Acid Solutions."

The results obtained from Ipatieff's investigations reported in his dissertation had suggested to him that the same reaction should be studied with other types of hydrocarbons. At that time, diolefins containing two nonadjacent double bonds had been studied very little. The hydrocarbon C_5H_8, isoprene, had long (1860) been known as a decomposition product of natural rubber and turpentine; but its structure was entirely unknown, and Beilstein's *Handbook* of 1895 placed a question mark after its formula.

Ipatieff immediately started to prepare isoprene by the dry distillation of raw paracaoutchouc. His study of isoprene was postponed, however, and it was not until 1897 that he proved its structure and then synthesized it.

During 1896 he was advised by A. E. Favorsky to continue his study of organic chemistry in Munich under the great Adolf von Baeyer. Baeyer's laboratory was equipped for some eighteen students who were working toward the Doctor's degree, and also a small number of postdoctorate research chemists, among whom were Willstätter, Beshorn, Gomberg, Piccard, and others. Ipatieff worked directly under Baeyer's supervision.

Ipatieff's nearest co-workers were Gomberg, the American, and Koch, the Englishman. Gomberg was born in the southern part of Russia, had emigrated to the United States at the age of nineteen and, fortunately for Ipatieff, could speak Russian.

Ipatieff's work progressed rapidly. He obtained caronic acid and proved its structure. Considerable brown tar was formed during the reaction by the oxidation of carone ($C_{10}H_{16}O$, a cyclic ketone

1282

of the terpene series) and when Ipatieff asked Baeyer what to do with it he always said, "Throw it out." Ipatieff thought he might extract some substance from this tar which would explain the low yield of acid. Keeping his work to himself, he managed to extract a new acid which turned out to be a spatial isomer of the first acid.

Back at the Academy Ipatieff's work in the laboratory was concentrated upon an investigation of the little-known allene class of hydrocarbons. The action of sodium malonic ester on the dibromides obtained from allene hydrocarbons and also the action of nitrosyl chloride upon the double bond were especially interesting to him. These investigations served later as the subject of his professorial dissertation.

Studying the action of sodium malonic ester on the dibromides of olefins (the Perkin reaction), he found that one does not always obtain a cyclic acid when one atom of bromine is located on the tertiary carbon atom in the dibromide, as was proposed by Perkin.

On the night of November 12, 1897, when his youngest son, Vladimir, was born, he went to bed on the couch in his study much later than usual. As he lay there he was haunted by this mysterious compound. Suddenly the idea came to him that it had the structure of acetylene tetracarbonester

$$\begin{array}{c} \text{(EtOOC} \\ \text{(EtOOC} \end{array} \overset{\overset{\displaystyle H}{|}}{>}\overset{}{C} - \overset{\overset{\displaystyle H}{|}}{C} < \begin{array}{c} \text{COOEt)} \\ \text{COOEt)} \end{array}$$

formed by the condensation of two molecules of sodium malonic ester with the loss of two atoms of sodium under the influence of the unstable dibromide. He jumped out of bed and looked in Beilstein's *Handbook* and was amazed and delighted to find that the physical and chemical properties given in the literature for this compound agreed perfectly with those of the compound that he had obtained.

Ipatieff had started to write his dissertation for the rank of professor in the fall of 1898, and by the end of that year it was ready for publication under the title, "Allene Hydrocarbons, the Reaction of Nitrosyl Chloride and of Nitric Oxide on Organic Compounds Containing a Double Bond, and the Synthesis of Isoprene."

In 1900 Ipatieff also became interested in unsaturated hydro-carbons, which induced him to study Thiele's method for the preparation of 1,3-butadiene by pyrolysis of isoamyl alcohol. Ipati-eff found the yield of butadiene quite small. Little or no attention had been paid to the nature of the liquid products obtained in this reaction. Ipatieff investigated the residual liquid which he found to be isovaleric aldehyde when he used an iron tube in his experiments, but very little, if any, of this substance was formed when he used a glass tube. This work proved that pyrolytic de-composition which previously had been considered uncontrollable with the formation of products such as carbon, hydrogen, methane, ethane, ethylene, etc., could be controlled by the use of catalysts to produce individual compounds. Ipatieff was the first to recognize this important principle. As a further example, when alcohol is heated in the presence of brass, zinc, or copper, it produces acetal-dehyde plus hydrogen, and when heated in the presence of alumina the products are ethylene and water. With these discoveries, the basis of Ipatieff's scientific career began to emerge.

From the very beginning of the study of the decomposition of alcohols in the presence of iron Ipatieff had realized that he was dealing with a new phenomenon which the Russian chemists called a contact reaction and other European chemists called a catalytic reaction. The novelty in his discovery was that these re-actions could take place at high temperatures; previously it had been assumed that there was a complete breakdown of the alcohol molecule under such conditions, and that no clean-cut reactions would occur.

The discovery of the catalytic decomposition of alcohol into aldehyde and hydrogen opened an entirely new field of investigation for him. The reaction was one of catalytic dehydrogenation (the removal of hydrogen), and a detailed study was necessary to eluci-date the mechanism and gather sufficient information to predict new catalysts for the reaction.

After reporting his first work in catalysis at the January, 1901, meeting of the Russian Physical-Chemical Society, he sent the article on the catalytic removal of hydrogen from an organic mole-cule to Berlin to be published in the *Berichte* of the German Chemical Society. It was published in March of that year, which meant that his work appeared ahead of the first and famous article by Sabatier (Paul, 1854–1941) and Senderens (Jean Baptiste, 1856–1937) in the *Comptes rendus* on the hydrogenation of benzene in the presence of reduced nickel.

At another meeting of the Russian Physical-Chemical Society, Ipatieff gave a detailed report on the catalytic decomposition of alcohols under the influence of various metallic catalysts, and proposed a reaction mechanism. To test his hypothesis, he studied the catalytic effect of various metal oxides, and his views—that if a metal causes the aldehyde decomposition of alcohols its oxide should do the same—where completely confirmed.

In the fall of 1901 Ipatieff discovered the effect of alumina on olefinic decomposition of alcohol into ethylene. The enormous field of the dehydration of organic compounds opened before Ipatieff. He began by examining the catalytic action of silica, alumina, and finally clay, in the preparation of olefin from alcohol. Alumina proved to be the best catalyst.

In the spring of 1902 Ipatieff systematized his lectures in organic chemistry at the Artillery Academy and the following year used them as the basis for a textbook "Inorganic Chemistry" suitable for technical institutions and universities. In all, seven editions of this book appeared, and the later editions were considered especially useful for their systematic and understandable presentation of the different types of organic compounds.

Ipatieff's greatest discovery in this period (1903) was the isomerization of the olefin isopropylethylene into trimethylene and, also, that ether hydrocarbons, cyclic and open chain, could be isomerized in the presence of catalysts. These catalytic isomerizations attracted the attention of the scientific world, but they were not applied practically until thirty-five years later. It was not until the 1930's that the reactions were seriously considered by scientists as well as petroleum technologists as a means of obtaining high quality gasoline.

In 1903, Ipatieff showed for the first time that in the presence of powdered aluminum, ethyl alcohol decomposed at 600°C. to give not only aldehyde and ethylene but also butadiene. Later Lebedev studied this reaction in greater detail and, by using mixed catalysts, so increased the yield of butadiene that this method could be used in the manufacture of synthetic rubber.

In 1903, also, in order to study the reversibility of reactions discovered in 1900, Ipatieff experimented laboriously for a whole year to construct an apparatus suitable for high-pressure work.

In the fall of 1904, using high-pressure technique, he began the study for hydrogenating organic compounds in the liquid phase. This study established for the first time the reversibility of catalytic reactions in the presence of such catalysts as nickel, iron and zinc

In spite of the war between Russia and Japan, which began early in 1904, and the political disorders of 1905, Ipatieff was able to continue his research without interruption. The results obtained in this work as well as previous work started Ipatieff on the study of what was later called destructive hydrogenation. These data were used later by Friedrich Bergius (1884–1948), in decomposing various types of coals, tars, etc., in the presence of hydrogen to produce low-boiling hydrocarbons for motor fuels.

Toward the end of 1909 Ipatieff discovered a very interesting phenomenon while studying the hydrogenation of organic compounds containing a double bond. The hydrogenation of amylene or cyclohexene in the presence of a copper oxide catalyst is slow and incomplete in a bronze-lined, high-pressure bomb. But the reaction is rapid and complete in an iron bomb in the presence of copper oxide. The idea then came to him that the iron walls of the bomb increased the catalytic action of copper oxide. Ipatieff considered this one of the most important of his discoveries.

In 1911 Ipatieff showed for the first time the cyclization of aliphatic hydrocarbons. The formation of the abnormal product of polymerization—paraffin hydrocarbons—was explained as well as possible on the basis of the experimental data; a complete picture of its formation had to await further study. Not until twenty years later, when Ipatieff was in the United States, was he able (with his co-worker Dr. Pines) to study this reaction thoroughly in the presence of phosphoric acid catalysts. They were able to give a complete explanation of the formation of aromatic hydrocarbons. The formation of the latter from cyclized olefins must be

1286

accompanied by the liberation of hydrogen, and it is this hydrogen that adds to the olefinic polymers to convert them to paraffins.

This complicated reaction of ethylene, which Ipatieff named "conjunct polymerization," is an example of intermolecular hydrogenation, hydrogen being removed from one molecule and transferred to another.

During 1912 Ipatieff hydrogenated carbohydrates at relatively low temperatures. Emil Fischer had reduced monosaccharides (glucose, fructose, and others) to the corresponding alcohols (mannite, sorbite, etc.) by means of sodium amalgam. Ipatieff's experiments indicated that hydrogen under pressure easily converts mono- and polysaccharides to the corresponding alcohols.

In 1912 Ipatieff showed for the first time that the reduction of carbon monoxide and carbon dioxide by means of hydrogen at a high temperature does not proceed to completion and that the reaction is reversible, that is, the water that is formed during this reaction can oxidize methane back again to hydrogen and carbon monoxide. This reaction was later used industrially for the production of hydrogen.

The desirability of studying the pyrolysis (cracking) of petroleum and its distillates under pressure, in the presence and absence of catalysts, for the purpose of obtaining gasoline was discussed with the director of Nobel Brothers Laboratory at Baku, Russia. (The Nobel Brothers Laboratory had been formed by Robert (1829–1896) and Ludwig (1831–1888), brothers of Alfred Nobel, founder of the Nobel Prize.) The director approved this idea, and permission was obtained from the Board of Directors to do work on it. When the first data were reported to the Board of Directors they decided to continue the investigations. The World War of 1914–1918 forced them to halt their work, and it was not published until 1920. When Ipatieff arrived in the United States in 1931 he became acquainted with the various American methods for cracking petroleum, and he realized that the processes were practically the same as those which he and his co-worker had worked out.

Investigations in 1913 dealt with both organic and inorganic compounds. He was particularly interested in the separation of acids under pressure by means of carbonic acid. Experiments showed that carbonic acid can replace acetic acid from its salts, and when the carbonates of the metal are insoluble in water, the salt separates in the form of crystals.

That same year, a Finnish chemist, working under Ipatieff's supervision, made two investigations in the field of high pressure. His study of the polymerization of ethylene in the presence of catalysts was the more interesting. For the first time it was shown that ethylene polymerizes in the presence of aluminum chloride to a liquid at room temperature. This important discovery was later used by the petroleum industry for the production of gasoline from olefins and for the manufacture of synthetic lubricating oils.

Ipatieff's other consulting work was in the new branch of industrial chemistry—the hardening of vegetable oils into solid fats. As an industrial consultant Ipatieff spent part of his time studying various technical problems. Ipatieff carried out one series of experiments on different catalysts which might be suitable for the hardening of fats. The number of articles which were beginning to appear in English and German scientific literature on the application of metal oxides as catalysts in the hydrogenation of organic compounds indicated the influence of Ipatieff's work abroad.

From 1913 on, Ipatieff became more and more interested in the actual application of his scientific knowledge to the needs of industry. Unfortunately, the Russian chemical industry was too immature to use these scientific discoveries even then available. Ipatieff did not take out patents, indicating that he was a scientist and wanted complete freedom in his work, which he would not have if he had to be concerned with patents.

Ipatieff's research early in 1914 centered around the precipitation of zinc from a solution of its salt by means of hydrogen under pressure. According to the Nernst theory on the dissolving of metals, hundreds of thousands of atmospheres of hydrogen would be required to separate zinc from a solution of its salt. Ipatieff achieved this result at a pressure of 400 atmospheres and at 350°C.

In the Russian Empire before World War I, there was no department, despite the existence of the special Ministry of Trade and Industry, which could direct the development of Russia's national economy in time of war. The Ministry had little knowl-

1288

edge of Russian industry as a whole, and it knew even less about its infant chemical industry. The history of the Russian chemical industry during the war and immediately after is best given by an account of the activity of the Chemical Committee of which Ipatieff was chairman. This committee united all branches of the chemical industry, it served the needs of the Army, and also prepared for the eventual return of industry to a peacetime role.

World War I brought new and responsible assignments to Ipatieff. The first of these was the organization of all chemical defense. Russia did not have a sufficient accumulation of munitions or individual munitions plants. In a short time Ipatieff mobilized all Russian industry for this work, and the production of explosives increased in six months from 60 tons per month to 3300 tons. In two years' time an enormous chemical industry was brought into existence, and Ipatieff was justly recognized as its creator. This and other items of interest are detailed in the Second Period.

SECOND PERIOD, FROM 1917 TO 1931

The second period of Ipatieff's life began with very trying days in Petrograd (now Leningrad). In this period a number of events in the life of Ipatieff are enumerated which proved trying, time-consuming, and ineffective. The accumulation of events forced upon Ipatieff the belief that scientific thought and expression would be continually curtailed and that freedom for such activities would, of necessity, need to be pursued elsewhere.

According to Ipatieff, the October Revolution (1917), masterfully led by Lenin, saved the conutry from anarchy, and at least temporarily preserved its intelligentsia and material wealth. Ipatieff also maintained that but for the Bolsheviks in 1917 and 1918 he probably would have lost his life.

Since the problem of changing the chemical industry from a wartime to a peacetime basis was paramount, Ipatieff, as chairman of the Chemical Committee, called a special meeting in January, 1918. The results were frustrating and indefinite, and little or nothing came from the discussion.

Life in Petrograd during 1919 to 1920 became more and more

unpleasant, and Ipatieff's research almost stopped. Toward the end of 1919 he acted as consultant in the reorganization of a soap and candle factory in Kazan. Later, he was sent to inspect government arsenals.

In 1920 Ipatieff became director of the National Institute of Scientific and Technical Investigations (formerly the Central Chemical Laboratory). Because of the acute sugar shortage in 1920, Ipatieff served as consultant to a small factory producing saccharin.

On the other hand, 1921 was a record year for Ipatieff. In order to speed the rebuilding of Russian industry it was voted to combine trade and industry under one commissariat as in the tsarist days. Ipatieff was asked to head the newly established Chemical Administration which was finally approved by Lenin and the All-Russian Central Executive Committee, with the assignment to secure foreign aid in the redevelopment program of the chemical industry.

In 1923, Ipatieff studied the destructive hydrogenation of naphthalene. It was demonstrated for the first time that molecules of polycyclic organic compounds can be cracked into simpler molecules without the formation of polymers or noticeable quantities of carbon. Also, naphthalene and tetrahydronaphthalene (the product of the hydrogenation of naphthalene) give a large quantity of aromatic compounds, such as benzene, toluene, etc., in the presence of the mixed hydrogenating catalyst nickel oxide and alumina.

Government duties occupied Ipatieff's time in 1923; that fall, in accordance with previous commitments, he spent a month in Germany negotiating for the production of mustard gas. This was followed in 1924 by work on the Russian-German Commission for the construction of poison gas factories. Research duties occupied the remainder of his time. During 1926 changes took place which strongly influenced Ipatieff's entire future in the U.S.S.R.

The Russian-German Commission on poison gas production had become very time-consuming, and the Chemical Administration meetings spent endless hours discussing current and tentative problems of the chemical industry. Ipatieff advised that Russia establish its own production of calcium cyanamide since this could be used directly as a fertilizer for agriculture. This advice received slight consideration.

Also, there were many disputes over the future development of various branches of the chemical industry, particularly those relating to dyes and to nitrogen fixation. One of the most heated controversies had to do with the establishment of the production of naphthol by-products. Other unpleasant incidents occurred in carrying out Ipatieff's duties, and in the end Ipatieff decided to leave the Chemical Administration.

About this time also, significant changes in the independence of the Academy of Sciences were taking place. Within a year the government appointed a commission of academicians and party officials to discuss basic reforms which would ensure that the Academy's activities conformed in great measure to the needs of the Socialist government. This action ended the Academy's independence.

Toward the close of 1926 Ipatieff prepared to organize another laboratory for catalytic experiments under high pressure, the one at the Artillery Academy being too small for his needs. Accordingly, the year 1927 saw the official launching of the Institute of High Pressures in Leningrad, its expenses being included in the budget of the Institute of Applied Chemistry.

From the High Pressures laboratory Ipatieff and associates published more than twenty completed research reports during 1927 to 1928.

About this time Ipatieff was chosen as chairman of a commission to study the conversion of benzene and toluene to explosives. During the Scientific Week in Berlin to honor Russian scientists, Ipatieff, at a dinner given by Walther Nernst, met Albert Einstein. During the dinner Ipatieff was asked why he did not take up permanent residence abroad. He replied that he had not the slightest intention of leaving his country because he sincerely believed that he could serve her. He was sure that civilized life could be reestablished only by the united efforts of all Russians.

Professor Einstein, overhearing his remarks, commented: "I agree with the Professor; a man can act no differently." Within three years, however, both Ipatieff and Einstein left their native countries for the United States.

About this time it was determined that there was a possibility of developing a process in which all of the phosphorus employed in a given experiment would be completely converted into pure phosphoric acid. The results were remarkable: he and Carl Freitag, graduate assistant of the Technological Institute of Charlottenburg, were able to oxidize phosphorus into phosphoric acid at about 300°C. and to obtain pure hydrogen without any phosphines. Dr. Caro, head of the Bayer plant, was exuberant. He told Ipatieff that I. G. Farbenindustrie was greatly interested in the process since they had bought a patent from a Swedish engineer for the oxidation of phosphorus, but the acid obtained was impure, containing the lower acids, and the hydrogen produced required purification from phosphines.

In mid-October, Ipatieff went abroad again, this time with a delegation of Soviet scientists to attend the centennial celebration of the birth of Marcellin Berthelot (1827–1907) in Paris. For the first time since the war German scientists were invited to attend a French celebration, and for this occasion Germany sent the greatest in German chemistry, Willstätter, Wieland, Haber, and Nernst. Ipatieff renewed his acquaintance with them, and for the first time met Paul Sabatier, then seventy years old.

Ipatieff accepted an invitation to attend the International Congress of Pure and Applied Chemistry held at The Hague in 1928, and from there went to Strasbourg. His report to the Congress on Industrial Chemistry was scheduled for the final session at which Raymond Poincaré (1860–1934) was to be present. Speaking in French, Ipatieff summarized the development of his basic ideas on hydrogenation under pressure which had resulted in the production of liquid fuels from coal and heavy oils as developed by Bergius and by the I. G. Farbenindustrie.

During this meeting it was announced that the French Society of Industrial Chemistry had awarded Ipatieff the Berthelot Medal.

During the year Ipatieff made several trips to Essen to test a special gasproof fabric which could be used in making clothing for the army. In the days when Ipatieff was concerned with the manufacture of phosgene he was impressed with the work of E. I. Spitalsky (professor of chemistry at Moscow University) on the

various methods for the synthesis of phosgene. He found Spitalsky's advice on chemical problems, gases, gas masks, science industry invaluable, and in time Spitalsky was made Ipatieff's
assistant in his various activities for the U.S.S.R. Spitalsky was
quite critical of the government, and since he had worked hard to
develop poison gas preparations he disliked abandoning this field.
With great consternation Ipatieff learned, in 1929, that Spitalsky
had been arrested. It was incredible to Ipatieff that such a valuable
and talented man, who had worked incessantly for the good of the
U.S.S.R., could be charged with any criminal activity. Following
Spitalsky's arrest rumors circulated in Leningrad that many other
important men in the chemical industry, including Ipatieff, soon
would be arrested.

When the names for the Twelfth International Power Congress
to be held in Berlin on June 30, 1930, were announced, Ipatieff's
was not among them. He was sent, however, as a replacement for
one of the Communists. On the threat of otherwise refusing to go
to the Congress, he managed also to obtain a passport for his wife.

Since Ipatieff had become increasingly aware that freedom of
scientific thought in the Soviet Academy would be restricted and
that academicians would be publicly criticized for their scientific
labors, he and his wife left Russia early in 1930. He could not
free himself from the sad feeling that he would never again see
his beloved country, his beloved Leningrad, and those laboratories
in which he had spent the happiest hours of his life.

THIRD PERIOD, FROM 1931 TO 1953

It has been suggested that the life of Ipatieff reads like a tale
from the Arabian nights. Under the tsarist regime he became an
honored and wealthy Russian. He was richly rewarded by his scientific endeavors, but the Revolution took everything from him
except his knowledge and scientific skill. Under the Soviet regime
he again rose to outstanding recognition. The loss of freedom made
him practically an exile from his country at the age of sixty-two,
while working on chemical processes in Germany. A year later he
came to the United States and in this country, not then too friendly

to one of his nationality and with whose language, habits, and customs he was quite unfamiliar, he started to build again.

In the United States Ipatieff[3] successfully continued his scientific work in the research laboratories of the Universal Oil Product Company, (Riverside) Chicago, Illinois, where he came to be considered "the foremost expert in catalytic reactions in connection with petroleum refining." After strenuous work in the laboratory, Ipatieff, at the age of sixty-four, took lessons in English. His success in his newly adopted land is scientific history.

Before coming to the United States from Russia Ipatieff had accomplished more than most men do in a lifetime, having served both the tsarist and the Soviet regimes; each had awarded him its highest recognition. Among his achievements are the early recognition of the catalytic principle, invention of high pressure processes, and outstanding work on dehydration. One of his most revolutionary discoveries was the alkylation of paraffins with olefins, which was thought to be impossible. This reaction along with catalytic dehydrogenation, isomerization, and polymerization made possible the high octane gasoline and the synthetic rubber so vital in war and peace.

As the years went by, Ipatieff applied his favorite processes, his catalysts and his promoters, more and more to the field of petroleum. The great developments in the petroleum industry in the last few decades, together with the triumph of modern internal combustion engines, have been due to the work of thousands of different scientists and engineers. However, if one were to select one man who more than any other was responsible for these developments, one would cite the discoveries, the genius, the development, and the indefatigable energy of Ipatieff.

In the United States Ipatieff enlarged upon his original discoveries of hydrogenation and dehydrogenation. In polymerization he continued his work on the changing of gases, which were too volatile for motor fuels, into liquids capable of being used. He extended his work of alkylation in the field of isomerization, and the application of his catalysts and promoters to cyclization in order to produce new products and more efficient fuels.

His work in the United States is further characterized by the discovery of the "solid phosphoric acid" catalyst for the polymerization of olefins, for the discovery of the alkylation of olefins by isoparaffins, and for work on the isomerization of alkanes.

Early in the work of polymerization of olefins it was realized that the less reactive olefins are accelerated by the presence of more active olefins. For example, pure alpha butylene was not polymerized by a weak catalyst under certain experimental conditions, whereas a commerical sample of butylenes containing 30 per cent of isobutylene mixed with alpha and beta butylenes was polymerized by the same catalyst to the extent of 50 per cent under identical experimental conditions.

By the use of the "solid phosphoric acid" catalyst Ipatieff and co-workers were able to obtain gasoline from ethylene and to convert gases from the cracking process to high octane fuel. Ipatieff conducted many experiments on the polymerization of propylene and other olefins in the presence of so-called "solid phosphoric acid." Mixing phosphoric acid with various substances permits the preparation of contact masses rich in phosphoric acid which are solid at the temperature at which polymerization of propylene and other olefins occur.

In 1938, in order to pursue purely academic research more easily and to be able to teach his techniques to students, Ipatieff established (with the support of the Universal Oil Products Company) the Ipatieff High Pressure Laboratory at Northwestern University. His interest in this work may be seen from the fact that he donated $26,000 toward this research laboratory. He also established a trust fund of $35,000, the interest from which after his death would be used for prizes in chemistry, to be awarded under the jurisdiction of the American Chemical Society to students in chemistry in any country, irrespective of creed or race.

Evans' account of Ipatieff's connection with Northwestern University is quite interesting and is recounted below:

In July 1931, Dr. Egloff called at my home, and he had with him a tall, dark, distinguished looking man that he introduced as Dr. Ipatieff. Now, fortunately, I had heard of a Russian chemist called Ipatieff, who had done a great deal of work on high pressure catalysis. In my ignorance, I imagined that the Ipatieff whose work was familiar to all chemists had been dead many years, and so I said to Dr. Egloff, "But surely this is not Ipatieff?" Egloff bowed not too gracefully, and said, "Yes, this is the great Ipatieff."

Because of that visit I was instrumental in having Northwestern University take him on the staff. This was not any easy task, for Ipatieff was just an unknown Russian as far as the president and board of trustees were concerned. But I accomplished my task, and when I cash in, and they see fit to enumerate the little things I have been able to do, I hope they say, "He brought Ipatieff to Northwestern University." This will be glory enough for me.

In 1940 a committee of American scientists awarded Ipatieff (for his achievements in chemistry) the highest and most coveted of American prizes, the Willard Gibbs Medal. Russia should feel especially proud of this award because up to that time it had been given to only three European scientists: Arrhenius (1911), Curie (1921), and Willstätter (1933).

Beginning his career in the United States at an age when most men retire, Ipatieff published thereafter about 150 scientific papers and obtained more than 200 patents. He had already published some 200 papers before he left Russia.

Of all the compliments Ipatieff ever received, he indicated that none pleased him as much as the one from the late Homer Adkins, who stated that: "There is no chemist in the world today who has been so productive over so long a period of time as yourself. Neither time nor place nor political nor economic conditions has stopped the flow of your creative and fruitful work in chemistry."

During his long and fruitful career many honors came to him. He was elected a member of the Academy of Sciences, in both Russia and America (the only man to have held regular membership in the National Academies of both the U.S.S.R. and the United States), he received an honorary Doctor of Chemistry degree at St. Petersburg University, Doctor Honoris Causa at the German University of Munich and at the French University of Strasbourg, and was elected Honorary Member of the Deutsche Chemische Gesellschaft and of the Göttingen Academy of Science. The French Government made him Commander of the Legion of Honor; he was the recipient of the Berthelot Medal in France; of

1296

small and large prizes of A. I. Butlerov of the Russian Academy of Sciences. After the revolution he became President of the Central Chemical Bureau in Moscow and was the founder of the High Pressure Research Institute in Leningrad. For this valuable work he received the Lenin Prize. His book entitled "Catalytic Reactions at High Pressure and Temperature" outlines the work on catalysis in which he specialized.

In reference to his own life Ipatieff said:

> I have lived a long and busy life; I have had contact with a very large number of people of all types and all occupations; I have lived through several wars and revolutions; and I cannot say that fate has been unkind to me. I am happy that in my later years, despite the troublesome times through which I have lived, I have kept my love for my chosen science, and that I still retain my physical strength. And I am most happy that I can spend these later years in this wonderful country where I have found so many talented assistants and friends.

Ipatieff was a man of charm and kindness who enjoyed social contacts. He was always ready with encouragement and assistance to anyone interested in advancing science. He was an indefatigable worker who set himself a hard schedule, any disturbance to which upset him.

Several months before his death the Universal Oil Products Company entered into negotiations with Northwestern University to establish the Vladimir Ipatieff Research Professorship by which the company grants the university $25,000 annually for the salaries of a professor and an assistant and for other expenses. It was the source of much gratification that Ipatieff had been notified of the final details of this professorship, a few days before his death on November 29, 1952. His wife, Barbara, with whom he had celebrated their sixtieth wedding anniversary, survived him but a few days and died on December ninth.

NOTES AND REFERENCES

1 Evans, Ward G., *Chem. Eng. News, 25,* 3720, December 15, 1947.
2 Ipatieff, Vladimir N., "The Life of a Chemist, Memoirs of V. N. Ipatieff," Stanford University Press, 1946. Background cited in the first and second

period of this biography was obtained from this reference, edited by Xenia J. Eudin, Helen D. Fisher, and Harold H. Fisher. (Permission to use this material was granted by Stanford University Press by letter dated February 18, 1959.)

3 "Catalytic Reactions at High Pressures and Temperatures," Macmillan, New York, 1936.

4 *Time*, January 10, 1937.

CARL B. MARQUAND

HELEN H. MARQUAND

·· *91* ··

Fritz Haber

1868-1934

Haber's scientific spirit was not contemplative in nature. He loved science and lived for it, not merely for its own sake, but because he affirmed its molding influence on human life. He served science because he believed it held a key position in the domains of culture and civilization. Imbued with the necessity of research for the preservation of our existence, he saw no degradation when science was applied to technical problems, and he certainly regarded pure science as being but little higher than applied science. He measured each with its proper scale of values.

The versatility of his talents and proclivities could have been a danger to his career. However, the success of his life and the benefits it brought to his fellow men were due to his ability in his youth to concentrate on factual accomplishment. Who can determine now whether it was chance, external circumstances, or internal predilection that led him to specialize in chemistry? In later years, he often left the impression that he would have been just as pre-eminent in other lines. He tried himself out in other directions but remained true to chemistry.

Born at Breslau on December 9, 1868, Haber started his scientific activity as an organic chemist. After studying at Berlin under A. W. Hofmann, at Heidelberg under Bunsen, and at Charlottenburg under Liebermann, he took his doctorate at Berlin with an organic thesis. Later he worked at Jena under Ludwig Knorr in a field that was completely in the interest of the older man, and they published a joint paper on diacetosuccinic ester. He put down no roots, however. The clarification of chemical structures and the working-out of syntheses, which constitute the bulk of organic chemistry, could not satisfy his scientific imagination. His main interest lay always in the material side of Nature and its diversity. He consistently considered himself to be a chemist and freely acknowledged this even in later years when developments brought him frequently into purely physical problems. Once when one of his younger colleagues brought up the matter of changing from chemistry to physics, he jokingly said: "As a matter of fact, the

1301

most interesting thing in physics is chemistry." In his opinion, the art of the organic chemist was not sufficient to enable him to penetrate as deeply as he desired into material aspects. This method of approach was too specialized to suit him and too highly developed; the possibilities of the organic chemist seemed to him to be as foreseeable as those of a mature man. In comparison, what great potentialities were present in the then young field of physical chemistry which, in the hands of van't Hoff, Arrhenius, and Nernst, was in those years disclosing very remarkable, fruitful, and novel methods of attacking chemical problems?

In 1894, Haber was offered an assistantship at Karlsruhe by Hans Bunte, professor of chemical technology. He accepted because the post offered him two things that he was seeking; the professional responsibilities and connections which it entailed were welcomed by Haber. He once said that he would not have been satisfied with a research position without obligations; he wanted to make himself useful and to fit himself in, and thus get the feeling of belonging to a solid scientific group.

However, the official duties of this post were not so demanding that he did not find time for extending his scientific depth and production. Teachers who might have advanced him in his special field of interest, physical chemistry, were not to be found at Karlsruhe. Bunte's special field was combustion chemistry, particularly gases; Carl Engler was also there, but he was interested in petroleum and the phenomena of autoxidation. The problems with which Haber came in contact at Karlsruhe had a decisive influence on his later scientific investigations, and during the last years of his life he repeatedly returned to the problem of the combustion phenomena in gases and of autoxidations.

It was only two years after he became assistant that he qualified as Privatdozent with the habilitation essay "Experimental studies of the decomposition and combustion of hydrocarbons." Apart from its technical importance, the question of the mechanism of the decomposition of the hydrocarbons offers, even at the present more advanced state of our knowledge of reaction kinetics, something of special interest and is still the subject of serious researches in many countries. It is well to recall that Haber was the first to carry out well-planned studies in this field and recognized the essence of several aspects of these problems. After another two years he published his textbook "Technische Elektrochemie." It was based on the lectures he gave at the Technische Hochschule, and it reveals the intensity with which Haber had attacked this field in which he had hardly begun to publish. The intention, expressed in the preface, to establish a contact between the most recent researches and the industrial practices which up to then had developed with almost no attention to such studies, can be regarded in an extended sense as the basis of his entire life work. That same year he reported to the meeting of the *Bunsengesellschaft* on a major experimental study of electrolytic reduction. Here he succeeded in showing that order could be brought into the bewildering maze of organic cathode processes if attention were paid to the potential at the cathode, and that definite reduction products result if the electrode potential is kept constant. The manner in which nitrobenzene is reduced in stages at the cathode was thus clearly set forth and became the prototype of a number of similar reduction processes.

The next ten years saw a host of electrochemical researches joined to the initial excursion into this field. Only a few can be cited here. The continuation of the study of electrolytic reduction reactions of organic compounds led him to the general realization that the velocity of chemical reactions at the electrodes is not infinitely great, but rather true chemical reaction rates prevail just as in homogeneous reactions. He advocated this view, which everyone shares now, in opposition to the then modern notions about the course of such reactions. In this connection he studied, among others, the establishment of the quinone-hydroquinone equilibrium at the cathode, and through this research laid the foundations of the quinhydrone electrode as developed by Bijlman, which has become a useful instrument to obtain accurate data regarding the acidity of a liquid. He himself created an instrument for the same purpose that was at least as good, namely, the glass electrode which was developed in conjunction with Cremer. It has the advantage that nothing need be introduced into the liquid being tested except the indifferent glass material and, consequently, it now finds wide use in factory operations as well as in research. This discovery was intimately connected with a group of studies, in which Haber

1303

made the first experimental investigations of the potential differences that arise between solid electrolytes and their aqueous solutions, and in which he found laws similar to those that apply to the contact of metal solutions. These observations are of much physiological interest, since the bioelectric systems show greater similarity to the Haber elements than to the usual galvanic cells with their metal electrodes. In addition to the electromotive behavior of the solid electrolytes, studies were made of their conduction characteristics, and for the first time there was detected an electrolysis of a solid crystal of salt in accord with Faraday's law.

However, another fundamental problem of electrochemistry occupied Haber even more during these years. When steam engines, turbines, and motors are driven by fuels, a large part of the energy is inevitably lost. The theories of physical chemistry indicate how a combustion process can be guided by electrochemical means so that the loss of energy is limited to the physically necessary fraction. But the construction of such so-called reversible fuel elements encounters great difficulties. Haber spent much work on this topic, which is one of the cardinal problems of industrial physical chemistry, and he succeeded in finding at least the fundamental solution for the laboratory combustion of carbon monoxide (and also hydrogen) even though the road to the commercial application remains difficult.

His interest in electrochemical problems gradually receded, and two problems from gas chemistry claimed more and more of his attention. These were the elucidation of the combustion processes in flames and the fixing of the nitrogen from the air. Haber's investigations of the Bunsen flame have become fundamental to an understanding of the processes occurring there. By chemical analysis of the gases, which he drew off from the region between the inner cone and the mantle of the Bunsen flame, he demonstrated that in the luminous inner cone there is established the thermodynamic water gas equilibrium, whose temperature can be calculated from the composition; a combustion of water gas takes place in the outer mantle. These studies then led to a chemical method of determining flame temperatures which, when direct measurements are possible, agree very well with the latter.

As at the start of his electrochemical researches, Haber at the

1304

beginning of his studies of gas reactions published a monograph. His fundamental text on "The thermodynamics of technical gas reactions" appeared in 1905. The foreword stated that the book was written from the industrial rather than the theoretical viewpoint. Nevertheless, it is a model of scientific rigor and thoroughness, which in its treatment of the so-called thermodynamically undetermined constants led directly to the door of the Nernst heat theorem. In this book there are appraisals of the approximate position of the ammonia equilibrium on the basis of observations which he had made the preceding year. At 1000°C., with the aid of iron as catalyst, small amounts of ammonia were produced from N_2 and H_2. A new approach to the fixing of atmospheric nitrogen was thus indicated, but the yields were so hopelessly low that Haber did not choose to follow this road. Yet the problem gave him no rest, and he spent several years studying the then customary method of oxidizing nitrogen by electrical arc discharges. It was not until 1908, when he became better acquainted with the possibility of working on an industrial scale under high pressures, and after more exact data were made available to him by others regarding the position of the ammonia equilibrium, that he became convinced, in the face of the skeptical opinions of all the experts, that the method of the future lay in the synthesis of ammonia. Together with Le Rossignol he made a systematic search for good catalysts and, when these had been found, built a small model with which, in June, 1908, he was able to demonstrate to the industrialists the synthesis of ammonia on the laboratory scale.

The consequences of this exploit were stupendous in comparison with what was foreseen at the time. In the hands of Carl Bosch, there arose in the next few years the great Oppau and Leuna ammonia works, which first of all provided Germany with the raw materials for munitions in World War I and then, after peace had come, furnished the means for making the soil more fruitful and remunerative. The principle employed in the ammonia synthesis proved to be of use in other important technical processes, and the further development, namely, the art of controlling catalytic reactions at high pressures and temperatures, made possible the synthesis of methyl alcohol by Alwin Mittasch and the hydrogenation of coal by the Bergius method.

The years just preceding World War I saw a change in the structure of physical chemistry. The period of classical physical chemistry appeared to be passing. The thermodynamic problems, so far as they related to chemical equilibrium, seemed to have been brought to a certain degree of conclusion by the Nernst theorem, and the first victorious dawning of the quantum ideas in energetics and atomistics were making their appearance. With these it was possible to gain a deeper insight into chemical equilibria with the aid of statistical methods, as shown by the calculation of chemical constants, and also to approach closer to the chemical events themselves. It is interesting to note a parallel turning toward atomistic problems in Haber's studies. The problems which Haber pursued were invariably the questions of his time. He lived in the present, he did not become rigid, and he shared the interests of the constantly renewed younger generation. Accordingly, his scientific work was a mirror of the development of physical chemistry during his adult life, and the influence which he exerted was founded on his scientific successes as well as on the prestabilized harmony between his own development and the spirit of his time.

Among the experiments leading into the new epoch are the study of the ion emission of platinum wires during the course of catalytic reactions, and the proof that electrons can be sent out during certain chemical reactions.

In this sense, it is more than chance that the first paper of the transactions of the Kaiser Wilhelm Institut für physikalische Chemie in 1911 is a paper by Fritz Haber dealing with the ultraviolet and infrared natural frequencies of crystals and the relation between chemical heat effects and energy quanta. Although the findings of this study, except for an interesting empirical relationship for the crystal's natural frequencies, were later superseded, because the questions dealt with were not mature enough at the time, the study nevertheless shows that a completely new set of problems had gained entrance to his world of ideas, problems which were to have a part in determining the nature of the work carried out in the laboratory of which he had become the director. However, it was eight years before he again took up a portion of these trains of thought and followed them through to a conclusion. The few years preceding the war were occupied by getting the Institut into running order and no new fundamental studies were begun. In the main, the ammonia synthesis was further developed from the quantitative standpoint. Three things, however, are worth mentioning: (1) for mining: the invention of the firedamp whistle; (2) for laboratory practice: the development of a quartz thread manometer for low gas pressures; and (3) for chemical detection: the observation that the adsorption powers can be due to unsaturated valence forces of a solid body. Langmuir built his adsorption theory on the latter finding.

Then came the war and with it an interruption of the scientific output; this was destined to have a serious effect on Haber himself. This is not the place to discuss in detail Haber's activities during the war. At the start he was attached to the Ministry of War as a consultant and later was given an independent section. He developed the first gas attack procedures and later organized the entire gas warfare and gas defense. Eventually this organization included 150 university personnel and about 2000 assistants. The Kaiser-Wilhelm-Institut für physikalische Chemie became the center for the necessary investigations. In addition, Haber advised the Ministry with respect to the most varied problems regarding raw materials and industrial matters. It was an overpowering burden, and he paid for it in terms of his health.

When the collapse of the German resistance and economy came in 1918, he did not immediately return to pure research activities. Rather he sought to devote his organizational and technical abilities to the restoration of the stricken nation. The great commerical success of the ammonia synthesis, his activities during the war, and the bestowal of the Nobel Prize (1918) had brought him so much respect that he was in demand everywhere. He took a prominent part in the creation of the great relief organization *Notgemeinschaft*. He accepted the chairmanship of large scientific societies and battled with skill and success for the recognition of German representatives in international organizations. He worked particularly on the effort, planned by him, to set up an elaborate undertaking to recover the traces of gold that were alleged to be in sea water. He expended much time and thought on this from 1920 to 1926. These studies ended in practical failure, a result that wounded Haber seriously. Already somewhat weakened in health,

1307

the shattered hopes of thus enabling Germany to meet its war reparations were ascribed by him as due to his decreasing efficiency, and he was deeply depressed. But, driven by unrest, he soon found another field of activity.

The reorganization of the Institut was his first concern after the war. He succeeded in enlisting prominent scientists as collaborators in this research center and, thanks to the quality of his leadership and despite the many difficulties, in a few years it was one of the best institutions of its kind in the world. The most varied types of work were nurtured by him but conducted in completely independent fashion. The constantly increasing number of publications testified to the healthy growth of this establishment. The fundamental studies by James Franck and his associates on the electron bombardment of atoms were published in the years immediately following the war. Here could be discerned the essence of chemiluminescence and the nature of the photochemical primary processes. Our ideas of the primary fission products of molecules when struck by electrons were greatly enriched by the investigations from this laboratory, and almost all that was known up to the time of Haber's death regarding the chemistry and reaction kinetics of the free metalloid and metal atoms came from his laboratory. The resonance phenomena due to collisions of certain molecules were here given their first clear experimental proof. New kinds of molecular absorption spectra, which represent a transition to x-ray absorption spectra, were found in the extreme ultraviolet. The predictions of quantrum mechanics were confirmed by the discovery of parahydrogen. Measurements were made of the life span of atoms in various states of excitation. Information about the constitution of atoms was obtained from studies of hyperfine structures. The chemistry of silicon was extended by the discovery of a new group of most unusual compounds. Nowhere else in Germany was more done to advance colloid chemistry. The whole multiplicity of colloid phenomena was disclosed in these researches. Fundamental studies of the electrokinetic potential and its relation to the thermodynamic electrical equilibrium potential were made here, and the significance of the former with respect to the flocculation of colloid systems was investigated experimentally. Special interest was given to the shape of the colloid particle and to the structures in gel and sol form. This problem was attacked by mechanical, optical, and magnetic methods and yielded many surprising findings as the result and expression of these structures. Nor did these investigations neglect the problems of colloid chemistry encountered in biological and industrial fields.

And what was Haber doing during this development of the Institut? He by no means exhausted himself in caring for the material and organizational needs or in collecting the necessary funds. Rather, by virtue of his sovereign superiority, he held together the apparently heterogeneous and divergent tendencies within the establishment. The colloquium, at which he assembled the entire staff every fortnight, was a prime example of his guiding talent. Often, at the close of a hazy and too specialized lecture, he took the floor himself and in two or three sentences put the problem in such succinct terms that the darkness was dispelled—at least to a considerable extent. How often the audience derived more from his few sentences than from the entire preceding hour! Care was exercised that absorption in special problems did not result in the loss of proper perspectives and standards. Nothing was less welcome to Haber during discussions than indefiniteness. In order to make himself clear, he often spoke in terms of plastic comparisons, frequently only as a matter of experiment to arouse discussion when he had possibly misunderstood something. And then, with a gentle smile, he put the Socratic questions from which clarity eventually emerged from the discussion. Just as his inventive spirit made him a research man, his organizing talent made him a model director of a large laboratory. His ability to permit full freedom to the individual workers and yet to keep the mental control of the whole in his own grasp was almost unbelievable.

When, disillusioned, he had given up the attempts to recover gold from sea water commercially and thus had more time to devote to the investigations being conducted in the Institut, it was this writer's good fortune that Haber, at the close of the 1920's, turned his attention to the group in which I was the leader. The probable reason was that he saw in the results that we had obtained concerning the behavior of free atoms and free radicals the possibility of applying new methods to problems that had engaged him in his early years, the field of flames, particularly the Bunsen flame, and autoxidations. He now reverted to purely scientific work. Although handicapped by a serious cardiac condition accompanied by painful angina pectoris, he energetically collected all of his powers, participated in our inner group colloquium, occupied himself with the theory of spectra, and again took up his old studies. It was not to be expected that decisive results would be obtained immediately by this method, but through these investigations he pointed out the way which later investigations pursued. His last researches, in 1933, dealt with hydrogen peroxide catalysis. At this point, the anti-Semitic barbarism of the Nazi regime entered the picture. He left the institute shortly after addressing the Minister (May 2) as follows:

My tradition requires of me in a scientific post that in choosing fellow workers I take into account only the professional qualifications and the character of the applicants without asking about their racial disposition. You will hardly expect a man of sixty-five to alter his mode of thought that had guided him in the thirty-nine years of his academic career, and you will appreciate that it is the pride with which he has served his German homeland through all of his life which now dictates the request for retirement.

Shortly thereafter Haber left Germany to open a small laboratory at Cambridge where he had been invited by English colleagues. He did not withstand this transplanting well, his thoughts were constantly on his homeland, his health worsened, and he feared the rigors of the English winter. Within a few months he moved to Switzerland but his spirit was broken, his health was gone. He died January 29, 1934, at Basel, an outcast rejected by the authorities of the country he had served so well.

Richard Willstätter once said: "To judge Haber by his published work would be like trying to learn about the sculptor Hildebrand from his books or about the painter Van Gogh from his letters." Although this statement is somewhat exaggerated, it contains much truth. The basic nature of scientific research is such that the individual and personal qualities of the man are subordinate to his accomplishments. However, Haber was a very forceful and unusual person. Those who knew him will never forget this personality, its memory will enrich their lives always.

The bitterness and tragedy surrounding the close of this brilliant career have yielded to the inexorable softening influences of time. A ceremonial session was held at the Kaiser Wilhelm Institut für physikalische Chemie und Elektrochemie on December 9, 1952, and an impressive tablet was unveiled to Haber's memory. The inscription reads:

> Themistocles has come down in history not as the exile at the court of the Persian king but as the victor at Salamis. Haber will go down in history as the gifted discoverer of the process of combining nitrogen with hydrogen, which is the basis of the industrial fixing of nitrogen from the atmosphere, who in this way, as was stated when the Nobel Prize was conferred on him "created an exceedingly important means of improving agriculture and the welfare of mankind, who made bread from the air and scored a triumph" in the service of his country and all mankind.

From: *Z. Elektrochem.*, 57, 2 (1953). Translated by Ralph E. Oesper.

K. F. BONHOEFFER

·· *92* ··

Phoebus Aaron Theodor Levene

1869-1940

PHOEBUS AARON THEODOR LEVENE was a great pioneer in biochemistry who arrived on the scene after structural organic chemistry was well established and after Emil Fischer had completed his work on the fundamental nature of the components (*Bausteine*) of proteins and carbohydrates. Although Levene was trained as a physician and held no other degree than that of M.D., he worked as an isolative and structural organic chemist and was not averse to applying physicochemical concepts and techniques when such were indicated. He continually read and studied, attended classes in advanced chemistry, and worked in many laboratories of Europe. He utilized well the capabilities of his co-workers. He possessed great energy and drove himself mercilessly. As a member of the first group of scientists assembled by Dr. Simon Flexner at the founding (1905) of the Rockefeller Institute for Medical Research in New York City, he contributed greatly to the establishment of biochemical research in this country. He initiated research which has been continued by veritable hosts of other workers in the universities and research institutes of the world— investigators who have found that the foundations laid by him were firm and solid.

Levene was born into an Orthodox Jewish family of Sagor, Russia, on February 25, 1869, and was named (as transliterated from the Russian) Fishel Aaronovich Levin.[1] He was the second of eight children of Aaron and Etta (Brick) Levin. When he was four years old his family moved to St. Petersburg (later called Petrograd and then Leningrad) where the Hebrew name "Fishel" was changed to the Russian "Feodor"; his family and intimate friends always called him Fedia, which is the Russian diminutive of Feodor. When he came to the United States, the name Feodor Aaronovich Levin somehow became transliterated as Phoebus Aaron Levene. Some years later, after he had realized that the proper English translation of Feodor was Theodor(e) and not Phoebus, he decided it was too late to change his name, then appearing in scientific publications, from Phoebus to Theodore. He therefore decided to insert Theodor as a third name and listed himself as Phoebus Aaron Theodor Levene (he dropped the final "e" in Theodore as such vowel endings are not found in Russian). This caused some confusion when initialed on circulars as P. A. T. and there were over-zealous clerks who decided that such abbreviations were undignified and should be changed to the proper address of Patrick Levene. All this tumult was obviated in most of his publications by adopting the simplified form P. A. Levene.

Levene's father was a custom shirtmaker and operated three stores in St. Petersburg, one of which was on Nevsky Prospect, the Fifth Avenue of that city. Fedia graduated in 1886 from the Classical Gymnasium where he was subjected to eight years of Latin and Greek—he was able later to read Newton's "Principia" in the original Latin. The eldest son, Isaac, was set on becoming a physician and was able to realize this ambition. Fedia did not have the same consuming desire to study medicine but went into it because the difficult examination for entrance to the St. Petersburg Imperial Medical Academy was an intriguing challenge to him. He passed the examination with flying colors and entered the Academy. There he came into contact with Alexander Borodin[2] and could recall the grief of Rimsky-Korsakov on the death of Borodin in 1887. Ivan Pavlov was docent in physiology at the time. Borodin, who had succeeded Nikolaï N. Zinin, was assisted by Alexander Dianin.[3] Levene participated in some of Dianin's researches concerned with the condensation of phenols with aldehydes and ketones. This experience introduced the young medical student to chemical research and he was advised by his teachers to study chemistry further. Thereafter he leaned more toward chemistry than medicine.

Before Levene had completed his medical training, because of the growing anti-Semitism in Russia as well as to find broader opportunities and a fuller life, his family decided to emigrate to America, and the young Levene accompanied them to New York where they arrived on the Fourth of July, 1891. He returned to Russia in the fall to complete his examinations for the M.D. degree which he received in the autumn of 1891. He rejoined his family

1316

in New York in March of 1892, passed his examinations for the profession of medicine in New York, and practiced in the Russian-Jewish colony on the lower East Side until 1896. In later years he maintained occasional contact with the remnants of this section through the Russian Bear, an authentic Russian restaurant boasting a balalaika orchestra.

Orthodox Jews and Russian medical students wore full beards, but this was shortened to a mustache by Levene, who then bore a striking resemblance to his sister Vera's husband, Morris Hillquit, with whom he shared an office. Morris Hillquit (1869–1933), later a leading socialist of this country, was then a budding lawyer. As neither could afford to lose a patient or a client, it was their custom to "bluff it out" for the other when either was alone in their mutual office.

While a medical practitioner, he enrolled at Columbia University and attended the lectures in organic chemistry of Professor Marston T. Bogert. At the same time he was given working space in the laboratory of Professor John G. Curtis of the department of physiology of the College of Physicians and Surgeons, Columbia University, then on 59th Street, from where he published, in German, his first paper entitled "Die zuckerbildende Function des N. vagus (The Sugar-Forming Function of the Vagus Nerve)." He also worked on the physiology of sunstroke, then prevalent in New York City during the summer. During the summer of 1896 he took over, in addition to his own, the medical practice of his brother Isaac Levin (Isaac had not changed the Russian form of his surname), who had gone to Europe. On Isaac's return, he found that his brother had contracted tuberculosis; after consulting an eminent diagnostician, Fedia was sent to Switzerland to recuperate. After spending a year there, which included a short term in the laboratory of Professor E. Drechsel in Bern, he returned to recuperate further in the Trudeau Sanatorium at Saranac Lake, New York. While at Saranac he utilized their laboratories for further research.

Following this period, and while still far from well, Levene decided to discontinue the practice of medicine and dedicate his life to chemical research in relation to medicine. He was appointed

"Director of the Physiological Chemistry Division of the Pathological Institute of the New York State Hospitals for the Insane," but this unit underwent some political vicissitudes. He held a position as chemist at the Saranac Laboratory for the study of tuberculosis. He studied abroad in the laboratories of Professors A. Kossel (Marburg), H. Hofer (Munich), and E. Fischer (Berlin). His name appears on a publication of E. Fischer on the analysis of gelatin by the ester method. In 1902 he returned to the chemical laboratory of the reorganized Pathological Institute of the New York State Hospitals on Welfare Island and continued there until 1905. By 1905 he had published 84 papers and had been invited to present the Herter Lectures in pathological chemistry at New York University Medical College. Those papers included his first studies on the preparation and analysis of nucleic acids, work on the chemical nature of mucins and of chondroitinsulfuric acid (*Glycothionsäure*), studies on the biochemistry of the tubercle bacillus, and on the enzymic reactions of autolysis. He therefore was well established in biochemistry in this country on the basis of a publication record, and this led to his selection by Dr. Simon Flexner for an appointment as assistant in chemistry in the newly formed Rockefeller Institute for Medical Research, where he remained for the rest of his life. In 1907 he was made a member of the Institute in charge of the Division of Chemistry. He was made a member emeritus in 1939 but continued work unabated until his death of a heart condition on September 6, 1940. On one of his periodic visits to Saranac Lake he met Anna M. Erickson, a native of the Norwegian Lutheran colony of Evanston, Illinois, whom he married in 1920 when he was fifty-one years of age. This marriage was a very happy one and Anna Levene proved to be an ideal helpmate for him. They had no children.

Dr. Levene was a thin, wiry man of short stature. He had very penetrating, dark-brown eyes, and an intense, rather stern, expression. He wore a small mustache and his head was covered with a heavy shock of hair which in later life became steel gray and which he was wont to toss about or run his hands through in characteristic fashion. He moved rapidly and loved to work in the laboratory with his own hands, assisted only by his *Diener,* Joe Lender, whom he always addressed in German. When the writer knew him first, in 1927, Levene's routine was to rise early and read and write at home. At eight o'clock the telephone would ring on his floor and he would talk to members of his group on ideas that may have come to him regarding their work. At about 9:30 he would appear in the laboratory and plunge into experiments of his own in his neat and excellently equipped personal laboratory. After a short rest following lunch he would literally tear out of his office and make the rounds of his co-workers, after which he would resume his own experimentation. In the afternoon he would write up his notes on easily filed cards and then proceed homeward with a briefcase full of the journals which had arrived in the library that day. His summers were mainly spent away from New York as soon as his wife could pry him loose from his activities. Although he traveled widely in Europe, he never did so in the States and he held very naïve and astonishing concepts of the hinterland west of the Hudson River.

His temperament was strictly artistic. He published all of his work in the *Journal of Biological Chemistry*, established by the Rockefeller Institute group, and his manuscripts were sent to press immediately with no refereeing and little editing. Although he had numerous co-workers who provided experimental portions, he wrote all his own introductions, and I have known him to dash one off in twenty minutes, complete with references. In all he published over 700 articles. Levene spoke an excellent German and a perfect French. His English had a heavy accent, said to be Russian. One morning the writer entered Dr. Levene's laboratory to use his microscope in the customary search for crystals in a sugar sirup, and Dr. Levene maintained a running conversation simultaneously with the writer in English, with Dr. Steiger (from Paris) in French, and with Joe Lender in German, while at the same time carrying on his laboratory work on the bench. Dr. Levene directed his laboratory group with a firm hand and ordinarily brooked no suggestions from its members, unless it could be claimed that they were derived from the papers of Emil Fischer. The writer shared a double laboratory with one of Dr. Levene's collaborators who was working on configurational relationships in simple compounds involving straightforward, though difficult, organic syntheses utilizing Grignard reagents and the like. With this type of technique, Levene was not overly familiar and his co-worker had an excellent method worked out. He would first try to find what "worked" and then, by adroit conversation, get Dr. Levene to suggest that he try this. The next day Dr. Levene would be delighted to find that the experiment had been quickly and successfully carried through. This method, however, was inapplicable to laboratory work, such as that with the sugars, with which Dr. Levene was thoroughly familiar in minute detail.

Away from the laboratory, as in his New York apartment, Dr. Levene could relax and become a gay and charming host. He had numerous friends about the city, and his home was the center for the gathering of many interesting groups. He maintained a keen interest in contemporary art, and the walls of his home, where not covered by the multitudinous bookcases present, were decorated with many paintings he had purchased from young artists who he hoped had a future. He was a regular attendant at the concerts of the New York Philharmonic Orchestra and also enjoyed the better theatrical productions. As might be expected, Dr. Levene held liberal views; although thoroughly pleased with the Kerensky revolution he was not in sympathy with the Bolshevist counterrevolution. His home and laboratory formed a mecca for the constant stream of refugees reaching these shores from the excesses and trials incident to the vast changes then occurring in Russia.

Levene's scientific work embraced all classes of tissue constituents and the basic chemistry related thereto. He liked to find groups of compounds susceptible to investigation by graded hydrolysis and was very successful in this. He was a master in the isolation of pure substances from complex mixtures and in the crystallization of intractable sirups. He placed great reliance on the test tube. He had little patience with micromanipulations and worked with relatively large quantities. His favorite expression, when a line of work petered out due to a lack of material, was "next time we will make a kilo!" He was ever on the lookout for new techniques or "tricks," as he was wont to call them. He introduced the Pregl organic microanalyses to this country when he brought to New

York one of Pregl's students in the person of Oskar Wintersteiner, who in turn trained Dr. A. Elek. Dr. Elek remained with Dr. Levene throughout Levene's career.

Levene's main mark was made in the structural chemistry of the nucleic acids. He defined the nucleotide and, with Dr. R. Stuart Tipson, he explored its fine structure through methylation techniques. He isolated and characterized the two sugars by which the modern biochemist classifies the nucleic acids into their two characteristic groups. Both sugars were at the time unknown. The first was D-ribose and the second was its 2-deoxy derivative (2-deoxy-D-*erythro*-pentose). The discovery of the first was made in 1909, but the second was not uncovered until twenty years later, although many attempts to attain this goal were doggedly made in the intervening years. This was because the deoxypentose was destroyed by the acidity required to break it loose, and the appropriate enzyme could not be found. Finally, success was obtained by passing a solution of nucleic acid through a gastrointestinal segment of a dog by introducing it through a gastric fistula and withdrawing it by an intestinal fistula. This difficult experiment was done in cooperation with the Russian physiologist, E. S. London. There followed a great rush to establish the configuration of the 2-deoxypentose but it did not fit any of the known structures quickly synthesized. Then, in 1930, a paper appeared in the *Journal of Biological Chemistry* with data to show it *was* "2-deoxy-D-ribose." The discrepancy was caused by the circumstance that Joe Lender had, in the excitement, mixed two bottles of D- and L-arabinose of unequal content with a consequent utter confusion in the rotatory powers of the resultant, partially racemized preparations.

Levene was a pioneer in determining the nature of those tissue constituents containing proteins, uronic acids, N-acetylhexosamines, and sulfuric acid, of which the main member is chondroitinsulfuric acid from cartilage. He found that the hexosamine component of this substance was then unknown 2-amino-2-deoxy-D-galactose (its exact 2-epimeric nature was not established until later by others). He was much intrigued with the D-galactose-containing components of the brain and nervous tissues and carried out significant work in the isolation and characterization of these cerebrosides. The structure of several of the important sugar phosphates, of significance as intermediates in alcohol fermentation and in carboyhdrate metabolism in tissues, was elucidated with Albert L. Raymond. In the protein field, he presented evidence in favor of the linear polypeptide theory of protein structure.

Requisite to the sugar work in relation to tissue constituents, the Levene laboratory carried out an enormous amount of experimentation in fundamental carbohydrate chemistry. The synthesis and reactions of the hexosamines were studied and several were described for the first time. With Walter A. Jacobs, he synthesized the new hexoses D-allose and D-altrose and their aldonic acids, through the cyanohydrin reaction on natural D-ribose.

In attempting to determine the configuration of the second carbon in the hexosamines, Levene encountered the puzzling phenomenon of Walden inversion. In an attempt to solve the question of when or when not does a Walden inversion occur, he carried out a series of masterly investigations on the configurational relationships in a group of simple structures synthesized by methods obviating the possibility of Walden inversions. This work was done mainly with H. L. Haller and R. E. Marker and, while it did not solve the problem of Walden inversion, it did lead to the establishment of reference substances which have been of great value to later investigators.

It is obvious that the above summary does not do justice to the some 720 publications of P. A. Levene and his co-workers, but it is hoped that it has delineated some of the high lights in the picture. Levene was a member or fellow of the American Association for the Advancement of Science, the American Chemical Society, the American Philosophical Society, the American Physiological Society, the American Society of Biological Chemists (charter member), the American Society of Naturalists, Bayerische Akademie der Wissenschaften, Deutsche Akademie der Naturforscher (Halle), Deutsche chemischen Gesellschaft, the Harvey Society, the National Academy of Sciences, the Royal Society of Science (Sweden), Société de chimie biologique, Société chimique de France, Société Royale des sciences médicales et naturelles de Bruxelles, Société Suisse de Chimie, the Society of Experimental Biology and Medicine, and Phi Lambda Upsilon (honorary member). He was awarded the Willard Gibbs Medal of the Chicago Section of the American Chemical Society in 1931 and the William H. Nichols Medal of the New York Section in 1938. Levene was quite proud of the fact that he had never served on a committee nor held an office in any society, and in general he was impatient with what he considered to be the lack of scholarship and culture exhibited by most of the members of the American scientific societies of the time. He did enjoy the symposia of the Organic Division of the American Chemical Society and occasionally attended meetings of the National Academy. He encouraged his younger co-workers to attend meetings, especially those of the American Chemical Society.

The stature of P. A. Levene as a pioneer of modern biochemistry increases with time. His rapid and piecemeal publication in so many fields was bewildering to his contemporaries and made his work very difficult to follow in its entirety. He trained many men, most of whom entered the expanding field of biochemical research then being established in the research institutes, hospitals, and government laboratories of the country. He always stood behind his men and spent a great deal of time in aiding them to obtain suitable positions. Very few of his co-workers became established in the American universities. This is perhaps to be ascribed to the rather aloof attitude toward the universities adopted by the Institute (or perhaps it was the reverse). The Rockefeller Institute and the Rockefeller Foundation, whose leaders stemmed largely from the Johns Hopkins Medical School, cooperated with Johns Hopkins in revolutionizing medical training and medical research in this country. They set a pattern and were successful in doing so. In this effort Phoebus A. Levene made his sterling contribution. The award of the Willard Gibbs Medal in 1931 was made to P. A. Levene as "the outstanding American worker in the application of organic chemistry to biological problems." That citation is one which will go unchallenged for many years to come.

NOTES AND REFERENCES

1 The writer is indebted to Dr. Levene's youngest brother, Alexander, for much information regarding the early life of P. A. Levene.

2 Alexander Porfirievich Borodin (1834–1887). Professor of chemistry at the St. Petersburg Imperial Military Academy; organic chemist and famous Russian nationalist musical composer; introduced coeducation into the Russian universities.

3 Nikolaï Nikolaevich Zinin (1812–1880). Established the reduction of nitrobenzene to aniline; discovered azoxybenzene.

D. D. Van Slyke and W. A. Jacobs, "Phoebus Aaron Theodor Levene," *Biographical Memoirs, National Academy of Sciences of the U.S.A.*, XXIII, 75–126 (1944); R. S. Tipson, "Phoebus Aaron Theodor Levene," *Advances in Carbohydrate Chem.*, 12, 1–12 (1957).

MELVILLE L. WOLFROM

·· 93 ··

Fritz Pregl

1869-1930

IN THE beginning of our century, when organic chemists began to increase their work on the chemistry of special substances which are active in the organisms of plants and animals, the quantities of these substances that could be obtained were often extremely small. Thus, the problem of carrying out elementary analyses with the smallest possible quantities of a substance became more urgent from day to day. In his own research on the constitution of specific acids obtained from gall, Pregl in 1909 obtained such a tiny yield of a cholic acid derivative that he was confronted with the decision as to whether to abandon further studies of this compound or to start with such large quantities of bovine galls that the expenditures in time and cost would have become excessive and unbearable. In this dilemma, he decided to follow a new path which led him to the quantitative microanalysis of organic substances, an almost virgin field. His decision to elaborate micromethods of elementary analysis may have been facilitated by the fine success achieved by Friedrich Emich (1860–1940) at the Technische Hochschule in Graz. At about that time, Emich had shown that working with small quantities of substances is fundamentally reliable and advantageous. This method was especially congenial to Pregl's gifts and interests. He was a man of painstaking skill which enabled him to carry out difficult work in glass blowing. He had also demonstrated his great skill as a young physician, when he acted as an eye doctor during vacations and performed many a difficult surgical operation. In addition, Pregl had spent several years on improving the methods of elementary analysis. He constructed a time-saving automatic combustion oven for determining carbon and hydrogen in organic substances.

When he started his microanalytical research, Pregl recognized immediately that he needed an exceptionally sensitive microbalance. In Emich's laboratory he had seen the assay balance built by W. Kuhlmann of Hamburg for precious metals. He discovered that this balance, which can be loaded with up to 20 grams, was capable of much greater precision than claimed by Kuhlmann, provided it was treated and handled right. The guarantee stated an accuracy of 0.01 to 0.02 of a milligram but Pregl showed how to use it for weighing to plus or minus one-thousandth of a milligram.

Within two years of work, Pregl succeeded in reducing the quantity needed for an elementary analysis to about one-fiftieth of the usual amount. In a lecture with experiments before the German Chemical Society in Berlin on February 27, 1911, he demonstrated for the first time that the quantitative analysis for carbon, hydrogen, nitrogen, sulfur, and the halogens can be carried out using only 7 to 13 milligrams of a substance.

During the following years, Pregl improved and simplified the micromethod for determining the most important elements in organic compounds so far that only 3 to 5 milligrams was necessary, and the accuracy was the same as with the usual macroanalysis. In a lecture at the scientists convention in Vienna, 1913, he demonstrated to his audience that the molecular weight and composition of an organic substance—he used acetanilid—could be determined in one hour. Thus he aroused a wide interest in organic microanalysis. From that time on, increasing numbers of chemists came to Pregl's laboratory to learn the methods from the master himself. He liked the personal contacts and introduced many colleagues to microanalytical methods, first in Innsbruck and later in Graz. These occasional instructions developed into regular courses, held several times a year and attended by hundreds of chemists from all over the world. The author of this biography continued these courses at the Pregl Laboratory after Pregl's death in 1930 and as his successor until 1938; they were resumed after international relations were restored in 1949. After Pregl had seen that the procedures worked not only in his laboratory, but had proved successful for years at other institutions, he published his experimental results in a book on quantitative organic microanalysis ("Die quantitative organische Mikroanalyse," Berlin, Julius Springer, 1917). New editions appeared in 1923, 1930, 1935, and 1947, the last two under the care of Hermann Roth. The book was translated into several languages.

Recognition of Pregl's great achievements did not fail to come soon. In 1914 the Vienna Academy of Sciences awarded him the

Lieben Prize in chemistry. The University of Göttingen gave him an honorary degree in philosophy (1920) stating: "Pregl has thought out the methods of organic microanalysis, and he has completed them in undefatigable work. He has thus greatly promoted applied chemistry and has enabled medicinal chemistry to solve new tasks." The highest recognition and honour was the Nobel Prize in chemistry in 1923.

Thanks to the pioneering work of Fritz Pregl, the further progress in quantitative organic microanalysis was rapid. There are chemists who feel that this was the most significant advance in organic elementary analysis since Liebig's times.

In 1930 Pregl donated a substantial sum of money to the Vienna Academy of Sciences for the purpose of establishing a Fritz Pregl Prize in microchemistry, to be awarded, if possible annually, to Austrian microchemists.

In the years since Pregl's death microchemistry has advanced and expanded in all special fields of chemistry. Elementary analysis has been further enriched by the microanalytical procedure for oxygen determination according to Schütz-Unterzaucher. Automatizations and simplifications have been developed in the laboratories of industry. Further refinements and work with still smaller quantities of substance have been achieved. Thus, Unterzaucher succeeded in reducing the quantity required for the measurement of carbon, hydrogen, and nitrogen to a few tenths of a milligram and still obtain reliable results.

The development of microchemistry and the increased number of publications in this field made it appear desirable to establish a new journal in which the new experiences of working with smallest quantities could be brought together and made available to the microchemists. R. Strebinger in Vienna prepared the steps leading to such a publication. Under his editorship the first volume of *Mikrochemie* came out in Vienna, 1923. The size was rather modest at first. Since 1929, the staff of editors was expanded by including several outstanding microchemists, among them Emich and Pregl, and now the journal has grown in size and has an international readership.

Pregl's life and development was that of a scientist who made his own way. Born September 23, 1869, the son of an official at the savings bank of Krain, Fritz Pregl attended the German gymnasium there. After the early death of his father, he moved with his mother to Graz and there began to study medicine in 1887. As a student he far exceeded the average. Consequently, the physiologist Alexander Rollett made him an assistant even before he had completed his studies. Pregl remained in this position, which he liked very much, for fourteen years. He became doctor of medicine in 1894, Privatdozent in physiology five years later. At that time he also studied chemistry, stimulated by his friendship with Zdenko Skraup (1850–1910) who was then director of the chemistry department. This was of decisive influence on his later career. His work on acids obtained from gall, called cholic acids, gradually led him almost completely into chemistry. After the death of A. Rollett in 1903, Pregl gave the main lecture in physiology and became associate professor in 1904. He then went to Germany for a year, studying with Georg von Hüfner in Tübingen, Wilhelm Ostwald in Leipzig, and finally with Emil Fischer in Berlin. There he began work on protein chemistry. He continued this work after his return to Graz, but his main effort was concerned with the chemistry of cholic acids. In this connection he began to elaborate micromethods of elementary analysis. In 1910 he accepted a call to the University of Innsbruck from where he was called back, after three years, to the Medicochemical Institute at Graz. Declining several flattering offers from Berlin and Vienna, he remained faithful to the medical faculty at Graz until he died, December 13, 1930.

Pregl was a forceful personality. He was kindly without being soft, practical without being stolid, a felicitous example of thorough matter-of-factness. The attributes of his life were enduring friendships and lasting, although not hateful, oppositions. When relaxed he could be gay and witty. Unpretentious in his mode of living, open-hearted and direct even in the time of his greatest successes, he was attractive and fascinating. His strongest influence was on his students. His lectures were always interesting and greatly admired because of his clear and precise style, his outstanding skill in experimenting, and his humorous remarks. He was a good friend, adviser, and helper to the academic youth, and he was one of the most active promoters of help during the time of great need after the First World War. Through his efforts many a student was enabled to complete his studies.

GENERAL REFERENCES

On Friedrich Emich, see: A. A. Benedetti-Pichler, in *Ind. Eng. Chem., Anal. Ed., 12,* 226 (1940).
On Zdenko Skraup, see: Hugo Schrötter, in *Ber. deut. chem. Ges., 43,* 3683 (1910).

From: *Mikrochemie ver. Mikrochim. Acta,* XXXV, 123 (1950), abbreviated. Translated by Eduard Farber.

HANS LIEB

·· *94* ··

Victor Grignard

1871-1935

O N MAY 6, 1871, at 11 o'clock at night, at 51 rue des Carrières in Cherbourg, François-Auguste-Victor Grignard was born to Theophile-Henri Grignard, a chief sailmaker, and his wife, Marie Hebert.

Victor Grignard went to the secondary school of his native city. There he distinguished himself among his co-students. Each year, from 1883 to 1887, his efforts were rewarded by the "prize of excellence." After two years of preparation, he was the winner in the competition for the École Normale Spéciale of Cluny (1889). This school, although scarcely twenty years old, was closed during the reform of the secondary school system in 1891. Grignard acquired the right to one more year of study and was thus transferred to Lyon.

He began to prepare for a degree in mathematics, but he failed, in spite of high intellectual abilities, because his memory was deficient. At that time he fulfilled his obligatory military service without any high ambitions, and thus we shall find him as a corporal at the mobilization in 1914.

After one year in the service he returned to Lyon where he obtained the degree in mathematics and, at the advice of his friend Rousset, also the degree as assistant in the Service de Chimie Générale de la Faculté des Sciences, in 1894. He did this without enthusiasm; from his previous studies he had a very low opinion of chemistry. This science seemed to him unimportant, purely empirical, requiring a memory much better than his. After a short time at the laboratory of Bouveault and Ph. Barbier, those two outstanding representatives of French organic chemistry, what a revelation, what a red face!

In Bouveault, the young lecturer, he found the logician of chemistry, the scholar who was after the crucial experiment to obtain a decisive yes or no answer to a problem. Then, Grignard sought contact with Barbier, and it really was a rude contact with this teacher who was famous for his infinite knowledge. An impetuous, robust researcher, he demanded everything from everyone. This scientific milieu of fruitful activity quickly inflamed Grignard. He obtained his license *ès Sciences physiques* and succeeded his unfortunate friend Rousset in 1898 as *Chef des Travaux*.

In the same year, Grignard published his first scientific paper, together with Ph. Barbier, on the isopropyl derivative of the ethyl ester of acetylbutyric acid and the stereoisomers of diisopropyl-hexane dioic acids. After a short publication on a method for obtaining hydrocarbons that have, at the same time, ethylene and acetylene bonds (enines), and on a hydrocarbon with three twin double bonds, Barbier authorized him to continue and generalize a study made by his teacher in 1898. By reacting simultaneously methyliodide and a ketone, natural methylheptenone, with magnesium, that is replacing zinc by magnesium in the method of Saytzeff, Barbier had obtained the corresponding tertiary alcohol, methylheptenol and thus demonstrated that the use of magnesium permitted to penetrate into the series of the methylketones that is absolutely closed to zinc. This event reached far beyond the narrow confines of synthesis of a new alcohol. However, when Grignard tried to pursue the same principle that should have formed the basis for a general synthetic method, he ran up against the same inconsistent and irregular results that Barbier had encountered. In his calm and slow reasoning Grignard examined the problem more thoroughly. He thought that his chance for success would be improved if he first prepared the organomagnesium compound and only then brought it together with the substance containing the functional group ($-CO-CH_3$).

Unfortunately, the method of Löhr for preparing symmetric organomagnesium compounds had to be rejected, especially after the experiences at the laboratory of Lothar Meyer, and even with the modifications by Fleck and Wage. The substances obtained were noncrystallizable, infusible, and insoluble substances of high reactivity, which spontaneously caught fire in contact with dry air or dry carbon dioxide. Therefore, Grignard approached the problem from a new basis.

Frankland and Wanklyn had discovered that by preparing organozinc compounds in the presence of anhydrous ethyl ether, the ether compounds were not inflammable in the air and yet reactive. Grignard hoped that the same reaction could be obtained with magnesium, which is more electropositive and reactive than zinc. This actually happened, and Grignard thus discovered that, in the presence of dry ether, magnesium reacted with halogenated alkyls at ordinary temperature, and that this reaction, which is practically complete, resulted in ether-soluble organomagnesium compounds.

The first publication of these results appeared in the *Comptes rendus* of the Académie des Sciences on May 14, 1900, presented by Moissan. In a few months Grignard explored various directions and established an impressive number of synthetic procedures. This work on mixed organomagnesium compounds and their use in the synthesis of acids, alcohols, and hydrocarbons was presented at the University of Lyon in July, 1901, for the degree of doctor in physical sciences. Moissan suggested to him that he present his thesis in Paris, but Grignard remained faithful to his spiritual cradle and honored it with his first book.

The mixed organomagnesium compounds have such a wide range of reactivities that it was impossible for a single experimenter to develop all the applications. Collaboration was soon begun, and it proved to be of two kinds, voluntary and involuntary. The first proceeded in accord with the inventor and brought him sweet satisfaction. His school was established, a school which, at present (1936) numbers hundreds of experts. The second kind of collaboration was, as usual with all far-reaching discoveries, a contradiction which sometimes makes polemics inevitable and yet was useful for Grignard.

Grignard's scientific life can be divided into three periods: before, during, and after World War I.

From 1901 to 1914 he was mainly occupied with perfecting the initial discovery, interrupted only by social functions. From 1901 on, his collaborator was Tissier, who later became a Senator.

The first discussion on the constitution of organomagnesium compounds occurred between Blaise and Grignard. Both admit the formula R—Mg—X, not free, however, but combined with one or several molecules of ether. For the monoether compound, two structures are possible:

$$
\begin{array}{ccc}
\underset{C_2H_5}{\nearrow}\,\underset{R}{\nwarrow} & & \underset{C_2H_5}{\nearrow}\,\underset{MgR}{\nwarrow} \\
O & \text{and} & O \\
\underset{C_2H_5}{\nearrow}\,\underset{MgX}{\nwarrow} & & \underset{C_2H_5}{\nearrow}\,\underset{X}{\nwarrow}
\end{array}
$$

Grignard   Baeyer and Villiger,
Blaise

(X represents a halogen atom)

It was particularly interesting to study the behavior of halo-hydrines toward organomagnesium compounds. The simplest case is that of the monochlorohydrine of glycol, $CH_2OH—CH_2Cl$. At low temperature, the reaction involves only the alcoholic group:

$$
\begin{array}{c}
CH_2{-}CH_2 \\
|\qquad\ | \\
Cl\quad OH
\end{array}
+ R.MgX \longrightarrow
\begin{array}{c}
CH_2{-}CH_2 \\
|\qquad\ | \\
Cl\quad OMgX
\end{array}
+ RH
$$

The complex thus obtained is capable of reacting with a new molecule of organomagnesium which may well be different from the first:

$$R'MgX + Cl.CH_2.CH_2.O.MgX \rightarrow R'CH_2.CH_2.OMgX \rightarrow R'CH_2.CH_2.OH$$

When R′ is the phenyl radical, the result is the phenylethyl alcohol, $C_6H_5 \cdot CH_2 \cdot CH_2 \cdot OH$, which has the fragrant odor of roses. With this reaction Grignard's discovery first entered industry, in the plant of Descollonges at Lyon.

On November 1, 1905, Grignard started lectures at the Faculté des Sciences in Besançon. The following year he returned to Lyon as Maître des Conférences, so that he was again a member of the department of organic chemistry together with Barbier, and, in addition, had to direct student work at the laboratory. He developed a double activity. Together with Barbier he carried forward a study of the terpenes, and with his students Reif and Abelman he investigated methods of preparing ethylenic alcohols and aldehydes.

Slowly, Grignard climbed the ladder of the academic hierarchy. In 1908 he became associate professor and received the rosette of an Officer of Public Instruction. Not seeing a future for himself at Lyon, he accepted a position at Nancy in November, 1909. A year later, he became professor at Nancy with one of the best equipped provincial laboratories. On the campus of the school, the 150 students of the chemical institute talked about chemistry.

The echoes of the magnificent public garden of the city were full of words like coupling, condensation, grignardization. The followers of Hermes could be easily traced by the strong and characteristic odors with which their clothes were impregnated.

On August 22, 1910, Grignard set up housekeeping. The next year, his worthy companion, Augustine-Marie Boulant, presented him with a son who today is also a chemist.

Wednesday morning, November 13, 1912, at the Faculté des Sciences of Nancy, the rumor of an unprecedented success for the University spread like wildfire. The Nobel Prize in chemistry had been awarded to two scientists of France, Paul Sabatier, dean of science at the University of Toulouse, for his method of catalytic hydrogenation, and Victor Grignard for his discovery of the organomagnesium compounds. The joy over this great news was immense. At forty-one, Grignard was then the youngest of the Nobel Prize winners.

The Congress of the French Association for the Advancement of Science took place at Le Havre, toward the end of July, 1914. A conference was scheduled on "a tunnel under the Channel," a question of burning actuality, when the headlines of the newspapers announced in big capital letters: "To the Austrian ultimatum Serbia replies: No!"

Grignard was mobilized the second of August. The military authorities had known him as a corporal in 1893, for them he was still a corporal in 1914. Professor at the university, Chevalier of the Légion d'honneur, Nobel Prize winner in Chemistry, Grignard became a guard in the Cherbourg region. However, he was soon discovered by the military. Toluene threatened to be in short supply, and Grignard was asked to study the cracking of heavy benzenes. He returned to Nancy where he made a quantitative investigation of the reaction between methylbenzenes and aluminum chloride.

Shortly afterward, on July 10, 1915, practically one year after the mobilization, he was a member of the Chemical War Production Board in Paris where Professor Urbain welcomed his provincial colleague at his laboratory in the Sorbonne. As the director of one of the laboratories for research on war gases, Grignard rendered inestimable services. First he analyzed the combat gases used by the enemy. More than 2000 analyses were thus carried out on more than 600 samples. Furthermore, numerous investigations were made of our own combat gases, and the control he established in the factories on the basis of laboratory work brought considerable progress in the manufacture of these products. Grignard worked marvels with regard to the many problems in the defense of the country, and he was for World War I what Berthelot had been to the War of 1870.

Of the research done during this period we mention only that part which Grignard was able to publish. He studied the preparation of phosgene by means of oleum and by ordinary sulfuric acid, as well as the utilization of the residues. Sulfuric acid gives twice the yield, with regard to SO_3, as the reaction of Schützenberger, who uses SO_3 dissolved in pyrosulfuryl chloride. In the first case the reaction is:

$$H_2SO_4 + SO_3 + CCl_4 \rightarrow COCl_2 + 2Cl.HSO_3$$

whereas in the second:

$$2SO_3 + CCl_4 \rightarrow COCl_2 + Cl_2S_2O_5$$

At 75 to 80°C., ordinary sulfuric acid, with diatomaceous earth as the catalyst, permits obtaining phosgene without having recourse to oleum, although the phosgene is mixed with hydrochloric acid.

The industrial method of producing phosgene with oleum had left several hundred tons of chlorosulfonic acid as a by-product. Grignard utilized it by reaction with ethylene. At temperatures below 20°C. he obtained the chlorosulfate of ethyl, a tear gas.

Yperite, the terrible "mustard gas," ravaged the Allied troops after the fall of 1917. Grignard discovered that a 30 per cent solution of sodium iodide easily replaces the chlorine of yperite by iodine and yields the crystallizable β-β'-diiodide of ethyl sulfide. By studying this reaction, he arrived at a method for detecting one-tenth of a gram of yperite in one cubic meter of air.

On May 30, 1917, Grignard was delegated to represent chemistry in the mission sent over the Atlantic when America joined the Allies. He remained in the United States till the end of January, 1918.

After the armistice, Grignard returned to Nancy and, in November, 1919, he succeeded Barbier in Lyon. We thus approach the third period of his work during which the number of his students grew considerably. Twice he declined offers of a professorship in Paris.

Grignard's profound studies brought us well-rounded knowledge of aldols, ketols, their dehydration products, and the unsaturated alcohols to which they are converted by organomagnesium compounds. These unsaturated alcohols were catalytically hydrogenated, and the splitting of tertiary alcohols did not escape his attention; the dienes from monoethylenic alcohols were closely studied. The chemical constitution of these molecules was frequently established by ozonization. In addition to the normal reactions of the organomagnesium compounds, Grignard observed anomalies like reductions, enolizations of ketones, and condensations. Grignard was not content with observing the phenomenon and exploring its range of application; often he elaborated a theory.

For the saturation of double carbon bonds by hydrogen, two great classic methods appeared normally available, the catalysis by nickel or by platinum. With the method of Sabatier and Senderens, an unsaturated alcohol is completely dehydrated, even at relatively low temperature, and the hydrogenation occurs with the corresponding diene. Grignard avoided the difficulty with great elegance by hydrogenating under reduced pressure. Thus, reducing the concentration on the surface of the catalyst, he avoided the dehydration of the alcohol, at least in part. The remarkable results that he obtained in hydrogenating under reduced pressure seemed contrary to the concepts and theories of the time. Grignard sought new applications for this technique in many directions. Thus he reduced benzaldehyde with a yield of 67 per cent to benzyl alcohol at 150°C. and 100 mm. pressure, and the aldehyde which is not reduced can almost completely be recovered. From benzylidene acetone he obtained increasing yields of the enol by successive reductions of temperature and pressure over a nickel catalyst. The case of the phenols is still more interesting. From several derivatives, and from phenol itself, he produced the tetrahydrophenol or cyclohexanone enol. This, as Grignard wrote, was a new and clear-cut illustration for Kekulé's benzene formula. Everything occurs as if three double bonds existed in the nucleus; two of them are hydrogenated together, they are those not adjacent to the phenolic function.

Chemical nomenclature was one of the foremost didactic concerns of Grignard. He was an active member of the Commission of Nomenclature of Organic Chemistry in 1912 and, again, in 1921. He collaborated in establishing the rules which this Congress at Liège published, and we find very judicious remarks on these rules in his great opus "Chimie Organique" of which only two volumes appeared before his death, while others have been published posthumously under his name since he had revised them page by page.

This immense work, which he wanted to be perfect, accelerated his end. Full of plans and work he disregarded the illness which undermined him and which, too soon, overpowered him. Grignard died at the age of sixty-four, on December 13, 1935.

GENERAL REFERENCES

M. S. Kharash, Carl W. Eisendrath, and Otto Reinmuth, "Grignard Reactions of Non-metallic Substances," Prentice-Hall, Englewood Cliffs, N. J., 1954.

S. T. Yoffe and A. N. Nesmeyanov, "A Handbook of Magnesium-Organic Compounds," compiled by the Metallo-Organic compounds Laboratory of the Institute of Organic Chemistry of the Academy of Sciences of the U.S.S.R., Pergamon Press, London, (1957).

From the biography by Charles Courtot in *Bull. soc. chim. France,*
5ᵉs., 3, 1433 (1936). Translated by Eduard Farber.

CHARLES COURTOT

·· 95 ··

Lord Rutherford

1871-1937

NEW ZEALAND, 1871–1894

IF A NEW country is peopled with a good stock, its future is assured. Such has been the happy fortune of New Zealand, which today justly claims Rutherford as her greatest son. New Zealand was sighted by Tasman and visited by Captain Cook, F.R.S., who stayed long enough to bequeath the flea, the black rat, and the pig to the Maoris. The country received its first white settlers in 1817, but the main colonization followed about 1840—less than a hundred years ago.

Among the early settlers was one of the Rutherfords, for the most part Scots and a virile border folk. His son James, and Martha his wife, another New Zealand settler from Sussex, had four and eight daughters. Ernest, the second son and fourth child, was born on August 30, 1871, near Nelson, at Brightwater, and there he went to the State primary school, whence he obtained a scholarship to the Nelson School. About this time his father had moved to Pungarehu, Taranika Province, where he had a flax farm and mill and a rope walk. Rutherford is reported on good authority to have been a normal, happy, unassuming boy, but with unusual powers of concentration—the secret of his success in life. He shot pheasants and wild pigeons, played forward at Rugby football, caught eels and brook trout, nearly drowned himself bathing, took clocks to pieces, made water wheels (like Newton), photographed, loved reading and music; he also won prizes and scholarships for English, History, French, and Latin. He was greatly helped by a good schoolmaster, W. S. Littlejohn, who taught him sound mathematics, and, in a very small class, chemistry and physics. He obtained a scholarship to Christchurch College, Canterbury (part of the University of New Zealand), which at that time (1890) had seven professors and about one hundred and fifty students. Here two men in particular influenced him: Professor A. W. Bickerton, who taught physics and chemistry and was highly original, although "heterodox in all his views and erratic in his methods;" and Professor G. H. H. Cook, whose mathematics was sound and orthodox.

Rutherford's thesis in physics was on "Magnetization of Iron by High-Frequency Discharges," and the necessary experiments were carried out in a cold and draughty den. He showed that high-frequency currents from a small Tesla coil, with a frequency of about 100 million cycles a second, would strongly magnetize iron, contrary to the belief of the day. The explanation was given by the late Lord Rayleigh, who pointed out that with damped oscillations the balance of the total current must necessarily be unidirectional.

Rutherford's second paper was on "Magnetic Viscosity," published 1896 in the *Transactions of the New Zealand Institute*. By this time he was able to send wireless (Hertzian) waves down the 60 feet of the shed, and through walls, detecting them at the other end. He had also, with prophetic insight, read a paper to the Science Society (1891) entitled "The Evolution of the Elements."

For a time he endeavored to impart some of his knowledge to some restless and rather unruly boys of the High School, Christchurch, N.Z.; but—the great opportunity came—the spirit of the Prince Consort kindled New Zealand, and the Commissioners of the great 1851 Exhibition elected the brilliant and promising youth to a scholarship, and he sailed for Cambridge University.

Most of the preceding account is culled from a description of the early years of Rutherford collected by Professor C. C. Farr, F. R. S., Canterbury College, N. Z.

CAMBRIDGE, 1895–1898

On his arrival in England Rutherford joined Trinity College, Cambridge, where later he was elected to a Coutts Trotter Studentship. A wise University regulation had just been made which enabled graduate students of other universities to join Cambridge as research students and obtain a B.A. degree after two years' residence. Sir J. J. Thomson has stated that Rutherford was the very first research student to join him in the Cavendish Laboratory, while J. S. Townsend was a close second.

Rutherford at first continued and developed his work on the magnetic detector already begun in New Zealand and his results were published in *Phil. Trans.*, A, Vol. 198, p. 1 (1897), in a paper which may still be read with great interest. After testing many types of iron and steel of various lengths and diameters, he finally made a bundle of 20 steel wires (1 cm. long, each 0.007 cm. diameter) and wound them with 80 turns, 2 layers, of fine insulated wire having a total length of 6 inches! The ends of this small solenoid were connected between two straight rods in line, which formed the aerial. The waves came from the oscillator through space and caused a current in the aerial. This current passing round the coil altered the magnetism of the steel and this change was indicated by the deflection of an adjacent small mirror magnetometer. Rutherford used a vibrator or oscillator such as Hertz employed in his classic experiments on wireless waves; the plates were about 16 inches square, but for long ranges he used zinc plates, 6 feet by 3 feet. The sparks between the central knobs were excited either by a Wimshurst machine or a Ruhmkorff coil, and these were equally effective. There was one drawback; the detector had to be remagnetized after the receipt of a signal, a difficulty which Marconi later overcame by the revolution of an endless steel band passing a "washout" magnet. Detection of wireless waves, 6 or 7 meters long, by this method was first made by Rutherford across Jesus Common, Cambridge, over a distance exceeding a quarter of a mile, and later from the top of the Cavendish Laboratory to Park Place, with many brick and stone buildings between oscillator and receiver half a mile apart. Sir Joseph Larmor states that there were also signals sent in this manner from the Cavendish to the Observatory about two miles away. No apology is needed for dwelling at some length on this important pioneer experiment. He received no benefits or specific recognition for his invention, and refused to act as "expert witness" with reference to the discovery.

Rutherford next joined in the investigations on the "Conduction of Electricity through Gases," about which Sir J. J. Thomson published his famous book in 1903—a book which opened great vistas of new regions of physics and was for a number of years almost a bible for physicists. In the index are 25 references to the five or six years of Rutherford's work. Rutherford had ingenious methods for measuring the velocities of the ions produced by Röntgen rays. First he measured the ionization current between two parallel plates; then he switched off the rays, instantly put on a high potential and thus swept out all the ions of one sign to a plate and measured the charge that this carried with an electrometer. Thus, without knowing either the number or the charge of the ions, it was easy to find the sum of the velocities of the ions in air or in any chosen gas. These added velocities were found to be 10 cm./ sec. for hydrogen and 3·2 for air, as for a gradient of 1 volt per centimeter. By another method he measured the velocities of each kind of ion; while his most ingenious scheme was to toss negative ions up and down by an alternating potential until they just reached an upper parallel plate joined to an electrometer. Rutherford was the first to measure the coefficient of the rate of recombination of ions. All of which justified his remark that "Ions are jolly little beggars, you can almost see them!"

In the meantime great events were happening in France. Henri Becquerel had shown that uranium was radioactive (1896); Marie Curie had discovered polonium; Pierre and Marie Curie had found radium (1898); the next year Debierne produced actinum. All of these bodies had new, strange, complex properties. At Cambridge, Rutherford, now highly trained, began to study the radiations from uranium, and when he was appointed Macdonald Research Professor of Physics at McGill University, Montreal, to succeed H. L. Callendar, he carried this work with him with far-reaching results.

McGILL UNIVERSITY, 1898–1907

At Montreal, Rutherford continued his work on the radiations from uranium and found that there were two types, which he named alpha and beta rays, whose absorptions by aluminum foil were in the ratio of a hundred to one. He noted in the case of thorium a yet more penetrating type, but the name gamma rays was given later by Villard. About the same time R. B. Owens began work at McGill on the radiations from thorium compounds and found some perplexing new properties, for a draft of air would reduce his electroscope readings to a third of their value in still air, and "something" would pass through paper which could not get through quite thin layers of mica or metal foil. Rutherford

1348

examined this problem in a systematic way and found that there was an "emanation," quite different from ionized air, for it would pass through cotton wool or red-hot metal tubes, losing half its strength about every minute. Moreover, this substance would render other bodies radioactive, so that there were now four things to think about in the case of thorium—alpha rays, beta rays, emanation, and "induced" or "excited" activity, later known as "active deposit." It was well remarked at the time that "it will be seen that radioactivity is a very complicated phenomenon." This discovery of thorium emanation (thoron) was an important advance, followed by Dorn (1900) finding radium emanation with a half-value period of about four days. This, too, gave rise to "induced radioactivity" as Mme. Curie found.

Sir William Crookes ingeniously extracted by chemical methods uranium X—a highly radioactive material relatively small in quantity—from uranium nitrate, which thereby became weaker; but the new substance grew weak (half-value period one month) and the original uranium recovered at the same kind of rate. Rutherford and Soddy somewhat similarly extracted thorium X from thorium and watched the former, at first strongly radioactive, weaken day by day, following an exponential law, while the original thorium recovered its radioactivity in a strictly complementary manner. In this case the period of half-value, regardless of age, was four days.

With this somewhat scanty but definite evidence, (Rutherford had also found an exponential law of decay for thorium emanation and active deposit) Rutherford and Soddy (1902) boldly set forth the theory of radioactive change. They claimed that radioactivity was an *atomic* property, independent of physical surroundings or chemical composition, and it was stated that "the normal or constant radioactivity possessed by thorium is an equilibrium value, where the rate of increase of radioactivity due to the production of fresh active material is balanced by the rate of decay of radioactivity of that already formed" (*Phil. Mag.*, vol. 6, 3, p. 569, 1902).

The importance of the word "material" may be emphasized. A year later came a clearer statement; writing of a single radioactive substance, the principle is laid down: "The rate of the change of the system at any time is always proportional to the amount remaining unchanged." Here speaks the perfect actuary dealing with the mortality tables of disintegrating atoms. He continues: "The proportional amount of radioactive matter that changes in unit time is a constant." This constant for any given material is here called for the first time the "radioactive constant." It is of course simply and closely connected with the half-value period, and its reciprocal is the average life of the atoms.

After these general principles had thus been laid down there was little stumbling in their application. Rutherford, with consummate skill, mastered the radium family, viz., radium, radon, radium A–F, all in strictly linear descent. He identified radium F with Mme. Curie's polonium, for the two had the same period of decay to half-value. He also postulated the existence of two "rayless" changes RaB and RaD, which are now known to project beta particles, but at the time they were mere go-betweens, devoid of all physical properties, but none the less "real." He presented the whole fabric complete with theory to the Royal Society in his Bakerian Lecture. (*Phil. Trans.* A, vol. 204, pp. 169–219, 1904.)

In 1908 Boltwood was praising the then recent papers of Rutherford and Geiger. "These are quite up to the top notch of your own standard and I think the best since the Bakerian Lecture period, which in my opinion can never be beaten. That Bakerian Lecture is going down through history as *the classic,* and every time that I turn to it I am comforted with the thought that I possess a copy."

Rutherford was elected Fellow (1903) and awarded the Rumford Medal (1905). Before this, however, he had revisited his home in New Zealand and married (1900) Mary G. Newton, only daughter of Arthur and Mary de Renzy Newton, Christchurch, N.Z.

The great benefactor of McGill, Sir William Macdonald, presented to the laboratory a liquid air machine and a hundred milligrams of Ra Br$_2$; with these Rutherford quickly showed that radium emanation was a gas which would condense in a spiral tube immersed in liquid air at a temperature of about 153°C. At

1350

ordinary temperatures, the emanation behaved like a gas and diffused at a rate suggestive of high molecular weight. Moreover, it disintegrated at a rate independent of the volume it occupied, so that atoms were not disintegrated by the radiation from adjacent atoms.

Curie and Laborde had found that a gram of radium would produce heat continuously at the constant rate of about 100 calories an hour. Rutherford and Barnes confirmed this and found how the heat arose with reference to the different types of radiation, also with respect to the various members of the radium family. Rutherford made a calculation relating to this high output of energy and added "there is no reason to suppose that this enormous store of energy is possessed by radioelements alone" (*Phil. Mag.*, vol. 6, 5, p. 587, 1903). Indeed, were it possible to collect a pound of radium emanation the rate of output of its radiant energy would at first be equivalent to 10,000 or 100,000 horsepower. Rutherford and Soddy had stated that "on the disintegration hypothesis this energy is derived from the latent energy in the radium atoms and is released in the successive stages of their disintegration."

In 1903 Rutherford published important results on the nature and measured properties of alpha rays from radium, which he passed between parallel plates and deflected with magnetic and electrostatic fields. He found the ratio of charge to mass of an alpha particle to be about 6000, which suggested a helium atom of mass 4 and with charge $+ 2 e$, as was finally proved. He found the velocity of the alpha particle to be about $2 \cdot 5 \times 10^9$ cm./sec.— rather too large a value. But these early results gave a clear enough picture of the nature of this radiation. In 1905, while still at McGill, Rutherford had fired alpha particles into a testing chamber and determined the total charge carried per second. Knowing the double charge that each carried, he was able to state that the number of alpha particles issuing from a gram of radium every second was about 6×10^{10}, and of beta particles $7 \cdot 3 \times 10^{10}$, while the half-value period of radium was estimated at 1850 years. (*Phil. Mag.*, vol. 6, 10, p. 193, 1905.) These figures were based on an erroneous radium standard and on too low a value of the electronic charge, yet for first measurements they were astonishingly, perhaps luckily, good.

MANCHESTER, 1907–1919

In 1907 Rutherford accepted the Langworthy Chair of Physics in the University of Manchester. His predecessor in the chair, Professor Arthur Schuster, was largely responsible for the invitation which was sent from Manchester to Rutherford. The laboratories to which he came were fairly new (they had been opened in 1900), and Schuster had devoted much care to their design and equipment. Two subdepartments, electrotechnics (later separated into an independent department under Professor R. Beattie) and electrochemistry, were housed in the physics building and under the control of the Langworthy Professor. The laboratories as a whole were well equipped for electrical work, and there was an efficient liquid air machine. In other words, the laboratories were so equipped that Rutherford could continue, with a minimum of delay, the work he had begun in Canada. He was not hampered by excessive teaching or administrative duties, he had a capable teaching staff to assist him, and he found in Mr. William Kay a young, energetic, and exceptionally capable laboratory steward. The department ran smoothly and Rutherford was able to throw a large part of his amazing energy into the development of a school of radioactive research. In a short time he attracted so many research workers from all parts of the world that the laboratory became seriously overcrowded. Conditions were much relieved by the building, some four or five years later, of additional research rooms and the removal of the subdepartment of electrotechnics to a separate block.

Two circumstances facilitated the beginning of work in Manchester. He found there Schuster's young assistant, H. Geiger, who became an admirable second in furthering the development of a research school; and in 1908 the Akademie der Wissenschaften of Vienna lent him 250 milligrams of radium, a very considerable amount of radium in those days. The radium preparation was of low concentration and so bulky that it was unsuitable for most experiments. Rutherford therefore developed a new way of using radium—the use of radium in solution as a source for its emanation, which could be pumped off when required. The apparatus for this purpose and the method of purifying the emanation were worked out with the aid of Royds (*Phil. Mag.*, November, 1908). This was a significant advance in technique, for it made possible a regular supply of radium emanation and an active deposit for the many experiments in progress in the laboratory.

Rutherford's work at McGill had firmly established the transformation theory propounded by himself and Soddy, and the general scheme of the radioactive families was sufficiently clear, at least in outline, by 1907. At the time of his arrival in Manchester he was more keenly interested in the radiations from the radioactive substances, and especially in the x-rays, than in the substances themselves.

One of his earliest major contributions in Manchester was the beautiful work with Geiger (*Proc. Roy. Soc.*, A, vol. 81, p. 141, 1908), in which the number of α- particles emitted per second per gram of radium was accurately and directly measured for the first time. It is difficult now to realize the many difficulties which had to be overcome before they were able to detect a single α-particle by means of its electrical effect. It was a technical feat of a high order, all the more impressive for having been accomplished with the simplest apparatus and in a very short time. The result of this measurement was of the utmost value in general atomic theory, as well as in radioactivity. When combined with the measurement of the total charge carried by a stream of α-particles (Rutherford and Geiger, *Proc. Roy. Soc.*, A, vol. 81, p. 162, 1908) this result showed clearly that the normal α-particle was doubly charged, and gave a value for the unit of charge which was at least as reliable as any available at the time.

Rutherford's earlier work had convinced him (and most other physicists) that the α-particles were doubly charged helium atoms. Although the new work with Geiger strongly supported this view, he evidently felt the need of a direct identification. This followed in the experiment with Royds (*Phil. Mag.*, vol. 17, p. 281, 1909). They succeeded in preparing glass tubes with walls so thin that α-particles could pass through and yet so strong as to withstand atmospheric pressure. Such an "α-ray tube" was filled with radon and the emitted α-particles were allowed to emerge into a previously evacuated space. After a few days, an electrical discharge was passed through this space and the characteristic spectrum of helium appeared. This experiment created great interest on account of its simple directness and beauty.

It was, however, the experiments on the scattering of α-particles which led to Rutherford's greatest and most fruitful contribution to atomic theory. In the experiments on the counting of the particles it had been noticed that traces of residual gas in the long tube down which the α-particles passed had an influence on the counts. This effect was ascribed to a small scattering of the α-particles, which was investigated later by Geiger (*Proc. Roy. Soc.*, A, vol. 81, p. 174, 1908; vol. 83, p. 492, 1910). Then came the surprising observation by Geiger and Marsden (*Proc. Roy. Soc.*, A, vol. 82, p. 495, 1909) that an α-particle sometimes experienced an exceptionally violent deflection, seldom, it is true, but far too often to be explained on the basis of the previous measurements of the scattering. Rutherford must have pondered deeply on this curious effect. Professor Geiger writes: "One day (in 1911) Rutherford, obviously in the best of spirits, came into my room and told me that he knew now what the atom looked like and how to explain the large deflections of the α-particle. On the very same day I began an experiment to test the relation expected by Rutherford between the number of scattered particles and the angle of scattering." The genius of Rutherford had seized upon an apparently unimportant detail and transformed it into a clue to the problem of the inner structure of the atom. The nuclear theory of atomic structure was published in a surprisingly complete form in 1911 (*Phil. Mag.*, vol. 21, p. 669, 1911). Supported at first by the preliminary experiments of Geiger on the variation of scattering with angle, it was in the next few months confirmed in its minutest details by a beautiful series of accurate quantitative tests. It would be difficult to exaggerate the influence of the nuclear theory of atomic structure on the whole range of the exact natural sciences, and the theory will surely rank as the greatest of all Rutherford's contributions to physics.

Soon after the publication of the nuclear theory came two researches which are now classic. The first of these was Bohr's earliest contribution to atomic physics, in which he applied quantum-mechanical principles to the Rutherford model of the atom. Bohr had spent a few months in Manchester in the early summer of 1912, where he began to think about the rôle played by the quantum of action for the stability of the Rutherford atom. Only after his return to Denmark, however, did he produce his great paper on the constitution of the atom, in which he showed how the fundamental rules of the spectra of the elements could be explained in a very simple way. The second piece of work was Moseley's brilliant investigation of the x-ray spectra of the elements, in which he demonstrated the function of the nuclear charge in determining x-ray spectra and established the importance of the concept of atomic number. These two researches, which are among the most illustrious of a long line depending upon Rutherford's nuclear atom, undoubtedly owed much to his personal inspiration.

Not long afterward, the Manchester research school was almost completely dispersed as a result of the outbreak of war. Much of Rutherford's time was taken up by war work, as well as by the difficulties of running his department with a heavily depleted staff. In 1919, however, he was able to publish the results of yet another epoch-making research, again made with α-particles. In four papers published in the *Philosophical Magazine,* Vol. 37, he proved conclusively that the long range particles earlier shown by Marsden to be produced when α-particles were fired into hydrogen were in fact fast hydrogen nuclei, and he showed that identical particles were produced by the collisions of α-particles with nitrogen. The explanation—that these protons were the result of the disruption, or "artificial disintegration," of the normally stable nitrogen nucleus—was so revolutionary, and so pregnant with far-reaching implications, that it clearly needed to be supported by very complete experimental evidence. Rutherford obtained the necessary support by an admirably designed series of control experiments. He did the whole of the experimental work, with Kay's assistance in taking observations of scintillations. The further development of this work, and its extension to other nuclei, belongs to the Cambridge period.

WAR WORK, 1914–1918

World War I produced marked changes in Rutherford's laboratory in Manchester. The "family" of research workers dispersed—joining various branches of the fighting forces.

In July, 1915, the Admiralty Board of Invention and Research (B.I.R.) was organized under the presidency of Lord Fisher. Rutherford was on the Panel of the Board and on the Sub-Committee dealing with submarine detection and location, besides other important matters. At that time, enemy submarines were just becoming troublesome; later they became a menace.

It might have been supposed that a man like Rutherford could not "switch over" from atoms to submarines. No doubt such a change required a great effort on his part, but he was equal to it and tackled the problem with his customary energy. The large research laboratory on the ground level was transformed into an acoustics laboratory with a large tank for studying underwater acoustics, about which little was known. His early work in this laboratory with Broca tubes, diaphragms, microphones, and various underwater senders and receivers demanded tests under service conditions. A research station was started at Hawkeraig, Aberdour, in November, 1915. Rutherford supplied a contant stream of apparatus and ideas to be tried out on ships and submarines at Aberdour.

CAMBRIDGE, 1919–1937

When Rutherford went to Cambridge in the summer of 1919 he took with him a great deal of apparatus from Manchester, including the Vienna radium, so that he was ready to start work immediately. He continued his investigation of the effects accompanying the passage of α-particles through nitrogen and oxygen, recorded in the series of papers in the *Philosophical Magazine* of 1919. The results of these experiments were given in his second Bakerian Lecture of 1920, "The Nuclear Constitution of Atoms." He gave further and conclusive proof that the long range particles

1356

from nitrogen were swift protons, by measuring their deflection in a magnetic field. This was the first great step in the deliberate transmutation of matter. He also discussed the nature of the "short range atoms" observed in nitrogen and oxygen, and concluded that they were a new kind of particle of mass 3 and charge 2, that is, an isotope of helium, liberated in the disintegration of nitrogen and oxygen. This conclusion proved to be wrong, for these "short range atoms" were found later to be "long range α-particles" emitted by the source of radium C. This is one of the very few instances in which Rutherford made a wrong deduction from his experiments. The apparent occurrence of this new particle—part of the structure of the nitrogen and oxygen nuclei—led him to consider generally the constitution of atomic nuclei. Using as the ultimate constituents the hydrogen nucleus and the electron, he suggested that simple combinations of these might exist which had not yet been discovered. It may be of interest to quote his own prophetic words forecasting deuterium and neutron:

> . . . it seems very likely that one electron can also bind two H nuclei and possibly also one H nucleus. In the one case, this entails the possible existence of an atom of mass nearly 2 carrying one charge, which is to be regarded as an isotope of hydrogen. In the other case, it involves the idea of the possible existence of an atom of mass 1 which has zero nuclear charge. Such an atomic structure seems by no means impossible. On present views, the neutral hydrogen atom is regarded as a nucleus of unit charge with an electron attached at a distance, and the spectrum of hydrogen is ascribed to the movements of this distant electron. Under some conditions, however, it may be possible for an electron to combine much more closely with the H nucleus, forming a kind of neutral doublet. Such an atom would have very novel properties. Its external field would be practically zero, except very close to the nucleus, and in consequence it should be able to move freely through matter. Its presence would probably be difficult to detect by the spectroscope, and it may be impossible to contain it in a sealed vessel. On the other hand, it should enter readily the structure of atoms, and may either unite with the nucleus or be disintegrated by its intense field, resulting possibly in the escape of a charged H atom or an electron or both.

1357

And further:

> The existence of such atoms seems almost necessary to explain the building up of the nuclei of heavy elements; for unless we suppose the production of charged particles of very high velocities it is difficult to see how any positively charged particle can reach the nucleus of a heavy atom against its intense repulsive field.

The idea that there might exist small particles with no electric charge had, of course, been suggested many times before, but none of these suggestions so closely forecast the properties of the neutron we now know. Rutherford thought that these neutral particles might be formed in the electric discharge through hydrogen. Several experiments were made to test this idea, but they gave, of course, negative results. Rutherford never abandoned the idea that the neutron might exist, and in later years both he and Chadwick made unsuccessful attempts to detect this particle (cf. Rutherford and Chadwick, *Proc. Camb. Phil. Soc.,* vol. 25, p. 190, 1929).

After going over the ground of his previous work in this way, Rutherford, with Chadwick, extended the work on disintegration by the impact of α-particles on other elements. Improvements in the technique of scintillation counting made observations much easier and more reliable, and it was rapidly shown that many of the lighter elements could be disintegrated, with the emission of long range particles (Rutherford and Chadwick, *Phil. Mag.,* vol 42, p. 809, 1921). In a later paper it was shown with reasonable certainty that the long range particles were in all cases swiftly moving protons. In subsequent papers the observations were further extended and it was shown that nearly all the light elements, up to argon, were disintegrated in this way. The mechanism of the disintegration process was not at first clear. It was gradually realized that a kind of synthesis of the atomic nucleus probably took place, in which the α-particle was captured and incorporated into the nuclear structure, and a proton emitted. This capture of the α-particle was later shown very clearly and decisively in the beautiful experiments of Blackett in which he observed and photographed disintegrations of nitrogen in the expansion chamber. The general view (*cf.* Rutherford and Chadwick, *Proc. Phys. Soc.,* vol. 36, p. 417, 1924) was that, while the ordinary Coulomb force must hold outside the nucleus, there must be attractive forces inside in order to hold the particles together. There must then be a critical surface around the nucleus at which the force is zero or the potential a maximum. In order to promote a disintegration, the α-particle had to penetrate within this critical surface. There should thus be a minimum velocity which the α-particle must have to produce a disintegration and the proton must escape from the nucleus also with a certain minimum velocity. The experiments gave general support to this view of the disintegration process. Estimates of the critical potential (which we should now call the height of the potential barrier) agreed reasonably well and the probability of disintegration also fitted in with this view. It is not without point to remark how well this general picture corresponds to our present ideas.

Pursuing this conception, Rutherford attempted to obtain further information about the potential barriers around atomic nuclei by investigating the scattering of the α-particles (Rutherford and Chadwick, *Phil. Mag.,* vol. 50, p. 799, 1925). He found that the scattering by light elements departed in a striking way from the normal scattering calculated on Coulomb forces. While the deviations occurred in about the expected region it was not possible to give a satisfactory explanation of the results. A still more striking result was obtained from the examination of the scattering by uranium. As uranium emits α-particles of 2·7-cm. range it was expected that α-particles of radium C', of much greater energy, would be able to penetrate with ease into the uranium nucleus; such penetration would be revealed by strong divergences from normal scattering. No such divergences were observed; the forces experienced by the α-particle were the ordinary Coulomb forces. The radioactive data gave a radius of at least 7×10^{-12} cm. for the uranium nucleus, the scattering experiments said it was less than 3×10^{-12} cm. To escape from this dilemma, the suggestion was made that the outer parts of a nucleus were composed of neutral satellites. Rutherford himself developed this point of view

1359

later in great detail (*Phil. Mag.*, vol. 4, p. 580, 1927) in an interesting way, but without real success. The difficulty was too deep-seated. Classical mechanics failed to describe these events. The explanation was given by Gurney and Condon, and by Gamow, a year or so later, when they pointed out that the wave mechanics allowed the α-particle to escape from a nucleus through the potential barrier, and did not force it, as did the classic mechanics, to climb over the top.

The transmutation of elements, so long and so often sought and at last by him achieved, the crowning triumph of his life's work, held for Rutherford a profound fascination. Perhaps he dimly foresaw the boundless possibilities, not yet conceivable. He was able to convey some of this quiet satisfaction and enthusiasm in that last book of his, "The Newer Alchemy," which has given so much pleasure to many readers of varied types of thought.

This work on disintegration by high-speed ions was pushed on with great vigor, and he and Oliphant, with various collaborators, obtained a great many interesting and important results. The energy relations in some of the processes led Rutherford and Oliphant to the conclusion that the values accepted for the atomic masses of the light elements were inconsistent. They deduced, from their experiments, a new set of atomic masses and this work acted as a fresh stimulus to measurements by Aston using the mass spectrograph.

During his years in Cambridge, Rutherford's influence spread far and wide. As his insight and sound judgment became more widely appreciated, the claims on his time and services grew. He was consulted on awards and appointments by societies, universities and government departments. There were his annual lectures at the Royal Institution, of which he was professor of physics, where he demonstrated admirably his latest discoveries. He was in demand for lectures, meetings, and addresses both at home and abroad.

HONORS

In 1893 Rutherford obtained his M.A. degree with honors in mathematics and physics from the University of New Zealand, and in 1894 he was elected to an 1851 Exhibition Scholarship. He became fellow of the Royal Society in 1902, and three years later was awarded the Rumford Medal. He was Nobel Laureate for chemistry, 1908, and received the honor of knighthood in 1914. He was elected fellow of Trinity College, Cambridge (1919), and awarded the Copley Medal of the Royal Society (1922). He was president of the British Association for the Advancement of Science (1922). He received the great distinction of the Order of Merit (1925). He was president of the Royal Society (1925–1930), and he was professor of natural philosophy at the Royal Institution. He was president of the Institute of Physics and an 1851 Exhibition Commissioner. He received the Barnard Medal from Columbia University, the Franklin Medal (1924) from the Franklin Institute, Philadelphia; the Albert Medal (1928) from the Royal Society of Arts; the Faraday Medal (1930) from the Institute of Electrical Engineers; and, as early as 1908, the Bressa Prize (£384) from the Academy of Sciences at Turin—his first substantial recognition. He received honorary degrees from about twenty universities scattered over the world, and he was an honorary member of numerous societies and academies, as recorded in the Year Book of the Royal Society.

In 1931 he was created Baron Rutherford of Nelson and took his seat in the House of Lords.

In 1937 he was elected president of the twenty-fifth (silver jubilee) meeting of the Indian Science Congress joined by nearly a hundred representatives of the British Association for the Advancement of Science. His presidential address, prepared about two months before his untimely death, was read (January, 1938) by his successor, Sir James Jeans, who paid a noble tribute to this friend he so admired and respected. He said:

> In truth most of his investigations were key investigations, each brilliant in its simplicity of conception and far-reaching in its consequences . . . In his flair for the right line of approach to a problem, as well as in the simple directness of his methods of attack, he often reminds us of Faraday, but he had two great advantages which Faraday did not possess—first, exuberant bodily health and energy,

and second, the opportunity and capacity to direct a band of enthusiastic co-workers. Great though Faraday's output of work was,
it seems to me that to match Rutherford's work in quantity as well
as in quality, we must go back to Newton.

Voltaire once said that Newton was more fortunate than any
other scientist could ever be, since it could fall to only one man to
discover the laws which govern the universe. Had he lived in a later
age, he might have said something similar of Rutherford and the
realm of the infinitely small; for Rutherford was the Newton of
atomic physics. In some respects he was more fortunate than Newton; there was nothing in Rutherford's life to compare with the
years which Newton spent in a vain search for the philosopher's
stone, or with Newton's output of misleading optical theories, or
with his bitter quarrels with his contemporaries. Rutherford was
ever the happy warrior—happy in his work, happy in its outcome,
and happy in its human contacts.

Like Faraday, Rutherford lived to be a centre of universal affection as well as esteem . . . He had, of course, a volcanic energy and
an intense enthusiasm—his most obvious characteristic—and an
immense capacity for work. A "clever" man with these advantages
can produce notable work, but he would not be a Rutherford.
Rutherford had no cleverness—just greatness.

He could not fail to be aware of this, but, like his honors, it
left him quite unspoiled. On the occasion of one of his discoveries,
the writer said to him: "You are a lucky man, Rutherford, always
on the crest of the wave!" To which he laughingly replied, "Well!
I made the wave, didn't I?" and added soberly, "At least to some
extent." Truly his wave went with him wherever he went, a fine
wave, lit by the sunbeams, for he had the three precious gifts of
the poet—deep insight, powerful imagination, and a profound
love of truth. And so it came to pass that he was "always a charming blend of boy, man, and genius."

There came a short, sharp illness, an operation, and in spite of
every care he died on October 19, 1937.

Six days later his remains were laid to rest in the Abbey near
the graves of Newton, Kelvin, Darwin, and Sir John Herschel.
He had been created Baron Rutherford of Nelson in 1931, but he
will always be Rutherford. The words of the Sub-Dean of West-

minster remain with us: "We thank thee for the life and works of Ernest our brother."

GENERAL REFERENCES

A. S. Eve, "Rutherford 1871–1937, being the life and letters of the Rt. Hon. Lord Rutherford," Macmillan, New York, 1939.

"Rutherford by those who knew him; being the collections of the first five Rutherford-lectures of the Physical Society," The Physical Society, London, 1954.

Selections from: *Obituary Notices of Fellows of the Royal Society,* No. 6, 2, 395 (January 1938).

A. S. EVE

J. CHADWICK

·· *96* ··

Richard Willstätter

1872-1942

LIKE Wilhelm Ostwald, Richard Willstätter left us an autobiography, with the difference, however, that its publication occurred after his death, through the devotion of his former assistant
Arthur Stoll.[1] Again like Ostwald, Willstätter resigned from his
professorship, the former at the age of fifty-three, the other at
fifty-two, and both for reasons connected with religion. There the
likeness ends; Willstätter resigned in protest against anti-Semitism
among the faculty at his university. In fact, the differences between these two great men are more pronounced than the similarities. Willstätter was not a prolific writer; he collected his research
papers in only three books: on chlorophyll, on the assimilation of
carbon dioxide by the green leaf, and on enzymes. This reveals
another difference from the outstanding physicochemist, Ostwald.
They also differed in their outlook on philosophy and in their
relationship to art. Willstätter had little inclination toward music:
"I experienced more strongly through the eye than by ear."[2]
Ostwald was, in a creative sense, self-centered; in his autobiography he describes mostly his own life story, seen as the result of
certain generally valid laws which it exemplified. Willstätter in his
autobiography relates much more about his friends and colleagues.
He says many penetrating and, often, humorous things about
them. A deep interest in the history of their science was shared
by both, but Ostwald expressed it in historical studies, while
Willstätter confined his activities in this field to the search and
acknowledgment of predecessors in his special research work. Both
disliked to search the literature before they started work on a
new idea, but Willstätter expressed the reason differently:

What I was not always inclined to do was to examine the literature of the adjacent sciences, physics, botany, physiology, *before*
the experiment. It is too difficult, it is often enough repelling, to
distinguish the dim path between right and wrong before one's own
experimenting. It is different when clear experimental results have

1367

been achieved, then you can always find predecessors and previous accomplishments.[3]

Richard Willstätter was born on August 13, 1872, in Karlsruhe, as the second son of Max Willstätter, a textile merchant, and his wife Sophie, née Ulmann. Both parental families had lived in southern Germany for many centuries. The great-grandfather of Richard's grandfather, a rabbi, came to Karlsruhe in 1720 from the small Alsatian town of Willstätt. Two great-uncles also were rabbis. The father was not too successful in his business; he went to New York for several years, so that the responsibility for the education of the boys rested largely on the mother's shoulders.

During his school years, at the age of twelve, Richard "was decidedly for chemistry and the natural sciences in general."[4] Thus, when he entered the Technische Hochschule at Munich in 1890, he gave much time to botany in addition to chemistry. Medicine and physiology also attracted him, but his mother opposed them as a preparation for a profession.

In Munich, Richard assisted Alfred Einhorn (1857–1917) in his work on cocaine, the main alkaloid of the coca leaves, which had great medical importance. His doctor's thesis of 1895 was in this field, and he concluded the work four years later with the proof that cocaine contained a seven-membered carbon atom ring.

The new scientific result had interesting practical consequences. The new products synthesized by Willstätter were of great medical value as narcotics. The house of Merck in Darmstadt had offered Willstätter an agreement for the industrial development of these findings. "I did not work with an industrial application in mind. However, the solution to an industrial problem, or some new technical method, frequently happened without being intended or expected."[5]

Sometimes, however, the application was clearly intended and predicted by Willstätter. When a derivative of trichloroethanol proved to be a mild sedative, he directed work toward the corresponding substances containing bromine instead of chlorine. Thus, Voluntal and Avertin came to be added to the chemical pain relievers and anesthetics. They were by-products of his later work on fermentations and enzymes. The name Voluntal was coined by Carl Duisberg (1861–1935), head of the Farbenfabriken vormals Fr. Bayer and Co., who told Willstätter: "We are going to treat you like Emil Fischer."[6] This meant a very substantial support of Willstätter's work, until the dramatic change in his life.

After his graduation Willstätter had become a private assistant to Adolf von Baeyer, a cooperation which developed into personal friendship. Willstätter remained in Munich till 1905 as Privatdozent (1896), associate professor (1902) and head of the department of organic chemistry. In 1903, he married the daughter of professor Emanuel Leser. She died five years later. A son and a daughter were born to them.

In 1905, Willstätter accepted a call to the Technische Hochschule in Zürich and occupied the chair in chemistry till 1912. These were particularly fruitful years, devoted mostly to substances of the quinone group and to the chemistry of chlorophyll.

The study of the quinone group was related to the work at Munich. A continuation of the cocaine investigations led to an intriguing new substance, obtained from an alkaloid present in the root bark of the pomegranate tree. This new substance resembled benzene in structure insofar as its eight carbon atoms formed a ring and were alternately connected by single and double bonds. It was, therefore, designated as cyclooctatetraene. In spite of the structural analogy to benzene, it behaved like an unsaturated aliphatic compound.

Through new methods of extraction, solvent application, and judicious use of acid and alkali as specific splitting agents, he made important contributions to chlorophyll chemistry. "My third paper on chlorophyll was the high point on my scientific way."[7, 8] Twenty-two more articles on chlorophyll followed. They were all combined in a book by Richard Willstätter and Arthur Stoll which came out in 1913. Among the new results were the magnesium content, the uniformity of chlorophyll throughout the plant kingdom, its composition of two components (a and b), the close relationship to the red pigment of blood, and the presence of a complex alcohol, phytol, as part of the chlorophyll molecule. This was purely scientific work, yet it led to many practical applications.

For example, phytol has become a starting material for synthesizing vitamin E, and the corresponding acid (phytic acid) is used in industry.

And yet, after this great success, Willstätter abandoned the field of chlorophyll chemistry and turned to other plant pigments, the yellow pigments in carrots, called carotenes, and those of the flower petals in their rich tints and shades, called anthocyanins. This was mainly carried out at the Chemical Institute of the Kaiser-Wilhelm-Gesellschaft for the Promotion of the Sciences at Berlin-Dahlem from 1912 to 1914. The material for these studies was collected from a large flower plantation on the institute grounds to make sure that the petals used were in their natural state, not altered during transportation or by drying and conserving. A new laboratory method again was essential, this time the specific adsorption on inert carriers as a means of separating the delicate substances from one another.

Once again, this work was abandoned after it had brought highly interesting new results. One very powerful reason was the start of World War I. Although he was not at first directly involved in war work like his friend Fritz Haber, the development of gas warfare resulted in an appeal to Willstätter for protective measures. Within a few months, he completed a gas mask with three layers of absorbents including activated charcoal and hexamethylenetetramine. The use of this chemical remained a secret for many years.

He did not continue the work on flower pigments after he returned to Munich in 1915. "I did not want to give the example of an investigation which required the very greatest consumption of organic solvents. Thus I declined to take up the interrupted work again. However, I doubt that the reason was really so simple. The difficulties could naturally have been overcome in time. Was it not actually the case that the deep darkness of enzyme chemistry was more alluring to me than the detailed work on the chemical structure of chlorophyll derivatives, exploration of nature more than systematic organic chemistry, adventure more than system and synthesis?"[9]

In Dahlem and in Munich he studied how carbon dioxide is assimilated by the green leaf. Isolated chlorophyll cannot do it, the entire living leaf seemed to be necessary. The work was considered completed in 1917 and published in book form the following year by Willstätter and Arthur Stoll.

From then on, Willstätter concentrated on a new great topic, catalysis, by two different kinds of agents, metals and enzymes.

For the addition of hydrogen to unsaturated compounds, called hydrogenation, Adolf von Baeyer had used sodium amalgam, which develops hydrogen upon the addition of water. Catalytic hydrogenation with platinum metals as catalysts furnished the surprising result that traces of oxygen were necessary for the effect. Willstätter and Ernst Waldschmidt-Leitz had discovered that fact during the Dahlem years. In Munich, the study was resumed. The main effort, however, was on the nature and action of enzymes, which had already played a role in the chlorophyll work. The leaf contains a chlorophyll-splitting enzyme, chlorophyllase, which had to be inactivated in order to obtain unchanged chlorophyll. Now, many other enzymes were extracted from yeasts and leaves and roots. They were purified by the then almost forgotten method of chromatography which Michael Tswett (1872–1920) had published in 1906.

Enzymes were considered as mysterious agents connected with life processes. Willstätter strongly emphasized the view that enzymes are chemical substances. They were, in his opinion, characterized by complex formation with proteins to what he designated as "simplexes," aggregates of substances which acquire special new properties through the aggregation.

In order to produce the special adsorbents for enzymes, Willstätter went far into the field of inorganic chemistry. He found methods for making solutions of silicic acid and for obtaining the hydroxides of aluminum, iron, and tin in chemically specific and defined forms. Here he was often in conflict with authoritative pronouncements of colloid chemists. "When I found something new in organic chemistry, it was accepted as valid. When, however, I entered a neighbouring field, like for example inorganic chemistry, I did not readily find acceptance and willingness from my colleagues."[10]

Not all of his colleagues were willing to acknowledge the value of his enzyme work. Henry E. Armstrong remarked, after Willstätter's Faraday lecture on enzymes in London, 1927, "May I say that it is a matter of our deepest regret that you have ceased from inquiry into the field of plant pigments."[11]

Experimental work was only part of Willstätter's activities in the difficult postwar years. The burden of lecturing was great, the care for the students and the institute took much time, willingly and abundantly given. "A researcher who does not let his students watch his experiments, a scientist who does not invite his students to his desk when he writes, appears to me not to be the right kind of teacher."[12]

His efforts found high recognition by his peers in the award of the Nobel Prize (1915), and in the love of his students. However, political events soon caused a drastic decision. The Nazi movement had started with a *Putsch* in Munich. Anti-Semitism grew among the faculty. On three occasions in 1924, when new department heads had to be elected, Jewish candidates were rejected. One of them was Richard M. Goldschmidt, obviously the most outstanding candidate for the chair, held until then by the mineralogist Paul von Groth. Richard Willstätter thereupon handed in his resignation and remained firm in spite of many entreaties. He succeeded in getting Heinrich Wieland to be nominated for his chair. Willstätter remained active in the several scientific organizations that requested his help, but he never entered his institute again. The only assistant who continued his experimental work was Margarete Rohdewald with whom he communicated by telephone and at the writing desk in his home.

The study of enzymes thus continued at a reduced pace. Work in scientific organizations, publications, special lectures, and industrial consultations filled his time. Thus he gave the Willard Gibbs Memorial Address at the American Chemical Society meeting in Chicago, September 14, 1933, and he followed the development of a process for producing sugar from wood, based on his patent of 1913 with Laslo Zechmeister. He declined all the offers of important positions that came to him from universities and industry in Germany, Spain, and America.

When Hitler took over the German government, Willstätter still refused to leave Germany. It was one thing to resign from a professorship, quite another decision to give up one's country. His friend Fritz Haber resigned from his offices and emigrated. If Willstätter deceived himself about the intentions and practices of the Nazi government, it was not for very long. In March of 1939, after grueling experiences, he finally crossed the border into Switzerland. His former assistant and younger friend, Arthur Stoll, provided a new home for him near Locarno.

Here he wrote the memoirs of his work and life, with many poignant remarks about his friends and colleagues. These memoirs show him as a keen observer not only of chemical substances and biochemical reactions, but also of human life. With Fritz Haber he formed a pair like Liebig and Wöhler, and if the comparison could be carried further, the more impetuous Haber would appear closer to Liebig than to Wöhler in this friendship. Willstätter devoted a memorial chapter to him in the memoirs, as he did to his revered older friend, Adolf von Bayer. In addition, he continued some work on the enzyme system of the muscle, again with the experimental help of Miss Rohdewald. On June 7, 1940, he wrote to Stoll: "Garlic is, besides yeast, the most important and the most widely applicable means for improving the whole metabolism, and, which is not recognized, of the metabolism of the skin in particular."[13]

He continued to be interested in biochemistry, plants, and paintings until his heart began to fail. "I do not notice that my illness requires patience; it only demands some attention, perhaps also initiative. Regrettably, I lack the medical knowledge, and also literature, to understand it more deeply."[14] He died August 3, 1942.

NOTES AND REFERENCES

1 Richard Willstätter, "Aus meinem Leben. Von Arbeit, Musse und Freunden," ed. und mit einem Nachwort versehen von Arthur Stoll, Verlag Chemie, 1949.
2 *Ibid.*, p. 367.
3 *Ibid.*, p. 181.
4 *Ibid.*, p. 19.
5 *Ibid.*, p. 74.
6 *Ibid.*, p. 329.
7 *Ann.*, 354, 205 (1907).
8 See Ref. 1, p. 174f.
9 *Ibid.*, p. 184.

10 *Ibid.*, p. 358.
11 *Ibid.*, p. 332.
12 *Ibid.*, p. 216.
13 *Ibid.*, p. 420.
14 *Ibid.*, p. 433.

Richard Kuhn, *Naturwissenschaften*, 36, 1 (1949); Sir Robert Robinson, *Obituary Notices of Fellows of the Royal Society*, No. 22, 1953, 609–634, with bibliography.

EDUARD FARBER

·· 97 ··

Nevil Vincent Sidgwick

1873-1952

NEVIL SIDGWICK (born May 8, 1873) was sent to Summer Fields School, near Oxford, for one year from 1885 to 1886, when his parents were living in London. Previously to that he had been educated entirely at home, mainly by his mother, who early imbued him with that love and wide knowledge of botany and natural history which was one of his most marked characteristics and which was to add so much to the interest of his travels. He entered Mr. Scott's House (School Field) at Rugby School in September, 1886, but became a day boy in 1888 when his parents moved to Rugby. He must have been an ungainly boy, physically unattractive and useless at any kind of game. (In later years he became an expert skater, and a competent player of golf, to which he was introduced by one of his Magdalen pupils.) This does not seem to have affected him at all, even in those days when most small boys at public schools had to contend with serious difficulties if their main assets were their brains rather than their athletic accomplishments. Possibly his wit was too biting and his good humor too disarming for his tormentors, if indeed there were any. There is no indication that he had any difficulty in making friends.

Rugby School was then in the forefront of the new movement for the teaching of science at public schools, but there was no concentration on science to the exclusion of literary subjects. Throughout his school career Sidgwick studied classics as well as science. In 1892 he was elected to an open scholarship in natural science at Christ Church, Oxford. Two of his contemporaries were elected at the same time to science scholarships at Balliol and Trinity. Sidgwick applied to the headmaster for the customary half holiday in recognition of these successes, but met with a refusal. The custom was confined to the winners of classical scholarships!

Sidgwick entered into residence at Christ Church in the autumn of 1892. He was fortunate in his tutor, Vernon Harcourt, the Dr. Lees Reader in Chemistry, who was a pioneer in the new domain of physical chemistry, and one of the first to measure the velocity of chemical reactions and to study the conditions that

1377

determine it. The brunt of the teaching of chemistry was borne at that time by the Colleges, and Sidgwick did the whole of his practical work in the Christ Church laboratory. He was placed in the first class of the Honor School of Natural Sciences in 1895. Sidgwick demonstrated in the Christ Church laboratory for a year, and was then elected to a Dixon scholarship which enabled him to go to Germany. He went first to Ostwald's laboratory in Leipzig, in order to acquire modern techniques for the physical study of organic compounds. Unfortunately he fell ill there, and returned to Oxford, where he spent the summer of 1899 investigating the action of alcohol and other organic substances on stannic chloride. He then went to Germany again in the autumn to work under von Pechmann in Tübingen, where he spent two happy and fruitful years, becoming a fluent German scholar, and carrying out a research on derivatives of acetone dicarboxylic acid for which he obtained the degree of D.Sc. in July, 1901. This was published as a dissertation (dedicated to his mother) in Tübingen, but only appeared in the *Berichte* in 1904, the delay being caused by von Pechmann's illness and death.

Before he left Tübingen Sidgwick was elected to a fellowship at Lincoln College, where he went into residence in October, 1901, and remained for the rest of his life. Apart from his unsuccessful candidature for the Dr. Lees Readership in the following year, and a not very serious application for the professorship of inorganic chemistry in 1920, when Soddy was elected, he appears never to have sought any other appointment, or seriously considered any invitation. Lincoln College became his cherished home, and Oxford the center of his life's work.

I well remember my first meeting with Sidgwick in 1905. He was then responsible for teaching the chemists at Magdalen as well as at Lincoln. I had been reading mathematics for a year, and was told at the end of the summer term to go and introduce myself to the man who would be my tutor for my remaining years at Oxford. I called to see him in the rooms which he was to occupy for nearly fifty years. An elderly looking man, almost bald, with a fringe of gray hair, rose and greeted me pleasantly. It was not till long afterwards that I realized he was then in his early thirties. He asked when I had last done any serious chemistry. I told him.

"Oh," he said, "in that case you must settle down to some serious reading in the long vacation." Observing, perhaps, a lack of enthusiasm in my face, he turned to his shelves and picked out a new-looking book entitled "Chemical Statics and Dynamics" by Mellor. "This is an important subject," he said, "but the book is rather too mathematical for me. I wish you'd take it away and see how many mistakes you can find in it." I believe that this was the first time that any senior man had indicated that I might know more than he did about something that was worth knowing, and the first time that anyone had suggested to me that there might be mistakes in a printed book of science. I took it away: an early discovery of a mistake in the first chapter aroused a detective spirit and led me to consult works of reference; and I returned in October with a list the length of which surprised my tutor as well as the author (who wrote a charming letter of acknowledgement), and I learnt a lot of chemistry in the process. This was characteristic of Sidgwick's method of dealing with his pupils. He was a great tutor, except of a few men whom he did not understand and whose difficulties did not appeal to him. Most of his pupils will always remember him with gratitude and affection, although they may find it hard, as I do, to describe the unusual nature of his influence. He did not appear to take very much trouble. He read one's essays casually and uncritically, but with stray illuminating comments. He would spend the rest of the time discussing irrelevant topics, often unconnected with chemistry. He would advise one to go to lectures to see what they were like, but did not blame one for irregular attendance. I did not even regularly attend his own lectures on the organic chemistry of nitrogen; I found it more convenient to borrow the typescript from which he read them, and study it at leisure. He was never caustic about one's ignorance, so long as he detected a desire to improve. He was nearer than anyone else I have known to Stephen Leacock's description of an Oxford tutor in "My Discovery of England":

I understand that the key to this mystery (of an Oxford education) is found in the operations of the person called the tutor. It is from him, or rather with him, that the students learn all that they know: one and all are agreed on that. Yet it is a little odd to know just how he does it. "We go over to his rooms," said one student, "and he just lights a pipe and talks to us." "We sit round him," said another, "and he simply smokes and goes over our exercises with us." From this and other evidence I gather that what an Oxford tutor does is to get a little group of students together and smoke at them. Men who have been systematically smoked at for four years turn into ripe scholars.

Sidgwick did smoke in those days; a pipe was hardly ever out of his mouth in waking hours except for meals; and by the time he had smoked at one for three years one had a pretty firm foundation of a liberal scientific education on which to build if one had a mind to. But he fell short in one respect: he was not inspiring as an investigator in the years of which I write. His researches, such as they were, were haphazard. At first he continued, in a desultory fashion, his work on the organic compounds of tin, but soon abandoned it without publishing any results. He lost interest in the subject so much as actively to discourage one of his pupils from pursuing it on the reasonable ground that organometallic compounds could be poisonous. But in 1923, when their importance to the study of valency became obvious to him, this objection seemed to lose its force and all his pupils were set to work on them, fortunately without mishap. The fact is that Sidgwick, though accurate, was never an ardent experimenter. He liked to have a band of disciples round him to do most of the work in the laboratory. He was not even very good in selecting topics or advising on methods of research; where he excelled was in the interpretation of results; he could see further than could most of those who produced them. But he had no clear line of work before him until much later. His scientific reputation in 1914 was largely confined to Oxford, and even there mainly to the younger men; some of the older were inclined to regard him as an organic chemist gone wrong. To the outside world of the Chemical Society he was known rather as an acute critic and the author of the "Organic Chemistry of Nitrogen" than for the merits of his original work. The coveted distinction of the fellowship of the Royal Society, for which he yearned, seemed terribly slow in coming; and his closest friends felt that there was some danger of his becoming a disappointed and disheartened man, like his father.

1380

The "Organic Chemistry of Nitrogen" was published in 1910. In the preface Sidgwick wrote: "It is becoming generally recognized that organic chemistry cannot be treated satisfactorily without reference to those questions of physical chemistry which it involves. To attempt a separation of the two is to refuse all the assistance which can be derived from what is the quantitative side of chemistry."

The book was not enthusiastically received by the scientific press; one reviewer went so far as to criticize the author's English— a bold man indeed. It was, however, a great success. The clear, logical, and convincing discussions of controversial matters were of a kind that had never been seen before, and gave the book an altogether outstanding quality. Its educational value was immense. Many of the theories put forward did not survive the passage of time; but the masterly assembly of facts remained invaluable.

The year 1914 was a turning point in Sidgwick's career. He was one of the members of the party chosen to represent the British Association for the meeting held in Australia. This was the first of the many travels overseas which added so much to his enjoyment of life. It was an especial stroke of good fortune for him that Rutherford was a fellow passenger on board the ship. He fell at once under the spell of Rutherford's genius and gaiety. He conceived for him a respect which ripened into a deep devotion in later years. He could not bear at any time to hear even a playful criticism of him; and if anyone was so rash as to differ from Rutherford in print, one felt that Sidgwick would gladly have had the offending article or book burnt by the common hangman! Any pronouncement of Rutherford was right in Sidgwick's eyes; he brought, for instance, the whole weight of his classical erudition in support of Rutherford's suggestion of diplogen as the right name for heavy hydrogen. He felt that this was too serious a matter to be left to the discoverer. However, he took the final decision philosophically: we can at least agree, he said, to denote the new hydrogen by the symbol D.

Perhaps it was Rutherford who supplied the spark that released into its right channels the pent-up energy of Sidgwick's mind. Certainly the curve of his achievements rose thenceforward like the pressure of an explosion. But the period of induction was lengthened by the war of 1914 to 1918, during which Sidgwick, who was clearly unfitted though not unfit for any normal form of military service, stayed quietly at Oxford, acting as an unpaid consultant to the Department of Explosive Supplies.

In 1922 Sidgwick was elected a fellow of the Royal Society. The distinction did not, in his case, mark the end of his best work for science; it marked the beginning. His horizon extended to embrace the whole of chemistry. He was then forty-nine years of age, full of vigor, and quite unchanged in appearance from what he was twenty years previously. But his friends observed a change in other respects: he became more mellow, more confident, more masterly, and yet more tolerant.

Ever since his first discussions with Rutherford on the way to Australia in 1914 Sidgwick had been interested in the bearing of the nuclear theory of the atom on problems of chemical combination, but he had taken no direct part in the various speculative theories that were put forward after the discovery of the atomic numbers of the elements. The position in 1921 was that there was general acceptance of the view that in the simpler ionic compounds there is a transfer of an electron, or electrons, from the positive to the negative atom, so that each ion is surrounded by a number of electrons equal to the atomic number of the nearest inert gas. This theory, which was first given a precise form by Kossel in 1916, gave a fresh meaning to the century-old idea of electrovalency; but it did not apply to nonpolar compounds. G. N. Lewis, on the other hand, had made an advance of fundamental importance in the same year by suggesting the possibility that in nonpolar compounds atoms could share electrons in such a way as to bring about a more stable grouping of the system as a whole. The most stable grouping, in his view, was one of eight valency electrons arranged in cubic formation. This "octet" theory, which was elaborated by Langmuir and others, received considerable attention; but it was abundantly clear by 1921 that the postulate of stationary electrons was not in harmony with physical evidence. Neither theory, nor any combination of them, could account at that time for the formation and stability of the complex inorganic compounds which Werner had been studying for many years, but in which chemists had taken singularly little interest until he succeeded in predicting

1382

and demonstrating that certain of them could be resolved into optically active components.

This was obviously an unsatisfactory state of affairs, which, in Sidgwick's view, would remain unsatisfactory until more was known about the distribution and function of electrons in atoms. The further information for which chemists were waiting was provided by Bohr's note on "Atomic structure" which appeared in *Nature* in March, 1921, and by the publication of his extended "Theory of Spectra and Atomic Constitution" in 1922. The first fruits of Sidgwick's heightened interest in the subject appeared in his note on "The structure of basic beryllium acetate" and in his paper on "Co-ordination compounds and the Bohr atom," which were published in 1923. In June of the same year Lewis visited Oxford and stayed with Sidgwick. They both attended the meeting of the British Association at Liverpool, where Sidgwick opened a discussion on "The Bohr atom and the periodic law." Their interchange of views, and the publication of Lewis's "Valence and the Structure of Atoms and Molecules" later in 1923 provided Sidgwick with an additional stimulus. He saw his way at last to develop an electronic theory of valency which could be applied to all the known facts without infringing the conditions that physical research showed to be necessary. But to do so it would be necessary to survey the whole field of chemistry.

To this formidable task he now addressed himself. It was a task for which he was pre-eminently fitted. It needed a man with an acute penetrating intellect, an orderly and critical mind, a prodigious memory, an exceptional power of assimilation, and a dogged perseverance. All these qualities Sidgwick possessed; and he buttressed them with a determination to synthesize the sciences of physics and chemistry; never to stretch his inductive logic so far as to reach conclusions which, however attractive to the chemist, would be regarded as untenable by the physicist.

Sidgwick's "Electronic Theory of Valency" was published in 1927. It was rightly said of it when he was awarded a Royal Medal in 1937 that for the first time the most diverse structural phenomena covering the whole field of chemistry were rationally systematized, and that it had more widespread influence on the views of chemists in this country than any other of this generation.

1383

The most original part of this now classic work, of which some 10,000 copies have been sold, was that which dealt with coordination compounds. His original paper on "Co-ordination compounds and the Bohr atom" was indeed a carefully laid foundation stone, now almost lost in the magnitude of the structure that has risen around it. He expounded the results of five years of further study and research in a brilliant Presidential Address to Section B of the British Association at the meeting at Leeds in 1927. Nothing is more illustrative of his powers of induction than his conclusion that the covalency of carbon atoms did not differ fundamentally from the coordination of inorganic compounds. He reached this conclusion after an exhaustive study of all the relevant facts that he could find. It provided a firm basis for the general electronic theory of valency. It followed that the special theory of coordination, which Werner had evolved with so much skill and insight, was unnecessary; and it became clear that the coordinate link is of the first importance throughout the whole of chemistry. His views have since been modified in detail; but their general validity remains unimpaired.

In the last chapter of his book Sidgwick considered in a preliminary way the application of the new principles to the individual elements; and he indicated in the preface his intention to develop this in a second volume. Over twenty years were to elapse before he achieved this ambition.

This highly productive period of his life from 1920 to 1930, during which Sidgwick published the book which brought him international fame, and was also responsible wholly or in part for over forty original contributions to scientific journals, was not without major relaxations. In 1924 he visited Canada with the British Association, and after the final meetings in Toronto crossed the prairies and the Rockies to the West Coast before returning to Oxford. In 1929 he had an even more extended tour to South Africa with the British Association, ending by traveling north to Livingstone by train, then by road to Dar-es-Salaam, and then after two days in Zanzibar sailing home via Aden and Suez.

Toward the end of 1930 he was invited to spend a semester at Cornell University as George Fisher Baker Non-Resident Lecturer in Chemistry. He accepted with alacrity, sailed to New York in

1384

January, 1931, spent a fortnight there, visited Princeton, and settled down in Ithaca early in February, "with every luxury that an American laboratory can supply. Two offices, four telephones, a private laboratory, and a stenographer, all to myself. . . . It is a wonderful place, with a great deal of good work going on, and everybody is most kind, so that I can see that I am going to have a very pleasant time here."

By 1932 Sidgwick had abandoned his intention to revise the "Organic Chemistry of Nitrogen" after writing four new chapters; so when the "Covalent Link in Chemistry" was out of the way he was free to concentrate on volume 2 of the "Electronic Theory of Valency." He made a start on this early in 1935, and in the summer was writing to America: "I have accumulated a lot of material, but I don't want to spend all my time in accumulating and not to live to use it." He soon found that he had taken on a far greater task than he had anticipated. The science of inorganic chemistry had been given a new lease of life through the discoveries and theories of physicists, and it became almost impossible to keep abreast of the flood of papers on new classes of compounds and new elements. And then there was wave mechanics to be reckoned with. Quantum mechanics had been bad enough for a nonmathematician to swallow and digest; but wave mechanics was worse still. It could not be neglected, however. Had it not produced the concept of resonance, which, as he wrote in his introduction to the new edition of the "Organic Chemistry of Nitrogen," is the most important development which structural chemistry has had since it was extended to three dimensions by van't Hoff in 1874?

It was not so much the mathematical as the literary language of the wave mechanicians that he objected to. Resonance was a bad name; for it implies that a molecule is oscillating between two states, which is what the theory denies. It reminded him, he said, of a remark by Mrs. Wilfer, one of his favorite characters in the works of Dickens, of which he was a master: "When I use the term attractions, I do so with the qualification that I do not mean it in any way whatever." However, he did not encourage chemists to rechristen the phenomenon: "For the present we have to accept the terminology of the physicists."

I do not know when the full magnitude of his task broke upon him, and volume 2 was abandoned in favor of an entirely new treatise. Not before 1939, I fancy, if indeed so early. By then he had revisited the United States six times. America drew him like a magnet. He loved the country; few Americans can have known it so well as he did. Before he died he had visited 46 of the 48 states, and had at least one friend in each. No British scientist was better known in the United States. He was made a Foreign Member of the American Academy of Arts and Sciences in 1938; but by then he had become, so to speak, an honorary American.

The war of 1939 to 1945 was really a blessing in disguise for Sidgwick—or rather for the accomplishment of his purpose. Traveling was out of the question; even visits to London were rare, and held no attractions. Oxford, of all English cities, was the least affected by war, especially if one was a bachelor don living in College. More important still, from his point of view, the gradual cessation of purely scientific work meant that the flood of new information abated, became a stream, and then a trickle. He was able to get abreast of the literature at last. The chief worry now was whether his health, which was steadily deteriorating, would last. It did: his will power and his sense of humor sustained him.

The book, which had grown to two volumes of 750,000 words, was finished at the end of October, 1947, but for a final revision and the compilation of an index.

"The Chemical Elements and Their Compounds" is a monumental work of scholarship. As one reviewer (D. Ll. H.) wrote: "Never before has the content of chemistry been reviewed with such penetrating perception of its structure and such illuminating criticism of its philosophy." Its aim was to discuss in detail the properties of all the elements and their compounds in the light of modern theory; and especially to bring the same order into the study of inorganic chemistry as had existed so long in organic chemistry. No one had attempted a task of such magnitude before; and it is safe to say that no one else could have achieved it with such remarkable success. It contains nearly 10,000 references to original papers, the greater part of which had been studied and documented, and their essential points stored in Sidgwick's capacious mind, which never seemed to reach saturation. It was not to be expected that a work of such dimensions could be altogether free from errors and omissions; indeed the book was still hot from the press when chemists from many countries wrote to combine with their congratulations gentle complaints that their own work had been overlooked or misinterpreted. Other criticisms have been made—not without foundation. But few great works of art or scholarship have been free from imperfections; and I can imagine no more instructive task for a young chemist than to compile a list of the mistakes in Sidgwick's last and greatest book. It will take him many months of labor, and into many fields of knowledge, still only partially explored. For the mature chemist it is a mine of information into which he cannot dip at any point without being led to read on by interest in the subject matter and the attraction of the style. Sidgwick's own estimate of its circulation— "judging from the number of enquiries I get about the book's progress from both sides of the Atlantic"—was from 3000 to 5000 copies within three years. Up to date about 9000 copies have been sold. It will be surpassed in time; but it will long remain a standard work, and a pattern for future authors to emulate.

Sidgwick's place in the history of chemistry is assured. His own researches, embodied in a long list of contributions to scientific journals, are not outstanding for originality. He was a natural philosopher rather than a researcher; inductive rather than deductive; a weaver rather than a spinner. He would weave the threads of the discoveries of others into an ordered and harmonious pattern on a grand scale. He exerted a great influence on his contemporaries. His wide interests and knowledge, his forceful and clear speaking, illumined all discussions, whether in private gatherings or before large audiences. He was a most welcome visitor to international conferences, a cosmopolitan in the true tradition of science.

He died on March 15, 1952.

Selections from *Obituary Notices of Fellows of the Royal Society,* IX, 237–258 (1954).

H. T. TIZARD

·· *98* ··

Marc Tiffeneau

1873-1946

M ARC TIFFENEAU was born November 5, 1873, the sixth of eight children. In 1883, he went from grammar school to the Institut Saint-Joseph, directed by the Maristes brothers at Pont-Saint-Maxence. There, he excelled in intelligence and assiduity to the point that the head of the school, a distinguished Latin scholar, gave him additional lessons in Greek and Latin, although this was not the special province of the Institut Saint-Joseph. He was barely fifteen when he started his apprenticeship at the pharmacy Frigaut in Pont-Saint-Maxence while continuing his studies at Saint-Joseph. In 1892, after working at the pharmacy Vigier in Paris, he concluded his apprenticeship and began to study at the Faculté de Pharmacie in Paris. I met him for the first time in that year.

While preparing for an examination, I had gone to the Hôpital du Midi to see the collection of medications, and there I met a small, vivacious young man with a joyous and almost boyish expression, to whom I was drawn by a spontaneous sympathy. Almost every day we met again at the same place. This was the beginning of a friendship which lasted, without a cloud, until, regretfully, my friend died.

After my military service, I started my studies at the School of Pharmacy and renewed my relations with Tiffeneau. The course given by Auguste Béhal (1859–1941), which played such a great role in French chemistry, was attended by about a dozen young enthusiasts, among them Tiffeneau and I, and this brought us still closer together.

During my three years in Germany we remained in continuous correspondence. Then we went into industry, I to Poulenc Frères, Tiffeneau to the Matières Odorantes De Laire, and our scientific collaboration began. I became engaged in the study of the simple amino alcohols, because I was convinced that the natural local anesthetics, cocaine and tropacocaine, owed their properties not to their heterocyclic nucleus, but to the fact that they are benzoic acid esters of amino alcohols. It will be recalled that the amino

1391

alcohols are obtained by reacting amines with chlorohydrines. At that time, around 1902, the number of known chlorohydrines was quite small and, naturally, so was that of the amino alcohols. By applying the method of Grignard to chloroacetone, Tiffeneau prepared for me the chlorohydrine which enabled me to find stovaine (the hydrochloride of amyl aminoethyl-p-aminobenzoate, $H_2N.C_6H_4.COO.(CH_2)_2.NH.C_5H_{11}.HCl$). Thus, the first industrial application of the Grignard reaction can be said to have been started by Tiffeneau. I might add that when I asked Grignard about the possibility of treating 30 to 50 kilograms of magnesium at one time; he advised against trying such a dangerous reaction in a closed metallic apparatus in which one could not see what went on. In fact, the first trial with 20 kilograms of magnesium was so violent that the apparatus exploded, and I almost finished my industrial career that same day.

We both left industry almost at the same time in order to devote ourselves completely to pure and applied science. The communications between us became even more frequent than before.

Our friendship was still closer after Tiffeneau married my sister to whom I had introduced him as my noblest and dearest friend, a man whom one could trust completely for life and who could best understand her artistic and intellectual interests. Few marriages were more perfect than theirs, and I believe that if I have done any good things in my life, this was the most successful of all.

In 1903, Tiffeneau and I had formed a group of young chemists, called La Molécule. Later, at the beginning of the war in 1914, a number of young industrialists joined us. We met once a month exchanging ideas and helping each other in many ways. It was due to this group, of which Tiffeneau was one of the founders and the most active, that the Société Chimique de France was able to overcome the many difficulties connected with the war which had almost stopped the development of the Société.

We shared a great interest in music too. The composers whom Tiffeneau preferred were Bach, Beethoven, and Wagner. He knew by heart all the quartets by Beethoven and the operas by Wagner, text and music. His tenor voice had a wide register; he read any musical score at sight, singing all the parts in succession. Gradually, we formed a group of rabid melomaniacs that performed every week at Marc's house, or at mine, or on Sundays at Justin Dupont's where the hospitality was marvelous.

Tiffeneau traveled much, most often to fulfill missions and to attend congresses. He was seen in Rome, Frankfurt, Ghent, Leningrad, Brussels, Edinburgh, Madrid, Zürich, and particularly in Geneva, since he was an expert for the League of Nations. His last great trip, which he undertook in my place with his usual devotion, was across South America in all directions. There he gave a large number of lectures on theoretical chemistry, chemotherapy, and pharmacology. He was greatly helped by his wife who spoke English, German, and Spanish fluently and who, in spite of delicate health, accompanied him everywhere.

In the year of his death he prepared to go to Basle in order to present a survey of his research on molecular rearrangements. He had also accepted an invitation to lecture in the United States. He gladly sacrificed his health and his convenience in the interest of French science. At the same time he used these travels to increase his already extended knowledge of art. He was familiar with all the museums in Europe. Some of his most beautiful trips were undertaken for the artistic education of his family. Ever since his student days, until 1914, he went to Bayreuth every year.

As I mentioned above, Tiffeneau held many important honorary positions. It frequently happens that such honors and activities connected with them make it impossible to devote time to the laboratory. The lasting interest which Tiffeneau extended to his research and his collaborators is one of the most astonishing facts in his life. Up to the time of his death he published, either alone or with his students, highly interesting papers.

On Pentecost Sunday, 1945, Marc Tiffeneau rose early. He arrived at the railroad station around 8 o'clock because he intended to visit a friend who was sick. As he was walking to the platform to board the train he fell down dead.

The largest part of Tiffeneau's scientific work was devoted to the study of certain molecular transpositions. This work started in 1902 and continued to the end of his life. A few weeks before his death he presented a summary of this research at the Institut Pasteur.

A molecular transposition generally is any permutation (re-arrangement) within a molecule. When only atoms migrate, the structure of the initially present skeleton does not change. How-ever, the migration of carbon-containing groups (radicals) gen-erally produces modifications of the structure, as can be seen in the following typical examples. Here are two iodohydrines from which one molecule of hydroiodide is removed by the action of silver nitrate:

In the first example, the branched chain is straightened, in the second the straight chain is transformed into a branched one. In both, the radical phenyl changes its place. These transformations in structure can be classified into two groups: In the first group, migration occurs without reactions of addition or diminution, e.g., methyl aniline to paratoluidine, etc. In the second group, the trans-position follows upon a reaction of elimination of water, hydro-halogenide, ammonia, or amine. A phase of desaturation is thus followed by a phase of rearrangement. In most cases, only the second phase can be verified by experiment.

The studies which Tiffeneau carried out with so much ingenu-ity and perseverance belong exclusively to this second group. He and his collaborators investigated almost all the possible variations to be derived from the following general formula in which R, R_1, R_2, and R_3 may designate hydrogen, aromatic and aliphatic radicals, cyclohexyl, and others:

These transpositions are governed by two factors working in the same direction or in opposition, depending upon the nature of the radicals: the degree of affinity and the ability to migrate. They go together for aromatic radicals, and they are in opposition to each other for the aliphatic radicals. The nature of the reagent causing the transposition interferes with the validity of these rules.

This extended work on molecular transpositions required the preparation of many substances for which new methods had to be developed. Particularly in the field of glycols, ethylene oxides, and halohydrines, Tiffeneau, aided by outstanding collaborators, showed his wisdom, perseverance, and profound knowledge of organic synthesis.

Tiffeneau's activities were not all on problems of pure chemistry. He did not forget that he was, at the same time, a chemist, a pharmacologist, and a physician. A great chemist, he also was the greatest pharmacologist of his time. His study of the relationships between chemical constitution and pharmaceutical action was mainly directed to hypnotizing substances, to sympathomimetic and analeptic amines, and to local anesthetics.

One of his outstanding studies that has become a classic dealt with phenolic derivatives of benzylamine, part of which formed his thesis for the doctorate in medicine (1910). He prepared isomers and homologs in the series of hordenine, ephedrine, and adrenaline. He studied analogs of the analeptic substance benzedrine (amphetamine) and local anesthetics related to benzydryl amines. For these, and for derivatives of barbituric acid and of hydantoin, he derived general relationships between chemical constitution and pharmaceutical action.

One of the well-established rules of pharmacodynamics is that amino alcohols become good local anesthetics when they are benzoylated or, quite generally, acylated. However, some amino alcohols themselves have that action (Ogata, 1920). Tiffeneau, Fourneau, Torrès, and Mrs. Benoît studied a large number of benzydryl amines, starting with $C_6H_5—CH(NH_2)—C_6H_4—OR$. Some of these amines are powerful anesthetics, up to twenty times stronger than cocaine; unfortunately, they are also irritants for the cornea and other tissues which makes their use impossible and even dangerous. Tiffeneau and his collaborators stated certain relationships between constitution, anesthetic, and irritating effects. As in many other series of chemical compounds, accessory factors intervene to make general rules impossible.

In the group of barbiturates, the presence of an ethyl radical had been thought indispensable. Tiffeneau introduced other radicals: butyl, isoamyl, hexyl, heptyl, etc. From this research came one of the best sedatives and hypnotics, soneryl (butethal, 5-butyl-5-ethylbarbituric acid).

GENERAL REFERENCES

E. Choay, "Auguste Béhal," in *J. pharm. chem.*, 1, 512–8 (1941). with bibliography.

Selections from *Bull. soc. chim. France*, *1–5*, 905–932 (1948). Translated by Eduard Farber.

ERNEST FOURNEAU

·· *99* ··

Carl Bosch

1874-1940

O N AUGUST 27 of this year (1949), Carl Bosch would have attained the age of seventy-five years. Since his death on April 26, 1940, great changes have taken place in the world of politics, in the field of natural sciences and technology, and also in the industrial plants established by Bosch. Meanwhile the achievements through which Bosch has enriched industry have remained as a permanent possession of all mankind. The development of high pressure technique, for which he received the Nobel Prize in December 1931, has led to an industry of nitrogenous fertilizer materials, which has attained a magnitude never before imagined, and which is capable of satisfying the demand by agriculture for nitrogen in all countries of the earth for all time. Besides additional new chemical industries, of which that of synthetic methanol with its diversity of additional manufactured products, as well as the metallurgy of carbonyl metals, are to be mentioned only briefly, high pressure technique has realized above all the large-scale industrial production of benzene and middle oils from coal and heavy oils. Much has been written in detail about the history of these developments and the extent of their application; in the year 1920, Bosch himself reported on the development of the nitrogen industry in an extensive lecture at a convention of scientific investigators in Nauheim, and in lectures in Stockholm (1932) and in Oslo (1933) on high pressure technique in general.

Carl Bosch's life work, however, did not consist exclusively of his great accomplishments as a technologist—chemist and engineer—and as director first of the Badische aniline and soda factory and then of the IG Farbenindustrie. Bosch was an inventor and entrepreneur of the first rank, as well as a promoter of research; he was infused with the noblest scientific spirit. He always attached the greatest importance to the complete clarification of technical processes in his plants, and at every opportunity supported, both in word and deed, the cultivation of science, especially of pure basic research. In the years following World War I, he helped research overcome the serious financial difficulties it en-

1399

countered. He was useful to science through the many tasks and suggestions which he gave to the most diverse groups whenever possibilities arose for a thorough scientific treatment and clarification of problems in connection with his technical work.

The love for science, indeed the irresistible urge to get to the basis of all phenomena by scientific means, was apparent in Bosch in his first years of study. The status of metallurgy and mechanical science at that time, to which Bosch devoted himself at first on the advice of his father, did not satisfy the young student at the Technical High School in Berlin-Charlottenburg, not only because he felt that his real interest was in chemistry, but also because the science of materials needed for metallurgy and mechanical science was still influenced by empiricism. The refined methods of the study of metals, as they were developed a few years later, were still unknown or in the beginning stages. "What kind of knowledge is this," Bosch said at a later time in his typical drastic manner of expression, "One calculates the cross section with a complicated formula and then makes it five times as thick so that it will hold up!" Thus it came about that Bosch went to Leipzig and there devoted himself to the study of chemistry at the university. On occasion, Bosch expressed his regret over the fact that technological subjects are taught at technical schools rather than at the universities. Of course Bosch always recognized the achievements of the technical schools, for much that he learned there was of great benefit to him in his subsequent work. If he possessed complete mastery of metal working and of the properties of metals and later was able to contribute considerable practical and scientific progress in these fields, it was chiefly because the basis for this had been given him in Charlottenburg.

His completely scientific manner of thinking and working became evident soon after entering industry, particularly when, in 1909, he was given the task of developing the synthesis of ammonia. Here his actions were guided by the principle that technology must not be satisfied merely with accepting and making use of science for its practical purposes, but that it must contribute to propagating and deepening scientific knowledge in larger fields. He was convinced that this is the only way in which technology could ensure its permanent progress.

1400

In the ammonia plant in Oppau, which was still being built when the First World War broke out, he had constructed a large three-story laboratory which was equipped with all accessory materials, and which was to serve for purposes of pure research as well as for the requirements of the plant. The constant close contact between this laboratory, called the "Ammonia Laboratory," the directorship of which was given to Alwin Mittasch, and the technical works proved to be an excellent means of constantly supplying new tasks for scientific research and thus serving the progress of the newly opened fields. Thus, for example, Bosch stated that we must not be satisfied with the practical mastery of the synthesis of ammonia, but that we must also investigate why this synthesis takes place under certain conditions; why, for instance, iron and moylbdenum serve as catalysts while tin and lead do not. Workers in the laboratory also were to occupy themselves with the theory of catalysis; well-known investigators, like Walter Frankenburger and Rudolf Brill, took part in these projects. The theoretical phase relationships of saline manures, especially of double salts and combined mixed fertilizers, were investigated by Ernst Jaenecke and represented by means of exact phase diagrams. At the Agricultural Experiment Station of Limburgerhof, which was founded in the year 1914 at Bosch's suggestion, Bosch not only instituted a general study of the behavior of nitrogen fertilizers made from synthetic ammonia, but also called for a thorough examination of new nitrogen fertilized materials, such as potassium chloride with ammonium nitrate, ammonium sulfate, and nitrate (Nitrophoska), and, furthermore, of the behavior of the most diverse nitrogen-containing organic compounds, such as guanidin, thiourea, oxamide, formamide, and many others.

As a supplement to this work, a special "biolaboratory" was established in Oppau for the investigation of general questions concerning the growth and nourishment of plants, in which the research extended from the effects of enzymes into the field of medicine. Photochemical studies and investigations on the polymerization of butadiene and macromolecular compounds in general were also included, in addition to further topics, in the work of the Ammonia Laboratory.

The effect, unknown at that time, of hydrogen at high pressure and high temperatures on the carbon content of steel, which gives it tenacity, had caused serious difficulties in the production of high pressure apparatus for the synthesis of ammonia. This impasse led to the establishment of a large material-testing laboratory for the testing and investigation of metals and alloys with equipment; this laboratory was more complete than any owned by university institutes or by the laboratories of the large steel companies.

It became possible to explain and avoid fatigue phenomena in parts of machines that were under great, and especially pulsed, stress, as well as attacks on the metal structure by the effect of different agents. The construction of steam boilers was considerably furthered by this. By means of constant collaboration with the steel industry, Bosch thus gave valuable stimulation to the metallurgy of iron and steel and their alloys as well as to the utilization of these metals.

Another physical laboratory, designed for an extensive "plant control," with large workshops under the direction of the physicist Paul Gmelin, constructed the most delicate apparatus for measurement and analysis on the basis of physical methods, attaining the highest accuracy. The indication of 1/100 per cent and the triggering of an alarm at 1/10 per cent of carbon monoxide in air should be mentioned as examples of their productive ability. Colorimetric procedures were worked out for the measurement of concentrations of colored solutions, e.g., copper solutions, as well as photoelectric methods for indicating the dew point; analytical methods using qualitative spectral analysis in the regions of ultraviolet and infrared wavelengths using the Raman effect; and roentgen rays and electron diffraction were put to use in the study of metals. Another large laboratory, the "technological testing station," under Prof. Wilhelm Wilke, was concerned with the testing of the engine characteristics of fuels for Otto and Diesel motors.

From the very beginning, after entering the field of technology, Bosch placed great value on measuring everything which could be measured in any way. He owed a great measure of his successes to this thorough method of working, which he also demanded of his co-workers.

Bosch radically departed from the system customary in the

chemical industry at that time of the seclusion of different laboratories and plants from one another; it now became the rule in the individual factories to discuss new advances in colloquia and meetings.

More and more, the policy of giving the public some insight into the newest technical and scientific experiences of the factories was followed, even if there were places here and there in the plants where this was not approved of. Bosch considered it a self-evident point of honor to pay to science a part of the debt of gratitude it deserved for the foundations which had been obtained from it for the establishing of the great factories. Thus a large-scale compromise between the requirements of safeguarding an advantage acquired at high cost and a furthering and strengthening of science which in turn would benefit technology was established. As a consequence, the scientific reputation of the factory, and of industrial work in general, was increased; this involved a publicity potential not to be underestimated.

Several hundred thousand copies of a monthly periodical, "Agriculture and Technology," were distributed to farmers.

Bosch had such high esteeem for the significance of thorough scientific working procedures that, even during times of economic depression when other industries began to reduce their research budgets, he maintained the large laboratories and testing institutes in which he saw the indispensable basis of a rational technological method of working. "Today, technology in the best sense is organized science." This was the theme of his acceptance speech which he addressed to the festive gathering after having been awarded the Nobel Prize in 1931.

In October, 1917, Bosch was elected to the governing board of the Kaiser Wilhelm Society and of the Kaiser Wilhelm Institute (KWI) for Chemistry, in recognition of his achievements on behalf of scientific research which he accomplished, in the midst of a very heavy work load, by the establishment of the great Leuna factory and the simultaneous expansion of the ammonia plant in Oppau.

After the war, he devoted himself more and more to super· vising the pursuit of research and the training of successors, the deficiencies in which, as a result of the war years and postwar problems, frequently became clearly apparent in the newly employed academic personnel. Trips to the United States showed him the exceptional means for technology and research in that country, and the general wealth there made the financial distress of the homeland appear all the more pronounced. "We have neither money, nor do we have cheap raw materials, nor do we have enormous sales. All that we have left to us are the people. Therefore we cannot do enough to make it clear to ourselves where our strength lies. It lies only in research, or intensive work." Thus he summarized his experiences in a lecture in Kissingen in 1924. On another occasion, Bosch stated that the training of chemists cannot be too intensive and many-sided, especially since he was convinced that the future rests on the common border fields of several disciplines.

In his essay in the economic journal of the *Frankfurter Zeitung* of April, 1927, Bosch paraphrased the tasks of the chemist in a very comprehensive manner:

> Our leading chemists should also be at home in the new frontier of chemistry which was won through the productive development of physics and of physical chemistry in the past decades. I am thinking here of the marvelous development which atomic physics and atomic chemistry have undergone in recent times. The new discoveries about the fine structure of atoms and molecules, about the exchange effect of this material on the one hand and of the electrical forces and electromagnetic radiations on the other hand, will surely lead technology into new fields of thought and work sooner or later. Furthermore it is certain that the new knowledge gained in atomic physics will also be fruitful in photochemistry. This is true for the production of chemical substances whose photochemical formation nature shows us daily in the mighty experiment of the assimilation of carbonic acid by the green plant, as well as for the introduction of new ways of thought into the field of light-sensitive substances, of photographic-chemical technology.

How clearly Bosch anticipated the developments of the future!

In the year 1933, Bosch became a member of the Kuratorium of the Institute for the Physical Foundations of Medicine in

Frankfurt a.M.; in 1935, of the KWI for Physical Chemistry and Electrochemistry in Berlin-Dahlem and the KWI for Carbon Research in Mülheim-Ruhr; and, in the following year, of the KWI for Physics. The institute in Frankfurt, which was taken over in 1936 by the KWG and continued as KWI for Biophysics under Dr. Rajewski, enjoyed special advancement through Bosch. For a long time, he said, he had given considerable thought to the causes for the transformation of organisms and the origin of the geological ages, in which high altitude radiation plays a greater role. He did not allow the objection to stand that the tasks of the institute overlapped those of the Institute of Internal Medicine in Munich. "Furthermore," he added, as we quote here to show a characteristic trait of his way of thinking, "the contact of physics with biology and medicine is so great that not enough institutes can work in this field." His great merits in connection with the institute in Frankfurt found expression in his being named an honorary citizen of the Johann-Wolfgang-Goethe University in Frankfurt a.M. on July 1, 1939. In numerous additional Kaiser-Wilhelm Institutes Bosch occupied leading positions in the administrative and advisory bodies.

Finally, Bosch obtained the highest recognition that could be bestowed upon the leader of an industrial enterprise by the representatives of pure science: he was named to the presidency of the Kaiser-Wilhelm Society on June 22, 1937, the chairmanship of the governing board of the Society had been transferred to him two years before.

In the difficult times between two wars, German science was indebted to Bosch in many respects for extraordinarily valuable support.

His entire love and enthusiasm for natural science found expression in the speech which Bosch delivered on September 16, 1934 in Hannover as chairman of the Society of German Natural Scientists and Physicians during its ninety-third convention. As testimony of a deep, downright philosophical penetration into the nature of research, it is a panegyric more beautiful than has been put into words on almost any other occasion. At the same time it was a courageous and deeply moving cry of despair in view of the oppression to which the establishing of goals for research was subjected at that time in Germany. He said, in part:

> It is inherent in the peculiar character of natural science research, as in each field of science, that it cannot set mental or geographical limits for itself without endangering its goals. Also, it fights for its progress in all philosophical-political situations, because it is timeless in its character. . . . The present limits of scientific research have been pushed far beyond the distance of the starry sky and below the realm of subatomic processes. It is conscious of these limits and, beyond them, sees the path free for metaphysical needs by separating the field of research from that of surmising.

Bosch, the investigator, who was so matter-of-fact and sober in his thinking and very reserved, made it clear that there is a region beyond the boundaries of that which can be explored, where one cannot do research, but merely surmise and revere.

Bosch's comprehensive knowledge and great amiability won for him the highest esteem, an enduring reverence, and in many instances, permanent close friendships. With open-minded foresight Bosch was also interested in research projects which, at the time, were of a purely abstract nature. Einstein's astrophysical observatory in Potsdam was constantly supported by him with considerable contributions which aided greatly in its development. Bosch also had a friendly relationship with Fritz Haber, who provided the scientific basis and the impetus for the synthetic ammonia industry which Bosch created so magnificently. It is to be remembered how energetically Bosch insisted on the carrying out of the memorial celebration for Haber planned by the Kaiser Wilhelm Society, even though the National Socialist Party prohibited the participation of university teachers and of the members of scientific and technical organizations. Bosch not only visited the festivities himself, but also was instrumental, through zealous endeavors in scientific and industrial circles in filling every seat in the lecture hall. Nothing was farther from Bosch's mind— whether in his personal relationships with learned men or in his endeavors toward the support of scientific teaching and research— than to let himself be led by any viewpoints that were not of purely factual nature. If such influences asserted themselves after

1406

1933, they were for him additional cause for taking a stand, with the full power of his being, for that which he considered right and necessary.

Activity in natural science was also a source of relaxation from his many occupational duties. The joy in nature which he had experienced during his school years in Cologne on excursions in the meadows and fields of the nearby surroundings where, among other things, he could collect many interesting aquatic animals in swampy places, later became the foundation for his hobbies, to which he devoted a large part of his free time. Here, too, he did not lack in scientific thoroughness. In Charlottenburg, as well as in Leipzig, he attended lectures and experiments on the lower native animals, mineralogy, petrography, and plant identification as voluntary elective subjects. Later on, when he entered the field of technology in Ludwigshafen, he became an avid collector in the nearby surroundings, in the Palatinate and in the Odenwald, and on his numerous travels in foreign countries—an activity directed mostly toward the collecting of beetles, snails, minerals, and rocks. He entered his findings, and the circumstances of their discovery, in his diary with great accuracy. He established large collections, increased later by purchases, in his house, including in them the diverse fields of his hobbies.

As an indication of the deep knowledge and the sharp power of observation which he acquired over the years, one example merits mention. Once, during an automobile trip to Munich, he had the car stopped suddenly in the vicinity of Ulm. On a slope he had seen a flowering plant which interested him. He left the car and took along a few leaves and a blossom of the plant, in order to identify it at home. He found that it was a tropical plant whose occurrence he could not explain. Later on he found in his books that this tropical plant was indeed to be found in Germany in a few rare locations in the surroundings of Ulm. He was now very happy that he had found such a rare specimen by a glance out of the car, and that he could include it in his herbarium.

Bosch also enjoyed occupying himself in the workshop which he had set up in his house; there, with great skill, he made apparatus for his collecting activities and for physical experiments. He also found recreation and diversion in astronomy and astrophysics, for which he had an observatory built next to his house in Heidelberg. On clear nights, he often spent many hours in this observatory, making observations and taking photographs.

His last years were characterized by a glaring disharmony between his happy family life and the high esteem in which he was held by the scientific and technological world, on the one hand, and the dismal political developments, on the other, which embittered his life by creating bad moods and gloomy forebodings in him. He repeatedly spoke in almost prophetic-sounding pronouncements about the impending disaster. A peaceful death prevented him from having to experience the actual occurrence of his grim presentiments.

From: *Naturwissenschaften*, 36, 161–165 (1949). Translated by Elisabeth Lanzl.

K. HOLDERMANN

·· 100 ··

John Edgar Teeple

1874-1931

JOHN E. TEEPLE was, in his own words, "an habitual consultant." It was an apt description: he was one of the greatest of the last generation of American chemists and chemical engineers who rendered to their clients personal, professional service. To this rather exacting task he brought sound training in chemistry and engineering as well as an unusual combination of traits and talents, almost bound to guarantee his success in his profession.

He had a passion for problems. Each morning and evening, commuting between his home in Montclair, New Jersey, and his office in New York City, he did the crossword puzzle in his newspaper, and he thoroughly enjoyed piecing together jigsaw pictures, the bigger and more complicated, the better. His favorite extra-curriculum reading was a good detective story.

Out of this abiding interest in all sorts of puzzling problems grew a hobby, surely a strange one for a busy chemical engineer, but one through which Teeple was able, in his own way, to make an unusual scientific contribution. He became deeply interested in the Mayan civilization, fascinated by its curious hieroglyphics and calendar. He never went on a "dig." He never even visited the marvelous ruins in Central America. He became, however, a research associate in this field of the Carnegie Institution of Washington and a regular correspondent with many leading archeologists all over the world. He wrote a scholarly monograph—one of his two published books—that helped to solve some riddles of the Mayan calendar and to correlate it more accurately with our own chronology. A respected reference found in many archeological texts is: "Teeple, John E., *Maya Astronomy*, Publ. No. 403, Carnegie Inst., Washington, 1930."

In addition to his searching curiosity, Dr. Teeple had a high, almost an exalted, sense of professional responsibility. His relationships with his clients were always on an exceedingly confidential basis. Even his closest friends seldom knew the character of the work in which he was engaged nor the firms that were employing his services.

Over and beyond his most famous contribution in the separation of potash and borax from the Searles Lake brines, he did important work in the industrial production of the three mineral acids, in chlorine and activated carbon, in the purification and standardization of C.P. chemicals, in the distillation of hard woods and the utilization of their by-products, in the production of citric and tartaric acids by fermentation, and of naval stores by distillation from pine wood and stumps. The fruits of these researches were garnered in detailed reports to his clients: they were never published. He considered them the property of his clients and he disdained, as he once phrased it, "to build up my personal reputation at the expense of my employers."

John Teeple had a realistic brain. Habitually he penetrated superficialities to get to the core. Hence he was not easily fooled by appearances nor persuaded by plausible argument. His matter-of-fact point of view made him an exceedingly interesting, sometimes a disconcerting, friend but always an extraordinarily valuable adviser. In conference, when the discussion became involved or repetitious, he would suddenly ask, "So what?"—a devastating, or an inspiring, question.

The 1926 Williamstown Institute of Politics was devoted to an appraisal of the world's raw materials; Dr. Teeple was a member of the panel devoted particularly to fertilizer supplies. At one of the general evening sessions, a most attractive little lady read a paper on "Our Vanishing Woods." So dramatically did she picture the ruthless exploitation of our timber resources that she almost dissolved her listeners in tears. She sat down amidst great applause and John Teeple strolled almost carelessly to the center of the platform.

He was a tallish man with a big, loose-jointed frame. His thick shock of hair, prominent nose, and wide mouth, his deeply lined face, were somewhat reminiscent of Abraham Lincoln; like him, he had a winning smile. He propped his right hand on the low lecturn from which she had read her emotional appeal. Leaning forward, he hooked his left thumb in the armhole of his waistcoat and began speaking in his low, penetrating voice.

"Friends," he said, "let us look the facts of our future wood supplies straight in the face."

1412

His distinguished audience shivered with apprehension. Surely now they would learn the worst. Many of them recognized this great chemical engineer, builder of new industries, keen business analyst, outspoken critic of all flubdubbery. The general tenor of the conference had been dismal. Most of its sessions had developed into the gloomy contemplation of a cheerless, comfortless, very hungry future for the bedeviled human race—after we had squandered all of our irreplaceable raw materials.

"Wood," Teeple continued, "is our most ancient and honorable raw material. Man's first fuel was a handful of sticks; his first weapon was a club."

Then he proceeded to show how for most of its seemingly irreplaceable uses wood has already been largely replaced. Coal and oil have become our principal fuels. Wars are no longer fought with clubs and bows and arrows. Wood is no longer the most important material for our buildings, our bridges, our tunnels. Wood is not now a chemical raw material for the production of methanol or acetic acid or acetone. In fact, our chief, apparently irreplaceable, use of wood today is as a source of cellulose which, he pointed out, could be obtained from annual plants. Then he sketched swiftly the tree-farming activities of the Southern paper mills which since that time have so expanded that the kraft paper industry is self-supporting in its wood supplies. It was a masterful job of exposition, beautifully executed.

"Wood," he went on, "is continually disappearing—in the newspaper headlines—bringing modern civilization to an end. But just suppose it did disappear. What would happen?

"If wood were to vanish from the face of the earth—which God forbid—this horrible calamity would hardly change the trend of modern existence. For if wood were to disappear, I can think of but one important American industry that would be seriously embarrassed. Without wood, I really do not know what would become of the manufacturers of imitation antique furniture."

He grinned broadly and cheerfully at his audience and strolled off the platform amid gusts of wholesome laughter.

Upon another occasion he privately described an ardent crusader for the conservation of natural resources: "The worthy Mr. Blank is just the kind of a near-sighted 'fraid-cat who a century ago would have busied himself organizing an Association for the Relief and Succor of Sperm Whales, because, forsooth, our civilization would be impossible without whale-oil lamps. It is the greatest mistake to save anything for your grandchildren, they are not going to need it."

He was quite as sharp a critic of the manufacturer who committed the economic crime of throwing any valuable material on the dump heap, and he became a specialist in wastes and by-products, their recovery and use. Again his approach was thoroughly realistic. He had not use for "waste for waste's sake," but insisted always that a reclaimed material must be employed in some practical process or sold in a profitable market.

All this is, of course, a strictly chemical point of view, and Dr. Teeple was intensely chemical-conscious. He had unbounded faith in the chemist's ability to provide all the necessities for an ever-increasing population in an ever-advancing civilization. He continually emphasized that the dozen odd chemical elements vital to human life on this planet—oxygen and nitrogen, carbon and silicon, chlorine, iodine, and bromine, sodium, potassium, phosphorus—are all abundant in the composition of our globe. He did not live to see the Atomic Age. Had he done so, one can be sure that he would have hailed it (provided we do not blast ourselves into oblivion) not only as a promise of almost infinite power, but also as a pledge of vastly increased chemical knowledge.

"We know what happens in a chemical reaction," he often said. "Oh, but if we only knew how and why it happens!"

How he would have rejoiced in the opportunities laid bare by recent discoveries in subatomic physical chemistry. He was an habitual chemical consultant and an incorrigible chemical optimist.

John Edgar Teeple was born January 4, 1874, on a farm near the little hamlet of Kempton, Illinois, 70 miles southeast of Chicago. His parents, William Harvey and Abby M. (Hinckley) Teeple, were of old New England stock which two generations before had migrated to the Midwest. When he was ten years old he was left an orphan and was brought up by a neighbor. He never talked of his boyhood except to say that, when he was growing up, a farm boy in the Middle West was expected to earn his keep and that he learned very early to pay his own way. He attended the local public schools and became an omnivorous reader, absorbing an extraordinary cultural background, particularly in history and literature.

In 1888, at fourteen years of age, he began working his way through Valparaiso University. In 1892 he won a B.S. and the following year, a B.A. degree. That same year he became professor of chemistry and physics at Freemont (Nebraska) College, a double post he held until 1898. While at Fremont he met and married Linda Pease. They had two sons, John Hazen and Granger Odell Teeple, and a daughter, Marion, who became Mrs. Earl Hayner.

In 1898 Teeple accepted a position as instructor in organic and physiological chemistry at Cornell with the opportunity to do graduate work. He received a B.S. in 1899 and his Ph.D. in 1903.

Young Dr. Teeple, thirty years old, came to New York in 1904 as director of the Industrial Laboratories. Four years later he hung out his own shingle as consulting chemist and chemical engineer. During 1917–18 he served as interim professor of chemical engineering at Columbia University, but he declined a pressing invitation to an academic career in order to return to his chosen profession as consultant.

For many years he occupied a modest little office in the Chemists' Club Building in East Forty-first Street, New York. From here he served a diverse group of clients: Charles Pfizer & Company, Naugatuck Chemical Company, Niagara Alkali Company, Tartar Chemical Works, J. T. Baker Chemical Company, Darco Corporation, Binns Chemical Works, the Georgetown Chemical Works, the Southern Extracting Company, and the American Trona Corporation, now the American Potash & Chemical Corporation.

Despite his busy professional life, he found time for worthwhile outside activities. For twelve years he was treasurer of the American Chemical Society and between 1917 and 1924, a member of the National Research Council. For two terms, 1920 and 1921, he was president of the Chemists' Club. He was one of the original Board of Consulting Editors of *Chemical Industries* (now *Chemical Week*) and much of his published writing was contributed to this industrial journal. Many of these were short, pungent, unsigned editorials, but he also wrote articles on the broader aspects of chemical economics.

It is a pity that Teeple wrote so little. His forthright style was arrestingly vivid, his figures of speech always illuminating. He coined the now-familiar phrases "patient money" and "progress by injunction." He always had something to say and he said it not only effectively, but boldly. His only chemical book, "The Industrial Development of the Searles Lake Brines," is unique in chemical literature. Published as one of the American Chemical Society's monographs, it contains 60 equilibrium diagrams, 86 systems of from four to six components, water and the chlorides, sulfates, and carbonates of potassium and sodium, an expert, highly technical mathematical performance. But the book also deals ably with chemical industrial history and applied chemical enonomics. Furthermore, it sets forth a pragmatic philosophy of management, workday rules for good personnel relations, and far-sighted chemical prophecies, a goodly number of which have already come true.

Because of this slender volume of only 182 pages, Dr. Teeple is best remembered for his work on the separation of the Searles Lake brines. He well deserves to be, for this was not only a notable chemical accomplishment, but it set up a memorable milestone marking an important stage in the growth of a completely rounded, self-contained American chemical industry.

During World War I this country faced three critical chemical shortages. Two were of basic raw materials, potash and nitrate, for which we were dependent upon natural monopolies in Germany and Chili. At that time, the German chemical industry also had a virtual monopoly, technical and commercial, on the organic compounds synthesized from coal-tar intermediates. During the war, nitrogen was fixed from the air, breaking the God-given Chilean monopoly, and through herculean efforts we met our needs for modern explosives, aniline dyes, and coal-tar medicines, laying the foundation for an American synthetic organic chemical industry. But to achieve permanent independence in our supplies of potash appeared to be impossible. By hook and crook we had been able to supply only a fifth of our growing normal requirements for this essential fertilizer and useful reagent. No source, no method of recovery, was found that could compete on either a

1416

cost or quality basis with the remarkably pure potassium salts mined from the Stassfurt deposits. John Teeple's outstanding accomplishment was the breaking of this strongly entrenched natural monopoly.

Potassium can be recovered from many sources and to meet our wartime needs most of these were tapped. The historic method of leaching wood ashes with water which was evaporated in great iron pots (the original pot-ashes) was revived. Potash was recovered from the flue dusts of cement plants and blast furnaces; from the minerals, alunite in Colorado, Wyoming leucite, and the greensands of New Jersey; from beet sugar and molasses wastes; from kelp along the Pacific Coast. The greatest production came from the brine lakes of Nebraska and California.

Insatiable demand shoved the price up from $.75 prewar to $6 per unit, that is, per 20 pounds, or one-hundredth of a ton, of K_2O. Tempted by famine profits there were 128 plants producing potash from one or another of these sources when the war ended. Teeple clearly described their dilemma: "Only two courses were open to them; either to succumb, or to make a scientific and technical study of their problems such as they should have made in the first place. Most of them elected the former procedure; it was easier and less expensive to die."

Shortly after the Armistice the German potash companies announced a price of $.64 per unit. This was less than half the production costs of the most efficient American plants. Obviously the Germans were determined to rewin the world market and they were strategically placed to do so. They were united in a compulsory cartel, the Kali Syndikat, and could act in unison. They knew the American situation and were confident that in opposition to the powerful Farm Block, Congress, despite the war-taught lesson, would not give this infant chemical industry tariff protection. Their quick, deep price cut had just the effect they wanted. Within two years, of the 128 American potash companies only three were operating.

One of these was the American Trona Corporation working the Searles Lake brines. They had called in Dr. Teeple. Already they had junked over 1½ million dollars' worth of unsatisfactory equipment and were rebuilding their triple-effect evaporators, planning to expand. To gird themselves for the battle the company was re-organized, with fresh working capital, as the American Potash & Chemical Corporation. They had been warned to expect no quarter.

Periodically, throughout hostilities, a representative of Kali, Paul Freudrichen, appeared at the little plant in the heart of the California desert. Plainly he was keeping an eye on a potential competitor, and on one visit he issued an ultimatum swathed in a smiling warning.

"How foolish are your stockholders," he said, "to invest money in any potash enterprise in the United States. Don't you know that as soon as this war is finished the Kali Syndikat and the Imperial Government will absolutely destroy the whole American industry by selling German potash in this country at such low prices as to crush all competition?"

Teeple had been summoned to a very tough assignment. Not only must he effect the separation of the exceedingly complex mixture of native salts much more economically, but the recovered products must be salable. Borax contamination of potash was a fatal handicap in the fertilizer market. Complaints of crop injury by the Trona product, especially to cotton and tobacco in the Carolinas and to potatoes in Maine, had been numerous; back in 1918 the Hubbard Fertilizer Company had brought suit for damages of $275,000. The case came to trial in Baltimore, May, 1922, and Judge Stanton of the Maryland Supreme Court found Trona blameless. Hubbard had set their own specifications as to borax content and the potash delivered had met their standards. Furthermore, at the first complaints, Trona had shut down, ceased shipping, and at great expense revamped its operation to produce virtually borax-free potash. But the initial prejudice was widespread and had to be overcome. Teeple must maintain and, if possible, raise quality and drastically lower costs.

He first undertook an exhaustive study of the equilibrium data of the 18 consistent salts in the brine. Upon this factual foundation, the triple-effect evaporators were redesigned and the filters were replaced by settlers in order to effect a continuous production of borax and potash. The removal of sulfates and the prevention of the formation of glaserite ($Na_2SO_4:3K_2SO_4$) was much helped by the discovery of the double salt, burkeite (Na_2CO_3:

1418

$2Na_2SO_4$) isolated by his collaborator, William E. Burke. This and the complete separation of borax and potash by rapid cooling of the hot concentrated liquor were vital steps in the operation. The process was not fully perfected in all details until a third new plant was built in 1924.

In 1927, when Teeple was awarded the Perkin Medal, he was able to report that the Trona plant was the largest borax recovery operation in the world and that it was producing virtually pure potassium chloride and selling it at about \$.70 per unit in competition with the German and French mined salts.

This outstanding achievement has overshadowed his other notable contributions to the development of the American chemical industry. He was distinguished, as L. V. Redman said in his medal presentation address, by "his capacity for highly specialized scientific research and his ability as a businessman to hold the confidence of capital till he had turned red figures into black." His greatest contributions were in the perfection of plant processes. Here he was an audacious innovator. Repeatedly he introduced unorthodox design of equipment and novel hook-up of apparatus with amazingly successful results even in operations so standardized that they had become what he delighted to call "family heirlooms."

After a long, painful illness, induced by gallstones, John Teeple died in the Presbyterian Hospital, New York City, on March 23, 1931. He was fifty-seven years old and at the height of his career. In these days of richly endowed research institutions and huge engineering firms with their staffs of draftsmen, lawyers, accountants, and purchasing agents, and all sorts of technical specialists, his individual, personal services seem sadly outmoded, even a bit pitiful. Yet for all its stunning accomplishments, our present-day highly organized research tends to smother individual initiative and to gloss over personal responsibility. It is a healthy antidote to recall the sturdy individualists of the past.

GENERAL REFERENCES

The best material is in his own and the other addresses at the Perkin Medal Award, *Chem. & Met. Eng., 34,* 122 (1927); *Ind. Eng. Chem., 19,* 318 (1927).

See also "Who Was Who," I, 1222; "Am. Men of Sci.," 4th ed., 1927; "Dict. Am. Biog., XXI," 682.

Obits, *J. Am. Chem. Soc.*, 53, 61 (1931); *Chemicals,* Mar. 30, 1931, p. 12; *Chem. & Ind.* (London), *1931*, 327; *New York Times*, Mar. 24, 1937.

For early history of U.S. potash industry: Geo. W. Stocking, "The Potash Industry: A Study of State Control," New York, 1931, Chap. 13; John W. Turrentine, "Potash in North America," New York, 1943; Williams Haynes, "American Chemical Industry," Van Nostrand, New York, 1945–54, vol. II, Chaps. 13, 14, 15.

WILLIAMS HAYNES

·· *101* ··

Alfred Stock

1876-1946

ALFRED STOCK, born July 16, 1876, went to school at the Friedrich Werder Gymnasium in Berlin from October, 1882, to October, 1894. "As a small boy already I showed my inclination to science. It started with catching salamanders, collecting plants and raising butterflies. It continued with chemical and physical experiments at home." (A. Stock)

In October, 1894, he passed the final examinations with the mark "very good" and received valuable scholarships. They were of great help to him after he started his studies at the University of Berlin in 1894.

Of the two chemical institutes of this university, one was directed by the organic chemist Emil Fischer, the other by the physicochemist Hans Landolt. Alfred Stock selected Fischer's institute. Its laboratories were overcrowded, so that Stock had to wait one year for a laboratory place. While waiting, he attended lectures not only on chemistry, physics, and mathematics, but also on history of art, physiology (Du Bois-Reymond), and history (von Treitschke).

Twice during his university years he used the summer vacations to work in the private laboratory of van't Hoff. Here, Stock succeeded in solving various analytical problems, e.g., the determination of a little alkali in the presence of much magnesium, while taking part in van't Hoff's investigations on the formation of oceanic salt deposits.

Soon Stock became a teaching assistant to Oscar Piloty (1866–1915). Oscar Piloty, the organic chemist, music lover, mountain climber, hunter, sportsman, and son-in-law of Adolf von Baeyer, had accompanied Emil Fischer from Würzburg as assistant and director of the inorganic division and became Stock's sponsor (1898).

The great skill in experimenting shown by Alfred Stock during his studies and work on his doctor's thesis induced Emil Fischer to select him as his lecture–assistant for the winter of 1898 and the summer of 1899.

1423

With financial support from the Prussian Ministry of Culture, Alfred Stock went to Paris in September, 1899. Henri Moissan, then at the height of his fame, had just become the successor of the inorganic chemist and examiner at the mint, Alfred Riche, at the École superieure de Pharmacie.

It was a gay, international little group that Stock met in Moissan's laboratory. America, England, Austria, Norway, Germany, France, and Russia were represented by men who wanted to study Moissan's methods, particularly the handling of his *four électrique*. While working with this apparatus, one was "constantly in danger of losing one's life, either from carbon monoxide which could only escape through the small windows of the basement, or through glowing iron which threatened to fall from the weak resistance wire fastened to the ceiling."

In November, 1899, Moissan began to give the general lecture on inorganic chemistry, formerly presented by Riche. Its clear organization and its elegant, often humorous, rhetorically splendid form provided a great aesthetic pleasure. Alfred Stock was greatly stimulated; his subsequent lectures and speeches were also characterized by superior and elegant eloquence, by clear arrangement of the subject matter, and by a humor that was masterful and, when necessary, ironic.

Moissan assigned to the young scholar the preparation of new compounds from silicon and boron. This was Stock's first encounter with these two elements which were to be the foundations of his scientific fame. First they presented problems of apparatus construction for him. Moissan's electric oven was not suited to this task because it yielded only carbon-containing products. Therefore, Stock constructed his own resistance oven which soon made it possible to produce two compounds analogous to silicon carbide, $Si B_3$ and $Si B_4$. Stock himself admitted that he always particularly liked constructing and improving such tools. His gift in this direction found its highest achievement in the Stock high-vacuum pump.

After attending the splendid Paris Jubilee–World Exhibition, Stock returned to Berlin in August, 1900, and became laboratory assistant in Emil Fischer's new institute.

YEARS OF GROWTH: 1900 TO 1909

The greatest part of the investigations during these years were concerned with the elements phosphorus, arsenic, and antimony from the fifth group of the periodic system. They resulted in an intimate elucidation of their elemental modifications and their compounds with hydrogen, sulfur, and nitrogen. Several publications dealt with improvements in laboratory apparatus. One of them was the vapor-tension thermometer which later on was developed into Stock's tension-thermometer. With the description of the *cuve à mercure,* first introduced by Berthelot and used in Moissan's laboratory, Stock made this tool known in Germany. However, it also became the source of his chronic mercury poisoning which even in these early years caused him headaches, dizziness, and catarrhs.

In spite of many and prolonged experimental studies, he found time to publish, together with Arthur Stähler, a 152-page book "Praktikum der quantitativen anorganischen Analyse" which appeared in 1909. All the figures in this book, as in almost all of his many publications, were drawn by Stock himself. The "Stock-Stähler" came out in a fifth edition, 1941, and in English, Portugese, Serbian and Turkish translations.

On April 1, 1906, he was promoted to head of the division, and a few days later he received the title of professor. He was married on August 21, 1906. In July, 1909, he became full professor and director of the new Institute of Chemistry at the Techmische Hochschule in Breslau.

THE BRESLAU PERIOD: SEPTEMBER 1909 TO FEBRUARY 1916

In Breslau Alfred Stock started on the exploration of the boron hydrides with a series of studies which continued for a quarter of a century. The plan for this work dates back to 1900, after his return from Paris. At that time he had begun to ask himself whether boron, the neighbor of versatile carbon in the periodic system, really was as monotonous and tedious as was generally assumed. Specifically, the question was whether the chemical affinities of boron were restricted to strongly negative elements, like oxygen and chlorine. Would it be possible to detect hidden inclinations to other partners, perhaps even to build up a boron chemistry similar to the carbon-based organic chemistry? The first five studies on boron, carried out in Breslau (1912–1914), showed that this "brittle" element possessed a rich "personality" which, however, it made accessible only to the chosen few.

By decomposing magnesium boride with acid and separating the gases so obtained by liquefaction and fractional distillation, B_4H_{10} was discovered as the first liquid boron hydride, and its physical and chemical characteristics were measured. Upon heating, it formed B_2H_6, subsequently proved to be the simplest member of the borohydride series. Thermal decomposition of B_2H_6 yielded $B_{10}H_{14}$, a crystalline compound. Studies of the reactions with alkali and halogens led to the knowledge of hypoborates and halogenated borohydrides. Besides, there were indications of other derivatives and modes of reaction.

This work was temporarily interrupted by the outbreak of war in 1914. It also appeared necessary to study the silicon hydrides which were admixed with the boron hydrides and made their purification very difficult. Thus, the last borohydride publication from Breslau (1914) was continued nine years later in Berlin (1923), and the interim was filled with 16 publications on silicon hydrides (1916–1923), during Stock's Berlin period.

Other work in Breslau was concerned with inorganic carbon compounds, carbon subsulfide, C_3S_2, carbon sulfotelluride, CSTe, and carbon sulfoselenide, CSSe. Stock returned to carbon subsulfide, a terribly irritating substance, during the war when he was charged with a study of its effect as a war gas. It proved active in very small quantities. A practical application was prevented by its great tendency to polymerize.

MASTER YEARS, BERLIN: MARCH 1916, TO
SEPTEMBER 1926

In April, 1916, Stock took over Willstätter's laboratory at the Kaiser Wilhelm Institute for Chemistry in Berlin-Dahlem. Unfortunately, Stock had the laboratory available only for a few months, since it was taken over by the "military" Kaiser Wilhelm Institute, under Fritz Haber's direction, early in November, 1916. During this time, Stock, whose chronic ailments of the respiratory organs and increasing loss of hearing, consequences of the then-unknown mercury poisoning, excluded him from military service, moved over to the chemical institute of Berlin University with all his equipment and staff. The end of the war made it possible for him to return to Dahlem and to elaborate the chemistry of silicon and boron hydrides.

By improving the production of silicon hydrides from magnesium silicide and hydrochloric acid he succeeded in obtaining not only the superficially known gases monosilane SiH_4 and disilane Si_2H_6, but additionally two liquid silanes, Si_3H_8 (trisilane) and Si_4H_{10} (tetrasilane), and the penta- and hexasilanes, Si_5H_{12} and Si_6H_{14}. Halogenation of these compounds with elementary halogen, halogen hydride in the presence of aluminum halogenide, or chloroform led to numerous halogen derivatives.

Reaction with water yielded the group of siloxanes like disiloxane $(SiH_3)_2O$, the first gaseous compound of silicon with hydrogen and oxygen (silicomethylether), or prosiloxane SiH_2O, the volatile and easily polymerized starting member of the series (silicoformaldehyde).

With ammonia, halogenated silanes form compounds like the liquid, monomeric silicotrimethylamine $(SiH_3)_3N$, or silicoguanidine $Si(NH_2)_2NH$.

Thus arose a silicon chemistry corresponding to organic chemistry in richness. It was mainly a child of the laboratory, but its results were fruitful for industry as shown by the alkyl derivatives of the siloxanes, the silicones.

Research on beryllium also became industrially important and introduced this metal and its alloys into technology. In December, 1919, Hans Goldschmidt (1861–1923), the inventor of the Thermit process, had proposed to finance collaborative work with Stock. He suggested the production of metallic beryllium, which had been discovered by Wöhler in 1828, refined by Lebeau seventy years later, and had been disregarded since then. Electrolysis of a molten mixture of beryllium, barium, and sodium fluorides at 1300°C. with a water-cooled cathode which was gradually raised out of the melt furnished crystalline beryllium in good yield. A beryllium study group was formed. The price per kilogram was reduced from 200,000 marks in 1927 to 250 marks in 1940.

Parallel to the experimental work ran many organizational tasks which alone would have sufficed to fill the life of a man completely. The number of his honorary positions in professional groups, charitable organizations, committees on education, etc., was great. Without regard to his health, he worked on their many problems. Unforgettable is his help in reshaping German chemistry and supporting young chemists after the First World War. Yet he said he "could have done much more in every respect" if he had not been ill.

The beginning of his mercury poisoning dated back to his school years, when he frequently worked with mercury in his little laboratory at home and obviously laid the foundation for his oversensitivity to mercury. The symptoms became stronger after his return from Paris in 1900. They were aggravated in Berlin (from 1916 on). In 1923 and 1924 he suffered from an almost complete loss of memory. In March, 1924, after an unbearable winter, he discovered, by accident, the sudden illness of his collaborator Dr. Wolfhart Siecke, and recognized the cause of all his symptoms. A very small mercury vapor content in the air (a few thousandths of a milligram per cubic meter) can cause illness upon prolonged inhalation.

After a rest period, he attacked the exploration of mercury sickness from which, as he found, many other scientists (e.g., Faraday, Pascal, Berzelius, Liebig, Wöhler, Hertz, and Ostwald) had suffered. In 1926 he warned the public of the dangers of this volatile odorless, slowly attacking and long-acting metal:

> In deciding to report publicly about personal distress—which is itself would not concern others and would not be worth publishing—I am driven by the urgent wish to warn all those who work with metallic mercury most impressively of the dangers of the volatile

metal, and to save them from the harassing experiences that have spoiled a great part of my life.

Thus he starts his deeply moving report. He describes the symptoms, proposes preventive measures, points out the danger of amalgams in dentistry, and describes analogous cases among colleagues.

The prospect of leaving the mercury-infested rooms of the Kaiser Wilhelm Institute and establishing new unobjectionable laboratories contributed to his decision to accept a call as successor of Karl Freudenberg at the Technische Hochschule in Karlsruhe.

THE KARLSRUHE DECADE: OCTOBER 1926, TO AUGUST 1936

In Karlsruhe, he immediately started to establish several laboratory rooms which were models of efficiency and were frequently studied by visitors from many countries. By means of extensive precautionary measures the air in the laboratories was kept free of mercury vapor, although hundreds of pounds of mercury were in use.

In this decade at Karlsruhe Stock's experimental love belonged to the borohydrides and the study of mercury poisoning. First he improved the methods of preparation by using borides other than magnesium boride and acids other than hydrochloric. Then he adapted and elaborated the method found in 1931 by H. I. Schlesinger and A. B. Burg, which consisted of electrical discharges through a mixture of boron halogenides with hydrogen. Research on the reactions with alkali and earth-alkali amalgams enlarged the knowledge of these interesting addition-reactions to compounds like $Na_2(B_2H_6)$, $Ca(B_2H_6)$, $K_2(B_4H_{10})$, and $K_2(B_5H_9)$. Reaction with ammonia yielded, among other compounds, $B_3N_3H_6$ which is isosteric with benzene.

In general he did not think very highly of speculative discussions and theoretical deliberations. "The splendid development of theory must not mislead to contempt for patient experimental work."

To start his offensive against mercury poisoning, it was necessary to develop micromethods for measuring quantities as low as

1/100,000 milligram. Colorimetric methods were not reliable enough. The goal was reached by micrometry of the tiny mercury globe obtained by cathodic deposition on copper wire and vacuum distillation. Analytical studies were amplified by experiments on animals. It was shown that ingested mercury was less to blame than inhaled metal vapor which traveled from the nose to the brain and accumulated in the hypophysis (pituitary gland).

During his years at Karlsruhe Stock was, as always, interested in educational questions. In collaboration with his lecture assistant Hans Ramser and with Carl Zeiss-Jena he developed a teaching epidiascope. It was a universal apparatus, containing an experimentation chamber for the projection of prone or upright objects in incident and reflected light. I vividly remember the impressive production of a small sodium drop by means of Davy's electrolysis of molten sodium hydroxide, which was visible in the entire large lecture hall. Without the epidiascope it could only be shown to a very small group.

At the Thirty-Eighth Congress of the German Bunsen Society in Karlsruhe (May 1933) Stock published a booklet on "The International Congress of Chemists, Karlsruhe, September 3 to 5, 1860, before and behind the curtain." On the basis of old records and letters, found in Karlsruhe, he described the organization and the course of this congress which was to solve the confusion about Avogadro's hypothesis, the theories of radicals and types, the dualistic concepts, and so on. The reader of this enjoyable presentation of the various temperaments and the clashing opinions at the congress will certainly agree with Stock's facetious statement that there were at that time dualists and several "types" and "radicals" among the chemists as well as in the science of chemistry.

In October 1927, he represented the Verein Deutscher Chemiker in Paris at the celebration of Marcelin Berthelot's one-hundredth anniversary. From February to June, 1932, he was guest professor at Cornell University under the George Fisher Baker Nonresident Lectureship in Chemistry. This gave him a welcome opportunity for collecting his experimental work on "Hydrides of Boron and Silicon" (Ithaca, 1933).

During all these successes, representative duties, and honors

Stock's health continued to worsen. In addition, he had increasing difficulties with the political party influences in education. Thus he decided to ask for his retirement, and it was granted to him, effective October 1, 1936.

In September 1936, he returned with his family to Berlin-Dahlem.

IN RETIREMENT:
SEPTEMBER 1936, TO AUGUST 1943

In small laboratories in Dahlem he continued his research on mercury. The micrometric method of mercury determination was improved to such a degree that the quantity of the metal in a monomolecular film of $HgCl_2$ on $1/20$ square centimeters (0.01 millionth of a gram) became reliably measurable. The chemical path of mercury poisoning was thoroughly investigated, confirming the previous results.

From 1939 on Stock was plagued by hardening of the muscles (myogelosis). In May 1943, he discontinued his laboratory activities in Dahlem because the two small rooms at the Kaiser Wilhelm Institute were needed for war work. With his wife he moved to Bad Warmbrunn in Silesia, into the house of his brother-in-law.

THE LAST YEARS IN BAD WARMBRUNN AND AKEN:
SEPTEMBER 1943, TO AUGUST 12, 1946

Toward the end of February 1945, the advance of the Russians came closer and closer. Alfred and his wife had to leave Warmbrunn in the midst of war confusion, an enterprise beset with unspeakable difficulties because of his greatly impaired mobility. He sought refuge with his old collaborator and friend, Ernst Kuss, who, having been bombed out in Duisburg, had obtained emergency quarters in Dessau and was working, with his staff, in the I.G. magnesium plant in nearby Aken. After four days of the most exhausting train rides with thirteen changes, loaded with the last remains of his possessions, he arrived with his wife in Dessau. Here, his friend Kuss received them with loving care. Because of the destruction of Dessau they had to move to barracks in Aken.

In January 1946, he gave again a first lecture on boron chemistry before the chemists of I.G.'s plant in Bitterfeld. On February 1 he wrote an urgent appeal to the authorities: "Save the German chemistry!"

He died in the early morning of August 12, 1946.

Selected from the biography by Egon Wiberg, *Chem. Ber.*, 83, XIX (1950). Translated by Eduard Farber.

EGON WIBERG

·· 102 ··

Franz Fischer

1877-1947

FRANZ FISCHER spent his childhood in Freiburg i. Breisgau where he had been born on March 19, 1877. His main interests at the gymnasium were chemistry and physics, with little love of languages. After his graduation in 1896 he decided to study electrochemistry, after an interlude of one year in military service.

As a student in Munich, from October, 1897, on, he was anxious to complete the requirements quickly so that he could follow his own ideas. For his doctorate work, under Karl Elbs (Giessen), he studied the chemical events in the lead-acid storage battery. In a few months he had the experimental confirmation for a theory proposed by Elbs. The thesis was quickly completed, and at Christmas, 1899, he surprised his parents with the news that he had acquired the title of doctor.

To reward him for his quick and successful conclusion of university study, his parents permitted him to spend a semester in Paris, doing research under Moissan. There Franz Fischer learned to work with the electric oven and to prepare metals and their carbides.

After an interim course at Wilhelm Ostwald's institute in Leipzig, he went to Berlin and worked in Emil Fischer's institute. Since a paid assistantship did not become available, he accepted a position with an industrial firm at Freiburg. Soon he became convinced that he would not be happy in industrial work, and that scientific research was his field.

He began his academic career at the physiochemical institute at Freiburg. His research centered around electrochemistry.

In 1904, he returned to Berlin, this time as an assistant in the inorganic division of Emil Fischer's new chemical institute. His teaching duties left him time for research. Among other things he discovered an explosive nitride of cadmium formed by exposing the metal in liquid nitrogen to electrical discharges. Of technical interest was his method of depositing iron electrolytically in any thickness; such iron is characterized by ductility and good magnetic properties.

In 1908 he obtained the title of professor and became head of

1435

the department which Alfred Stock had directed. Three years later, he accepted full professorship of electrochemistry at the Technische Hochschule in Berlin-Charlottenburg. There he started work on electrochemical reactions under pressure. By cathodic hydrogenation, he produced hydrogen peroxide with oxygen, formic acid with carbon dioxide. Whereas hydrogen peroxide had so far been obtained only in aqueous solutions, he synthesized pure hydrogen peroxide, using dark electrical discharge and cooling in liquid air.

Through Emil Fischer's interest in this work, Franz Fischer was invited to direct the new institute which the Kaiser Wilhelm Gesellschaft planned to erect in the Ruhr valley. This institute was to be devoted to the study of coal on a purely scientific basis, as the president of the Kaiser Wilhelm Gesellschaft declared in the opening ceremonies on July 27, 1914, a few days before the First World War broke out. In his autobiographical notes, Franz Fischer included a chapter on "scientific freedom" in which he stated that during his term of office he always had the necessary freedom in selecting his objectives and his collaborators. That this scientific freedom of the institute had not always remained undisputed he showed by a few examples, but he gratefully recognized the protection of the institute by the governing agency.

The results of work done at the institute are presented in 12 volumes of "Gesammelte Abhandlungen zur Kenntnis der Kohle" (collected papers on coal research), supplemented since 1936 by the journal *Brennstoff-Chemie* founded and edited by Franz Fischer.

During the first years of operations, the work was dominated by questions of raw material supplies resulting from the war. Thus, Franz Fischer had to delay his intentions to study the conversion of coal or heat into electricity by a direct path. Research on this subject remained very limited later on when again other subjects took precedence, particularly the synthesis of hydrocarbons. The war of 1914 to 18 had drastically demonstrated Germany's lack of natural petroleum and the necessity of providing other sources of motor fuel and lubricants. Such sources could be found, if at all, only in refined coal. In this direction lay the first comprehensive work at the institute.

1436

All important types of German coal were studied as to their suitability for producing tar by low temperature carbonization. Another problem that Franz Fischer and his collaborators attacked early, and to which they returned again and again, was the extraction of coal by means of solvents. Under elevated pressure, and especially with benzene as the solvent at 270° C., the yields in extracts were many times those obtained at atmospheric pressure. Particle size influences the course of the extraction. By fine grinding the yield can be greatly increased.

Many publications by Franz Fischer and his collaborators are devoted to the problem of the origin of coal. He emphasized the decisive importance of biological processes to which other scientists did not give due prominence. On the basis of experimental work, carried out together with Hans Schrader, Fischer formulated the so-called lignin theory, according to which the biological decomposition of plant materials consumed mainly the cellulosic part and thus left the more resistant lignin to be transformed into humus coal.

The numerous chemical and biological investigations on this subject at the institute did not remain unchallenged as to their conclusions. Whether or not the lignin theory, in its original form, is correct or has to be modified, the experimental results obtained in this connection are valuable for our chemical knowledge of coal.

The hydrogenation of coal under high pressure, initiated by Friedrich Bergius, was the subject of detailed studies at the Mülheim Institute.

The use of coal in fertilizers was also studied, and best results were obtained with lignitic brown coal pretreated with ammonia. Biological gas reactions and biological purification of illuminating gas to remove poisonous substances were investigated. Synthetic resins, called Kolonit, were produced from lignites. Mobile generators of motor fuel from solid fuels were constructed.

The conversion of methane into more valuable hydrocarbons was thoroughly investigated. Reactions at high temperatures at precisely regulated temperatures and time periods led to acetylene under reduced pressures, to benzene at normal atmospheric pressure. Acetylene was also obtained through electrical discharge. Another way was the production, at relatively low temperatures, of

1437

carbides, e.g., of barium, with methane, and their decomposition, again, to acetylene.

The high point in this research was the catalytic hydrogenation of carbon monoxide. This work of the institute under Franz Fischer achieved scientific and technical success of world-wide importance. Systematic experiments on the hydrogenation of carbon monoxide began at Mülheim after the war, starting from the thought that besides the high-pressure hydrogenation undertaken by Friedrich Bergius, only the gasification of coal and the conversion of the gases could lead to the desired liquid and solid hydrocarbons. First there were attempts to use pressure and catalysts to produce salts of formic acid and then to decompose them. Then, in 1925, the synthesis of hydrocarbons at ordinary atmospheric pressure was found by Franz Fischer and Hans Tropsch.

Ten years of intensive work were necessary before this process was ready to be taken over by industry (Ruhrchemie A.G., Oberhausen-Holten). The problems comprised the manufacture of the gases for synthesis, extremely fine purification, disposal of the heat of reaction, and development of highly active catalysts. During these ten years there occurred times of standstill in view of apparently overwhelming difficulties when everything depended upon untiring continuation of efforts to find the solutions. Franz Fischer remained unerringly persistent and imparted this spirit to his collaborators. On November 16, 1934, he summarized the development of hydrocarbon synthesis and ended with the communication that Ruhrchemie A.G. had decided to build a large pilot plant.

Between 1935 and 1939, six synthesis plants in the Ruhr valley and three in other parts of Germany came into existence and produced an annual maximum of 600,000 tons of primary products. Outside of Germany too, several Fischer-Tropsch plants were erected.

Work on the further development of hydrocarbon synthesis continued after 1935; the progress was important. I mention only the synthesis under moderate pressures with cobalt catalysts, the peculiar synthesis of mainly hard paraffin with ruthenium catalysts, and finally the use of iron catalysts. A new type of carbon monoxide hydrogenation was found with oxidic catalysts; it was called isosynthesis. A vast field of research was the detailed analytical investigation of the primary products obtained by synthesis and their further refinement. Lubricating oils of exceptional quality were thus produced. New ways led to special high-grade fuels required for the new motors.

There is scarcely a topic of chemical elucidation and upgrading of coal to which Franz Fischer did not make a contribution. He had no periods of scientific unproductivity during his entire life. For his collaborators, it was sometimes not quite easy to follow experimentally what he frequently thought up during the night hours. Gifted with thorough human knowledge, he was able to attract and to train many young chemists and engineers as well as able technicians.

In lectures and publications, Franz Fischer regularly reported the new results obtained at the institute, always pointing out the contributions of those who participated in the work. He also encouraged his collaborators to publish experimentally completed themes, in order to make the results available to the public.

He was opposed to interferences by past regimes. He energetically opposed every political dictate.

Because of the excellent reputation of the institute, many foreign colleagues came to visit Mülheim. Franz Fischer cultivated these relationships and frequently visited foreign countries to lecture at international congresses. After the Second World War, the institute received many signs of friendliness, due mainly to the high regard for Franz Fischer. He received the Lord Melchett Medal of the British Institute of Fuel and many other distinctions.

He found his recreation in sociability and close contact with Nature. From his youth he was inclined to catarrhal attacks, and he counteracted them most effectively by long journeys at sea. He came to the United States three times.

After 1943, he lived in retirement in Munich where his wife had moved two years before. In Munich he intended to lecture at the Technische Hochschule where he was an honorary professor. This plan was prevented by the war, as his home was completely destroyed in the summer of 1944; his second home had the same fate. Personal grief and sorrow came to him in the same year. His wife died after long suffering, and shortly before that his daughter and son-in-law were arrested by the Gestapo and brought to the concentration camp at Dachau.

After the end of the war, Franz Fischer managed, after long labor, to found a very modest new home. It is tragic that the inventor of one of the most important processes of modern chemistry had to struggle tenaciously to obtain even such a modest place of living. He was not even allowed to use his automobile, at a time when the Fischer-Tropsch process was destined to produce millions of tons of motor fuel.

All these adversities and sorrows did not discourage Franz Fischer, who found new strength in the pursuit of science. When a company in Regensburg placed a laboratory at his disposal, he accepted the offer and carried out research on lignin.

He died on the first of December, 1947.

GENERAL REFERENCES

Hermann Kellermann, *Brennstoff-Chem.*, 30, 9 (1949).

Franz Fischer, "Leben und Forschung; Erinnerungen aufgezeichnet in den Jahren 1944 bis 1946," Max Planck-Institut für Kohleforschung, Mülheim a.d.Ruhr, 1957.

J. R. Kummer and P. H. Emett, *J. Am. Chem. Soc.*, 75, 5177 (1953).

From Herbert Koch's memorial lecture, Dec. 1, 1948, *Brennstoff-Chem.*, 30, 3 (1949). Translated by Eduard Farber.

HERBERT KOCH

·· 103 ··

Heinrich Wieland

1877-1957

Heinrich Wieland was born June 4, 1877, in Pforzheim where his father was a chemist in a gold and silver refinery. Heinrich started his chemical studies in Munich and obtained his doctorate there in 1901. His sponsor was Johannes Thiele (1865–1918), the originator of a valence theory for organic compounds containing several "double" bonds. It is of interest here to take a look at this theory, because its further development foreshadowed the fate of a basic theory which Heinrich Wieland developed a few years later in a quite different field.

A double bond between carbon atoms, like the one in ethylene $CH_2=CH_2$, is not stronger but, somewhat to the contrary, more reactive than a single bond. For example, hydrogen is readily added to form ethane, $CH_3—CH_3$. In a sequence of such double bonds:

$$\overset{1}{-HC}=\overset{2}{CH}-\overset{3}{CH}=\overset{4}{CH}-$$

the addition of hydrogen occurs primarily at the ends, saturating carbons 1 and 4, and with the production of a new double bond in the middle. Thiele concluded (1899) that the formula as usually written did not represent this fact, and he proposed a different formulation: The double bonds actually leave

$$-CH-\underline{CH-CH}-CH-$$

free valences which are mutually bound between the internal two carbon atoms. This causes addition reactions to occur on the outside, leaving one double bond in the middle at carbons 2 and 3. Thiele coined the name conjugated double bonds for such structures. At first, he claimed that all such conjugations should result in the addition of hydrogen, or halogen, on the carbons 1 and 4, instead of 1 and 2, or 3 and 4. However, it was soon found that this is not as generally true as the theory would have required it. Even the simplest of the compounds with conjugated bonds, butadiene, $H_2C=CH—CH=CH_2$, does not react exclusively at the carbons 1 and 4; the phenyl-substituted butadienes add halogen predominantly at the site of the double bond itself. The enticing simplicity of the theory had to be abandoned, but the specificity which had to take its place was gradually recognized to be still more beautiful.

In 1902, Heinrich Wieland began to study the addition of dinitrogen trioxide, N_2O_3, to single double bonds. He characterized the various ways in which this can occur as having one important aspect in common. Contrary to previous thoughts, the nitrogen is always directly connected with carbon, forming nitroso-nitro compounds:

$$R—CH=CH—R + N_2O_3 \rightarrow R—\underset{NO}{\underset{|}{CH}}—\underset{NO_2}{\underset{|}{CH}}—R$$

Nitrogen dioxide, in its usual dimeric form N_2O_4, acts similarly. Wieland concluded that N_2O_3 is constituted as $ON—NO_2$, and N_2O_4 correspondingly $O_2N—NO_2$. Theoretically, they are analogous to the halogens $Cl—Cl$ or $Br—Br$. Practically, N_2O_4 should be effective as a nitrating agent with many advantages over concentrated nitric acid.

Wieland submitted these results in his habilitation thesis and became a Privatdozent at the University of Munich in 1904. From then on, his work expanded in several directions, most of it on problems requiring great experimental skill and, after many years, yielding results of wide importance with the help of his excellent students and assistants.

One problem of this kind was to explain the reaction which produced a blue color when diphenylamine, dissolved in concentrated sulfuric acid, was treated with oxidizing agents. At first, it was thought that two molecules of the amine lost hydrogen to the oxidant and combined to tetraphenylhydrazine. This was later found to be erroneous; the tetra-substituted hydrazine is formed only when the amine is dissolved in an inert medium, e.g., in ether. In such a solvent, the hydrazine showed a peculiar color reaction which led to a new series of studies. This striking color reaction occurs, in the absence of water, with hydrogen chloride, or with the chlorides of iron, tin, and others known to form complex addition compounds. With tetraphenylhydrazine the color quickly disappears, because the products undergo a molecular rearrangement. When the para positions are occupied by methyl groups, this rearrangement does not occur and the color is more stable. In 1911, Wieland discovered that a similar reaction takes place by simply heating the substituted hydrazines in xylene. A few years before, Moses Gomberg had found that hexaphenylethane breaks apart into two halves, "radicals" containing carbon in the unusual trivalent form, and Wilhelm Schlenk (1879–1943) had just expanded the methods of identifying them as such (1910). It appeared to Wieland that his hydrazines also dissociated into radicals, and that they contained nitrogen in the unusual divalent state. The relative stability of this state is influenced by the nature of the groups replacing the hydrogen atoms of hydrazine $H_2N—NH_2$. A systematic study of the substituted hydrazines showed that the influences are characteristically different from those found for the radicals with trivalent carbon. The analogy, which exists between carbon and nitrogen in this respect, is modified by the differences between these elements.

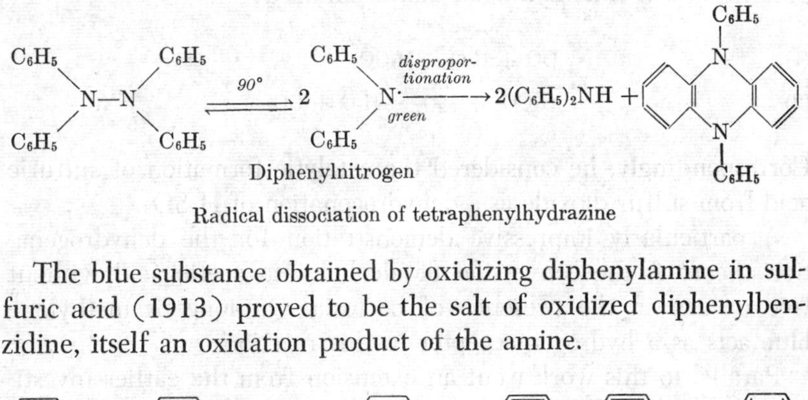

Radical dissociation of tetraphenylhydrazine

The blue substance obtained by oxidizing diphenylamine in sulfuric acid (1913) proved to be the salt of oxidized diphenylbenzidine, itself an oxidation product of the amine.

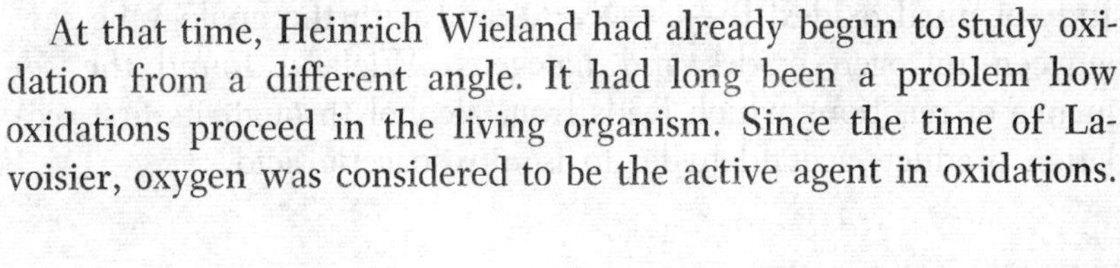

diphenylamine

At that time, Heinrich Wieland had already begun to study oxidation from a different angle. It had long been a problem how oxidations proceed in the living organism. Since the time of Lavoisier, oxygen was considered to be the active agent in oxidations.

1445

During the nineteenth century, and particularly in its last two decades, various theories were proposed, all relating to "activations" of the oxygen. Johann Ernst Ostwald Schmiedeberg (1838–1921), however, suggested that the explanation should be sought in an "activation" of the substrate, i.e., the substance to be oxidized (1881). Moritz Traube (1826–1894) showed that when a metal like zinc is attacked in the presence of water, oxygen actually combines with hydrogen, and not primarily with the metal; he expressed the reaction by a formula which explains how hydrogen peroxide is formed in this reaction:

$$Zn + \begin{matrix} H—O—H \\ H—O—H \end{matrix} + \begin{matrix} O \\ O \end{matrix} \rightarrow Zn \begin{matrix} OH \\ OH \end{matrix} + \begin{matrix} H—O \\ | \\ H—O \end{matrix}$$

From his experiments with platinum metal as a catalyst, Wieland concluded (1912) that hydrogen, not oxygen is activated. When carbon monoxide is "oxidized" to carbon dioxide, water must be present, and it is its hydrogen that is oxidized:

(1) $$CO + H_2O \rightarrow H_2CO_2$$

(2) $$H_2CO_2 + \tfrac{1}{2}O_2 \rightarrow H_2O + CO_2.$$

Correspondingly, he considered the catalytic formation of sulfuric acid from sulfur dioxide as a dehydrogenation of H_2SO_3.

A particularly impressive demonstration for the dehydrogenation theory is the conversion of alcohol into acetic acid without free oxygen in the presence of bacteria. Quinone or methylene blue acts as a hydrogen-acceptor in this reaction.

Parallel to this work went an extension from the earlier investigation on reactions with nitrogen oxides. Thus Wieland solved an old riddle which had interested Justus Liebig—the reaction between alcohol and nitric acid, in the presence of mercury or silver salts, by which fulminating compounds are formed. Through his study of nitril oxides, $R—C{\equiv}N{=}O$, and with the analogy he saw between nitrogen oxides and halogens, Wieland found the sequence of reactions which leads from alcohol through its first oxidation product, acetaldehyde, to isonitrosoacetic acid,

1446

$$HO—N—CH_2—COOH,$$

and then to fulminic acid,

$$H—C{\equiv}N{=}O \rightleftharpoons C{\equiv}N—OH$$

(1907). This acid polymerizes readily. Liebig's fulminuric acid is a trimeric form of it. Wieland also found the structure of a tetrameric product, isocyanilic acid, and these exist in various isomeric forms.

$$
\begin{array}{ccccc}
HC—C & & & C—CH \\
\| \ \| & & & \| \ \| \\
HO—N \ \ N & & & N \ \ N—OH \\
& \searrow & \swarrow & \\
& & O &
\end{array}
$$

Isocyanilic acid

The year 1912 also brought a publication by Wieland on the chemistry of bile acids. Again the problem had been pursued for a long time, since Thenard, in 1806, discovered a bittersweet substance (picromel) and a resinous, acidic material in bile. Twenty years later, Leopold Gmelin separated 22 different substances from this material, among them cholesterin, cholic acid, and nitrogen-containing acids. These were later hydrolytically split into amino acids and bile acids. Just before Wieland started his work in this field, three particular bile acids appeared to be characteristic: cholic acid, deoxycholic acid, and lithocholic acid. Wieland proved the close chemical relationship among these three by converting them into the same substance, cholanic acid. The steps consisted in dehydration and then addition of hydrogen in the presence of the same kind of catalysts which he used in developing his hydrogen-activation theory of oxidation. The three bile acids were thus shown to differ only in the number of hydroxyl groups attached to the same basic compound; cholic acid has three, deoxycholic two, and lithocholic acid one hydroxyl group. In their basic structure, they are related to cholesterin, which Wieland's friend, Adolf Windaus (1876–1959) had been investigating since 1903.

Research in all these fields, organic nitrogen compounds, dehydrogenation, and bile acids, continued with shifting emphasis when Heinrich Wieland became full professor at the Technische Hochschule in Munich, intensified after the war at the University of Freiburg (1921–25), and particularly after Wieland returned to the University in Munich, as Richard Willstätter's successor, in 1926.

From 1921 on, Wieland concentrated his research of organic nitrogen compounds on alkaloids, particularly those of the plant *Lobelia inflata*. Predominant among the lobelia alkaloids is lobeline. When methyl iodide is added to this substance, it can easily be transformed into 1,7-dibenzoyl heptane, $C_6H_5—CO—(CH_2)_7—CO—C_6H_5$. Oxidation to the so-called scopolinic acid and other reactions revealed the structure of lobeline.

Lobeline

In a similar manner, the other two groups of alkaloids, called lelobine and lobinine, were shown to differ from the main group in containing a C_2H_5 group for one of the phenyls. Synthesis gave the final confirmation for these structures (1929–1939).

The various kinds of curare, the arrow poison of South American Indians, yielded a substance, toxiferine I, of which 0.3 millionth of a gram was sufficient to paralyze a 40-gram frog (1937–41).

The poison of the mushroom death cup (*Amanita phalloides*) contains several amino acids in an arrangement which Theodor Wieland (b. 1913), Heinrich's son, only recently succeeded in establishing.

At the suggestion of Clemens Schöpf (b. 1899) Wieland turned his attention to the pigments of butterflies, the pterins. They proved to be related to uric acid.

The venom of toads (*Bufo vulgaris*), which acts upon the heart, has an entirely different structure. It is related to the sterols of yeast (1941), and the nitrogen is carried by the side chains, not in the ring structure of the molecule.

Wieland extended his dehydrogenation theory more and more to biological systems, such as the enzymes of bacteria which form acetic acid, and those of yeast, milk, muscle, and plants. He found

1448

Bufotoxin
Structure of toad venoms

an opponent of great experimental skill in Otto Warburg (b. 1883), who explained that biological oxidations are governed by metals, particularly iron (in rarer instances copper), which act by activating the oxygen. Hydrocyanic acid (HCN) or carbon monoxide inhibits respiratory reactions by "poisoning" the iron surface. The catalytic, oxygen-activating action of blood pigment persists even after charring the hemine because its iron is still present in this charcoal (Warburg, 1921). Wieland thereupon showed that amino acid oxidation in the presence of such charcoal can still be carried out, in the absence of free oxygen, with such hydrogen acceptors as quinone, alloxan, or dinitrobenzene. What the catalyst activates is the hydrogen of the amino group, not oxygen. Warburg countered with experiments on the absorption spectra and the influence of carbon monoxide on them. In light, the effect on respiration is as reversible as the iron compound formation with carbon monoxide. Finally, Warburg had to admit that there are systems in which the substrate, not the oxygen, is activated, and Wieland had to relent insofar as phenol oxidase enzymes of plant materials are concerned.

Warburg received the Nobel Prize for his work on the respiratory enzyme in 1931, four years after Wieland obtained it for his research on the constitution of bile acids and related substances.

One of the first stations on the long way toward a structural formula for bile acids had been to recognize that cholic, deoxycholic, and lithocholic acid are derivatives of one common acid, called cholanic acid (1912). The next great advance was made by gradual oxidations which attacked the molecules only where the hydroxyl groups are located (1919). Then, however, an analogy to the behavior of known dicarboxylic acids led in the wrong direction, until it was found that acids of the structure present in the oxidized bile acids were exceptions to the supposed general rule. At the same time, in 1932, O. Rosenheim and H. King concluded from J. D. Bernal's x-ray crystallography of these materials that they are to be formulated as derivatives of phenan-

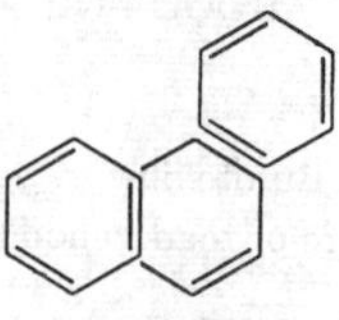

phenanthrene

threne, and Wieland found a new chemical way which proved such a structure. This structure was also consistent with the results which Otto Diels (1876–1954) had obtained in 1925. He dehydrogenated sterins (sterols) and bile acids by heating them with selenium and found two hydrocarbons: chrysene, and a second one for which the formula of γ-methyl cyclopentanophenanthrene was established in 1934.

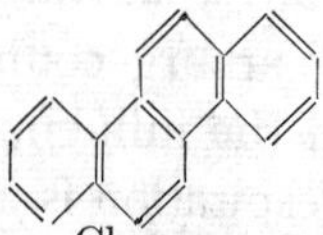

Chrysene 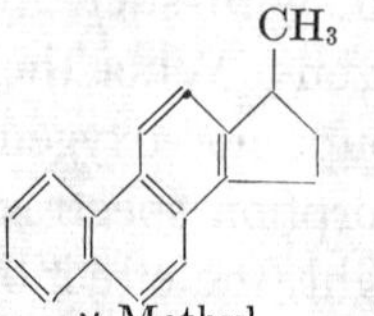   γ-Methyl   Cholanic acid
cyclopentanophenanthrene $C_{24}H_{40}O_2$

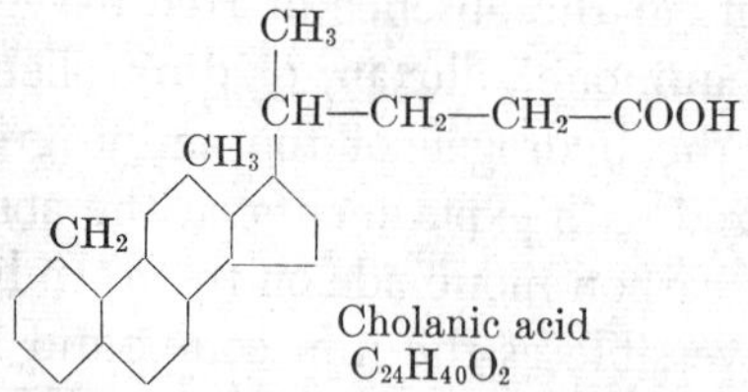

Now it only remained to establish the sites of the original carboxyl group and the methyl groups in cholanic acid. Bromination, Grignard reactions, oxidations, and reductions finally permitted to derive the place for each of the atoms and their arrangement in space in the formula $C_{24}H_{40}O_5$ for cholic acid (1936). Wieland may have felt like Adolf von Baeyer when he had experimentally established the place of every atom in the molecule of indigo half a century before. And whereas the knowledge of the indigo molecule was of greatest importance in dyestuff technology, the results from the investigation of the bile acids

1450

had far-reaching consequences in the biochemistry of hormones.

Like Baeyer, Wieland was able to derive deep insight from apparently simple test tube experiments, and like his great predecessor at the University of Munich, he enjoyed experimenting and teaching to the last years of his long life.

In his memorial lecture before the Chemical Society, delivered on May 8, 1958, Rolf Huisgen said about Wieland's last years: "His sense of justice forced Wieland into a dangerous opposition in the difficult years before and during the war when political tyranny did not spare the halls of science. His uprightness and his personal courage remain unforgotten. He made no secret of his hatred for a totalitarian regime. In defiance of official orders, he protected in his Institute a group of persons persecuted for so-called racial reasons. In 1944 some of his students became involved in a trial for what was then termed high treason. His favorable testimony and his loyalty to the defendants in front of the court demonstrated his courage and his political stand."

"On August fifth, 1957, eight weeks after Wieland's eightieth birthday which was celebrated quietly, a great life ended. A living symbol of human and academic dignity had ceased to exist."

GENERAL REFERENCES

Naturwissenschaften issued a double-number on June 2, 1942, in which Heinrich Wieland's students and friends celebrated his 65th birthday. Elisabeth Dane, Wilhelm Franke, Friedrich Klages, and Clemens Schöpf gave surveys of Wieland's work, quoting many of the over 400 papers with the names of the co-authors.

The *Proceedings of The Chemical Society* published The Wieland Memorial Lecture, delivered before the Chemical Society in London, May 8, 1958, by Rolf Huisgen, in the issue of August, 1958.

EDUARD FARBER

·· *104* ··

Francis William Aston

1877-1945

ASTON'S name is associated in the minds of men of science with the mass spectrograph and the discoveries concerning isotopes to which it lead. In the history of British physics it is rare that a man's work should thus be associated with an instrument, although it is common enough to be almost the rule among the great names of American science. Although, in fact, in Aston's case the instrument was devised to test a specific theory and not developed for its own sake, it is yet true that Aston's mind was fundamentally that of an instrumentalist to whom experimental methods and actual manual dexterity are a joy in themselves, approaching that to be gained from the results they give. This habit of mind can be traced throughout his life, and the skill of hand that went with it found expression as well in games and in music.

F. W. Aston was born in September, 1877, at Tennal House, Harborne, Birmingham, which is still occupied by a member of the family. He was the second son and third child of a family of seven. From an early age he showed a passion for mechanical toys. After a preparatory education at Harborne Vicarage School, he went for two years to Malvern College, where he began the study of science. He left in 1893, head of the school in chemistry and physics and in the highest mathematical set, to enter Mason College, Birmingham. Here he worked under Tilden and Frankland for chemistry, and under Poynting for physics, of whom he often spoke with affection in later years. At Birmingham, too, he laid the foundation of his skill as a glass blower which was to be so important to him later on. In 1898 he was awarded the Forster Scholarship and worked on the preparation and optical rotatory properties of a complex tartaric derivative, the results of which were published in collaboration with Frankland in 1901. For financial reasons he then took up fermentation chemistry and was engaged for three years at a brewery in Wolverhampton. During this period his thoughts were turning to physics under the influence of the new science that followed the discovery of x-rays.

Quite naturally his interest expressed itself in terms of apparatus. He designed and made a new pattern of the Sprengel pump, and with it exhausted small focus tubes, made from chemical test tubes, in a tiny workshop at home. The Sprengel pump led to a Tœpler, also of new design, and he discovered a type of rectifying valve depending on a gas discharge.

In 1903 Aston definitely returned to physics, with a scholarship to the University of Birmingham, as Mason College had by then become, where he worked on properties of the gas discharge, in particular of the dark space. His measurements of the length of the Crookes' dark space and its variation with current and pressure are still classical and appeared in the *Proceedings of the Royal Society* of 1905. Two years after, he discovered the narrow region which appears in some gases inside the Crookes' dark space and is known as the "Aston dark space." Then came a tour round the world, as the result of a legacy, which confirmed him in a love of travel, and especially of ocean travel, that never left him and was the source of much happiness.

In 1909 Aston took the step which, as it turned out, determined his future scientific career, by accepting the invitation of J. J. Thomson to work as his assistant in the Cavendish Laboratory, a post which left him time for independent research. By then Thomson had developed the parabola method of analyzing positive rays, and produced for the first time clear evidence that atoms and molecules were, at least in certain cases, of definite weights for any particular substance. Besides continuing his own work on the dark spaces and measuring the distribution of force in this region of discharge, Aston helped in the further development of the analysis of positive rays. Among the photographs taken on his improved apparatus were some showing a curious effect with neon. Instead of a single parabola due to the atoms of this gas there were two, corresponding to weights of about 20 and 22 units. Isotopes among radioactive substances were already an accepted fact, due to the work of Soddy, and Thomson, not without some hesitation, attributed the two lines to isotopes of neon. The lines were undoubtedly due to neon, since they only occurred when this gas was present. The alternative was to suppose the weaker 22 line to be due to a compound NeH_2 (in this early work it was practically impossible to get rid of hydrogen). Such a compound was contrary to chemical ideas, but since the method of positive rays had already disclosed several compounds which violated the ordinary laws of valency, the chemical evidence was not very strong, and the decision had to rest on the character of the second line, its variation with conditions, and in particular the appearances of a corresponding line showing a double charge for which there was then no precedent among compounds.

Aston set to work to decide the question. There were two ways of doing so. The first was to try to separate the isotopes if they really existed. The second was to compare the values of e/m of the positive rays with that to be expected from the density of the gas, which gave an atomic weight of 20·2. If the weaker line was due to a compound, the stronger should show a mass of 20·2; if to an isotope, the weight 20·2 must be a mean and the stronger line have a smaller mass, probably about 20. The parabola method was not accurate enough to decide between these possibilities.

Aston started with the first, and as we should now think it, the harder method. At first, indeed, he had some slight success, and an ingenious apparatus for fractional distillation, which of course he made himself, had given a positive result just outside the experimental error when the First World War broke out. During this war Aston worked at Farnborough at the Royal Aircraft Factory, as it then was, as a chemist studying the peculiarities of the doped canvas with which airplanes were then covered, and its preservation by pigments. All the time, however, he was thinking over the neon problem. He lived in a civilian mess known from its location first as "Arnold House" and then as "Chudleigh." Here he discussed physics and the then new quantum theory in its relation to isotopes with Lindemann (now Lord Cherwell), with results which appeared shortly after the war in two joint theoretical papers in the *Philosophical Magazine*. The "Chudleigh" atmosphere was conducive to the spread of ideas; among the others who lived there from time to time being Sir Geoffrey Taylor, Sir Melville Jones, F. M. Green, then chief engineer of the Factory, Prof. E. D. Adrian, W. S. Farren, later director of the R.A.E., D. H. Pinsent, a young man of great brilliance killed during an experiment in the air, H. Glauert, and the Author. Aston was inclined to be shy in discussing his work, and the ability to do so with men with whom he was really intimate was probably valuable to him. Certainly he always referred to those times with pleasure in afteryears.

The end of the war brought a great disappointment. Two successive pieces of apparatus designed to achieve the separation of the neon isotopes by diffusion failed to do so. It says much for Aston's faith and courage that he was undeterred by these failures, which must have been particularly hard after his previous partial success. The failures were due, not to any error of principle, but to insufficient mixing in the diffusing bodies of gas.

Aston accordingly turned to plans which he had developed while at Farnborough for an attack on the problem by the second method. He devised the well-known apparatus with which his name is so closely associated, in which the ingenious use of electromagnetic focusing of a special type makes great improvements possible in intensity, dispersion, and resolving power. The more delicate parts, such as the slits, of this new apparatus he made himself. The new mass spectrograph, as he called it, was an almost instantaneous success. Not merely did Aston show that neon is indeed a mixture of isotopes, but also that the same is true of chlorine and many other elements.

Aston's discovery was quickly acclaimed. He became a fellow of Trinity in 1920, where he lived ever after until his death. He received the Nobel Prize for chemistry and the Hughes Medal of the Royal Society within two days in 1922; he had been elected a fellow of the Royal Society in 1921.

The earlier work with isotopes was done with gaseous compounds, and many of the metals were missing. In order to get beams of metallic ions, special methods have to be used. Dempster in 1921 analyzed magnesium, and soon after Aston and the author, simultaneously but independently, discovered means of analyzing lithium, which was closely followed by many of the other metals of the early groups of the periodic classification. Later on, Aston succeeded in producing beams of ions from most of the remaining elements, even including the rare earths. In all but a few cases he made the first isotopic analysis.

1458

The original mass spectrograph, now in the Science Museum, South Kensington, analyzed more than fifty elements during its active career and established the whole-number rule. The task of its successor was to measure the deviations from this rule which are so vitally important in nuclear physics, especially for atomic energy.

The new mass spectrograph was accurate to 1 in 10,000. It was characteristic of Aston that to ensure the complete reliability of a battery of 500 small lead accumulators which supplied the field for the deflector plates, he decided to make them himself. He was now concerned with high accuracy, and exerted his ingenuity to devise methods of comparing masses with the utmost precision. These measurements are extremely difficult and in some cases, as might be expected, appreciable alterations had to be made in the results first obtained. By a curious accident a mistake in the ratio of the masses of helium and oxygen stimulated the discovery of heavy hydrogen by Urey and Brickwedde by predicting a larger discrepancy between the physical and chemical atomic weights of hydrogen than in fact exists.

Aston never forgot his early training as a chemist; and his next task, that of determining the relative abundance of isotopes, interested him partly because of its connection with the atomic weights of chemistry. His method was a photographic one, in which exposures were adjusted to make the blackening caused by two isotopes the same or nearly so. His last apparatus, the third mass spectrograph, aimed at an accuracy of 1 in 100,000, and although it did not have quite the resolving power he had hoped for, it achieved valuable results in fixing the mass defects of a number of important isotopes.

Although in the later years work of equal quality was being done in the field of mass spectrography by Dempster, Bainbridge, Neier, and others in the United States, there are few instances in modern science in which the first discoverer of a major field of research has had it so much his own way for such a long time. This is evidence of the technical difficulties involved, not only, or even perhaps mostly, on the measurement side, but also in the production of beams of ions of all sorts of elements with measurable intensity. For this, Aston's training in chemistry and in the peculiarities of the gaseous discharge were of the greatest value. But to this training he added that combination of patience and intuition which marks the great experimenter. There is scarcely a research in nuclear physics which does not use his work, directly or indirectly, and usually many times over. The use of isotopes as tracer elements both in chemistry and in biology is only in its early stage, but even now the results are highly important and it is difficult to put a limit on the possibilities of this field. It is true that most of the isotopes used for this purpose are either radioactive or were discovered by the analysis of band spectra, but the method would scarcely be possible without the knowledge of the isotopic structure of ordinary elements which we owe to Aston. Nor is it likely that the rare isotopes of the light elements, such as heavy hydrogen, which his method is not well fitted to discover, would have been found without his work.

Outside his work Aston's interests were most strongly held by sport, by travel, and by music, although any sort of mechanical or scientific device attracted him. In sport he was an ardent skier and made almost yearly visits both to Switzerland and to Norway. He preferred expeditions, often long ones, to trick turns, although he had jumped a little. He liked to do his own climbing and to be independent of funiculars. It was perhaps the greatest grief of his life that a strained heart produced by skiing in the winter of 1934–35 put a stop to winter sports. But skiing was only one of many sports. As a young man he once cycled two hundred miles in twenty-two hours; he was a good lawn tennis player of tournament class, a good swimmer and used to say that the surf-riding he learnt at Honolulu was in many ways the finest sport in the world. He was a golfer well above the average, and the Sunday four with Rutherford, Fowler, and Taylor was an institution. During the First World War he took up rock climbing. On several occasions he led courses classed as of "exceptional severity." Among his miscellaneous activities were photography, bridge, and the special Trinity game of *vingt,* and the collection of Chinese porcelain. He played the piano and violin, but gave most attention to the 'cello.

1460

His love of travel was intense, especially sea travel, and he contrived to combine it with science by going on eclipse expeditions and on British Association visits, although these were by no means his only journeys.

Aston was a man in whom a great zest for life was combined with a simplicity of character almost approaching naïvety. He was interested in people, especially his numerous friends, and probably more interested in things and places. This gift of interest in the outside world made him an ideal holiday companion. The pleasure he clearly took communicated itself to the rest of the party. He was precise in his habits, although it would be unfair to call him old-maidish, for he enjoyed changing from one routine of life to a totally different one. Although a good occasional lecturer, he had no gift for teaching and a few early attempts were not persisted in. He enjoyed scientific meetings, but was essentially an individualist and never attempted to form a school. I think he realized that much of his skill was incommunicable, and that in any event he needed quiet to work his best. His attitude to physics was essentially that of the experimenter and visualizer. He preferred the model to the equation; the concrete to the abstract. The philosophical aspect did not appeal to him. He was a Conservative in politics as in life, and though he would admit that a change might be good, he preferred it to happen as gradually as possible. I last saw him when he received the Duddell Medal of the Physical Society. In a characteristic speech he remarked with some feeling that his researches would never have been passed by any competent planning committee.

In addition to many papers in the *Proceedings of the Royal Society* and *Philosophical Magazine,* Aston's principal published work was his book on "Isotopes," of which the first edition came out in 1922, the second in 1924. In 1933 the name was changed to "Mass Spectra and Isotopes," although much of the material was the same; in 1941 it appeared in final form. He was twice on the Council of the Royal Society, was awarded a Royal Medal and gave the Bakerian Lecture in 1927. He was an honorary member of the Russian Academy of Sciences, and of the Accademia dei Lincei. He received an Hon. LL.D. from the University of Bir-

1461

mingham, and an Hon. D.Sc. from Dublin. He took a prominent part in the work of the International Atomic Weights Committee.

From: *Nature, 157,* 296 (1946).

SIR GEORGE PAGET THOMSON

·· *105* ··

Frederick Soddy

1877-1956

FREDERICK SODDY was born at Eastbourne in September, 1877, and died on September 22 of this year (1956). If he had been an only child many of us who knew him in middle life would have thought him an excellent specimen of the class. His aloofness, his desire to go his own way, his assumption that possibly his word was law, his shyness with others, his desire not to be one of the crowd, would have struck us as almost right. In fact, however, Soddy was the youngest of a large family of boys brought up in Sussex. The mother died early, when Soddy was quite small, and he was left to his own devices in the home. From Eastbourne College, which he left at seventeen, he went to Merton College, Oxford, to read chemistry for his degree after, characteristically, spending a year at University College, Aberystwyth. In 1900, after finishing at Oxford, he went as demonstrator in chemistry to McGill University in Montreal. There he met the great Rutherford, the professor of physics. At that time radioactivity was a major subject of study in physics but no one had an inkling what was its cause. The very brilliant physicist and the brilliant and younger chemist, by their joint work, opened a new chapter in natural science. Their disintegration theory, now so obvious, then so sensational, was put forward in 1902–03. The very heaviest elements were in part unstable. One element could produce another by expelling from its center small portions of its mass or of its electricity. There were three main disintegration series.

After these three fruitful years Soddy returned to England and worked with Sir William Ramsay at University College in London. There he showed spectroscopically that radium produced helium. In 1904 he was made lecturer in physical chemistry and radioactivity at the University of Glasgow where he remained till his appointment to a chair of chemistry in Oxford in 1919. His big research at Glasgow was the proof that carefully purified uranium very, very slowly at first, and later with increased speed, was producing radium. From his results he deduced that between uranium and radium in the disintegration series there must be a third element, stabler than one and less stable that the other—an important result later confirmed by the discovery (by others) of the element ionium. In Glasgow also he worked on nonseparable radio elements. Concentrating as a chemist mainly on the chemical properties of radioactive material he found that there were far more chemical species showing radioactivity than there were places in the periodic table. He and others showed there were about fifty of the former for twelve of the latter. Soddy triumphed over his contemporaries by coining the word "isotope," now almost a household word. Isotopes are elements chemically identical, and consequently nonseparable, but physically different. The novelty of this idea, thanks largely to the experiments of Aston and the insight of Rutherford, was later shown to have important implications well outside of the narrow field where it was first recognized. The culmination of Soddy's Glasgow period was the formulation of the rules connecting the expulsion of α- and β-particles from a parent radioactive atom and the nature of the resulting product.

In 1914 Soddy was made professor of chemistry at Aberdeen and in 1919 at Oxford. Part of his Aberdeen time was spent on isotopes and part on war work. At Oxford he was very unhappy in his early years. It was his own university; he knew what the college system there was; yet he found himself often at loggerheads with the powerful body of tutors in chemistry. Owing to foolish, quite out-of-date, and long since remedied regulations he found himself at first excluded from all boards and governing bodies connected with his subject. Laboratory instruction, moreover, was only partly a university affair. Half a dozen of the colleges had their own chemical laboratories and were not subject to Soddy's control. His attempts to close these small institutions and concentrate effort in University buildings—the right thing to do—led him to be thought perverse and obstructive. His case was that he was not master in his own department. The tutors thought him cranky. They thought he was always doing unpopular things tactlessly from the highest motives. Even his most adverse Oxford critic, however, would admit "that the worst of Soddy is that he is always three-quarters in the right." Gradually he dropped research in radioactivity and physical chemistry as his interest in social questions began and increased. He became a strident and adverse critic of economics, the businessman, and the financial world. He was undoubtedly unnecessarily violent in his condemnation of what he thought was wrong. As a man of science he recognized that nature and the factory could bring all the good things of life, on its bread-and-butter side, into everybody's home with great ease. All the good things in life, he said, existed in plenty and could easily be put on the highway, thanks to discovery, but the hell's brew of the financial world and the perverseness of the middleman and the banks were robbing mankind of its birthright. His books and pamphlets on "Cartesian economics," on "wealth and debt," on "money and man," and on "the arch-enemy of economic freedom" made many forget that he had written with great power and insight also on radioactivity, the structure of the atom, matter and energy, and on science and life. His unpopularity with many of his colleagues at Oxford may be illustrated by the statement that although he was a member at different times of three of its Colleges none of them on his early retirement at fifty-nine in 1936 then or later made him an honorary fellow.

Soddy was made a fellow of the Royal Society in 1910 and obtained a Nobel Prize in Chemistry in 1921. He was LL.D. of Glasgow University. He was awarded the Cannizzaro Prize by Rome in 1913. He was a Foreign Member of several continental Academies of Science. In 1908 he married Winifred the only daughter of Sir George and Lady Beilby of Glasgow. They had no children. She died in 1936. Their life together was a very happy one. Soddy might thunder on the platform or curse in committee but in private life and especially in the home he was the soul of courtesy, gentleness, and good manners. He had a fine appearance, tall, fair-haired, Scandinavian—a splendid head. To the Scots of Glasgow and Aberdeen he appeared to be the typical English public-school and Oxford man. Quietness, aloofness, and even superciliousness concealed at times thoughtfulness, kindness, and generosity. Many of his needy pupils remember his generosity to them at the right moment in the days before scholarships and university grants had become common. One of his last acts was to come to Oxford, knowing he was a dying man, and to give hand-some checks to laboratory stewards and assistants who had served with him twenty and more years ago.

From: *Chem. & Ind., 1956, 1420.*

ALEXANDER S. RUSSELL

·· *106* ··

Johannes Nicolaus Brønsted

1879-1947

IT IS a difficult task to commemorate and appraise a great man like Brønsted, especially for one thirty years his junior in age, and so much his junior in science. This difficulty is increased by a difference in nationality, and I feel therefore that I ought to begin by acknowledging my debt to the many friends in Denmark who have helped me in the preparation of this lecture. I must mention especially Mrs. Brønsted, who has provided me with much material, especially about Brønsted's early life, and Professor Christiansen, who has made available to me the manuscript of his own memorial lecture to Brønsted. What I have to say owes a very great deal to their willing cooperation.

I shall begin by giving an outline of Brønsted's life and career, followed by some account of his scientific work, and finally I shall try to give a general picture of him as a scientist and as a man.

Johannes Nicolaus Brønsted was born on February 22, 1879, in Varde, a small town in West Jutland. His father was a civil engineer employed by "Hedeselskabet," a corporation founded to reclaim moorland by draining, irrigation, and planting. His mother died shortly after his birth, but his father remarried shortly afterward, and the family moved to a farm in the heart of Jutland, where the young Brønsted and his elder sister spent most of their childhood. This period laid the foundation for the love of country things and country people which played such a great part in his later life. When he was twelve years old his family moved to Aarhus, the second largest city in Denmark, but still an essentially rural environment. He went to school there and seems to have been an apt pupil, particularly in mathematics. There was, of course, no school instruction in chemistry at that time, but Brønsted's interest in the subject was a very early one, his first source of information being an agricultural dictionary which he found in the attic. He did primitive experiments at home in the usual fashion, and the spirit lamp and balance which he used are still in existence.

His father died in 1893, leaving the family in straitened circumstances. Several friends of the family felt that the young Brønsted ought to begin to earn his living, but his mother recognized his promise and was determined to give him and his sister a good education even if it meant considerable sacrifices. The family moved to Copenhagen, and Brønsted attended the Metropolitan School there, where he found not only a high educational standard, but also a remarkably stimulating set of schoolfellows. Of the twenty boys in his class, two became bishops, two distinguished physicians, and five professors. One of the latter was Niels Bjerrum, his closest friend for many years, and his chief rival in making Danish physical chemistry world-famous. Brønsted matriculated in 1897, and went to study at the Polytechnic Institute in Copenhagen, where he met Charlotte Louise Warberg, whom he married in 1903. His studies seem to have sat lightly on his shoulders, and he found plenty of leisure to cultivate other interests such as philosophy, art, poetry, and music. It was at first intended that he should become an engineer like his father, but after taking his first degree in that subject in 1899 he changed over to pure science, and took his "Magister" degree in chemistry in 1902. At that date this degree was something of a rarity, especially in chemistry, and Brønsted's friends used "Magister" as a nickname for many years afterwards.

There was no academic position immediately available, and Brønsted worked for a short time in an electrotechnical concern. However, he soon returned to the University Chemical Laboratory, and was made an assistant there in 1905. He worked there on his affinity measurements, and in May 1908 presented the third paper in this series (on mixtures of sulfuric acid and water) for his doctorate degree. In the same year a new chair of chemistry was instituted in Copenhagen which combined the duties of teaching physical chemistry to the university students, and inorganic chemistry to students at the Polytechnic Institute. The two competitors for this chair were Brønsted and Niels Bjerrum, who had been Brønsted's classmate at school, and had taken his doctorate degree in the same year. It must have been a very difficult decision for the judges to make; but their choice finally fell on Brønsted, who was appointed at the early age of twenty-nine. The news reached the

Brønsted family in a dramatic way: one day just before Christmas a goods train stopped at the bottom of their garden in the country, and a railway official descended bearing a telegram of congratulation from Bjerrum.

This appointment fixed the whole of Brønsted's subsequent career, as he held the chair until his death thirty-nine years later. His laboratory was at first in the Polytechnic Institute, and for a time facilities were very limited, as physical chemistry was a new subject and the laboratory had to be equipped from scratch. However, conditions gradually improved, and in 1919 he was relieved from the onerous task of teaching elementary inorganic chemistry. The greatest change in his working conditions resulted from his visit to the United States in 1926–27, when he was able to discuss the possibility of financing a new physicochemical laboratory in Copenhagen. The International Education Board finally met the cost of a new University Physicochemical Institute, which was completed in 1930. Here Brønsted had not only ideal working conditions, but also a delightful official residence where he and his family could exercise their hospitality and charm.

I shall now give some account of Brønsted's contributions to physical chemistry, not in strict chronological order, but under their main headings.

The most important general interest in Brønsted's scientific work was undoubtedly thermodynamics. His earlier work dealt entirely with this topic, and even his later work on reaction kinetics has a strong thermodynamic flavor. His series of thirteen experimental papers on "Affinity" appeared during the years 1906–18, and constitute a veritable textbook of thermodynamics. Although Brønsted is well known for his later work on the thermodynamics of dilute electrolyte solutions, it is probably not generally realized how much he contributed to the fundamentals of chemical thermodynamics, where he can be ranked with Nernst and G. N. Lewis. At that time, although it was generally accepted that the affinity of a chemical process was measured by the maximum work and not by the heat of reaction, there were very few accurate or systematic measurements of affinity, and it was this gap which Brønsted set out to fill. In 1906 he showed how the heat and free energy changes in the interconversion of rhombic and monoclinic sulfur could be measured over a range of temperature, and he also speculated as to how affinity changes could be calculated from purely thermal quantities. It was, of course, Nernst, and not Brønsted, who first solved this last problem successfully, but Nernst himself acknowledged the importance of Brønsted's work in pointing the way. In a later paper in the same series (1910) Brønsted dealt with the thermodynamics of water-sulfuric acid mixtures, and gave one of the first correct treatments of the relations between the various differential and integral thermodynamic quantities in a mixture. In this paper he showed great ingenuity in combining vapor pressure, E.M.F., and calorimetric measurements, and (as in all these early papers) in obtaining accurate results with very modest resources.

Brønsted was always skilled at devising applications of E.M.F. measurements, and one example of this was his measurement of the free energy of formation of naphthalene picrate from its solid constituents, not at first sight a promising system for study by E.M.F. methods. Brønsted pointed out in 1911 that the free energy of this change was measured by the E.M.F. of the cell:

picrate electrode|solution I|H₂Pt, PtH₂|solution II|picrate electrode

where solution I is saturated with picric acid, and solution II with naphthalene + naphthalene picrate. Brønsted suggested using mercury-mercurous picrate for the picrate electrode, but was unable to make measurements on the above cell because the picrate solutions were reduced at the hydrogen electrodes. He was therefore compelled to use a very ingenious but laborious indirect method of measurement. It is interesting to note that in Oxford we have recently been able to measure the E.M.F. of the cell originally proposed by Brønsted by replacing the hydrogen electrodes by glass ones (which of course were not available to him): the value obtained for the free energy of formation is exactly the same as that obtained in 1911 by the indirect method (Bell and Fendley, *Trans. Faraday Soc.*, 1949, 45, 121).

Brønsted's thermodynamic studies soon led him into the field of electrolytes, first through E.M.F. measurements, and later through

1474

studies of solubility. It was becoming clear, partly through the work of Bjerrum, that very many electrolytes were completely dissociated in solution, and that their deviations from ideal thermodynamic behavior could not be explained in terms of any association equilibrium. The concept of "activity" had been introduced by G. N. Lewis, and various authors had suggested that electrostatic forces between the ions might be of importance. Brønsted's approach was essentially an experimental one, and his solubility measurements became famous in 1924, when with LaMer he published data on activity coefficients of ions in very dilute salt solutions which provided a most striking confirmation of the theoretical treatment of Debye and Hückel, published while the work was in progress. It should, however, be stressed that this publication with LaMer was really the fifth of a series of papers on solubility, starting in 1919, interspersed with a number of other papers on the properties of ionic solutions. It is in fact remarkable how many important laws Brønsted was able to discover on the basis of his carefully designed and accurate experiments, in most cases before any theoretical basis for these laws was available. Thus he was able to show that the deviations of ionic solutions from ideal behavior increase greatly with an increase in the charges on the ions present, and that in a solution containing several electrolytes the thermodynamic behavior of a given ion is mainly a function of the ionic strength μ, defined as

$$\mu = \tfrac{1}{2}\Sigma m_i z_i^2,$$

where m_i is the concentration of an ion of charge z_i, and the summation extends over all the ions in the solution. In more cencentrated solutions ions show individual properties not depending only on their charge, and Brønsted's "Principle of the Specific Interaction of Ions" (1921) states that the individual properties of a given ion depend mainly on the ions of opposite charge which are present in solution. Brønsted's investigations on the effect of salts of ionic equilibria will be described under his kinetic work, but one simple principle is worth mentioning here: that even an ionic equilibrium will obey the classical law of mass action in presence of a large excess of nonparticipating salt. All these principles were later shown to have theoretical bases, and if we add to Brønsted's work the equally important investigations of his countryman Bjerrum, it will be seen that Denmark has had an altogether disproportionate share in the experimental foundations of the modern theory of electrolytes.

Most of Brønsted's solubility determinations, and many of his other researches, were carried out with the cobaltammines. These had been studied in great detail from the preparative point of view by S. M. Jörgensen, Brønsted's teacher, and he therefore had to hand large numbers of specimens and much information about these compounds. This was naturally a piece of good fortune, but Brønsted's genius lay in realizing how admirably suited they were for his purposes. By suitable variations in the nature of the six groups coordinated to the central atom, ions can be produced with valencies varying from $+3$ to -3, and by combining these ions with one another or with other anions or cations it is possible to obtain salts of many charge types and of widely varying solubility. Most of these salts are well defined and crystalline, and they can be determined accurately even in very dilute solution by the simple process of treatment with sodium hydroxide and distillation of the ammonia into standard acid. These properties made them almost ideal for investigation of solubilities in salt solutions, but there was a great deal of groundwork to be done before the most suitable salts could be chosen: thus in his 1920 paper he measured the solubilities of 90 salts at two temperatures. The salts finally used by Brönsted and LaMer were the following:

$$[Co(NH_3)_4C_2O_4]^+[Co(NH_3)_2(NO_2)_2C_2O_4]^- \qquad s = 4\cdot9 \times 10^{-4}$$
$$[Co(NH_3)_4(NO_2)(CNS)]^+[Co(NH_3)_2(NO_2)_2C_2O_4]^- \qquad s = 3\cdot3 \times 10^{-4}$$
$$[Co(NH_3)_4C_2O_4]_2^+[S_2O_6]^- \qquad s = 1\cdot5 \times 10^{-4}$$
$$[Co(NH_3)_6]^{+++}[Co(NH_3)_2(NO_2)_2C_2O_4]_3^- \qquad s = 5\cdot0 \times 10^{-4}$$

The saturated solutions were obtained by the simple expedient of letting the solvent trickle slowly down a long vertical tube packed with crystals, a method which had been used by Brønsted much earlier in his measurements on rhombic and monoclinic sulfur. In spite of the low solubilities involved, an accuracy of about 0.3% was attained. . . .

The cobaltammines also played a considerable part in the development of Brönsted's ideas on acids and bases, and there is one other example of their use which may be mentioned here. On a simple electrostatic picture the solubility of a salt in different solvents should be a smooth function of the dielectric constant, but this is not so in practice, no doubt largely because of the part played by nonelectrostatic factors. In a paper given to the 1931 meeting of the British Association Brønsted reported solubility measurements on the two substances $Co(NO_2)_3(NH_3)_3$ and $[Co(NO_2)_2(NH_3)_4]^+[Co(NO_2)_4(NH_3)_2]^-$ which contain exactly the same chemical groupings, but are respectively a nonelectrolyte and a uniunivalent salt. By considering the ratio of the solubilities of these two substances, rather than the solubility itself, he hoped to eliminate the nonelectrostatic factors, and he did in fact find a fairly regular behavior for nine solvents with dielectric constants ranging from 21 to 84.

Apart from electrolytes, a particular thermodynamic problem which interested Brønsted from 1930 onward is the effect of molecular size on thermodynamic properties. He carried out experiments on the solubilities and distribution between phases of molecules (or colloidal particles) which were chemically very similar, and differed mainly in size. These led him to the concept of an "isochemical series," and he established several laws governing the solubilities and other properties of such a series. Although he did not realize that large entropy effects might be present in mixtures of molecules of different sizes, Brønsted's laws are essentially the same as those developed recently for high polymers such as rubber. Some of Brønsted's last published work was on the vapor pressures of mixtures of the normal paraffins, for which he obtained experimental results of very high accuracy, and established some new regularities which have not yet been explained theoretically. This work contains some very neat experimental devices: for example, in order to weigh a vessel containing liquid and vapor without detaching it from the rest of the apparatus, he suspended it from an ordinary balance and used as a connecting tube such a fine glass capillary that it had little effect within the sensitivity of the balance.

Brønsted's work on isochemical series is of particular interest, because it represents one of the few cases in which he gave a molecular interpretation for the laws which he had established experimentally. In general he was curiously reluctant to consider any detailed molecular picture, preferring to derive from experiment empirical regularities which should be independent of any particular features of the molecules concerned. For example, one sometimes felt that he regretted the mechanistic explanation given by the Debye-Hückel theory for the laws which he had established experimentally, and other examples of a similar attitude will be given later. I well remember his indignation when I suggested to him, shortly before his death, that a statistical approach was helpful in explaining the laws of thermodynamics to students.

Certainly there was no suggestion of any molecular interpretation in his writings on the fundamental bases of thermodynamics, which occupied him to an increasing extent during the last ten years of his life. Although he criticized severely the conventional approach to the second law, his treatment remained a strictly phenomenological one. It is diffcult to give an estimate of the value of this work, and I shall not attempt to summarize its content here. It roused violent controversy in Denmark, but has received little attention elsewhere: it is usually regarded as formally correct, but rather sterile. It is true that a similar view was at one time held about Brønsted's acid-base definition, which proved to have such a widespread importance, and it would indeed be interesting if his concepts of heat and entropy should eventually prove equally fruitful. They may perhaps be helpful in treating processes in which a steady state is set up by the irreversible flow of energy or matter through the system, a field which Brønsted had begun to study experimentally shortly before his death.

The second main field of Brønsted's activities was reaction kinetics, and in particular catalysis by acids and bases. This interest arose comparatively later in Brønsted's scientific development, but is probably the work for which he is best known, especially outside Denmark. It was closely connected with his work on electrolytes. and it is difficult to trace the exact order in which the various interwoven ideas arose, since papers on both kinetic and thermodynamic topics followed one another with bewildering rapidity in the nineteen-twenties.

1478

Brønsted first used kinetic measurements in 1921 in connection with the effect of salts on acid-base equilibria. He was particularly concerned to show that the effect of salt concentration on hydrogen-ion concentration depends on the nature of the equilibrium involved: for example, in the system

$$CH_3 \cdot CO \cdot OH \rightleftharpoons CH_3 \cdot CO \cdot O^- + H^+$$

the hydrogen-ion concentration will be increased by added salt, while the equilibrium

$$NH_4^+ \rightleftharpoons NH_3 + H^+$$

will be little affected by salt additions, and in the system

$$[Fe(H_2O)_6]^{+++} \rightleftharpoons [Fe(H_2O)_5OH]^{++} + H^+$$

the hydrogen-ion concentration will be decreased by addition of salt. These results follow directly from the Debye-Hückel expression for activity coefficients, but were derived by Brønsted from the experimental evidence on the activity coefficients of ions of different charges. In order to test his conclusions it was necessary to measure the hydrogen-ion concentrations in these solutions, and for this purpose he used the rate of reaction of diazoacetic ester with water to give glycolic ester and nitrogen, a well-known example of hydrogen-ion catalysis. This at once raised questions of fundamental importance, for it was held in many quarters that the reaction velocity in such a system was proportional to the activity rather than to the concentration of hydrogen ions. Brønsted showed definitely that the concentration was the appropriate quantity: for example, when only a strong acid is present, the effect of added salt on the reaction velocity is much less than its effect on the hydrogen-ion activity. This justified the use of the diazoacetic ester reaction for measuring hydrogen-ion concentrations, and the salt effects observed with solutions of weak electrolytes agree with those predicted from activity data. This type of kinetic salt effect, depending on the displacement of an equilibrium, was termed by Brønsted a "secondary salt effect."

There existed at the time a mass of uncoordinated data on the effect of added salts on reaction velocities, including many reactions involving only strong electrolytes, where no secondary salt effect could be involved. In this latter class of reaction it is customary to speak of "primary salt effects." Brønsted next showed in 1922 that all the existing data for primary salt effects could be summarized by the following simple statement: reactions between ions of like charge exhibit a large positive salt effect, reactions between ions of unlike charge a large negative salt effect, and reactions between an ion and a neutral molecule a small salt effect which may be either positive or negative. This classification was in itself a great step forward, but Brønsted gave it a further interpretation in terms of his famous expression for the effect of environment on the rate of chemical reaction. For a reaction between two species A and B the expression for the reaction velocity v is

$$v = k[A][B]\frac{f_A f_B}{fX} \quad \dotfill \quad (1)$$

where k is independent of environment, f is an activity coefficient, and X represents the "critical complex" of A and B through which they must pass in order to react. It now seems obvious to us that the correct expression must involve the activity coefficient of some intermediate complex, as well as those of the reacting species, but Brønsted was the first to realize this, although the concept of a critical complex had previously been employed by Marcellin. We know very little about the nature of X, but we do know that its charge is the algebraic sum of the charges on A and B, and this is sufficient to predict approximately how its activity coefficient will vary with salt concentration. Nowadays this prediction would be made on the basis of the Debye-Hückel theory, but Brönsted again had to use the experimental data available for ionic activity coefficients, and was able to show that equation (1) corresponds to the rules for the salt effect given above, and agrees approximately with the magnitude of the observed effects. In particular it shows that in a reaction involving an ion and a neutral molecule (such as the decomposition of diazoacetic ester ion in presence of hydrogen ions) the activity coefficient factor will be near to unity, and hence the reaction velocity will be proportional to the concentrations of ester and hydrogen ions, and not to their activities. After the advent of the Debye-Hückel theory Brønsted made more measurements on salt effects in very dilute solutions, and found a complete confirmation of equation (1). It is interesting to note that Brønsted did not attempt to give any detailed molecular explanation of this equation, and the semithermodynamic derivation which he gave in

1922 was not made much clearer by a more detailed treatment in 1925. Brønsted's equation is now of course regarded as a special case of the transition-state expression for reaction velocity, but Brønsted himself showed little interest in later developments in this field.

The second major advance which served to clarify a large mass of kinetic work was Brønsted's extended definition of acids and bases, first published in 1923. Identically the same definition was put forward almost simultaneously by Lowry in this country. This definition is now generally accepted: it states that *an acid is a species which has a tendency to split off a proton, and a base is a species which has a tendency to add on a proton.* All acids and bases can therefore be arranged in conjugate or corresponding pairs according to the scheme

$$A \rightleftharpoons B + H^+$$

This definition of acids includes not only uncharged molecules such as $CH_3 \cdot CO_2H$, but also anions like HSO_4^-, $HPO_4^=$ and cations like NH_4^+, $[Fe(H_2O)_6]^{+++}$. The new definition of bases was even more fruitful, since there had previously been great confusion, for example, as to whether the ammonia molecule or the hypothetical ammonium hydroxide should be regarded as a true base. The Brønsted-Lowry definition includes unchanged bases like NH_3, NMe_3 and anion bases such as $CH_3 \cdot CO \cdot O^-$, OH^-, $CO_3^=$. It was not so easy to find an example of a cation base, but once again the cobaltammines and similar compounds came to the rescue: for example, the ion $[Co(NH_3)_3(H_2O)_2OH]^{++}$ is a base in virtue of the reaction

$$[Co(NH_3)_3(H_2O)_2OH]^{++} + H^+ \rightarrow [Co(NH_3)_3(H_2O)_3]^{+++}$$
$$\text{Base} \qquad\qquad\qquad\qquad\qquad \text{Acid}$$

It is immediately clear that the hydroxyl ion is not in any way unique, since it is only one member of a whole class of anion bases. On the other hand the hydrogen ion does appear to occupy a privileged position as long as we write it as H^+, i.e., a bare proton. However, following Fajans and others, Brønsted realized that the free proton could not exist in any significant concentration in the presence of other molecules, and that in aqueous solution it existed as the hydroxonium ion, H_3O^+, entirely analogous to the ammonium ion, NH_4^+. In fact, the "hydrogen ion" is a different entity in each solvent, in each case being only one of a class of cation bases.

Once the claim of hydrogen and hydroxyl ions to uniqueness has been abandoned, it becomes possible to write all the reactions of acids and bases (variously described as dissociations, neutralizations, hydrolyses, buffer systems, etc.) in the symmetrical form:

$$\text{Acid (1)} + \text{Base (2)} \rightleftharpoons \text{Base (1)} + \text{Acid (2)}$$

Some examples of this are given in the following table, and a similar set could be given for nonaqueous solvents.

A_1	+	B_2	$\rightleftharpoons$	A_2	+	B_1	Description.
$CH_3 \cdot CO_2H$		H_2O		H_3O^+		$CH_3 \cdot CO \cdot O^-$	Dissociation in water *or* buffer action in acetic acid + acetate.
$CH_3 \cdot CO_2H$		NH_3		NH_4^+		$CH_3 \cdot CO \cdot O^-$	Dissociation of acetic acid in liquid ammonia, *or* dissociation of ammonia in glacial acetic acid, *or* neutralization of $CH_3 \cdot CO_2H$ by NH_3, with or without solvent.
H_2O		$CH_3 \cdot CO \cdot O^-$		$CH_3 \cdot CO_2H$		OH^-	Hydrolysis of acetate solutions.
NH_4^+		H_2O		H_3O^+		NH_3	Hydrolysis of ammonium salts, *or* buffer action in $NH_3 + NH_4Cl$.
H_2O		HPO_4^-		$H_2PO_4^-$		OH^-	Hydrolysis of secondary phosphates.
H_2O		NH_3		NH_4^+		OH^-	Dissociation of ammonia in water.
$H_2PO_4^-$		H_2O		H_3O^+		HPO_4^-	Dissociation of primary phosphate *or* buffer action in mixtures of primary and secondary phosphate.

Since the hydrogen and hydroxyl ions are not unique among acids and bases, there is no reason why they should have the monopoly of catalytic cation in chemical reactions, and Brønsted's next important contribution was the experimental demonstration of *general acid-base catalysis* in a number of reactions. Brønsted and Pedersen's paper on the nitroamide decomposition, published in 1924, showed that the reaction was catalyzed by the following classes of base:

(1) Anion bases like acetate ion, oxalate ion, etc.

(2) Uncharged bases like aniline and pyridine.

(3) Cation bases like $[Co(NH_3)_5OH]^{++}$.

Brønsted and Pedersen made a detailed study of catalysis by anion bases, and later papers (1925–34) extended this to the other types of base and also to nonaqueous solvents. The mutarotation of glucose offered rather more complications, since it is catalyzed by both acids and bases. Thus, in an acetate buffer solution the full expression for the reaction velocity is

$$v = k_0 + k_1[H_3O^+] + k_2[OH^-] + k_3[HOAc] + k_4[OAc^-]$$

However, by carefully designed experiments it was possible to separate the effects of different species, and the 1927 paper by Brønsted and Guggenheim demonstrated the catalytic effect of anion bases, uncharged bases, cation bases, uncharged acids like acetic acid, and cation acids like the ammonium ion. Very similar conclusions were published by Lowry in the same year, although his investigations were less complete.

The idea of catalysis by species other than hydrogen and hydroxyl ions was not altogether a new one, and in particular the "dual theory," suggested by Acree, Snothlage, and H. S. Taylor, had assumed catalysis by undissociated acid molecules. However, most of their deductions were based upon incorrect values for the degree of dissociation of electrolytes, and did not allow for primary and secondary salt effects. In his monograph on "acid-base catalysis" (published in Danish in 1926, English translation in 1928) Brønsted devoted a good deal of space to a severe criticism of this earlier work, and was in fact able to show that in almost all cases the supposed catalytic effect of acid molecules was based on a misinterpretation of the data, or could reasonably be attributed to a salt effect. The only notable exception to this statement was Dawson's work on the acetone-iodine reaction, and here Brønsted's strictures were rather less than just. It is true that Dawson did not take into account recent views on electrolytes and that his experiments were planned in such a way as to involve complicated salt effects. Nevertheless, there is no doubt that his work definitely establishes catalysis by carboxylic acid molecules, and in fact still provides the most extensive set of data for this type of catalyst, although his numerical values need some revision in the light of modern developments.

If we consider a series of similar acids and bases, it is natural

1483

to expect that their catalytic power for a given reaction will depend on their acidic or basic strength. In his first paper on the nitroamide decomposition Brønsted gave a quantitative form for this dependence which has been found to be generally valid, and which is commonly known as the "Brønsted relation." For basic catalysis it can be written in the form:

$$k_b = GK_b{}^\alpha$$

where k_b is the catalytic coefficient of a base of dissociation constant K_b, and G and α are constants characteristic of the reaction, the temperature, and the solvent, α being less than unity. . . . As in many other cases Brønsted arrived at the form of this relation primarily by considering the experimental data. The only theoretical basis which he gave for it was a vague and unsatisfactory one, and he was not particularly interested in later attempts to interpret the relation in terms of molecular potential-energy curves.

I must now attempt some kind of summing up of Brønsted as a scientist and as a man. His skill as an experimentalist was not immediately apparent because of the simple nature of many of his methods, and it took some time to realize how much skill and discrimination lay behind an apparently simple piece of experimental work. His great strength lay in the choice of the most suitable substance or reaction, and in the planning of a series of experiments to attain the desired end with the greatest certainty and economy. For this reason his researches always had a much wider application than the immediate purpose in hand, and one of the greatest benefits of working with him was the opportunity of sharing his insight into general methods and planning of research. Many of his pupils have modeled their subsequent work on Brønsted's prototypes: for example, most later work on activity coefficients from solubility measurements and on general acid–base catalysis follows closely on some lead originally given by Brønsted.

It is more difficult to place Brønsted as a theoretical physical chemist in relation to the main developments of his time. We have already seen several examples of his absorption in thermodynamics and his love of an experimental approach, and the adjective "classical" seems an appropriate one to describe his contributions to physical chemistry. In the field of solutions his work has had a clarifying effect to which it is difficult to find a parallel. Although his mind was a most agile one, several of the major trends in modern physical chemistry failed to rouse his interest: for example, the experimental and theoretical study of molecular structure, and the theoretical treatment of reaction velocities. Looking back, it seems strange that one of the greatest investigators of reaction kinetics in solution should never have deliberately measured an activation energy. On the other hand, there is no doubt that this limitation of interest enabled him to attack his chosen field with greater intensity and singleness of vision.

Brønsted was an individualist in his work, and owed little to the influence of other scientists, although the tradition of Julius Thomsen fostered his early interest in thermodynamics, and his training under S. M. Jörgensen introduced him to the cobaltammines and gave him high standards of preparative and quantitative work. There is only one instance where he collaborated with another scientist outside his own field, and that was in his famous work with Hevesy on the separation of the isotopes of mercury and chlorine by ideal distillation at low pressures. In his earlier days he had few junior collaborators, but in the period 1922–37 many chemists from other countries, particularly England and the United States, went to work with him. I myself spent four years in his laboratory, and I remember very clearly the impression of integrity and intensity of scientific endeavor which I received. One guest worker described his laboratory as a place of "high chemical potential," and the phrase does give something of the tense and personal feeling which Brønsted inspired. He showed great kindness and consideration to his collaborators from overseas, and the subsequent work done by many of them shows the lasting effect of his influence. On first acquaintance he seemed rather reserved, but one soon realized that this arose from an unwillingness to talk carelessly or lightly on scientific matters. When he had once embarked on a discussion his acuteness and remorseless logic were remarkable, and there can be very few occasions on which he was worsted in a scientific argument. He did in fact very much enjoy a keen polemical discussion, and never hesitated to express his criticisms in an edged and sometimes personal manner. This involved him in a number of controversies, beginning in 1908 with his criticism of Nernst's concept of "ideal concentrated solutions," and ending with a lengthy argument with Danish physicists about the foundations of thermodynamics.

Brønsted's duties as a professor involved a considerable amount of elementary teaching, especially in his earlier days, and his lectures were elegant in delivery and content. Their concentrated exactness made them perhaps rather indigestible for the average student, and the same was true of his textbook of physical chemistry. The later editions of this book incorporated his own treatment of thermodynamic principles, and we can sympathize with the polytechnic student who had to use terms like "heat" and "work" in one sense in his physics and engineering, and in another sense in his chemistry. The Danish system involves a large amount of oral examination, and in his earlier days Brønsted gained some reputation for severity as an examiner: his standards were certainly high, and he was not much given to compromise, least of all in scientific matters. There are many anecdotes about these examinations, and I remember one candidate who had rashly professed some knowledge of the occurrence and properties of the silicates, and who was finally driven by Brønsted's remorseless logic into maintaining that a paving stone would probably dissolve completely if stirred up with a little water! However, as he became older Brønsted became more lenient toward his younger students, although he could still be a formidable opponent to candidates for the doctorate degree.

In private life Brønsted had great personal charm and a wealth of interests outside his science. The chief of those was his love of the countryside and its people, which remained with him all his life. His family holidays were usually spent in some remote part of the country, and he had a very extensive knowledge of Danish wild life, especially of birds. It is interesting to note that his last publication, just before his death, was a note describing some observations on insect behavior made during his summer holiday. He felt very keenly about the preservation of natural beauty and nature reserves, and took a prominent part in campaigns to this end. Music and painting were also among his accomplishments, and through

1486

his marriage he came into close contact with many of Denmark's leading artists and musicians. He had a wide knowledge of literature in several languages and a remarkable gift not only for accuracy but also for elegance in expression in both Danish and English.

Brønsted traveled widely in Europe, and made several visits to the United States. In spite of his strong Danish patriotism he had a great deal of sympathy and understanding for other countries, and especially for England. His early contacts were mostly with German scientists, but after the First World War his sympathies turned decisively toward this country. In 1920 he spent several months in England, mainly with Professor Donnan at University College, and he made at least seven more visits before 1939, including several to attend meetings of the Faraday Society. Among many other honors he was made an honorary member of the Academy of Arts and Sciences in 1929, an honorary fellow of the Chemical Society in 1935, and an honorary doctor of London University in 1947.

The Second World War served only to strengthen the ties which bound him to English things and English people, and he never had any doubts as to the rightness or the eventual outcome of the struggle. From the first day of the German occupation he spent several hours daily listening to the broadcast news from London, and he also read widely in English history and biography: when I visited him in 1945 he still had on his table a list of English Foreign Secretaries from 1769 onward. The occupation also turned his attention to public affairs in general, in particular the vexed question of Schleswig and the Danish-German frontier, about which he spoke and wrote in his usual forthright manner. Nevertheless, it was a surprise to many of his friends when in 1947 he accepted nomination as a candidate for the Danish parliament, and a still greater one when on October 28 he was elected. He took this responsibility seriously, and immediately began to study parliamentary procedure, but he was overtaken by his last fatal illness before he could take his seat, and died on December 17. It is interesting to speculate how he would have fared in Parliament and how his logical and uncompromising mind would have dealt with the half-truths of politics. He himself believed that many of the ills of mankind were due to the lack of logic and precise definition in public affairs, and it is an open question whether the application of this principle would have brought success or frustration.

The Brønsted Memorial Lecture, delivered before the Chemical Society in London, Feb. 3, 1949. Selections from J. Chem. Soc., *1950*, 408.

RONALD PERCY BELL

Niels Janniksen Bjerrum

1879-1958

NIELS JANNIKSEN BJERRUM was born on March 11th, 1879, the son of the well-known eye-specialist and professor of ophthalmology Jannik Petersen Bjerrum (born 1851, died 1920) and his wife Anna Katrine Lorentine Johansen (born 1856, died 1941). Both his father and his mother came of families of North Schleswig farmers. He can trace his descent through eight generations, with the names Niels, Jannik, and Peder alternating, back to Peder Nielsen Bierum born on October 12th, 1635. Niels was the eldest of eight children. Bjerrum's paternal aunt Dr. Kirstine Meyer, a distinguished physicist, lived in their home from 1880 to 1885 and was like a second mother to him. She undoubtedly stimulated his interest in the physical sciences.

During Bjerrum's childhood and youth, frequent and numerous visitors to his home included well-known professional men, especially doctors, scientists, and politicians. On Sunday evenings their house was open to all their intimate friends and there would often be a full score of guests for dinner. Thus did young Niels grow up in a happy, liberal, intelligent, and tolerant milieu throughout the period when his character was developing.

Niels spent all his summer holidays at the home of his maternal grandfather in Kolding in Jutland. Here he acquired at an early age his lifelong love of the countryside and more especially of the sea. His grandfather was a cabinetmaker, and Niels when a small boy learnt to use carpentry tools which he applied especially to making model ships of gradually increasing complexity.

Niels began to go to school at the age of five. Between the ages of twelve and eighteen he was at the Metropolitan School. He had several outstanding schoolfellows, including J. N. Brønsted who remained for many years his friendly rival. Niels found mathematics and natural history easy, but languages difficult. However, he passed the university entrance examination with overall high marks to the pleasant surprise of his languages teacher.

On leaving school in the summer of 1897 Bjerrum was still undecided whether he wanted to read chemistry or mathematics, but in the end he chose chemistry and in February, 1898 he began a university course lasting four years. His teachers included Professor Jørgensen, the contemporary and rival of Werner in the field of metal complexes.

In January, 1902 Bjerrum obtained his master's degree for which he was required to submit a thesis entitled "A critical-historical survey of the isomerism of fumaric and maleic acid." His examiner, Professor Jørgensen, nearly failed him because the candidate had the temerity to extend his criticism to the chemistry instead of confining it to the history!

The very same month by good fortune a post of assistant at the University Chemical Laboratory fell vacant. Bjerrum applied for this post and was appointed at a commencing salary of 1000 Kr. (about £50) per annum with some small extras. However, this gradually increased so that by the time he married in 1907 he was earning about 3000 Kr. per annum.

Bjerrum's enthusiasm for research received no encouragement from his seniors. In August, 1902 Professor Martin Knudsen put him on to the thrilling problem of investigating the accuracy of the determination of chloride in sea water. He published a couple of papers on this subject but was glad to drop it and work on something more interesting. Bjerrum had learnt from Jørgensen many of the experimental facts, if not much theory, concerning complexes and had been struck by certain parallels between green chromium chloride and cobaltammine salts. He accordingly chose for his research the field of chromic compounds which kept him actively occupied and interested for the next six or seven years.

In the summer of 1905 Bjerrum spent three months in the Institute of Physical Chemistry in Leipzig of which Ostwald was still nominally director but Luther was in active control. Here Bjerrum met and became friendly with Luther, Bodenstein, von Halban, Drucker, and C. Benedicks. It was during this visit that Bjerrum published his famous paper containing a theoretical and experimental study of the use of a bridge of concentrated potassium chloride to reduce the overall liquid–liquid junction potentials. It is unfortunate that the title of this paper contained the word "elimination" instead of "reduction" because subsequent history indicates that many people read the title but few read the text of this valuable paper.

When Bjerrum began his research on chromic compounds, salts of the bluish-violet $[Cr,aq_6]^{3+}$ and of the green $[CrCl_2,aq_4]^+$ were well known. Bjerrum studied the hydrolysis of green $[CrCl_2,aq_4]Cl$ to violet $[Cr,aq_6]Cl_3$ and came to the conclusion that the ion $[CrCl,aq_5]^{2+}$ was formed as a relatively unstable intermediate. He succeeded in isolating green salts containing this ion, in particular the chloride and sulphate. He proved that the sulphate $[CrCl,aq_5]SO_4$ was identical with a compound previously prepared by Recoura and erroneously supposed by Werner to have the structure of the double salt $[Cr,aq_6][CrCl_2,aq_4][SO_4]_2$ which had been obtained both by Werner and Huber and independently by Weinland and Krebs. All this may seem to be rather ordinary inorganic chemistry of interest only to specialists in the chemistry of chromium. In fact this work was a striking example of the application of physical chemistry to a problem of inorganic chemistry. Bjerrum gave three independent proofs of the constitution of Recoura's compound. The first was from conductance measurements. The second was based on rates of hydrolysis. The third was based on extinction coefficients. A paper, 122 pages long, entitled "Studies on chromic chloride" was published by the Royal Danish Academy in 1906 and awarded their silver medal which had been awarded to only three other chemists over the previous twenty years.

In the spring of 1907 Bjerrum married Ellen, the beautiful and lively daughter of Peter Dreyer a wine-importer in Randers. The same summer he again visited Germany and, what is more important, went to Zürich to see Werner. He told Werner about his research on Recoura's compound $[CrCl,aq_5]SO_4$. Contrary to the forebodings of Professor Emil Petersen, Bjerrum's chief, Werner, was interested and recognized that Bjerrum's conclusions were right while his own earlier interpretation was wrong.

In the continuation of this work Bjerrum's interest was directed especially to basic chromic compounds obtained by hydrolysis of salts of the bluish-violet ion $[Cr,aq_6]^{3+}$. He showed that there are two distinct types which he called "manifestly basic" and "latently basic." Typical of the former class are the soluble green

$[CrOH,aq_5]Cl_2$ and $[Cr(OH)_2,aq_4]Cl$ and the grey-green insoluble $[Cr(OH)_3,aq_3]$. Equilibrium between these is established rapidly and is determined by the acidity of the solution. Bjerrum showed that "even in rather involved cases the law of mass action in combination with the theory of electrolytic dissociation gives a correct evaluation of the factors governing hydrolysis when one confines oneself to the investigation of dilute solutions." Bjerrum determined the several equilibrium constants at two or three temperatures and derived values for the heats of reaction. The "latently basic" compounds, also green, are easily soluble in water, contain no Cl bound in the complex, react slowly with acid and contain more than one chromium atom per ion, e.g.,

$$\left[aq_4Cr \begin{array}{c} OH \\ \\ HO \end{array} Cr\ aq_4 \right] Cl_4$$

an early example of what is now called hydroxyl bridging. The physical chemistry of these compounds is complicated and, although this early work of Bjerrum was continued in collaboration with Faurholt over the years 1924 to 1927 there is still much to be learnt about them. They apparently play an important part in tanning. This work was published in 1908 as a thesis which earned Bjerrum the degree of Doctor of Philosophy in the University of Copenhagen (awarded only for completely independent unaided work and thus only distantly related to Anglo-Saxon Ph.D. degrees). The detailed results of this research are of rather specialized interest, but the physicochemical methods used were revolutionary (in the best sense of the word). The study of complex compounds had hitherto been mainly restricted to preparation and identification. Reagents were mixed and precipitates recrystallized. The chemical reactions of the purified compound were studied, but usually the only physicochemical measurement was that of conductance. Bjerrum introduced several new methods of study. He used the hydrogen electrode to determine equilibrium constants some years before Sørensen had introduced the term pH. He made such measurements at several temperatures and used thermodynamics to derive heats of reaction. Instead of merely recording visual observation of colour he made quantitative determinations of absorption spectra and drew quantitative conclusions

1494

concerning the concentrations of molecular or ionic species in solution. Not only were the techniques new, so was the point of view. Bjerrum was not satisfied with qualitative conclusions concerning the products of some process. He set out to determine the several species present in solution, their respective amounts, their rates of transformation into one another, and the equilibria between them. It is not surprising that Werner was favourably impressed. What is most surprising is that Bjerrum must have learnt physical chemistry almost entirely by independent reading of Ostwald's books. There was certainly no professor in Copenhagen who could have taught him these methods of approach, with the possible exception of Julius Thomsen—but Thomsen gave only first-year lectures and had retired before Bjerrum graduated.

This work set the pattern for all subsequent quantitative research on complexes. First and foremost must be mentioned Bjerrum's own comprehensive work, begun in 1909 and published in 1915, on the whole family of thiocyanatochromium compounds $Cr(CNS)_n,aq_{6-n}$ where n has all values between 1 and 6. Of especial interest is the nonelectrolyte ($n = 3$) coming between the cations ($n < 3$) and the anions ($n > 3$). Bjerrum succeeded in proving the existence of all six thiocyanatochromic complexes, isolating four of them and finding analytical methods for determining the amounts of all six. He determined the six equilibrium constants at 50° and the rate constants of interconversion at 17°. This work was rewarded with the rarely bestowed gold medal of the Royal Danish Academy: during the first half of the present century the gold medal was awarded to only two other scientists, a geologist and a physicist. Also worthy of mention is analogous work by Bjerrum with the collaboration of Kirschner on thiocyanatoaurous and thiocyanatoauric compounds published in 1918. It is interesting that as late as 1947 Bjerrum published work of a similar kind on equilibria involving chloroauric and chloroaurous compounds. Last, but not least, must be mentioned that in the wide field of quantitative work on the stability constants of all kinds of complex ions one of the world's leading authorities is Niels Bjerrum's son and pupil Jannik Bjerrum.

In 1907 both the chemistry chairs in the University of Copenhagen fell vacant. They were filled by Biilmann, the organic chemist, and by Julius Petersen, the inorganic chemist. Neither chair was likely to fall vacant again for many years. A third chair was created in 1908. It is not altogether clear to what extent its first holder had to be a physical chemist. Anyhow the two candidates for the chair were Bjerrum and Brønsted. Both were exceptionally outstanding physical chemists and either in the absence of the other would have had a walk-over. It was decided that the two candidates should compete by delivering five lectures, three on a subject chosen by the candidate and two on a set subject. Bjerrum chose "Colour and structure of electrolytes," *i.e.*, the subject of his own research work; Brønsted chose "Gaseous equilibria," a subject of classical thermodynamics. Bjerrum was at a disadvantage because his public defence of his thesis, which is the final stage of obtaining the doctor's degree, took place only a week before the beginning of the competition whereas Brønsted had completed the formalities for his doctor's degree some months earlier. The selection committee, contrary to custom, issued a public statement praising both candidates but voted unanimously for Brønsted. If the candidates had been judged on their research work it is an open question who would have won. But they were in fact judged on their ability as lecturers. Brønsted had a natural gift for public speaking. Bjerrum always found it an effort. This defeat was a hard blow for Bjerrum who was honestly convinced that he was the better physical chemist. It was also a depressing thought that no other chair was likely to be vacant for many years. However, he soon recovered his good spirits and the next half dozen years were in many ways the most active and productive years of his career.

In 1909 Bjerrum attended the Seventh International Congress of Applied Chemistry in London and presented a paper entitled "A new form for the electrolytic dissociation theory." In his work on chromic salts he had shown that, whereas salts containing the ions $[Cr,aq_6]^{3+}$, $[CrCl,aq_5]^{2+}$, and $[CrCl_2,aq_4]^+$ have distinct absorption spectra, the absorption of light per chromium atom in salts containing $[Cr,aq_6]^{3+}$ is constant over a five-fold range of concentration and nearly constant over a twenty-five-fold range of concentration, and is identical for chloride, nitrate, and sulphate. At first Bjerrum interpreted this to mean that ionization had no effect

1496

on colour, but he gradually became aware of the much more reasonable explanation which he expounded in the above-mentioned paper. In this paper Bjerrum wrote, "These colour-relations found in connection with electrolytic dissociation can best be explained by changing Arrhenius's hypothesis in the following manner: We suppose that the strong electrolytes always are completely separated into ions, and that this is the reason why they always have the same colour in all concentrations. If changes of colour take place in solutions of an electrolyte, the ions have more or less entered into combination with each other, the dissociation is not complete. If this hypothesis is correct, then the decrease in molecular conductivity and in molecular depression of the freezing-point that accompanies the increase in concentration must be due to the action of the electric charges of the ions on each other." "It accords well with this new form for the dissociation theory that the 'degree of dissociation' which has been calculated from the molecular conductivity is, in the case of strong electrolytes, approximately determined by the valency of the ions (Ostwald-Walden's rule), by the dielectric constant of the solvent (Walden), and by the concentration of the salt. The fact that the so-called 'degree of dissociation' depends upon the electric constants of the substances without admitting of any specific influence by chemical affinity becomes quite natural when this quantity in reality is the decrease in electrolytic friction due to the electric forces among the ions. And the fact that the law of mass action does not apply to the influence of the concentration on the degree of dissociation of strong electrolytes will no longer be an inexplicable anomaly." Arrhenius was present at the meeting. He regarded Bjerrum's modification of his theory of ionic dissociation as a personal affront which he refused even to discuss with Bjerrum. Walden and Donnan, who were also present, were among the first to take the new theory seriously. It is interesting that G. N. Lewis at the same period observed that the additivity of properties of electrolyte solutions pointed to complete dissociation but was unwilling to accept this interpretation. He wrote:[1] "If we had no other criterion for the degree of dissociation, these facts would undoubtedly lead us to regard salts, up to a concentration of normal or half normal as completely dissociated . . .

I believe that we shall make no great error in assuming that the degree of dissociation calculated from the conductivities is in most cases substantially correct."

Bjerrum wrote nothing further on this subject until 1916 when he presented a paper at a Congress in Christiania in which he marshalled the evidence in favour of complete dissociation. He recalled the evidence from optical properties and the fact that the thermodynamic properties of electrolyte solutions are determined mainly by the concentration and electric type. In 1912 Milner had developed the first sound, though only approximate, theory of the effect on the thermodynamic properties of the Coulomb interaction between the ions. Bjerrum showed that freezing points could be explained at least semiquantitatively by this Milner effect without any need for assuming incomplete dissociation, but it was impossible to obtain agreement by assuming incomplete dissociation and ignoring the Milner effect. Bjerrum also used experimental data on the catalysis of esterification by hydrochloric acid. The experimental facts were that the rate of esterification is within the experimental accuracy directly proportional to the stoicheiometric concentration of hydrochloric acid. It was generally accepted that the catalysis is due to hydrogen ion and there was no reason to suppose that the rate was not directly proportional to the concentration of hydrogen ion. It follows that the hydrochloric acid is completely ionised.

As already mentioned, Arrhenius was violently opposed to this modification of his ionic theory. Whether owing to the opposition of Arrhenius or owing to a general epidemic of shortsightedness among the physical chemists of that generation, Bjerrum's theory was not generally accepted until most people had forgotten its origin.

The years intervening between the two papers on complete dissociation were both active and fruitful. In the summer of 1910 Bjerrum spent a month in Perrin's laboratory. He made quantitative measurements on the Brownian movement of rubber-latex particles in a glycerol–water mixture having a viscosity a hundredfold that of water. The results led to the value of Avogadro's constant previously obtained by Perrin and so showed that the law of equipartition of energy of the particles is unaffected by the viscosity of the medium. This visit to France was a great joy to Bjerrum's wife who had been to school in France and always remained a Francophile.

In the spring of 1910 Nernst visited Copenhagen and invited Bjerrum to spend a year in his laboratory in Berlin. Thanks to a grant from the Carlsberg Foundation he was able not only to accept but also to take his wife and baby son with him. This year 1911 was one of the highlights of Bjerrum's life. He had no teaching duties and was free to devote himself entirely to research and study. He worked on the determination of the heat capacity of various gases at high temperatures by the explosion method. He improved the apparatus and introduced corrections for errors hitherto unnoticed. What is more important he became interested in explaining the temperature-dependence of gaseous heat capacities. He did this successfully by applying the quantum theory of a harmonic oscillator to the internal vibrations of molecules. The expressions which he first formulated for the total energy of linear and nonlinear molecules are still used today. This is the earliest known example of correlation between a measured macroscopic quantity, the heat capacity, and a completely molecular quantity, the characteristic frequency. Thus did Bjerrum become the pioneer of the new kind of science on the borderland between physics and chemistry. In 1933 it was given the name "Chemical Physics."[2]

Through gaseous heat capacities Bjerrum became interested in the internal degrees of freedom of molecules and so in their infrared spectra. He made a fundamental contribution to general theory in the particular case of HCl. It had been shown that HCl had an absorption band at 2800 cm.$^{-1}$ due to vibrational motion and also a broad band in the far-infrared region at 67 cm.$^{-1}$ ascribed to rotational motion. Bjerrum predicted that through combination of vibrational and rotational motions the absorption band in the near-infrared region should have two peaks at approximately (2800 −67) and (2800 + 67) cm.$^{-1}$ respectively. Almost a year later this prediction was confirmed experimentally by Burmeister. This phenomenon is still called a Bjerrum double band. More refined measurements made shortly afterwards by von Bahr showed that each of the two bands, now called P-band and R-band respectively, can be resolved into a series of equally spaced lines.

In 1912 Bjerrum was promoted to become docent (tutor) while

retaining at the same time the post of assistant (demonstrator) to Professor Biilmann.

In the summer of 1914 Bjerrum succeeded Odin T. Christensen, lately deceased, as professor of chemistry in the Royal Veterinary and Agricultural College where he remained until his retirement in 1949 and where he continued to work until a few days before his death. Many people have expressed the opinion that it was wasteful for such a brilliant scientist to devote so much of his life to teaching veterinary and agricultural students, but Bjerrum himself considered good teaching as important as good research. No one could be more painstaking than Bjerrum in teaching, especially elementary teaching. Some of his scripts are models of perfection. Particularly worthy of mention is his book "Inorganic Chemistry" which includes a comprehensive but elementary exposition of all the fundamentals of physical chemistry. The book went through six editions, the first in 1916 and the last in 1956. Nearly ten thousand copies have been sold in all. The third edition, in which Brønsted's definitions of acids and bases were adopted for the first time in a text-book, was translated into German in 1933, into Russian in 1935, and into English by R. P. Bell in 1936. Equally impressive for clarity and comprehensiveness, but on a higher plane, is a paper published in 1917, entitled "On acid and basic reaction." This paper includes a rigorous, yet simple, analysis of the factors determining the accuracy of an acid–base titration, i.e., concentration, pK_a of the two reactants, pK_a of the indicator. For anyone with a taste for clear thought and accurate exposition this paper is a delight.

It must not be concluded from the above remarks that when Bjerrum became a professor his teaching responsibilities, which he took so seriously, interfered with research in his department. Quite the contrary, but naturally and gradually less experimental work was done with his own hands and more with those of his juniors.

Bjerrum attracted research workers from several lands and more than a dozen became professors: England (Guggenheim), Finland (Sihvonen), Germany (Ebert, Manegold, Heitler), Hungary (Zechmeister), Norway (Schreiner), Poland (Józefowicz), Sweden (Brosset, Bäckström, Larsson, Ljunggren, Widmark). This distribution is undoubtedly due largely to the fact that most of

Bjerrum's published papers are written either in Danish or in German. By contrast Brønsted published mostly in English and almost all the visitors to his laboratory were American or English.

Nearly all Bjerrum's work after he became professor is related to electrolytes. I have already mentioned the work with Faurholt on the hydrolysis of chromic compounds. With the collaboration of Lannung he made an extensive experimental and theoretical study of the distribution between two solvents of, on the one hand, alkali halides and, on the other, the inert gases. The ratio of the distribution coefficients of these two classes of substance is related theoretically to the permittivity of the medium and the size of the ions. The extent of agreement between theory and experiment is unimpressive, probably because the macroscopic permittivity accounts inadequately for the interaction between ion and solvent. What is of special interest from a general thermodynamic point of view is that the well-known expression of Born was shown by Bjerrum to relate to the free energy and not to the total energy as previously supposed. This is not the only occasion when Bjerrum corrected a mistake, in what is now called statistical thermodynamics, by a world-famous physicist. In the original papers of Debye and Hückel on interionic attraction they gave the right formula for the free energy but their formula for the total energy was wrong and was corrected by Bjerrum.[3] These two mistakes are both examples of an incomplete understanding of the fundamental role of free energy as the most secure connecting link between statistical mechanics and thermodynamics. The clarification of this by Bjerrum in these two particular cases was finally and completely generalized by Onsager.[4]

Another much earlier contribution to the thermodynamics of solutions was the derivation from the Gibbs-Duhem relation of the formula relating the activity coefficient γ (first mentioned in print by Noyes and Bray in 1911 but attributed by them to G. N. Lewis) to the osmotic coefficient ϕ (first introduced by Bjerrum in 1916). The use of this formula leads to values of γ from freezing-point measurements which give directly values of ϕ.

In 1919 Bjerrum and his assistant Gjaldbaek published a paper on the acidic and basic properties of soil, which raised the study of soils from pure empiricism to a science. At that time it was fashionable to measure the pH of anything one could lay one's hand on, but there had been little, if any, attempt to interpret the experimental pH values. Bjerrum and Gjaldbaek pointed out that to understand the acidic and basic properties of a soil it was not sufficient to measure its pH; equally important was the manner in which the pH is changed on the addition of strong acid or alkali, In other words, complete titration curves were required. Moreover, the details of such titration curves would depend on the conditions of the titration, such as the rate of titration, the temperature, the presence or absence of carbon dioxide, the acid or base used (since insoluble precipitates might be formed). When all such experimental information had been obtained, it should be possible to correlate it with the acid-base equilibria of the substances in solution and with the solubility equilibria of the solid phases present. Bjerrum and Gjaldbaek accordingly formulated a programme involving a systematic study of the part played in soil equilibria by the important slightly soluble solids. The programme was a tremendous one and will probably never be completed, but its conception and commencement was the first milestone in a new science. In connexion with this programme Bjerrum himself became especially interested in the several forms of calcium orthophosphate, and his last work was a monograph on this subject published in his eightieth year.

In 1923 Bjerrum made a discovery of outstanding importance for the physical chemistry of proteins. It was well known that an α-amino-acid exists in strongly acid solution as the cation $^+H_3N \cdot CHR \cdot CO_2H$ and in strongly alkaline solution as the anion $H_2N \cdot CHR \cdot CO_2{}^-$. It had always been assumed that the intermediate form preponderant near the isoelectric point was the neutral molecule $H_2N \cdot CHR \cdot CO_2H$. Bjerrum, by elementary reasoning based on the numerical values of the two acidity constants, showed that the intermediate form is in fact the "ampho-ion" $^+H_3N \cdot CHR \cdot CO_2{}^-$. This deduction, once made, was so obviously right that one could not but wonder that it had not been self-evident. Yet no less an authority than Michaelis had written in 1922 concerning the amino-acid ampho-ion "Seine Menge ist zweifellos auch stets verschwindvend klein."

In 1926 Bjerrum contributed an important modification to the

1502

theory of ionic interaction given by Debye and Hückel in 1923. In its original form the theory contains the assumption that configurations in which the mutual potential energy of a pair of ions exceeds kT are negligibly rare. This assumption is valid for $1:1$ electrolytes but not for $2:2$ electrolytes in water, while in solvents with much smaller dielectric constant it is not even valid for $1:1$ electrolytes. Bjerrum showed how this restriction can be avoided by treating separately and differently the interaction between (a) pairs of ions distant apart more than $z^2e^2/2\epsilon kT$ and (b) pairs of ions distant apart less than $z^2e^2/2\epsilon kT$ (in which class only pairs of oppositely charged ions need be considered). The interaction (a) can be completely taken care of by the formulae of Debye and Hückel modified only to exclude the ion pairs accounted for under (b). The interaction (b) was taken care of in a simple approximate manner as a short-range interaction analogous to a chemical equilibrium. This method of extending the theory to higher valencies and lower dielectric constants is simpler than any of the alternative methods and at least as effective. Bjerrum conventionally called the ions of (a) "free ions" and those of (b) "associated ion pairs." This terminology has unfortunately been misunderstood and misinterpreted.

In 1929 Bjerrum and his assistant Augusta Unmack published a two-hundred-page paper describing several years' work on the measurement and interpretation of electromotive force of cells containing a hydrogen electrode in various dilute aqueous solutions, a standard calomel electrode, and a bridge of concentrated potassium chloride: in other words, the type of cell associated with the name of Sørensen and the expression pH. The solutions contained hydrochloric acid or sodium hydroxide or a phosphate buffer or a citrate buffer or a glycine buffer. A wide range of concentrations was covered with various concentrations of added sodium or potassium chloride. Measurements were made at four temperatures. From these measurements, by judicious estimation of the effect of the liquid–liquid junctions and careful extrapolation to infinite dilution, values were obtained for the thermodynamic ionization constant of water and for the thermodynamic equilibrium constants of eight other acid–base equilibria. Each of these constants was determined over the range of temperature from 0° to 37° C., and

1503

the heat changes of the several acid–base equilibria were deduced. These values are of necessity not quite as accurate as those obtainable by cells without liquid–liquid junctions, but for several of the acid–base equilibria and at several of the temperatures the values obtained by Bjerrum and Unmack are after thirty years still the best available.

I have mentioned briefly less than a score of the odd hundred publications of Bjerrum. I hope this suffices to establish my contention that Bjerrum was without any comparison the most versatile physical chemist of his generation. In 1949 a collection of his most important papers, translated into English, was published to celebrate his seventieth birthday.

In 1931 Bjerrum was offered the chair of inorganic chemistry at the University of Copenhagen, but being well settled and happy at the Agricultural College he preferred to stay there. Over the period 1939 to 1946 Bjerrum was director of the Royal Veterinary and Agricultural College. This was a period of unprecedented strain owing to the five-years' occupation by the Germans. Bjerrum retired from his chair in 1949 and had the satisfaction of being succeeded by his able assistant Aksel Tovborg Jensen. After retirement Bjerrum continued his research work and indeed was able to resume work which he had been compelled to set aside when he had been too busy with administrative duties. In 1951 he published a fifty-page article entitled "Structure and properties of ice." The positions of the oxygen atoms in ice are unambiguously determined by X-ray diffraction but the positions of the hydrogen atoms were still a matter of controversy. This late paper by Bjerrum shows that he still retained his full power for original thought. His last paper, published in 1958, was a monograph on the solid calcium orthophosphates, a continuation of work which he had to put aside twenty years earlier.

The death of his charming and versatile wife in 1934 was a terrible shock for Professor Bjerrum from which he seemed never to have completely recovered. Fortunately there remained four children of whom he was justly proud. The eldest is his brilliant son Jannik born in 1909 (the same year as the theory of complete dissociation of electrolytes). Niels Bjerrum's three attractive daughters are all happily married. Niels Bjerrum's greatest joy in his last years was being a fifteen-fold grandfather. Jannik's eldest boy and another grandson are appropriately named Niels.

Bjerrum was elected to membership of the Royal Danish Academy in 1916 and was its treasurer from 1927 to 1931. He became honorary member or corresponding member of over twenty learned societies including the Chemical Society (1938) and honorary doctor of Göttingen and Åbo.

Niels Bjerrum had three great loves: the first, his wife and family; the second, physical chemistry; the last, but perhaps not the least, sailing. Strictly speaking, the last had precedence for it began when he was only ten years old, spending his summer holidays at his maternal grandfather's home in Kolding. Throughout his life Bjerrum spent his summer holidays sailing. In 1927 he became a member of the Royal Danish Yacht Club. During the terrible years of the German occupation, when the open sea was barred, it was a great solace still to be able to sail in the Ise Fiord. Not until he was over seventy did Bjerrum consent, with some reluctance, to have a boat with a motor.

In the morning of Thursday, September 25th, 1958, Bjerrum was working, as was still his custom, in the library of the chemistry department where he had spent over forty years of his life. That afternoon he had a stroke and he died on Tuesday, September 30th. Thus ended abruptly and peacefully in its eightieth year the life of a great man. No one who knew Bjerrum can lament the suddenness of his death. His life was happy and active to the end.

Of Bjerrum's personal characteristics the following were outstanding. He was profoundly interested in everything around him, and his scientific curiosity was insatiable. He was intolerant of tyranny, arbitrariness, hypocrisy, pomp, conceit, and loose thinking, but tolerant of almost everything else. If he seemed to some people impatient, the explanation is that he expected others to be as reasonable as himself and in this he was unduly optimistic. He had all the qualities of a leader and he knew it. Above all he was kind. He will be sadly missed by his many friends.

I am grateful to Professor Tovborg Jensen and to Fröken Unmack for furnishing certain details concerning Bjerrum's life and work. Above all I am grateful to Professor Jannik Bjerrum for letting me have a copy of his father's autobiographical notes, which were invaluable in the preparation of this Lecture.

NOTES AND REFERENCES

1 Lewis, Z. *phys. Chem.*, 70, 215, 218 (1910).
2 See J. *Chem. Phys.*, 1, 1933, editorial.
3 Since the obituary lecture was delivered, Dr. Redlich has reminded the author that this mistake was corrected independently by Gross and Halpern (May 1925), by Adams (October 1925), and by Bjerrum (November 1925).
4 Onsager, *Chem. Rev.*, 13, 73 (1933).

From The Niels Bjerrum Memorial Lecture delivered before the Chemical Society on October 15, 1959, printed in the Proceedings of the Chemical Society, March, 1960, page 104, and shortened by the author.

E. A. GUGGENHEIM

·· *108* ··

Irving Langmuir

1881-1957

SCIENTIFIC WORK

IRVING LANGMUIR'S scientific work covered a period of fifty years, starting in 1904 with his doctorate dissertation at Göttingen "Ueber partielle Wiedervereiningung dissociierter Gase im Verlauf einer Abkühlung" and terminating in 1955 with an unpublished report on "Widespread Control of Weather by Silver Iodide Seeding." Between these two extremes his work exhibits a great diversity of interest and achievement, and can be grouped into seven categories. This grouping follows rather closely that used by Langmuir himself in the Introduction to "Phenomena, Atoms and Molecules," a reprint[1] of some twenty of his papers selected by him in 1950. The dates associated with each category indicate when most of the relevant work was published, although it will be clear from the span of some of these dates that Langmuir's productive interest in certain areas continued throughout a large part of his active scientific life. The categories are as follows and are listed, as nearly as possible, in rough chronological order.

Publication dates

1906 to 1921	Chemical Reactions at High Temperatures and Low Pressures
1911 to 1936	Thermal Effects in Gases
1919 to 1921	Atomic Structure
1913 to 1937	Thermionic Emission and Surfaces in Vacuum
1916 to 1943	"Chemical Forces" in Solids, Liquids, and Surface Films
1923 to 1932	Electrical Discharges in Gases
1938 to 1955	Science Out-of-Doors

1. Chemical Reactions at High Temperatures and Low Pressures. In 1904 Langmuir commenced his doctoral work at Göttingen and Prof. W. Nernst suggested as a thesis subject the study of the formation of nitric oxide from air in the vicinity of a glowing Nernst filament. It was thought that the filament would act catalytically on the reaction between oxygen and nitrogen and that the final equilibrium would correspond to the temperature of the filament. This method of studying equilibria looked extremely attractive because of the simplicity of the apparatus involved as compared with the complexity of the equipment more generally used in such studies. This simple hypothesis proved not to be applicable to the interaction of nitrogen and oxygen in the vicinity of a glowing Nernst filament and the thesis effort was shifted to studying other gaseous equilibria, such as the dissociation of carbon dioxide brought about by a glowing platinum filament, where the hypothesis was found to be valid. This very early work is especially interesting as a foreshadowing of Langmuir's predilection for experiments requiring only simple apparatus but where understanding of the experimental results might involve new, bold concepts and extended theoretical analysis. In this case the work led to an understanding of the unexpectedly much greater importance of thermal conduction, as compared with convection, in determining the heat loss from a filament through the first few tenths of a millimeter of gas surrounding it.

This thesis work was also important in orienting Langmuir's scientific interests in July, 1909, when, at Dr. W. R. Whitney's invitation, he came to the relatively new Research Laboratory of the General Electric Company. Dr. Whitney suggested that Langmuir should spend a few days looking around the laboratory to see what was going on; the first entry in his notebook reads:

> July 19–July 21, Spent these two days looking thru lab and seeing what work was being done.

Apparently these two days (or was it three?) were sufficient to show Langmuir that the laboratory was intensely interested in problems connected with making good incandescent lamps out of the the new ductile tungsten wire just introduced by W. D. Coolidge. The first experiments of his choice were therefore concerned with preparing pure hydrogen and studying the effects of heating tungsten wire in it. At that time all incandescent lamps were vacuum lamps and the general feeling was that if the vacuum could be made better the life of the lamp would be improved. Langmuir, on the other hand, had been impressed with how much better lamp-factory vacuum was than university vacuum and, not knowing how to improve this, resolved to see what effects the opposite approach of adding various gases would have on the life of tungsten lamps. He was also impressed with the ready availability of tungsten wires capable of being heated electrically to very high temperatures, and from this environment of good vacuum and high-temperature filaments grew his important scientific work on chemical reactions at high temperatures and low pressures. These studies included the discovery and detailed investigation of the formation of atomic hydrogen by contact of molecular hydrogen with a hot tungsten filament, a careful analysis of the effects of water vapor in incandescent lamps, and a systematic investigation of the mechanisms of "clean-up" of oxygen, nitrogen, and other gases at low pressure by hot tungsten and molybdenum filaments.

2. *Thermal Effects in Gases.* This work was a logical outcome of the studies of chemical reactions in lamps described in the preceding section. Langmuir had established that, apart from the special chain reaction with water vapor, the life of a tungsten vacuum lamp was insensitive to the residual gases usually present and was determined entirely by the evaporation of tungsten. This encouraged him to experiment with lamps containing much higher pressures of inert gases and to study heat losses from filaments under these conditions. He found that the evaporation of tungsten in nitrogen at approximately atmospheric density is essentially a diffusion process and obeys laws similar to those of conduction or convection of heat from a wire; that is, for wires of small diameters, the actual amount of tungsten evaporated is almost independent of the size of the wire, an unfavorable result for the very small filaments used in most lamps. On the other hand, experiment showed that, for several reasons, life and efficiency were better for large filaments in nitrogen. This dilemma was resolved by coiling the small wire tightly into a helix of substantially larger diameter, a form of construction which led to widespread adoption of the gas-filled lamp.

The dissociation of hydrogen by a hot tungsten filament had been postulated by Langmuir to explain the sudden increase in heat loss

1511

from a filament in hydrogen at high temperatures. Estimates of the heat of dissociation were made and some properties of atomic hydrogen were observed, such as its adsorption on a cold glass wall. Several years later Langmuir's attention was attracted by R. W. Wood's preparation of concentrated atomic hydrogen in an electric discharge tube and Wood's observations on the heating effects produced by the recombination of the atomic hydrogen on a variety of surfaces. This led Langmuir to the invention of the atomic hydrogen welding torch, in which large amounts of atomic hydrogen are produced by an arc between tungsten electrodes in hydrogen and the atoms are allowed to recombine on the metal to be heated.

3. *Atomic Structure.* Some of Langmuir's most productive thinking was guided by consideration of the differences between what he called "physical forces" and "chemical forces." This thinking led to his concept of the adsorption process and also to his rather brief sortie into the field of atomic structure during 1919 to 1921. The Bohr theory was then well established by reason of its spectacular spectroscopic successes. Langmuir considered this to be a typical "physical force" theory based on forces acting according to simple laws between mathematical points separated by relatively large distances. The chemist, on the other hand, did not think of molecules as point centers of force but rather as complex entities having structures which made the outward acting "chemical force" at one part of the molecule quite different from that at another. Moreover, the "chemical forces" were usually of shorter range than the "physical forces." This thinking, together with G. N. Lewis' theory of the "cubical atom" and a keen felling for the complex chemical phenomena to be explained, led Langmuir to his "octet theory" of atomic structure in which Bohr's centrally orbiting electrons were replaced by electrons distributed in regions throughout the atom, each electron being stationary in its region or describing a restricted orbit within the region.

With these concepts, and a limited number of postulates, Langmuir was able to correlate a tremendous variety of chemical phenomena. Further detailed calculations, however, led to the need for more assumptions and it was not long until the advent of quantum-mechanical concepts of chemical bonds led him to transfer his efforts to other problems. Langmuir, while appreciating the great conceptual contributions made by quantum mechanics, was impressed by the tremendous mathematical difficulties of attempting to understand chemical properties in detail by this route. Because of this he apparently made a decision not to develop a working knowledge of these new tools for himself but to continue his work where more classical methods were still fruitful.

4. *Thermionic Emission and Surfaces in Vacuum.* As a natural outgrowth of his earlier work on tungsten lamps, Langmuir entered the field of thermionic emission in 1913 to answer the specific problem of why relatively large electron currents did not appear as shunt currents from the negative leg to the positive leg of a tungsten lamp with a hairpin filament. At that time the true origin of thermionic emission was still in doubt, and there were even suggestions that the thermionic electrons were by-products of a chemical reaction and, therefore, that the absence of the shunt current in lamps was due to the very high vacuum. Langmuir made experiments with lamps containing two separate hairpin filaments and soon arrived at the concept that the shunt currents were small because the charges on the electrons in the space between the legs of the filament shielded the negative leg from the accelerating field due to the positive leg. This hypothesis was at once submitted to theory and calculation resulting in the Child-Langmuir[2] space charge equation, according to which the electron current between electrodes of any shape in vacuum is proportional to the 3/2 power of the potential difference between the electrodes. This celebrated law was followed through in great detail for various electrode configurations, and corrections for the initial thermal velocities of the electrons were introduced. The 3/2 power law became the major issue in a hard-fought patent suit.

Thorium oxide is added to tungsten lamp filaments to improve their mechanical behavior at high temperatures, and it had been observed sporadically that abnormally high thermionic emission was obtained from some lamp filaments. Langmuir undertook a systematic study of this problem; he soon showed that the abnormally high emission was definitely associated with the presence of thoria in the filament, and worked out in great detail the temperature treatment needed to obtain thoriated emission and the magnitude of the emission under various conditions. His theoretical study of the phenomenon showed that the enhanced emission could be explained in terms of the formation by diffusion of a single, more or less complete layer of thorium atoms on the surface of the filament. These rather detailed and involved concepts were obtained by interpretation of experiments with the simplest of vacuum tubes and current measurements with a portable micro-ammeter.

It is interesting to observe here that the interpretation of such simple experiments, even in the hands of so great a master, can at times be incorrect in detail. Langmuir interpreted the transient behavior of the surface film in formation as being due to a combination of the diffusion of the thorium atoms through the tungsten lattice plus a reasonable assumption of "induced evaporation" when a new thorium atom arrived under one already in the surface layer. It was not until considerably later that more complicated experiments by P. Clausing showed that the thorium really diffused to the surface through the intercrystalline material and then spread over the surface from these lines of access in a two-dimensional diffusion.

Another extended series of thermionic studies, done in collaboration with K. H. Kingdon and J. B. Taylor, involved new phenomena observed when cesium is put into a vacuum tube containing a tungsten filament. At low filament temperatures, and particularly if the filament is first coated with a monatomic layer of oxygen, the cesium atoms are strongly adsorbed from the vapor onto the surface of the filament. Such a Cs–O–W surface is the most efficient thermionic emitter known, and high hopes were entertained at first for its application in radio tubes. However, the advent of conventional barium oxide cathodes heated from the alternating current supply replaced this possible application.

Another new phenomenon observed was that, at higher filament temperatures, cesium atoms (ionizing potential 3.9 volts) striking a tungsten filament are robbed of an electron by the filament (work function 4.5 volts) and come off as positive ions which may be collected at a negative electrode. Langmuir gave a theoretical interpretation of these phenomena in terms of his concepts of adsorbed films and the Saha equation. This equation gives the equilibrium concentrations of ions, electrons, and neutral atoms at a known temperature in a gas with known ionization potential, and for this application must be modified to include the electron emitting capability of the hot filament, since this shifts the temperature equilibrium. Langmuir had great hopes for the use of this controlled source of ionization for neutralizing electron space charge in power tubes, but experiment, and later theory, showed that only modest effects could be obtained. The principle of ionization at a hot surface found early application as a molecular beam detector and at present is being investigated as a source of ion propulsion for space vehicles.

All kinds of studies and processes requiring evacuated enclosures were aided tremendously by Langmuir's invention of the condensation pump. This pump was simple to construct, had very high speed and, with the aid of refrigerants, produced an extremely high vacuum. It rapidly came into widespread use.

5. *"Chemical Forces" in Solids, Liquids, and Surface Films.* This area of science is one to which about one-quarter of Langmuir's publications are devoted and for which he received the Nobel prize in 1932. His ideas on the short-range character of "chemical forces" led him to a new concept of adsorption in which every molecule striking a surface remained in intimate contact with the surface for a short or long time and then evaporated. This adsorption contact was so intimate that it might be thought of as a chemical bond, and thus the concept of a firmly held, single layer of adsorbed atoms replaced the existing idea of a relatively thick adsorbed sheath extending some distance out from the surface with concentration decreasing with distance.

Langmuir made an early application of his ideas on surface films to the study of films on water surfaces, an area of science to which his attention had been drawn by the beautifully simple experimental techniques developed over the years by Miss Pockels, Lord Rayleigh, Devaux, and Marcelin. Langmuir made a tremendous extension of this technique by the introduction of a surface

1515

balance method for measuring the spreading force of the films; he showed that these films were truly monomolecular. In collaboration with Katharine Blodgett and V. J. Schaefer, a whole series of techniques was developed for working with surface films and used to study gaseous, liquid, and solid films, including such complicated molecules as proteins.

Langmuir's ideas on adsorbed films were also applied to films on solids and led to the development of the Langmuir adsorption isotherm, which gives an expression for the fraction of the surface covered by the adsorbed layer in terms of ambient pressure and a temperature dependent variable characterizing rates of condensation and evaporation at the surface. A theory was developed for the catalytic effect of an adsorbing surface which considered the chemical reaction as actually occurring in the adsorbed film and elucidated many features of such reactions which had hitherto been obscure. This theory became the basic approach to surface kinetics.

6. *Electric Discharge in Gases*. In 1914 mercury arc rectifiers were in common use, and Langmuir gradually became interested in some of the scientific problems of electric discharges in gases. Langmuir was impressed with the opportunities for electron tubes capable of controlling high power and endeavored to apply the newly understood phenomena of vacuum electron amplifier tubes to the much larger currents of gas tubes. E. F. W. Alexanderson pointed out in conversation that in alternating current power circuits the important thing was to be able to control the initiation of the current in any part of the circuit and that if this were done the circuit reversal of voltage could be used to extinguish the current at a later time in the cycle. This led Langmuir, in 1914, to the idea of inserting a grid in a mercury arc device to control the starting of current to a main anode. The study of such devices was carried on in collaboration with A. W. Hull and others.

Langmuir's activity in the gas-discharge field developed rather slowly, but in 1923 he was analyzing the current-voltage characteristics of currents to probe electrodes placed in a mercury arc. He found that the current to a negatively charged plane collector was independent of voltage over a wide range and showed by

1516

gridding tests that the current was due to the arrival of positive ions rather than the emission of photoelectrons. The independence of voltage was explained in terms of a plane parallel "positive ion space-charge sheath" in front of the plane electrode, whose thickness increased with voltage in accordance with the 3/2 power space-charge law, but whose outer surface was entered by an invariant stream of positive ions.

This initial work with collecting electrodes, or probes, led to a most fruitful series of experiments in collaboration with H. M. Mottsmith, Jr., and Lewi Tonks. The current-voltage characteristics of probe electrodes of all sorts were studied experimentally and theoretically, the results being used to elucidate the mechanism and behavior of electric discharges in gases under a wide range of conditions. One of the most important concepts arising from this work was the interpretation of the volt-ampere characteristic of a probe collecting electrons in terms of a Maxwellian temperature distribution of the electrons. The temperatures found were very high, of the order 15,000°K., and showed that the electrons were continually receiving energy from the drift gradient in the discharge and were far from being in temperature equilibrium with either the positive ions or the neutral gas. The production of ionization in the discharge could be explained quantitatively in terms of the ionization effectiveness of the electrons in the high energy Maxwell tail.

Langmuir and Tonks also made a study of electrical oscillations in an ionized gas. Langmuir was so impressed with the implication of organization and structure in the ionized gas evidenced by the capability of oscillation that he adopted the word "plasma" to indicate the fundamental nature of a volume of ionized gas essentially free of space-charge. At the same time he was much impressed with the instabilities and the energy transfer capabilities of a plasma, properties which have come to the fore in recent studies of fusion plasmas.

7. *Science Out-of-Doors.* Langmuir had a keen and continuing interest in the scientific basis of outdoor phenomena. One of the earlier examples of this was his explanation of the streaks or wind-

1517

rows of seaweed and bubbles which form on the ocean parallel to the direction of a moderate wind. He had noticed this phenomenon especially during an Atlantic crossing in August, 1927, and studied windrows for several years at Lake George, New York, where he had a summer camp. By simple but carefully planned experiments, using such apparatus as oriented umbrellas and lamp-bulb floats, Langmuir was able to establish that the windrows were caused by wind-induced circulation of the surface water, the water on the surface flowing toward the windrows, downward under them, and up again at a point halfway between them.

An extended series of experiments with V. J. Schaefer was devoted to the production of particles of various desired sizes in atmospheric air, their behavior in filters, and the development of apparatus for generation of oil smokes for military use. The resulting smoke generator was of the order 100 times more effective than existing generators and was adopted by the United States forces in World War II.

Another series of studies with Schaefer concerned the nucleation of ice crystals in supercooled clouds by seeding with particles of solid carbon dioxide; Schaefer showed that the low temperature is the important thing. This led to a great deal of outdoor experimentation related to possible modification of the weather by such processes and was the last field of science in which Langmuir took an active part.

PERSONAL AND WORK CHARACTERISTICS

The diversity of Langmuir's scientific work shows his great breadth of interest and also indicates his characteristic approach, which was to seize on some unusual phenomenon or technique, exploit this until the returns showed signs of diminishing, and then pass on to something else. Examples of this were his realization that the ready availability of tungsten filaments and good vacuum conditions offered an excellent opportunity for the study of chemical reactions at high temperatures and low pressures; his attack on the random, anomalously high electron emission observed from tungsten filaments containing thoria; his appreciation of the possibilities of the surface tension trough for the study of surface film phenomena coupled with the insight which his ideas on localized "chemical forces" gave him into the fundamentals of the problem; and his realization of the power of the probe characteristic technique for studying the mechanism of electric discharge in gases.

This brilliant insight into fruitful directions for applying his effort was coupled with the characteristic of being a tremendous worker. Although not by any means a slave to science, science was never far from his thoughts, whether in the laboratory, at home, traveling or out-of-doors.

Perhaps the best demonstration of this work effort is given by Langmuir's notebooks. During his 37 active years in the laboratory, Langmuir filled 54 notebooks of 330 pages each with the details of his scientific work. These notebooks exhibit the vast foundation of data, theory, and numerical calculation on which the structure of Langmuir's published scientific work was erected. There was always a notebook with him and he wrote in it at any time, even in a sleeping-car berth. His records were especially detailed regarding the genesis of ideas and must have been the delight (or the embarrassment?) of all patent lawyers who encountered them.

Langmuir combined his unusual scientific ability with a strong practical bent and was always on the lookout for practical applications of any idea or new piece of knowledge with which he came in contact. For example, he was keenly aware of the great opportunities for electron tubes capable of controlling power circuits and his notebooks contain detailed schemes for using "trapped ions" and cesium thermions for neutralizing electron space charge. Both of these possibilities were later made obsolete by the development of controlled plasma tubes. Langmuir made 138 personal patent disclosures, of which 63 led to issued patents. Some of these were of great practical importance, such as the gas-filled lamp, high-vacuum electron tube principles, the condensation pump, the thoriated tungsten filament, atomic hydrogen welding, the grid-controlled arc, and the military smoke generator. Much of Langmuir's scientific work lay in areas where there was little scope for patent protection, but whenever the opportunity existed Langmuir was quick to recognize it.

1519

Langmuir had well-developed abilities as an applied mathematician. His notebooks are filled with theoretical work related to his experimental investigations and with the results of extended computations made in test of the theories. Most of these computations were on the desk-computer scale since much of his work was done before the advent of large computers.

Most of Langmuir's scientific work was accomplished with the assistance of relatively few people. He never directed a large research team. In much of his earlier experimental work he was assisted by Samuel P. Sweetser, whose name appears in many of the early publications. Sweetser prepared the experimental equipment and, with meticulous care, took volumes of characteristic curves for analysis by Langmuir. At one time when the electron emission studies were very active, Langmuir's notebook gave a list of some 82 experiments which he was interested in having Sweetser do. With such a backlog of work it would seem that the direct experimental staff might have been expanded, but apparently Langmuir preferred not to do this.

This may have been partly because Langmuir was usually closely connected with experimental work by some of the younger scientists in the laboratory, as noted elsewhere. These younger people were often working on problems suggested by Langmuir but had opportunity to contribute to the work according to their own talents instead of working under very close supervision.

In addition to these activities, the notebooks are filled with suggestions for work made to many people inside and outside the laboratory who were not at all directly connected with Langmuir. In this way, without formal organization, his scientific influence touched a great many people.

Langmuir's personal characteristics may be described by such words as sincerity, intensity, vigor, intellectual integrity, breadth of interest, depth of approach. His speech was rapid, emphatic, and filled with the intensity of his interest in the ideas which he was trying to convey. In spite of these hard-driving characteristics Langmuir was always approachable and willing to give his best attention to any sensible problem brought to him. If he passed you in the hall without recognition this was not a demonstration of aloofness, but

1520

rather of his complete absorption in the current scientific problem. If the problems of others demanded too much of his time he could always retire to his study at home until his own current idea was satisfactorily advanced. Monday morning was frequently dedicated to an exposition of the scientific developments of the weekend to those who he thought might be interested.

The photograph of Langmuir communicates the atmosphere of the laboratory and reveals a little of his breadth of scientific interest. The large bottle at the upper left corner contains a colloidal suspension of vanadium pentoxide used in some polarization studies, the shelves are filled with surface active chemicals, and the inner surface of the glass bulb is flecked with crystals from a nucleation-adsorption study.

Langmuir was an enthusiastic skier and mountain climber and for several years owned and piloted an airplane.

BIOGRAPHICAL

Irving Langmuir was born in Brooklyn, N. Y., on January 31, 1881, the son of Charles and Sadie Comings Langmuir. His mother was a descendant of the Lunt family, which came to this country on the "Mayflower." After obtaining elementary education in public schools in Brooklyn, he traveled with his parents to Paris, where he studied for three years. He then returned to the United States, studied for a year at Chestnut Hill Academy, Philadelphia, then in Brooklyn at Pratt Institute, and at the School of Mines, Columbia University. In 1903 he graduated from Columbia with a degree in metallurgical engineering. Again he visited Europe, this time to study at the University of Göttingen in Germany, where he was awarded M.A. and Ph.D. degrees in 1906.

Until July, 1909, he taught chemistry at Stevens Institute of Technology. He then joined the staff of the General Electric Company's Research Laboratory at Schenectady, N. Y., to begin his colorful career in scientific research.

Dr. Langmuir and his wife, the former Marian Mersereau of South Orange, N. J., whom he married in 1912, made their home at 1176 Stratford Road, Schenectady, N. Y., with a son, Kenneth, and a daughter, Barbara.

HONORS

Among scientific honors that were bestowed upon him, the Nichols Medal, awarded by the New York Section of the American Chemical Society, was twice given to Langmuir, once in 1915 for his work on chemical reactions at low pressures, and again in 1920 for his work on atomic structure.

The Hughes Medal of the Royal Society of London was awarded him in 1918 for his researches in molecular physics. In 1920, the American Academy of Arts and Sciences gave him the Rumford Medal for his thermionic researches and for his development of the gas-filled incandescent lamp. In 1925, the Royal Academy of Lincei at Rome, Italy, bestowed upon him the Cannizzaro Prize. In 1928 he was the recipient of the Perkin Medal, and in 1930 he was awarded the Chandler Medal and the Willard Gibbs Medal.

In 1932, Langmuir became the first American industrial chemist to be awarded the Nobel Prize, granted him for researches in surface chemistry. In the same year, Popular Science Monthly Magazine awarded him its annual medal and honorarium of $10,000 as "an American who has done notable scientific work."

The Franklin Medal of the Franklin Institute and the Holly Medal of the American Society of Mechanical Engineers were given him in 1934, and the City of Philadelphia presented him the John Scott Award in 1937. In 1940 he received a plaque as a "Modern Pioneer of Industry" from the National Association of Manufacturers, and in 1943 became an honorary member of the British Institute of Metals. In 1944, Langmuir became the fourth American to receive the coveted Faraday Medal of the British Institute of Electrical Engineers.

The Mascart Medal of the Société Française des Electriciens was presented to Langmuir in 1950. He was a foreign member of the Royal Society of London and a fellow of the American Physical Society. He had served as president of the American Chemical Society, and as president of the American Association for the Advancement of Science.

He was also an honorary member of several societies, including the Chemical Society of London. Langmuir held honorary degrees from the following colleges and universities: Northwestern, Union,

Edinburgh (Scotland), Columbia, Kenyon, Princeton, Lehigh, Harvard, Oxford, Johns Hopkins, Rutgers, Queens (Canada), and Stevens Institute of Technology.

NOTES AND REFERENCES

1 Philosophical Library, New York (1950). A complete reprinting of Langmuir's papers, together with critical comments and biographical material, will be published soon by Pergamon Press.
2 Independent derivations of this equation were made by Langmuir for electrons, and by C. D. Child for positive ions about two years earlier.

K. H. KINGDON

·· *109* ··

Hans Fischer

1881-1945

Hans FISCHER was born at Höchst am Main on July 27, 1881. His father had a responsible position at the dye factory there and later also in Biebrich. Hans obtained his doctor's degree in 1904 at Marburg under Theodor Zincke (1843–1928). After completing a course in medicine, he became assistant to Emil Fischer in Berlin. Then Friedrich von Müller (1858–1939), who had tried to find a relationship between the pigments of bile and those of blood, and had come to Munich in 1902, invited Fischer to join him there. Hans Fischer accepted the position at the medical clinic to work in this new field of research which required close cooperation between medicine and chemistry.

It is to the great credit of Friedrich Müller that he did not burden his chemical protégé with clinical duties but, instead, allowed him to devote himself entirely to scientific pursuits. The same credit should be given to the physiologist Otto Frank (1865–1944), in whose laboratory Fischer took an assistantship before the beginning of the First World War, a position which involved no teaching studies.

At this time, Oscar Piloty, Adolf Baeyer's son-in-law, was also studying the chemistry of the bile pigment bilirubin. This engendered a certain amount of tension and prevented the two young rivals from entering into closer personal relations with each other and the associates at the University of Munich.

The external conditions were favorable in every sense for Fischer's scientific activity, and almost his only worry lay in procuring adequate amounts of steer gallstones as the raw material from which to prepare bilirubin. From the start, Fischer worked entirely independently. The writer has never heard that Fischer ever sought any advice in chemical matters. He was not inclined to discuss his plans nor the results of his researches before they were published. During the many years of our friendship, he seldom spoke of the way his work was going. It was the custom in those years for chemists to keep their current researches in complete secrecy in order to protect the field from intrusion by others; many teachers solemnly swore their doctorate candidates to exercise discretion. In my opinion, the exchange of ideas that is the general practice in research laboratories now is much preferable to the former custom, even though there is a certain danger of loss of priority.

Shortly after the outbreak of World War I, Adolf Windaus was called from Innsbruck to succeed Otto Wallach at Göttingen. Fischer took over the vacant chair of medical chemistry at Innsbruck in 1915. Fritz Pregl, Adolf Windaus, and Hans Fischer have brought fame to this modest, small laboratory. No further advance was made there with respect to bilirubin after the valuable progress achieved in several directions at Munich. The war made experimental activity difficult. The marvelous scenery around Innsbruck enticed the young chemist to go on long walks and, in the winter, to slip away into the wonderland of snow. The sudden and tragic death of his father clouded the lighter moments of the years at Innsbruck. While making a not very dangerous climb of a peak in the Zillertal Alps, the elder Fischer fell into a covered crevasse, from which he could not be saved despite the efforts of the Alpine herdsman who was summoned at once. The unfortunate victim had been brought almost to the edge of the crevasse when his strength gave out! Before the eyes of his son, he fell back into the chasm and was irretrievably lost.

The following years, Hans Fischer spent as head of the Institut für Medizinische Chemie of the University of Vienna, as successor to Ernst Ludwig (1842–1915). Because of the war and its consequences, this was not a propitious time for pure research. However, in the spring of 1921, he took over the direction of the Institut für Anorganische Chemie at the Technische Hochschule (Technical University) at Munich, and there he quickly cleared away the external and internal hurdles. In an incredibly short time, he organized the laboratory from which issued his impressive work for twenty-four years. There was some doubt at that time of the wisdom of calling a medically minded chemist to a technical university. The doubts proved to be unjustified. The development of the Fischer school at Munich demonstrated the importance of the scientific personality at the head of a laboratory. The medical man from Vienna not only accomplished much pure research at the

Munich Technical University, but he trained there many excellent chemists for industry and science. Those who came from the Hans Fischer laboratory and had been so thoroughly trained to carry out experimental studies were well received everywhere, especially at the great dye manufacturing plants; many of these young men eventually rose to be leaders in chemical industry. Numerous others from Fischer's school distinguished themselves in academic careers.

In marshaling all of the resources of his laboratory into research activities, Fischer introduced much that was new and exemplary. The usually rather difficult preparation of the innumerable compounds that were needed in large amounts as intermediates in the tortuous paths of the syntheses provided the students with valuable exercises. Great stress was laid on purity and yields. A staff of microanalysts had to take care of tremendous numbers of samples. No other institute had ever turned out so many new compounds. Special laboratories were set up for measuring absorption spectra, for calorimetric determinations, and later for taking x-ray diagrams. The conscientious study of the current literature constantly inspired Hans Fischer to try out and introduce new methods.

The problem of the structure of hemin, i.e., of the colored components of the blood pigment, was attacked in Munich even before the nature of the bile pigments, especially bilirubin, had been cleared up. The previous studies by Marcel Nencki, Wilhelm Küster, Richard Willstätter, Oskar Piloty, and others had shown that the two groups of substances are chemically closely related. The structure first proposed by Küster for hemin was rejected vigorously by Hans Fischer at the start, but the subsequent synthesis of this pigment forced him to acknowledge his error. After the analytical method, namely, the study of the pyrrole derivatives obtained by the reductive cleaving of hemin, had produced no well-defined structure for the starting compound, Fischer began to put the pyrrole segments together in mosaiclike arrangements and then to weld together, by brilliant synthetic procedures, the semi-molecules of the pyrromethenes produced in this manner. The hemin problem was solved in 1929 by several methods of synthesis; the 1930 Nobel Prize for chemistry was awarded to Hans Fischer for this work.

However, the problem of the structure of the bile pigments and their synthesis was not solved until much later. The discovery that bilirubin is formed in the organism through oxidative fission of the porphin ring with loss of a methine group led to the answer which had been sought by Friedrich Müller in the 1890's.

From the start, Hans Fischer had set for himself the goal of combining the analytical elucidation of the natural pyrrole pigments with the systematic exploration of all the phases of the chemistry of the parent substance, namely, pyrrole. What he accomplished as a result of this endeavor would, in itself, have been enough to constitute the lifework of an extensive chemical career.

The ring skeleton of porphin, which is made up of four pyrrole nuclei bound to each other by methine groups, has been entrusted by nature to perform some of her most essential biological tasks. The blood pigment carries oxygen, in loose combinations, to all of the living cells and assures their metabolism. The respiratory enzymes, which likewise are porphin derivatives containing coordinatively bound iron, bring about the chemical action of the oxygen, an action that, in essence, consists in the reoxidation of the bivalent iron formed from the trivalent iron during the dehydrogenation processes.

No less important is the third porphin derivative, chlorophyll. Its role need not be discussed here, but the mere fact that in chlorophyll magnesium takes the place of the iron in the respiratory enzymes reveals the difference in the functions of the two groups of natural products.

Willstätter, who was then a Privatdozent at the University of Munich, began to study chlorophyll in 1902. He was the first to isolate and purify the two components of chlorophyll, namely, the bluish-green chlorophyll-a and the yellowish-green chlorophyll-b, to make them accessible by preparative methods. He also showed that chlorophyll contains two carboxyls esterified with methanol and phytol; by reductive cleavage of the pigment, he arrived at substituted pyrrols similar to those already known from hemin. The transformation into porphyrins was also accomplished. Although no insight into the inner structure of chlorophyll was obtainable at this stage, Willstätter left the field. Today, it is difficult to understand why almost twenty years went by before anyone took up where Willstätter left off in 1912. After he had established

1530

the structure of hemin, Hans Fischer was almost impelled to turn to the chlorophyll problem. This was done with the full consent of Willstätter, who had returned to Munich in 1916 as head of the Chemical Institute of the University of Munich.

The structural differences between chlorophyll and hemin appear slight. One of the four pyrrole rings is partially hydrogenated, and between it and its neighbors, there has attached itself, from a side chain, a fifth ring, namely, an isocyclic outer ring. This was sensed rather soon in superb intuitional manner by Hans Fischer, whereas the hurdle of the divergent degree of saturation in one of the pyrrole rings impeded the progress of the study for some time. Today, we have clearly before us the results of the gigantic task of unraveling the structure of chlorophyll. A few partial steps in the complete synthesis are still lacking. These will doubtless be supplied soon because three of his best students have banded together to finish the task as a memorial to their revered teacher.

On chlorophyll alone, Hans Fischer published 129 papers. They are not easy reading, even to those familiar with the topic. He was not particularly concerned with literary style, and furthermore the relationships are often not brought out clearly. Usually, important findings are not properly stressed. Even in his later years, Hans Fischer had to cope with embarrassment when lecturing. It often happened that an important success, which should have been highlighted, was relegated to the status of an incidental remark in a subordinate sentence. In his retiring and withdrawn manner, he lacked all sense for the importance of external expressions and impressions, and this shows up clearly in the lack of form and emphasis in his oral and written reports.

Those who met Hans Fischer for the first time probably concluded from his massive, compact build and from his energetic, duel-scarred face that he was a decidedly dynamic person. In a physical sense this was quite correct. He was skilled in all kinds of sports; he was an excellent mountain climber and skier. This physical dexterity and endurance was all the more remarkable because he was tubercular from his twentieth year on, necessitating the removal of a kidney in 1917. He had to fight the onslaught of this disease on his spine for the rest of his life. His exceptional vitality always prevailed. He required no recreation, and the idea of rest was foreign to him. His short vacations were usually spent on long and strenuous automobile trips. His mode of life was extremely moderate and unassuming in all respects. In his early years, it was his custom to carry his luggage with him in a knapsack, even when on lecture trips abroad; this included even the inevitable frock coat. The adjustment of his behavior to the accepted social customs was improved somewhat under the influence of his wife, who was about thirty years his junior, and with whom he enjoyed a very happy married life. Contrary to his usual reticence, he once told me how much his life had been enriched by his marriage despite the great difference in their ages.

The unwavering devotion to his research activities, a real *furor experimentalis,* dominated him to such an extent that hardly any other interest could gain a footing—except his love of nature and his passion for wheeled vehicles which he had maintained from the bicycle through all the various stages of the development of the motorcycle and automobile. He had no connections with art; music played no part in his life.

In scientific questions, Fischer was very sensitive. He watched over his wide field of work with a careful eye and was always ready to meet opponents with his sword bared. Differences that involved his findings could stir up his usually even temperament and turn his pen into a feared weapon. And yet this man of iron will and inflexible bodily strength was innately a tender, sensitive person, who attracted all who came to know him intimately. Although he despised all sentimentality, he felt a strong need to help where he could and to the extent of his abilities, no matter who appealed to him. The responsibility for and to his students lay closest to his heart; their unlimited devotion to him provided the most convincing testimony of the warm-hearted human understanding that shone from his light blue eyes.

This brief characterization of Hans Fischer has admittedly not exhausted the full depth of his real nature. The direct reasons that led to the sudden, voluntary termination of this meaningful life lay entirely beyond anything that might have been anticipated even by those who knew him best. The calamitous events of the closing years of World War II were obviously too much for his powers of resistance, whose weakening had already become apparent to some

1532

degree. The ringing of the Easter bells could no longer restrain him from taking the final step. Thus, there passed from this world a man, who, like few others, was capable of being the support and leader of German science. The date was March 31, 1945.

From: *Angew. Chem.*, *62*, 1 (1950). Translated by Ralph E. Oesper.

HEINRICH WIELAND

·· 110 ··

Claude Silbert Hudson

1881-1952

THE name of Claude S. Hudson is listed among the great leaders in the development of the chemistry of the carbohydrates. His main contribution was the establishment of the stereochemical nature of the labile hydroxylated carbonyl or cyclic hemiacetal function of the sugars and the concomitant development of the relations between structure and optical rotatory power in this group of stereoisomers. Thus, in the case of glucose (I), Emil Fischer[1] established the basic stereochemistry of carbons 2 to 5, the ring size was established by Haworth,[2] Hirst,[3] and associates, and the stereochemical assignment to carbon 1 was made by Hudson.

I

Although essentially all of his work was carried out in various laboratories of the United States government, he nevertheless established his mark as a great teacher. His published work attracted many young men to study in his laboratory and to come under his inspirational tutelage. His personality was very forceful and most unusual. It was cloaked in an outer sheath of informality and gracious manner, but his associates knew that under this was a strong critical spirit holding them and himself to exacting standards of scientific performance. His work was his life and his life was his work. After periods of intense concentration he was able to relax with kindred spirits and rejuvenate himself for the next round of intense scientific activity. He had a complete disregard for conventions and was, in all respects, a true creative artist. He was a great writer in his specialty and was an even greater speaker. He could apply a relatively simple organic reaction to the carbohydrates and hold an audience completely spellbound by describing to them the results he had obtained. He never spoke from notes but always offered a thoroughly logical and polished presentation. As an informal raconteur he was without peer, and this gift had its root in his background in the leisurely life of the old American deep South with its emphasis upon good manners and pleasant conversation.

Hudson came of early American southern stock that was a mixture of English, Scotch, Irish, and Huguenot French. His maternal great-grandfather and grandfather were physicians and the latter, John S. Wilson (1821–1892), was a surgeon in the 40th Georgia Regiment of the Confederate Army. His paternal great-grandfather, Robert Hudson (1786–1861), was a wealthy plantation owner in Williamsburg County, South Carolina. Hudson's paternal grandfather and father lived in South Carolina but in the disturbed period following the close of the war between the States, his father entered the mercantile business and at one time was the president of the Mobile Fertilizer Co., of Mobile, Alabama. It was in this beautiful southern city on the shores of Mobile Bay that Claude Hudson spent his childhood and early youth, a period upon which he looked back with fond nostalgia. Claude had been born in Atlanta, Georgia, but was moved as an infant to Greenville, Alabama, and shortly thereafter to Mobile. The French influence in this Gulf Coast region was prominent, and Hudson recalled the Mardi Gras festivities which were similar to those of New Orleans. His father's home in Mobile comprised four acres with six beautiful live oaks shading its long entrance way. There was a large vegetable garden in the rear and Claude was early introduced to the cultivation of plants. His mother was interested in church and charitable work and the son planned to enter the Presbyterian ministry. He received a good secondary school education in private schools in Mobile where he came under the influence of two excellent teachers, Mr. Julius T. Wright and the Rev. Archibald C. Harte.

At sixteen, Claude Hudson arrived at Princeton University to initiate his college work in preparation for the ministry. Thereafter he was to spend all of his time in the North and was to return to his beloved Alabama only on occasional visits. While he always enjoyed these returns, he was in later life irked and disappointed at the cultural and economic backwardness of this area of the states. The reasons for this state of affairs were complex but were in no small measure due to the tendency of their inhabitants to look backward upon vanished glories rather than forward to new challenges. Claude's arrival at Princeton also initiated a love and devotion for this institution which remained with him to the end of his life; indeed his mortal remains are interred in his beloved Princeton village. Never had any college a more devoted and loyal alumnus!

At Princeton, Hudson elected a course in chemistry given by Professor L. W. McCay, who offered brilliant showmanship in lecture demonstrations. Thereupon the Presbyterian ministry lost a candidate and the science of chemistry gained a votary. His college chum, a minister's son, said: "Console yourself by believing that you have conferred a favor on your imaginary future parishioners!" Hudson received the B.Sc. degree *cum laude* from Princeton in 1901 and was rewarded with an endowed fellowship (Class of 1860) in experimental science. He embarked immediately upon scientific research. While recrystallizing some milk sugar for Professor William F. Magie,[4] of the department of physics, to be used by him in measuring the specific heat of its aqueous solution, Hudson encountered the phenomenon of mutarotation[5] and immediately proposed its study for his investigational problem. This was not agreeable to the professor of organic chemistry who stated that Emil Fischer had just completed his studies with the sugars and there were no problems left in that area. It was then agreed that the student could use the laboratory facilities of the chemistry department but could report his results to Professor Magie and take his M.Sc. degree in the department of physics; this was done in 1902. Then followed a year of study in Germany, in accordance with the custom of the times.

Hudson began his studies abroad with Professor Walther Nernst[6] at Göttingen but spent the following summer semester with J. H. van't Hoff[7] in Berlin. In Germany, Hudson continued his work on the mutarotation of lactose, later published, and did not accept an assigned problem from either professor. In addition, he proposed to Professor G. Tammann of Göttingen the measurements which resulted in the publication of the now famous closed-ring curve solubility relation in the nicotine-water system. Hudson attended an International Chemical Congress at Berlin in the summer of 1903 and there met Emil Fischer, whose work in organic chemistry did not at the time especially interest Hudson. He did meet Arthur A. Noyes, from the United States, who offered him a position in the newly established Research Laboratory of Physical Chemistry at the Massachusetts Institute of Technology. This Hudson was pleased to accept since a stringency in his father's finances eliminated further study abroad. This year of study in two of the great European universities of the time was a fruitful period. The contact with van't Hoff, although short, was especially stimulating. A fine relationship existed between these great research professors and their students. Hudson and another American taught Nernst the intricacies of the game of poker prior to the professor's visit to the United States on a mission concerned with patent rights on the Nernst lamp. On being told of the dangers of Indian scalpings in the vicinity of New York, the eminent professor observed that his baldness absolved him from any such fears.

On Hudson's return he worked for one year (1903–1904) as a research assistant in Boston with A. A. Noyes and W. R. Whitney. Again he continued on his own path with further studies on the mutarotation of sugars and elaborated his theory of the maximum rate of solution whereby the rotation of an unknown anomer[8] could be evaluated by measuring the solubility and polarimetric changes with time in a solution saturated with respect to the known anomer. The grant for this fellowship originated with the Carnegie Foundation and when the renewal application listed studies in the preparation of rare sugars to be used in the measurements, the whole approach was considered to be too "organic" in nature and the grant was not renewed, even though the proposal carried the signed recommendations of Nernst and van't Hoff.

After this experience with the Leipzig-trained American physical chemists, Hudson turned to physics and Professor Magie, who obliged him with an instructorship in physics at Princeton (1904–1905) and then helped him to obtain a similar post at the University of Illinois which he held from 1905 to 1907. This was no better and Hudson approached the newly appointed head of the

Illinois Chemistry Department, W. A. Noyes, who promptly informed him that he did not qualify as a chemist. Meanwhile Hudson had married (1906) Miss Alice Abbott of Urbana and they were having difficulties, even at that time, in living on his salary of $900 per year. A Göttingen chum then helped him obtain a position in the technologic branch of the U. S. Geological Survey at a salary of $1600. On his way to accept this post, he stopped at Princeton to take the final examination for the degree of Doctor of Philosophy. At the time, this title was taken rather literally and a member of the department of philosophy was required to sit in on the examination in physics, a discipline which was considered to be a branch of the subject of natural philosophy. Professor A. T. Ormond represented the philosophy department; his specialty was the history of philosophy, on which subject he had written a book. A hasty perusal of this by Hudson failed to assure him of success and he bethought himself of the mile walk the professor was required to take from his home to the university. Hudson stated, "I can see now his beaming, round countenance when I appeared at his home with horse, victoria and colored coachman to drive him in regal splendor to the examination hall." The scientific part of Hudson's examination passed off brilliantly and Professor Ormond declined to question. The candidate was dismissed and some considerable time later Professor Magie emerged to inform him that he had been awarded the degree *magna cum laude*. Hudson then politely asked if he might inquire why the committee took so long in arriving at the decision. The reply was, "Oh, it was because of that philosophy professor, he was holding out for a *summa cum laude*."

While Hudson was at Princeton to complete his Ph. D. work, he spent a few days in the laboratory of Dr. G. A. Hulett, who had just been appointed professor of physical chemistry. In this time he measured the pH dependency of the mutarotation of D-glucose and established the formulation

$$k = 0.0096 + 0.258[\text{H}^+] + 9750[\text{OH}^-].$$

This equation shows that the catalytic activity of hydroxyl ions is 40,000 times that of hydrogen ions and the first term allowed the ionic dissociation of water to be evaluated as 1.0×10^{-14} at 25°.

In 1907 Claude Hudson made the acquaintance of Dr. Harvey
W. Wiley, then chief of the Bureau of Chemistry of the United
States Department of Agriculture, and in 1908 Hudson was appointed chemist aid to Mr. Frederick Weber in the laboratory
concerned with the analyses involved in Dr. Wiley's famed "poison
squad" tests of food preservatives. Wiley had once carried out
research in the technology of cane sugar and during a slack period
in the analytical work, Hudson persuaded Wiley to allow him to
conduct some investigations on the action of invertase on sucrose.
Hudson then completed the work, one of the first of its kind,
which showed that this enzymic reaction followed the laws of
mass action. Thereafter, Wiley allowed Hudson to conduct research of his own choice and provided him with an assistant,
H. S. Paine, the two of them forming a new section designated
the physical chemistry laboratory. There resulted his famous series
of articles on the action of invertase on sucrose in which it was
shown that the reaction was not reversible and that the D-fructose
component was combined in sucrose in an unusual form. He also
published (1909) his famous paper entitled "The Significance of
Certain Numerical Relations in the Sugar Group" wherein he
enunciated his rule, originally empirical, that the more dextrorotatory member (D-series) of an anomeric pair was to be designated α and its hydroxyl, or substituted hydroxyl, was to be written
to the right in the Fischer projection formula:

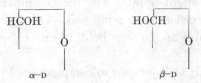

This paper further contains his rules of isorotation which state
that if the rotation is divided into that A contributed by the
anomeric center and that B of the remaining centers, then in any
anomeric pair the sum of their molecular rotations is a constant
characteristic of the B portion and the difference is a constant
characteristic of the A part.

For the α-D anomer, $A + B = [M]$
For the β-D anomer, $-A + B = [M]$

In 1910 he published his lactone rule wherein he demonstrated that the asymmetric center concerned in the ring closure controlled the rotation. It was later shown that in acyclic aldonic acid functions the center adjacent to the carboxyl function controlled the rotation. These rules have some limitations but have been extremely useful to the chemist. They established an early reputation for Hudson and in 1916 he was recognized by the award of the Nichols Medal of the New York Section of the American Chemical Society. On a later visit to the department of chemistry of the University of Illinois, Professor Roger Adams invited Dr. Hudson to sit in on the oral examination of a candidate for the degree of Doctor of Philosophy. On being asked by Professor Adams to state Hudson's rules the candidate replied that he only knew one, to wit, "Any drink with gin in it is a good drink." Dr. Hudson then remarked that the answer was correct since this was also one of his rules (gin being free of aldehydes and fusel oil) and he had indeed expounded it to the candidate on the previous evening.

In 1911, Dr. Wiley resigned from the Bureau of Chemistry and was replaced by Dr. C. L. Alsberg, who backed Dr. Hudson even more and placed him in charge of a carbohydrate laboratory with an augmented staff.

From 1911 to 1912, Hudson was away from Washington on leave of absence substituting for Professor G. A. Hulett at Princeton, who was in turn on leave of absence in Washington. At Princeton, Dr. Hudson attracted a graduate student, Julian K. Dale, and they initiated their classical measurements on the kinetics of mutarotation of the α and β forms of D-glucose. Hudson taught a course in physical chemistry at Princeton which consisted of a résumé of his own researches followed by instruction in the reading of German chemistry. On his return to the Bureau of Chemistry, Hudson embarked upon an intensive period of research (1912–1919) with a number of co-workers. He initiated his valued series of publications on exact methods of preparation of sugars from natural sources. He found a new source for melezitose and discovered (with F. B. LaForge) the new heptulose "sedoheptose" in *Sedum spectabile*. They became interested in this common garden plant because a large bed of it was growing in Hudson's home flower garden and they could find no record of an examination of the sap of the plant for sugars. Many years later this sugar was established (M. Calvin) as an important member of the photosynthetic carbon cycle in all green plants. Hudson turned to the acetate esters of the sugars for a rich source of readily preparable and crystallizable anomers and in the course of this investigation found that the sugar galactose could exist in more than one ring form by the preparation (made with J. M. Johnson) of its four isomeric pentaacetates in two anomeric pairs.

During World War I Hudson initiated experiments in the preparation of activated carbon for gas masks at Trenton, New Jersey, in association with Professor W. F. Magie of Princeton and Dr. Edward Mack, Jr., who had just completed his Ph.D. work with Professor G. A. Hulett. This interest in activated carbon persisted and led to the only deviation from carbohydrate research undertaken by Dr. Hudson. He left the government service to act as a consulting chemist in Trenton where he was concerned with the manufacture of activated carbon and with malt sirups of the prohibition era. Dr. J. K. Dale was associated with him in this work which extended over the period 1919–1923, with one year added later in 1924 for consulting service in the Hawaiian Islands related to the use of activated carbon in the pineapple canning industry. Brewing was a subject of personal interest to Hudson; during the prohibition era he made his own home brew according to an exacting procedure with excellent results. After his retirement from the government service many years later, he continued this interest by acting as a consultant to the Anheuser-Busch Brewing Co. of St. Louis.

In 1923 Mr. Frederick J. Bates, chief of the Polarimetry Section of the National Bureau of Standards in Washington, D. C., offered Hudson a research position for the study of sugars which Hudson gladly accepted; he remained there until 1928. This period was notable for the attraction to his laboratory of fellowship students from this country and abroad: A. Kunz, E. Pacsu, C. B. Purves, W. C. Austin, and the writer. Dr. Hudson worked with his own hands and seemed mainly concerned with a large assortment of small beakers in each of which he was attempting to crystallize a sirup. These beakers did not appear to be labeled but he knew what was contained in each. He was an early riser and walked to the laboratory with a sandwich in his pocket which, with a quart of delivered milk, served for his lunch; it was partaken while watching experiments so that no time was lost over the lunch period. He never returned in the evening but utilized this time for writing and study. He interested one of the physicists, an expert in optics, in his sugar experiments and published a number of papers with him. While Hudson was away on a trip, I discussed the purification of a sugar derivative with this eminent physicist and mentioned that the main impurity present was acetamide. He inquired about the optical rotatory power of acetamide. On being informed that it had none he was very skeptical and I was forced to bring out the books and back my statement. This was not easily done, as nowhere in the description of acetamide was there any mention that it was optically inactive. Indeed, I am not sure whether I convinced him at all.

When I was at the Bureau of Standards, one of the storeroom attendants had published a paper with Hudson. It was said that at one time Hudson interested a janitor in his experiments so much that the man took out a subscription to the *Journal of the American Chemical Society* in order to follow the publications of the laboratory as they appeared.

The writer studied with Hudson just as long as Hudson had studied with van't Hoff—that was for one summer. The impact of his personality and creative artistry, however, was tremendous and was unequaled by any other experience I have ever had. During this period, Hudson initiated his program on the higher-carbon sugars in a search for members having the upper structures of the very rare aldoses. He discovered (with A. Kunz) the configurational inversion, by aluminum chloride, of the second and third carbons in the reducing portion of the disaccharides lactose and cellobiose. Studies on the kinetics of the hypobromite oxidation of aldoses were initiated with H. S. Isbell.

In 1929 Hudson accepted an invitation to continue his work on a larger scale in the Hygienic Laboratory (later the National Institutes of Health) of the United States Public Health Service.

The position carried the title of Professor of Chemistry, and so at long last Hudson had achieved a professorship. He enjoyed telling the academic professors that he was no ordinary professor but was a professor by Act of Congress. At the 1926 Meeting of the American Chemical Society, the rather pompous and always highly critical Professor Harold Hibbert of McGill made the public statement that it was unfortunate Hudson did not hold an academic post, whereupon Hudson arose and remarked that there were *some* universities in which he would not care to hold a professorship. During the move to the laboratory at Bethesda, Maryland, Hudson quietly took along several kilograms of melezitose which he had prepared from "gritty honey." This caused a great uproar, at the Bureau chief level, which eventually subsided.

At this time Hudson had published a new classification of sugar ring types based upon deviations from his isorotation rules. Thus, methyl α-D-mannoside was assigned a furanoside structure because its A_{OMe} value was in disagreement with that of the methyl D-glucosides for which Hudson accepted a pyranoside structure. This came into conflict with the methylation studies of Haworth and Hirst in England, and both sides presented their cases before the Conference on Carbohydrates of the International Union of Chemistry at Liège, Belgium, in September, 1930. The English investigators presented a valid proof independent of rotatory considerations, and Hudson returned to the United States to spend much time in a fruitless attempt to prove that methyl α-D-mannoside was a mixture or molecular compound. Together with E. L. Jackson, he then applied the periodate α-glycol-splitting agent of Malaprade to verify the methylation experiments in a most elegant manner and, in addition, to correlate the configurations of the anomeric carbons of the methyl pyranosides of the pentoses and hexoses. The results gave an experimental verification of the 1909 assignments which had been based on optical rotatory power alone. In spite of this scientific disagreement, the personal relations between Hudson, Haworth, and Hirst remained eminently cordial.

The period at Bethesda, from 1929 to his retirement at the age of seventy in 1951, was extremely productive with emphasis on organic structural and synthetic aspects of the sugars. He had many co-workers from both the government service and from visiting fellows. Through Dr. C. H. Herty of the Chemical Foundation, a well endowed fellowship was placed in Hudson's laboratory and filled by a succession of worthy young men. Hudson's principal assistant during this period was Raymond (Ray) M. Hann. He was an indefatigable worker who understood Hudson and his methods and kept the whole group in smooth operation. For example, Hudson was notorious for not answering such letters as were considered by him to involve routine or trivial matters, but any letter addressed to Ray Hann would be tactfully brought to the attention of Hudson and answered promptly by Ray. The researches of the laboratory in this period covered many topics and are recorded in over 200 journal publications.

Although Hudson often remarked that he was accepted as a colleague by neither the physicists, the physical chemists, nor the organic chemists, he was a regular attendant at the meetings of the American Chemical Society and particularly enjoyed those held in the southern cities. A favorite whimsy of his was that on occasion an L-Hudson could be brought out from behind the mirror. D-Hudson was the serious, sober, gentlemanly scientist. The L-Hudson was the convivial one who partook of intoxicating beverages, was strongly attracted by beautiful women, and was in general sinful. On the occasion of the Organic Symposium of the American Chemical Society at Richmond, Virginia, L-Hudson was in charge. It became necessary for him to leave the auditorium, but alas, the only inconspicuous exit was a spiral staircase which was dextrorotatory. With the aid of friends he finally mounted it, but claimed ever after that he had been racemized in the process.

Hudson was elected chairman (1934) of the Organic Division of the American Chemical Society, but in later years he was closely associated with the Carbohydrate Division. With William B. Newkirk and Norman F. Kennedy he organized (1939) the Starch Round Table, an annual meeting held in some secluded spot under the auspices of the Corn Industries Research Foundation. Hudson showed little interest in organic chemistry not directly connected with the carbohydrates. On the other hand, he was intensely critical of physical chemists who attempted to grapple with the problems of polysaccharide chemistry without exhibiting any knowledge or appreciation of the established organic structures of these substances.

Hudson was associated with the *Advances in Carbohydrate Chemistry* from its inception in 1944; this is an annual journal publishing review chapters. He insisted that a high level of scholarship be maintained in this endeavor. He served as an associate editor of the *Journal of the American Chemical Society* and was a close friend of its great editor, Arthur B. Lamb.[9] He spent much time reviewing manuscripts in the carbohydrate field and insisted on holding their authors to the same rigid criteria by which he judged his own writings, an excellent principle but one not always appreciated by the contributors. When the editorship of the journal changed, one of Hudson's manuscripts in his internationally famed series of sugar preparations was returned to him with the statement that the improvements cited, which indeed made the difference between crystals or no crystals at the finish, were of insufficient novelty to warrant space in the journal. The resultant near-volcanic eruption in the suburbs of Washington was such that this decision was hastily reconsidered and the paper entitled "Improvements in the Preparation of L-Arabinose from Mesquite Gum" appeared under his name alone in 1951 as the last in this great series of authoritative publications.

Claude Hudson was married four times, the first three marriages ending in divorce. His last marriage, in 1942, was to his childhood sweetheart, the then-widowed Erin Gilmer Jones of Selma, Alabama.

In addition to being the recipient of the Nichols Medal (1916) mentioned previously, Claude Hudson was the recipient of the Willard Gibbs (Chicago Section, American Chemical Society, 1929), Richards (Northeastern Section, 1940), Borden (American Chemical Society, 1941) and Cresson (Franklin Institute of the State of Pennsylvania, 1942) Medals, the Hillebrand Prize (Washington Chemical Society, 1931) and the Sugar Division Citation (1946). He was elected to membership in the National Academy of Sciences (U.S.A.) in 1927, and to the Kaiserlich Leopoldinisch-Carolinisch Deutsche Akademie der Naturforscher

(Halle) in 1932. He was a charter member (1936) of the Academy of Medicine of Washington, D.C., and was an honorary fellow of the Chemical Society (London). He received the honorary degree of D.Sc. from Princeton University (1947), the grand prize of $10,000 from the Sugar Research Foundation of New York (1950), and the first Federal Security Agency Award (1950).

Hudson survived official retirement by only two years and died in his Washington apartment of a coronary thrombosis on December 27, 1952. His scientific work will long stand as a monument of rigorous mathematical reasoning, exceptional clarity, and experimental cleverness. His influence upon carbohydrate chemistry and upon the rising science of biochemistry was great and profound.

GENERAL REFERENCES

C. S. Hudson, Autobiography in "The Collected Papers of C. S. Hudson," R. M. Hann and N. K. Richtmyer, eds., Vol. I, Academic Press, New York, 1946, pp. xi–xxviii.

R. M. Hann and N. K. Richtmyer, eds., "The Collected Papers of C. S. Hudson," Academic Press, New York, Vol. I, 1946, 898 + xxxv pp., Vol. II, 1948, 795 + xvi pp.

E. L. Hirst, The Hudson Memorial Lecture, *J. Chem. Soc., 1954,* 4042–4058.

M. L. Wolfrom, "Claude Silbert Hudson," *Advances in Carbohydrate Chem., 9,* xiii–xviii (1945).

L. F. Small and M. L. Wolfrom, "Claude Silbert Hudson," Biographical Memoirs, National Academy of Sciences of the United States of America, *XXXII* (1959), pp. 181–220.

NOTES AND REFERENCES

1 "Das Buch der Grossen Chemiker," Band II, G. Bugge, ed., Verlag Chemie, Berlin, 1930, p. 408 ff.

2 Walter Norman (Sir Norman) Haworth (1883–1950), Nobel laureate in chemistry, 1937, was a student of W. H. Perkin, Jr. and O. Wallach and was Professor of Chemistry at Birmingham, 1925–1946.

3 Edmund Langley Hirst (1898–   ), student and associate of Sir Norman Haworth; since 1944 Professor of Chemistry at Edinburgh.

4 William F. Magie (1858–1943), professor of physics at Princeton University from 1890 to 1929.

5 The change in optical rotation with time exhibited by a freshly prepared sugar solution.

6 Hermann Walther Nernst (1864–1941), Nobel laureate in chemistry, 1920; one of the founders of the science of chemical thermodynamics.

7 "Das Buch der Grossen Chemiker," Band II, G. Bugge, ed., Verlag Chemie, Berlin, 1930, p. 391 ff.

8 Anomers are stereoisomeric sugars differing only in the configuration of the reducing carbon (carbon 1 in formula I on p. 1537).

9 Arthur Becket Lamb (1880-1952), student of Arthur Michael and T. W. Richards, professor of chemistry, Harvard University, 1920–1948, and editor of the *Journal of the American Chemical Society*, 1917–1949.

MELVILLE L. WOLFROM

· · *111* · ·

Ernst Späth

1886-1946

WHEN a second son was born on May 14, 1886, to the blacksmith Späth in the small village of Barn, in the Northern Silesian province of the Austro-Hungarian Empire, nobody expected that this boy was destined to become one of the leading organic chemists of our time. In line with the traditional custom, the limited family finances were used to allow for a higher education for the elder son, but the younger boy, Ernst, was to continue in his father's modest trade. Ernst inherited from his father an enormous energy which the village blacksmith Späth thought to be the right quality for success in his trade.

It was Ernst Späth's mother who recognized her son's love for learning and especially for the natural sciences. She persuaded her husband that their younger son should also be permitted a high school and college education. This meant that the family had to tighten the belt considerably to be able to bear the expenses; Ernst Späth never knew the word "plenty" throughout his whole period of education.

In his early high school years Ernst Späth was fortunate to have a teacher who instilled in him an interest in natural sciences—especially chemistry. Many years later, Ernst Späth used to speak gratefully to his friends and students about this teacher and the guidance he had received from him during the early period of his education. It was his good fortune to find another inspiring teacher later on, when he studied chemistry at Vienna University. This other teacher was Rudolf Wegscheider, who quickly discovered his student's abilities and helped guide him toward an academic career.

When Ernst Späth graduated with full honors from high school, he had proven to his parents that their efforts had not been wasted, and he was then allowed to continue his studies. His first goal was to become a high school teacher. Later, when he found support in his teacher Wegscheider, he quickly decided to devote himself to chemistry.

In order to facilitate the studies of his student, Rudolf Weg-scheider offered him an assistantship at the Chemical Institute of Vienna University. The small income from this position allowed Ernst Späth to supplement the meager allowance which his parents were able to give him, but what was still more important, this first academic position determined the young man to seek the career of a college professor.

After obtaining his doctorate in 1910, he had to interrupt his professional career at the University of Vienna for military duty during World War I. Nevertheless, he was allowed to continue in a professional capacity at the laboratories of the university. Once the war was over, he returned to the academic career at the same university, and even though he had obtained several very tempting offers from a number of German universities, he decided to stay in his beloved Vienna. In 1917 he became a full-fledged member of the academic faculty of Vienna University in the field of chemistry; he advanced in 1921 to the title of assistant professor, in 1923 to professor and one year later, in 1924, he became *ordinarius* and head of the Second Chemical Institute. This opportunity arrived when his predecessor, Wilhelm Schlenk, went to the University of Berlin.

His untiring energy, his clear vision of the goal which he had set for himself, and his never-ending optimism served well in the building and expansion of the Second Chemical Institute and inspired his students and co-workers. The students working on their theses for the doctorate were especially privileged to have his help and attention. He gave them many hours of patient advice, and he also inspired them by his own research activity, his skill in all laboratory techniques, and the long hours which he devoted to research. It was not unusual for him to return in the evening to the laboratory and work into the early hours of the morning. His lectures were alive and inspiring. He did not use a written text to deliver them; instead, he spoke freely, supplementing his lecture with many demonstrations, and he always tried to adjust his teaching to the latest developments in chemistry. At the end of the lecture he was usually surrounded by students asking him many questions which he would patiently answer. These seminars after the lecture would last nearly as long as the lecture itself and gave him the opportunity to pick the ablest among his audience and invite them to collaborate with him in his research studies. It was easy to notice how much he enjoyed the close contact with his students. In addition, he used to walk through the many laboratories of the Second Institute, stop and talk with his students and often remain for a considerable time at a student's work bench, advising him how to conduct the experiment, demonstrating proper techniques, and personally making adjustments to the apparatus in order to improve the experiment. In the many research projects which he conducted with the cooperation of his assistants and students, there was hardly a decisive experiment which he would not perform himself. Through his active participation in the experimental portion of each research project conducted by his group of collaborators and students, he made certain that in the final report the conclusions were based on exhaustive and accurate experimentation. Himself a master of the latest experimental techniques, he insisted that his students acquaint themselves with all of them. The temporary lack of a special piece of laboratory glassware was never a reason for him to stop the experiment. He was skilled in building or improvising the needed equipment. Often he demonstrated to his students his ability as a glass blower and taught them how to make and design their own equipment.

With his enormous capacity for work Späth was able simultaneously to conduct and supervise a number of research projects, deliver the lectures, devote considerable time to his younger students, and conduct the administration of a large institute in the most efficient manner. The administration of the Second Chemical Institute was accomplished with only a few clerical assistants.

At all times there were about twenty students working on their doctoral theses under his guidance and with his active and close collaboration. Many of them came from abroad. It was not unusual to hear several different languages spoken in this part of the institute. Racial or religious discrimination was foreign to Ernst Späth's thinking, and one could find there students of different races and creeds working side by side, getting acquainted, and developing friendship with one another. This happened at a time when racial and religious discrimination was becoming extremely noticeable all over Central Europe and especially at the Central European universities. Once, when students from other sections of the university tried to invade the Second Chemical Institute in order to stage an anti-Semitic demonstration and to eject the Jewish students who were working there, the intruders were stopped by Ernst Späth and told that they had invaded a place of learning which had no use for their shallow ideologies. This personal courage was demonstrated later on repeated occasions when Späth used all his personal influence to protect colleagues and students who were exposed to the hatred of political extremists. Ernst Späth had no political affiliations. All of his energy was devoted to the service of humanity through his beloved chemistry at a time when some of his colleagues had lost their way from science and education and had surrendered the traditional liberalism of the university to violence and mob psychology.

Ernst Späth had started his chemical work as the student of the physical chemist Wegscheider, but he soon changed to organic chemistry. The chemistry of the natural plant substances became his special field of interest. According to his own statement, Späth made the decision to devote his research activity to the chemistry of the natural plant substances shortly after the conclusion of the First World War. In 1918, while spending a vacation on the beautiful Adriatic island of Brioni, he made a literature search of the alkaloids. Because of the important position of the alkaloids in pharmacology and their use in medicine, Späth earned for himself an international reputation by conducting brilliant and thorough research to establish the chemical configuration of these substances. There were two reasons for Ernst Späth's decision. Austria had become a very small country after the conclusion of the war in 1918. Its resources were very limited, and there was not much money in the budget of the university laboratory. Therefore, Späth had to choose a field of research which did not require large sums of money. The second reason was that the necessity to work with small quantities of the product he was investigating had a special attraction to him. The then usual, not too accurate methods of the organic chemist did not appeal to him. The order and tidiness of

1556

not only the master's private laboratory, but also of the others in the Second Chemical Institute was characteristic of his personality. The exactness that was required in the research operations dealing with very small quantities led to many discoveries in chemical research methods which have since become valuable tools in fields other than alkaloid chemistry.

In the nineteenth century, Austrian chemists like Rochleder, Hlasiwetz, and Redtenbacher had pioneered in the research of the chemical constituents of plants and were able to show considerable achievements. Ernst Späth's predecessors at the Second Chemical Institute of Vienna University, Zdenko Skraup and Guido Goldschmiedt, were also interested in research on alkaloids. It was therefore tempting to Späth to resume the tradition, especially since this trend had been interrupted by his immediate predecessor Schlenk who had devoted his work to the theory of organic chemistry.

When Ernst Späth started his fruitful activity in alkaloid chemistry, there were still many questions unanswered, and there were several that also gave promise of financial success.

Although he was able to inspire many of the people around him, nevertheless some of them had to make a considerable effort to penetrate through the hard surface of this introvert personality in order to recognize his true nature. Some of his most brilliant students experienced this difficulty at the beginning of their contact with the master. It was then that Späth's deep sense of justice and discernment finally effected a mutual understanding.

There are 160 finished research projects in the field of alkaloids from Ernst Späth's laboratory. His first researches were devoted to the alkaloids belonging to the isoquinoline group to which ephedrine, papaverine, and others belong. He devoted work to the constituents of curare, to the chemical identity of chelidonine, the main alkaloid contained in the herb celandine (*Chelidonium Majus*), and to the alkaloids of the narcissus plants. Among the latter was tazettine whose chemical formula he ascertained. He also studied alkaloids contained in angotura bark, for instance, cusparine.

In many of his researches Späth tried to identify all the bases contained in a drug; this procedure involved experimentally difficult work. Many of his results are of great importance in the field of plant physiology. Together with H. Bretschneider he developed a convincing synthesis of nicotine, and alone he proved the existence of a number of secondary alkaloids. He also described for the first time anabasine, nicotine, N-methylanabasine, and others. His thorough knowledge of the tobacco alkaloids is demonstrated in the monograph entitled "The Alkaloids of Tobacco" which he wrote with F. Kuffner.

Späth's synthesis of nicotine[1] starting with the ethyl ester of nicotinic acid (I) and N-methylpyrrolidone (II)

Together with F. Galinowski he elucidated the chemical configuration of cytisine, the main alkaloid of *Laburnum Anagyroides* and other leguminous plants. Among other alkaloids which had attracted Späth's attention, one must mention harmaline because of the pharmacological importance of this drug in the treatment of influenza.

1558

Späth's synthesis of harmine[2] starting with 3-methoxy-phenol hydrazine and gamma-aminobutyraldehyde

In the last fifteen years of his life, Späth devoted his scientific activity to another group of plant substances, the coumarins. More than sixty publications in this field witness his activity. His research started with a domestic Austrian plant from which Hlasiwetz had previously isolated pencedamine. Among other members of this group was khellin, which Späth isolated. This drug is interesting because of its pharmaceutical use in the treatment of asthma and angina pectoris. Späth's research on the coumarins is the foundation for the work that is being conducted at present and undoubtedly will be continued in the future because of the numerous derivatives which have significant physiological properties.

3, 4, 6-Triacetoxy-cumaran   Bergaptol   Bergapten

Allo-bergaptol

Späth's synthesis of bergapten[3]

1559

Späth occasionally conducted other investigations dealing with natural products that belong to different chemical groups. Some of them are: cotoin, kynurenic acid, lactucin, podophyllotoxin, protocotoin, pseudobaptigenin, pseudobaptisin, saponins, and sparrasol, Among the methods he developed is the dehydrogenation of heterocyclic substances by using palladium.

During thirty years of an extensive scientific activity, Späth produced more than 300 major publications. The world recognized his genius by bestowing many honors upon him. In 1931 he became a member of the Carolinisch-Leopoldinische Academy for Natural Sciences in Halle, Germany; in 1934 he was elected to the corresponding membership of the Academia de Ciencias Exactas, Físicas y Naturales in Madrid; in 1937 he was awarded the nonresident membership of the Hungarian Academy in Budapest, and then he was made corresponding member of the Academy in Bologna, Italy.

From 1936, he was a member of the Comité d'Experts Scientifiques de l'Organisation de Cooperation Intellectuelle de la Société des Nations (Committee of Scientific Experts of the Organization for Intellectual Cooperation of the League of Nations). In 1937 he was elected an honorary member of the Associazione Italiana di Chimica and the Société de Chimie Industrielle of Paris.

The Vienna Academy of Sciences honored Späth in 1920 by awarding to him the Lieben Prize. In 1933 he was awarded the Lavoisier Medal of the Société Chimique de France and in 1937 the Liebig Medal of the Verein Deutscher Chemiker. In 1937 he was also given the Wilhelm Exner Medal of the Chamber of Commerce of Lower Austria.

Ernst Späth had very close ties with Vienna which he had adopted as his home and the site of his intellectual activity. When he was elected to the corresponding membership of the Academie der Wissenschaften in Wien (Vienna Academy of Sciences) in 1925, it was the fulfillment of his greatest ambition. In 1926 he became a full member of this venerable institution. Within the framework of the Vienna Academy of Sciences, Späth found the opportunity to honor his teacher Wegscheider. In 1929 he initiated and sponsored the Wegscheider Foundation on the occasion of the seventieth anniversary of the great chemist who had started Ernst Späth on the path of chemical research. Späth devoted considerable effort and time in the service of the Vienna Academy, and in 1938 he was elected general secretary of the Mathematics and Natural Sciences Section of the Academy. One of his important achievements for the Academy was the enlargement of its library.

Ernst Späth possessed a profound love for his country, its science, and art. He had no use for political parties and their ideologies. The raucous year 1938 gave Späth the opportunity to become the champion of the persecuted, and he used his influence and the respect which he commanded to protect many of his colleagues whom he respected as scientists, but who had attracted the hatred of the ignorant and misled masses. At a time when Austria was at its most difficult position, impoverished and marred by the destruction of war, on October 30, 1945, he was elected president of the Vienna Academy of Sciences.

The re-establishment of the Vienna Academy is entirely his achievement. The old and venerable building which had housed this learned society was demolished by bombs during the war. It was Ernst Späth's achievement that the structure was rebuilt. He obtained the needed funds and, what was still harder, the building materials to do the job. His firm and quiet personality gained many friends and supporters among the members of the Austrian government, the military and civil authorities of the occupying powers, and many admirers abroad. His untiring efforts were crowned when he obtained the facilities of the Biological Station in Linz, Austria, from the Russians who occupied it.

On September 30, 1946, in Zurich, Switzerland, came the last act of the great scientist. He had come there as the delegate of the Vienna Academy of Sciences for the celebration of the two-hundredth anniversary of the Schweizer Naturforschende Gesellschaft (Swiss Society of Natural Sciences). Without any warning he succumbed that day to a heart attack. Only shortly before, he had celebrated his sixtieth birthday in the quiet of his home among his beloved family. This great and honest man, who was possessed by an untiring energy and love for science and his fellowmen, died quietly in the midst of his work and among his fellow scientists.

REFERENCES

Almanach Österr. Akad. Wiss., 97, 123, 304 (1947).
Österr. Chemiker-Z., 48, 57 (1947).

1 E. Späth, "Récentes synthèses d'alcaloides," *Bull. Soc. Chim.*, ser. 4, 53, 1379, 1933.
2 E. Späth, *loc. cit.*, p. 1383.
3 E. Späth, "Die natürlichen Cumarine," *Ber.*, 1937 A, p. 107.

ALFRED A. BACHER

·· 112 ··

Victor Moritz Goldschmidt

1888-1947

T HE basic problem of geochemistry," said Victor Moritz Goldschmidt, "is to determine the quantitative chemical composition of the earth and to find the laws which underlie the frequency and distribution of the various elements in nature."

During the nineteenth and early twentieth centuries attempts were made, mainly by chemists, to collect the chemical and physical-chemical data relating to mineralogical and geological chemistry. In Switzerland, Schoenbein coined the name "geochemistry"; in Germany Carl Gustav Bischof published, between 1848 and 1854, his famous treatise on "Physical and Chemical Geology" which presented the chemical knowledge of his time. The great Berzelius in Sweden did much to elucidate the chemical genesis of minerals and rocks, and at the beginning of the century J. H. van't Hoff laid the foundation of the physical chemistry of salt minerals. The greatest contributions came from the work of the American petrologists F. W. Clarke and H. S. Washington. Modern geo-chemistry, however, had its origin in Oslo. The laws which determine the geochemical distribution of the elements were postulated by V. M. Goldschmidt from 1917 on.

Goldschmidt was born on January 27, 1888, in Zürich. His father, Heinrich Jacob Goldschmidt, was a distinguished physical chemist who came from Prague which was then, of course, part of the old Austro-Hungarian monarchy. His mother was Amelie Köhne, and Victor Moritz was their only child. In quick succession his father became professor in Amsterdam, then Heidelberg—where V.M. received his early schooling and in 1905 he was appointed professor of chemistry, succeeding Waage at the University of Oslo (then Christiania), at that time the only university in Norway. Famous for its tradition in the mathematical sciences, Oslo was also famous for its school in the earth sciences. V. M. matriculated in 1905 to study mineralogy, geology, inorganic and physical chemistry, and came under the inspiring influence of the great W. C. Brøgger, whom he soon equaled in the importance of his geological and petrological work. Except for the winter terms of 1908 and 1911 when he worked under F. Becke in Vienna and P. von Groth in Munich, he finished his studies in Oslo and obtained his doctor's degree in 1911. After two years as a lecturer he was appointed, in 1914, at the early age of twenty-six, full professor and director of the Mineralogical Institute of the University of Oslo.

By then, shortly before the outbreak of World War I, the first scientific harvest was brought in. His earliest paper on the pyroluminescence of quartz[1] was published when he was a first-year student. The main work of this period, which has since become a classic, was his 480-page study on the contact metamorphism of the Oslo region[2] published in 1911. Throughout this monograph Goldschmidt applied physical-chemical considerations to geological problems, rightly regarding the whole planet earth as one single physicochemical system. It was perhaps the first time that, by Goldschmidt's mineralogical phase rule, the applications of Nernst's heat theorem and the law of mass action on complex systems of rocks mineralogy have come of age as an exact science.

It took Goldschmidt eight years to complete the fundamental investigations that followed his work on contact metamorphism: an intensive geological-petrographical study of regional metamorphism of the mountains of southern Norway.[3]

Long before war broke out the Goldschmidt family had become Norwegian citizens. When the general situation in the neutral countries deteriorated, and after the intensified U-boat warfare, Norway was largely cut off from overseas; sources of raw materials were badly needed. The result was that in 1917 the Norwegian government decided upon thorough research into the mineral resources of Norway, and entrusted Goldschmidt with this task. He became chairman of a Government Commission for Raw Materials and director of the Raw Materials Laboratory. This work, which was directed entirely toward practical ends during the war, was continued afterward along general lines from which developed a new branch of science, geochemistry, which from the theoretical and the practical point of view is of the greatest importance. Several schools of geochemistry existed already and a mass of material was available. Apart from the American school, pre- and postwar Russia had produced some outstanding personalities such as W. J. Vernadsky, who did pioneer work notably in biogeochemistry, i.e., the frequency and distribution of elements in plants and animals. The work of today's leading expert on the origin of primitive life, Oparin, has its roots in Vernadsky's earlier work and is mainly a geochemical and biogeochemical complex of problems. There is also the school of the other leading Russian geochemist, A. E. Fersman, who died during the last war. Unfortunately his four-volume treatise on geochemistry has never been translated. However, the fundamental laws and principles underlying frequency and distribution of elements—the basic problem of geochemistry—were developed by V. M. Goldschmidt in Oslo between 1920 and 1928 and, when he was in Göttingen, by systematic research into the geochemistry of individual elements. That Russia alone has produced some 25,000 geochemists after the war gives some idea of the importance of modern geochemistry.

With an excellent team of co-workers, and with great energy, every conceivable method of chemical and physical analysis was used for the accumulation of data for a formidable task. Analytical methods had to be checked and adopted or new ones developed; carbon arc optical spectrography was developed; chemical analysis by characteristic x-ray spectra, already used by von Hevesy and by Assar Hadding in Sweden for geochemical purposes and mineral analysis, proved very useful; plans were also made by V. M. Goldschmidt for the construction of a mass spectrometer for the determination of the mass ratio of isotopes. The outbreak of the Second World War prevented Goldschmidt from introducing this instrument to geochemical research. Today mass spectroscopy has become a widely used tool in geochemical laboratories.

One of the methods extensively used by Goldschmidt was the analysis of crystal structure by x-rays, the great discovery of Max von Laue, and of W. H. and W. L. Bragg. The use of this method broadened the original views considerably, and almost as a by-product a new scientific discipline, crystal chemistry, was created.

One of the principal problems in the history of the earth that Goldschmidt approached is the partition of the chemical elements during the geological evolution between gas and coexisting liquid phases, the subsequent crystallization of these liquid phases, of molten iron, iron sulfides, and fused silicates, and the distribution of the chemical constituents in these phases. According to their tendency to enter one or the other of these phases, the elements could be classified into siderophile (metal melt), chalcophile (sulfide melt) and lithophile groups (silicate melt). A fourth group, the atmophile group, includes those elements which in pregeological times differentiated into the primordial atmosphere. It is of great interest that the distribution of the chemical elements among the three phases (iron, sulfide, silicate) is closely related to their atomic volume and the structure of their electronic shells.

The main controlling factors during these stages of differentiation are the chemical affinities of the various elements toward oxygen and sulfur and their latent heat of vaporization as compared with the affinity of the most common terrestrial heavy metal, iron. Goldschmidt took as a measure of these affinities the free energy of oxidation per gram atom of oxygen of the lowest oxides of the electropositive elements and the corresponding data for their sulfur compounds. Elements which are extremely rare in the earth crust— the lithosphere—are gold, the elements of the platinum group, and also nickel, cobalt, and germanium. They can be expected in the iron phase, the siderosphere. On the other hand the alkali and alkali-earth elements, silicon, aluminum, titanium, elements with a higher free energy of oxidation than iron, will, in the primordial differentiation, have concentrated in the outer silicate crust of the earth. Incidentally, it is known that the siderophile elements— gold, platinum metals, etc.—enter fused iron and iron alloys and are thus found as by-products in iron and steel works. The other analogon in metallurgical practice is the concentration of lithophile elements in the slag.

The next step after the primordial differentiation is the cooling of our planet and the crystallization of the silicate crust, a process which is still going on in rock formation from volcanic magmas.

Goldschmidt attacked the problem of finding the general laws and principles of geochemistry "from the viewpoint of atomic physics and atomic chemistry and to find out the relationships be-

1568

tween the geochemical distribution of the various elements and the measurable properties of their atoms and ions." He soon discovered that the principal factor regulating the entrance of atoms and ions and the distribution of the rarer elements in the crystalline phases of igneous and metamorphic rocks was the size of the atoms and ions and not their weight. During the gradual crystallization of liquid solutions, those atoms or ions of rare metals are caught in the already existing three-dimensional lattice which, because of their size, fit into this lattice. Those atoms and ions which are either too small or too big to be caught remain in the liquid. This idea led to the discovery of the fundamental relationship between crystal structure and chemical constitution:

> The structure of a crystal is conditioned by the numerical propor-
> tions, the proportion of size and the properties of polarization of its
> ultimate particles, and not only the structure but also other impor-
> tant properties of crystals, such as hardness, solubility and melting
> temperature, could be predicted from the properties of the atoms,
> and so, in the course of our geochemical investigations, the founda-
> tions of modern crystal chemistry were laid. These relationships
> were not limited to crystalline phases, but applied as well to the
> properties of solidified glasses . . .

Until then crystallography was for the mineralogist and the practical chemist: as Goldschmidt wrote, "a purely descriptive auxiliary science which made possible the recognition and distinction of crystalline materials whether they were minerals or technical products." Goldschmidt with his excellent team of co-workers— T. F. W. Barth, G. Lunde, I. Oftedal, L. Thomassen, W. H. Zachariasen and others—embarked on a hitherto unsurpassed systematic series of x-ray studies. In 1926 the atomic and ionic sizes, i.e., the radii of the greater part of the chemical elements in their different stages of electrical charge or ionization, were determined. Goldschmidt was now in a position to predict in which minerals, rocks, or ores a certain element could be found—an achievement equally important scientifically and practically. To give only one example from innumerable cases which had been proved: Nickel and magnesium have as divalent positive ions the same radius of 0.78 A; this is the reason why nickel is found in magnesium silicates of igneous rocks, and the percentages of both follow each other closely. Goldschmidt could soon predict the sequence of fractionated crystallization, taking into account the electrostatic forces between the positive metal ions and the negative silicate ions.

However, there are additional forces which support the electrostatical attraction of the ions in the crystal frame work, i.e., van der Waals forces, polarization forces, and the electron pair forces. They result in a measurable contraction of the lattice which is highest in the case of nickel orthosilicate, followed by magnesium and then by iron (ionic radius = 0.83 A). Nickel, in the fractionated crystallization from magmatic or other solutions, is the first, and iron the last to enter the mixed crystal. The concentration of nickel in magnesium-orthosilicate is sometimes of economic importance.

Goldschmidt could further predict the sequence of crystallization in cases of elements of the same size and practically the same ionic radius, but different electrical charge. If a divalent element, such as magnesium, is the main constituent in a crystal in contact with a saturated solution containing, as minor constituents, a trivalent element, such as scandium, and a monovalent, such as lithium, then, owing to the excess of electrostatic attraction, the trivalent scandium is preferentially built into the crystal—"captured"— whereas the univalent element lithium, owing to its smaller electrostatic charge, is only "admitted" to the lattice toward the end of the crystallization period. We understand now that scandium is not nearly as rare as it was formerly considered, but is a frequent constituent of many igneous rocks, especially magnesium silicates.

The problem of ionic substitution in minerals, which has occupied the mind of every mineralogist, was simply and elegantly solved by Goldschmidt's fundamental laws of crystal chemistry.

The chemical and geochemical behavior of elements with the same valency and almost the same ionic radii is of especial interest. The classical examples are the pairs aluminum/gallium and zirconium/hafnium. The trivalent gallium (radius = 0.57 A) is "hidden" in aluminum (radius = 0.62 A) and practically every aluminum mineral, every bauxite contains up to 100 grams of gallium per ton of aluminum. It accompanies aluminum through all the stages of industrial manufacture, and can be detected in practically every aluminum alloy. The tetravalents zirconium and hafnium have the ionic radii Zr = 0.87 A; Hf = 0.86 A. It will be remembered that in zirconium minerals von Hevesy discovered hafnium, the existence of which was predicted by Bohr's atomic theory. Goldschmidt called this hiding of a rare element in another "camouflage." The most famous example of camouflage is found in the rare earth elements, and the celebrated elucidation of the geochemical and chemical behavior of this fascinating group of elements, closely related to their ionic radii and valency, is one of the most magnificent achievements of Goldschmidt's work.

In his monumental work "Geochemische Verteilungsgesetze der Elemente, I–IX,"[4] Goldschmidt laid down the fundamental laws of geochemistry and crystal chemistry. These 600 pages contain the life work of one who, more than anyone else, has laid in two branches of science the foundations on which later generations will build. Nos. I–VIII contain the result of his work in Oslo, IX (the "ninth symphony" as he used to call it) originated from one of his happiest periods of life in Göttingen. No. VII contains the famous laws of crystal chemistry and No. VIII the relations between the structure and properties of crystals. One of the problems Goldschmidt approached in the latter communication are the factors influencing the hardness of crystals. Based on earlier work by Reis and Zimmermann, and by Friedrich, Goldschmidt systematically— supported by hundreds of investigated substances—extended our knowledge by showing how the hardness of a crystal was determined by the interatomic distance, the valency, and the structure type. Goldschmidt, however, did not stop here and went on to the question of whether it is possible to "construct" crystals of certain well-defined and desired properties, such as hardness, melting point, solubility, optical refraction, chemical reactivity, etc. Unfortunately this work on "model structures" of crystallized silicates and silicate glasses has remained comparatively unknown in the English-speaking world, as it was published in a journal not easily accessible (*Zeitschr. für technische Physik,* 1927). In this paper, readers will find the scientific basis of a problem of quite fundamental importance—how to construct solid materials of certain physical, chemical, and mechanical properties.

The year 1929 was a decisive year for V.M. (as he was affectionately called). In that year he was invited to join the faculty of natural sciences of Göttingen as full professor and head of the Mineralogical Institute. Other invitations from foreign universities had come to him, and more than one university was anxious to obtain the collaboration of the recognized leader in his field. Stockholm had previously tried before; V.M. decided in favor of Oslo. A few years before he went to Göttingen the University of Munich had planned to appoint V.M. to the vacant chair of Paul von Groth. The failure of this proposal is a typical and ominous sign of the political influence of a small group of professors in the town which later became the hotbed of Nazism. Unfortunately at the decisive meeting of the faculty a number of politically moderate and reliable people were absent, believing that Goldschmidt's appointment was already decided. As a result the invitation was turned down because "We already have one Jew at the Faculty." In protest against this racial discrimination, the "Jew at the Faculty" resigned. He was Richard Willstätter, Nobel Laureate, and one of the greatest organic chemists of his time.

In view of this experience, V.M. may have been reluctant to accept an invitation from another German university. However, Göttingen was not Munich and, in the tradition of its great permanent Under-Secretary Althoff, the Prussian Minister of Education, treated V.M. with the greatest courtesy and, fully aware of the great importance of this appointment, agreed to all V.M.'s wishes. It is said that after a meeting for Goldschmidt's official acceptance and final decisions the very dignified Under-Secretary and his advisers joined in a dance of joy.

Goldschmidt, with his father and their Norwegian housekeeper, Frökken Marie Brendigen (his mother had died shortly before), moved to Göttingen where V.M. bought a house in Wagnerstrasse. On arriving in Göttingen, father and son found the town "dressed over-all"—not to greet the distinguished scientist, but to honor Colonel Düsterberg, the leader of a somewhat nationalistic organization of soldiers called "Stahlhelm" (the Steel Helmet). The Stahlhelm was harmless compared with those organizations that replaced it after 1933; Colonel Düsterberg, being only "partly" Aryan, was forced by the Nazis and S.S. to resign. Nevertheless, it gave the Goldschmidts an ominous foretaste of things to come.

There was a galaxy of eminent men of science in Göttingen at that time. The mathematical tradition—uninterrupted from the days of Gauss—was carried on by David Hilbert, Courant, Landau, and others; the organic chemist and Nobel Laureate Wallach was living in retirement and his successor (also a Nobel Laureate), A. Windaus, of cholesterol fame, was at the height of his career. Another Nobel Prize winner was Zsigmondy; the physics department was headed by the triumvirate James Franck, Max Born, and W. Pohl—after 1933 the first two, both Nobel Laureates, became "unbearable." Prandtl, one of the founders of modern aerodynamics, was one of Göttingen's great men; so was G. Tammann, the physical chemist who was still very active after his retirement, and who was succeeded by A. Eucken. The zoologist Kühn and the astronomer Kienle became great personal friends of the Goldschmidts. There was also a young generation, many of whom have since become world-famous.

The few years before 1933 were perhaps the happiest in Goldschmidt's life. In Oslo he was something of a lone wolf; in Göttingen he not only inspired his own students and colleagues, but drew inspiration from them all—the physical chemists, the inorganic chemists, the physicists, astronomers, and biologists. It was an almost ideal cooperation among scientists of every branch, and nobody sat in an ivory tower, anxiously guarding the results of his own work from intruders. In addition there was a constant exchange of ideas with foreign visitors and guests.

The Mineralogical Institute was housed in a former school which was adapted according to V.M.'s requirements. One wing contained the lecture theater, students' working rooms and laboratories, and the teaching collections of crystals, minerals, and rocks. The teaching department was connected to the third-floor research wing by a wide corridor in which magnificent specimens of minerals were displayed. There, a group of young and very able scientists set out under the direction and guidance of V.M. to study the geochemistry of individual elements. The laws which govern the distribution of elements were postulated in Oslo. They were now applied to the systematic survey of a large number of elements.

This period between 1929 and 1935 or, to be more precise, 1933, was the happiest epoch in the lives of V.M. and his aging father H.J. There the lonely man found not only devotion of his collaborators, which he had enjoyed in Oslo, but also the warm friendship and admiration of his colleagues.

In those pre-war days Goldschmidt was a heavily built, stout man, shy and often difficult to approach. He had an almost old-fashioned courtesy which could change to an outspoken but equally courteous frankness in scientific and other arguments. Shortly before he died he told me a story which is a clue to his strange personality. When his father moved to Heidelberg young V.M., who was about six years old, attended a private school. His mother had impressed upon him that he must always be polite and also tell the truth, however disagreeable. After a few days at his new school, the headmaster, a big man with a black beard and of alarming appearance, asked young V.M. how he liked the school, and ended by saying: "I hope we will become good friends. Do you already like me?" Aware of his mother's admonition, after a moment's pause V.M. replied: "Nicht so besonders, Herr Göckel" (not particularly, Sir).

As well as this "truthful politeness" which is found in some of his polemics and in many of the discussions after scientific meetings (not always to the delight of those concerned), he had a grim and sarcastic sense of humor, and was very quick-witted. In all scientific and personal affairs he was completely sincere, honest, and incorruptible. There was no room in his department for anyone who did not measure up to his own scientific and moral standards, nor for sloppy and untidy workers. He was enthusiastic about new, exciting, scientific results wherever they came from; but his criticism of unsound or too highly publicized work could be devastating. He had a certain naive streak of vanity, and he was easily hurt if insufficient credit was given to his work. I well remember his reaction to a long review article on some fundamental problems of geochemistry by a well-known chemist, in which only one reference was given to a paper by V.M., and that, on a minor subject. However, this was after 1933 and the author had undergone a color metamorphosis to brown—the Nazi color. (It is only fair to emphasize that in the case of V.M.G. this was one of the rare exceptions. Almost all of his collaborators and colleagues stood by him in the dark days after 1933. Only one case is reported in which a younger and presumably ardent Nazi scientist dared to refer to V.M.'s name in the Nazi prescribed form—V.M. (Israel) Goldschmidt—in the Nazi-sponsored *Zeitschrift für die gesamte Naturforschung* (in the Germany of those days nicknamed "Zeitschrift *gegen* die gesamte Naturforschung").

He was by nature a pessimist and, partly perhaps because of his Jewish origin and of the anti-semitism which he had experienced from his childhood on, he occasionally suffered from a feeling of persecution. This was why he did not readily trust people until he knew them well and also why he was so responsive to genuine overtures of friendship. His kindness and generosity were unfailing, even to people unknown to him personally. He was a real animal lover and his garden was almost a bird sanctuary. There is the story about his learning the cat language, an attempt which came to an abrupt stop when he was attacked by a large tomcat to whom he had, apparently, unwittingly been extremely rude. The household, in addition to its human inhabitants, consisted of the famous dachshund "Bazi"—which tyrannized father and son; three squirrels demanded and received a home in the bathroom, a toad hibernated in the cellar, and a family of bats resided in the loft. Each had a name, and the toad shared his with a well-known and not too endearing character in Göttingen. One of the squirrels was named Parsifal ("because he was indescribably stupid") another was Richard (Weil er so stark riecht"), but the most notorious was Magdalena, who came to a sad and untimely end. V.M. gave a birthday party for Bazi and several dog guests were invited to share the birthday cake. In the excitement, Bazi concluded that on this special day everything was permitted and ended the feast by devouring Magdalena.

Only a few of his devoted assistants and collaborators in Göttingen can be mentioned—most of them are today heads of university departments: F. Laves, Zurich; Th. Ernst, Erlangen; H. Hauptmann, São Paolo; W. v. Engelhardt, Tübingen; H. Witte, Darmstadt; R. Mannkopff, Göttingen; C. Peters, Vienna.

The scientific harvest of this short Göttingen period was particularly rich. From 1930 to 1935 Goldschmidt published an inspiring series of papers on the geochemistry of rarer elements. In each case terrestrial material from all parts of the world was analyzed; meteoritic matter was also included. New analytical methods were developed, such as the cathode layer technique which proved to be one of the most valuable methods for the detection of elements down to and below 0.01 per cent. It is impossible to condense into a few paragraphs the results of well over two dozen papers, dealing with the geochemistry of the alkali metals, nickel, the noble metals, germanium, gallium, scandium, boron, arsenic, and selenium. In almost every case the abundance of the elements in the earth's crust, in meteorites, and in stellar atmospheres were investigated. One typical example is the investigation by V.M. of the geochemistry of germanium and its occurrence—with other rare elements—in coal and coal ashes.

This element is distributed in silicates of the upper lithosphere, owing to the similarity of the ionic radii of Ge and Si. It is also present in iron meteorites, and Goldschmidt found striking concentrations of it in the ashes of certain coals. A preliminary spectrographic analysis of the ashes of the boiler in V.M.'s institute and the soot in the chimney led to a systematic investigation of the geochemistry of coal ash. The highest amount—1.6 per cent GeO_2—was found by V.M. in ash from samples of Northumberland coal. Still higher amounts (up to 9 per cent) were found later in lignites from the District of Columbia, and in certain Russian coals.

The biochemical, or rather biophysical, mechanism of the enrichment of this and other rare elements—boron, arsenic, beryllium, cobalt, nickel, platinum metals—is still far from clear and needs further elucidation. Among those elements most highly concentrated in coal ash is arsenic. V.M. thought that one of the causes of the professional disease of chimney sweeps, skin cancer, may be the high content of arsenic in soot and flue dusts. It should

1576

be noted that petroleum shows a still greater affinity for trace elements than coal, and certain ashes of petroleum are used as a vanadium ore containing up to 70 per cent V_2O_5.

Some thirty years ago the metallurgy and the industrial uses of minor elements were practically unknown. It did not "pay" to recover rare elements or to develop industrial uses for these. Today, thirteen years after Goldschmidt's death, some of the minor elements have become of the utmost industrial importance. Goldschmidt showed where to find them and laid the foundation of their geochemical and crystal-chemical behavior.

The peaceful lives of Goldschmidt, father and son, were fundamentally changed and their work interrupted in 1933. The "thousand years" of the Third Reich had begun. Monsieur François Poncet, French Ambassador in Berlin, summed it up "C'est la victoire des Boches sur les Allemands." Göttingen and the other German centers of learning were systematically destroyed by the Nazis. Many eminent scientists deeply regretted this—but they did not protest, or make a firm stand against the measures taken by the Nazis against science and the arts. Some of V.M.'s students went to Berlin in the hope of convincing the Ministry of Education that V.M. must remain in Göttingen. Goldschmidt and his father, who had not previously belonged to any faith, ostentatiously joined the small Jewish community in Göttingen. V.M. was determined, in the interests of his students, to continue his work at the University as long as he could, knowing that soon he too would be dismissed and forced to leave the country. He became more lonely and withdrawn than before, constantly careful not to "compromise" or endanger his non-Jewish friends and colleagues. His sense of humor became more grim than ever. His father was once perturbed at being greeted by someone with "Heil Hitler." Goldschmidt retaliated by remarking that surely no atheist could be offended if greeted by "Grüss Gott."

He continued to work on his extensive research program; early each morning and again until late each night he sat at his ancient double-keyboard typewriter, writing scores of letters to colleagues and friends abroad, recommending young scientists who had lost their positions for racial reasons. Many young scientists owe to

V.M. not only their careers in countries outside Germany, but even their lives.

In 1935, after a new wave of anti-Semitism, Goldschmidt resigned his chair and returned to Norway. The Norwegian citizenship which he had to resign when he went to Göttingen was immediately granted and a chair at Oslo University offered to him. The Goldschmidts arrived back in Norway almost penniless; although emigrants and refugees from Germany were allowed to take their personal belongings with them, the money allowed was only ten marks per person. Much later part of Goldschmidt's money was transferred to Oslo as the result of a very courageous and outspoken letter written by F. K. Drescher-Kaden, V.M.'s successor in Göttingen, to the president of the German Reichsbank, Hjalmar Schacht. The house in Wagnerstrasse and all his other possessions were lost without compensation from Germany.

He rented the top floor of a small house in Holmenkollen, and divided all his energies between his scientific work and helping refugees from Germany and the countries invaded by the Germans before the war. He wrote the ninth and final publication of the "Verteilungsgesetze", a book of 150 pages covering the abundance and distribution of the individual elements and atomic species, and geochemical and cosmochemical data; in this attempt to estimate the mineral mass ratios of the chemical elements he also included isotopes, thus laying the foundation stone of isotope geology. He resumed his work for the Norwegian Raw Materials Laboratory, assisted by his devoted collaborator Aslak Kvalheim (who later became his successor in this government laboratory), and he continued his geochemical research. As a side line, and a money-making hobby, he resumed the industrial work he had done after World War I, when he did so much to develop the utilization of Norwegian raw materials. On the west coast of Norway there are large deposits of olivine; Goldschmidt discovered that it has refractory properties, and he himself developed the methods successfully used in industrial furnaces and ceramic kilns of transforming olivine rock into industrial refractories. In addition he made use of olivine sand and crushed dunite rocks instead of quartz sand for making molds for foundries. The olivine molds not only produce excellent castings of steel and high-melting ferro-alloys, but also reduce, and may even eliminate, the danger of silicosis in foundries.

In the tranquility of his new home Goldschmidt was at peace again, although he was distressed by tension and oppression in Germany and anxious about many of his friends still living there. His correspondence was greater than ever, and the file marked "N.A." (non-Aryan) grew daily. A personal tragedy for him was the sudden death of his father, and he became more lonely and withdrawn than before. Future and worse developments in the political theatre, however, soon made him realize that death had spared his father from participation in the coming cataclysm.

I went to stay with him in Oslo shortly after his father's death. He had aged, his health had deteriorated, and he was embittered and tired. But he went on with his scientific and his relief work with almost inexhaustible energy. He spent more than he could afford on helping other people and managed to bring an aged aunt and a niece—still a child—from Germany to Oslo, and the niece from there to the U.S.A. He still enjoyed his food and an occasional drink and he maintained his old-fashioned courtesy. His humor had become more whimsical, more grim, and sometimes even caustic. I remember one day when I asked him to come with me to take some flowers to the crematorium as a tribute to his parents. We stood reverently in front of the urns, all made of beautiful green Norwegian olivine, two with the ashes of his parents and a third, empty and destined to hold his own, and finally V.M. remarked dryly: "Ja, ja, the whole family in magnesium orthosilicate."

His pessimism in those pre-war days was sometimes almost unbearable. He knew the omens and foresaw the coming pandemonium from which there was no escape, and yet he worked and made plans for further research. The spectrographic unit was in full swing, and plans were ready for a new mass spectrometer with which to study the abundance and distribution of isotopes. And then war broke out, bringing the darkest days of Goldschmidt's life. He had always been a man of strong likes and dislikes and could not always see eye-to-eye with his colleagues. During the war, and especially when Norway was overrun by the

Germans, he forgot all his animosities in a personal attempt to resist the waves of evil which swept over Europe. He kept in touch with those friends in Germany who still dared to write to him and, in order not to compromise them during censorship, signed his letters illegibly. His main correspondence was with English friends; even during the Nazi occupation many messages reached the Allies through Goldschmidt's help.

By nature timid and anxious, he grew in stature during the war years, but his health suffered. Finally he was arrested by the S.S., his property was confiscated and he was sent to one of the concentration camps which the new masters had installed. These camps were full of the Norwegian intelligentsia—university teachers, lawyers, writers, etc.—regarded as dangerous by the regime. It is true, and it should never be forgotten, that nearly everyone in Norway was engaged in the resistance. Goldschmidt's case, however, was a special one: in addition to being one of the most prominent Norwegians, he was also a Jew, and therefore earmarked for extermination in the gas chamber. In November, 1942, he was listed for deportation to Poland, but at the last moment, probably through the clever intervention of the Norwegian police, and owing to his poor health, he was temporarily released. Then, with the help of the Norwegian resistance he was smuggled across the Swedish frontier in a load of hay which some German soldiers prodded with a fork.

Goldschmidt did not stay long in Sweden. He was eager to offer his services to the Allies, and in the spring of 1943 he was brought to England. It was in this country, and especially in Scotland, that, although seriously ill, he felt at peace again. Under the auspices of the Agricultural Research Council he first went to Craigiebuckler, near Aberdeen, to work at the Macaulay Institute for Soil Research. He was warmly received by its director, Dr. (now Sir) William Ogg and his wife, and for the first time in many years he knew what it meant to live in a free country. He took a great interest in soil research and, when Ogg became director of Rothamsted Experimental Station, he moved with him to Harpenden. He was liked by everybody and soon affectionately called "Goldie"; he took the greatest interest in the Institute's work on

1580

trace element distribution, and used to remark that it was in England, and through his contacts with Dr. Ogg, Dr. Alex Muir, and others that he began "to understand what geochemistry really is"—put with great modesty, this was certainly a great appreciation of the excellent work of British soil chemists.

Goldschmidt always hated the writing of papers and books, and he used to tell his pupils in Göttingen to write their papers as concisely as a Scotsman would if they were to be sent by telegram. It was with difficulty that Dr. Ogg and his colleagues eventually persuaded V.M. to write his last magnum opus, and gave him every facility for his work. But the task was too great and his health already too seriously undermined. Seven hundred folios were written, but he could not finish the rest. The ultimate book "Geochemistry" was completed after years of hard work by Alex Muir with the collaboration of A. Kvalheim and published posthumously by O.U.P. in 1954.

Many honors came to Goldschmidt—he received an honorary degree at Aberdeen University, and also the highest award of the Geological Society, the Wollaston Medal; but nothing pleased him more than his election, as one of its fifty foreign members, to the Royal Society, London. Perhaps, had he lived longer, he would have received a Nobel Prize, which he so richly deserved. His deepest satisfaction, however, was the kindness he received, and the fact of his freedom—in Göttingen, when one Nazi riot followed another, he and his father carried hydrocyanic acid in a capsule for emergency use as a final evasion of Nazi cruelty. In Norway, too, during the occupation, he carried poison in his pocket. On one occasion a university colleague of his in Oslo asked Goldschmidt for a capsule. "This poison," answered V.M., "is for professors of chemistry only. You, as professor of mechanics will have to use the rope." This was the typical grim humor of Goldschmidt. In England he did not need the poison any longer, and in a gay ceremony at Rothamsted it was solemnly buried deep in the garden.

I saw Goldschmidt again in January, 1946, after a long interval, and found him greatly changed in appearance. From then on I went to Harpenden once or twice every wek to spend the day with him. His agonizing experiences in Norway and his recent illnesses had made him lose weight and he looked more like a pathetic survivor of a Nazi concentration camp. In spirit, however, he was indestructible; he was still easily hurt if somebody failed to give credit to his work and he suffered, often with justification, from a sense of persecution. His English, although grammatically correct and even fluent, was known as "Goldschmidt English" because of his quaint pronunciation. As usual he was more generous than his means really allowed and the pockets of his suits, which always became baggy, bulged with dozens of small pieces of paper: notes of atomic constants, old bills, bus tickets, and the addresses of people to whom he wished to write, or whom he wished to help in their academic career.

In one fundamental way he had changed: the bitterness had gone—he no longer hated those who, in so grim a way, had twice interrupted his work, undermined his health, and shortened his life. One episode influenced V.M. deeply and occupied his mind until the end of his life: it happened early in November, 1942, in the County Hospital in Tönsberg, Norway, which was then the internment camp for Norwegian Jews. After a day of humiliation and torment by his Nazi jailers, V.M. talked to two other prisoners, whose names deserve to be recorded: Moses Katz, an orthodox Jew and a hosiery peddler, and Lesser Rosenblum, socialist, atheist, and manufacturer of umbrella handles. V.M. suggested that they should remember the names of their tormentors, so that any survivors might exact retribution. The reply of the pious Moses Katz was a surprise to V.M.: "Revenge is not for us; that must be left to the Almighty." With the arrogance of a scientist confident of his superior knowledge, V.M. asked what prayers would be permissible to God from men in their position. Katz replied without hesitating a moment: "You may pray that the hearts of your enemies may be enlightened." Goldschmidt, still not admitting defeat, turned to the atheist Rosenblum and asked for his view. His reproof was equally unexpected: "We must break the evil circle of retribution, or there can never be an end to evil."

Goldschmidt became very humble after this experience. He had escaped, but his two friends from Tönsberg were facing death in

Poland's gas chambers. He regarded their sayings as lucid and practical improvements on the Old Testament. Through them he learned not to forget, but to forgive.

The prolonged strain he had undergone, his escape, and the frequent adjustments to new countries and languages and people had completely undermined V.M.'s health, and for weeks he had to stay in bed. On one occasion he was staying with the Oggs. Dr. Ogg, on his way to bed very late, heard groans coming from V.M.'s bedroom. He had had a heart attack and was convinced that he was dying. Between groans he kept saying "This is the end. I have done my best for Norway and Britain." A doctor was called at once and Goldschmidt was given oxygen; but his condition was critical and the doctor, scarcely expecting him to live until the morning, gave Dr. Ogg the name and telephone number of an undertaker. V.M. appeared to be unconscious but evidently heard these remarks. He had enormous will power and was not yet prepared to be defeated by illness. When he was being carried out to the ambulance in the morning he was joking about the undertaker.

His mind worked constantly; many fascinating theories occupied him and were developed in talks with visiting friends. No record of these is available as Goldschmidt never committed to paper, or published, ideas which he could not yet prove. He strongly disliked the premature publication of theories: "Make two thousand experiments, and then you have your theory and can publish both," he used to say.

However, he did write two papers which, for different reasons, he was unwilling to publish. There exists a handwritten manuscript, "Geochemical Aspects of the Origin of Complex Organic Molecules on the Earth as Precursors to Organic Life." It was published after his death in a series of popular scientific books but has remained practically unknown to scientists, and Goldschmidt himself would never have agreed to its publication in its unfinished form. Some of the ideas expressed in this draft may one day reappear and their significance be recognized.

The second paper—actually more a note—was written in cooperation with G. Nagelschmidt and was never published because Goldschmidt felt it was, perhaps, undignified to end his fundamental scientific work with a note on album Graecum (dog feces), a prosaic and unattractive product, however interesting in its chemistry, in which insoluble phosphates are transformed into white and soluble ones. It may be recalled that before World War I it was used in the manufacture of fine, high-grade leather. The idea of this note must have come to V.M. during the war, when he grew vegetables in a small suburban garden outside Oslo where many people kept dogs. Album Graecum is an ideal phosphate fertilizer for a poor soil; but if it would be undignified as a scientific paper V.M. thought it would be even more undignified for a middle-aged professor to collect album Graecum from suburban pavements for his garden. He was in any case a very reluctant gardener, and had a widely representative collection of weeds in his allotment.

For several months in Harpenden, when he was too weak to leave his bed, he must have felt that his life was slowly drawing toward its close. He did not speak of the disappointments, the sorrows, the pains, and the dangers he had experienced, but of bygone and happy days; of Göttingen and his friends and pupils who resumed contact with him after the war. He was happy that his old Institute had two of his friends as his successors, first F. K. Drescher-Kaden and after him C. W. Correns; and he was happy that his work was carried on by the younger generation which had been so strongly influenced by him. In his weakness V.M., who had never spoken German since 1939, sometimes lapsed unconsciously into his mother tongue. It was a moving experience to visit Goldschmidt in those days—the lonely man with some enemies, but with many devoted friends. These he remembered in gratitude, the others he forgot. "Should you see Dr. Lonsdale or Professor Tilley, and if you write to my old friend Eskola, please remember me to them," he would say, wanting them all to know that he was still alive. He could no longer go to see the Oggs, but they came and looked after him and he kept his friendship and gratitude for them until he died.

However, his time had not yet come. He recovered sufficiently to prepare for his return to Oslo. Once he felt better, his unfailing will power took possession of him, and he made plans to resume his scientific work on a large scale. At the end of June, 1946, he left England and arrived safely in Oslo. "Father's Return" was celebrated enthusiastically at the Raw Material Research Laboratory, and he was delighted to see among other friends W. Zachariasen of Chicago University, one of the pupils of whom he was most proud. At his flat much of his furniture had been recovered with the help of the government, and there were letters from Göttingen, offering him his old chair and from China, inviting him to organize raw materials research in that country. Soon, however, he had to undergo examination and treatment in several hospitals. His reports were optimistic, heart, kidneys, and lungs seemed to be satisfactory, and he hoped to have several years ahead in which he could work, provided he "followed the recognized principles of Moses Katz." Miss Brendigen had again joined his household, and had provided him with what he regarded as a delicious specialty, fresh whale meat! In October for the first time he mentioned a black spot on his leg; he received x-ray treatment, but the growth proved to be malignant and required surgery. The carcinoma could not be removed completely, and again Goldschmidt had to go into the hospital. Still he continued working on his book, directing scientific and industrial research and writing letters to his friends. In March, 1947, he entered the surgical ward for the sixth operation. On March 19 I had a few scribbled lines that the operation had been successful and that he would be allowed to go home on the following morning. He arrived home on the twentieth, complained of a sudden intense pain in his head, and died almost immediately.

In one of his last letters to me he wrote:

The wisdom of the Moses Katz principles is undeniable. . . . And I am fully convinced that it is my duty towards science and decency to stand firm in continuing my work as long as health permits, thus giving an example to at least some of my junior colleagues. Often I think that (to maintain these principles) to be even more important than my contributions to scientific and industrial research and my scientific teaching. To set a new standard of morality is a matter of great urgency in these times . . .

NOTES AND REFERENCES

1 "Die Pyroluminescenz des Quarzes," *Kgl: Norske videns.-skab. Selskabs. Skrifter,* No. 5, 1–15 (1906).

2 "Die Kontaktmetamorphose im Kristiania-Gebiete," *Ibid.*, No. 1, 1–483 (1911).

3 "Geologisch-petrographische Studien im Hochgebirge des suedlichen Norwegens. I–V" *Ibid.* (1912, 1915, 1916, 1920).

4 "Geochemische Verteilungsgesetze der Elemente. I–IX," *Ibid.* (1923–1937).

ACKNOWLEDGMENTS

I gratefully acknowledge the help and advice of friends of V. M. Goldschmidt: Professor C. W. Correns, Göttingen; Dr. Alex Muir, Harpenden; Sir William Ogg, Edzell, Angus; Professor C. E. Tilley, F.R.S., Cambridge.

PAUL ROSBAUD

·· *113* ··

Thomas Midgley, Jr.

1889-1944

THOMAS MIDGLEY, JR., discovered a new tool for chemical research: with its aid he invented two new, very important industrial chemicals. Twice he set out deliberately to put together a new chemical compound with exact specifications for its chemical and physical properties, intended to do a very particular job. His synthesis of the antiknock agent, tetraethyl lead, and the refrigerant, trichlorofluoromethane, now used also as an aerosol propellent, were beautiful pieces of pure, or at least deliberately planned chemical research. Midgley is memorable for the new, time-saving idea he introduced into modern research techniques.

There was a rich strain of inventiveness in his blood. His mother's father, James Emerson, invented the insert-tooth saw. His own father made half a dozen notable inventions.

Thomas, Sr., born in London in 1860, came to the United States with his parents as a small boy and received his education in the public schools of Worcester, Massachusetts. In 1874 he got a job in a shoe factory and four years later, at eighteen, he was a foreman in a wire-drawing plant. In 1884 he moved to Beaver Falls, Pennsylvania, as superintendent of the Hartford Steel Company, and it was here that Thomas, Jr., was born on May 18, 1889.

When his son was a year old, Thomas Midgley ventured into his own business, making wire-goods specialties, but in 1896 he became factory manager of the Columbus Bicycle Company, Columbus, Ohio. Again, four years later, he began on his own to manufacture steel wire wheels for bicycles and automobiles. In 1905 the father was back in New England as consultant to the Hartford Rubber Works and Morgan & Wright. In 1914 he launched the Midgley Tires Company in West Virginia, but soon moved to Ohio. Here he was joined by his son, who had been graduated three years before from Cornell.

The father held many patents in wire-drawing, in specialties made from wire, and in rubber-compounding. His various business ventures were based upon his own inventions, notably a woven wire wheel with detachable tires, which was replaced by the more popular "clincher" tires, and the Midgley collapsible core tire,

1589

which had the advantage of being quite puncture-proof, but it never supplanted the pneumatic tube which, at this time, was being rapidly improved.

Young Tom Midgley was sent to Betts Academy at Greenwich, Connecticut, a small private school with a superior faculty. Among his teachers was a former professor at the Naval Academy, Annapolis, who gave him his first instruction in chemistry and with whom he long remembered an argument on the periodic table. This sophomoric debate on God *vs.* the tiny particles was a forecast of the novel application he was to make years later of Mendeleev's periodic law. But when he entered Cornell, Tom elected, not chemistry or chemical engineering, but mechanical engineering, in which he received his M.E. in 1908 and his Ph.D. in 1911.

Without tarrying for graduation exercises and his diploma, he hurried to Dayton, Ohio, to report on his first job in the Inventions Department of the National Cash Register Company. For the compelling reason that he was very much in love with a young lady just graduating at Ohio Wesleyan, he wanted to get on the payroll as quickly as possible. Within two months, on August 3, 1911, he and Carrie M. Reynolds of Delaware, Ohio, were married. As he said, "Like all good fairly tales, we lived happily ever afterwards." They had two children; a son, Thomas III, and a daughter, Jane, who became Mrs. Edward Z. Lewis.

Research and development work at the National Cash Register Company was then presided over by Dr. Charles F. Kettering, and Midgley later acknowledged that "it was his dynamic personality; a bigger salary than anyone but an optimist could hope I could possibly earn; and the Ohio address of National Cash, that made me choose this job—but mostly it was Boss Kett."

Kettering handsomely returned the compliment. More than once he said, "The greatest discovery I ever made was Tom Midgley."

Certainly it was the influence of Boss Kett that brought him back to Dayton from his association with his father in the Midgley Tires Company. Meanwhile, Kettering had set up the Dayton Engineering Laboratory (Delco) to develop his own inventions. Among these was a home lighting system for which he had modified the regular internal combustion engine to use kerosene because at that time many cities had fire laws forbidding the storage of gasoline in residential property. The kerosene-fueled engine developed such a bad knock that it occasionally cracked the cylinder head. Midgley, who was working on battery hydrometers, was assigned the job of finding the cause of knocking and how it might be eliminated.

He arranged a series of optical lenses to magnify and record the shape of the pressure wave which soon indicated that the knock was not caused by preignition, as had been supposed, but was due to the rapid rise in pressure after ignition and near top dead center. Kettering suggested that kerosene dyed red might absorb radiant heat and so vaporize more quickly and run more smoothly.

Had Midgley been a good physicist he would have recognized that this hypothesis was not workable, but as an experimentalist he went to the laboratory stockroom for an oil-soluble red dye. Finding none, at the suggestion of Fred L. Chase, he used iodine. The knocking stopped. They tried a dozen different red dyes, to find a cheaper reagent, but none eliminated the knock. When they found that colorless ethyl iodide was a capital antiknock agent, it was clear that iodine, not color, stopped the knock. Thus Midgley at once discovered by chance the first antiknock and identified scientifically the cause of this phenomenon. He patented the Midgley High Speed Indicator, which won him the Longstreth Medal of the Franklin Institute.

These researches turned Midgley into a chemist. Realizing his shortcomings in chemistry, he began a stiff course of self-education. For the next three years, given a few free moments, he was to be found deep in some stout chemical text and he acquired the habit of buttonholing his chemical associates to ask them very pointed questions.

We were in the midst of World War I: better aviation gas was a sore need. Collaborating with the Bureau of Mines, the Dayton laboratory staff attacked the antiknock problem under Midgley's leadership. He tackled this job with all his celebrated gusto backed by do-or-die determination. He had plenty of expert help: Alan R. Albright, T. A. Boyd, Carrol A. Hochwald, and Charles A. Thomas, all of the Delco group, later Robert E. Wilson and Charles S. Venable, then both professors at M.I.T.; finally Charles M. A. Stine, Willis Harrington, Elmer K. Bolton, and others from Du

Pont, to name but a few of the many whose advice and assistance Midgley time and again acknowledged gratefully. They went to work by the good old Edisonian method: "Try everything on the laboratory shelf and if nothing works make up some new ones."

From the front lines a cable reported that captured German aviation gas contained cyclohexane; Midgley and three associates worked one night through, attempting to hydrogenate benzene. Leo Baekeland, who was assisting the Army in this frantic fuel hunt, skeptically offered a wooden medal for the first pint of cyclohexane, which was actually produced at Dayton, October 26, 1917, using nickel oxide as a catalyst with a yield of 23 per cent. Tests showed that while the freezing point of cyclohexane is 40°F., a mixture of 80 per cent cyclohexane and 20 per cent benzene did not freeze till −40°. By July a pilot plant, built by Boyd, produced 50 gallons, and a liter bottle in a plush-lined mahogany case was sent to Baekeland. Plant experience nearly doubled the yield and flying tests modified the mixture to two-thirds cyclohexane and one-third benzene. Christened Hecter, this additive made it possible to increase the compression of an aviation engine from 5.5:1 to 8:1. The war ended before the 500-gallon-a-day cyclohexane plant was completed.

The cut-and-dry search continued. "From melted butter and camphor to ethyl acetate and aluminum chloride" was how Midgley ruefully described these tests, "and most of them had no more effect than spitting in the Great Lakes."

Hydrogen peroxide had the distinction of being the first positive knock-promoter found and zinc ethyl the first metallic alkyl tested. On January 30, 1919, it was discovered that two cubic centimeters of aniline was a more effective antiknock than a gram of iodine. This was the first tangible encouragement. It came at the right time, for the war was over, and it was agreed that after the turn of the year "this wild goose chase should be abandoned." So the hunt went on, and during the following summer two college professors—McPhearson of Ohio State and Ebaugh of Denison—brought down suitcases full of different chemicals for trial.

March 1, 1920, the Dayton Laboratory was taken over by General Motors. Splendidly housed in the former Dayton-Wright airplane factory, they received general instructions to continue the antiknock work and raise the sights to include carbon-dissolving compounds and the broad problem of more, better, and cheaper motor fuel.

The hawk-eyed Kettering picked up in a newspaper item that selenium oxychloride had been hailed as a "universal solvent," and at his suggestion Midgley very skeptically tried this out. By many experiments both chlorine and oxygen had been classified as elements that generally increase knocking, but the selenium compound was a capital antiknock agent. Simultaneous tests with sulfur oxychloride demonstrated that it was a splendid knock promoter. This chemical contradiction arrested Midgley's attention. Hochwald prepared diethyl, methyl, propyl, and phenyl selenium and the corresponding tellurium compounds. All proved to be more or less successful antiknock additives to gasoline.

To this hint Midgley's inventive brain responded immediately. He was disgusted with the slow, wasteful, hit-and-miss procedure. Why not narrow the field by an investigation of compounds based upon the periodic arrangement of the elements?

This was the germ of Midgley's new, time-saving research technique. He used a special arrangement of the elements by Robert E. Wilson, based on Irving Langmuir's theory of atomic structure. This new approach suggested a study of the metallo-organic compounds, and in four months Midgley demonstrated indubitably that antiknocking is a periodic function of the elements and highest as one went down the table.

Tetraethyl tin having proved exceptionally effective, on December 9, 1921, Midgley and Hochwald prepared tetraethyl lead. They tested 1/40 of 1 per cent of it in kerosene and it gave better results than 1.3 per cent of aniline, their adopted standard. The long hunt, started in July, 1917, for a satisfactory antiknocking agent had ended.

Midgley played an important supporting role in the commercial development of ethyl gas. The primary problem was an economical, large-scale manufacturing process. It was solved by a combination of methods devised by Midgley, the Du Pont and the Standard Oil of New Jersey research staffs. This led to the joint organization of Ethyl Corporation of which he was vice-president, and at the beginning, general manager. Initial formation of lead oxide and its

1593

deposition on valves was cured by the addition of ethylene dibromide. This created a demand for far more tons of bromine than had ever been dreamed of, which prompted the recovery of bromine from the sea according to a process suggested by Midgley, but perfected naturally enough by the Dow Chemical people. Since 1892 this company had been the largest American producer of bromine, extracted from Michigan brine. Another jointly owned company, the Ethyl-Dow Corporation, opened its famous bromine-from-seawater plant at Kure Beach, North Carolina, in 1934.

Amid these industrial developments, Dr. Lester S. Keilholtz, chief engineer of the Frigidaire Division of General Motors, came to Dayton with a message from Kettering. Artificial refrigeration was blossoming luxuriantly. Ammonia was still the great industrial refrigerant: methyl chloride and sulfur dioxide were the leading rivals in the household field. A disastrous accident in a Cleveland hospital dramatically emphasized the poisonous character of the former and the American Medical Association took pains to point out that sulfur dioxide (used in the early Frigidaire machines) was not less dangerous. A number of bad-smelling warning additives to the refrigerants were suggested and made obligatory by state and municipal health ordinances. But Kettering, keenly apprehending all the implications of this situation, was not satisfied with a warning.

"We must have," he said to Midgley through Keilholtz, "a nontoxic, nonflammable, cheap refrigerating agent, quick! What can you do about it?"

Here was a challenge with definite specifications—nontoxicity and nonflammability—but also with rigid limitations, for the much-needed chemical must have a boiling point between $0°$ and $-40°C$.

While waiting to join Midgley and the Frigidaire envoy at lunch, Albert L. Henne and Robert McNary went to the library; they checked the International Critical Tables of volatile organic compounds, and noted the obvious mistake that recorded the boiling point of carbon tetrafluoride as $-15°C$. Discussion of this error over coffee focused attention on fluorine compounds, possibly chlorofluorides, and the probability that the chemical they sought would be a reasonably complex compound.

Midgley thought of the periodic table arranged according to the Langmuir theory of atomic structure which had so profitably narrowed the antiknock search. It was quickly found that only elements on the right side with vacant spaces were volatile; that flammability is reduced from left to right; that toxicity declines from the heavy toward the light elements. Midgley himself has described what followed:

> Plotting boiling points, hunting toxicity data, corrections; slide rules and log paper, eraser dirt and pencil shavings, all the rest of the paraphernalia that take the place of tea leaves and crystal spheres in the life of the scientific clairvoyant were brought into play.

By this paper-and-pencil research they concluded the most likely fluorine compound, probably the simplest to produce in quantity, was dichlorodifluoromethane. This seemed an unlikely selection. Chlorine and fluorine are highly toxic and the flammability of methane is almost notorious. But its physical properties as a refrigerant were perfect, and they began to check its toxicity.

In the preparation of this new refrigerant they had used five one-ounce bottles of antimony trifluoride, purchased through a laboratory supply house which had scoured the country for this tiny stock. Selecting one of these bottles at random, a few grams of the first Freon was prepared for trial. A guinea pig under a bell jar with a sample was not even irritated, but scampered merrily about most contentedly.

A second batch was prepared from another bottle. It killed guinea pig Number Two almost instantly. Something was radically wrong—but what?

Before making the third batch from a third bottle, Midgley applied the good old nose test. The unmistakable odor of phosgene revealed the trouble. Four of those five little bottles contained antimony trifluoride contaminated with a double salt-containing water of crystallization. This was enough to produce phosgene in ample quantity to be lethal. A simple caustic wash cleared this grave difficulty.

"The chances were four to one against us," said Midgley afterward, "and I often wonder if the sudden decrease of our first guinea pig would not have so completely shaken our confident expectation that our new compound could not possibly be toxic, that —well, I still wonder if we would have been smart enough to have continued the investigation. Even if we had, the chances were still three to one against our using the one pure sample. I still wonder."

This sensationally successful research was completed in three days, quick enough to astonish everyone connected with it. It was a striking demonstration of the time-saving possible by applying Midgley's new technique in attacking the problem of a new synthesis. His method, with all sorts of modifications, has since been applied to every kind of hitherto unknown compounds for many purposes—from lubricant antioxidants and synthetic detergents to insecticides and medicinals.

With a frank disclosure of his new method, Midgley announced the new product at the Atlanta meeting of the American Chemical Society, April, 1930. Several years later, when he was awarded the Perkin Medal, he gave a striking demonstration of its salient properties. Before that distinguished and dignified audience he breathed in a great gulp of Freon and then exhaled it through a rubber tube under a bell jar where it quickly extinguished a lighted candle. Here was proof positive that Freon was neither poisonous nor flammable. It was also a fine example of his instinct for the dramatic, his inborn sense of clever showmanship.

Tom Midgley was a jovial man. His good spirits fairly bubbled over. He was an outgoing man, fond of all sorts of people, a human being with such a relish for life that he had fun performing the most routine and monotonous tasks. Beneath this almost Pickwickian exterior was a keenly analytical intelligence, ambition to excel, and a dogged determination. He was as capable as he was popular, which, on both counts, is high praise.

Few chemists have won more awards for their accomplishments: the Nichols Medal, 1923; the Longstreth Medal, 1925; the Perkin Medal, 1937; the Priestley Medal, 1941; the Willard Gibbs Medal, 1942. But no other chemist had so many honors that were also personal tributes. He was elected president of the American Chemical Society and was named American delegate to the International Congress of Applied Chemistry and a member of the National

Academy of Science. Significantly, he was honored with membership in an exceptional number of professional fraternities: Sigma Xi, Phi Kappa Phi, Tau Beta Phi, Alpha Chi Sigma, and Atmos.

His death was tragic and untimely, for although crippled by an attack of polio in 1940, he was mentally active and busied with chemical affairs. He had devised a harness with pulleys to aid himself in arising from bed, and somehow he became entangled in it and was strangled. He died at his home in Worthington, Ohio, near Columbus, November 2, 1944, at the age of fifty-five.

NOTES AND REFERENCES

Midgley was granted 117 U.S. patents and was a prolific contributor to technical and scientific journals so that his pressional career is well documented.

Robt. E. Wilson's presentation address of the Perkin Medal [*Ind. Eng. Chem.,* 29, 239 (1937)] and his informal sketch in *Ethyl News,* February 1948, are outstanding; see also "Who Was Who," II, 371.

For tetraethyl lead development, a full account, based on unpublished reports in files of General Motors Corp. with complete documentation, is in Williams Haynes, "American Chemical Industry," Van Nostrand, New York, 1945–54, vol. IV, pp. 396–405; also Kettering, *Trans. Soc. Automotive Engrs.,* 4, 269 (1919); H. S. Tegner, *Petrol. Times,* 19, 750 (1928).

For Freon: *Chem. Met. Eng.,* 37, 261, 286 (1930); *Ind. Eng. Chem.,* 22, 542 (1930); Haynes, *op. cit.,* V, 181–85.

For Ethyl Corp., *Ibid.,* VI, 151. For Thos. Midgley, Sr., *India Rubber World,* 62, 676 (1920).

Obits, *Chem. Ind.,* 55, 806 (1944); *Chem. Eng. News,* Nov. 10, 1944; *Rubber Age,* 56, 202 (1944); *New York Times,* Nov. 3, 1944.

WILLIAMS HAYNES

·· *114* ··

Wallace Hume Carothers

1896-1937

WALLACE HUME CAROTHERS, who died on April 29, 1937, was born in Burlington, Iowa, on April 27, 1896. His contributions to organic chemistry were recognized as outstanding and, in spite of the relatively short span of time for his productive accomplishments, he became a leader in his field with an enviable international reputation.

His paternal forbears were of Scotch origin and settled in Pennsylvania in prerevolutionary days. They were farmers and artisans. His father, Ira Hume Carothers, who was born in 1869 on a farm in Illinois, taught country school at the age of 19. Later he entered the field of commercial education and for forty-five years has been engaged in that type of work as teacher and vice-president in the Capital City Commerical College, Des Moines, Iowa. Wallace Hume Carothers was the first scientist in the family.

His maternal ancestors were of Scotch-Irish stock and were also, for the most part, farmers and artisans. They were great lovers of music, and this may account for the intense interest in and appreciation of music which Carothers possessed. His mother, who was Mary Evalina McMullin of Burlington, Iowa, exerted a powerful influence and guidance in the earlier years of his life.

To his sister Isobel (Mrs. Isobel Carothers Berolzheimer), of radio fame as Lu in the trio Clara, Lu and Em, he was especially devoted. Her death in January 1936, was a staggering shock to him and he was never able to reconcile himself completely to her loss.

On February 21, 1936, he married Helen Everett Sweetman of Wilmington, Delaware. Her father is Willard Sweetman, an accountant, and her mother, Bertha Everett. The family is of English-Welsh descent. Mrs. Carothers received her bachelor's degree in chemistry at the University of Delaware in 1933 and was employed in the patent division of the chemical department of the Du Pont Company from 1933 to 1936. A daughter, Jane, was born November 27, 1937.

Wallace was the oldest of four children. His education began

1601

in the public schools of Des Moines, Iowa, to which city his parents moved when he was five years of age. In 1914 he graduated from the North High School. As a growing boy he had zest for work as well as play. He enjoyed tools and mechanical things and spent much time in experimenting. His school work was characterized by thoroughness and his high school classmates testify that when he was called upon to recite his answers revealed careful preparation. It was his habit to leave no task unfinished or done in a careless manner. To begin a task was to complete it.

He entered the Capital City Commerical College in the fall of 1914 and graduated in the accountancy and secretarial curriculum in July 1915, taking considerably less time than the average. He entered Tarkio College, Tarkio, Missouri, in September 1915, to pursue a scientific course, and simultaneously accepted a position as assistant in the Commercial Department. He continued in this capacity for two years and then was made an assistant in English, although he had specialized in chemistry from the time he entered college. During World War I the head of the department of chemistry, Dr. Arthur M. Pardee, was called to another institution, and Tarkio College found it impossible to secure a fully equipped teacher of chemistry. Carothers, who previously had taken all of the chemistry courses offered, was appointed to take over the instruction. Since he was rejected as a soldier on account of a slight physical defect, he was free to serve in this capacity during his junior and senior years. It is interesting that during his senior year there were four senior chemistry-major students in his class and every one of them later completed work for the doctorate, studying in the universities of this country and abroad. Today they bear testimony to the fact that as undergraduates they owed much to the inspiration and leadership of Carothers.

Upon entering college his interest in chemistry and physical sciences was immediate and lasting, and he rapidly outdistanced his classmates in accomplishment. As a student he showed mature judgment and was always regarded by his fellow students as an exceptional person. Invariably he was the brightest student in the class regardless of the subject. Financial necessity required that he earn a large portion of his educational expenses. He always found time, however, to associate with the other students, though he showed little interest for the boisterous enthusiasms of the average underclassman. During his last two years in college he was entrusted with a number of student offices to which he gave freely of his time and energy.

Leaving Tarkio College in 1920 with his bachelor of science degree, he enrolled in the chemistry department of the University of Illinois where he completed the requirements for the master of arts degree in the summer of 1921. His former instructor at Tarkio College, then head of the chemistry department at the University of South Dakota, desired a young instructor to handle courses in analytical and physical chemistry and was fortunate in securing Carothers for this position during the school year, 1921–1922. He went to South Dakota only with the intention of securing sufficient funds to enable him to complete his graduate work, but the careful and adequate preparation of his courses, as well as his care of the students under his direction, showed that he could be a very successful teacher of chemistry. He was still the same quiet, methodical worker and scholar, not forceful as a lecturer, but careful and systematic in his contact with the students. He always required adequate preparation of assigned work and was able to get a large volume in student accomplishment.

Simultaneously with his teaching work he started to develop some independent research problems. He was especially interested in the 1916 paper of Irving Langmuir on valence electrons and desired to investigate some of the implications it held in organic chemistry. Pursuing this idea he carried out laboratory studies which were reported in his first independent contribution to the Journal of the American Chemical Society, "The Isosterism of Phenyl Isocyanate and Diazobenzene-Imide." His second independent paper, published while still a student, was that on "The Double Bond." In this he presented the first clear, definite application of the electronic theory to organic chemistry on a workable basis. He described the electronic characteristics of the double bond and in essence included in his discussion everything that has since been written on this particular subject.

It was evident, even at this stage of his career, that teaching was not his forte. Literally he spent all of his spare time on research problems in which he became interested. A number of his newly found friends in South Dakota tried to induce him to relax somewhat from his constant and sustained application to work, but without avail. He appeared to be driven by the many things that occurred to him as worthy of investigation in the laboratory.

He returned to the University of Illinois in 1922 to complete his studies for the degree of doctor of philosophy, which he received in 1924. His major work was in organic chemistry with a thesis under the direction of Dr. Roger Adams, on the catalytic reduction of aldehydes with platinum-oxide platinum-black and on the effect of promoters and poisons on this catalyst in the reduction of various organic compounds. His minors were physical chemistry and mathematics. He exhibited the same brilliance in all of his courses and in research which characterized his earlier accomplishments. Although specializing in organic chemistry, he was considered by the physical chemists to have a more comprehensive knowledge of physical chemistry than any of the students majoring in that field. During 1920–1921 he held an assistantship for one semester in inorganic chemistry and for one semester in organic chemistry. He was a research assistant during 1922–1923, and during 1923–1924 held the Carr Fellowship, the highest award offered at that time by the department of chemistry at Illinois. During these two years his seminar reports demonstrated his wide grasp of chemical subjects. The frequency with which his student colleagues sought his advice and help was indicative of his outstanding ability. At graduation he was considered by the staff as one of the most brilliant students who had ever been awarded the doctor's degree. A vacancy on the staff of the chemistry department of the University of Illinois made it possible to appoint him as an instructor in organic chemistry in the fall of 1924. In this capacity he continued with unusual success for two years, teaching qualitative organic analysis and two organic laboratory courses, one for premedical students and the other for chemists.

Harvard University, in 1926, was in need of an instructor in organic chemistry. After carefully surveying the available candidates from the various universities of the country, Carothers was selected. In this new position he taught during the first year a course in experimental organic chemistry and an advanced course in structural chemistry, and during the second year he gave the

1604

lectures and laboratory instruction in elementary organic chemistry.

President James B. Conant, of Harvard University, was professor of organic chemistry at the time that Carothers was instructor. He says of him:

Dr. Carothers' stay at Harvard was all too short. In the brief space of time during which he was a member of the chemistry department, he greatly impressed both his colleagues and the students. He presented elementary organic chemistry to a large class with distinction. Although he was always loath to speak in public even at scientific meetings, his diffidence seemed to disappear in the classroom. His lectures were well ordered, interesting, and enthusiastically received by a body of students only few of whom planned to make chemistry a career. In his research, Dr. Carothers showed even at this time that high degree of originality which marked his later work. He was never content to follow the beaten track or to accept the usual interpretations of organic reactions. His first thinking about polymerization and the structure of substances of high molecular weight began while he was at Harvard. His resignation from the faculty to accept an important position in the research laboratory of the Du Pont Company was Harvard's loss but chemistry's gain. Under the new conditions at Wilmington, he had facilities for carrying on his research on a scale that would be difficult or impossible to duplicate in most university laboratories. Those of us in academic life, however, always cherished the hope that some day he would return to university work. In his death, academic chemistry, quite as much as industrial chemistry, has suffered a severe loss.

In 1928 the Du Pont Company had completed plans to embark on a new program of fundamental research at their central laboratory, the Experimental Station at Wilmington, Delaware. Carothers was selected to head the research in organic chemistry. The decision to leave his academic position was a difficult one. The new place demanded only research and offered the opportunity of trained research men as assistants. This overbalanced the freedom of university life and he accepted. From then on until his death his accomplishments were numerous and significant. He had the rare quality of recognizing the significant points in each problem he undertook, and unusual ability for presenting his results in a most explicit and precise way, which led to clarity and understanding. In these nine years he made several major contributions to the theory of organic chemistry and discoveries which led to materials of significant commercial importance. Dr. Elmer K. Bolton, Chemical Director of the Du Pont Company, writes concerning Carothers:

At the time the Du Pont Company embarked upon its program of fundamental research in organic chemistry in the Chemical Department, Dr. Carothers was selected to direct this activity, because he had received the highest recommendations from Harvard University and the University of Illinois, and was considered to have unusual potentiality for future development. There was placed under his direction a small group of excellently trained chemists to work on problems of his own selection. The results of his work, extending over a period of nine years, have been of outstanding scientific interest and have been considered of great value to the Company as they have laid the foundation for several basically new developments of commercial importance.

In our association with Dr. Carothers, we were always impressed by the breadth and depth of his knowledge. He not only provided inspiration and guidance to men under his immediate direction, but gave freely of his knowledge to the chemists of the department engaged in applied research. In addition, he was a brilliant experimentalist. Regarding his personal characteristics, he was modest, unassuming to a fault, most uncomplaining, a tireless worker— deeply absorbed in his work, and was greatly respected by his associates. He suffered, however, from a nervous condition which in his later years was reflected in poor health and which became progressively worse in spite of the best medical advice and care, and the untiring efforts of his friends and associates. His death has been a great loss to chemistry and particularly to the Chemical Department. In my judgment, he was one of the most brilliant organic chemists ever employed by the Du Pont Company.

His reputation spread rapidly; his advice was sought continually, not only by his colleagues but also by chemists throughout the world. In 1929 he was elected associate editor of the Journal of the American Chemical Society; in 1930 he became an editor of Organic Syntheses. He took an active part in the meetings of the organic division of the American Chemical Society. He was invited frequently to speak before various chemical groups. He addressed the Johns Hopkins summer colloquium in 1935 on "Polymers and the Theory of Polymerization." That year he also spoke on the same subject before the Faraday Society in London, when his paper was considered one of the outstanding presentations on the program. His achievements were recognized by his election to the National Academy of Sciences in 1936—the first organic chemist associated with industry to be elected to that organization. During these years, from 1928 to 1937, several attractive academic positions were offered him but he chose to remain to the end with the company which had given him his opportunity for accomplishment.

Very early in life he displayed a love for books. From the time when *Gulliver's Travels* interest a boy on through Mark Twain's books, *Life of Edison,* and on up to the masters of English literature, he was a great reader. He possessed a singing voice that might have developed under training into something very worthwhile. Though he had no technical training in music, he was a lover of the great masters, and possessed a large and much-used collection of phonograph records of their works. He said occasionally that were he to start over he would devote his life to music.

Carothers was deeply emotional, generous and modest. He had a lovable personality. Although generally silent in a group of people, he was a brilliant conversationalist when with a single individual, and quickly displayed his broad education, his wide fund of information on all problems of current life, and his critical analysis of politics, labor problems and business, as well as of music, art, and philosophy. With all his fine physique he had an extremely sensitive nature and suffered from periods of depression which grew more pronounced as he grew older, despite the best efforts of his friends and medical advisors.

SCIENTIFIC WORK

His early scientific work involved an extension to organic compounds of Langmuir's idea of isosterism. He demonstrated that it was valid in the case of phenyl isocyanate and azoimide. Reactions of the double bond were interpreted in terms of the electronic theory, using a point of view that has since gained wide acceptance.

His next efforts were devoted to demonstrating that any idea of "negativity" alone is inherently incapable of accounting for the relative reactivity of organic halides. He measured the base strength of a series of amines. His work on the thermal decomposition of alkali alkyls threw light on the inherent properties of the simplest organic anions.

The first field of which he was in a position to make an exhaustive study was that of acetylene polymers and their derivatives. With vinylacetylene and divinylacetylene made available to him, he completed a detailed study of these substances. It was his discovery that it was possible to add hydrogen chloride to monovinylacetylene with formation of 2-chloro-1, 3-butadiene, called chloroprene. This substance is analogous structurally to isoprene but polymerizes several hundreds of times more rapidly and leads to a product much superior to all previously known synthetic rubbers. It was the first synthetic material to show rubber's curious property of developing fibrous orientation when stretched and instantly reverting to the amorphous condition when released from stress. In resistance to aliphatic hydrocarbons and to most chemical reagents it is definitely superior to natural rubber. It has, moreover, a greater resistance than rubber to corona and sunlight. Carothers' work laid the foundation for the development by other chemists and by chemical enginers of the Du Pont Company of the commercial product which has found wide industrial use and which is marketed as neoprene.

These practical results, however, were of no greater importance than the theoretical. In the course of the investigation, many analogs and homologs of chloroprene were prepared and studied. Their behavior threw light on the relationship between the chemical structure of a diene and its suitability as a precursor of rubber. Fundamental information concerning the character and formation of the various polymers from these compounds was revealed and their structures clarified. The reactivity of the vinylacetylenes and the mechanism by which the products formed was studied in detail. New light was thrown on 1,4 addition and on α,γ rearrangements. His work in this field was a basic contribution to acetylene chemistry.

The most outstanding scientific accomplishment of Carothers was his work on linear polymers. In a letter written to Dr. John R. Johnson of Cornell University on February 14, 1928, Carothers made a statement which demonstrated the careful thought and study which he had given previously to polymerization and polymeric molecules. It follows:

One of the problems which I am going to start work on has to do with substances of high molecular weight. I want to attack this problem from the synthetic side. One part would be to synthesize compounds of high molecular weight and known constitution. It would seem quite possible to beat Fischer's record of 4200. It would be a satisfaction to do this, and facilities will soon be available here for studying such substances with the newest and most powerful tools.

Another phase of the problem will be to study the action of substances xAx on yBy where A and B are divalent radicals and x and y are functional groups capable of reacting with each other. Where A and B are quite short, such reactions lead to simple rings of which many have been synthesized by this method. Where they are long, formation of small rings is not possible. Hence reaction must result either in large rings or endless chains. It may be possible to find out which reaction occurs. In any event the reactions will lead to the formation of substances of high molecular weight and containing known linkages. For starting materials will be needed as many dibasic fatty acids as can be got, glycols, diamines, etc. If you know of any new sources of compounds of these types I should be glad to hear about them.

These initial ideas culminated in the publication of a series of thirty-one papers in the field of polymerization. In these he proposed a general theory of condensation-polymerization and a logical and systematic terminology suitable for use in this previously disorganized field. The implications of his theory were illustrated by a series of experimental studies dealing with polyesters, hydrocarbons, polyamides, and polyanhydrides. These studies provided experimental material for correlating chemical structure and physical properties of materials of high molecular weight, and furnished evidence favoring a view now generally accepted for the structure of such natural high polymers as cellulose. In these investigations a new technique—molecular distillation—was applied to the propagation of chemical reactions.

In this study a method new in principle was developed for the synthesis of many-membered cyclic compounds. A large number of many-membered cyclic compounds was synthesized, including several of entirely new types. Some of these compounds had musk-like odors and are otherwise similar in their properties to the genuine musks. One of these new many-membered ring compounds has found industrial application. The large amount of experimental material made possible important deductions bearing on the relationship between chemical structure and ease of ring formation. His contribution was a major one to the field of many-membered ring compounds, which is one of growing significance in organic chemistry.

He investigated the means by which polymers structurally analogous to cellulose and silk could be prepared, and synthesized a large number. These materials constituted the first completely synthetic fibres with a degree of strength, orientation, and pliability comparable with natural fibres. Their study made possible the development of a theory for the relation between structure, fibrous properties, and other physical properties. The work was brilliant and the most important aid in recent years to the understanding of such polymers. This information, and the modification of the physical and chemical properties of polymers by slight changes in the mode of preparation, has made possible the exploration of a wide variety of substances of most promising industrial application.

Based on this work, nylon was developed by the Du Pont Company. This consists of a synthetic fibre-forming polymeric amide with a protein-like chemical structure, characterized by extreme toughness, strength and peculiar ability to be formed into fibres and into various shapes such as bristles and sheets. Filaments of extreme fineness can be spun, much finer than the filaments of either silk or rayon.

1610

NOTES AND REFERENCES

This biography is an abbreviated reprint of Roger Adams, "Wallace Hume Carothers, 1896–1937," *National Academy of Sciences of the U.S.A., Biographical Memoirs, 20, 1939.*

ROGER ADAMS

Epilogue

T HE foregoing biographies present selected aspects of the efforts by which the edifice of chemistry has been built. These efforts, extended over so many years, continue at an increased rate. At certain periods during these years, the edifice appeared to be complete, and there were actually times when it seemed to some chemists that nothing more of any importance could be added, that a solid body of facts and laws were "now" available to be preserved and transmitted in writing and teaching. Yet, new thoughts and facts claimed attention. The feeling grew that each advance was not concluding a tradition but starting an unforeseen development.

Two apparent contradictions accompany this development—the first is the accelerated advance, the second is the attitude toward the future. The greater the body of discoveries was, the more prolific became the production of new ones. Obviously, it is a fallacy to assume that because the field of the unknown was so much greater before, it should have been easier to make new findings. One of the fascinating questions answered in the biographies of these chemists is how they recognized new problems and were successful in finding ways through the unknown. Increasing success established confidence in the future, and here lies the answer to the second of those contradictions. Earlier science relied greatly on the past. As time progressed, the past became enriched and more reliable. The tradition, thus founded, was often invoked against new theories, especially by chemists in their old age who earlier had set the example that the younger chemists now followed. The process almost seemed to conform to a generalization from the law of chemical kinetics which van't Hoff had formulated in 1884, the rate of transformation was proportional to the active mass of the transformable.

In looking back to such changes—their accelerated progress and the men who brought them about—we gain a strong feeling for

1615

the men who brought them about—we gain a strong feeling for the effects of time. The year 1900 seemed so far off to Wöhler in 1843 when he admonished his friend Liebig:

> Imagine what will happen in the year 1900 when we shall be returned into carbon dioxide, ammonia and water . . . Who will then be concerned with whether we live in peace or in anger . . .? Nobody, but your good ideas, the new facts you discovered, they will remain known and valued, cleansed of everything that is not permanent, in the most distant times.

It is such a simple truth, and yet it contains the great experience that our lasting work is achieved during the fleeting moment of our present. Thus we see many of these men concentrating on the moment to the point of exhaustion, summoning all their energies like the athlete at the peak of his performance. The effort is dictated by the inner law of the work and the worker, in freedom from a law imposed from the outside. By the height thus reached, we judge the greatness of the man. There is considerable value in the regular duty, faithfully and constantly performed, but we see greatness more in high peaks than in constant levels.

As the effort of the moment extends to the future, so the work on one particular detail has its bearing on the whole of science. When Mitscherlich reported about his investigation of selenic acid to Berzelius, he replied on March 27, 1827: "Thank you for your wonderful discoveries . . . You are going on a straight path to the heart of Nature . . ." To go on this path to the heart of Nature, the chemists require all the meticulous care about methods of operation, recognition and exclusion of impurities, accuracy of measurement, manipulative skill and precise interpretation. Some of the chemists can be occupied completely by these details which they enlarge and refine. Others devote much effort to describing the place of details in a system of chemistry. A third group becomes interested in the industrial applications, while a fourth takes active parts in professional, social, and political affairs. The groups were not sharply separated; in fact, there was a unity between all their special efforts, the unity that Berzelius indicated as leading to "the heart of Nature."

1616

When we single out a few men as great, we remain conscious of their own, often expressed conviction that they could not have created their work without that of many others. This recognition is necessary, yet it must not lead to a leveling-off process. In 1792, Lavoisier appealed to his readers:

> The theory is therefore not, as I hear it said, the theory of the French chemists, it is mine, and it is a property that I claim before my contemporaries and before posterity. There is no doubt that others have added to it new degrees of perfection . . .

At first glance, this reads like a very egotistic statement, but we must appreciate its wider meaning as a plea to recognize the value of the individual.

Lavoisier experienced, in the most tragic way, the ingratitude of his contemporaries. Fortunately, he was an exception. More often, we find contemporaries who exalted their heroes too highly, a trend that even shows, somewhat, in a few of the older biographies assembled here. Taken together, these biographies enable us to find the right way between ingratitude and hero worship, the way that leads to an understanding and appreciation of our great chemists.

Index

In the following index, those names appearing in *italic type indicate authorship,* while entries in **boldface type denote biographies.**